PARKIN/BADE

ECONOMICS

CANADA IN THE GLOBAL ENVIRONMENT

TEST BANK

Harvey B. King *University of Regina*
Patricia J. Euzent *University of Central Florida*
David E. Spencer *Brigham Young University*

Addison-Wesley Publishers Limited
Don Mills, Ontario • Reading, Massachusetts • Menlo Park, California
New York • Wokingham, England • Amsterdam • Bonn • Sydney •
Singapore • Tokyo • Madrid • San Juan

Dedicated to Tracy

ISBN 0-201-52456-2

Printed and bound in Canada

A B C D E F G -ALG- 95 94 93 92 91

PROJECT EDITOR: Shirley Tessier
PRODUCTION EDITOR: Valerie Jones
COPYEDITOR: Edie Franks
INTERIOR DESIGN: Artplus Design Consultants Ltd
TYPESET AND LAYOUT: Anthony Leung
TEXT FORMATTING: Judy Petersiel
COVER DESIGN: Pronk & Associates
COVER ART: Calvin Nichols Paper Sculpture
PRINTER: Alger Press Ltd

CONTENTS

INTRODUCTION

This *Test Bank* for Parkin and Bade, *Economics: Canada in the Global Environment* contains over 4,000 multiple-choice questions, providing comprehensive coverage of the entire textbook. Each question was written using the final draft manuscript to ensure consistency between the textbook and the *Test Bank* in terminology and methodology. The distribution of questions per concept is proportional to the importance of each concept in the text. The authors and editors who have worked with the *Test Bank* believe such careful preparation has resulted in an excellent resource for evaluating your students' progress in understanding the principles of economics.

This *Test Bank* contains the following features:

- Each question has a page reference for quick, easy access to the hardcover text page or pages on which the question is based.
- Each question is labelled by topic for the easy selection of appropriate material for your exam.
- The correct answer appears to the left of each test item.
- Each question is labelled by difficulty level so you can easily achieve a balanced exam in terms of difficulty. The difficulty levels range from 1 (lowest) to 5 (highest). Most questions fall in the range of 2–4, with a level of 1 or 2 usually assigned to definitional questions, and with 3 and above assigned to analytical questions.
- The graphs included in the *Test Bank* have been professionally drawn, and correspond in style and notation to the graphs in the text and the *Study Guide*.
- The *Study Guide* that accompanies the textbook contains practice multiple-choice questions. To encourage students to work through the *Study Guide*, within each chapter of the *Test Bank*, certain of the *Study Guide* multiple-choice questions have been included and identified.
- A very special feature of the *Test Bank* is that it is offered to adopters in two forms for maximum flexibility: in printed form ("hard copy"), and on diskettes for IBM computers in 3 1/2 and 5 1/4 inch disk versions. The microcomputer form is very useful for large classes, as tests built using it can be "scrambled" to provide tests with identical questions arranged in different orders, and with the answers "scrambled" (but still remembered by the computer). In addition, answer keys are constructed and printed automatically. Tests can be automatically built by the computer program, based on certain topic areas, or they can be built randomly. You can also add your own questions to the *Test Bank*, or edit existing questions. Please contact your local Addison-Wesley representative for more information on the computerized *Test Bank*.

Harvey B. King

GUIDE TO CONTENTS OF PAPERBACK SPLITS

Chapter 1 What is Economics?

1.1
Correct: d)
Difficulty: 3
Page(s): 9
Scramble range: a)–d)
Topic: Scarcity

1.1
The problem of scarcity
a) exists only in economies which rely on the market mechanism.
b) could be eliminated if we could force prices to fall.
c) means that there are shortages of some goods.
d) exists because human wants cannot be satisfied with available resources.
e) none of the above.

1.2
Correct: a)
Difficulty: 2
Page(s): 9
Scramble range: All
Topic: Scarcity

1.2
There would be no economic problems if
a) scarcity were eliminated.
b) unemployment were eliminated.
c) everyone had a $1 million annual income.
d) inflation were controlled.
e) everyone was self-sufficient.

1.3
Correct: e)
Difficulty: 4
Page(s): 9
Scramble range: None
Topic: Scarcity

1.3
In a world without scarcity
a) it would still be necessary to choose among alternatives.
b) opportunity costs would determine choices.
c) all goods would be free.
d) the market would be irrelevant.
e) both c) and d).

1.4
Correct: a)
Difficulty: 3
Page(s): 9
Scramble range: All
Topic: Scarcity

1.4
In a world characterized by scarcity
a) people must make choices among alternatives.
b) opportunity costs are zero.
c) we need not sacrifice in order to obtain what we want.
d) individuals need not work in order to obtain goods.
e) people are always hungry.

1.5
Correct: b)
Difficulty: 3
Page(s): 10
Scramble range: a)–d)
Topic: Opportunity cost

1.5
To an economist, the term “cost” means
a) accounting cost.
b) opportunity cost.
c) monetary cost.
d) social cost.
e) all of the above.

1.6
Correct: e)
Difficulty: 3
Page(s): 10
Scramble range: a)–d)
Topic: Opportunity cost

1.6
Opportunity cost means
a) the value of the best activity.
b) the value of the leisure forgone.
c) the indirect costs of an activity.
d) the monetary costs of an activity.
e) none of the above.

1.7
Correct: c)
Difficulty: 4
Page(s): 10
Scramble range: a)–d)
Topic: Opportunity cost

1.7
Which of the following is *not* a part of the opportunity cost of attending college?
a) The cost of tuition.
b) The cost of textbooks.
c) The cost of meals.
d) The income that could have been earned by working.
e) All of the above.

1.8
Correct: e)
Difficulty: 4
Page(s): 10
Scramble range: a)–d)
Topic: Opportunity cost

1.8
When a choice is made, we call the value of the best alternative choice the
a) implicit choice.
b) explicit choice.
c) apparent cost.
d) accounting cost.
e) none of the above.

1.9
Correct: b)
Difficulty: 5
Page(s): 10
Scramble range: None
Topic: Opportunity cost

1.9
During the next hour John can choose one of the following three activities: playing basketball, watching television, or reading a book. The opportunity cost of reading a book
a) depends on how much the book cost when it was purchased.
b) is the value of playing basketball if John prefers that to watching television.
c) is the value of playing basketball *and* the value of watching television.
d) depends on how much John enjoys the book.
e) both a) and b).

1.10
Correct: a)
Difficulty: 3
Page(s): 10
Scramble range: a)–d)
Topic: Opportunity cost

1.10
Wanda makes $20 an hour as a welder. She must take two hours off work (without pay) to go to the dentist to have a tooth pulled. The dentist charges $100. The opportunity cost of Wanda's trip to the dentist is
a) $140.
b) $120.
c) $100.
d) $40.
e) none of the above.

1.11
Correct: e)
Difficulty: 4
Page(s): 9
Scramble range: None
Topic: Scarcity

1.11
Which of the following is a necessary consequence of scarcity?
a) Racial discrimination.
b) High profits.
c) The requirement of making choices.
d) Unfulfilled wants.
e) Both c) and d).

1.12
Correct: d)
Difficulty: 2
Page(s): 10
Scramble range: All
Topic: Optimizing

1.12
Balancing benefits against costs and doing the best within the limits of what is possible is called
a) competition.
b) choice.
c) opportunity cost.
d) optimizing.
e) capitalism.

1.13
Correct: e)
Difficulty: 3
Page(s): 10
Scramble range: All
Topic: Optimizing

1.13
In order to optimize, people must
a) be able to carry out complex mathematical calculations.
b) have unlimited resources.
c) be free from government constraint.
d) have unlimited access to information at no cost.
e) evaluate the costs of alternative actions.

1.14
Correct: b)
Difficulty: 2
Page(s): 10–11
Scramble range: None
Topic: Competition

1.14
Sam offers Bill a higher price for his compact disc player than Walter. This is an example of
a) opportunity cost.
b) competition.
c) cooperation.
d) positive economics.
e) both a) and b).

1.15
Correct: d)
Difficulty: 2
Page(s): 14
Scramble range: All
Topic: Factors of production

1.15
Which of the following is *not* an example of a factor of production?
a) Oil in Saudi Arabia.
b) A shovel.
c) Knowledge about the operation of a computer.
d) A diamond ring.
e) The strength to use a shovel.

1.16
Correct: c)
Difficulty: 1
Page(s): 14
Scramble range: None
Topic: Factors of production

1.16
Which of the following is *not* one of the major classifications of factors of production?
a) Capital.
b) Land (natural resources).
c) Bonds.
d) Labour.
e) Neither b) nor c).

1.17
Correct: a)
Difficulty: 1
Page(s): 14
Scramble range: a)–d)
Topic: Capital

1.17
A tractor is an example of
a) capital.
b) labour.
c) land (natural resources).
d) management.
e) none of the above.

1.18
Correct: b)
Difficulty: 2
Page(s): 15
Scramble range: All
Topic: Mixed economy

1.18
The Canadian economy
a) relies exclusively on the market mechanism.
b) is a mixed economy that relies heavily on the market mechanism.
c) relies exclusively on the command mechanism.
d) is a mixed economy that relies heavily on the command mechanism.
e) is a mixed economy that relies equally on the market and the command mechanism.

1.19
Correct: e)
Difficulty: 3
Page(s): 15
Scramble range: All
Topic: Market mechanism

1.19
Under a market mechanism the determination of *what, how,* and *for whom* is the result of
a) decisions by the wealthy.
b) decisions by the government.
c) the political process.
d) the amount of shortages in the economy.
e) price adjustments.

1.20
Correct: c)
Difficulty: 2
Page(s): 16
Scramble range: All
Topic: Open economy

1.20
An open economy is one that
a) has free borders.
b) allows private ownership of factors of production.
c) engages in trade with other economies.
d) allows a free press.
e) allows exports to other countries.

1.21
Correct: a)
Difficulty: 3
Page(s): 16
Scramble range: None
Topic: Open economy

1.21
An economy that imports goods from and exports goods to other countries
a) is called an open economy.
b) is called a closed economy.
c) must always maintain a balance between exports and imports.
d) both a) and c).
e) both b) and c).

1.22
Correct: e)
Difficulty: 1
Page(s): 16
Scramble range: None
Topic: Open economy

1.22
The Canadian economy is
a) an open economy.
b) a closed economy.
c) a mixed economy.
d) both b) and c).
e) both a) and c).

1.23
Correct: c)
Difficulty: 2
Page(s): 15
Scramble range: None
Topic: Mixed economy

1.23
A mixed economy is one in which
a) there are aspects of both a closed and open economy.
b) labour, natural resources, and capital are all used in production.
c) both the market mechanism and command mechanism are used.
d) trade is sometimes restricted and sometimes free.
e) both c) and d).

1.24
Correct: b)
Difficulty: 1
Page(s): 17
Scramble range: All
Topic: Positive–normative

1.24
Statements about "what ought to be" are called
a) positive statements.
b) normative statements.
c) economic statements.
d) scientific statements.
e) hypotheses.

1.25
Correct: a)
Difficulty: 1
Page(s): 17
Scramble range: All
Topic: Positive–normative

1.25
Statements about "what is" are called
a) positive statements.
b) normative statements.
c) economic statements.
d) scientific statements.
e) hypotheses.

1.26
Correct: d)
Difficulty: 2
Page(s): 17
Scramble range: All
Topic: Positive–normative

1.26
A positive statement is one about
a) what is usually the case.
b) the assumptions of an economic model.
c) what ought to be.
d) what is.
e) the real world.

1.27
Correct: a)
Difficulty: 3
Page(s): 17
Scramble range: None
Topic: Positive–normative

1.27
Which of the following is an example of a normative statement?
a) Scientists should not make normative statements.
b) Warts are caused by handling toads.
c) As the price of compact discs falls, people will buy more of them.
d) If income increases, sales of luxury goods will fall.
e) Both c) and d).

1.28
Correct: e)
Difficulty: 3
Page(s): 17
Scramble range: None
Topic: Positive–normative

1.28
A positive statement is
a) about what ought to be.
b) about what is.
c) always true.
d) a statement that can be settled by scientific research.
e) both b) and d).

1.29
Correct: a)
Difficulty: 3
Page(s): 17
Scramble range: All
Topic: Positive–normative

1.29
"The rich should face higher income tax rates than the poor." This is an example of
a) a normative statement.
b) a positive statement.
c) a negative statement.
d) economic reasoning.
e) neither a normative nor a positive statement.

1.30
Correct: c)
Difficulty: 3
Page(s): 18–20
Scramble range: All
Topic: Economic models

1.30
Economic *models*
a) do not answer questions about the real economy.
b) include most of the detail of the real economy.
c) rely on abstraction.
d) make no assumptions in advance.
e) are very realistic.

1.31
Correct: c)
Difficulty: 3
Page(s): 18–20
Scramble range: None
Topic: Economic models

1.31
The scientific purpose of simplifying assumptions in an economic model is to
a) avoid confronting difficult issues.
b) eliminate the need for further testing of the implications of the model.
c) abstract from the complexities of the real world those issues that are not important for the issues under examination.
d) eliminate the possibility of personal bias in the model.
e) both b) and c).

1.32
Correct: c)
Difficulty: 4
Page(s): 20–21
Scramble range: All
Topic: Model testing

1.32
Model *A* is superior to model *B* if
a) it contains more real world detail than model *B*.
b) it contains fewer unrealistic assumptions than model *B*.
c) its predictions correspond more closely to the facts than the predictions of model *B*.
d) it is preferred by a majority of researchers in a public opinion poll.
e) it is scientifically "elegant."

1.33
Correct: d)
Difficulty: 2
Page(s): 19
Scramble range: All
Topic: Rational choice

1.33
A choice by an individual which is intended to make him or her as well-off as possible is called a(n)
a) economic choice.
b) market choice.
c) normative choice.
d) rational choice.
e) positive choice.

1.34
Correct: d)
Difficulty: 4
Page(s): 19
Scramble range: None
Topic: Rational choice

1.34
For economists, assuming that people economize is the same as assuming that people
a) have complete information.
b) are selfish.
c) are normative.
d) are rational.
e) both b) and d).

1.35
Correct: a)
Difficulty: 1
Page(s): 20
Scramble range: All
Topic: Micro–macro

1.35
The branch of economics that studies the economy as a whole is called
a) macroeconomics.
b) microeconomics.
c) Keynesian economics.
d) positive economics.
e) normative economics.

1.36
Correct: b)
Difficulty: 3
Page(s): 20–21
Scramble range: All
Topic: Micro–macro

1.36
Which of the following would *not* generally be considered a microeconomic issue?
a) The effect of a rise in the price of sugar on the market for soft drinks.
b) The effect of the federal government budget deficit on interest rates.
c) The factors determining the amount a firm will produce.
d) The cause of a decline in the price of peanut butter.
e) The effect of government regulation on the airline industry.

1.37
Correct: e)
Difficulty: 3
Page(s): 20–21
Scramble range: All
Topic: Micro–macro

1.37
Macroeconomics
a) is primarily concerned with the operation of individual markets in the economy.
b) deals mainly with the economic behaviour of households.
c) is the only part of economics to deal with goverment decisions.
d) is primarily concerned with the behaviour of the stock market.
e) is the study of the economy as a whole.

1.38
Correct: d)
Difficulty: 2
Page(s): 20–21
Scramble range: a)–d)
Topic: Micro–macro

1.38
The determination of prices in individual markets is primarily a concern of
a) positive economics.
b) negative economics.
c) macroeconomics.
d) microeconomics.
e) all of the above.

1.39
Correct: b)
Difficulty: 1
Page(s): 22–23
Scramble range: All
Topic: Adam Smith

1.39
The author of *An Inquiry into the Nature and Causes of the Wealth of Nations* is
a) John M. Keynes.
b) Adam Smith.
c) Alan Greenspan.
d) Alfred Marshall.
e) Michael Parkin.

1.40
Correct: e)
Difficulty: 1
Page(s): 22–23
Scramble range: All
Topic: Adam Smith

1.40
The founder of the discipline of economics was
a) the Duke of Glasgow.
b) George Stigler.
c) Alfred Marshall.
d) Antoine-Augustine Cournot.
e) Adam Smith.

1.41 (SG 1.1)
Correct: b)
Difficulty: 2
Page(s): 9
Scramble range: All
Topic: Scarcity

1.41
The fact that human wants cannot be fully satisfied with available resources is called the problem of
a) opportunity costs.
b) scarcity.
c) normative economics.
d) what to produce.
e) positive economics.

1.42 (SG 1.2)
Correct: c)
Difficulty: 4
Page(s): 9
Scramble range: All
Topic: Scarcity

1.42
The problem of scarcity
a) exists only in economies that rely on the market mechanism.
b) exists only in economies that rely on the command mechanism.
c) exists in all economies.
d) means that at least some prices are too high.
e) can be solved by economists.

1.43 (SG 1.3)
Correct: e)
Difficulty: 2
Page(s): 10
Scramble range: All
Topic: Opportunity cost

1.43
When the government chooses to use resources to build a dam, those resources are no longer available to build a highway. This illustrates the concept of
a) microeconomics.
b) macroeconomics.
c) rational choice.
d) optimizing.
e) opportunity cost.

1.44 (SG 1.4)
Correct: e)
Difficulty: 4
Page(s): 10
Scramble range: None
Topic: Opportunity cost

1.44
Sally has the chance to either attend an economics lecture or play tennis. If she chooses to attend the lecture, the value of playing tennis is
a) the opportunity cost of attending the lecture.
b) greater than the value of the lecture.
c) less than the value of the lecture.
d) equal to the value of the lecture.
e) both a) and c).

1.45 (SG 1.5)
Correct: c)
Difficulty: 2
Page(s): 10
Scramble range: All
Topic: Opportunity cost

1.45
The opportunity cost of getting a $10 haircut is
a) the best alternative use of the $10.
b) the best alternative use of the time it takes to get a haircut.
c) the best alternative use of both the $10 and the time it takes to get a haircut.
d) the value of $10 to the barber.
e) $10.

1.46 (SG 1.7)
Correct: c)
Difficulty: 3
Page(s): 14
Scramble range: a)–c)
Topic: Capital a factor of production

1.46
Which of the following is an example of capital as a factor of production?
a) Money held by General Motors.
b) A General Motors bond.
c) An automobile factory owned by General Motors.
d) All of the above.
e) None of the above.

1.47 (SG 1.9)
Correct: e)
Difficulty: 2
Page(s): 16
Scramble range: a)–c)
Topic: Closed economy

1.47
A closed economy is one that
a) has strict government control of production.
b) has economic links with other economies.
c) maintains strict control of its borders.
d) is characterized by a dominant agricultural sector.
e) none of the above.

1.48 (SG 1.11)
Correct: c)
Difficulty: 2
Page(s): 17
Scramble range: All
Topic: Normative statements

1.48
A normative statement is one about
a) what is usually the case.
b) the assumptions of an economic model.
c) what ought to be.
d) what is.
e) economic situations.

1.49 (SG 1.12)
Correct: b)
Difficulty: 2
Page(s): 17
Scramble range: All
Topic: Positive statements

1.49
"The rich face higher income tax rates than the poor" is an example of a
a) normative statement.
b) positive statement.
c) negative statement.
d) theoretical statement.
e) normal statement.

1.50 (SG 1.14)
Correct: b)
Difficulty: 2
Page(s): 18–20
Scramble range: a)–c)
Topic: economic models

1.50
An economic model is tested by
a) examining the realism of its assumptions.
b) comparing its predictions with the facts.
c) the Testing Committee of the Canadian Economic Association.
d) all of the above.
e) none of the above.

1.51 (SG 1.15)
Correct: b)
Difficulty: 4
Page(s): 19–20
Scramble range: All
Topic: Economic models

1.51
Which of the following is *not* a key assumption of an economic model?
a) People have preferences.
b) People live in a market economy.
c) People are endowed with a given technology and a fixed amount of resources.
d) People's choices are coordinated.
e) People economize.

1.52 (SG 1.16)
Correct: b)
Difficulty: 3
Page(s): 19
Scramble range: All
Topic: Rational behaviour

1.52
When economists say that people are rational, they mean that people
a) do not make errors of judgement.
b) make the best decision from their perspective.
c) act on complete information.
d) will not later regret any decision made now.
e) make calculated, mathematical decisions.

1.53 (SG 1.17)
Correct: b)
Difficulty: 1
Page(s): 20–21
Scramble range: All
Topic: Microeconomics

1.53
The branch of economics that studies the decisions of individual households and firms is called
a) macroeconomics.
b) microeconomics.
c) positive economics.
d) normative economics.
e) Smithian economics.

1.54
Correct: e)
Difficulty: 3
Page(s): 20–21
Scramble range: None
Topic: Macroeconomics

1.54
Which of the following would be considered a macroeconomic topic?
a) The reasons for a decline in the rate of unemployment.
b) The cause of recessions.
c) The effect of the government budget deficit on inflation.
d) The determination of aggregate income (GDP).
e) All of the above.

1.55
Correct: a)
Difficulty: 2
Page(s): 9
Scramble range: All
Topic: Scarcity

1.55
Scarcity refers to
a) the fact that human wants cannot be fully satisfied with available resources.
b) positive economics only.
c) normative economics only.
d) what to produce.
e) what to consume.

1.56
Correct: e)
Difficulty: 4
Page(s): 9
Scramble range: All
Topic: Scarcity

1.56
Command economies
a) do not face the problem of scarcity, whereas market economies do.
b) face the problem of scarcity until their economy becomes more sophisticated.
c) face the problem of scarcity, whereas market economies do not.
d) avoid the problem of scarcity by not using the market economy.
e) as well as market economies face the problem of scarcity.

1.57
Correct: a)
Difficulty: 4
Page(s): 10
Scramble range: All
Topic: Opportunity cost

1.57
Sally has to decide whether to study for her economics test or her accounting test. If she chooses to study for accounting, the value of studying economics is
a) the opportunity cost of studying accounting.
b) greater than the value of studying for accounting.
c) not comparable to the value of studying economics.
d) equal to the value of studying for economics.
e) the future lost wages that will occur if she fails her accounting exam.

1.58
Correct: b)
Difficulty: 2
Page(s): 16
Scramble range: All
Topic: Open economy

1.58
An open economy is one that
a) has no government control of production.
b) has economic links with other economies.
c) allows limited immigration.
d) is characterized by a manufacturing sector.
e) has no economic links with other economies.

1.59
Correct: d)
Difficulty: 4
Page(s): 17
Scramble range: All
Topic: Positive statements

1.59
Which of the following is a positive statement?
a) The finance minister should lower interest rates and this will create jobs.
b) If the finance minister lowers interest rates, this should make the economy better off.
c) If more jobs are created, this should make the economy better off.
d) If the finance minister lowers interest rates, this will create more jobs.
e) The finance minister should not lower interest rates because this will raise inflation and make the economy worse off.

1.60
Correct: a)
Difficulty: 3
Page(s): 17
Scramble range: a)–d)
Topic: Normative statements

1.60
"The rich face higher income tax rates than the poor, which is not good since it is the rich who provide jobs for the poor." This is an example of
a) a normative statement.
b) a positive statement.
c) a negative statement.
d) a theoretical statement.
e) none of the above.

1.61
Correct: b)
Difficulty: 3
Page(s): 18–20
Scramble range: None
Topic: Economic models

1.61
An economic model is
a) tested by examining the realism of its assumptions.
b) useful if it predicts well even if its assumptions are not realistic.
c) tested by the Testing Committee of the Canadian Economic Association.
d) not useful unless it predicts with 100 percent accuracy.
e) both a) and d).

1.62 (SG 1.15)
Correct: d)
Difficulty: 2
Page(s): 18–20
Scramble range: All
Topic: Economic models

1.62
Which of the following is not a key assumption of an economic model?
a) People have preferences.
b) People economize.
c) People are constrained by a given technology and a fixed amount of resources.
d) People's choices are not coordinated.
e) People are endowed with a fixed amount of resources.

1.63
Correct: a)
Difficulty: 2
Page(s): 20–21
Scramble range: All
Topic: Microeconomics

1.63
Microeconomics is
a) the branch of economics that studies the decisions of individual households and firms.
b) concerned with normative issues only.
c) concerned with the size of the total amount of income earned by all households in an economy.
d) unrelated to macroeconomics.
e) concerned exclusively with the role of the government in the economy.

1.64
Correct: e)
Difficulty: 2
Page(s): 20–21
Scramble range: a)–c)
Topic: Microeconomics

1.64
Which of the following would be considered a microeconomic topic?
a) The reasons for a decline in the rate of unemployment.
b) The cause of unemployment in the economy.
c) The effect of the government budget deficit on inflation.
d) The determination of aggregate income (GDP).
e) None of the above.

1.65
Correct: c)
Difficulty: 4
Page(s): 17
Scramble range: a)–d)
Topic: Normative statements

1.65
Which of the following is a normative statement?
a) Pollution is an example of an external cost.
b) The presence of pollution makes people worse off.
c) We should force firms to close down if they pollute.
d) The presence of pollution in a market setting with no government interference leads to an efficiency loss.
e) None of the above.

1.66
Correct: a)
Difficulty: 1
Page(s): 9
Scramble range: a)–d)
Topic: Scarcity

1.66
The inescapable economic fact is that
a) there are unlimited wants and limited resources.
b) there are unlimited resources, we just have to figure out how to allocate them.
c) capitalists are always exploiting the workers.
d) unions are always exploiting firms.
e) all of the above.

1.67
Correct: e)
Difficulty: 3
Page(s): 14
Scramble range: a)–d)
Topic: Coordination

1.67
The solutions to the economic coordination problem are
a) command, the market, and religion.
b) the market, random chance, and tradition.
c) the market and tradition.
d) communism and capitalism.
e) none of the above.

1.68
Correct: d)
Difficulty: 4
Page(s): 9–10
Scramble range: a)–c)
Topic: Scarcity/choice

1.68
Which of the following illustrates scarcity?
a) Billionaire Donald Trump deciding whether to buy a hot dog.
b) A poor street child deciding whether to buy a hot dog.
c) The government deciding whether to spend an extra $100 million in tax revenues on hospitals or whether to return it to taxpayers.
d) All of the above.
e) None of the above.

1.69
Correct: e)
Difficulty: 4
Page(s): 10–11
Scramble range: a)–c)
Topic: Competition

1.69
Which of the following statements is true?
a) Competition and cooperation cannot exist together in the same market.
b) The problem of scarcity can only be solved by competition.
c) The problem of scarcity can only be solved by cooperation.
d) Competition necessarily means unconstrained stealing by the most powerful in society.
e) None of the above.

1.70
Correct: a)
Difficulty: 2
Page(s): 12
Scramble range: All
Topic: Decision makers

1.70
The crucial decision makers in an economy are
a) households, firms, and governments.
b) labour, land, and capital.
c) foreign governments, the federal government, and the voter.
d) the municipal, provincial, and federal governments.
e) the rich only.

1.71
Correct: c)
Difficulty: 3
Page(s): 18
Scramble range: a)–c)
Topic: Economic models

1.71
Economic models will generally contain
a) an exact description of the relevant part of the economy.
b) assumptions about the economy that will be extremely realistic.
c) assumptions about the relevant part of the economy and implications about the economy that are the outcome of the model.
d) all of the above.
e) none of the above.

1.72
Correct: e)
Difficulty: 4
Page(s): 20
Scramble range: None
Topic: Models

1.72
Select the best statement.
a) An economic model always must be correct in its predictions or it must be discarded.
b) An economic model is evaluated based on the realism of its assumptions.
c) An economic model should generate predictions about actual events in the real world so that it can be tested.
d) An economic model will be discarded if its predictions are often in conflict with the facts.
e) Both c) and d).

1.73
Correct: b)
Difficulty: 2
Page(s): 22–23
Scramble range: None
Topic: Adam Smith

1.73
Adam Smith argued
a) that the economy was best served by individuals cooperating, not competing.
b) that it was the self-interest of the individuals in society that lead to the best possible social outcome.
c) that it was the self-interest of the individuals in society that lead to the worst possible social outcome.
d) both a) and c).
e) none of the above.

1.74
Correct: a)
Difficulty: 3
Page(s): 17
Scramble range: All
Topic: Positive/normative

1.74
Which of the following statements is positive?
a) Low rents will restrict the supply of housing.
b) High interest rates are bad for the economy.
c) Housing costs too much.
d) Owners of apartment buildings ought to be free to charge whatever rent they like.
e) The government should restrict the rents that apartment owners are allowed to charge.

Chapter 2 Making and Using Graphs

2.1
Correct: a)
Difficulty: 1
Page(s): 29-37
Scramble range: All
Topic: Data/graphs

2.1
Refer to Figure 2.1. Which of the following statements is true?

a) All four graphs indicate ways to represent data.
b) Only graphs like (a) can be used to represent data.
c) All but graph (a) can be said to represent data.
d) Only graphs like (b) and (c) can be used to represent data.
e) Graph (d) cannot be used to represent data because it has dots, not lines.

Figure 2.1

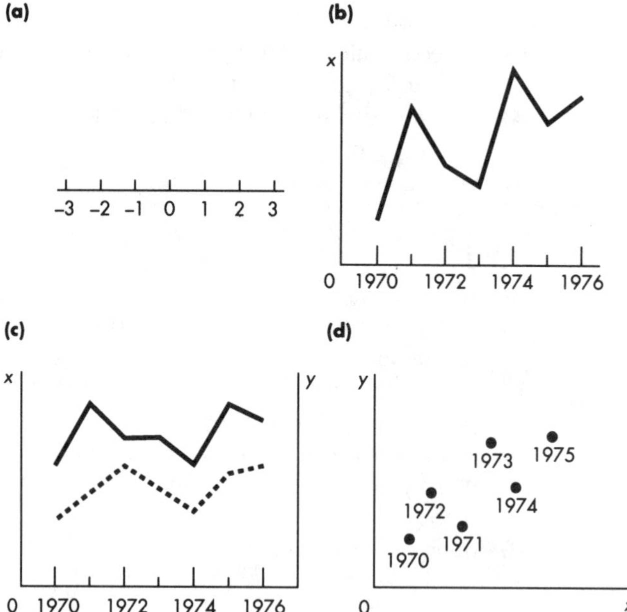

2.2
Correct: d)
Difficulty: 2
Page(s): 33-37
Scramble range: a)-d)
Topic: Data/graphs

2.2
Refer to Figure 2.1. Which of the graphs is a scatter diagram?

a) (a).
b) (b).
c) (c).
d) (d).
e) None of the above.

2.3
Correct: a)
Difficulty: 3
Page(s): 30-31
Scramble range: All
Topic: Data/graphs

2.3
Refer to Figure 2.1. Which of the diagrams illustrates a time-series graph?
a) Both (b) and (c).
b) (b) only.
c) (c) only.
d) (d) only.
e) (b), (c), and (d).

2.4
Correct: c)
Difficulty: 2
Page(s): 33–36
Scramble range: All
Topic: Data/graphs

2.4
Refer to Figure 2.1. Which of the diagrams illustrates a two-variable time-series graph?
a) (a).
b) (b).
c) (c).
d) (d).
e) (c) and (d).

2.5
Correct: e)
Difficulty: 4
Page(s): 30–35
Scramble range: All
Topic: Data/time-series

2.5
The solid line in Figure 2.2 represents variable x. In that figure, the value of x
a) increased more rapidly between 1978 and 1979 than in any other period.
b) decreased more rapidly between 1972 and 1973 than between 1971 and 1972.
c) decreased more rapidly between 1975 and 1976 than in any other period.
d) ended the period below its 1974 value.
e) increased more rapidly between 1974 and 1975 than in any other period.

Figure 2.2

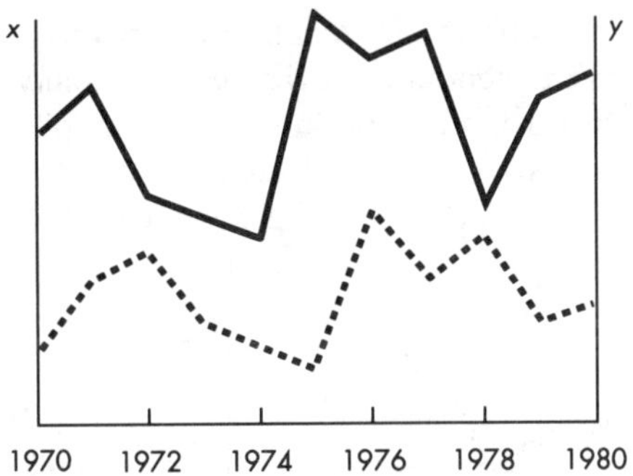

2.6
Correct: c)
Difficulty: 3
Page(s): 30–35
Scramble range: All
Topic: Data/time-series

2.6
Refer to Figure 2.3. If we define a recession as any time the unemployment rate exceeds 8 percent,
a) there were no recessions over the period 1970–1987.
b) 1982 and 1983 were the only recession years.
c) 1975, 1982, and 1983 were the only recession years.
d) 1975–1977 and 1982–1985 were all recession years.
e) 1975, 1976, and 1981–1984 were all recession years.

Figure 2.3

2.7
Correct: d)
Difficulty: 4
Page(s): 30–35
Scramble range: None
Topic: Data/time-series

2.7
Refer to Figure 2.3. Which of the following statements is true?
a) The unemployment rate rose more rapidly between 1981 and 1982 than between any other years.
b) The unemployment rate was generally higher during the period 1984–87 than it was during 1977–80.
c) The early 1970s was a period of relatively low unemployment.
d) Both b) and c).
e) None of the above.

2.8
Correct: a)
Difficulty: 2
Page(s): 30–35
Scramble range: All
Topic: Data/time-series

2.8
Consider Figure 2.4. The behaviour of x over time is best characterized as exhibiting
a) an upward trend and increasing variability.
b) an upward trend and decreasing variability.
c) a downward trend and increasing variability.
d) a downward trend and decreasing variability.
e) a constant trend and increasing variablility.

Figure 2.4

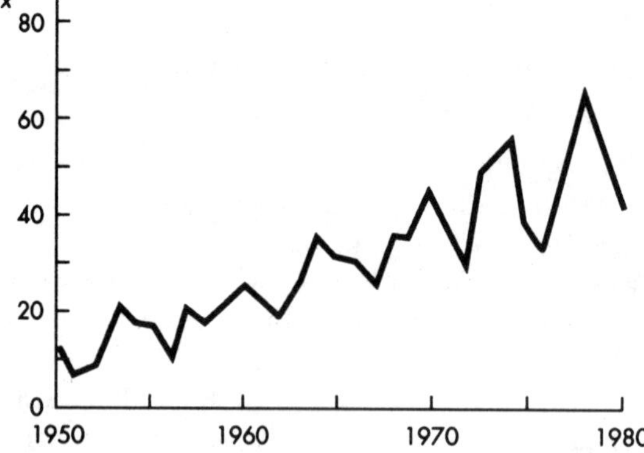

2.9
Correct: a)
Difficulty: 2
Page(s): 38
Scramble range: None
Topic: Data/scatter

2.9
Consider the graphs in Figure 2.5. Which of them indicates a positive relationship between x and y?
a) (a).
b) (b).
c) (c).
d) (d).
e) Both (a) and (d).

Figure 2.5

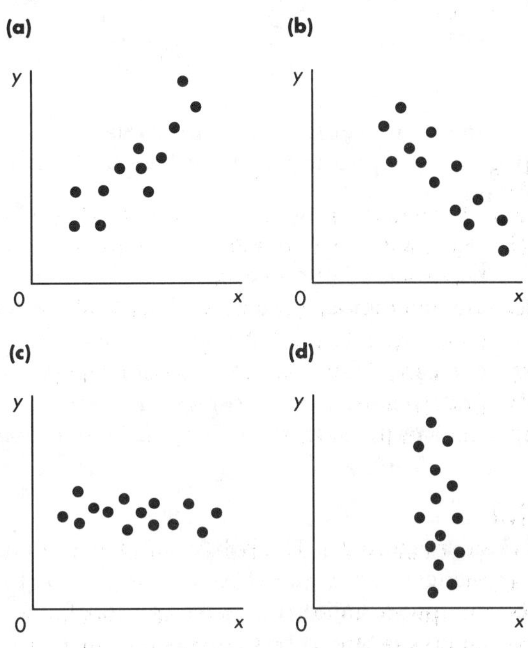

2.10
Correct: d)
Difficulty: 1
Page(s): 35–37
Scramble range: a)–d)
Topic: Data/scatter

2.10
The graphs in Figure 2.5 are examples of
a) dot graphs.
b) one-variable time-series graphs.
c) two-variable time-series graphs.
d) scatter diagrams.
e) none of the above.

2.11
Correct: b)
Difficulty: 2
Page(s): 37–39
Scramble range: None
Topic: Data/scatter

2.11
Consider the graphs in Figure 2.5. Which of them indicates a negative relationship between x and y?
a) (a).
b) (b).
c) (c).
d) (d).
e) Both (b) and (d).

2.12
Correct: d)
Difficulty: 2
Page(s): 40–41
Scramble range: None
Topic: Data/scatter

2.12
Consider the graphs in Figure 2.5. Which of them seems to indicate no relationship between *x* and *y*?
a) (a) only.
b) (b) only.
c) (c) only.
d) (c) and (d).
e) None of the above.

2.13
Correct: c)
Difficulty: 2
Page(s): 38–41
Scramble range: None
Topic: Data/scatter

2.13
Consider the graph in Figure 2.5(a). Which of the following statements is true?
a) *x* and *y* appear to be negatively related.
b) *x* and *y* appear to be unrelated.
c) *x* and *y* appear to be positively related.
d) *x* and *y* appear to move in opposite directions.
e) Both a) and d).

2.14
Correct: e)
Difficulty: 2
Page(s): 39–41
Scramble range: None
Topic: Data/scatter

2.14
Consider the graph in Figure 2.5(b). Which of the following statements is true?
a) *x* and *y* appear to be negatively related.
b) *x* and *y* appear to be unrelated.
c) *x* and *y* appear to be positively related.
d) *x* and *y* appear to move in opposite directions.
e) Both a) and d).

2.15
Correct: b)
Difficulty: 2
Page(s): 38–41
Scramble range: None
Topic: Data/scatter

2.15
Consider graph in Figure 2.5(c). Which of the following statements is true?
a) *x* and *y* appear to be negatively related.
b) *x* and *y* appear to be unrelated.
c) *x* and *y* appear to be positively related.
d) *x* and *y* appear to move in opposite directions.
e) Both a) and d).

2.16 (SG 2.6)
Correct: a)
Difficulty: 1
Page(s): 38–39
Scramble range: All
Topic: Graph/ relationship

2.16
If variables *x* and *y* move up and down together, they are said to be
a) positively related.
b) negatively related.
c) conversely related.
d) unrelated.
e) proportional.

2.17
Correct: b)
Difficulty: 2
Page(s): 38–39
Scramble range: All
Topic: Graph/ relationship

2.17
Two variables are positively related if
a) increases in one are associated with decreases in the other.
b) increases in one are associated with increases in the other.
c) decreases in one are associated with increases in the other.
d) any change in one causes an increase in the other.
e) any change in one causes a decrease in the other.

2.18
Correct: a)
Difficulty: 2
Page(s): 38–39
Scramble range: All
Topic: Graph/ relationship

2.18
Two variables are negatively related if
a) increases in one are associated with decreases in the other.
b) increases in one are associated with increases in the other.
c) both variables are below zero.
d) any change in one causes an increase in the other.
e) any change in one causes a decrease in the other.

2.19
Correct: c)
Difficulty: 2
Page(s): 38–39
Scramble range: All
Topic: Graph/ relationship

2.19
Two variables are positively related if
a) when one is positive the other is positive.
b) when one is negative the other is negative.
c) they increase or decrease together.
d) they move in opposite directions.
e) they both are always positive.

2.20
Correct: e)
Difficulty: 2
Page(s): 38–39
Scramble range: All
Topic: Graph/ relationship

2.20
Two variables are negatively related if
a) when one is positive the other is positive.
b) when one is negative the other is negative.
c) they increase or decrease together.
d) they both are always negative.
e) they move in opposite directions.

2.21
Correct: a)
Difficulty: 2
Page(s): 38–39
Scramble range: All
Topic: Graph/ relationship

2.21
The relationship between two variables that are positively related is shown graphically by a line that
a) slopes upward to the right.
b) is horizontal.
c) slopes downward to the right.
d) is vertical.
e) is always in the positive part of both the x-coordinate and the y-coordinate.

2.22
Correct: c)
Difficulty: 2
Page(s): 38–39
Scramble range: All
Topic: Graph/ relationship

2.22
The relationship between two variables that are negatively related is shown graphically by a line that
a) slopes upward to the right.
b) is horizontal.
c) slopes downward to the right.
d) is vertical.
e) is always in the negative part of both the x-coordinate and the y-coordinate.

2.23
Correct: a)
Difficulty: 3
Page(s): 38–39
Scramble range: All
Topic: Graph/ relationship

2.23
The relationship between two variables that move up and down together is shown graphically by a line that
a) is positively sloped.
b) is steep.
c) is relatively flat.
d) is negatively sloped.
e) has increasing volatility.

2.24
Correct: c)
Difficulty: 2
Page(s): 40–41
Scramble range: a)–d)
Topic: Slope

2.24
The slope of a horizontal line is
a) positive.
b) negative.
c) zero.
d) infinite.
e) none of the above.

2.25
Correct: e)
Difficulty: 3
Page(s): 38–39
Scramble range: All
Topic: Graph/relationship

2.25
Consider Figure 2.6. The variables *x* and *y*
a) are negatively related.
b) have a nonlinear relationship.
c) move down together.
d) are unrelated.
e) are positively related.

Figure 2.6

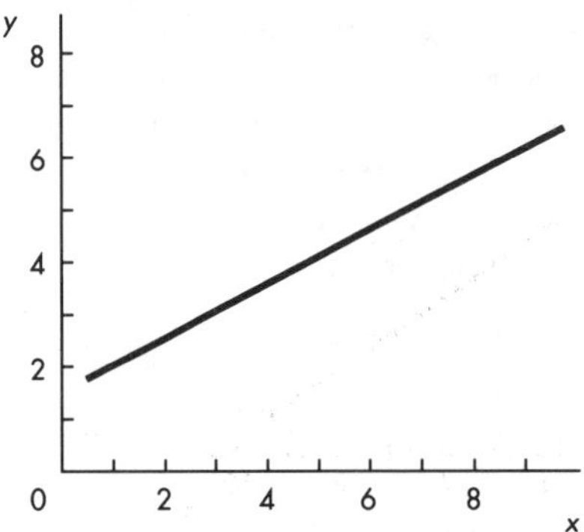

2.26
Correct: d)
Difficulty: 2
Page(s): 38–45
Scramble range: All
Topic: Graph/interpret

2.26
In Figure 2.6 the value of *y* is 5 when *x* is
a) 4.
b) 5.
c) 6.
d) 7.
e) 8.

2.27
Correct: b)
Difficulty: 2
Page(s): 38–45
Scramble range: All
Topic: Graph/interpret

2.27
Refer to Figure 2.6. If *x* decreases from 5 to 4, *y*
a) decreases from 4 to 3.
b) decreases from 4 to 3 1/2.
c) decreases from 4 to 2.
d) increases from 4 to 5.
e) increases from 3 1/2 to 4.

2.28
Correct: c)
Difficulty: 2
Page(s): 38–45
Scramble range: All
Topic: Graph/interpret

2.28
Refer to Figure 2.6. In order for *y* to increase from 5 to 6, *x* must
a) increase from 5 to 6.
b) increase from 7 to 8.
c) increase from 7 to 9.
d) decrease from 9 to 7.
e) increase from 7 to 7 1/2.

2.29
Correct: c)
Difficulty: 4
Page(s): 41–43
Scramble range: All
Topic: Slope/calculate

2.29
The slope of the line in Figure 2.6 is
a) 1.
b) –1.
c) 1/2.
d) 2.
e) dependent on where you measure it.

2.30
Correct: b)
Difficulty: 3
Page(s): 38–39
Scramble range: All
Topic: Graph/straight

2.30
In Figure 2.7 the variables *x* and *y*
a) move up and down together.
b) are negatively related.
c) are time-series variables.
d) reach a maximum when *x* is zero.
e) are positively related.

Figure 2.7

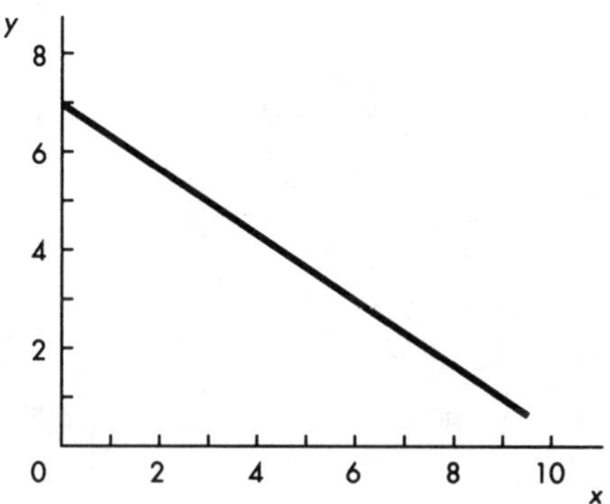

2.31
Correct: d)
Difficulty: 4
Page(s): 41–43
Scramble range: a)–d)
Topic: Slope/straight

2.31
The slope of the line in Figure 2.7 is
a) 3/2.
b) 2/3.
c) –3/2.
d) –2/3.
e) none of the above.

2.32
Correct: a)
Difficulty: 3
Page(s): 41–42
Scramble range: All
Topic: Graph/straight

2.32
The slope of a straight line
a) is the same at every point.
b) increases as the variable on the *x*-axis increases if the slope is positive.
c) decreases as the variable on the *x*-axis increases if the slope is negative.
d) is the same at every point only if the line is horizontal.
e) depends on where you measure it.

2.33
Correct: a)
Difficulty: 4
Page(s): 38–43
Scramble range: All
Topic: Graph/relationship

2.33
From Figure 2.8 we know that household expenditure
a) is linearly related to household income.
b) is negatively related to household income.
c) decreases only if household income increases.
d) and household income movc up and down independently of each other.
e) increases as household income increases, and this slope increases as income increases.

Figure 2.8

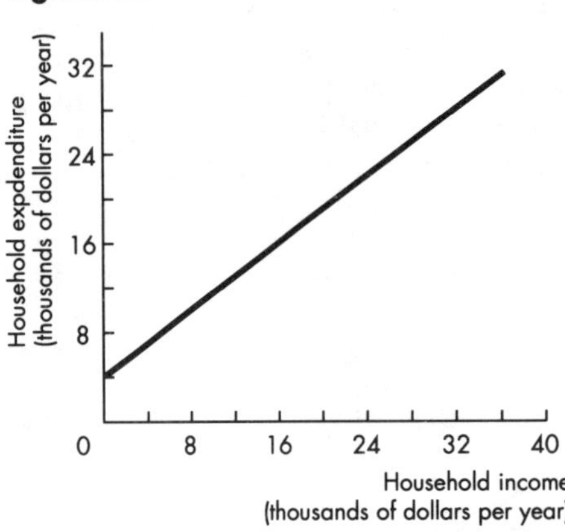

2.34
Correct: e)
Difficulty: 4
Page(s): 38–45
Scramble range: All
Topic: Graph/interpret

2.34
Refer to Figure 2.8. If household income increases by $1,000, household expenditures will
a) increase by $1,333.33.
b) increase by $1,000.
c) remain unchanged.
d) increase but we cannot tell by how much unless we know the initial value of household income.
e) increase by $750.

2.35
Correct: c)
Difficulty: 2
Page(s): 38–45
Scramble range: All
Topic: Graph/interpret

2.35
Refer to Figure 2.8. If household income is $16,000, household expenditures will be
a) $10,000.
b) $12,000.
c) $16,000.
d) $18,000.
e) $20,000.

2.36
Correct: b)
Difficulty: 2
Page(s): 38–45
Scramble range: All
Topic: Graph/interpret

2.36
Refer to Figure 2.8. If household income is zero, household expenditures
a) will be 0.
b) will be $4,000.
c) will be $8,000.
d) will be –$4,000.
e) cannot be determined from the graph.

2.37
Correct: c)
Difficulty: 2
Page(s): 38–45
Scramble range: All
Topic: Graph/interpret

2.37
Refer to Figure 2.8. If household income is $24,000, household expenditures

a) will be $18,000.
b) will be $20,000.
c) will be $22,000.
d) will be $24,000.
e) cannot be determined from the graph.

2.38
Correct: c)
Difficulty: 2
Page(s): 38–45
Scramble range: a)–d)
Topic: Graph/interpret

2.38
Refer to Figure 2.8. If household expenditure is $28,000 then household income must be

a) $24,000.
b) $28,000.
c) $32,000.
d) $36,000.
e) none of the above.

2.39
Correct: b)
Difficulty: 4
Page(s): 41–43
Scramble range: All
Topic: Slope/straight

2.39
The slope of the line in Figure 2.8 is

a) 0.5.
b) 0.75.
c) 1.
d) 1.25.
e) 1.5.

2.40
Correct: e)
Difficulty: 4
Page(s): 42–43
Scramble range: All
Topic: Slope/arc

2.40
Refer to Figure 2.9. The slope across the arc between *a* and *b* is

a) 2/5.
b) 2/3.
c) 1.
d) 2.
e) 1/2.

Figure 2.9

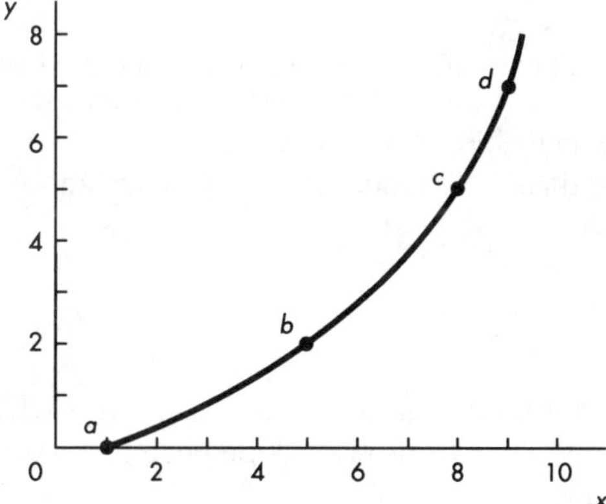

2.41
Correct: c)
Difficulty: 3
Page(s): 38–42
Scramble range: All
Topic: Graph/relationship

2.41
Figure 2.10 illustrates two variables, *x* and *y*, which are
a) negatively related, with a decreasing slope as *x* increases.
b) negatively related, with an increasing slope as *x* increases.
c) positively related, with a decreasing slope as *x* increases.
d) positively related, with an increasing slope as *x* increases.
e) unrelated.

Figure 2.10

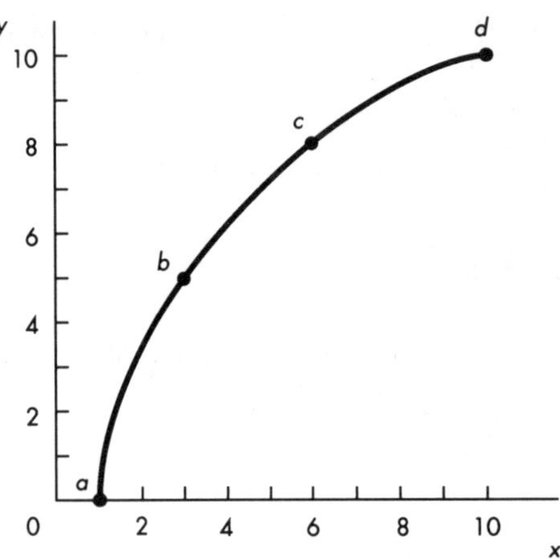

2.42
Correct: d)
Difficulty: 4
Page(s): 42–43
Scramble range: All
Topic: Slope/arc

2.42
In Figure 2.10, the slope across the arc between *a* and *b* is
a) 1/2.
b) 1.
c) 3/2.
d) 5/2.
e) 5/3.

2.43
Correct: c)
Difficulty: 5
Page(s): 42–43
Scramble range: All
Topic: Slope/point

2.43
In Figure 2.10, the slope at point *b* is
a) 3/2.
b) 1.
c) between 1 and 5/2, although the exact value cannot be determined from the available information.
d) less than 1, although the exact value cannot be determined from the available information.
e) 5/3.

2.44
Correct: a)
Difficulty: 4
Page(s): 38–42
Scramble range: All
Topic: Graph/interpret

2.44
Figure 2.11 illustrates two variables, *x* and *y*, which are
a) negatively related, with slope getting closer to 0 as *x* increases from 2 to 16.
b) negatively related, with slope getting farther from 0 as *x* increases from 2 to 16.
c) positively related, with slope getting closer to 0 as *x* increases from 2 to 16.
d) positively related, with slope getting farther from 0 as *x* increases from 2 to 16.
e) positively related, with the slope unchanging as *x* increases from 2 to 16.

Figure 2.11

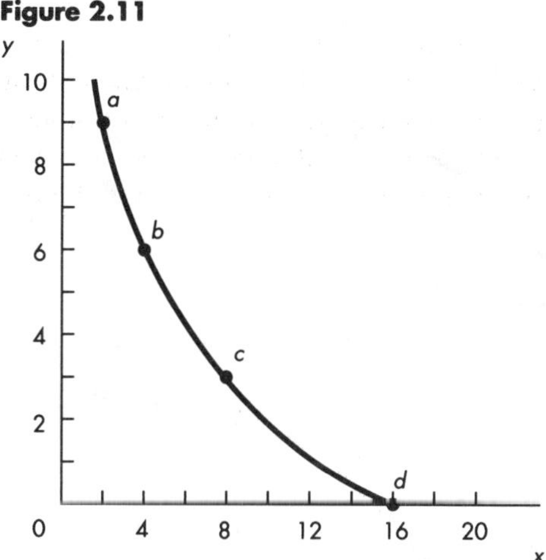

2.45
Correct: c)
Difficulty: 4
Page(s): 42–43
Scramble range: All
Topic: Slope/arc

2.45
In Figure 2.11, the slope across the arc between *a* and *b* is
a) 2/3.
b) –1.
c) –3/2.
d) –3.
e) –9/4.

2.46
Correct: e)
Difficulty: 4
Page(s): 42–43
Scramble range: All
Topic: Slope/arc

2.46
In Figure 2.11, the slope across the arc between *b* and *c* is
a) –2/3.
b) –3/2.
c) –2.
d) –4/3.
e) –3/4.

2.47
Correct: b)
Difficulty: 4
Page(s): 42–43
Scramble range: All
Topic: Slope/point

2.47
In Figure 2.11, the slope at point *b*
a) lies between –2/3 and –1.
b) lies between –3/4 and –3/2.
c) lies between –2/3 and –4/3.
d) lies between 1 and 3/2.
e) is greater than 3/2.

2.48
Correct: c)
Difficulty: 5
Page(s): 39–40
Scramble range: All
Topic: Graph/interpret

2.48
Refer to Figure 2.12. Which of the following statements is true?
a) *x* and *y* are positively related between points *a* and *d*.
b) *x* and *y* are negatively related between points *b* and *d*.
c) *y* reaches a maximum at point *c*.
d) *y* reaches a minimum at point *c*.
e) *x* and *y* are unrelated.

Figure 2.12

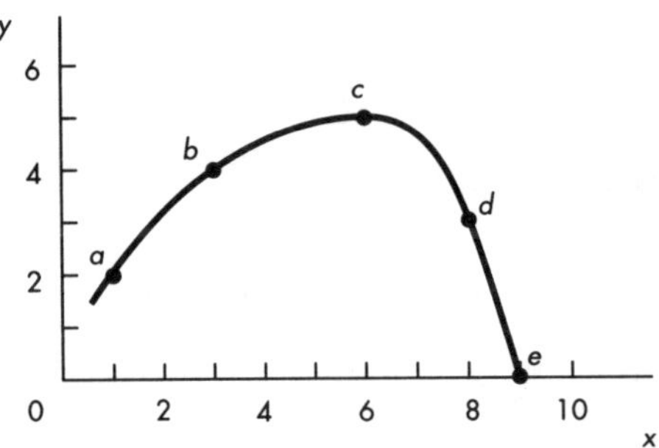

2.49
Correct: c)
Difficulty: 4
Page(s): 41–44
Scramble range: All
Topic: Slope

2.49
Refer to Figure 2.12.
a) The slope is less between points *a* and *b* than between points *b* and *c*.
b) The slope is greater between points *b* and *c* than between points *a* and *b*.
c) The slope at *c* is 0.
d) The slope at *c* is 1.
e) The slope at *c* is negative.

2.50
Correct: a)
Difficulty: 4
Page(s): 42–43
Scramble range: All
Topic: Slope/arc

2.50
In Figure 2.12, the slope across the arc between points *b* and *c* is
a) 1/3.
b) 1/2.
c) 1.
d) 2.
e) 5/6.

2.51
Correct: d)
Difficulty: 4
Page(s): 42–43
Scramble range: All
Topic: Slope/arc

2.51
In Figure 2.12, the slope across the arc between points *c* and *d* is
a) 1/2.
b) 1.
c) –1/2.
d) –1.
e) –5/8.

2.52
Correct: b)
Difficulty: 4
Page(s): 42–43
Scramble range: All
Topic: Slope/arc

2.52
In Figure 2.12, the slope across the arc between points *b* and *d* is
a) 1/5.
b) –1/5.
c) 1/2.
d) –1/2.
e) –3/8.

2.53
Correct: e)
Difficulty: 4
Page(s): 42–43
Scramble range: All
Topic: Slope/point

2.53
In Figure 2.12, the slope at point *b*
a) is 1.
b) is –1.
c) is 4/3.
d) lies between 1 and 3.
e) lies between 1/3 and 1.

2.54
Correct: a)
Difficulty: 4
Page(s): 42–43
Scramble range: All
Topic: Slope

2.54
In Figure 2.12, the slope at point *c*
a) is 0.
b) is 1.
c) lies between 1/3 and 1.
d) lies between –1/5 and –1.
e) lies between 1/3 and –1.

2.55
Correct: d)
Difficulty: 5
Page(s): 38–39
Scramble range: a)–d)
Topic: Graph/ relationship

2.55
Consider the values for *x* and *y* given in Table 2.1. Which of the graphs in Figure 2.13 represents the relationship between *x* and *y*?
a) (a).
b) (b).
c) (c).
d) (d).
e) None of the above.

Table 2.1

x	2	4	6	8	10
y	12	8	5	3	2

Figure 2.13

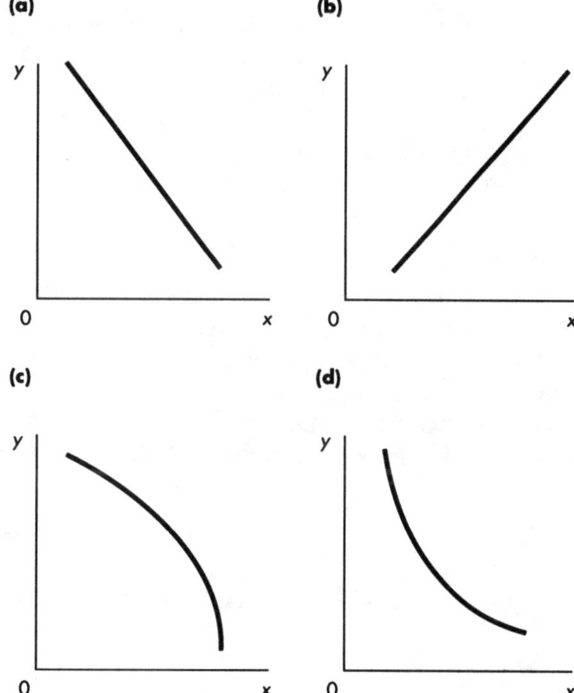

2.56
Correct: b)
Difficulty: 4
Page(s): 43–44
Scramble range: All
Topic: Graph/three variables

2.56
To graph a relationship among three variables we
a) hold two variables constant in order to graph the third variable.
b) hold one variable constant and graph the relationship between the other two variables.
c) graph each of the three using a separate time-series graph.
d) must be able to draw in three dimensions.
e) must be able to allow all three variables to vary at once in one graph.

2.57
Correct: e)
Difficulty: 5
Page(s): 38–45
Scramble range: All
Topic: Graph/variables

2.57
In Table 2.2,
a) x and y are positively related, holding z constant.
b) x and y are negatively related, holding y constant.
c) x and y are unrelated.
d) x and z are unrelated.
e) y and z are positively related, holding x constant.

Table 2.2

x	120	100	80	140	120	100	160	140	120
y	10	12	14	10	12	14	10	12	14
z	4	4	4	5	5	5	6	6	6

2.58
Correct: a)
Difficulty: 4
Page(s): 38–45
Scramble range: All
Topic: Graph/three variables

2.58
Given the data in Table 2.2, holding z constant, the graph of x and y
a) is a negatively sloped line.
b) is a positively sloped line.
c) reaches a maximum.
d) reaches a minimum.
e) does not have a constant slope.

2.59
Correct: b)
Difficulty: 4
Page(s): 38–45
Scramble range: All
Topic: Graph/three variables

2.59
Given the data in Table 2.2, holding y constant, the graph of x and z
a) is a negatively sloped line.
b) is a positively sloped line.
c) reaches a maximum.
d) reaches a minimum.
e) shows that x and z are not related.

2.60
Correct: d)
Difficulty: 5
Page(s): 43–44
Scramble range: a)–d)
Topic: Graph/three variables

2.60
Given the data in Table 2.2, which of the graphs in Figure 2.14 correctly represents the relationship between x, y, and z?
a) (a).
b) (b).
c) (c).
d) (d).
e) None of the above.

Figure 2.14

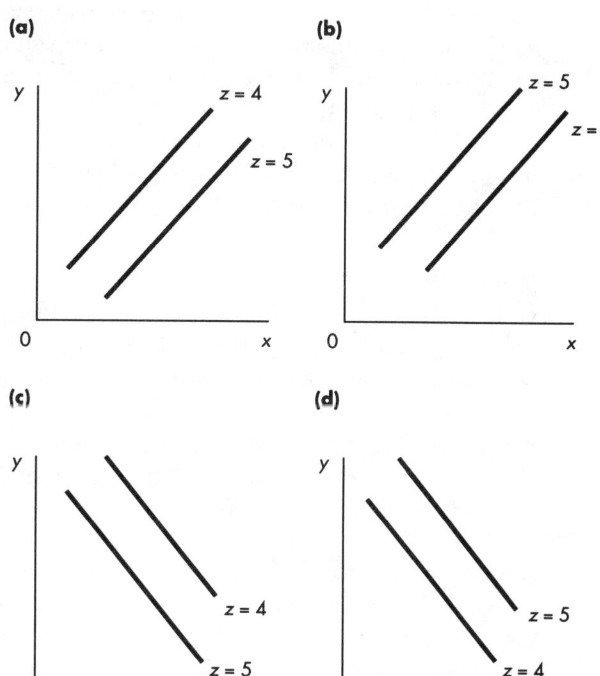

2.61
Correct: c)
Difficulty: 5
Page(s): 43–44
Scramble range: a)–d)
Topic: Graph/three variables

2.61

Given the data in Table 2.2, which of the graphs in Figure 2.15 correctly represents the relationship among *x*, *y*, and *z*?

a) (a).
b) (b).
c) (c).
d) (d).
e) None of the above.

Figure 2.15

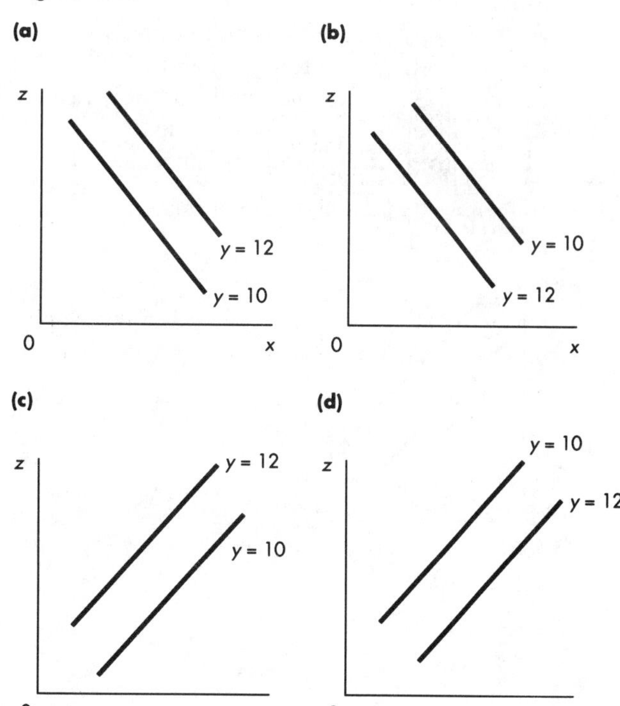

2.62
Correct: a)
Difficulty: 5
Page(s): 43–44
Scramble range: None
Topic: Graph/three variables

2.62
Consider the data in Table 2.2. Suppose *z* increases from 4 to 5. What will happen to the graph of the relationship between *x* and *y*?
a) It will shift to the right.
b) It will shift to the left.
c) It will become positively sloped.
d) Both a) and c).
e) None of the above.

2.63
Correct: a)
Difficulty: 5
Page(s): 43–44
Scramble range: None
Topic: Graph/three variables

2.63
From Table 2.3 we observe that, for the Smith family,
a) the number of boxes of strawberries purchased is negatively related to the price of strawberries, holding income constant.
b) the number of boxes of strawberries purchased is negatively related to income, holding the price of strawberries constant.
c) the price of strawberries is negatively related to family income, holding purchases of strawberries constant.
d) both b) and c).
e) both a) and b).

Table 2.3

x	300	300	300	400	400	400
y	$1.00	$1.25	$1.50	$1.00	$1.25	$1.50
z	5	3	2	7	5	4

Table 2.3 indicates how strawberry consumption by the Smith family depends on family income and the price of strawberries. In the table, *x* represents weekly family income, *y* represents the price of strawberries per box, and *z* represents the number of boxes of strawberries purchased per week.

2.64
Correct: c)
Difficulty: 4
Page(s): 38–45
Scramble range: All
Topic: Graph/three variables

2.64
In Figure 2.16, *x* is
a) positively related to *y* and negatively related to *z*.
b) positively related to both *y* and *z*.
c) negatively related to *y* and positively related to *z*.
d) negatively related to both *y* and *z*.
e) negatively related to *y* and unrelated to *z*.

Figure 2.16

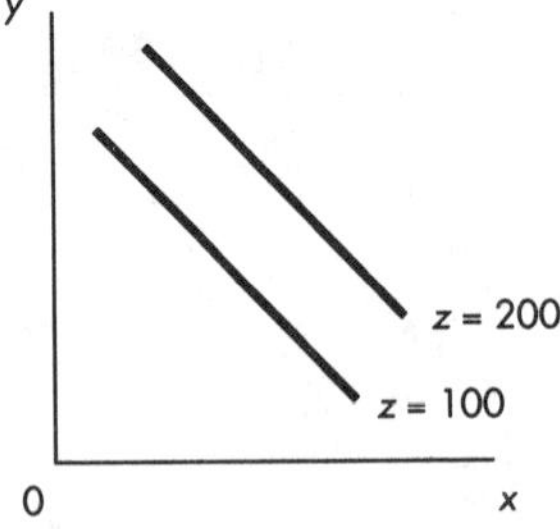

2.65
Correct: b)
Difficulty: 4
Page(s): 38–45
Scramble range: All
Topic: Graph/three variables

2.65
In Figure 2.17, *z* is
a) positively related to *x* and negatively related to *y*.
b) negatively related to *x* and positively related to *y*.
c) positively related to both *x* and *y*.
d) negatively related to both *x* and *y*.
e) related to *y* but not related to *x*.

Figure 2.17

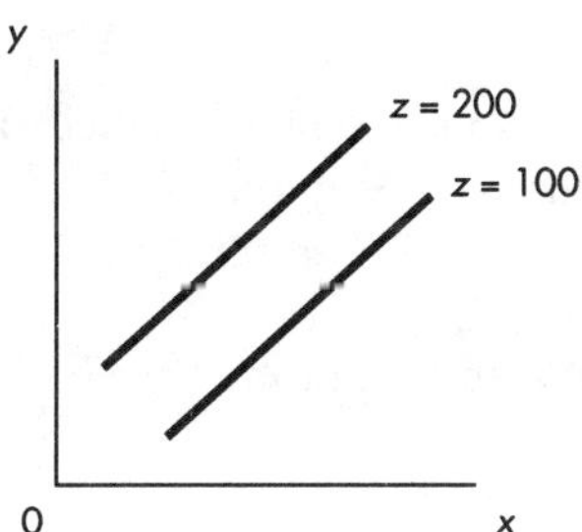

2.66
Correct: c)
Difficulty: 2
Page(s): 30–31
Scramble range: All
Topic: Time–series graph

2.66
The behaviour of a single economic variable over time is best illustrated by a
a) one-variable graph.
b) two-variable graph.
c) time-series graph.
d) scatter diagram.
e) three-dimensional graph.

2.67 (SG 2.2)
Correct: b)
Difficulty: 1
Page(s): 35–36
Scramble range: None
Topic: Two–variable time–series graph

2.67
Figure 2.18 is a
a) one-variable time-series graph.
b) two-variable time-series graph.
c) scatter diagram.
d) both a) and c).
e) both b) and c).

Figure 2.18

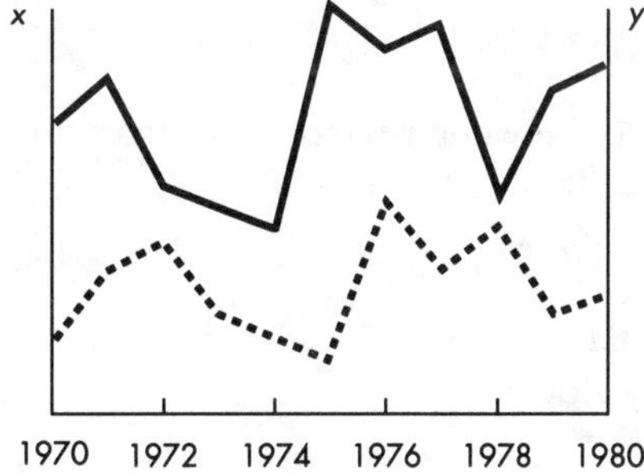

2.68 (SG 2.3)
Correct: d)
Difficulty: 5
Page(s): 35–36
Scramble range: All
Topic: Variable relationship

2.68
The dotted line in Figure 2.18 represents variable *y*. Which of the following statements best describes the relationship between *x* and *y* in Figure 2.18?
a) *x* and *y* tend to move in opposite directions over time.
b) *x* and *y* tend to move together over time.
c) *x* tends to move in the same direction as *y* but one year later.
d) *y* tends to move in the same direction as *x* but one year later.
e) *y* tends to move in the same direction as *x* but one year earlier.

2.69
Correct: e)
Difficulty: 2
Page(s): 29–37
Scramble range: All
Topic: Graphs

2.69
The data in Table 2.4 could not be represented by
a) two one-variable time-series graphs.
b) one two-variable time-series graph.
c) any sort of graph.
d) a three-variable time-series graph.
e) a scatter diagram.

Table 2.4

x	2	4	6	8	10
y	12	8	5	3	2

2.70
Correct: a)
Difficulty: 3
Page(s): 39–40
Scramble range: All
Topic: Negative relationships

2.70
From the information in Table 2.4, it appears that
a) *x* and *y* tend to exhibit a negative relationship.
b) *x* and *y* tend to exhibit a positive relationship.
c) there is no relationship between *x* and *y*.
d) there is first a negative and then a positive relationship between *x* and *y*.
e) there is first a positive and then a negative relationshiup between *x* and *y*.

2.71 (SG 2.6)
Correct: a)
Difficulty: 2
Page(s): 37–38
Scramble range: None
Topic: Positive relationships

2.71
If variables *x* and *y* move up and down together, they are said to be
a) positively related.
b) negatively related.
c) conversely related.
d) unrelated.
e) both b) and c).

2.72 (SG 2.7)
Correct: d)
Difficulty: 2
Page(s): 38–39
Scramble range: All
Topic: Negative relationships

2.72
The relationship between two variables that move in opposite directions is shown graphically by a line that is
a) positively sloped.
b) steep.
c) relatively flat.
d) negatively sloped.
e) perfectly flat.

2.73
Correct: e)
Difficulty: 4
Page(s): 41–42
Scramble range: All
Topic: Graph/ relationship

2.73
Consider Figure 2.19. If you were told that economic theory predicts that higher levels of the rate of interest (x) lead to lower levels of sales of houses (y), which graph would you pick to represent this economic relationship?

a) (a) or (d).
b) (d).
c) (b).
d) (c).
e) (a).

Figure 2.19

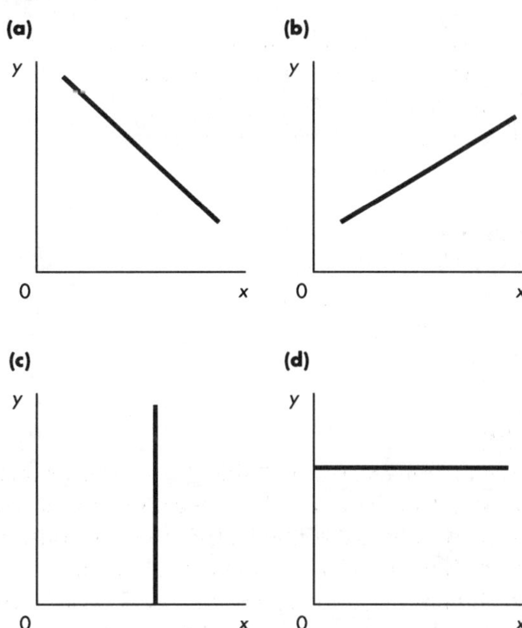

2.74
Correct: d)
Difficulty: 4
Page(s): 38–43
Scramble range: All
Topic: Graph/ relationship

2.74
Refer to Figure 2.19. If your theory predicted that a rise in the wage rate (x) leads to a rise in the amount of labour supplied in the economy (y), which graph would you use to represent this relationship?

a) (a) or (c).
b) (d).
c) (c).
d) (b).
e) (a).

2.75 (SG 2.10)
Correct: a)
Difficulty: 3
Page(s): 38–39
Scramble range: All
Topic: Increasing positive slope

2.75
In Figure 2.20 the relationship between x and y is

a) positive with slope decreasing as x increases.
b) negative with slope decreasing as x increases.
c) negative with slope increasing as x increases.
d) positive with slope increasing as x increases.
e) first positive, with a decreasing slope as x increases, then negative, with a decreasing slope as x increases.

Figure 2.20

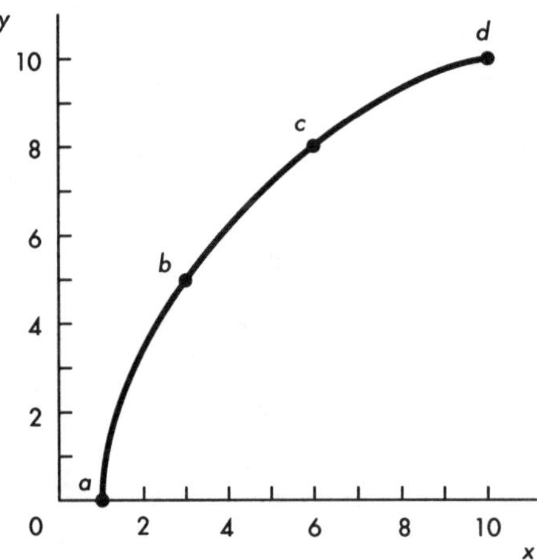

2.76 (SG 2.11)
Correct: c)
Difficulty: 4
Page(s): 41–43
Scramble range: All
Topic: Slope

2.76
In Figure 2.20, the slope across the arc between *b* and *c* is
a) 1/2.
b) 2/3.
c) 1.
d) 2.
e) 4/3.

2.77
Correct: e)
Difficulty: 4
Page(s): 41–43
Scramble range: All
Topic: Slope

2.77
In Figure 2.20, the slope at point *b*
a) is 2/3.
b) is 1.
c) is 5/3.
d) cannot be determined exactly from our information but is less than 1.
e) cannot be determined exactly from our information but lies between 5/2 and 1.

2.78 (SG 2.13)
Correct: b)
Difficulty: 4
Page(s): 43–44
Scramble range: All
Topic: Negative relationships

2.78
If the price of an umbrella is low and the number of rainy days per month is large, more umbrellas will be sold each month. On the other hand, if the price of an umbrella is high and there are few rainy days per month, fewer umbrellas will be sold each month. On the basis of this information, which of the following statements is true?
a) The number of umbrellas sold and the price of an umbrella are positively related, holding the number of rainy days constant.
b) The number of umbrellas sold and the price of an umbrella are negatively related, holding the number of rainy days constant.
c) The number of rainy days and the number of umbrellas sold are negatively related, holding the number of umbrellas sold constant.
d) The number of rainy days and the price of an umbrella are negatively related, holding the number of umbrellas sold constant.
e) The number of rainy days and the price of an umbrella are positively related, holding the number of umbrellas sold constant.

2.79 (SG 2.14)
Correct: b)
Difficulty: 4
Page(s): 38–39
Scramble range: All
Topic: Graphing two variables

2.79
Given the data in Table 2.5, holding income constant, the graph of the consumption of strawberries (horizontal axis) and the price of strawberries
a) is a positively sloped line.
b) is a negatively sloped line.
c) is a flat line.
d) reaches a maximum.
e) reaches a minimum.

Table 2.5

x	$300	300	300	400	400	400
y	$1.00	1.25	1.50	1.00	1.25	1.50
z	5	3	2	7	5	4

x = weekly family income, y = price of strawberries per box,
z = number of boxes of strawberries purchased per week.

2.80 (SG 2.15)
Correct: d)
Difficulty: 4
Page(s): 43–44
Scramble range: All
Topic: Shifts of the curve

2.80
Consider the data in Table 2.5. Suppose family income decreases from $400 to $300 per week. Then the graph of the price of strawberries (on the vertical axis) and the number of boxes of strawberries purchased will
a) no longer exist.
b) become positively sloped.
c) shift to the right.
d) shift to the left.
e) will not change at all.

2.81 (SG 2.16)
Correct: a)
Difficulty: 4
Page(s): 38–39
Scramble range: All
Topic: Graphing two variables

2.81
Given the data in Table 2.5, holding price constant, the graph of the consumption of strawberries (on the horizontal axis) and family income
a) will be a positively sloped line.
b) will be a negatively sloped line.
c) reaches a maximum.
d) reaches a minimum.
e) cannot be drawn if we hold price constant.

2.82 (SG 2.17)
Correct: e)
Difficulty: 3
Page(s): 38–42
Scramble range: All
Topic: Two-variable relationship

2.82
In Figure 2.16, x is
a) positively related to y and negatively related to z.
b) positively related to both y and z.
c) negatively related to z and unrelated to y.
d) negatively related to both y and z.
e) negatively related to y and positively related to z.

2.83
Correct: b)
Difficulty: 1
Page(s): 40–41
Scramble range: All
Topic: Slope

2.83
The change in a y variable (measured on the vertical axis) due to a change in an x variable is referred to as
a) an average.
b) slope.
c) run over rise.
d) calculus.
e) a maximum or minimum.

2.84
Correct: b)
Difficulty: 3
Page(s): 38–39
Scramble range: All
Topic: Positive relationship–variable

2.84
Refer to Table 2.6. What type of relationship exists between *y* and *z*?
a) Negative.
b) Positive.
c) Inverse.
d) No consistent relationship exists.
e) First a positive relationship, then a negative one.

Table 2.6

y	4	6	8	10	12
z	1	2	3	4	5

2.85
Correct: e)
Difficulty: 4
Page(s): 41–42
Scramble range: All
Topic: Calculating slope

2.85
Refer to Table 2.6. Assuming *y* is plotted on the vertical axis, the slope of the line is
a) constant at –2.
b) –2 when *x* is between 1 and 3.
c) –2 when *x* is between 1 and 3, and then +2 when *x* is between 4 and 5.
d) –2 when *x* is between 4 and 5.
e) constant at +2.

2.86
Correct: b)
Page(s): 39
Scramble range: All
Topic: Negative relationship–variable

2.86
Refer to Table 2.7. What type of relationship exists between *w* and *u*?
a) Positive.
b) Negative.
c) Direct.
d) No consistent relationship exists.
e) First a positive relationship, then a negative one.

Table 2.7

w	2	4	6	8	10
u	15	12	9	6	3

2.87
Correct: e)
Difficulty: 5
Page(s): 41–42
Scramble range: All
Topic: Calculating slope

2.87
Refer to Table 2.7. Suppose that *u* is the dependent variable. The slope of the line that could be drawn with *u* plotted on the vertical axis is
a) positive.
b) negative with a decreasing slope.
c) first negative, then positive.
d) positive with an increasing slope.
e) negative with a constant slope.

2.88
Correct: e)
Difficulty: 4
Page(s): 41–42
Scramble range: All
Topic: Calculating slope

2.88
Refer to Table 2.7. Suppose that *u* is the dependent variable. The slope of the line that could be drawn with *u* plotted on the vertical axis is
a) + 3.
b) –3.
c) –2/3.
d) +3/2.
e) –3/2.

2.89
Correct: b)
Difficulty: 1
Page(s): 38–39
Scramble range: All
Topic: Positive relationships

2.89
Refer to Figure 2.19. Which of the graphs shows a positive relationship between *x* and *y*?
a) (a).
b) (b).
c) (c).
d) (d).
e) Both (b) and (d).

2.90
Correct: a)
Difficulty: 1
Page(s): 38–39
Scramble range: All
Topic: Negative relationships

2.90
Refer to Figure 2.19. Which of the graphs shows a negative relationship between *x* and *y*?
a) (a).
b) (b).
c) (c).
d) (d).
e) Both (a) and (d).

2.91
Correct: d)
Difficulty: 2
Page(s): 40–41
Scramble range: All
Topic: Zero slope

2.91
Refer to Figure 2.19. Which of the graphs shows a line with a zero slope?
a) (a).
b) (b).
c) (c).
d) (d).
e) None of the graphs.

2.92
Correct: e)
Difficulty: 2
Page(s): 40–41
Scramble range: All
Topic: Infinite slope

2.92
Refer to Figure 2.19. Which of the graphs shows a line with an infinite slope?
a) None of the graphs.
b) (b).
c) (d).
d) (a).
e) (c).

2.93
Correct: e)
Difficulty: 4
Page(s): 38–43
Scramble range: All
Topic: Graph/ relationship

2.93
Consider Figure 2.19. Suppose our theory predicted that for low levels of quantity produced (*x*) a firm's profits (*y*) were low, for medium levels of output their profits were high, and for high levels of output their profits were low again. Which of the graphs would represent this relationship?
a) (a).
b) (b).
c) (c).
d) (d).
e) None of the graphs.

2.94
Correct: e)
Difficulty: 4
Page(s): 38–43
Scramble range: All
Topic: Graph/ relationships

2.94
Consider Table 2.8. If we were to draw a graph of this relationship, then when would the slope be positive?
a) Never.
b) Only if x is less than 5.
c) We do not have enough information to tell.
d) Only if x equals 5.
e) Only if x is greater than 5.

Table 2.8

x	0	1	2	3	4	5	6	7	8	9
y	10	8	6	4	2	0	2	4	6	8

2.95
Correct: d)
Difficulty: 4
Page(s): 38–43
Scramble range: All
Topic: Slope/calculation

2.95
Consider Table 2.8. When $x = 5$, the slope is
a) 5.
b) –2.
c) +2.
d) 0.
e) infinite.

2.96
Correct: b)
Difficulty: 2
Page(s): 38–43
Scramble range: a)–d)
Topic: Graph/ relationship

2.96
Consider Table 2.8. When $x = 5$,
a) y is at a maximum.
b) y is at a minimum.
c) the slope is positive.
d) the slope is negative.
e) none of the above.

2.97
Correct: a)
Difficulty: 5
Page(s): 38–43
Scramble range: All
Topic: Graph/ relationship

2.97
Consider Table 2.8. If y was the amount of pain that Jill Student gets from studying, and x was the amount of hours she has studied, then
a) Jill would never want to study more than 5 hours, other things equal.
b) Jill clearly hates studying, and will study zero hours, other things equal.
c) Jill clearly loves studying, and will study as many hours as she can, other things equal.
d) Jill will study zero hours, other things equal.
e) Jill will clearly study 9 hours, other things equal.

Chapter 3 Production, Specialization, and Exchange

3.1
Correct: b)
Difficulty: 2
Page(s): 51
Scramble range: All
Topic: Resources

3.1
The three major classes of resources used in production are
a) natural resources, unnatural resources, and consumption resources.
b) natural resources, human resources, and capital resources.
c) natural resources, production resources, and consumption resources.
d) water, land, and minerals.
e) capital goods, consumption goods, and service goods.

3.2
Correct: b)
Difficulty: 2
Page(s): 51
Scramble range: a)–d)
Topic: Resources

3.2
Which of the following is *not* a major class of resources used in production?
a) Natural resources.
b) Market resources.
c) Capital resources.
d) Human resources.
e) None of the above is a major class of resources.

3.3
Correct: c)
Difficulty: 2
Page(s): 51
Scramble range: All
Topic: Natural resource

3.3
Which of the following is an example of a natural resource?
a) Frank Sinatra's singing voice.
b) A computer program.
c) A dairy cow.
d) A road.
e) A dam.

3.4
Correct: c)
Difficulty: 3
Page(s): 51
Scramble range: All
Topic: Human resource

3.4
Which of the following is an example of a human resource?
a) An insurance policy.
b) A General Motors bond.
c) The skills of a welder.
d) An IBM stock certificate.
e) A computer program.

3.5
Correct: a)
Difficulty: 3
Page(s): 51
Scramble range: All
Topic: Capital resources

3.5
Which of the following is *not* an example of a capital resource?
a) Money.
b) A carpenter's hammer.
c) A shoe factory.
d) A bread-slicing machine.
e) The Skydome.

3.6
Correct: c)
Difficulty: 2
Page(s): 51
Scramble range: All
Topic: Goods and services

3.6
A shoe shine is an example of a
a) productive resource.
b) consumption good.
c) service.
d) property right.
e) human resource.

3.7
Correct: e)
Difficulty: 2
Page(s): 51–52
Scramble range: All
Topic: Human capital

3.7
Ted works as a clerk in a retail store during the day and is taking accounting classes in the evenings. Ted is
a) not producing a good or a service.
b) producing inside his production possibility frontier.
c) uselessly expending resources.
d) trying to produce outside his production possibility frontier.
e) accumulating human capital.

3.8
Correct: a)
Difficulty: 4
Page(s): 51–52
Scramble range: All
Topic: PPF

3.8
The production possibility frontier
a) is the boundary between attainable and unattainable levels of production.
b) illustrates the maximum quantities of all goods that can be produced for given resources and technology.
c) illustrates the fact that, in an economy using all its resources, to produce more of one good need not mean less of another good is produced.
d) shows prices at which production is possible and impossible.
e) illustrates why there need not be any scarcity in the world.

3.9
Correct: b)
Difficulty: 3
Page(s): 51–53
Scramble range: All
Topic: PPF

3.9
Which of the following concepts is *not* illustrated by a production possibility frontier?
a) Scarcity.
b) Monetary exchange.
c) Opportunity cost.
d) Attainable and unattainable points.
e) The tradeoff between producing one good versus another.

3.10
Correct: a)
Difficulty: 2
Page(s): 52–53
Scramble range: All
Topic: PPF

3.10
A point inside a production possibility frontier
a) indicates some unemployed resources.
b) is unattainable.
c) is better than points on the production possibility frontier.
d) indicates fully employed resources.
e) illustrates the idea of opportunity cost.

3.11
Correct: a)
Difficulty: 3
Page(s): 52–53
Scramble range: All
Topic: PPF

3.11
If Sam is producing at a point inside his production possibility frontier, then he
a) can increase production of both goods with no increase in resources.
b) is fully using all his resources.
c) must be doing the best he can with limited resources.
d) is unaffected by costs and technology.
e) has a high opportunity cost of moving from this point.

3.12
Correct: e)
Difficulty: 3
Page(s): 52–53
Scramble range: All
Topic: PPF

3.12
If Sam is producing at a point on his production possibility frontier, then he
a) cannot produce any more of either good.
b) is unaffected by costs and technology, since he is fully using his resources.
c) will be unable to gain from trade.
d) is not subject to scarcity.
e) can increase the production of one good only by decreasing the production of the other.

3.13
Correct: d)
Difficulty: 3
Page(s): 52–57
Scramble range: All
Topic: PPF

3.13
Refer to the production possibility frontier in Figure 3.1. Which of the following is true about point *a*?
a) It is unattainable.
b) While no more of good *Y* can be produced, more of good *X* can be produced.
c) It is preferred to point *b*.
d) Resources are not fully employed.
e) It is attainable only if we increase the amount of capital goods.

Figure 3.1

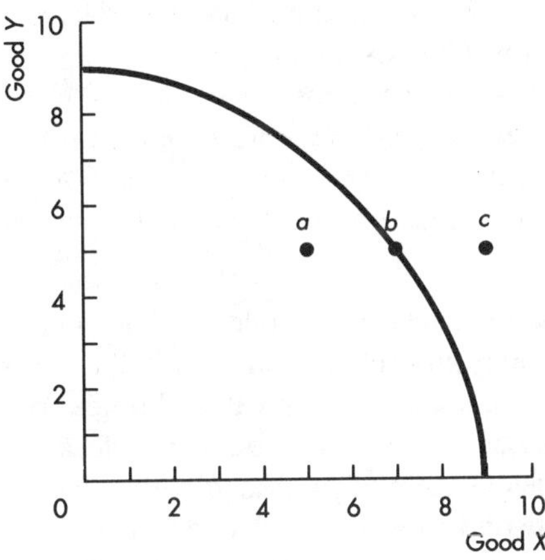

3.14
Correct: b)
Difficulty: 3
Page(s): 52–53
Scramble range: All
Topic: PPF

3.14
In Figure 3.1,
a) movement from *a* to *b* would require a technological improvement.
b) point *b* is superior to point *a*.
c) some resources must be unemployed at point *c*.
d) the concept of decreasing opportunity cost is illustrated.
e) movement from *c* to *b* would require a technological improvement.

3.15
Correct: a)
Difficulty: 4
Page(s): 54–55
Scramble range: All
Topic: Shape of PPF

3.15
The fact that individual productive resources are not equally useful in all activities
a) implies that a production possibility frontier will be bowed out.
b) implies that gain from specialization and trade is unlikely.
c) follows from the law of demand.
d) implies a linear production possibility frontier.
e) implies that an economy should not produce certain goods.

3.16
Correct: d)
Difficulty: 4
Page(s): 54–55
Scramble range: All
Topic: Shape of PPF

3.16
If additional units of any good could be produced at a *constant* opportunity cost, the production possibility frontier would be
a) bowed outward.
b) bowed inward.
c) positively sloped.
d) linear.
e) perfectly horizontal.

3.17
Correct: c)
Difficulty: 4
Page(s): 54–55
Scramble range: All
Topic: Shape of PPF

3.17
The existence of *increasing* opportunity cost
a) explains why specialization is frequently useful.
b) explains why resources are scarce.
c) explains the bowed out shape of the production possibility frontier.
d) follows from the existence of property rights.
e) explains why some societies are inside their production possibility frontier.

3.18
Correct: b)
Difficulty: 3
Page(s): 54–55
Scramble range: None
Topic: Shape of PPF

3.18
A production possibility frontier will be negatively sloped because
a) more goods are purchased as price falls.
b) of opportunity costs.
c) some resources are not fully utilized.
d) there is not enough capital in the economy.
e) both b) and c).

3.19
Correct: e)
Difficulty: 4
Page(s): 54–55
Scramble range: All
Topic: Shape of PPF

3.19
Refer to the production possibility frontier in Figure 3.2. If 6 units of *X* are currently being produced, then
a) 40 units of *Y* cannot be produced unless production of *X* is decreased.
b) 40 units of *Y* cannot be produced unless production of *X* is increased.
c) 60 units of *Y* can be produced with some resources *not* fully utilized.
d) 50 units of *Y* must be produced, regardless of resource utilization.
e) 50 units of *Y* can be produced if all resources are fully utilized.

Figure 3.2

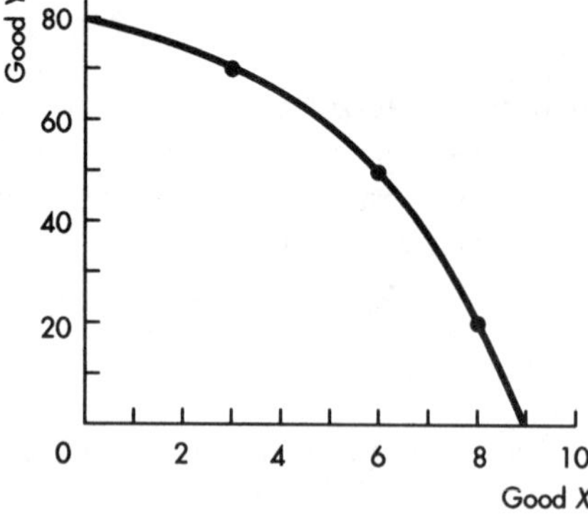

3.20
Correct: b)
Difficulty: 4
Page(s): 54–55
Scramble range: All
Topic: Shape of PPF

3.20
Refer to the production possibility frontier in Figure 3.2. Suppose that 50 units of *Y* are currently being produced. Then
a) 7 units of *X* are being produced.
b) 6 units of *X* can be produced if all resources are fully utilized.
c) 9 units of *X* can be produced if all resources are fully utilized.
d) resources are not being fully utilized.
e) 6 units of *X* are being produced.

3.21
Correct: d)
Difficulty: 3
Page(s): 53–54
Scramble range: All
Topic: Opportunity cost

3.21
Refer to the production possibility frontier in Figure 3.2. If 3 units of *X* are currently being produced, the opportunity cost of producing 3 more units
a) cannot be determined from the diagram.
b) is 30 units of *Y.*
c) is 3 units of *X.*
d) is 20 units of *Y.*
e) is 10 units of *Y.*

3.22
Correct: d)
Difficulty: 3
Page(s): 53–54
Scramble range: All
Topic: Opportunity cost

3.22
Refer to the production possibility frontier in Figure 3.2. If 70 units of *Y* are currently being produced, the opportunity cost of increasing production of *Y* to 80 units is
a) 10 units of *Y.*
b) 80 units of *Y.*
c) 2 units of *X.*
d) 3 units of *X.*
e) 1 unit of *X.*

3.23
Correct: d)
Difficulty: 2
Page(s): 54–55
Scramble range: All
Topic: Shape of PPF

3.23
A situation in which all resources are not fully utilized is represented in a production possibility frontier diagram by
a) any point on either the horizontal or the vertical axis.
b) a point above or to the right of the production possibility frontier.
c) a point outside the production possibility frontier.
d) a point inside the production possibility frontier.
e) a point on or inside the production possibility frontier.

3.24
Correct: e)
Difficulty: 1
Page(s): 53–55
Scramble range: All
Topic: Opportunity cost

3.24
When we choose a particular option, we must give up alternative options. Economists call the best alternative forgone the __________ of the chosen option.
a) monetary cost
b) comparative advantage
c) nonmonetary cost
d) absolute advantage
e) opportunity cost

3.25
Correct: c)
Difficulty: 2
Page(s): 53–55
Scramble range: All
Topic: Opportunity cost

3.25
Ted has chosen to study for his economics exam instead of going to the concert. Apparently, the concert he will miss is Ted's __________ of studying for the exam.

a) implicit cost
b) explicit cost
c) opportunity cost
d) discretionary cost
e) comparative cost

3.26
Correct: b)
Difficulty: 1
Page(s): 53–55
Scramble range: All
Topic: Opportunity cost

3.26
We have defined *opportunity cost* as the

a) best choice that can be made.
b) best alternative forgone.
c) monetary cost.
d) indirect cost.
e) direct cost.

3.27
Correct: a)
Difficulty: 3
Page(s): 53–55
Scramble range: All
Topic: Opportunity cost

3.27
As we increase the production of good *A* we find that we must give up larger and larger amounts of good *B* per unit of *A*.

a) This illustrates increasing opportunity cost.
b) As a result, we should not specialize in the production of *A*.
c) The production possibility frontier for *A* and *B* will be a straight line.
d) Good *B* will be more highly regarded by consumers than *A*.
e) We must be inside the production possibility frontier.

3.28
Correct: a)
Difficulty: 4
Page(s): 56–57
Scramble range: All
Topic: Technological change

3.28
A technological improvement is represented by

a) an outward shift of the production possibility frontier.
b) a movement along the production possibility frontier.
c) a point inside the production possibility frontier.
d) a point outside the production possibility frontier.
e) a movement from a point inside the production possibility frontier to a point on the production possibility frontier.

3.29
Correct: c)
Difficulty: 3
Page(s): 56–58
Scramble range: All
Topic: Capital accumulation

3.29
In general, if country *A* is accumulating capital at a faster rate than country *B*, then

a) country *A* will soon have a comparative advantage in the production of most goods.
b) country *A* is using a larger proportion of resources to produce consumption goods.
c) country *A*'s production possibility frontier will be shifting out faster than country *B*'s.
d) country *A* will have a higher rate of inflation than country *B*.
e) country *A* will have more unemployment than country *B*.

3.30
Correct: e)
Difficulty: 2
Page(s): 58–59
Scramble range: All
Topic: Capital accumulation

3.30
The principal reason for the fact that production possibilities have grown more rapidly in Japan than in Canada over the last 25 years is
a) cheap Japanese labour.
b) foreign aid to Japan.
c) the Japanese have smarter workers.
d) the Japanese have more natural resources.
e) the Japanese have devoted a larger proportion of their resources to the production of capital goods.

3.31
Correct: a)
Difficulty: 2
Page(s): 56–57
Scramble range: All
Topic: Capital accumulation

3.31
Which of the following would cause a production possibility frontier to shift outward?
a) An increase in the stock of capital.
b) An increase in the production of consumption goods.
c) Bad weather.
d) A decision to fully utilize unemployed resources.
e) A decrease in the population.

3.32
Correct: b)
Difficulty: 2
Page(s): 56–57
Scramble range: a)–c)
Topic: Shifting PPF

3.32
Which of the following would likely shift a production possibility frontier *inward*?
a) a technological improvement.
b) a drought.
c) a decrease in the price of natural resources.
d) All of the above.
e) None of the above, since production possibility frontiers do not shift inward.

3.33
Correct: c)
Difficulty: 2
Page(s): 56–57
Scramble range: All
Topic: Shifting PPF

3.33
Refer to the production possibility frontier in Figure 3.3. The production possibility frontier will shift out more rapidly if current production is at
a) 1.
b) 2.
c) 3.
d) 4.
e) 5.

Figure 3.3

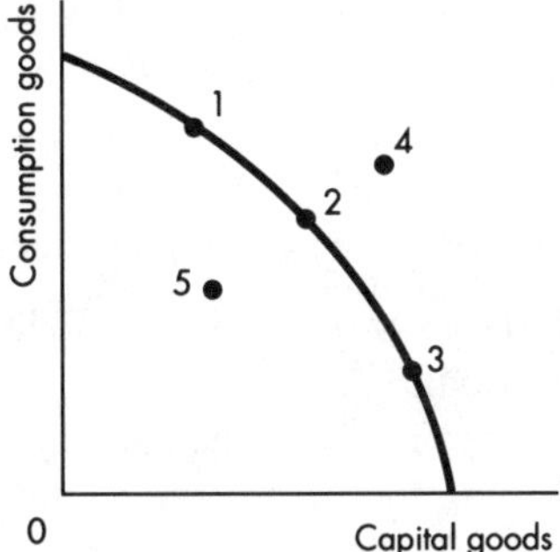

3.34
Correct: e)
Difficulty: 1
Page(s): 55
Scramble range: All
Topic: Shape of PPF

3.34
Refer to the production possibility frontier in Figure 3.3. Which point indicates that resources are not fully utilized?
a) 1
b) 2.
c) 3.
d) 4.
e) 5.

3.35
Correct: d)
Difficulty: 1
Page(s): 55
Scramble range: All
Topic: Shape of PPF

3.35
Refer to the production possibility frontier in Figure 3.3. Which point is unattainable?
a) 1.
b) 2.
c) 3.
d) 4.
e) 5.

3.36
Correct: d)
Difficulty: 3
Page(s): 53–54
Scramble range: All
Topic: Opportunity cost

3.36
Figure 3.4 illustrates Mary's production possibility frontier. If Mary wants to move from point *b* to point *c*,
a) it will be necessary to improve technology.
b) it will be necessary to increase the accumulation of capital.
c) it will be necessary to give up some of good *X* in order to obtain more of good *Y*.
d) it will be necessary to give up some of good *Y* in order to obtain more of good *X*.
e) she can accomplish this without any opportunity cost.

Figure 3.4

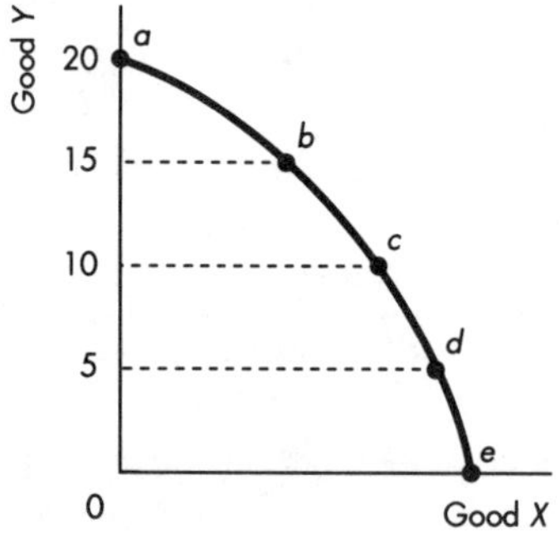

3.37
Correct: c)
Difficulty: 3
Page(s): 53–54
Scramble range: All
Topic: Opportunity cost

3.37
Figure 3.4 illustrates Mary's production possibility frontier. If Mary wants to move from point *d* to point *c*,
a) it will be necessary to improve technology.
b) it will be necessary to increase the accumulation of capital.
c) it will be necessary to give up some of good *X* in order to obtain more of good *Y*.
d) it will be necessary to give up some of good *Y* in order to obtain more of good *X*.
e) she can accomplish this without any opportunity cost.

3.38
Correct: a)
Difficulty: 4
Page(s): 53–54
Scramble range: a)–d)
Topic: Opportunity cost

3.38
Refer to the production possibility frontier in Figure 3.4. The opportunity cost of moving from *c* to *b* will be
a) greater than for moving from *d* to *c* but less than for moving from *b* to *a.*
b) less than for moving from *d* to *c* but greater than for moving from *b* to *a.*
c) the same as for moving from *d* to *c* or moving from *b* to *a.*
d) greater than for moving either from *d* to *c* or from *b* to *a.*
e) none of the above.

3.39
Correct: d)
Difficulty: 3
Page(s): 53–54
Scramble range: All
Topic: Opportunity cost

3.39
Refer to the production possibility frontier in Figure 3.4. Which of the following movements requires the largest opportunity cost of increased *Y*?
a) *e* to *d.*
b) *d* to *c.*
c) *c* to *b.*
d) *b* to *a.*
e) The opportunity cost is the same in each case.

3.40
Correct: d)
Difficulty: 4
Page(s): 53–54
Scramble range: All
Topic: Opportunity cost

3.40
Refer to the production possibility frontier in Figure 3.4. Which of the following movements requires the largest opportunity cost of increased *X*?
a) *a* to *b.*
b) *b* to *c.*
c) *c* to *d.*
d) *d* to *e.*
e) The opportunity cost is the same in each case.

3.41
Correct: b)
Difficulty: 2
Page(s): 53–54
Scramble range: All
Topic: Opportunity cost

3.41
Refer to the production possibility frontier in Figure 3.4. The fact that less of *X* must be given up when moving from *d* to *c* than when moving from *b* to *a* indicates
a) decreasing opportunity cost.
b) increasing opportunity cost.
c) comparative advantage in the production of *X.*
d) the consequences of technological improvement.
e) unemployed resources at *d.*

3.42
Correct: b)
Difficulty: 2
Page(s): 53–54
Scramble range: All
Topic: Opportunity cost

3.42
Refer to the production possibility frontier in Figure 3.4. The fact that more of *X* must be given up when moving from *b* to *a* than when moving from *c* to *b* indicates
a) decreasing opportunity cost.
b) increasing opportunity cost.
c) comparative advantage in the production of *X.*
d) the consequences of technological improvement.
e) unemployed resources at *c.*

3.43
Correct: b)
Difficulty: 3
Page(s): 53–54
Scramble range: All
Topic: Opportunity cost

3.43
Refer to Table 3.1. What does point *c* mean?
a) If 8 units of *X* are produced, then at least 28 units of *Y* can be produced.
b) If 8 units of *X* are produced, then at most 28 units of *Y* can be produced.
c) If 28 units of *Y* are produced, then more than 8 units of *X* can be produced.
d) If 8 units of *X* are produced, then only 36 units of *Y* can be produced.
e) There is unemployment at this point.

Table 3.1 Points on the production possibility frontier for goods X and Y.

Point	Production of *X*	Production of *Y*
a	0	40
b	4	36
c	8	28
d	12	16
e	16	0

3.44
Correct: d)
Difficulty: 2
Page(s): 53–54
Scramble range: All
Topic: Opportunity cost

3.44
Refer to Table 3.1. The opportunity cost of increasing the production of *X* from 8 to 12 units is
a) 4 units of *X*.
b) 4 units of *Y*.
c) 8 units of *Y*.
d) 12 units of *Y*.
e) 16 units of *Y*.

3.45
Correct: b)
Difficulty: 3
Page(s): 53–54
Scramble range: All
Topic: Opportunity cost

3.45
Refer to Table 3.1. The opportunity cost of increasing the production of *Y* from 16 to 36 units is
a) 4 units of *X*.
b) 8 units of *X*.
c) 12 units of *X*.
d) 16 units of *X*.
e) 20 units of *Y*.

3.46
Correct: d)
Difficulty: 2
Page(s): 53–54
Scramble range: a)–d)
Topic: Opportunity cost

3.46
The economy illustrated by the data in Table 3.1 exhibits
a) decreasing opportunity cost.
b) constant opportunity cost in the production of *X*.
c) constant opportunity cost in the production of *Y*.
d) increasing opportunity cost.
e) none of the above.

3.47
Correct: b)
Difficulty: 3
Page(s): 54–55
Scramble range: All
Topic: Shape of PPF

3.47
From the data in Table 3.1, the production of 7 units of *X* and 28 units of *Y* is
a) impossible given the available resources.
b) possible but leaves some resources less than fully utilized.
c) on the PPF between points *c* and *d*.
d) on the PPF between points *b* and *c*.
e) something whose possibility we cannot tell from the table.

3.48
Correct: c)
Difficulty: 2
Page(s): 53–54
Scramble range: All
Topic: Opportunity cost

3.48
Refer to Table 3.1. As we increase the production of *X*,
a) the amount of *Y* that is given up for each additional unit of *X* decreases.
b) the output of *Y* increases.
c) the opportunity cost of each new unit of *X* increases.
d) unemployment increases.
e) the amount of *X* increases at an increasing rate.

3.49
Correct: c)
Difficulty: 3
Page(s): 53–54
Scramble range: a)–d)
Topic: Opportunity cost

3.49
From the data in Table 3.1 we can infer that
a) the economy illustrated has a comparative advantage in the production of *Y*.
b) the economy illustrated has a comparative advantage in the production of *X*.
c) the opportunity cost of producing an additional unit of *Y* increases as the production of *Y* increases.
d) the opportunity cost of producing an additional unit of *Y* decreases as the production of *Y* increases.
e) none of the above.

3.50
Correct: a)
Difficulty: 2
Page(s): 59–60
Scramble range: All
Topic: Comparative advantage

3.50
Individuals *A* and *B* can both produce good *X*. We say that *A* has a *comparative advantage* in the production of good *X* if
a) *A* has a lower opportunity cost of producing *X* than *B*.
b) *A* can produce one unit of good *X* faster than *B*.
c) *A* can produce more units of *X* in a given time period than *B*.
d) *A* can produce *X* using newer technology than *B*.
e) *A* can produce less units of *X* in a given time period than *B*.

3.51
Correct: b)
Difficulty: 4
Page(s): 59–60
Scramble range: All
Topic: Comparative advantage

3.51
Individuals A and B can both produce goods *X* and *Y*. Individual *A* has a *comparative advantage* in the production of *X* if
a) *A* is faster than *B* at producing *X*.
b) the amount by which *A* must reduce production of *Y* is less than the amount by which *B* must reduce production of *Y* to produce a unit of *X*.
c) *B* has superior knowledge about how to produce *X*.
d) *A* has a preference to consume *X*.
e) the amount by which *A* must reduce production of *Y* is more than the amount by which *B* must reduce production of *Y* to produce a unit of *X*.

3.52
Correct: c)
Difficulty: 3
Page(s): 61
Scramble range: All
Topic: Absolute advantage

3.52
A person has an *absolute advantage* when he/she
a) has a comparative advantage in producing all goods.
b) can produce all goods at lower opportunity cost than anyone else.
c) can produce more of all goods than anyone else.
d) has exclusive rights to sell one good.
e) has better technology than anyone else.

3.53
Correct: e)
Difficulty: 3
Page(s): 60–61
Scramble range: All
Topic: Absolute advantage

3.53
A person who has an absolute advantage in the production of all goods will
a) also have a comparative advantage in the production of all goods.
b) not be able to gain from specialization and exchange.
c) produce all goods at lowest opportunity cost.
d) not have a comparative advantage in the production of any goods.
e) generally have a comparative advantage in the production of only some goods and not of others.

3.54
Correct: a)
Difficulty: 2
Page(s): 61–62
Scramble range: All
Topic: Absolute advantage

3.54
If a person can produce more of all goods than anyone else, that person
a) has an absolute advantage.
b) has a comparative advantage in the production of all goods.
c) will be unable to gain from specialization and exchange.
d) no longer is affected by scarcity.
e) will never be unemployed.

3.55
Correct: b)
Difficulty: 4
Page(s): 59–60
Scramble range: All
Topic: Comparative advantage]

3.55
Given Fact 3.1, the opportunity cost of producing 1 loaf of bread is
a) 20 minutes (1/3 hour) for Andy and 1 hour for Bob.
b) 1/3 pound of butter for Andy and 1 pound of butter for Bob.
c) 3 pounds of butter for Andy and 1 pound of butter for Bob.
d) 8 pounds of butter for both Andy and Bob.
e) not calculable from the given information.

Fact 3.1
In an eight-hour day, Andy can produce either 24 loaves of bread or 8 pounds of butter. In an eight-hour day, Bob can produce either 8 loaves of bread or 8 pounds of butter.

3.56
Correct: c)
Difficulty: 4
Page(s): 59–60
Scramble range: All
Topic: Comparative advantage

3.56
From Fact 3.1, we know that
a) Andy has the lower opportunity cost of producing bread, while Andy and Bob have equal opportunity costs of producing butter.
b) Andy has the lower opportunity cost of producing both bread and butter.
c) Andy has the lower opportunity cost of producing bread, while Bob has the lower opportunity cost of producing butter.
d) Andy has the lower opportunity cost of producing butter, while Bob has the lower opportunity cost of producing bread.
e) Andy has the higher opportunity cost of producing both bread and butter.

3.57
Correct: a)
Difficulty: 4
Page(s): 59–60
Scramble range: All
Topic: Comparative advantage

3.57
From Fact 3.1, we see that
a) Andy has a comparative advantage in the production of bread, while Bob has a comparative advantage in the production of butter.
b) Andy has a comparative advantage in the production of butter, while Bob has a comparative advantage in the production of bread.
c) Andy has a comparative advantage in the production of bread and neither has a comparative advantage in the production of butter.
d) Andy has a comparative advantage in the production of both bread and butter.
e) both Andy and Bob have a comparative advantage in the production of butter.

3.58
Correct: a)
Difficulty: 4
Page(s): 59–61
Scramble range: All
Topic: Absolute advantage

3.58
Refer to Fact 3.2. Which of the following statements is true?
a) Brenda has an absolute advantage over Agnes.
b) Agnes has a comparative advantage in the production of *Y*.
c) Brenda has a comparative advantage in the production of *X*.
d) Brenda cannot gain from trade.
e) Agnes cannot gain from trade.

Fact 3.2
Agnes can produce either 1 unit of *X* or 1 unit of *Y* in an hour, while Brenda can produce either 2 units of *X* or 4 units of *Y* in an hour.

3.59
Correct: a)
Difficulty: 4
Page(s): 59–60
Scramble range: All
Topic: Gains from trade

3.59
Given Fact 3.2, the opportunity cost of producing a unit of *X* is
a) 1 unit of *Y* for Agnes and 2 units of *Y* for Brenda.
b) 1 unit of *Y* for Agnes and 1/2 unit of *Y* for Brenda.
c) 1 hour for Agnes and 1/2 hour for Brenda.
d) 1 hour for Agnes and 2 hours for Brenda.
e) 1 hour for Agnes and 1/4 hour for Brenda.

3.60
Correct: e)
Difficulty: 4
Page(s): 59–60
Scramble range: All
Topic: Gains from trade

3.60
Given Fact 3.2, the opportunity cost of producing 1 unit of *Y* is
a) 1 unit of *Y* for Agnes and 2 units of *Y* for Brenda.
b) 1 unit of *Y* for Agnes and 1/2 unit of *Y* for Brenda.
c) 1 hour for Agnes and 1/2 hour for Brenda.
d) 1 hour for Agnes and 2 hours for Brenda.
e) 1 unit of *X* for Agnes and 1/2 unit of *X* for Brenda.

3.61
Correct: e)
Difficulty: 4
Page(s): 59–60
Scramble range: All
Topic: Specialization

3.61
Given Fact 3.2,
a) there can be gains from exchange, no matter what Brenda and Agnes specialize in, as long as they specialize in something.
b) there can be gains from exchange if Agnes specializes in the production of *Y* and Brenda in *X*.
c) there can be gains from exchange only if Agnes becomes faster at producing *X*.
d) there can be no gains from exchange because Agnes has an absolute advantage.
e) there can be gains from exchange if Agnes specializes in the production of *X* and Brenda in *Y*.

3.62
Correct: c)
Difficulty: 3
Page(s): 59–60
Scramble range: All
Topic: Specialization

3.62
Given Fact 3.2, what would be the total output of *X* and *Y* in an eight-hour day if Agnes and Brenda each specialized in producing the good for which they have a comparative advantage?
a) 3 units of *X* and 5 units of *Y*.
b) 8 units of *X* and 16 units of *Y*.
c) 8 units of *X* and 32 units of *Y*.
d) 24 units of *X* and 40 units of *Y*.
e) 16 units of *X* and 8 units of *Y*.

3.63
Correct: c)
Difficulty: 4
Page(s): 59–60
Scramble range: All
Topic: Comparative advantage

3.63
From Fact 3.2 we learn that
a) Agnes is the high opportunity cost producer of *X*.
b) Brenda has a comparative advantage in the production of both goods.
c) Brenda does *not* have a comparative advantage in the production of *X*.
d) Agnes cannot gain from trading with Brenda.
e) Brenda is the high opportunity cost producer of *Y*.

3.64
Correct: c)
Difficulty: 3
Page(s): 60
Scramble range: All
Topic: Gains from trade

3.64
Any two individuals can gain from exchange
a) unless one has an absolute advantage.
b) if each specializes in the production of the good for which he/she has the higher opportunity cost.
c) unless they have the same opportunity costs for producing all goods.
d) unless they have different opportunity costs.
e) unless they have the same absolute advantage.

3.65
Correct: d)
Difficulty: 4
Page(s): 59–60
Scramble range: All
Topic: Comparative advantage

3.65
Refer to Table 3.2. Which of the following is true?
a) Country *B* has both an absolute advantage and a comparative advantage in the production of *Y*.
b) Country *B* has both an absolute advantage and a comparative advantage in the production of *X*.
c) Country *A* has a comparative advantage in the production of *X*.
d) Country *B* has a comparative advantage in the production of *X*.
e) Country *A* should specialize in the production of *X*.

Table 3.2 Points on the production possibility frontiers of countries *A* and *B*.

Country *A*		Country *B*	
Good *X*	Goods *Y*	Good *X*	Good *Y*
0	16	0	12
2	12	2	9
4	8	4	6
6	4	6	3
8	0	8	0

3.66
Correct: d)
Difficulty: 4
Page(s): 59–60
Scramble range: All
Topic: Comparative advantage

3.66
Refer to Table 3.2. Which of the following is true?
a) The opportunity cost of producing more of good *X* is the same for both countries.
b) The opportunity cost of producing more of good *Y* is the same for both countries.
c) The opportunity cost of producing more of good *X* is lower in country *A*.
d) The opportunity cost of producing more of good *Y* is lower in country *A*.
e) The opportunity cost of producing more of good *Y* is lower in country *B*.

3.67
Correct: b)
Difficulty: 3
Page(s): 53–54
Scramble range: All
Topic: Opportunity cost

3.67
Refer to Table 3.2. For country *A*, the opportunity cost of producing an additional unit of *X* is

a) 4 units of *Y*.
b) 2 units of *Y*.
c) 2/3 units of *Y*.
d) 1 unit of *Y*.
e) dependent upon how many units of *X* are already produced.

3.68
Correct: e)
Difficulty: 3
Page(s): 53–54
Scramble range: All
Topic: Opportunity cost

3.68
Refer to Table 3.2. For country *B*, the opportunity cost of producing an additional unit of *X* is

a) 4 units of *Y*.
b) 2 units of *Y*.
c) 2/3 units of *Y*.
d) 1 unit of *Y*.
e) 3/2 units of *Y*.

3.69
Correct: a)
Difficulty: 3
Page(s): 53–54
Scramble range: All
Topic: Opportunity cost

3.69
Refer to Table 3.2. For country *B*, the opportunity cost of producing an additional unit of *Y* is

a) 2/3 units of *X*.
b) 1/2 units of *X*.
c) 2 units of *X*.
d) 3 units of *X*.
e) 3/2 units of *Y*.

3.70
Correct: b)
Difficulty: 3
Page(s): 53–54
Scramble range: All
Topic: Opportunity cost

3.70
Refer to Table 3.2. For country *A*, the opportunity cost of producing an additional unit of *Y* is

a) 2/3 units of *X*.
b) 1/2 units of *X*.
c) 2 units of *X*.
d) 3 units of *X*.
e) 4 units of *X*.

3.71
Correct: d)
Difficulty: 2
Page(s): 62–63
Scramble range: All
Topic: Property rights

3.71
Property rights

a) are social rules governing the ownership and use of real estate.
b) prevent trade from occurring.
c) are restricted by government regulation.
d) result in exploitation of privately held resources.
e) really do not play any important role in the economy.

3.72
Correct: c)
Difficulty: 2
Page(s): 63
Scramble range: All
Topic: Monetary exchange

3.72
Which of the following greatly facilitate(s) trade?

a) a barter economy.
b) Absence of property rights.
c) a monetary exchange system.
d) Prohibitions on formation of markets.
e) Absolute advantage.

3.73
Correct: c)
Difficulty: 1
Page(s): 63
Scramble range: All
Topic: Property rights

3.73
Social arrangements governing the ownership, use, and disposal of property are called
a) market mechanisms.
b) monetary exchange systems.
c) property rights.
d) private enterprise.
e) barter systems.

3.74
Correct: c)
Difficulty: 2
Page(s): 63
Scramble range: All
Topic: Barter

3.74
A barter system
a) exists only when there is no trade.
b) relies on the use of money in exchange.
c) involves the exchange of goods for goods.
d) is a very efficient system of exchange.
e) no longer exists in our modern world.

3.75
Correct: b)
Difficulty: 2
Page(s): 63–64
Scramble range: All
Topic: Money

3.75
Money can be defined as
a) anything backed by gold.
b) a medium of exchange.
c) coins and currency issued by the Canadian government.
d) any kind of deposit in a financial institution.
e) cigarettes.

3.76
Correct: e)
Difficulty: 3
Page(s): 63–64
Scramble range: All
Topic: Money

3.76
Which of the following would be considered money in Canada today?
a) Cigarettes.
b) Bonds issued by the Canadian government.
c) Gold.
d) The stock of major industrial corporations.
e) Chequing accounts issued by banks.

3.77
Correct: d)
Difficulty: 2
Page(s): 51–52
Scramble range: a)–c)
Topic: Capital resources

3.77
Which of the following is an example of a capital resource?
a) A hydroelectric dam.
b) A dentist's drill.
c) A shovel.
d) All of the above.
e) None of the above.

3.78
Correct: a)
Difficulty: 1
Page(s): 51
Scramble range: All
Topic: Services

3.78
A haircut is an example of a
a) service.
b) consumption good.
c) human resource.
d) capital good.
e) natural resource.

3.79
Correct: c)
Difficulty: 2
Page(s): 51, 60
Scramble range: All
Topic: Production possibility frontier

3.79
If Harold can increase production of good *X* without decreasing the production of any other good, then Harold
a) is producing on his production possibility frontier.
b) is producing outside his production possibility frontier.
c) is producing inside his production possibility frontier.
d) must prefer good *X* to any other good.
e) has a comparative advantage in the production of good *X*.

3.80
Correct: a)
Difficulty: 2
Page(s): 52–53
Scramble range: All
Topic: Concavity of the PPF

3.80
The bowed out shape of a production possibility frontier
a) reflects the existence of increasing opportunity cost.
b) reflects the existence of decreasing opportunity cost.
c) is due to technological improvement.
d) is due to the fact that less of a good is consumed as its price rises.
e) is due to the presence of unemployed resources.

3.81
Correct: e)
Difficulty: 3
Page(s): 53–54
Scramble range: All
Topic: Opportunity cost

3.81
Refer to the production possibility frontier in Figure 3.2. If 8 units of *X* are currently being produced, the opportunity cost of producing one more is
a) 1 unit of *Y*.
b) 1 unit of *X*.
c) 30 units of *Y*.
d) 20 units of *X*.
e) 20 units of *Y*.

3.82
Correct: b)
Difficulty: 3
Page(s): 53–54
Scramble range: All
Topic: PPF

3.82
Refer to the production possibility frontier in Figure 3.2. What is the opportunity cost of increasing the production of *Y* from 20 to 50 units?
a) 6 units of *X*.
b) 2 units of *X*.
c) 8 units of *X*.
d) 20 units of *Y*.
e) 30 units of *Y*.

3.83
Correct: d)
Difficulty: 1
Page(s): 53–54
Scramble range: All
Topic: Opportunity cost

3.83
Because productive resources are scarce, we must give up some of one good in order to acquire more of another. This is the essence of the concept of
a) specialization.
b) monetary exchange.
c) comparative advantage.
d) opportunity cost.
e) absolute advantage.

3.84
Correct: d)
Difficulty: 2
Page(s): 56–57
Scramble range: a)–c)
Topic: Shifting PPF

3.84
A production possibility frontier will shift outward if
a) there is a technological improvement.
b) there is an increase in the stock of capital.
c) there is an increase in the labour force.
d) all of the above.
e) none of the above.

3.85
Correct: e)
Difficulty: 3
Page(s): 56–57
Scramble range: All
Topic: Opportunity cost growth

3.85
The opportunity cost of pushing the production possibility frontier outward is
a) the value of the increase in new capital resources required.
b) the value of the increase in technological improvement required.
c) nothing; we are using unemployed resources.
d) the amount by which the production possibility frontier shifts.
e) the value of the reduction in current consumption required.

3.86
Correct: b)
Difficulty: 2
Page(s): 56–57
Scramble range: All
Topic: Technical improvement and PPF

3.86
In general, the higher the proportion of resources devoted to technological research in an economy,
a) the greater will be current consumption.
b) the faster the production possibility frontier will shift outward.
c) the faster the production possibility frontier will shift inward.
d) the closer it will come to having a comparative advantage in the production of all goods.
e) the less unemployed resources there will be.

3.87
Correct: c)
Difficulty: 3
Page(s): 53–54
Scramble range: All
Topic: Opportunity cost

3.87
Refer to Table 3.1. The opportunity cost of increasing the production of *X* from 4 to 8 units is
a) 4 units of *X*.
b) 4 units of *Y*.
c) 8 units of *Y*.
d) 28 units of *Y*.
e) 36 units of *Y*.

3.88
Correct: c)
Difficulty: 2
Page(s): 55–56
Scramble range: a)–d)
Topic: Slope of PPF

3.88
The diagram of the production possibility frontier corresponding to the data in Table 3.1 would be
a) negatively sloped and linear.
b) negatively sloped and bowed in.
c) negatively sloped and bowed out.
d) positively sloped for *X* and negatively sloped for *Y*.
e) none of the above.

3.89
Correct: a)
Difficulty: 2
Page(s): 55–56
Scramble range: All
Topic: Slope of PPF

3.89
From the data in Table 3.1, the production of 10 units of *X* and 28 units of *Y* is
a) impossible given the available resources.
b) possible but leaves some resources less than fully utilized.
c) on the production possibility frontier between points *c* and *d*.
d) something whose possibility we cannot infer from the table.
e) possible if we reduce the amount of capital goods.

3.90
Correct: a)
Difficulty: 2
Page(s): 53–54
Scramble range: None
Topic: Opportunity cost

3.90
If the opportunity cost of producing good *X* is lower for person *A* than person *B*, then
a) *A* has a comparative advantage in the production of *X*.
b) *A* has an absolute advantage in the production of *X*.
c) it is unlikely that *A* will specialize in the production of *X*.
d) both a) and b).
e) both b) and c).

3.91
Correct: d)
Difficulty: 3
Page(s): 53–54
Scramble range: All
Topic: Opportunity cost

3.91
Refer to Fact 3.1. The opportunity cost of producing 1 pound of butter is
a) 20 minutes (1/3 hour) for Andy and 1 hour for Bob.
b) 1 hour for Andy and 1 hour for Bob.
c) 3 loaves of bread for Andy and 1/3 loaf of bread for Bob.
d) 3 loaves of bread for Andy and 1 loaf of bread for Bob.
e) 8 loaves of bread for Bob and 24 loaves of bread for Andy.

3.92
Correct: b)
Difficulty: 3
Page(s): 59
Scramble range: All
Topic: Specialization

3.92
Refer to Fact 3.1. Andy and Bob
a) can gain from exchange if Andy specializes in butter production and Bob specializes in bread production.
b) can gain from exchange if Andy specializes in bread production and Bob specializes in butter production.
c) cannot gain from exchange because Bob does not have any comparative advantage.
d) can exchange, but only Bob will be able to gain.
e) can gain because Andy has an absolute advantage in the production of bread, and Bob has an absolute advantage in the production of butter.

3.93
Correct: b)
Difficulty: 3
Page(s): 59–60
Scramble range: All
Topic: Comparative advantage

3.93
If individuals *A* and *B* can both produce only goods *X* and *Y* and *A* does not have a comparative advantage in the production of either *X* or *Y*, then we know that
a) *B* has an absolute advantage in the production of *X* and *Y*.
b) *A* and *B* have the same opportunity cost for *X* and for *Y*.
c) *B* has a comparative advantage in the production of both *X* and *Y*.
d) the gains from trade will be large but only in one direction.
e) *A* must have lower opportunity costs of production in both goods.

3.94
Correct: a)
Difficulty: 3
Page(s): 62
Scramble range: All
Topic: Private property rights

3.94
Which of the following would *not* limit private property rights?
a) High prices.
b) Export restrictions.
c) Laws prohibiting slavery.
d) Income taxes.
e) Pollution laws.

3.95
Correct: e)
Difficulty: 2
Page(s): 63
Scramble range: All
Topic: Medium of exchange

3.95
Anything that is generally acceptable in exchange for goods and services is
a) a consumption good.
b) private property.
c) a barter good.
d) called an exchange resource.
e) a medium of exchange.

3.96 (SG 3.15)
Correct: e)
Difficulty: 3
Page(s): 63
Scramble range: All
Topic: Monetary exchange

3.96
Which of the following is an advantage of a monetary exchange system over barter?
a) A monetary exchange system eliminates the basis for comparative advantage.
b) Only in a monetary exchange system can gains from trade be realized.
c) A monetary system allows the government to control trade easier.
d) In a monetary system transactions costs are zero.
e) A monetary exchange system does not require a double coincidence of wants.

3.97
Correct: d)
Difficulty: 5
Page(s): 59–60
Scramble range: a)–d)
Topic: Comparative/absolute advantage

3.97
Consider the following household. In 5 hours, Brian can cook 5 meals or clean 6 rooms. In 5 hours, Mila can cook 30 meals or clean 10 rooms. Pick the best statement.
a) Brian has an absolute advantage in the production of both goods.
b) Since Mila is better at producing both goods, she should produce both.
c) Brian has a comparative advantage in cooking.
d) Mila should specialize in cooking.
e) None of the above.

3.98
Correct: e)
Difficulty: 2
Page(s): 51
Scramble range: All
Topic: Services

3.98
Teaching is an example of a
a) natural resource.
b) consumption good.
c) human resource.
d) capital good.
e) service.

3.99
Correct: a)
Difficulty: 3
Page(s): 51
Scramble range: All
Topic: PPF

3.99
If Harold must decrease the production of some other good to increase production of good *X*, then Harold
a) is producing on his production possibility frontier.
b) is producing outside his production possibility frontier.
c) is producing inside his production possibility frontier.
d) must prefer good *X* to any other good.
e) has too few capital goods.

3.100
Correct: d)
Difficulty: 2
Page(s): 55–56
Scramble range: All
Topic: Concavity of the PPF

3.100
If opportunity costs are increasing, then the production possibility frontier
a) will be bowed out and have a positive slope.
b) will be positively sloped.
c) will be linear and have a negative slope.
d) will be bowed out and have a negative slope.
e) reflects the fact that available resources are equally useful in all production activities.

3.101
Correct: e)
Difficulty: 2
Page(s): 53–54
Scramble range: All
Topic: Opportunity cost

3.101
The concept of opportunity cost

a) is measured by the amount of the direct costs of an activity.
b) explains that goods are swapped for goods.
c) implies that when one person is more efficient than another in the production of one good, then that person should produce that good and exchange it for some good that that person is relatively less efficient at producing.
d) implies that a double coincidence of wants must be present for exchange to take place.
e) implies that because productive resources are scarce, we must give up some of one good in order to acquire more of another.

3.102 (SG 3.6)
Correct: d)
Difficulty: 2
Page(s): 56–57
Scramble range: All
Topic: Shifting PPF

3.102
A movement along the production possibility frontier will occur if

a) there is a technological improvement.
b) there is an increase in the stock of capital.
c) there is an increase in the labour force.
d) resources are diverted from the production of one good into some other.
e) unemployed resources become employed.

3.103
Correct: e)
Difficulty: 3
Page(s): 59–60
Scramble range: All
Topic: Specialization

3.103
To be useful, specialization requires

a) a market system.
b) a command system.
c) monetary exchange.
d) barter exchange.
e) some system of exchange.

3.104
Correct: c)
Difficulty: 3
Page(s): 53–54
Scramble range: All
Topic: Opportunity cost

3.104
Refer to Table 3.3. The opportunity cost of increasing the production of *Y* from 4 to 8 units is

a) 4 units of *Y*.
b) 4 units of *X*.
c) 8 units of *X*.
d) 12 units of *X*.
e) 36 units of *X*.

Table 3.3 Points on the production possibility frontier for goods *X* and *Y*.

Point	Production of *X*	Production of *Y*
a	0	16
b	16	12
c	28	8
d	36	4
e	40	0

3.105
Correct: c)
Difficulty: 4
Page(s): 55
Scramble range: All
Topic: Slope of PPF

3.105
The diagram of the production possibility frontier corresponding to the data in Table 3.3 would be

a) negatively sloped and linear.
b) negatively sloped and bowed in.
c) negatively sloped and bowed out.
d) positively sloped for *X* and negatively sloped for *Y*.
e) positively sloped and linear.

3.106
Correct: a)
Difficulty: 3
Page(s): 53–54
Scramble range: All
Topic: PPF

3.106
From the data in Table 3.3, the production of 6 units of *Y* and 36 units of *X* is

a) impossible given the available resources.
b) possible but leaves some resources less than fully utilized.
c) on the production possibility frontier between points *c* and *d*.
d) something whose possibility we cannot infer from the table.
e) possible if we fully utilize some of the unemployed resources.

3.107
Correct: e)
Difficulty: 2
Page(s): 59–60
Scramble range: All
Topic: Comparative/absolute advantage

3.107
Given the information in Table 3.4, can Sheila and Bruce gain by specialization?

a) Yes, but only if Bruce gets paid more than Sheila.
b) No, not under the given circumstances.
c) It depends on the wages each earns.
d) Only if they are married to each other.
e) Yes, unconditionally.

Table 3.4 Production for one week by Sheila and Bruce

Sheila		Bruce	
Good *X*	Goods *Y*	Good *X*	Good *Y*
8	0	20	0
6	1	15	2
4	2	10	4
2	3	5	6
0	4	0	8

X is the number of rooms designed and *Y* is the number of cars repaired.

3.108
Correct: e)
Difficulty: 5
Page(s): 59–60
Scramble range: None
Topic: Comparative/absolute advantage

3.108
Given the information in Table 3.4, which of the following is true?

a) Sheila should specialize in designing rooms.
b) Bruce should specialize in designing rooms.
c) The opportunity cost to Bruce of designing one room is 0.4 car repairs.
d) Both a) and b).
e) Both b) and c).

3.109
Correct: d)
Difficulty: 5
Page(s): 59–60
Scramble range: All
Topic: Comparative/absolute advantage

3.109
Suppose that Jane and Joe each have differing production possibility frontiers, such that Jane specializes in cloth and Joe specializes in corn. Jane's island gets really good weather unexpectedly, and suddenly she is twice as productive at the production of both corn and cloth.

a) This is an example of the use of unemployed resources becoming employed.
b) As a result, Jane must have an absolute advantage in both corn and cloth.
c) As a result, it is possible that Jane and Joe will switch what they specialize in.
d) There will be no change in what Jane and Joe specialize in, because Jane's comparative advantage has not changed.
e) There will be a change in what Jane and Joe specialize in, because of the fact that Jane's opportunity cost of production will have risen.

3.110
Correct: d)
Difficulty: 3
Page(s): 59–60
Scramble range: All
Topic: Gains from trade

3.110
It pays people to specialize and trade with each other because

a) otherwise they could not survive.
b) this way they can take advantage of the fact they have an absolute advantage in the production of something.
c) otherwise they cannot take advantage of the fact they have a high opportunity cost of producing something.
d) this way they can consume outside their production possibilities frontier.
e) this way the strong can exploit the weak.

3.111
Correct: e)
Difficulty: 3
Page(s): 55–57
Scramble range: All
Topic: Growth

3.111
Which of the following is *not* something that will shift out the production possibilities frontier?

a) The accumulation of capital goods.
b) Improvements in the weather.
c) The accumulation of new ideas about better ways to produce goods.
d) The production of less consumption goods.
e) The use of unemployed resources.

Chapter 4 Demand and Supply

4.1
Correct: a)
Difficulty: 2
Page(s): 71
Scramble range: All
Topic: Demand/law

4.1
The law of demand states that, other things being equal,
a) the higher the price of a good, the lower is the quantity demanded.
b) the higher the price of a good, the lower is the quantity supplied.
c) price and quantity supplied are positively related.
d) as income increases, willingness to pay for the last unit increases.
e) the higher the price of a good, the higher is the quantity demanded.

4.2
Correct: a)
Difficulty: 4
Page(s): 71-73
Scramble range: All
Topic: Demand/law

4.2
The fact that a decline in the price of a good induces people to plan to purchase more is indicative of
a) the principle of substitution.
b) a reduction in scarcity due to a price decline.
c) the law of supply.
d) the law of demand.
e) a change in demand.

4.3
Correct: a)
Difficulty: 4
Page(s): 74
Scramble range: All
Topic: Demand/shift, movement

4.3
Which of the following could shift the demand curve for grape jelly to the right?
a) An increase in income.
b) A decrease in the price of strawberry preserves, a substitute.
c) A decrease in the price of grape jelly.
d) An increase in the price of peanut butter, a complement.
e) A fall in the population.

4.4
Correct: c)
Difficulty: 3
Page(s): 72-73
Scramble range: All
Topic: Demand/law

4.4
The demand curve slopes downward to the right because of
a) the fact that increases in income lead to increased purchases.
b) the law of supply.
c) the law of demand.
d) comparative advantage.
e) the fact that as income goes up, quantity demanded goes up.

4.5
Correct: c)
Difficulty: 3
Page(s): 71-72
Scramble range: All
Topic: Demand/law

4.5
The law of demand states that, other things being equal, an increase in the price of a good will result in
a) greater production of the good.
b) a surplus.
c) a decrease in the quantity willingly purchased.
d) an increase in the quantity willingly purchased.
e) an increase in income.

4.6
Correct: e)
Difficulty: 4
Page(s): 73-74
Scramble range: None
Topic: Demand/shift, movement

4.6
An increase in the price of ground beef will
a) increase the demand for chicken, a substitute.
b) increase the demand for hamburger buns, a complement.
c) increase the demand for ground beef.
d) decrease the demand for ground beef.
e) both a) and d).

4.7
Correct: c)
Difficulty: 2
Page(s): 73-74
Scramble range: All
Topic: Demand/shift, movement

4.7
Changes in which of the following variables would *not* shift the demand curve?
a) Income.
b) Price of other goods.
c) The price of the good itself.
d) Population size.
e) Preferences.

4.8 (SG 4.1)
Correct: b)
Difficulty: 5
Page(s): 73-74
Scramble range: All
Topic: Demand/shift, movement

4.8
If an increase in the price of good *A* causes the demand curve for *B* to shift to the left, then
a) *A* and *B* are substitutes.
b) *A* and *B* are complements.
c) the price of *A* must be higher than the price of *B*.
d) *B* must be a normal good.
e) consumer preferences for *B* must have fallen.

4.9
Correct: b)
Difficulty: 4
Page(s): 73-74
Scramble range: All
Topic: Demand/shift, inferior

4.9
An increase in income will
a) increase the demand for turnips if turnips are inferior goods.
b) increase the demand for turnips if turnips are normal goods.
c) increase the supply of turnips.
d) decrease the demand for turnips if turnips have a very low price.
e) decrease the supply of turnips.

4.10
Correct: b)
Difficulty: 3
Page(s): 73-74
Scramble range: All
Topic: Demand/normal, inferior

4.10
Turnips are inferior goods if
a) an increase in the price of turnips implies a decrease in the quantity of turnips consumers want to buy.
b) an increase in income implies a decrease in the demand for turnips.
c) an increase in income implies an increase in the demand for turnips.
d) it violates the law of demand.
e) turnips are a low quality good.

4.11
Correct: e)
Difficulty: 5
Page(s): 73-74
Scramble range: None
Topic: Market adjustment/*D* shift

4.11
A increase in income will
a) cause the price of turnips to fall if turnips are inferior goods.
b) cause the price of turnips to rise if turnips are inferior goods.
c) cause the quantity of turnips traded to decline if turnips are inferior goods.
d) cause a decrease in supply for turnips whether or not turnips are inferior goods.
e) both a) and c).

4.12
Correct: d)
Difficulty: 5
Page(s): 72-73
Scramble range: a)-d)
Topic: Demand/curve

4.12
Point *a* in Figure 4.1 indicates that
a) $1.00 is the least consumers are willing to pay for the 4-thousandth apple.
b) consumers will not be in equilibrium if the price of an apple is $1.00.
c) consumers will only pay $1.00 for any apple.
d) if the price is $1.00, consumers will plan to buy 4,000 apples.
e) all of the above.

Figure 4.1

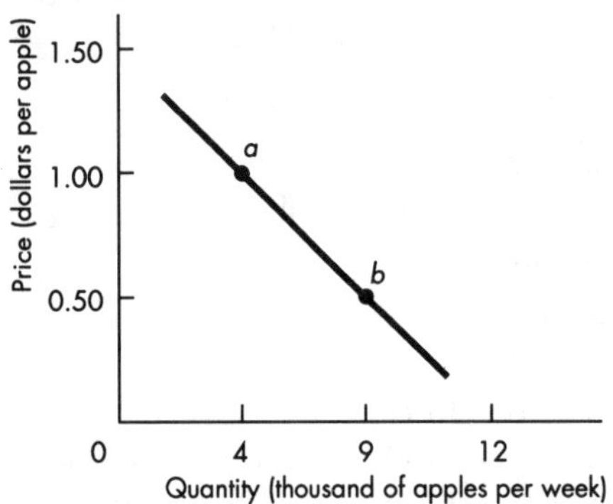

4.13
Correct: b)
Difficulty: 3
Page(s): 72-73
Scramble range: All
Topic: Demand/curve

4.13
Which of the following statements best characterizes point *b* in Figure 4.1?
a) Producers would be unwilling to sell the 9-thousandth apple for less than $0.50.
b) The most consumers would be willing to pay for the 9-thousandth apple is $0.50.
c) At a price of $0.50 consumers will be totally unwilling to buy apples.
d) At a price of $0.50 there will be an apple shortage.
e) At point *b*, the market is in equilibrium.

4.14
Correct: a)
Difficulty: 3
Page(s): 74
Scramble range: a)-d)
Topic: Demand/shift, movement

4.14
Which of the following would result in a movement from point *a* to point *b* in Figure 4.1?
a) A decrease in the price of apples.
b) An increase in the price of oranges.
c) An increase in population size.
d) Public concern over chemicals sprayed on apples.
e) None of the above.

4.15
Correct: b)
Difficulty: 3
Page(s): 74
Scramble range: All
Topic: Demand/shift, movement

4.15
Which of the following would cause a shift in demand from D_1 to D_2 in Figure 4.2?
a) An increase in the supply of pizza.
b) An increase in the price of hamburgers, a substitute.
c) An increase in the price of pizza.
d) A decrease in the price of pizza.
e) An increase in the price of Coke, a complement.

Figure 4.2

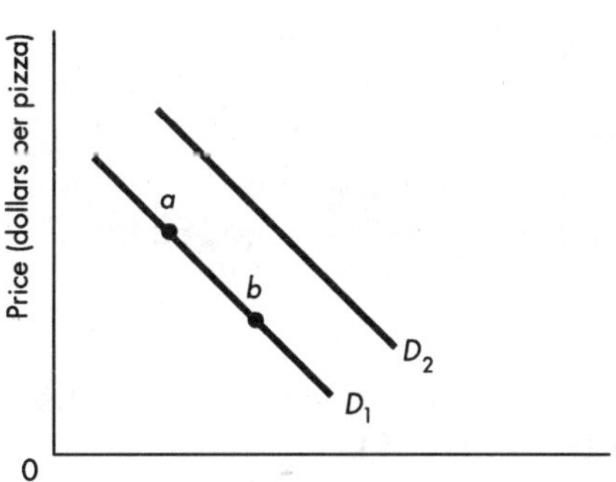

4.16
Correct: b)
Difficulty: 2
Page(s): 74
Scramble range: a)-d)
Topic: Demand/shift, movement

4.16
Refer to Figure 4.2. Which of the following represents a decrease in quantity demanded?
a) A shift from D_1 to D_2.
b) A shift from D_2 to D_1.
c) A movement from *a* to *b*.
d) A movement from *b* to *a*.
e) None of the above.

4.17
Correct: e)
Difficulty: 4
Page(s): 80-81
Scramble range: None
Topic: Equilibrium / surplus, shortage

4.17
Refer to Table 4.1. At a price of $3,
a) the market will be in equilibrium.
b) there will be a 180-unit surplus.
c) there will be a 180-unit shortage.
d) there will be a tendency for the price to rise.
e) both c) and d).

Table 4.1

Price (dollars)	Quantity demanded	Quantity supplied
1	1,100	50
2	800	200
3	600	420
4	500	500
5	420	580
6	350	640
7	320	680
8	300	700

4.18
Correct: c)
Difficulty: 2
Page(s): 80-81
Scramble range: All
Topic: Equilibrium/price

4.18
In Table 4.1, the equilibrium price is
a) $7.
b) $5.
c) $4.
d) $3.
e) $1.

4.19
Correct: d)
Difficulty: 3
Page(s): 80-81
Scramble range: All
Topic: Equilibrium / quantity

4.19
In Table 4.1, the equilibrium quantity is
a) 200 units.
b) 320 units.
c) 420 units.
d) 500 units.
e) none of the above; there is no equilibrium.

4.20
Correct: d)
Difficulty: 5
Page(s): 80-82
Scramble range: None
Topic: Equilibrium / surplus, shortage

4.20
Refer to Table 4.1. The quantity traded will be 420 if
a) the price is fixed at $3.
b) the price is fixed at $4.
c) the price is fixed at $5.
d) both a) and c).
e) none of the above.

4.21
Correct: a)
Difficulty: 3
Page(s): 76-77
Scramble range: All
Topic: Supply/law

4.21
The law of supply implies that, other things being equal,
a) as the price of gasoline decreases, the quantity of gasoline supplied will also decrease.
b) as the price of gasoline increases, the quantity of gasoline supplied will decrease.
c) as the supply of gasoline increases, the price of gasoline will decrease.
d) as the cost of producing gasoline falls, the supply of gasoline will increase.
e) as the cost of producing gasoline increases, the price of gasoline will increase.

4.22
Correct: b)
Difficulty: 4
Page(s): 76-77
Scramble range: All
Topic: Supply/law

4.22
The supply curve slopes upward to the right because of
a) technological improvements over time.
b) the law of supply.
c) the law of demand.
d) the existence of substitute goods.
e) the fact that prices tend to increase over time.

4.23
Correct: c)
Difficulty: 3
Page(s): 78-79
Scramble range: None
Topic: Supply/shift, movement

4.23
An increase in supply is represented by
a) a movement down the supply curve.
b) a movement up the supply curve.
c) a rightward shift in the supply curve.
d) a leftward shift in the supply curve.
e) both a) and c).

4.24
Correct: d)
Difficulty: 4
Page(s): 77-78
Scramble range: All
Topic: Supply/shift, movement

4.24
If goods *X* and *Y* are substitutes in production, then an increase in the price of good *X*
a) will cause the demand for good *Y* to increase.
b) will cause the demand for good *Y* to decrease.
c) will cause the supply of good *Y* to increase.
d) will cause the supply of good *Y* to decrease.
e) could cause anything to happen to the supply of *Y*; it depends on whether they are substitutes on the demand side.

4.25
Correct: e)
Difficulty: 5
Page(s): 77-78
Scramble range: None
Topic: Supply/shift, movement

4.25
If the production of good *A* is a by-product of the production of good *B*, then
a) *A* and *B* are substitutes in production.
b) *A* and *B* are complements in production.
c) an increase in the price of *A* will cause an increase in the supply of *B*.
d) an increase in the price of *A* will cause a decrease in the demand for *B*.
e) both b) and c).

4.26
Correct: e)
Difficulty: 4
Page(s): 77-78
Scramble range: None
Topic: Supply/shift, movement

4.26
If a producer can use its resources to produce either good *A* or good *B*, then an increase in the price of *A* will cause
a) an increase in the supply of *B*.
b) a decrease in the supply of *A*.
c) an increase in the supply of *A*.
d) a decrease in the supply of *B*.
e) both c) and d).

4.27
Correct: e)
Difficulty: 3
Page(s): 78
Scramble range: None
Topic: Supply/shift, movement

4.27
If the production of good *A* is a by-product of the production of good *B*, then an increase in the price of *A* will cause
a) an increase in the supply of *A*.
b) a decrease in the supply of *A*.
c) an increase in the supply of *B*.
d) a decrease in the supply of *B*.
e) both a) and c).

4.28
Correct: e)
Difficulty: 4
Page(s): 80-81
Scramble range: All
Topic: Equilibrium / surplus, shortage

4.28
At price P_3 in Figure 4.3,
a) this market will be in equilibrium.
b) there will be a shortage in the amount of $Q_5 - Q_1$.
c) there will be a tendency for the price to rise.
d) quantity traded will be Q_5.
e) there will be a surplus in the amount $Q_5 - Q_1$.

Figure 4.3

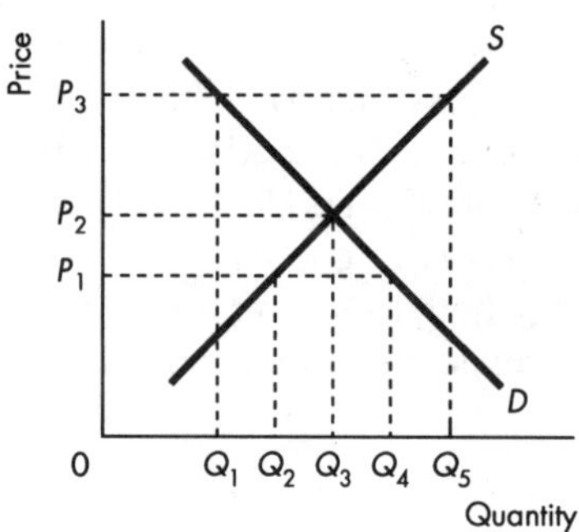

4.29
Correct: c)
Difficulty: 4
Page(s): 80-81
Scramble range: All
Topic: Equilibrium

4.29
At price P_2 in Figure 4.3, which of the following is *not* true?
a) This market will be in equilibrium.
b) The quantity demanded is equal to the quantity supplied.
c) The quantity demanded is Q_1.
d) There is no surplus.
e) The quantity supplied is Q_3.

4.30
Correct: b)
Difficulty: 3
Page(s): 80-81
Scramble range: All
Topic: Equilibrium / surplus, shortage

4.30
At price P_1 in Figure 4.3,
a) there will be a surplus in the amount of $Q_4 - Q_2$.
b) there will be a shortage in the amount of $Q_4 - Q_2$.
c) there will be a tendency for the price to fall.
d) the quantity traded will be Q_3.
e) the quantity traded will be Q_4.

4.31
Correct: a)
Difficulty: 3
Page(s): 80-81
Scramble range: All
Topic: Equilibrium/surplus, shortage

4.31
At price P_1 in Figure 4.3,
a) producers will be able to sell all they plan to.
b) consumers will be able to buy all they want.
c) producers will be unwilling to sell any goods.
d) a surplus will exist.
e) both sides of the market will be able to carry out their desired transactions.

4.32
Correct: c)
Difficulty: 2
Page(s): 80-81
Scramble range: a)-d)
Topic: Equilibrium

4.32
The equilibrium price in the market illustrated in Figure 4.4 is
a) \$2.
b) \$4.
c) \$6.
d) \$8.
e) none of the above.

Figure 4.4

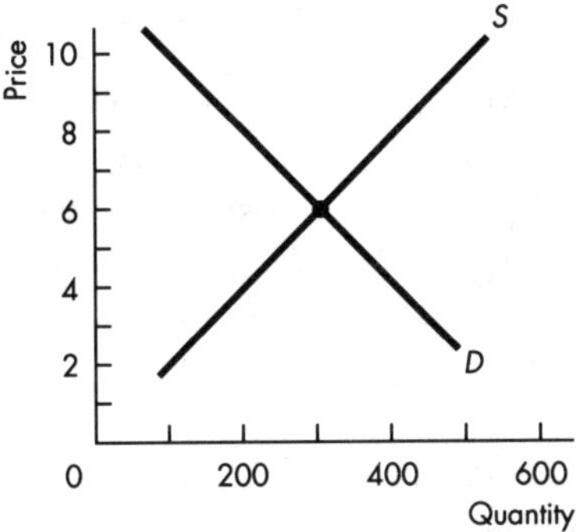

4.33
Correct: c)
Difficulty: 3
Page(s): 80-81
Scramble range: All
Topic: Equilibrium/surplus, shortage

4.33
At a price of $10 in Figure 4.4,
a) there will be a surplus of 200 units.
b) there will be a shortage of 200 units.
c) there will be a surplus of 400 units.
d) there will be a shortage of 400 units.
e) price will rise.

4.34
Correct: d)
Difficulty: 4
Page(s): 80-81
Scramble range: All
Topic: Equilibrium/surplus, shortage

4.34
At a price of $4 in Figure 4.4,
a) the quantity traded will be 400 units.
b) there will be a surplus of 200 units.
c) the quantity supplied will be 400 units.
d) there will be a shortage of 200 units.
e) the quantity demanded will be 200 units.

4.35
Correct: a)
Difficulty: 3
Page(s): 80-81
Scramble range: All
Topic: Equilibrium

4.35
If the demand curve is D_2 in Figure 4.5,
a) equilibrium price and quantity will be P_2 and Q_2.
b) equilibrium price and quantity will be P_2 and Q_0.
c) there will be a shortage in the amount of $Q_2 - Q_0$.
d) an increase in price will cause demand to shift to D_3.
e) price will rise.

Figure 4.5

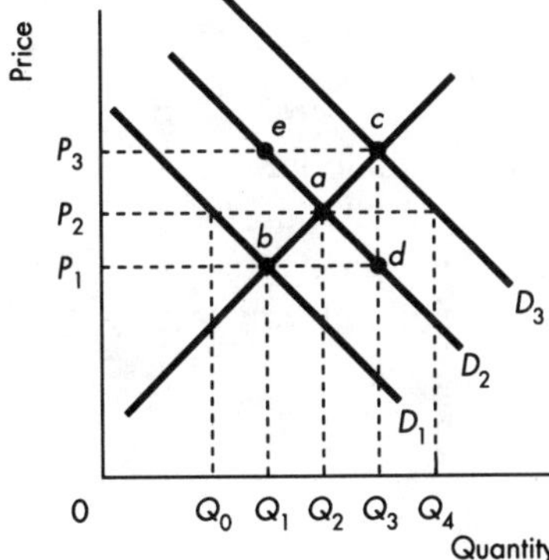

4.36
Correct: b)
Difficulty: 5
Page(s): 74
Scramble range: All
Topic: Market adjustment/*D* shift

4.36
Initially, the demand curve for good *A* is given by D_2 in Figure 4.5. Suppose good *B* is a substitute (in consumption). If the price of *B* falls,

a) the price of *A* will rise.
b) there will be a surplus of good *A* at P_2.
c) the demand for good *A* will rise.
d) the equilibrium quantity traded will rise.
e) the demand curve will shift from D_2 to D_3.

4.37
Correct: b)
Difficulty: 4
Page(s): 73-74
Scramble range: a)-d)
Topic: Market adjustment/*D* shift

4.37
Initially, the demand curve for good *A* is D_2 in Figure 4.5. If income increases and *A* is a normal good, the consequence would be represented graphically by a movement from point *a* to point

a) *b.*
b) *c.*
c) *d.*
d) *e.*
e) none of the above.

4.38
Correct: d)
Difficulty: 3
Page(s): 82
Scramble range: All
Topic: Market adjustment

4.38
Which of the following correctly describes how price adjustment eliminates a surplus?

a) As the price rises, the quantity demanded decreases while the quantity supplied increases.
b) As the price rises, the quantity demanded increases while the quantity supplied decreases.
c) As the price falls, the quantity demanded decreases while the quantity supplied increases.
d) As the price falls, the quantity demanded increases while the quantity supplied decreases.
e) As price falls, the demand for substitutes falls, getting rid of the surplus.

4.39
Correct: c)
Difficulty: 3
Page(s): 80-81
Scramble range: All
Topic: Equilibrium/surplus, shortage

4.39
If the price is above equilibrium, then

a) none of the good will be sold.
b) the price must rise to clear the market.
c) there will be a surplus.
d) there will be a shortage.
e) price will be unchanged, producers will cut back production until the market is in equilibrium.

4.40
Correct: b)
Difficulty: 4
Page(s): 80-81
Scramble range: All
Topic: Equilibrium/surplus, shortage

4.40
A shortage will exist if

a) the price is above equilibrium.
b) the price is below equilibrium.
c) there are not enough producers.
d) there are not enough consumers.
e) demand falls.

4.41
Correct: b)
Difficulty: 4
Page(s): 83-87
Scramble range: All
Topic: Market adjustment /*D*, *S* shift

4.41
The price of a good will increase if
a) demand for the good decreases.
b) supply of the good decreases.
c) there is a surplus of the good.
d) the price of a substitute decreases.
e) it is an inferior good and income increases.

4.42
Correct: c)
Difficulty: 2
Page(s): 83-84
Scramble range: All
Topic: Market adjustment/*D* shift

4.42
Suppose we observe both an increase in the price of good *A* and an increase in the quantity of good *A* traded. Which of the following is a likely explanation?
a) The law of demand is violated.
b) The law of supply is violated.
c) The demand for *A* has increased.
d) The supply of *A* has increased.
e) The supply of *A* has decreased.

4.43
Correct: a)
Difficulty: 2
Page(s): 83-84
Scramble range: All
Topic: Market adjustment/*D* shift

4.43
When the demand for good *A* increases,
a) both the price and quantity traded will increase.
b) the price will increase but quantity traded will decrease.
c) both the price and quantity traded will decrease.
d) the price will decrease but quantity traded will increase.
e) a surplus will result.

4.44
Correct: b)
Difficulty: 2
Page(s): 86-87
Scramble range: All
Topic: Market adjustment/*S* shift

4.44
When the supply of good *A* decreases,
a) both the price and the quantity traded will increase.
b) the price will increase but the quantity traded will decrease.
c) both the price and the quantity traded will decrease.
d) the price will decrease but the quantity traded will increase.
e) a surplus will result.

4.45
Correct: c)
Difficulty: 4
Page(s): 83-84
Scramble range: All
Topic: Market adjustment/*D* shift

4.45
If *A* is an inferior good and consumer income rises, the demand for *A* will
a) increase, and thus the price and the quantity traded will increase.
b) increase, and thus the price will rise but the quantity traded will decrease.
c) decrease, and thus the price and the quantity traded will decrease.
d) decrease, and thus the price will fall but the quantity traded will increase.
e) decrease, and thus the price will rise; as a result the quantity traded will decrease.

4.46
Correct: a)
Difficulty: 3
Page(s): 73-86
Scramble range: a)-d)
Topic: Market adjustment/*D* shift

4.46
If *A* and *B* are substitute goods (in consumption) and the price of *A* increases, we will observe
a) an increase in the price and the quantity traded of *B*.
b) a decrease in the price and the quantity traded of *B*.
c) an increase in the price but a decrease in the quantity traded of *B*.
d) a decrease in price but an increase in the quantity traded of *B*.
e) none of the above.

4.47
Correct: b)
Difficulty: 3
Page(s): 73-86
Scramble range: a)-d)
Topic: Market adjustment/*D* shift

4.47
If *A* and *B* are complementary goods (in consumption) and the price of *A* increases, we will observe

a) an increase in the price and the quantity traded of *B*.
b) a decrease in the price and the quantity traded of *B*.
c) an increase in the price but a decrease in the quantity traded of *B*.
d) a decrease in price but an increase in the quantity traded of *B*.
e) none of the above.

4.48
Correct: e)
Difficulty: 5
Page(s): 73, 78
Scramble range: All
Topic: Market adjustment / *D*, *S* shift

4.48
If *A* and *B* are substitute goods (in consumption) and the cost of a resource used in the production of *A* increases, then

a) the price of *B* will decrease but the price of *A* will increase.
b) the price of *B* will increase but the price of *A* will decrease.
c) the price of *A* will decrease, while the price of *B* will stay unchanged.
d) the price of *A* and the price of *B* will both decrease.
e) the price of *A* and the price of *B* will both increase.

4.49
Correct: b)
Difficulty: 4
Page(s): 77-78
Scramble range: All
Topic: Market adjustment/*S* shift

4.49
If *A* and *B* are substitutes in production and the price of *A* falls, the supply of *B* will

a) increase, and thus the price of *B* will increase.
b) increase, and thus the price of *B* will decrease.
c) decrease, and thus the price of *B* will decrease.
d) decrease, and thus the price of *B* will increase.
e) shift depending on whether *A* and *B* are substitutes in consumption.

4.50
Correct: d)
Difficulty: 4
Page(s): 77-80
Scramble range: All
Topic: Market adjustment/*S* shift

4.50
If *A* and *B* are complements in production and the price of *A* falls, the supply of *B* will

a) increase, and thus the price of *B* will increase.
b) increase, and thus the price of *B* will decrease.
c) decrease, and thus the price of *B* will decrease.
d) decrease, and thus the price of *B* will increase.
e) shift up or down depending on how close *A* and *B* are as complements.

4.51
Correct: c)
Difficulty: 3
Page(s): 78-79
Scramble range: All
Topic: Market adjustment/*S* shift

4.51
Crude oil is a very important resource used in the production of gasoline. If the price of crude oil increases, we would expect

a) the price of gasoline to rise due to an increase in demand.
b) the price of gasoline to fall due to an increase in demand.
c) the price of gasoline to rise due to a decrease in supply.
d) the quantity of gasoline to fall due to an increase in supply.
e) the quantity of gasoline to rise due to an increase in demand.

4.52
Correct: d)
Difficulty: 4
Page(s): 87-88
Scramble range: All
Topic: Market adjustment/*D, S* shift

4.52
If demand increases and supply decreases, then
a) the quantity traded will increase but the effect on the price is indeterminate.
b) the quantity traded will decrease but the effect on the price is indeterminate.
c) the price will fall but the effect on the quantity traded will be indeterminate.
d) the price will rise but the effect on the quantity traded will be indeterminate.
e) the effect on both price and quantity will be indeterminate.

4.53
Correct: c)
Difficulty: 4
Page(s): 87-88
Scramble range: All
Topic: Market adjustment/*D, S* shift

4.53
If demand decreases and supply increases, then
a) the quantity traded will increase but the effect on the price is indeterminate.
b) the quantity traded will decrease but the effect on the price is indeterminate.
c) the price will fall but the effect on quantity traded will be indeterminate.
d) the price will rise but the effect on quantity traded will be indeterminate.
e) the effect on both price and quantity will be indeterminate.

4.54
Correct: a)
Difficulty: 4
Page(s): 81-82
Scramble range: a)-d)
Topic: Market adjustment/*D, S* shift

4.54
If we observe an increase in the equilibrium price of good *A*, we know that either the demand for *A* has
a) increased or the supply of *A* has decreased (or both).
b) increased or the supply of *A* has increased (or both).
c) decreased or the supply of *A* has increased (or both).
d) decreased or the supply of *A* has decreased (or both).
e) none of the above.

4.55
Correct: c)
Difficulty: 4
Page(s): 81-82
Scramble range: a)-d)
Topic: Market adjustment/*D, S* shift

4.55
If we observe a decrease in the equilibrium price of good *A*, we know that either the demand for *A* has
a) increased or the supply of *A* has decreased (or both).
b) increased or the supply of *A* has increased (or both).
c) decreased or the supply of *A* has increased (or both).
d) decreased or the supply of *A* has decreased (or both).
e) none of the above.

4.56
Correct: b)
Difficulty: 4
Page(s): 80-81
Scramble range: a)-d)
Topic: Market adjustment/*D, S* shift

4.56
If we observe an increase in the equilibrium quantity traded, we know that
a) either the demand for *A* has increased or the supply of *A* has decreased (or both).
b) either the demand for *A* has increased or the supply of *A* has increased (or both).
c) either the demand for *A* has decreased or the supply of *A* has increased (or both).
d) either the demand for *A* has decreased or the supply of *A* has decreased (or both).
e) any of the above reasons could have occurred; it depends on the relative size of the effects.

4.57
Correct: d)
Difficulty: 4
Page(s): 87-88
Scramble range: a)-d)
Topic: Market adjustment/*D, S* shift

4.57
If we observe a decrease in the equilibrium quantity traded, we know that
a) either the demand for *A* has increased or the supply of *A* has decreased (or both).
b) either the demand for *A* has increased or the supply of *A* has increased (or both).
c) either the demand for *A* has decreased or the supply of *A* has increased (or both).
d) either the demand for *A* has decreased or the supply of *A* has decreased (or both).
e) any of the above could have occurred; it depends on the relative size of the effects.

4.58
Correct: c)
Difficulty: 4
Page(s): 83, 87
Scramble range: a)-d)
Topic: Market adjustment/*D, S* shift

4.58
Which of the following will cause an increase in the equilibrium price?
a) An increase in both demand and supply.
b) A decrease in both demand and supply.
c) An increase in demand combined with a decrease in supply.
d) A decrease in demand combined with an increase in supply.
e) Any of the above, depending on the circumstances.

4.59
Correct: d)
Difficulty: 4
Page(s): 83, 87
Scramble range: a)-d)
Topic: Market adjustment/*D, S* shift

4.59
Which of the following will cause a decrease in the equilibrium price?
a) An increase in both demand and supply.
b) A decrease in both demand and supply.
c) An increase in demand combined with a decrease in supply.
d) A decrease in demand combined with an increase in supply.
e) Any of the above, depending on the circumstances.

4.60
Correct: b)
Difficulty: 4
Page(s): 83, 87
Scramble range: a)-d)
Topic: Market adjustment/*D, S* shift

4.60
Which of the following will cause a decrease in the equilibrium quantity traded?
a) An increase in both demand and supply.
b) A decrease in both demand and supply.
c) An increase in demand combined with a decrease in supply.
d) A decrease in demand combined with an increase in supply.
e) Any of the above, depending on the circumstances.

4.61
Correct: e)
Difficulty: 3
Page(s): 78, 86
Scramble range: All
Topic: Market adjustment/*S* shift

4.61
A technological improvement in the production of good *A* will cause
a) an decrease in the supply of *A*.
b) an increase in the demand for *A*.
c) a decrease in the price of *A* and a decrease in the quantity traded.
d) a decrease in the quantity demanded of *A*.
e) an increase in the supply of *A*.

4.62 (SG 4.1)
Correct: b)
Difficulty: 2
Page(s): 73-74
Scramble range: All
Topic: Demand/shift

4.62
If an increase in the price of good *A* causes the demand curve for good *B* to shift to the left, then
a) *A* and *B* are substitutes.
b) *A* and *B* are complements.
c) *B* must be an inferior good.
d) *A* must be a normal good.
e) *A* must be an inferior good.

4.63
Correct: e)
Difficulty: 2
Page(s): 71-72
Scramble range: All
Topic: Demand/law

4.63
The law of demand implies that, other things being equal,
a) as the price of lobsters rises, the quantity of lobsters demanded will also increase.
b) as income increases, the quantity of lobsters demanded will decrease.
c) as income increases, the quantity of lobsters demanded will increase.
d) as the demand for lobsters increases, the price will rise.
e) as the price of lobsters rises, the quantity of lobsters demanded will decrease.

4.64
Correct: a)
Difficulty: 3
Page(s): 71, 73
Scramble range: All
Topic: Demand/shift, movement

4.64
Which of the following would lead to an increase in the demand for hamburgers?
a) A new fad hamburger diet.
b) A decrease in population size.
c) An increase in the price of french fries, a complement.
d) A decrease in consumer income.
e) A news report that hamburgers cause skin diseases.

4.65 (SG 4.4)
Correct: c)
Difficulty: 2
Page(s): 71, 73
Scramble range: All
Topic: Demand/shift, movement

4.65
Which of the following is *not* one of the "other things" held constant along a demand curve?
a) Income.
b) Prices of other goods.
c) The price of the good itself.
d) Tastes.
e) Population.

4.66 (SG 4.5)
Correct: d)
Difficulty: 4
Page(s): 73-74
Scramble range: All
Topic: Demand/shift, normal

4.66
Good *A* is a normal good if
a) an increase in the price of a complement causes the demand for *A* to decrease.
b) an increase in the price of a complement causes the demand for *A* to increase.
c) an increase in the price of a substitute causes the demand for *A* to increase.
d) an increase in income causes the demand for *A* to increase.
e) it satisfies the law of demand.

4.67
Correct: c)
Difficulty: 3
Page(s): 73-74
Scramble range: All
Topic: Demand/shift, inferior

4.67
An increase in income will
a) increase the supply of turnips if turnips are inferior goods.
b) decrease the supply of turnips if turnips are inferior goods.
c) cause the price of turnips to fall if turnips are inferior goods.
d) cause the price of turnips to rise if turnips are inferior goods.
e) increase the demand for turnips if turnips are inferior goods.

4.68 (SG 4.7)
Correct: c)
Difficulty: 3
Page(s): 74-75
Scramble range: All
Topic: Demand/movement, shift

4.68
A decrease in quantity demanded is represented by
a) a rightward shift of the demand curve.
b) a leftward shift of the demand curve.
c) a movement upward and to the left along the demand curve.
d) a movement downward and to the right along the demand curve.
e) either a leftward shift of the demand curve or a movement upward and to the left along the demand curve.

4.69
Correct: d)
Difficulty: 3
Page(s): 80-82
Scramble range: All
Topic: Equilibrium/surplus, shortage

4.69
The price of a good will tend to rise if
a) there is a surplus at the current price.
b) the current price is above equilibrium.
c) the quantity supplied exceeds the quantity demanded at the current price.
d) there is a shortage at the current price.
e) the current price is really low.

4.70 (SG 4.9)
Correct: a)
Difficulty: 3
Page(s): 76-77
Scramble range: All
Topic: Supply/law

4.70
The fact that a decline in the price of a good causes producers to reduce the quantity of the good they plan to produce illustrates
a) the law of supply.
b) the law of demand.
c) a technological change.
d) a change in supply.
e) a change in demand.

4.71
Correct: c)
Difficulty: 3
Page(s): 77-78
Scramble range: All
Topic: Supply/shift, movement

4.71
Which of the following would not shift the supply curve for good *X* to the right?
a) A reduction in the price of resources used in producing *X*.
b) An improvement in technology affecting the production of *X*.
c) An increase in the price of *X*.
d) An increase in the price of *Y*, a complement in the production of *X*.
e) A decrease in the price of *Y*, a substitute in the production of *X*.

4.72 (SG 4.11)
Correct: a)
Difficulty: 4
Page(s): 77-78
Scramble range: All
Topic: Supply/law

4.72
A decrease in quantity supplied is represented by
a) a movement down the supply curve.
b) a movement up the supply curve.
c) a rightward shift in the supply curve.
d) a leftward shift in the supply curve.
e) either a movement down the supply curve or a leftward shift in the supply curve.

4.73 (SG 4.13)
Correct: e)
Difficulty: 3
Page(s): 78-79
Scramble range: a)-c)
Topic: Supply/law

4.73
Which of the following will shift the supply curve for good *X* to the left?
a) A decrease in the wages of workers employed to produce *X*.
b) A decrease in the cost of machinery used to produce *X*.
c) A technological improvement in the production of *X*.
d) All of the above.
e) None of the above.

4.74 (SG 4.12)
Correct: a)
Difficulty: 2
Page(s): 77-78
Scramble range: a)-d)
Topic: Supply/law

4.74
If a producer can use its resources to produce either good *A* or good *B*, then *A* and *B* are
a) substitutes in production.
b) complements in production.
c) substitutes in consumption.
d) complements in consumption.
e) none of the above.

4.75 (SG 4.14)
Correct: d)
Difficulty: 3
Page(s): 80-81
Scramble range: All
Topic: Equilibrium/surplus, shortage

4.75
If the market for good *A* is in equilibrium, then
a) the scarcity of good *A* is eliminated.
b) producers would like to sell more at the current price.
c) consumers would like to buy more at the current price.
d) there will be no surplus.
e) price will be rising.

4.76
Correct: b)
Difficulty: 4
Page(s): 80-81
Scramble range: All
Topic: Equilibrium/surplus, shortage

4.76
A shortage
a) will exist if the price is above equilibrium.
b) is the amount by which quantity demanded exceeds quantity supplied.
c) is the amount by which quantity traded exceeds quantity supplied.
d) is the amount by which quantity demanded exceeds the equilibrium quantity.
e) always exists in a world with scarcity.

4.77
Correct: a)
Difficulty: 3
Page(s): 86-87
Scramble range: All
Topic: Market adjustment/shortage

4.77
Which of the following correctly describes how price adjustment eliminates a shortage?
a) As the price rises, the quantity demanded decreases while the quantity supplied increases.
b) As the price rises, the quantity demanded increases while the quantity supplied decreases.
c) As the price falls, the quantity demanded decreases while the quantity supplied increases.
d) As the price falls, the quantity demanded increases while the quantity supplied decreases.
e) As the price falls, the quantity demanded increases while the quantity supplied increases.

4.78 (SG 4.17)
Correct: d)
Difficulty: 3
Page(s): 86-87
Scramble range: None
Topic: Market adjustment/surplus

4.78
A surplus can be eliminated by
a) increasing supply.
b) government raising the price.
c) decreasing the quantity demanded.
d) allowing the price to fall.
e) both a) and c).

4.79
Correct: a)
Difficulty: 4
Page(s): 73-87
Scramble range: All
Topic: Market adjustment/*D*, *S* shift

4.79
Suppose we observe an increase in the price of oranges. Which of the following is the most likely cause?
a) An increase in the price of apples.
b) A scientific discovery that oranges cause hair loss.
c) A decrease in income.
d) Good growing weather in Florida.
e) A technological improvement in the production of oranges.

4.80
Correct: a)
Difficulty: 4
Page(s): 73-74
Scramble range: All
Topic: Demand/law

4.80
If *X* is a normal good and consumer income rises, the demand for *X* will
a) increase, and thus the price will rise and the quantity traded will increase.
b) increase, and thus the price will rise but the quantity traded will decrease.
c) decrease, and thus the price and quantity traded will decrease.
d) decrease, and thus the price will fall but the quantity traded will increase.
e) decrease, and thus both the price and the quantity traded will rise.

4.81 (SG 4.21)
Correct: b)
Difficulty: 5
Page(s): 76-77
Scramble range: All
Topic: Supply/law

4.81
If *A* and *B* are complementary goods (in consumption) and the cost of a resource used in the production of *A* decreases, then
a) the price of *B* will fall but the price of *A* will rise.
b) the price of *B* will rise but the price of *A* will fall.
c) the price of both *A* and *B* will rise.
d) the price of both *A* and *B* will fall.
e) the quantity traded of both goods will rise, since the price of both *A* and *B* will fall.

4.82 (SG 4.22)
Correct: c)
Difficulty: 4
Page(s): 87-88
Scramble range: All
Topic: Market adjustment/*D*, *S* shift

4.82
If both demand and supply increase, what will be the effect on the equilibrium price and quantity traded?
a) Both the price and quantity traded will increase.
b) Price will fall but the quantity traded will increase.
c) Quantity traded will increase but the equilibrium price could either rise or fall.
d) Price will rise but the quantity traded could either increase or decrease.
e) Price could either fall or rise, and quantity traded could either increase or decrease.

4.83
Correct: e)
Difficulty: 4
Page(s): 87-88
Scramble range: None
Topic: Market adjustment/*D*, *S* shift

4.83
Which of the following will cause an increase in the equilibrium quantity traded?
a) An increase in both demand and supply.
b) A decrease in both demand and supply.
c) An increase in demand combined with no change in supply.
d) A decrease in demand combined with a increase in supply.
e) Both a) and c).

4.84
Correct: e)
Difficulty: 5
Page(s): 73-86
Scramble range: None
Topic: Market adjustment/*D* shift

4.84
Consider the market for snack foods, specifically two goods — granola bars (a health food) and chocolate bars. Suppose a health craze sweeps the nation.
a) The price and quantity exchanged of granola bars will rise.
b) The price and quantity exchanged of chocolate bars will rise.
c) Granola bars and chocolate bars are complements.
d) Granola bars and chocolate bars are substitutes.
e) Both a) and d).

4.85
Correct: d)
Difficulty: 4
Page(s): 71, 73
Scramble range: All
Topic: Demand, shift, movement

4.85
Which of the following would lead to a decrease in the demand for hamburgers?
a) A fall in the price of french fries, a complement.
b) An increase in population size.
c) A rise in the price of hamburgers.
d) The release of a new study demonstrating that a steady diet of hamburgers will shorten one's life span by 10 years.
e) The release of a new study demonstrating that a steady diet of hamburgers prevents baldness.

4.86 (SG 4.4)
Correct: c)
Difficulty: 2
Page(s): 71, 73
Scramble range: All
Topic: Demand/shift, movement

4.86
Which of the following is *not* one of the "other things" held constant along a demand curve?
a) Income of buyers.
b) Prices of other goods related in consumption.
c) The price of the good itself.
d) Availability of the good.
e) Government regulation of sales of this good.

4.87
Correct: b)
Difficulty: 3
Page(s): 78-79
Scramble range: All
Topic: Supply/shift, movement

4.87
A rise in the price of a good will cause
a) the demand for the good to decrease.
b) a movement up and to the right along the supply curve.
c) a movement down and to the right along the demand curve.
d) the supply of the good to increase.
e) the demand for a complementary good to rise.

4.88
Correct: e)
Difficulty: 4
Page(s): 77-78
Scramble range: All
Topic: Supply/shift, movement

4.88
Which of the following will shift the supply curve for good *X* to the right?
a) An increase in the wages of workers employed to produce good *X*.
b) An increase in the cost of machinery used to produce good *X*.
c) A rise in the price of a substitute in production.
d) An increase in the price of good *X*.
e) A technological improvement in the production of good *X*.

4.89
Correct: b)
Difficulty: 2
Page(s): 80-81
Scramble range: All
Topic: Equilibrium

4.89
If a market is said to be in equilibrium, then
a) the quantity traded will be different from the quantity supplied.
b) the quantity demanded and the quantity supplied will be the same.
c) the surplus will be very small.
d) the shortage will be very small.
e) income levels of consumers must be rising in order for them to be able to afford this good.

4.90
Correct: b)
Difficulty: 4
Page(s): 80-81
Scramble range: All
Topic: Equilibrium/ surplus, shortage

4.90
If the market for a good is not in equilibrium, then
a) the quantity traded may be different from the quantity sold.
b) the quantity demanded may be different from the quantity traded.
c) the quantity demanded will equal the quantity supplied at the current market price.
d) either the demand or the supply curve will shift.
e) quantity supplied must be rising.

4.91
Correct: a)
Difficulty: 4
Page(s): 80, 81
Scramble range: All
Topic: Equilibrium/ surplus

4.91
A surplus
a) will exist if the price is above equilibrium.
b) is the amount by which the quantity demanded exceeds the quantity supplied.
c) is the amount by which the quantity demanded exceeds the equilibrium quantity.
d) is the amount by which quantity supplied exceeds the equilibrium quantity.
e) will lead to rising prices.

4.92
Correct: d)
Difficulty: 4
Page(s): 86-87
Scramble range: All
Topic: Market adjustment/surplus

4.92
Which of the following correctly describes how price adjustment eliminates a surplus?
a) As the price rises, the quantity demanded decreases while the quantity supplied increases.
b) As the price rises, the quantity demanded increases while the quantity supplied decreases.
c) As the price falls, the quantity demanded decreases while the quantity supplied increases.
d) As the price falls, the quantity demanded increases while the quantity supplied decreases.
e) As the price falls, the quantity demanded increases, while the quantity supplied must stay the same.

4.93
Correct: e)
Difficulty: 5
Page(s): 82-83
Scramble range: None
Topic: Market adjustment/price

4.93
A firm can use its resources to produce either good *A* or good *B*. If both markets are in equilibrium when the price of good *B* rises, then
a) the demand for good *B* will decrease.
b) the supply of good *A* will decrease.
c) the quantity supplied of good *B* will decrease.
d) the quantity supplied of good *B* will increase.
e) both b) and d).

4.94
Correct: e)
Difficulty: 5
Page(s): 83-86
Scramble range: All
Topic: Market adjustment/*S* shift

4.94
It has been revealed recently that there are severe problems in the Atlantic fishing industry, with large falls in the fish stocks. As a result of this,
a) the price of fish will fall, since no one will be able to eat them any more.
b) the quantity of fish sold will rise, as fishermen will catch more to make up for the shortage.
c) price and quantity will fall or rise depending on how large the fall in fish stocks is.
d) both price and quantity will rise, as consumers will desire even more fish, since they are scarce.
e) the fall in the fish stocks will lead to a shortage, and therefore a rise in price and a fall in quantity traded.

4.95
Correct: d)
Difficulty: 5
Page(s): 73-86
Scramble range: All
Topic: Market adjustment/*S* shift

4.95
Recently, it has been revealed that there have been severe falls in the fish stocks in the Atlantic fishing industry. As a result,
a) we would expect to see rises in the demand for meat (e.g. beef), since this is a complement to fish.
b) we would expect to see falls in the price of fish, leading to falls in the demand for meat, since meat and fish are substitutes.
c) we would expect falls in the price of fish, leading to rises in the demand for meat, since meat and fish are substitutes.
d) we would expect to see rises in the demand for meat, since meat is a substitute for fish.
e) we would expect to see rises in the price of fish, leading to falls in the demand for meat, since meat and fish are complements.

4.96
Correct: a)
Difficulty: 5
Page(s): 73-86
Scramble range: All
Topic: Market adjustment/*S* shift

4.96
A technological improvement in the production process of compact disc players will lead to
a) a fall in the price of CD players, and therefore a leftward shift in the demand curve for record turntables.
b) a fall in the price of CD players, and therefore an increase in demand for records.
c) a fall in the price of CD players, and therefore a leftward shift in the demand curve for compact discs.
d) a fall in the price of CD players, and therefore a fall in the demand for CD players.
e) a rise in the price of CD players.

4.97
Correct: e)
Difficulty: 5
Page(s): 73-86
Scramble range: All
Topic: Market adjustment/*D* shock

4.97
Suppose Canadians suddenly develop a strong urge to escape the cold winter by taking vacations in Hawaii. Therefore,

a) the price of vacations in Hawaii will rise and the overall quantity demanded will be lower.
b) the price of skiing vacations in the mountains will rise.
c) the initial result of the change is a surplus of vacations in Hawaii, leading to a price rise.
d) the price of airline tickets will fall, as ticket agents make lots of deals in response to this change.
e) the price of luggage will rise, because luggage and vacations are complements.

4.98
Correct: e)
Difficulty: 5
Page(s): 73-86
Scramble range: All
Topic: Market adjustment/*S* shift

4.98
Recently there have been very large technological improvements in the production process of video-cassette recorders (VCRs). As a result, we would expect the price of VCRs to

a) rise to reflect these technological improvements.
b) fall, leading to a rise in the demand for movies shown in theatres.
c) rise, leading to a rise in the demand for movies shown in theatres.
d) fall, leading to a fall in the demand for rented videotaped movies.
e) fall, leading to a rise in the demand for rented video movies.

4.99
Correct: a)
Difficulty: 4
Page(s): 73-86
Scramble range: All
Topic: Market adjustment

4.99
Which of the following will *not* increase the quantity of gasoline traded?

a) The price of cars rises.
b) The price of cars falls.
c) Robotic production plants lower the cost of producing cars.
d) The population doubles.
e) A massive and high-grade oil supply is discovered in northern Saskatchewan.

4.100
Correct: e)
Difficulty: 4
Page(s): 73-86
Scramble range: All
Topic: Market adjustment

4.100
Which of the following will decrease the quantity of gasoline traded?

a) The quality of gasoline rises (it gets more kilometres per litre).
b) The minimum age for drivers is decreased to 14.
c) All speed limits on highways are abolished.
d) The environmental lobby succeeds in closing down all nuclear power stations.
e) The price of cars rises.

4.101
Correct: d)
Difficulty: 4
Page(s): 73-86
Scramble range: All
Topic: Market adjustment

4.101
The Genius Software Company has developed an amazing new software package, to be used with Einstein Computers. As a result,

a) the price of all computers will rise.
b) the price of rival software packages will fall, leading to an overall increase in the quantity traded of these packages.
c) the price of all software packages will rise.
d) the price of Einstein computers will rise, accompanied by a rise in the quantity traded.
e) the price of Einstein computers will rise, leading to a fall in the quantity traded.

4.102
Correct: a)
Difficulty: 5
Page(s): 73-86
Scramble range: All
Topic: Market adjustment

4.102
A new study has been released, revealing that houses built with bricks are a health hazard, due to the fact that bricks release "cancoid" gas, which raises the probability of developing cancer. As a result,

a) the price of brick houses will fall, while the price of wood houses will rise.
b) the price of brick houses will fall, leading to a fall in the demand for all houses.
c) companies will switch from building wood to brick houses, since the price of the latter is lower.
d) the price of brick houses will rise, due to the fall in the quantity supplied once this news gets out.
e) the increase in the price of wood houses will lead to a fall in the quantity traded, as they will be too expensive.

Chapter 5 **Elasticity**

5.1
Correct: b)
Difficulty: 2
Page(s): 104-106
Scramble range: All
Topic: Price elasticity

5.1
A price elasticity of demand of 2 means that a 10 percent increase in price will result in a
a) 2 percent decrease in quantity demanded.
b) 20 percent decrease in quantity demanded.
c) 5 percent decrease in quantity demanded.
d) 2 percent increase in quantity demanded.
e) 20 percent increase in quantity demanded.

5.2
Correct: c)
Difficulty: 2
Page(s): 104-105
Scramble range: a)-d)
Topic: Price elasticity

5.2
The price elasticity of demand is a units-free measure of
a) the responsiveness of quantity demanded to changes in the price of a substitute or complement.
b) the responsiveness of quantity demanded to changes in income.
c) the responsiveness of quantity demanded to changes in the price of the good itself.
d) the responsiveness of price to changes in quantity demanded.
e) none of the above.

5.3
Correct: d)
Difficulty: 2
Page(s): 104-105
Scramble range: All
Topic: Price elasticity

5.3
The concept used by economists to indicate the responsiveness of quantity demanded to changes in price is the
a) cross elasticity of demand.
b) income elasticity of demand.
c) substitute elasticity of demand.
d) price elasticity of demand.
e) elasticity of supply.

5.4
Correct: a)
Difficulty: 2
Page(s): 104-106
Scramble range: All
Topic: Price elasticity

5.4
If a 10 percent rise in price causes a 5 percent decline in quantity demanded, the price elasticity of demand is
a) 0.5.
b) 2.
c) 5.
d) 0.2.
e) 50.

5.5
Correct: a)
Difficulty: 2
Page(s): 106-107
Scramble range: All
Topic: Price (in)elastic/unit

5.5
If a large percentage drop in the price level causes a small percentage increase in the quantity demanded,
a) demand is inelastic.
b) demand is elastic.
c) demand is unit elastic.
d) the price elasticity of demand is close to infinity.
e) the price elasticity of demand is zero.

5.6
Correct: a)
Difficulty: 2
Page(s): 106-107
Scramble range: All
Topic: Price (in)elastic/unit

5.6
Which of the following illustrates an inelastic demand curve?
a) A 10 percent increase in price causes a 5 percent decrease in quantity demanded.
b) A 10 percent increase in price causes a 20 percent decrease in quantity demanded.
c) A price elasticity measure of infinity.
d) A price elasticity measure of 1.0.
e) A price elasticity measure of 2.0.

5.7
Correct: b)
Difficulty: 2
Page(s): 106-107
Scramble range: All
Topic: Price (in)elastic/unit

5.7
Which of the following illustrates an elastic demand curve?
a) A 10 percent increase in price causes a 5 percent decrease in quantity demanded.
b) A 10 percent increase in price causes a 20 percent decrease in quantity demanded.
c) A price elasticity measure of 0.2.
d) A price elasticity measure of 1.0.
e) A price elasticity measure of zero.

5.8
Correct: c)
Difficulty: 3
Page(s): 104-106
Scramble range: All
Topic: Price elasticity

5.8
If a 6 percent decrease in price causes a 5 percent increase in quantity demanded, the price elasticity of demand is
a) 0.30.
b) 0.6.
c) 0.83.
d) 1.2.
e) 0.5.

5.9
Correct: e)
Difficulty: 2
Page(s): 106-107
Scramble range: All
Topic: Price (in)elastic/unit

5.9
The demand for good *A* is unit elastic if
a) a 5 percent decrease in the price of *A* causes an infinite increase in the quantity demanded.
b) a 5 percent increase in the price of *A* causes a 10 percent decrease in the quantity demanded.
c) any increase in the price of *A* causes a 1 percent decrease in the quantity demanded.
d) a 5 percent increase in the price of *A* results in no change in the quantity demanded.
e) a 5 percent increase in the price of *A* results in a 5 percent change in the quantity demanded.

5.10
Correct: c)
Difficulty: 2
Page(s): 106-107
Scramble range: All
Topic: Price (in)elastic/unit

5.10
Demand is inelastic if
a) a small change in price causes a large change in quantity demanded.
b) the quantity demanded is very responsive to changes in price.
c) the price elasticity of demand is 0.2.
d) its price does not change when supply increases.
e) a 10 percent change in price causes a 1 percent change in quantity supplied.

5.11
Correct: c)
Difficulty: 2
Page(s): 108-109
Scramble range: All
Topic: Price (in)elastic/unit

5.11
A horizontal demand curve
a) indicates 0 income elasticity.
b) has price elasticity of 0.
c) has infinite price elasticity.
d) is likely to arise in the short run.
e) is impossible.

5.12
Correct: e)
Difficulty: 2
Page(s): 108-109
Scramble range: All
Topic: Price (in)elastic/unit

5.12
A demand curve that has a price elasticity of
a) infinity will be vertical.
b) 0 will be horizontal.
c) 1 will be vertical.
d) 1 will be horizontal.
e) 0 will be vertical.

5.13
Correct: d)
Difficulty: 3
Page(s): 107-109
Scramble range: All
Topic: Price (in)elastic/unit

5.13
If a 10 percent increase in the price of goods causes a 10 percent decrease in quantity demanded, its demand curve
a) is vertical.
b) is horizontal.
c) has slope equal to 1.
d) is unit elastic.
e) is a straight line with slope equal to 10.

5.14
Correct: b)
Difficulty: 2
Page(s): 107-109
Scramble range: All
Topic: Price (in)elastic/unit

5.14
A unit elastic demand curve
a) means that the ratio of a change in quantity demanded to a change in price is equal to 1.
b) means that the ratio of a percentage change in quantity demanded to a percentage change in price is equal to 1.
c) means that the ratio of a percentage change in price to a percentage change in quantity demanded is equal to 1.
d) will be horizontal.
e) will be vertical.

5.15
Correct: d)
Difficulty: 3
Page(s): 104-106
Scramble range: All
Topic: Price elasticity

5.15
A 10 percent increase in the quantity demanded of good *A* results from a 20 percent decline in its price. The price elasticity of demand for good *A* is
a) 10.
b) 20.
c) 2.
d) 0.5.
e) 200.

5.16
Correct: c)
Difficulty: 3
Page(s): 104-106
Scramble range: All
Topic: Price elasticity

5.16
A 20 percent increase in the quantity demanded of good *A* results from a 10 percent decline in its price. The price elasticity of demand for good *A* is
a) 10.
b) 20.
c) 2.
d) 0.5.
e) 200.

5.17
Correct: e)
Difficulty: 4
Page(s): 104-106
Scramble range: All
Topic: Price elasticity

5.17
Suppose a rise in the price of good *A* from $5.50 to $6.50 causes a decrease in quantity demanded from 12,500 to 11,500 units. In this range of the demand curve, the price elasticity of demand is
a) 1.
b) 2.
c) 1000.
d) 20.
e) 0.5.

5.18
Correct: e)
Difficulty: 4
Page(s): 104-106
Scramble range: All
Topic: Price elasticity

5.18
A fall in the price of a good from $10.50 to $9.50 results in an increase in quantity demanded from 19,200 to 20,000 units. The price elasticity of demand in this part of the demand curve is
a) 0.8.
b) 1.25.
c) 1.2.
d) 8.0.
e) 0.41.

5.19
Correct: c)
Difficulty: 4
Page(s): 104-106
Scramble range: All
Topic: Price elasticity

5.19
A fall in the price of a good from $10.50 to $9.50 results in an increase in quantity demanded from 18,800 to 21,200 units. The price elasticity of demand in this part of the demand curve is
a) 0.8.
b) 1.25.
c) 1.2.
d) 8.0.
e) 2.4.

5.20
Correct: a)
Difficulty: 5
Page(s): 104-106
Scramble range: All
Topic: Price elasticity

5.20
Suppose that the quantity of root beer demanded declines from 103,000 litres per week to 97,000 litres per week as a consequence of a 10 percent increase in its price. The price elasticity of demand
a) is 0.6.
b) is 1.97.
c) is 6.
d) is elastic.
e) cannot be computed unless we know the before and after prices.

5.21
Correct: d)
Difficulty: 3
Page(s): 104-106
Scramble range: All
Topic: Price elasticity

5.21
Which of the following cases will yield a measured price elasticity of demand of 5.0? A 10 percent increase in the price results in a
a) 10 percent decrease in quantity demanded.
b) 5 percent decrease in quantity demanded.
c) 2 percent decrease in quantity demanded.
d) 50 percent decrease in quantity demanded.
e) 0.5 percent decrease in quantity demanded.

5.22
Correct: c)
Difficulty: 4
Page(s): 104-106
Scramble range: All
Topic: Price elasticity

5.22
Refer to Table 5.1. The price elasticity of demand between $6.00 and $7.00 is
a) 1.0.
b) 2.0.
c) 2.6.
d) 0.5.
e) 1.3.

Table 5.1 Demand schedule for good A.

Price ($)	Quantity demanded
8.00	2,000
7.00	4,000
6.00	6,000
5.00	8,000
4.00	10,000
3.00	12,000

5.23
Correct: d)
Difficulty: 5
Page(s): 104-106
Scramble range: All
Topic: Price elasticity

5.23
Refer to Table 5.1. Demand is unit elastic as price falls from
a) $8.00 to $7.00.
b) $7.00 to $6.00.
c) $6.00 to $5.00.
d) $5.00 to $4.00.
e) $4.00 to $3.00.

5.24
Correct: e)
Difficulty: 4
Page(s): 106-107
Scramble range: All
Topic: Price (in)elastic/unit

5.24
Refer to Table 5.1. If the price of good *A* is cut from $4.00 to $3.00,
a) total revenue will increase.
b) total revenue will remain constant.
c) we observe that demand is elastic in this range.
d) we observe that demand is unit elastic in this range.
e) we observe that demand is inelastic in this range.

5.25
Correct: a)
Difficulty: 3
Page(s): 106-107
Scramble range: a)-d)
Topic: Price (in)elastic/unit

5.25
For which of the following will demand be the most price inelastic?
a) Milk.
b) Happy Cow brand milk.
c) Happy Cow brand milk in Regina.
d) Happy Cow brand milk at Ralph's Grocery Store.
e) Each of the above will all exhibit the same demand elasticity.

5.26
Correct: d)
Difficulty: 2
Page(s): 109-110
Scramble range: All
Topic: Price (in)elastic/unit

5.26
For which of the following is the demand curve likely to be the most inelastic?
a) A new automobile.
b) A new Toyota automobile.
c) A compact disc player.
d) Toothpicks.
e) Travel.

5.27
Correct: b)
Difficulty: 2
Page(s): 109-110
Scramble range: All
Topic: Price (in)elastic/unit

5.27
For which of the following is demand likely to be most inelastic?
a) Diamonds.
b) Insulin for a diabetic.
c) Potatoes.
d) Gasoline.
e) Books.

5.28
Correct: d)
Difficulty: 3
Page(s): 109-110
Scramble range: All
Topic: Price (in)elastic/unit

5.28
Demand will be more inelastic
a) the higher the income level.
b) the lower the income level.
c) the longer the passage of time after a price increase.
d) the fewer good substitutes are available.
e) the larger the fraction of income spent on the good.

5.29
Correct: d)
Difficulty: 3
Page(s): 109-110
Scramble range: All
Topic: Price (in)elastic/unit

5.29
Demand will be more elastic
a) the higher the income level.
b) the lower the income level.
c) the longer the passage of time after a price increase.
d) the more good substitutes are available.
e) the smaller the fraction of income spent on the good.

5.30
Correct: b)
Difficulty: 3
Page(s): 109-110
Scramble range: All
Topic: Price (in)elastic/unit

5.30
Demand for a good is likely to be more price elastic
a) the higher the level of income.
b) the larger the proportion of monthly income spent on it.
c) if fewer good substitutes are available.
d) the higher the price of complementary goods.
e) the lower the price of substitute goods.

5.31
Correct: a)
Difficulty: 3
Page(s): 107-108
Scramble range: All
Topic: Price (in)elastic/unit

5.31
Figure 5.1 illustrates a linear demand curve. Comparing the demand elasticity in the $2 to $3 price range with the elasticity in the range $8 to $9, we can conclude

a) that demand is more elastic in the $8 to $9 price range.
b) that demand is more elastic in the $2 to $3 price range.
c) that the elasticity of demand is the same in both price ranges.
d) nothing without numerical information about quantities.
e) the elasticity of demand is zero in both price ranges, since we have a straight line demand curve.

Figure 5.1

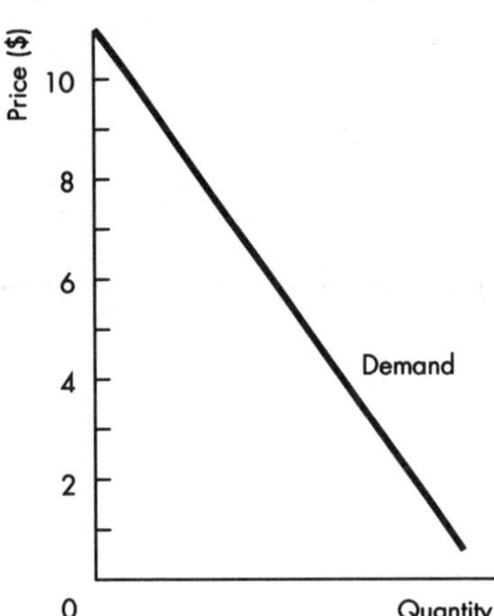

5.32
Correct: a)
Difficulty: 4
Page(s): 108,112
Scramble range: All
Topic: Price elasticity

5.32
Figure 5.2 illustrates a linear demand curve. If the price falls from $11 to $9 we know that

a) total revenue will increase.
b) total revenue will decrease.
c) total revenue will remain unchanged.
d) the effect on total revenue cannot be determined.
e) the effect on total revenue can be determined only with information on the quantities.

Figure 5.2

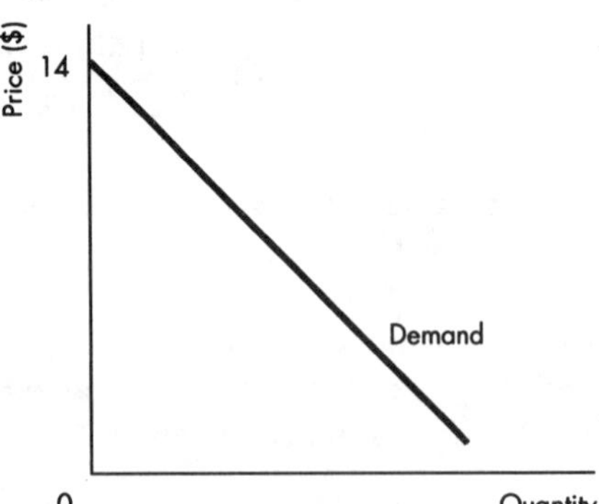

5.33
Correct: c)
Difficulty: 4
Page(s): 108,112
Scramble range: All
Topic: Price elasticity

5.33
Figure 5.2 illustrates a linear demand curve. If the price falls from $8 to $6 we know that

a) total revenue will increase.
b) total revenue will decrease.
c) total revenue will remain unchanged.
d) quantity demanded will increase by more than 10 percent.
e) the percentage change in quantity demanded will be more than the percentage change in price.

5.34
Correct: b)
Difficulty: 4
Page(s): 108,112
Scramble range: All
Topic: Price elasticity

5.34
Figure 5.2 illustrates a linear demand curve. If the price falls from $6 to $4 we know that

a) total revenue will increase.
b) total revenue will decrease.
c) total revenue will remain unchanged.
d) quantity demanded will increase by more than 10 percent.
e) the percentage change in quantity demanded will be more than the percentage change in price.

5.35
Correct: b)
Difficulty: 4
Page(s): 108,112
Scramble range: All
Topic: Price elasticity

5.35
Refer to the linear demand curve in Figure 5.2. If the price increases from $9 to $11 we know that

a) total revenue will increase.
b) total revenue will decrease.
c) total revenue will remain unchanged.
d) what happens to total revenue cannot be known without knowing the values of quantity demanded.
e) the percentage change in quantity demanded will be less than the percentage change in price.

5.36
Correct: c)
Difficulty: 4
Page(s): 108,112
Scramble range: All
Topic: Price elasticity

5.36
Refer to the linear demand curve in Figure 5.2. If the price increases from $6 to $8 we know that

a) total revenue will increase.
b) total revenue will decrease.
c) total revenue will remain unchanged.
d) we cannot tell what happens to total revenue without knowing the values of quantity demanded.
e) the percentage change in quantity demanded will be more than the percentage change in price.

5.37
Correct: a)
Difficulty: 4
Page(s): 108,112
Scramble range: All
Topic: Price elasticity

5.37
Refer to the linear demand curve in Figure 5.2. If the price increases from $4 to $6 we know that

a) total revenue will increase.
b) total revenue will decrease.
c) total revenue will remain unchanged.
d) we cannot tell what happens to total revenue without knowing the values of quantity demanded.
e) the percentage change in quantity demanded will be more than the percentage change in price.

5.38
Correct: e)
Difficulty: 2
Page(s): 112
Scramble range: All
Topic: Price elasticity

5.38
If a price decrease results in an increase in total revenue, then demand must be
a) inelastic in that range.
b) unit elastic in that range.
c) vertical.
d) horizontal.
e) elastic in that range.

5.39
Correct: c)
Difficulty: 3
Page(s): 112
Scramble range: All
Topic: Price elasticity

5.39
The demand for a good is elastic if
a) an increase in price results in an increase in total revenue.
b) a decrease in price results in a decrease in total revenue.
c) an increase in price results in a decrease in total revenue.
d) the good is a necessity.
e) the demand for the good is very insensitive to changes in price.

5.40
Correct: a)
Difficulty: 3
Page(s): 112
Scramble range: All
Topic: Price elasticity

5.40
The demand for a good is price inelastic if
a) an increase in price results in an increase in total revenue.
b) an increase in price results in a decrease in total revenue.
c) an increase in income results in a decrease in total revenue.
d) an increase in income results in an increase in total revenue.
e) the good is a luxury.

5.41
Correct: c)
Difficulty: 3
Page(s): 112
Scramble range: All
Topic: Price elasticity

5.41
If the demand for a good is unit elastic, then
a) a 5 percent increase in price will cause a 5 percent increase in total revenue.
b) a 5 percent increase in price will cause a 5 percent decrease in total revenue.
c) a 5 percent increase in price will cause total revenue to be unchanged.
d) a 5 percent increase in price will cause an increase in total revenue greater than 5 percent.
e) a 5 percent increase in price will cause an increase in total revenue less than 5 percent.

5.42
Correct: b)
Difficulty: 4
Page(s): 112
Scramble range: All
Topic: Price elasticity

5.42
Revenues from the sale of a good will decrease if
a) income increases and the good is normal.
b) its price rises and demand is elastic.
c) its price rises and demand is inelastic.
d) income falls and the good is inferior.
e) its price falls and demand is elastic.

5.43
Correct: c)
Difficulty: 4
Page(s): 112
Scramble range: All
Topic: Price elasticity

5.43
Revenues from the sale of a good will increase if
a) income increases and the good is inferior.
b) its price rises and demand is elastic.
c) its price rises and demand is inelastic.
d) income falls and the good is normal.
e) its price falls and demand is inelastic.

5.44
Correct: d)
Difficulty: 3
Page(s): 112
Scramble range: All
Topic: Price elasticity

5.44
If the country of Saudi Petrolia argues that an increase in the supply of OPEC oil will decrease total oil sales revenue, then Saudi Petrolia must believe the demand for oil to be

a) income inelastic.
b) income elastic.
c) price elastic.
d) price inelastic.
e) price unit elastic.

5.45
Correct: c)
Difficulty: 4
Page(s): 112
Scramble range: All
Topic: Price elasticity/revenue

5.45
Suppose there is an increase in the cost of resources used in the production of good *A*. Then

a) if the price of *A* rises, we know that the demand for *A* is elastic.
b) if the total revenue from sales of *A* rises, we know that the demand for *A* is elastic.
c) if the total revenue from sales of *A* falls, we know that the demand for *A* is elastic.
d) total revenue will increase since the price of *A* must rise.
e) total revenue must fall since the quantity traded of *A* must fall.

5.46
Correct: e)
Difficulty: 2
Page(s): 112-113
Scramble range: All
Topic: Income elasticity

5.46
The income elasticity of demand is computed by the percentage change in

a) price divided by the percentage change in income.
b) price divided by the percentage change in quantity demanded.
c) income divided by the percentage change in quantity demanded.
d) quantity demanded divided by the percentage change in price.
e) quantity demanded divided by the percentage change in income.

5.47
Correct: e)
Difficulty: 2
Page(s): 113-115
Scramble range: All
Topic: Income inelasticity

5.47
If the quantity of carrots demanded increases by a small percentage due to a large increase in income, we know that the demand for carrots is

a) price elastic.
b) price inelastic.
c) unit elastic.
d) income elastic.
e) income inelastic.

5.48
Correct: e)
Difficulty: 2
Page(s): 113-115
Scramble range: All
Topic: Income inelasticity

5.48
If the quantity of carrots demanded increases by a large percentage due to a small increase in income, we know that the demand for carrots is

a) price elastic.
b) price inelastic.
c) price elastic.
d) income inelastic.
e) income elastic.

5.49
Correct: a)
Difficulty: 2
Page(s): 113-115
Scramble range: All
Topic: Income inelasticity

5.49
Which of the following must be true if demand is income inelastic?
a) A large percentage increase in income will result in a small percentage increase in quantity demanded.
b) A small percentage increase in income will result in a large percentage increase in quantity demanded.
c) An increase in income will cause a decline in quantity demanded.
d) The good in question must be inferior.
e) A percentage rise in price will cause a smaller percentage rise in quantity demanded.

5.50
Correct: b)
Difficulty: 2
Page(s): 113-115
Scramble range: All
Topic: Income inelasticity

5.50
Which of the following must be true if demand is income elastic?
a) A large percentage increase in income will result in a small percentage increase in quantity demanded.
b) A small percentage increase in income will result in a large percentage increase in quantity demanded.
c) An increase in income will cause a decline in quantity demanded.
d) The good in question must be inferior.
e) A percentage change in price will lead to a larger percentage change in quantity demanded.

5.51
Correct: d)
Difficulty: 2
Page(s): 115
Scramble range: All
Topic: Income elasticity

5.51
To say that turnips are inferior goods means that
a) a small decrease in income will cause a large decrease in the quantity of turnips demanded at the current price.
b) a large decrease in income will cause a small decrease in the quantity of turnips demanded at the current price.
c) any increase in income will cause quantity demanded to increase at the current price.
d) any increase in income will cause quantity demanded to decrease at the current price.
e) turnips taste awful.

5.52
Correct: c)
Difficulty: 2
Page(s): 115
Scramble range: All
Topic: Income elasticity

5.52
To say that turnips are normal goods means that
a) a small decrease in income will cause a large decrease in the quantity of turnips demanded at the current price.
b) a large decrease in income will cause a small decrease in the quantity of turnips demanded at the current price.
c) any increase in income will cause quantity demanded to increase at the current price.
d) any increase in income will cause quantity demanded to decrease at the current price.
e) an increase in price will cause quantity demanded to decrease.

5.53
Correct: b)
Difficulty: 3
Page(s): 104-106
Scramble range: All
Topic: Income elasticity

5.53
A 10 percent increase in income has caused a 5 percent decrease in the quantity demanded (at the current price). The income elasticity is
a) 0.5.
b) –0.5.
c) 2.0.
d) –2.0.
e) –5.0.

5.54
Correct: d)
Difficulty: 3
Page(s): 112-113
Scramble range: All
Topic: Income inelasticity

5.54
Fred's income has just risen from $950 per week to $1,050 per week. As a result, he decides to increase the number of movies he attends each month by 5 percent. Fred's demand for movies is

a) price elastic.
b) price inelastic.
c) income elastic.
d) income inelastic.
e) income inferior.

5.55
Correct: e)
Difficulty: 4
Page(s): 112-113
Scramble range: All
Topic: Income elasticity

5.55
Fred's income has just risen from $940 per week to $1,060 per week. As a result, he decides to purchase 9 percent more bubblegum per week. The income elasticity of Fred's demand for bubblegum is

a) 0.9.
b) 1.33.
c) 1.0.
d) 0.12.
e) 0.75.

5.56
Correct: c)
Difficulty: 4
Page(s): 112-113
Scramble range: All
Topic: Income elasticity

5.56
Fred's income has just risen from $940 per week to $1,060 per week. As a result, he decides to purchase 12 percent more bubblegum per week. The income elasticity of Fred's demand for bubblegum is

a) 0.9.
b) 1.33.
c) 1.0.
d) 0.12.
e) 0.75.

5.57
Correct: b)
Difficulty: 4
Page(s): 112-113
Scramble range: All
Topic: Income elasticity

5.57
Suppose there is a 10 percent increase in income, which causes the quantity demanded of good *A* to increase from 19,200 to 20,800 units. The income elasticity of demand for good *A* is

a) 0.5.
b) 0.8.
c) 1.0.
d) 1.2.
e) 8.0.

5.58
Correct: d)
Difficulty: 4
Page(s): 112-113
Scramble range: All
Topic: Income elasticity

5.58
Suppose there is a 10 percent increase in income, which causes the quantity demanded of good *A* to increase from 18,800 to 21,200 units. The income elasticity of demand for good *A* is

a) 0.5.
b) 0.8.
c) 1.0.
d) 1.2.
e) 12.0.

5.59
Correct: a)
Difficulty: 2
Page(s): 114-115
Scramble range: All
Topic: Cross elasticity

5.59
The cross elasticity of demand between any two goods is defined as
a) the percentage change in the quantity demanded of one good divided by the percentage change in the price of the other good.
b) the change in the price elasticity of demand for one good divided by the change in the price elasticity of demand for the other good.
c) the percentage change in the quantity of a good demanded divided by the percentage change in its price.
d) the percentage change in the quantity of a good demanded divided by the percentage change in income.
e) the percentage change in the price of one good divided by the percentage change in the price of the other good.

5.60
Correct: d)
Difficulty: 3
Page(s): 115-116
Scramble range: a)-d)
Topic: Cross elasticity

5.60
If the cross elasticity of demand between goods *A* and *B* is positive, then
a) the demands for *A* and *B* are both price elastic.
b) the demands for *A* and *B* are both price inelastic.
c) *A* and *B* are complements.
d) *A* and *B* are substitutes.
e) none of the above.

5.61
Correct: c)
Difficulty: 2
Page(s): 115-116
Scramble range: a)-d)
Topic: Cross elasticity

5.61
If the cross elasticity of demand between goods *A* and *B* is negative, then
a) the demands for *A* and *B* are both price elastic.
b) the demands for *A* and *B* are both price inelastic.
c) *A* and *B* are complements.
d) *A* and *B* are substitutes.
e) none of the above.

5.62
Correct: a)
Difficulty: 2
Page(s): 115-116
Scramble range: All
Topic: Cross elasticity

5.62
If goods *A* and *B* are complements, then
a) the cross elasticity of demand between *A* and *B* is negative.
b) the cross elasticity of demand between *A* and *B* is positive.
c) their income elasticities of demand are both positive.
d) their income elasticities of demand are both negative.
e) their price elasticities are both inelastic.

5.63
Correct: d)
Difficulty: 2
Page(s): 115-116
Scramble range: All
Topic: Cross elasticity

5.63
An economic measure that indicates when the demands for two or more goods are related is
a) the income elasticity of demand.
b) the price elasticity of demand.
c) the substitute elasticity of demand.
d) the cross elasticity of demand.
e) the normal elasticity of demand.

5.64
Correct: a)
Difficulty: 3
Page(s): 115-116
Scramble range: All
Topic: Cross elasticity

5.64
If an increase in the price of good *B* causes the demand for good *A* to increase, then
a) *A* and *B* are substitutes.
b) *A* and *B* are complements.
c) the cross elasticity of demand between *A* and *B* is negative.
d) *A* is an input into production of *B*.
e) the price elasticity of *A* is elastic.

5.65
Correct: b)
Difficulty: 3
Page(s): 115-116
Scramble range: All
Topic: Cross elasticity

5.65
If a decrease in the price of good *A* causes the demand for good *B* to increase, then
a) *A* and *B* are substitutes.
b) *A* and *B* are complements.
c) the cross elasticity of demand between *A* and *B* is positive.
d) *A* is an input into production of *B*.
e) the price elasticity of *A* is inelastic.

5.66
Correct: c)
Difficulty: 3
Page(s): 115-116
Scramble range: All
Topic: Cross elasticity

5.66
If an increase in the supply of good *A* causes an increase in the demand for good *B*, then
a) the demands for *A* and *B* are independent.
b) the elasticity of supply for good *A* is greater than 1.
c) *A* and *B* must be complements.
d) *A* and *B* must be substitutes.
e) the elasticity of demand for *A* is elastic.

5.67
Correct: d)
Difficulty: 3
Page(s): 115-116
Scramble range: All
Topic: Cross elasticity

5.67
If an increase in the supply of good *A* causes a decrease in the demand for good *B*, then
a) the demands for *A* and *B* are independent.
b) the elasticity of supply for good *A* is greater than 1.
c) *A* and *B* must be complements.
d) *A* and *B* must be substitutes.
e) the elasticity of demand for *A* must be elastic.

5.68
Correct: b)
Difficulty: 4
Page(s): 115
Scramble range: All
Topic: Cross elasticity

5.68
An increase in the price of good *A* will
a) shift the demand curve of good *B* to the right if the cross elasticity of demand between *A* and *B* is negative.
b) shift the demand curve of good *B* to the right if the cross elasticity of demand between *A* and *B* is positive.
c) shift the supply curve of *B* to the right if the cross elasticity of demand between *A* and *B* is negative.
d) shift the supply curve of *B* to the right if the cross elasticity of demand between *A* and *B* is positive.
e) shift the demand curve of *B* to the right if the income elasticity of demand for *B* is positive.

5.69
Correct: c)
Difficulty: 1
Page(s): 115-117
Scramble range: All
Topic: Supply elasticity

5.69
The elasticity of supply is a (units-free) measure of the responsiveness of
a) quantity demanded to changes in supply.
b) quantity supplied to changes in demand.
c) quantity supplied to changes in price.
d) price to changes in quantity supplied.
e) quantity supplied of one good to changes in the price of another good.

5.70
Correct: a)
Difficulty: 1
Page(s): 117
Scramble range: All
Topic: Supply elasticity

5.70
Supply is elastic if

a) a small percentage change in price causes a large percentage change in quantity supplied.
b) a large percentage change in price causes a small percentage change in quantity supplied.
c) a small percentage change in demand causes a large percentage change in quantity supplied.
d) the good in question is inferior.
e) the good in question is normal.

5.71
Correct: d)
Difficulty: 2
Page(s): 117
Scramble range: All
Topic: Supply elasticity

5.71
If a large (percentage) decline in the price of good *A* causes a small (percentage) decline in quantity supplied, then

a) demand is elastic.
b) demand is inelastic.
c) demand in income inelastic.
d) supply is inelastic.
e) supply is elastic.

5.72
Correct: e)
Difficulty: 2
Page(s): 117
Scramble range: All
Topic: Supply elasticity

5.72
If a small (percentage) decline in the price of good *A* causes a large (percentage) decline in quantity supplied, then

a) demand is elastic.
b) demand is inelastic.
c) demand is income elastic.
d) supply is inelastic.
e) supply is elastic.

5.73
Correct: a)
Difficulty: 3
Page(s): 117
Scramble range: All
Topic: Supply elasticity

5.73
The two supply curves in Figure 5.3 are parallel. In the \$7 to \$8 price range,

a) S_1 is more elastic than S_2.
b) S_1 is more inelastic than S_2.
c) S_1 and S_2 have the same elasticity.
d) S_1 is steeper than S_2.
e) S_1 is flatter than S_2.

Figure 5.3

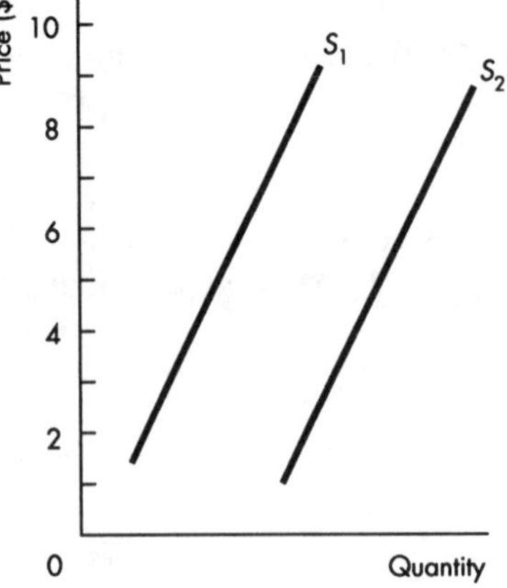

5.74
Correct: b)
Difficulty: 4
Page(s): 117
Scramble range: All
Topic: Supply elasticity

5.74
A rise in the price of good *A* from $7 to $9 results in an increase from 4,500 to 5,500 units supplied. Then

a) supply is elastic.
b) supply is inelastic.
c) supply is unit elastic.
d) demand is inelastic.
e) demand is elastic.

5.75
Correct: e)
Difficulty: 4
Page(s): 117
Scramble range: All
Topic: Supply elasticity

5.75
A rise in the price of good *A* from $7 to $9 results in an increase from 4,000 to 6,000 units supplied. Then

a) demand is elastic.
b) demand is inelastic.
c) supply is unit elastic.
d) supply is inelastic.
e) supply is elastic.

5.76
Correct: d)
Difficulty: 4
Page(s): 115-117
Scramble range: All
Topic: Supply elasticity

5.76
A rise in the price of good *A* from $7 to $9 results in an increase in quantity supplied from 4,000 to 6,000 units. Then the elasticity of supply is

a) 0.625.
b) 0.8.
c) 1.0.
d) 1.6.
e) 16.0.

5.77
Correct: e)
Difficulty: 3
Page(s): 117
Scramble range: All
Topic: Supply elasticity

5.77
If a 5 percent increase in price results in a 9 percent increase in quantity supplied,

a) the good in question is normal.
b) the good in question is inferior.
c) supply is unit elastic.
d) supply is inelastic.
e) supply is elastic.

5.78
Correct: e)
Difficulty: 3
Page(s): 117
Scramble range: All
Topic: Supply elasticity

5.78
If a 5 percent increase in price results in a 3 percent increase in quantity supplied,

a) the good in question is normal.
b) the good in question is inferior.
c) supply is unit elastic.
d) supply is elastic.
e) supply is inelastic.

5.79
Correct: d)
Difficulty: 4
Page(s): 115-117
Scramble range: All
Topic: Supply elasticity

5.79
If a 5 percent increase in price results in a 9 percent increase in quantity supplied, the elasticity of supply is

a) 0.3.
b) 0.6.
c) 1.2.
d) 1.8.
e) 9.0.

5.80
Correct: b)
Difficulty: 4
Page(s): 115-117
Scramble range: All
Topic: Supply elasticity

5.80
If a 5 percent increase in price results in a 3 percent increase in quantity supplied, the elasticity of supply is
a) 0.3.
b) 0.6.
c) 1.2.
d) 1.8.
e) 3.0.

5.81
Correct: c)
Difficulty: 3
Page(s): 117, 120
Scramble range: All
Topic: Supply elasticity

5.81
Suppose the price of television sets rises by 10 percent. Which of the following would we expect to be the most elastic following such a price change?
a) The momentary supply of television sets.
b) The short-run supply of television sets.
c) The long-run supply of television sets.
d) The momentary demand for television sets.
e) The normal demand for television sets.

5.82
Correct: b)
Difficulty: 2
Page(s): 117
Scramble range: All
Topic: Supply elasticity

5.82
A vertical supply curve
a) is impossible except in the long run.
b) has elasticity equal to zero.
c) has elasticity equal to infinity.
d) indicates that suppliers are unwilling to produce the good.
e) indicates a shortage of the good.

5.83
Correct: c)
Difficulty: 2
Page(s): 117
Scramble range: All
Topic: Supply elasticity

5.83
A horizontal supply curve
a) is impossible except in the long run.
b) has elasticity equal to zero.
c) has elasticity equal to infinity.
d) indicates that suppliers are unwilling to produce the good.
e) indicates that there is a fixed quantity of the good that can be supplied.

5.84
Correct: a)
Difficulty: 3
Page(s): 117, 120
Scramble range: All
Topic: Supply elasticity

5.84
The short-run supply curve is likely to be
a) more elastic than momentary supply but less elastic than long-run supply.
b) less elastic than momentary supply but more elastic than long-run supply.
c) less elastic than both momentary and long-run supply curves.
d) more elastic than both momentary and long-run supply curves.
e) as elastic as either the momentary or the long-run supply curves.

5.85
Correct: e)
Difficulty: 2
Page(s): 106-107
Scramble range: All
Topic: Price elasticity

5.85
The price elasticity of demand is calculated as
a) the change in quantity demanded divided by the change in price.
b) the change in price divided by the change in quantity demanded.
c) the percentage change in quantity demanded divided by the change in price.
d) the percentage change in price divided by the percentage change in quantity demanded.
e) the percentage change in quantity demanded divided by the percentage change in price.

5.86
Correct: b)
Difficulty: 2
Page(s): 107
Scramble range: All
Topic: Elastic demand

5.86
If a small (percentage) drop in the price level causes a large (percentage) increase in the quantity demanded,
a) demand is inelastic.
b) demand is elastic.
c) demand is unit elastic.
d) the price elasticity of demand is close to 0.
e) the price elasticity of demand is close to 1.

5.87
Correct: a)
Difficulty: 3
Page(s): 107
Scramble range: All
Topic: Elastic demand

5.87
If a 5 percent increase in price causes a 6 percent decrease in quantity demanded, demand is
a) elastic.
b) inelastic.
c) unit elastic.
d) income inelastic.
e) infinitely elastic.

5.88
Correct: c)
Difficulty: 4
Page(s): 105-106
Scramble range: All
Topic: Price elasticity

5.88
If a 5 percent decrease in price causes a 6 percent increase in quantity demanded, the price elasticity of demand is
a) 0.30.
b) 0.6.
c) 1.2.
d) 3.0.
e) 6.0.

5.89
Correct: a)
Difficulty: 2
Page(s): 107
Scramble range: All
Topic: Unit elastic demand

5.89
The quantity of apples demanded has fallen by 8 percent in the face of an 8 percent increase in price. The demand for apples is apparently
a) unit elastic.
b) inelastic.
c) elastic.
d) upward sloping.
e) very insensitive to price.

5.90
Correct: e)
Difficulty: 2
Page(s): 107-109
Scramble range: All
Topic: Vertical demand curves

5.90
A vertical demand curve
a) is unit elastic.
b) is perfectly elastic.
c) is likely to arise in the long run.
d) has price elasticity of infinity.
e) has price elasticity of 0.

5.91
Correct: a)
Difficulty: 5
Page(s): 106-116
Scramble range: All
Topic: Elasticity

5.91
Consider the information in Table 5.2. Select the best statement.
a) The price elasticity of demand is 0.5, and the income elasticity of demand is –2.5.
b) The price elasticity of demand is 0.5, and the income elasticity of demand is 2.5.
c) The price elasticity of demand is 1.33, and the income elasticity of demand is –3.33.
d) The price elasticity of demand is 1.33, and the income elasticity of demand is 3.33.
e) We cannot calculate the two elasticities, since both income and price are changing at the same time.

Table 5.2

Year	Quantity demanded	Price ($)	Income ($)
1989	25,000	1	4,000
1990	15,000	3	4,000
1991	5,000	3	6,000

5.92
Correct: a)
Difficulty: 5
Page(s): 108
Scramble range: All
Topic: Total revenue and elasticity

5.92
You have been hired as an economic consultant by OPEC. The current price of oil is $10 per barrel, with quantity demanded equal to 35,000 million barrels a day. It is estimated that the elasticity of demand is constant at 0.8. If supply is restricted such that price rises to $30, then quantity demanded will fall by
a) 80 percent, and total revenue will rise.
b) 8 percent, and total revenue will rise.
c) 80 percent, and total revenue will fall.
d) 8 percent, and total revenue will fall.
e) 24 percent, and total revenue will rise.

5.93
Correct: a)
Difficulty: 2
Page(s): 109-110
Scramble range: None
Topic: Substitutes and elasticity

5.93
The magnitude of the price elasticity of demand for a good depends on
a) the availability of substitutes.
b) the price of complementary goods.
c) income.
d) tastes.
e) choices b), c), and d) are correct.

5.94
Correct: d)
Difficulty: 3
Page(s): 109-110
Scramble range: a)-c)
Topic: Determinant of elasticity

5.94
A given percentage increase in the price of a good is likely to cause a larger percentage decline in quantity demanded
a) the longer the passage of time.
b) the larger the proportion of income spent on it.
c) the easier it is to obtain good substitutes.
d) all of the above.
e) none of the above.

5.95 (SG 5.9)
Correct: b)
Difficulty: 3
Page(s): 107-108
Scramble range: All
Topic: Inelastic demand

5.95
If a 4 percent rise in the price of peanut butter causes the total revenue from peanut butter sales to fall by 8 percent, then demand for peanut butter
a) must be elastic in the relevant price range.
b) must be inelastic in the relevant price range.
c) must be unit elastic in the relevant price range.
d) has elasticity equal to 0.5 in the relevant price range.
e) has an elasticity equal to 0.32 in the relevant range.

5.96
Correct: c)
Difficulty: 2
Page(s): 104-105
Scramble range: All
Topic: Price elasticity

5.96
If the country of Saudi Petrolia agrees that an increase in the supply of OPEC oil will increase total oil sales revenue, then Saudi Petrolia must believe the demand for oil to be
a) income inelastic.
b) income elastic.
c) price elastic.
d) price inelastic.
e) cross-price elastic.

5.97
Correct: d)
Difficulty: 3
Page(s): 115-116
Scramble range: All
Topic: Inferior goods

5.97
If a large increase in income results in a small decrease in quantity demanded at the current price, then
a) demand must be income elastic.
b) demand must be income inelastic.
c) demand must have positive income elasticity.
d) the good in question is inferior.
e) the good in question is normal.

5.98 (SG 5.19)
Correct: a)
Difficulty: 3
Page(s): 113-114
Scramble range: All
Topic: Income elasticity

5.98
A 10 percent increase in income has caused a 5 percent increase in quantity demanded (at the current price). The income elasticity is
a) 0.5.
b) –0.5.
c) 2.0.
d) –2.0.
e) 5.0.

5.99
Correct: e)
Difficulty: 4
Page(s): 113-114
Scramble range: All
Topic: Income elasticity

5.99
Fred's income has just risen from $950 per week to $1,050 per week. As a result, he decides to double the number of movies he attends each week. Fred's demand for movies is
a) price elastic.
b) price inelastic.
c) price unit elastic.
d) income inelastic.
e) income elastic.

5.100
Correct: e)
Difficulty: 3
Page(s): 115-116
Scramble range: All
Topic: Cross elasticity

5.100
The cross elasticity of demand is a measure of the responsiveness of
a) the demand for one good to changes in the supply of another.
b) the demand for a good to changes in its price.
c) the price elasticity of demand for one good to changes in the price elasticity of demand for another good.
d) the price elasticity of demand for one good to changes in income.
e) the demand for one good to changes in the price of another good.

5.101
Correct: c)
Difficulty: 2
Page(s): 115
Scramble range: All
Topic: Cross elasticity

5.101
If goods *A* and *B* are substitutes, then
a) the cross elasticity of demand between *A* and *B* is 0.
b) the cross elasticity of demand between *A* and *B* is negative.
c) the cross elasticity of demand between *A* and *B* is positive.
d) their income elasticities of demand are both negative.
e) they must have identical price elasticities.

5.102
Correct: b)
Difficulty: 3
Page(s): 115
Scramble range: All
Topic: Cross elasticity

5.102
Suppose the cross elasticity of demand between peanut butter and jelly is negative, then
a) an increase in the price of peanut butter will cause an increase in the equilibrium price of jelly.
b) an increase in the price of peanut butter will cause a decrease in the equilibrium price of jelly.
c) an increase in the price of peanut butter will have no effect on the equilibrium price of jelly.
d) a decrease in the price of peanut butter will cause a decrease in the equlibrium price of jelly.
e) peanut butter and jelly are substitutes.

5.103
Correct: b)
Difficulty: 5
Page(s): 115
Scramble range: All
Topic: Cross elasticity

5.103
Suppose that a decrease in the price of *A* from $10.50 to $9.50 causes an increase in the quantity of *B* demanded (at the current price of *B* from 7,960 units to 8,040 units. The cross elasticity of demand between *A* and *B* is
a) –0.01.
b) –0.1.
c) 0.01.
d) 0.08.
e) 0.1.

5.104
Correct: e)
Difficulty: 2
Page(s): 117, 120
Scramble range: All
Topic: Elasticity of supply

5.104
The elasticity of supply is calculated by
a) dividing the percentage change in quantity supplied by the change in price.
b) multiplying the percentage change in quantity supplied by the percentage change in price.
c) dividing the percentage change in price by the percentage change in quantity supplied.
d) dividing the change in quantity supplied by the change in price.
e) dividing the percentage change in quantity supplied by the percentage change in price.

5.105
Correct: b)
Difficulty: 1
Page(s): 117, 120
Scramble range: All
Topic: Elasticity of supply

5.105
Supply is inelastic if
a) a small percentage change in price causes a large percentage change in quantity supplied.
b) a large percentage change in price causes a small percentage change in quantity supplied.
c) the good in question is normal.
d) the good in question is inferior.
e) the good in question has lots of substitutes.

5.106
Correct: e)
Difficulty: 4
Page(s): 117, 120
Scramble range: All
Topic: Elasticity of supply

5.106
A rise in the price of good *A* from $10 to $12 results in an increase in quantity supplied from 5,000 to 6,000 units. Then the elasticity of supply is
a) 0.625.
b) 0.8.
c) 1.25.
d) 0.2.
e) 1.0.

5.107
Correct: d)
Difficulty: 2
Page(s): 120
Scramble range: All
Topic: Long-run supply elastic

5.107
The long-run supply curve is likely to be
a) more elastic than momentary supply but less elastic than short-run supply.
b) less elastic than momentary supply but more elastic than short-run supply.
c) less elastic than both momentary and short-run supply curves.
d) more elastic than both momentary and short-run supply curves.
e) as elastic as either the momentary or the short-run supply curves.

5.108
Correct: c)
Difficulty: 1
Page(s): 106-107
Scramble range: All
Topic: Price elasticity

5.108
The percentage change in __________ divided by the percentage change in __________ is the formula for the price elasticity of demand.
a) quantity demanded; quantity supplied
b) quantity supplied; price
c) quantity demanded; price
d) quantity supplied; quantity demanded
e) quantity demanded of *A*; price of *B*

5.109
Correct: e)
Difficulty: 4
Page(s): 107-108
Scramble range: None
Topic: Inelastic demand

5.109
If a very large percentage drop in the price level causes a very small percentage increase in the quantity demanded,
a) demand is inelastic.
b) demand is elastic.
c) demand is unit elastic.
d) the price elasticity of demand is close to zero.
e) both a) and d).

5.110
Correct: a)
Difficulty: 2
Page(s): 107
Scramble range: All
Topic: Elastic demand

5.110
If a 1 percent increase in price causes a 1.2 percent decrease in quantity demanded, demand is
a) elastic
b) inelastic.
c) unit elastic.
d) income inelastic.
e) infinitely elastic.

5.111
Correct: e)
Difficulty: 3
Page(s): 105-106
Scramble range: All
Topic: Price elasticity

5.111
If a 1 percent decrease in price causes a 1.2 percent increase in quantity demanded, the price elasticity of demand is
a) 0.012.
b) 0.6.
c) 0.83.
d) 1.0.
e) 1.2.

5.112
Correct: b)
Difficulty: 2
Page(s): 107
Scramble range: All
Topic: Inelastic demand

5.112
The quantity of apples demanded has fallen by 10 percent in the face of an 8 percent increase in price. The demand for apples is apparently
a) elastic.
b) inelastic.
c) unit elastic.
d) upward sloping.
e) infinitely elastic.

5.113
Correct: b)
Difficulty: 3
Page(s): 107
Scramble range: All
Topic: Perfectly elastic *D* curve

5.113
A horizontal demand curve
a) is unit elastic.
b) is perfectly elastic.
c) is likely to arise in the long run.
d) has price elasticity of zero.
e) is perfectly inelastic.

5.114
Correct: b)
Difficulty: 4
Page(s): 105
Scramble range: All
Topic: Price elasticity

5.114
Suppose a fall in the price of good *A* from $5 to $4 causes an increase in quantity demanded from 10 to 12 units. In this range of the demand curve, the price elasticity of demand is
a) 1.
b) 9/11.
c) 11/9.
d) 2.0.
e) 4.5/11.

5.115
Correct: d)
Difficulty: 3
Page(s): 109-110
Scramble range: a)-d)
Topic: Substitutes and elasticity

5.115
For which of the following will demand be the most price elastic?
a) Daily newspapers.
b) Ontario newspapers.
c) Toronto newspapers.
d) The *Toronto Star.*
e) Each of the above will exhibit the same demand elasticity.

5.116
Correct: e)
Difficulty: 5
Page(s): 115-120
Scramble range: a)-d)
Topic: Supply elasticity

5.116
Consider the information in Table 5.3. Select the best statement.
a) In the long run, the supply elasticity is 10.
b) In the short run, the supply elasticity is 2.0.
c) In the long run, the supply elasticity is 0.5.
d) In the short run, the supply elasticity is 1.5.
e) None of the above.

Table 5.3

Year	Price ($)	Quantity supplied
1990	2	10,000
1991	4	14,000
1992	4	30,000

5.117
Correct: b)
Difficulty: 3
Page(s): 113
Scramble range: All
Topic: Income elasticity

5.117
A 10 percent decrease in income has caused a 5 percent increase in quantity demanded (at the current price). The income elasticity is
a) 0.5.
b) –0.5.
c) 2.0.
d) –2.0.
e) 5.0.

5.118
Correct: e)
Difficulty: 5
Page(s): 104-110
Scramble range: a)-d)
Topic: Elasticity of demand

5.118
Suppose that this coming winter France will have unusually bad weather, and next year's wine crop will be very much reduced. Select the best statement.
a) French wine supply will rise as price rises.
b) If French wine has elastic price elasticity of demand, wine producers could be better off.
c) The initial change in the market will create a surplus of French wine.
d) In the final equilibrium, price and quantity will be higher.
e) None of the above.

5.119
Correct: e)
Difficulty: 5
Page(s): 112-115
Scramble range: None
Topic: Substitutes

5.119
Suppose that this coming winter France will have unusually bad weather, and next year's wine crop will be very much reduced. Select the best statement.
a) In the market for Canadian wine, price and quantity will rise.
b) The sign of the cross elasticity of the quantity of Canadian wine with respect to the price of French wine is negative.
c) In the Canadian market, the closer substitutes Canadian and French wines are, the higher the percentage change in quantity demanded.
d) Both b) and c).
e) Both a) and c).

Chapter 6 Markets in Action

6.1
Correct: b)
Difficulty: 3
Page(s): 128–129
Scramble range: All
Topic: Housing market

6.1
Why is the short-run supply curve for housing generally considered to be positively sloped rather than vertical?
a) Because the supply of housing is fixed in the short run.
b) Because the amount of the current housing stock can vary.
c) Because the cost of building an additional house is about the same whether 10 houses or 1,000 houses are built.
d) Because housing is a necessity.
e) Because housing demand is very flexible; people can always share it.

6.2
Correct: a)
Difficulty: 2
Page(s): 128–129
Scramble range: All
Topic: Housing market

6.2
The long-run supply curve for housing can be thought of as
a) perfectly elastic.
b) perfectly inelastic.
c) inelastic but not perfectly inelastic.
d) elastic but not perfectly elastic.
e) vertical.

6.3
Correct: c)
Difficulty: 3
Page(s): 128–129
Scramble range: All
Topic: Housing market

6.3
Why is the long-run supply curve for housing generally considered to be horizontal?
a) Because the intensity with which a given stock of housing is used can vary.
b) Because the more houses built, the greater is the cost.
c) The cost of building a house stays about the same regardless of the stock of housing in existence.
d) Because the demand for housing is almost constant.
e) Because the cost of building a house always falls in the long run.

6.4
Correct: b)
Difficulty: 2
Page(s): 128–129
Scramble range: All
Topic: Housing market

6.4
In an unregulated market, a sudden decrease in the stock of housing would likely evoke what kind of market response?
a) Higher quantity supplied.
b) Higher rental rates.
c) Persistent shortages.
d) More favourable lease terms for tenants.
e) Lower rental rates.

6.5
Correct: c)
Difficulty: 2
Page(s): 128–129
Scramble range: All
Topic: Housing market

6.5
The short-run supply curve for housing can be thought of as
a) perfectly elastic.
b) perfectly inelastic.
c) neither perfectly elastic nor perfectly inelastic.
d) vertical.
e) horizontal.

6.6
Correct: e)
Difficulty: 3
Page(s): 130–131
Scramble range: All
Topic: Rent ceilings

6.6
With rent controls we expect to see housing shortages. What sort of mechanisms might arise to bring about an equilibrium?
a) Decreased search activity costs.
b) Higher rents.
c) Added promotion by landlords to fill rent-controlled housing.
d) More favourable leases to attract tenants to rent-controlled housing.
e) Black market activity.

6.7
Correct: a)
Difficulty: 2
Page(s): 130–131
Scramble range: All
Topic: Housing market

6.7
Consider the market for housing illustrated in Figure 6.1 with demand given by *D*. The equilibrium in an unregulated market will be
a) 1,500 rooms rented at $150.
b) 1,500 rooms rented at $200.
c) 1,750 rooms rented at $175.
d) 1,750 rooms rented at $200.
e) 2,000 rooms rented at $150.

Figure 6.1

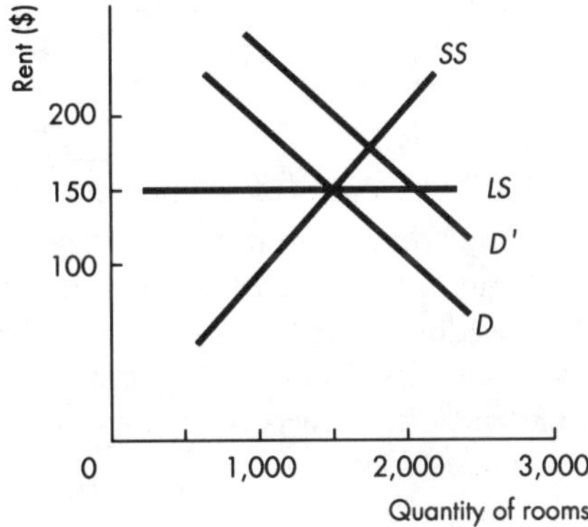

6.8
Correct: c)
Difficulty: 2
Page(s): 130–131
Scramble range: All
Topic: Housing market

6.8
Refer to Figure 6.1. If the demand for rental housing increases from *D* to *D′* and the market is unregulated, then in the short run the number of rooms rented will
a) remain unchanged but rent will rise to $200.
b) increase to 2,000 but rent will be at its initial level.
c) increase to 1,750 and rent will rise to $175.
d) increase to 2,000 and rent will rise to $200.
e) increase to 1,750 and rent will rise to $200.

6.9
Correct: b)
Difficulty: 2
Page(s): 130–131
Scramble range: All
Topic: Housing market

6.9
Refer to Figure 6.1. If the demand for rental housing increases from *D* to *D′* and the market is unregulated, then in the long run the number of rooms rented will

a) remain unchanged but rent will rise to $200.
b) increase to 2,000, but rent will be at its initial level.
c) increase to 1,750 and rent will rise to $175.
d) increase to 2,000 and rent will rise to $200.
e) increase to 1,750, and rent will rise to $200.

6.10
Correct: d)
Difficulty: 4
Page(s): 130–131
Scramble range: None
Topic: Rent ceilings

6.10
Refer to Figure 6.1. If the demand for rental housing increases from *D* to *D′* and there is a strictly enforced rent ceiling at $150 per room,

a) the number of rooms rented will increase to 1,750.
b) the number of rooms rented will remain unchanged.
c) there will be an excess quantity of rooms demanded in the amount of 500 rooms.
d) both b) and c).
e) none of the above.

6.11
Correct: c)
Difficulty: 4
Page(s): 130–131
Scramble range: a)–d)
Topic: Rent ceilings

6.11
Refer to Figure 6.1. Suppose that the demand for rental housing is given by D_1 and there is a rent ceiling at $150 per room. What is the highest rent that would be charged in a black market?

a) $150.
b) $175.
c) $200.
d) Cannot be determined from the graph, but we know it is greater than $200.
e) None of the above.

6.12
Correct: a)
Difficulty: 4
Page(s): 130–131
Scramble range: All
Topic: Price controls

6.12
Suppose the current price for corn is above the market price. This is a likely result of

a) government intervention in the corn market.
b) farmers holding inventories to increase price stability.
c) nonfarmers holding inventories to increase price stability.
d) a higher-than-expected demand for corn.
e) a lower-than-expected supply of corn.

6.13
Correct: c)
Difficulty: 1
Page(s): 130–131
Scramble range: All
Topic: Black market

6.13
Illegal trading activity at prices above a legal price ceiling is known as

a) a price ceiling.
b) wage controls.
c) a black market.
d) efficient markets.
e) search activity.

6.14
Correct: e)
Difficulty: 2
Page(s): 130–131
Scramble range: All
Topic: Black market

6.14
Which of the following would *not* be a black market activity?
a) Selling cocaine in Canada.
b) "Scalping" a ticket to a championship hockey game.
c) Selling a personal computer in a controlled market in Poland.
d) Charging rent higher than allowed in a rent-controlled community.
e) Offering to work for more than the minimum wage.

6.15
Correct: a)
Difficulty: 1
Page(s): 133, 136
Scramble range: a)–d)
Topic: Labour supply/long–run

6.15
In the text, the long-run labour supply curve is represented as
a) perfectly elastic.
b) perfectly inelastic.
c) neither perfectly elastic nor perfectly inelastic.
d) vertical.
e) none of the above.

6.16
Correct: d)
Difficulty: 1
Page(s): 133, 136
Scramble range: All
Topic: Labour supply/short–run

6.16
In the short run, the labour supply curve is thought to be
a) perfectly elastic.
b) perfectly inelastic.
c) negatively sloped.
d) positively sloped.
e) horizontal.

6.17
Correct: d)
Difficulty: 3
Page(s): 133, 136
Scramble range: All
Topic: Labour supply/long–run

6.17
If the long-run supply of labour is positively sloped, what would be the long-run equilibrium response to a decrease in the demand for labour?
a) An increase in the quantity of labour hired and an increase in the wage.
b) An increase in the quantity of labour hired and a decrease in the wage.
c) A decrease in the quantity of labour hired and an increase in the wage.
d) A decrease in the quantity of labour hired and a decrease in the wage.
e) It depends on the slope of the labour supply curve.

6.18
Correct: b)
Difficulty: 3
Page(s): 136–137
Scramble range: All
Topic: Minimum wage

6.18
Economists generally agree that minimum wage laws
a) hurt highly skilled workers.
b) hurt the unskilled workers the most.
c) increase the quantity of labour demanded.
d) shift the demand curve for low-skilled labour.
e) lower the supply of labour.

6.19
Correct: b)
Difficulty: 3
Page(s): 136–137
Scramble range: All
Topic: Minimum wage

6.19
Refer to Figure 6.2. Suppose a $5 minimum wage is in force. What is the lowest wage any unemployed person would be willing to accept?
a) $2.
b) $3.
c) $4.
d) $5.
e) We cannot tell from the diagram.

Figure 6.2

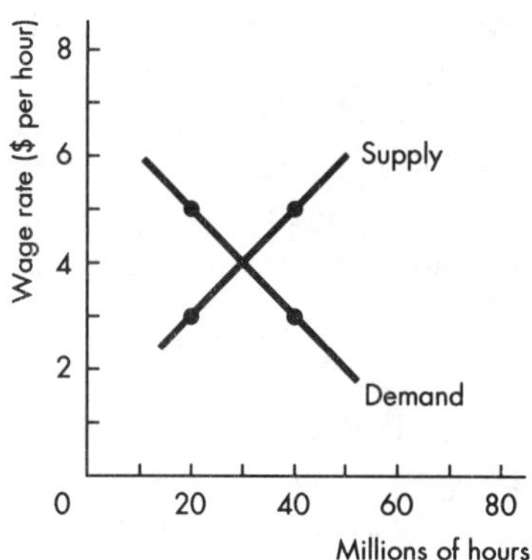

6.20
Correct: c)
Difficulty: 2
Page(s): 136–137
Scramble range: All
Topic: Minimum wage

6.20
Refer to Figure 6.2. What is the market clearing wage?
a) $2.
b) $3.
c) $4.
d) $5.
e) We cannot tell from the diagram.

6.21
Correct: a)
Difficulty: 3
Page(s): 136–137
Scramble range: All
Topic: Minimum wage

6.21
Suppose initially a minimum wage law is in force with wages at $4 per hour and an excess quantity of labour supplied of 10 million hours. Now the demand for labour increases with the intersection of supply and demand occurring at $5 per hour. What will happen to wages and employment?
a) The wage will be $5 and there will be no unemployment.
b) The wage will be $5 and there will be an excess supply of labour.
c) The wage will be $4 and there will be an excess supply of labour.
d) The wage will be $4 and there will be no unemployment.
e) The wage will be $4 and there will be unemployment.

6.22
Correct: e)
Difficulty: 2
Page(s): 130–131
Scramble range: All
Topic: Minimum wage/rent control

6.22
Minimum wage laws and rent controls are examples of
a) free enterprise.
b) market mechanisms.
c) black markets.
d) economies.
e) government intervention.

6.23
Correct: d)
Difficulty: 3
Page(s): 130, 136
Scramble range: All
Topic: Minimum wage/rent control

6.23
Which of the following would *not* affect the actual level of unemployment caused by minimum wage laws?
a) The strictness of enforcement of applicable laws.
b) The elasticity of the supply curve.
c) The elasticity of the demand curve.
d) The gap between demand and supply below equilibrium.
e) The gap between demand and supply above equilibrium.

6.24
Correct: b)
Difficulty: 2
Page(s): 136–137
Scramble range: All
Topic: Minimum wage

6.24
What type of firm would be affected the most by a minimum wage law?
a) A management consulting firm.
b) A fast food restaurant.
c) A manufacturing plant.
d) A hospital.
e) A university.

6.25
Correct: b)
Difficulty: 1
Page(s): 136–137
Scramble range: All
Topic: Minimum wage

6.25
Table 6.1 gives the supply and demand for teenage labour in the town of Normal. In an unregulated market,
a) there would be no teenage unemployment and the wage would be $4.00.
b) there would be no teenage unemployment and the wage would be $3.00.
c) teenage unemployment (measured in hours) would be 200 and the wage would be $4.00.
d) teenage unemployment (measured in hours) would be 200 and the wage would be $3.00.
e) teenage unemployment (measured in hours) would be 200 and the wage would be $2.00.

Table 6.1

Wage ($ per hour)	Labour supplied (hours per week)	Labour demanded (hours per week)
5.00	500	100
4.00	400	200
3.00	300	300
2.00	200	400

6.26
Correct: c)
Difficulty: 2
Page(s): 136–137
Scramble range: All
Topic: Minimum wage

6.26
Table 6.1 gives the supply and demand for teenage labour in the town of Normal. Suppose the Normal town council sets a minimum wage of $4.00 per hour. Teenage unemployment (measured in hours) will be
a) 400 hours.
b) 300 hours.
c) 200 hours.
d) 100 hours.
e) zero hours.

6.27
Correct: a)
Difficulty: 3
Page(s): 136–137
Scramble range: a)–d)
Topic: Minimum wage

6.27
Table 6.1 gives the supply and demand for teenage labour in the town of Normal. There is a minimum wage set at $4.00. Suppose that a new fast food restaurant opens in Normal and increases the demand for teenage labour by 400 hours per week at each wage. The result will be
a) elimination of teenage unemployment and a wage of $5.00.
b) elimination of teenage unemployment but the wage will remain at the ceiling of $4.00.
c) a reduction of teenage unemployment with the wage remaining at the ceiling of $4.00.
d) no change in teenage unemployment since the wage must remain at $4.00.
e) none of the above.

6.28
Correct: d)
Difficulty: 3
Page(s): 136–137
Scramble range: All
Topic: Minimum wage

6.28
Table 6.1 gives the supply and demand for teenage labour in the town of Normal. Suppose that a new fast food restaurant opens in Normal and increases the demand for teenage labour by 400 hours per week at each wage. If the teenage labour market is unregulated, there will be an increase in teenage employment to

a) 700 hours per week and a wage of $3.00.
b) 700 hours per week and a wage of $5.00.
c) 600 hours per week and a wage of $4.00.
d) 500 hours per week and a wage of $5.00.
e) 400 hours per week and a wage of $5.00.

6.29
Correct: c)
Difficulty: 4
Page(s): 136–137
Scramble range: All
Topic: Minimum wage

6.29
From the information in Fact 6.1 we know that the *market-clearing* wage is

a) at or above $3.50 in both A-town and B-town.
b) at or below $3.50 in both A-town and B-town.
c) above $3.50 in A-town but at or below $3.50 in B-town.
d) above $3.50 in B-town but at or below $3.50 in A-town.
e) above $3.50 in A-town, but it is impossible to tell what it is in B-town without more information.

Fact 6.1
The minimum wage is $3.50. In A-town the wage for unskilled labour is $5.50 per hour while in B-town the wage for the same type of labour is $3.50 per hour.

6.30
Correct: a)
Difficulty: 4
Page(s): 136–137
Scramble range: All
Topic: Minimum wage

6.30
Consider the information given in Fact 6.1. Suppose we also know that there are unemployed workers in A-town willing to work for $3.00 per hour. Then if the minimum wage were eliminated, the wage rate would

a) fall in A-town only.
b) fall in B-town only.
c) fall in both A-town and B-town.
d) rise in A-town only.
e) fall in A-town and rise in B-town.

6.31
Correct: b)
Difficulty: 2
Page(s): 130–131
Scramble range: All
Topic: Rent ceilings

6.31
Daisy and Donald live in a community with rent ceilings. Both are looking for an apartment to rent. Daisy has a job paying $10 per hour while Donald has a job paying $8 per hour. Both value an apartment equally. What is the most likely outcome?

a) Daisy will spend more time than Donald searching for an apartment.
b) Donald will spend more time than Daisy searching for an apartment.
c) Both of them will search equally.
d) Daisy will find the apartment.
e) Donald will find the apartment.

6.32
Correct: e)
Difficulty: 3
Page(s): 133–136
Scramble range: All
Topic: Price ceiling

6.32
With a price ceiling set below the market-clearing price, which statement is true?
a) The demand curve will shift downward.
b) Quantity supplied will exceed quantity demanded.
c) Quantity supplied will equal quantity demanded.
d) The supply curve will shift downward.
e) Quantity demanded will exceed quantity supplied.

6.33
Correct: e)
Difficulty: 3
Page(s): 133, 136
Scramble range: All
Topic: Price ceiling

6.33
Refer to Figure 6.3. If a rigorously enforced price ceiling is set at $10, then
a) 100 units will be sold at a price of $20.
b) 100 units will be sold at a price of $15.
c) 150 units will be sold at a price of $15.
d) 200 units will be sold at a price of $10.
e) 100 units will be sold at a price of $10.

Figure 6.3

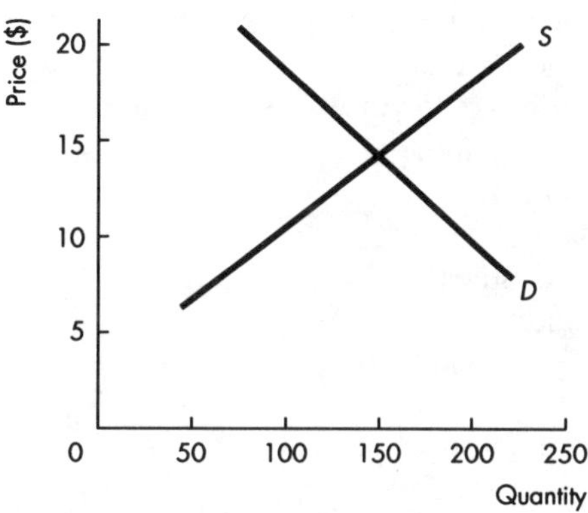

6.34
Correct: c)
Difficulty: 3
Page(s): 131–132
Scramble range: All
Topic: Black market

6.34
Refer to Figure 6.3. What would be the predicted black market price of the good if a price ceiling is set at $10?
a) $10.
b) $15.
c) $20.
d) 50 goods sold at $10 and 50 goods sold at $20.
e) 50 goods sold at $10 and 50 goods sold at $15.

6.35
Correct: a)
Difficulty: 3
Page(s): 133, 136
Scramble range: All
Topic: Price ceiling

6.35
One form of government regulation intended to stabilize farmers' incomes is limiting the amount of land used for production. This will have an impact on prices similar to
a) minimum wage laws.
b) rent ceilings.
c) efficient markets.
d) inventory holdings.
e) price ceilings.

6.36
Correct: e)
Difficulty: 4
Page(s): 133, 136
Scramble range: None
Topic: Price ceiling

6.36
Fill in the blanks with the best response. __________ are generally associated with prices being __________ market-clearing prices.
a) Minimum wages; above
b) Rent ceilings; above
c) Minimum wages; below
d) Rent ceilings; below
e) Both a) and d).

6.37
Correct: d)
Difficulty: 2
Page(s): 133, 136
Scramble range: All
Topic: Price ceiling

6.37
Which of the following is generally *false*?
a) Minimum wage laws set wages above market wage.
b) Rent ceilings set rent below market levels.
c) Rent ceilings generally result in housing shortages.
d) Minimum wage laws increase employment.
e) Minimum wage laws generally create surpluses.

6.38
Correct: d)
Difficulty: 2
Page(s): 130–131
Scramble range: All
Topic: Opportunity cost

6.38
A dentist, a lawyer, a business executive, and a student all equally enjoy watching the Toronto Maple Leafs hockey team. Considering opportunity cost, which person would you expect to wait in line for five hours to buy a ticket for a Maple Leafs game?
a) The dentist.
b) The lawyer.
c) The executive.
d) The student.
e) It is equally likely to be any of them.

6.39
Correct: d)
Difficulty: 2
Page(s): 138–139
Scramble range: All
Topic: Uncertainty

6.39
Which of the following would *not* lead to uncertainty about the demand curve?
a) The prices of substitutes and complements.
b) Income.
c) Tastes.
d) Uncertainty about new technology.
e) Population.

6.40
Correct: a)
Difficulty: 2
Page(s): 138–139
Scramble range: All
Topic: Uncertainty

6.40
Uncertainty about the supply curve results from uncertainty about
a) costs of factors of production.
b) household income.
c) the number of demanders.
d) tastes.
e) prices of complements in consumption.

6.41
Correct: e)
Difficulty: 1
Page(s): 138–139
Scramble range: All
Topic: Rational expectations

6.41
Expectations based on all relevant available information are known as
a) notional expectations.
b) logical expectations.
c) average expectations.
d) informed expectations.
e) rational expections.

6.42
Correct: a)
Difficulty: 3
Page(s): 138–139
Scramble range: All
Topic: Rational expectations

6.42
Cattle ranchers face uncertainty about the future price of beef and, therefore, must decide how much beef to produce based on a forecast of the price of beef. If demand turns out to be greater than expected, the market price of beef will be

a) above the forecast price.
b) equal to the forecast price.
c) below the forecast price.
d) a value that we cannot tell without knowing the forecast price.
e) below the forecast price, with the difference dependent upon how much demand is greater than expected.

6.43
Correct: a)
Difficulty: 4
Page(s): 139–140
Scramble range: All
Topic: Expected *D*/expected *S*

6.43
Refer to Figure 6.4. *ES* and *ED* are the expected supply and demand curves, respectively. *MS* is the momentary supply curve that results, and *D* is the actual demand curve. The expected price and quantity traded are

a) $4 and 250 units.
b) $5 and 250 units.
c) $7 and 250 units.
d) $5 and 350 units.
e) $4 and 400 units.

Figure 6.4

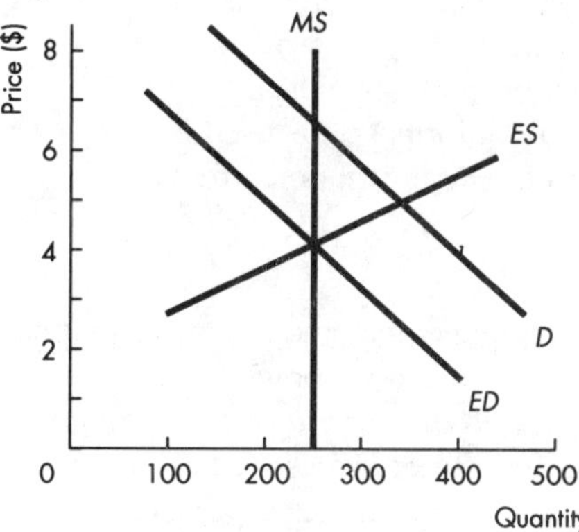

6.44
Correct: c)
Difficulty: 4
Page(s): 139–140
Scramble range: All
Topic: Expected *D*/expected *S*

6.44
Refer to Figure 6.4. *ES* and *ED* are the expected supply and demand curves, respectively. *MS* is the momentary supply curve that results, and *D* is the actual demand curve. The actual price and quantity traded are

a) $4 and 250 units.
b) $5 and 250 units.
c) $7 and 250 units.
d) $5 and 350 units.
e) $4 and 400 units.

6.45
Correct: b)
Difficulty: 4
Page(s): 139–140
Scramble range: All
Topic: Expected *D*/expected *S*

6.45
Refer to Figure 6.4. *ES* and *ED* are the expected supply and demand curves, respectively. *MS* is the momentary supply curve that results, and *D* is the actual demand curve. Which of the following is true?
a) The price forecast error is $3 and the quantity forecast error is 100 units.
b) The price forecast error is $3 and the quantity forecast error is 0.
c) The price forecast error is 0 and the quantity forecast error is 100 units.
d) The price forecast error is 0 and the quantity forecast error is 0.
e) The price forecast error is 0 and the quantity forecast error is 150 units.

6.46
Correct: e)
Difficulty: 3
Page(s): 139–140
Scramble range: All
Topic: Rational expectations

6.46
Jerry and Sally each own competing firms which sell forecasts of the price of tulips. What does rational expectations imply?
a) Jerry and Sally will predict the same price for tulips.
b) Whenever Jerry's forecast is higher than the actual price, Sally's forecast will be lower, so on average they both predicted correctly.
c) On average, Jerry and Sally will incorrectly predict the price.
d) Jerry and Sally will always correctly forecast the price.
e) On average, Jerry and Sally will correctly predict the price.

6.47
Correct: d)
Difficulty: 3
Page(s): 139–140
Scramble range: All
Topic: Rational expectations

6.47
Rational expectations implies
a) all people will make forecasts.
b) there is uncertainty in demand.
c) there is uncertainty in supply.
d) all relevant information is used in forecasting.
e) people's forecasts will be correct.

6.48
Correct: d)
Difficulty: 2
Page(s): 139–140
Scramble range: All
Topic: Rational expectations

6.48
Other things being equal, and assuming that no inventories are held, an increase in the expected supply of a good will cause
a) an increase in the current price of the good.
b) a decrease in the current price of the good.
c) an increase in the expected price of the good.
d) a decrease in the expected price of the good.
e) an uncertain change in the expected price of the good.

6.49
Correct: c)
Difficulty: 4
Page(s): 139–140
Scramble range: a)–d)
Topic: Rational expectations

6.49
Leslie needs to make a forecast of the number of widgets her office will receive in the coming year. She knows she will receive either 500 widgets or 1,000 widgets, and that receiving 1,000 widgets will be far more likely. What should Leslie's rational expectations forecast of the quantity of widgets be?
a) 750.
b) Less than 750.
c) Greater than 750.
d) 1,000.
e) None of the above.

6.50
Correct: b)
Difficulty: 4
Page(s): 139–140
Scramble range: All
Topic: Rational expectations

6.50
Linda needed to forecast the length of time required to write her English paper. If she found all of her reference material in the first trip to the library, writing the paper would take 10 hours. If she had to go to the library twice, the paper would take 15 hours. If she had to go to the library a third time, then writing the paper would take 20 hours. If it is equally likely that Linda will have to go to the library one, two, or three times, what is Linda's rational expectations forecast of her time needed to write the paper?
a) 10 hours.
b) 15 hours.
c) 12.5 hours.
d) 17.5 hours.
e) 20 hours.

6.51
Correct: b)
Difficulty: 4
Page(s): 142–144
Scramble range: All
Topic: Inventories

6.51
The current price of a stock is equal to its expected future price because
a) the actual supply of the stock is vertical.
b) the stock is bought and sold out of inventories if the current price deviates from expected price.
c) the demand for the stock is fixed.
d) investment bankers fix stock prices.
e) the expected supply of the stock is horizontal.

6.52
Correct: b)
Difficulty: 4
Page(s): 142–143
Scramble range: All
Topic: Inventories

6.52
Gerald is in the business of holding zwidget inventories. His long-run rational expectations forecast of the price for zwidgets is $5. A short-run fluctuation occurs which adds no information to the long-run forecast and raises the current price above $5. What will Gerald do?
a) Increase his inventories.
b) Decrease his inventories.
c) Leave his inventory unchanged.
d) Change his long-run rational expectations forecast.
e) Buy zwidgets.

6.53
Correct: a)
Difficulty: 3
Page(s): 144–145
Scramble range: All
Topic: Stock market efficiency

6.53
Which event would likely lead to a decrease in the stock price of a firm?
a) A fire in the firm's production plant.
b) Bankruptcy announcement of a rival firm.
c) Inauguration of a new prime minister of Canada.
d) Enactment of previously anticipated adverse legislation.
e) Settlement of a strike with wages as previously anticipated.

6.54
Correct: b)
Difficulty: 3
Page(s): 144–145
Scramble range: All
Topic: Stock market efficiency

6.54
Under rational expectations, the stock market crash of 1987 can be explained as
a) an unusual aberration that contradicts rational expectations.
b) a change in expectations from optimistic to pessimistic.
c) a statistical error.
d) a change in the supply of stocks.
e) a rise in the demand for stocks.

6.55
Correct: e)
Difficulty: 3
Page(s): 144–145
Scramble range: All
Topic: Stock market/paradox

6.55
What is the apparent paradox about efficient markets?
a) Supply does not always equal demand.
b) No one ever makes a profit.
c) The current price equals the expected price.
d) The current price embodies all information available.
e) Traders, seeking a profit, remove profit opportunities.

6.56
Correct: e)
Difficulty: 4
Page(s): 144–145
Scramble range: All
Topic: Stock market efficiency

6.56
Which of the following is *not* consistent with the efficient market hypothesis?
a) New information leads to price changes.
b) Wide fluctuation of stock prices.
c) Different prices for similar type firms.
d) The stock market crash of 1987.
e) Systematic profits can be made.

6.57
Correct: b)
Difficulty: 2
Page(s): 144–145
Scramble range: All
Topic: Stock market efficiency

6.57
A market in which current price equals expected future price is called
a) a futures market.
b) an efficient market.
c) a black market.
d) a rational expectations market.
e) a stock market.

6.58
Correct: b)
Difficulty: 2
Page(s): 144–145
Scramble range: All
Topic: Efficiency

6.58
Efficient markets imply
a) no profits can be made.
b) no profits can be predicted.
c) large profits can be realized.
d) profits can be predicted to be small but positive on average.
e) excess profits can be made.

6.59
Correct: e)
Difficulty: 4
Page(s): 144–145
Scramble range: All
Topic: Stock market efficiency

6.59
Sidney owns stock in Sunshine Corporation. One day he read in his local newspaper that the price of Sunshine stock was expected to fall. Which statement most closely corresponds to the efficiency hypothesis?
a) Sidney should sell all of his Sunshine stock immediately before the price falls.
b) The price of Sunshine stock would already have incorporated this information, and will be so low it can be expected to rise.
c) Sidney should buy up Sunshine shares to offset his losses.
d) The price of Sunshine stock will be constant over the long term.
e) The price of Sunshine stock will already incorporate this information.

6.60
Correct: b)
Difficulty: 2
Page(s): 130–145
Scramble range: All
Topic: Stock market/volatility

6.60
Which statement is false?
a) Stock market volatility can be explained by the arrival of new information which leads to price changes.
b) Inventories generally stabilize quantities.
c) Price controls generally result in market inefficiencies.
d) Inventories generally stabilize prices.
e) Price ceilings lead to black markets.

6.61 (SG 6.1)
Correct: e)
Difficulty: 2
Page(s): 128–129
Scramble range: All
Topic: Short–run *S* rent housing

6.61
The short-run supply curve for rental housing will be positively sloped because
a) the supply of housing is fixed in the short run.
b) as price goes up, demand falls.
c) the cost of constructing new buildings increases as the number of buildings in existence increases.
d) the cost of constructing a new building is about the same regardless of the number of buildings already in existence.
e) the current stock of buildings will be used more intensively for housing if rent rises.

6.62 (SG 6.2)
Correct: a)
Difficulty: 2
Page(s): 130–131
Scramble range: All
Topic: Rent ceilings

6.62
Rent ceilings imposed by governments
a) keep rental prices below prices that would exist in an unregulated market.
b) keep rental prices above prices that would exist in an unregulated market.
c) keep rental prices equal to prices that would exist in an unregulated market.
d) increase the stock of rental housing.
e) decrease the demand for housing.

6.63 (SG 6.3)
Correct: d)
Difficulty: 2
Page(s): 130–131
Scramble range: All
Topic: Rent ceilings

6.63
Which of the following is not a likely outcome of rent ceilings?
a) A black market for rent-controlled housing.
b) Long waiting lists of potential renters of rent-controlled housing.
c) A short-run shortage of housing.
d) Black market prices below the rent ceiling prices.
e) Intensified search activity by potential renters.

6.64 (SG 6.4)
Correct: e)
Difficulty: 3
Page(s): 130–131
Scramble range: All
Topic: Decrease in housing supply

6.64
In an unregulated market which of the following is not a likely result of an earthquake that suddenly destroys a large proportion of the stock of housing?
a) Higher rental prices.
b) Some people leaving town.
c) More basement apartments offered for rent.
d) More families sharing living quarters.
e) A shortage of rental housing.

6.65
Correct: d)
Difficulty: 4
Page(s): 130–131
Scramble range: a)–c)
Topic: Housing market

6.65
Which of the following is (are) true?
a) In the long run, the stock of available housing will be greater in an unregulated market than in a market with rent ceilings.
b) In the short run, the quantity of rental housing supplied will be greater in an unregulated market than in a market with rent ceilings.
c) Search activity costs will be higher in a housing market with rent ceilings than in an unregulated market.
d) All of the above.
e) None of the above.

6.66
Correct: d)
Difficulty: 2
Page(s): 136–137
Scramble range: a)–d)
Topic: Labour market

6.66
Refer to Figure 6.5. What is the level of unemployment (in millions of hours) if the minimum wage is set at $3 per hour?
a) 40.
b) 30.
c) 20.
d) 0.
e) None of the above.

Figure 6.5

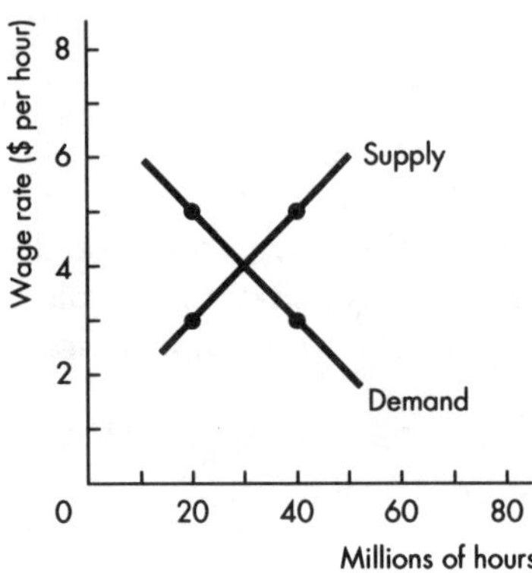

6.67
Correct: c)
Difficulty: 2
Page(s): 136–137
Scramble range: All
Topic: Labour market

6.67
Refer to Figure 6.5. What is the level of unemployment (in millions of hours) if the minimum wage is set at $5 per hour?
a) 40.
b) 30.
c) 20.
d) 10.
e) 0.

6.68 (SG 6.9)
Correct: b)
Difficulty: 2
Page(s): 136–137
Scramble range: All
Topic: Minimum wage

6.68
Which of the following types of labour would be most significantly affected by an increase in the legal minimum wage?
a) Professional athletes.
b) Young, unskilled labour.
c) Skilled union workers.
d) College professors.
e) Steelworkers.

6.69 (SG 6.10)
Correct: a)
Difficulty: 1
Page(s): 131–132
Scramble range: All
Topic: Search activities

6.69
Which of the following would not be considered a search activity?
a) Time spent moving from one job to another.
b) Time spent looking for a new job.
c) Reading a consumer magazine for information as you shop for a new stereo.
d) Time spent looking for the best price for a chair.
e) Time spent reading the apartment ads.

6.70
Correct: c)
Difficulty: 2
Page(s): 138–139
Scramble range: All
Topic: Uncertainty and demand

6.70
Which of the following would not cause uncertainty about the demand for peanut butter?
a) Uncertainty about the prices of substitutes and complements for peanut butter.
b) Uncertainty about household income.
c) Uncertainty about the costs of producing peanut butter.
d) Uncertainty about consumer tastes.
e) Uncertainty about the number of children who will be born.

6.71 (SG 6.13)
Correct: a)
Difficulty: 2
Page(s): 138–139
Scramble range: a)–d)
Topic: Uncertainty and demand

6.71
In the case of no uncertainty about demand but uncertainty about supply, which of the following combinations would generally yield the greatest price fluctuation?
a) Large supply fluctuations and inelastic demand.
b) Large supply fluctuations and elastic demand.
c) Small supply fluctuations and inelastic demand.
d) Small supply fluctuations and elastic demand.
e) All of the above are equally likely to yield the greatest price fluctuation.

6.72
Correct: d)
Difficulty: 2
Page(s): 139–140
Scramble range: All
Topic: Rational expectations

6.72
A rational expectation is best described as
a) determining price by equating demand and supply curves.
b) a rational explanation of current demand and supply curves.
c) any estimates of future demand and supply.
d) a forecast that uses all relevant available information and has the least possible error.
e) a forecast that is always correct.

6.73
Correct: d)
Difficulty: 3
Page(s): 139–140
Scramble range: All
Topic: Rational expectations

6.73
Refer to Figure 6.6. The rational expectations forecast of demand and supply are denoted by *ED* and *ES* and the realized demand and supply are given by *D* and *S*. What is the price forecast error?
a) 0.
b) $3.
c) $5.
d) $8.
e) $10.

Figure 6.6

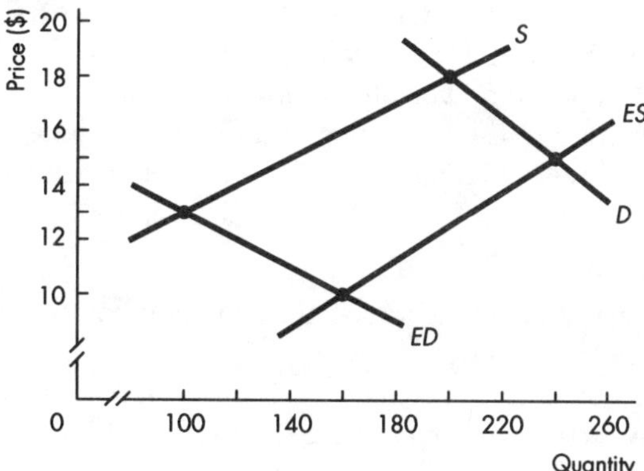

6.74
Correct: e)
Difficulty: 4
Page(s): 139–140
Scramble range: All
Topic: Rational expectations

6.74
Refer to Figure 6.6. The rational expectations forecast of demand and supply are denoted by *ED* and *ES* and the realized demand and supply curves are given by *D* and *S*. What is the forecast for price and quantity sold?
a) Price = $10, quantity = 100.
b) Price = $13, quantity = 100.
c) Price = $18, quantity = 160.
d) Price = $18, quantity = 200.
e) Price = $10, quantity = 160.

6.75
Correct: a)
Difficulty: 2
Page(s): 142–143
Scramble range: All
Topic: Inventories and quantity traded

6.75
The existence of inventories will generally
a) reduce price fluctuation but increase the fluctuation in quantity traded.
b) reduce price fluctuation and reduce the fluctuation in quantity traded.
c) increase price fluctuation and increase the fluctuation in quantity traded.
d) increase price fluctuation but reduce the fluctuation in quantity traded.
e) increase price fluctuation but have an uncertain effect on the fluctuation in quantity traded.

6.76 (SG 6.18)
Correct: c)
Difficulty: 4
Page(s): 142–143
Scramble range: All
Topic: Inventories and quantity traded

6.76
Which of the following statements is *not* true?
a) Buying goods to put into inventory is equivalent to decreasing supply.
b) If the current price is above the rationally expected price, goods will be supplied from inventory.
c) Inventories generally reduce fluctuations in the quantity of goods traded.
d) Inventory holders must forecast future prices.
e) If the current price is below the rationally expected price, goods will be added to inventory.

6.77 (SG 6.20)
Correct: d)
Difficulty: 4
Page(s): 144–145
Scramble range: All
Topic: Stock market

6.77
If the stock market is an efficient market, which of the following statements is *not* true?
a) The current price is equal to the expected future price.
b) The current price embodies all available information.
c) No predictable profit opportunities exist.
d) Prices are not volatile since holding stocks is holding inventories.
e) New information leads to changes in prices.

6.78
Correct: a)
Difficulty: 3
Page(s): 144–145
Scramble range: All
Topic: Volatility of stock price

6.78
The volatility of stock market prices is best explained as
a) resulting from frequently changing expectations due to new information.
b) due to the quantity smoothing effect of holding inventories.
c) due to the volatility in interest rates.
d) due to the manipulation of large investment institutions.
e) due to the falseness of the efficient market theory.

6.79
Correct: d)
Difficulty: 3
Page(s): 130
Scramble range: All
Topic: Rent ceilings

6.79
If a rent ceiling is imposed by the government at greater than the market rental rate for housing, then
a) the stock of rental housing will necessarily increase.
b) a shortage of housing will occur.
c) a surplus of housing will occur.
d) the market rate will prevail as long as all else remains constant.
e) the rental rate will rise.

6.80
Correct: a)
Difficulty: 2
Page(s): 130–131
Scramble range: All
Topic: Rent ceilings

6.80
Which of the following is a likely outcome of rent ceilings imposed below the market rental rate?
a) A black market for rent-controlled housing.
b) Long waiting lists of potential suppliers of rent-controlled housing.
c) A short-run shortage of housing; in the long run, no shortage will exist.
d) Black market prices below the rent ceiling prices.
e) A short-run rise in rents, followed by a fall back to the original value.

6.81
Correct: e)
Difficulty: 3
Page(s): 136
Scramble range: All
Topic: Labour market

6.81
Refer to Table 6.2. What is the level of unemployment (in millions of hours) if the minimum wage is set at $3 per hour?
a) 70.
b) 40.
c) 30.
d) 20.
e) 0.

Table 6.2

Wage rate ($ per hour)	Labour supplied	Labour demanded (millions of hours)
7	60	30
6	50	40
5	40	50
4	30	60
3	20	70

6.82
Correct: b)
Difficulty: 2
Page(s): 136–137
Scramble range: All
Topic: Labour market

6.82
Refer to Table 6.2. What is the level of unemployment (in millions of hours) if the minimum wage is set at $7 per hour?
a) 40.
b) 30.
c) 20.
d) 10.
e) 0.

6.83
Correct: b)
Difficulty: 3
Page(s): 136–137
Scramble range: All
Topic: Labour market

6.83
Refer to Table 6.2. What is the equilibrium wage rate in an unregulated market?
a) $5.00.
b) $5.50.
c) $6.00.
d) $6.50.
e) $7.50.

6.84
Correct: a)
Difficulty: 4
Page(s): 138–139
Scramble range: All
Topic: Uncertainty and supply

6.84
In the case of uncertainty about demand but no uncertainty about supply, which of the following combinations would generally yield the greatest price fluctuation?
a) Large demand fluctuations and inelastic supply.
b) Large demand fluctuations and elastic supply.
c) Small demand fluctuations and inelastic supply.
d) Small demand fluctuations and elastic supply.
e) Small demand fluctuations and a flat supply curve.

6.85
Correct: d)
Difficulty: 4
Page(s): 142–143
Scramble range: All
Topic: Inventories and quantity traded

6.85
Which of the following statements is true?
a) Buying goods to put into inventory is the same as increasing supply.
b) If the current price is below the rationally expected price, goods will be supplied from inventory.
c) Inventories generally reduce fluctuations in the quantity of goods traded.
d) Inventory holders must forecast future prices.
e) Inventories do not reduce fluctuations in the price of goods traded.

6.86
Correct: e)
Difficulty: 4
Page(s): 128–145
Scramble range: None
Topic: Minimum wage

6.86
Suppose the minimum wage was $4 per hour, and 1,100 units of labour are exchanged. Suppose the government raises the minimum wage to $6 per hour, and 900 units are now exchanged. Therefore,
a) total revenue paid to workers has fallen.
b) the elasticity of demand is 0.5.
c) there is an excess supply in this market.
d) supply has increased at the new wage.
e) all of the above except a).

6.87
Correct: e)
Difficulty: 2
Page(s): 137–141
Scramble range: All
Topic: Rational expectations

6.87
Suppose the market for wheat has the expected supply and demand in Table 6.3. If there are no inventories, the rational expectation of the price of wheat is
a) $3.
b) $3.50.
c) $6.
d) $5.
e) $4.

Table 6.3

Price ($)	Expected quantity demanded	Expected quantity supplied
1	700	100
2	600	200
3	500	300
4	400	400
5	300	500
6	200	600
7	100	700

6.88
Correct: c)
Difficulty: 5
Page(s): 137–141
Scramble range: All
Topic: Rational expectations

6.88
Suppose Table 6.3 represents the expected demand and supply in the market for wheat. There are no inventories. Suppose a drought occurs, and wheat production is 100 units less than expected. As a result, actual quantity traded is
a) 600 units at a price of $2.
b) 300 units at a price of $4.
c) 300 units at a price of $5.
d) 300 units at a price of $3.
e) 500 units at a price of $3.

6.89
Correct: c)
Difficulty: 5
Page(s): 137–141
Scramble range: All
Topic: Rational expectations

6.89
Suppose that Table 6.3 represents the expected demand and supply for wheat. There are no inventories and growing conditions turn out to be exactly as expected. However, a drought in the Soviet Union increases Soviet demand for Canadian wheat unexpectedly by 100 units. As a result, actual quantity traded will be
a) 400 units, and price will be $4.
b) 500 units, and price will be $5.
c) 400 units, and price will be $5.
d) 600 units, and price will be $6.
e) 500 units, and price will be $3.

6.90
Correct: c)
Difficulty: 3
Page(s): 142–145
Scramble range: All
Topic: Inventories

6.90
Suppose that Table 6.3 represents the expected demand and supply of wheat. There are inventories in this market. What is the expected price in this case?
a) $3.
b) $6.
c) $4.
d) $3.50.
e) $5.

6.91
Correct: e)
Difficulty: 5
Page(s): 142–145
Scramble range: All
Topic: Inventories

6.91
Suppose that Table 6.3 represents the expected demand and supply in the market for wheat. There are inventories. Suppose that a drought occurs and wheat production is 100 units less than expected. As a result, actual quantity traded is
a) 600 units and price is $2.
b) 500 units and price is $3.
c) 300 units and price is $5.
d) 300 units and price is $3.
e) 400 units and price is $4.

Chapter 7 Utility and Demand

7.1
Correct: c)
Difficulty: 2
Page(s): 157–158
Scramble range: All
Topic: Individual demand

7.1
Individual demand curves result from
a) utility maximization of a group of consumers.
b) minimizing the marginal utility of a good.
c) maximizing total utility of an individual subject to prices and income.
d) equating marginal utilities.
e) maximizing total utility.

7.2
Correct: b)
Difficulty: 2
Page(s): 157
Scramble range: All
Topic: Market demand

7.2
The market demand for a good will shift with
a) a change in the price of a resource used in making that good.
b) an increase in the income of all individuals.
c) a change in the price of the good.
d) a change in technology.
e) a change in the quantity of the good.

7.3
Correct: e)
Difficulty: 4
Page(s): 157
Scramble range: None
Topic: Individual demand

7.3
Which of the following would *not* shift an individual demand curve?
a) A change in the individual's income.
b) A change in the price of the good.
c) A change in the price of a substitute.
d) A change in production technology.
e) Neither b) nor d).

7.4
Correct: b)
Difficulty: 2
Page(s): 157,166
Scramble range: All
Topic: Individual demand

7.4
Negatively sloped demand curves are a direct result of
a) increasing prices.
b) decreasing marginal utility.
c) diminishing total utility.
d) increasing marginal utility.
e) decreasing income.

7.5
Correct: a)
Difficulty: 4
Page(s): 158–162
Scramble range: All
Topic: Utility

7.5
Martha and Sarah have the same preferences, face the same prices, and have the same income. Sarah's utility is measured in utils while Martha's is measured in utils squared. Choose the best response.
a) Martha and Sarah will choose to consume the same set of goods.
b) Martha's and Sarah's marginal utility per dollar will be equal.
c) Martha's and Sarah's marginal utilities will be equal.
d) Martha and Sarah will have equal total utility.
e) Martha and Sarah will not chose to consume the same set of goods.

7.6
Correct: c)
Difficulty: 5
Page(s): 158–162
Scramble range: All
Topic: Utility

7.6
John and Sally have identical preferences except that Sally's utility is exactly 10 times that of John's. Both have the same income and face the same prices. Choose the best response.
a) John consumes 10 times the amount that Sally consumes.
b) John receives 1/10 the satisfaction of Sally.
c) Both will consume the same amount of all goods.
d) John and Sally will have equal total utility.
e) John and Sally will have equal marginal utility.

7.7
Correct: d)
Difficulty: 3
Page(s): 158–161
Scramble range: All
Topic: Marginal utility

7.7
Table 7.1 gives utilities for Jim and Sally. Which of the following statements is true?
a) Jim has increasing marginal utility.
b) For Sally, the marginal utility of the 3rd unit consumed is 6.
c) If Jim consumes 2 units, his total utility will be 34.
d) Jim and Sally have identical marginal utilities.
e) If Sally consumes 2 units, her total utility will be 10 units.

Table 7.1

Units consumed	Jim's utility	Sally's utility
1	12	16
2	22	26
3	30	34
4	36	40

7.8
Correct: b)
Difficulty: 1
Page(s): 158–160
Scramble range: All
Topic: Marginal utility

7.8
The additional utility derived from the last unit of a good consumed is
a) total utility.
b) marginal utility.
c) average utility.
d) marginal utility per dollar spent.
e) a util.

7.9
Correct: c)
Difficulty: 1
Page(s): 158–159
Scramble range: All
Topic: Utility

7.9
Utility is best defined as
a) the value of a good.
b) the additional satisfaction received from consuming another unit of a good.
c) the benefit or satisfaction from consuming goods and services.
d) the practical usefulness of a good.
e) equal to the price of a good.

7.10
Correct: a)
Difficulty: 2
Page(s): 160
Scramble range: All
Topic: Marginal utility/diminishing

7.10
Diminishing marginal utility means that
a) Ralph will enjoy his second hamburger less than the first.
b) the utility from one hamburger is greater than the utility from two hamburgers.
c) the price of two hamburgers is less than twice the price of one.
d) the utility from eating two hamburgers will be more than twice the utility from eating the first.
e) hamburgers seem smaller as you eat more of them.

7.11
Correct: b)
Difficulty: 2
Page(s): 159–160
Scramble range: All
Topic: Marginal utility/diminishing

7.11
As increasing quantities of a good are consumed
a) marginal utility increases.
b) marginal utility decreases.
c) marginal utility remains unchanged.
d) total utility decreases.
e) total utility increases at an increasing rate.

7.12
Correct: e)
Difficulty: 2
Page(s): 159–160
Scramble range: All
Topic: Marginal utility

7.12
Marginal utility can be defined as
a) the total satisfaction from the consumption of goods.
b) the value of a good consumed.
c) units of measurement of total utility.
d) the total satisfaction from the consumption of one good.
e) the additional satisfaction from the last unit of a good consumed.

7.13
Correct: b)
Difficulty: 2
Page(s): 159–160
Scramble range: All
Topic: Marginal utility

7.13
As consumption of a good increases, marginal utility
a) increases.
b) decreases.
c) decreases and then increases.
d) stays the same.
e) increases and then decreases.

7.14
Correct: c)
Difficulty: 2
Page(s): 159–160
Scramble range: All
Topic: Utility

7.14
Utility can best be described as
a) the amount of satisfaction derived from consuming the last unit of a good.
b) a testable hypothesis about the level of happiness achieved from consumption of goods.
c) an abstract concept useful for obtaining predictions about human behaviour.
d) the units that measure a person's satisfaction.
e) the choice of rational individuals.

7.15
Correct: a)
Difficulty: 5
Page(s): 160–162
Scramble range: All
Topic: Utility maximization

7.15
Sarah can consume either pizzas or hamburgers. The price of a hamburger is \$1 and the price of a pizza is \$5. Let MU_h be the marginal utility of hamburgers and MU_p be the marginal utility of pizzas. In consumer equilibrium, what must the ratio MU_h/MU_p equal?
a) 1/5.
b) 5/1.
c) 1/1.
d) 1/6.
e) 6/1.

7.16
Correct: a)
Difficulty: 3
Page(s): 159–160
Scramble range: All
Topic: Marginal utility theory

7.16
Suppose John can consume apples, oranges, and pears. If John increases his consumption of oranges, marginal utility theory states that
a) the marginal utility of oranges decreases.
b) the marginal utility of apples decreases.
c) the marginal utility of pears decreases.
d) the marginal utility of oranges remains constant.
e) the marginal utility of oranges, apples, and pears all decrease.

7.17
Correct: c)
Difficulty: 2
Page(s): 164–165
Scramble range: All
Topic: Marginal utility theory

7.17
Harold can consume apples and oranges. He likes them equally well and currently is in consumer equilibrium. Now the price of oranges goes up while his income remains the same. What will happen to his consumption?
a) Consumption of oranges increases, consumption of apples decreases.
b) Consumption of oranges increases, consumption of apples increases.
c) Consumption of oranges decreases, consumption of apples decreases.
d) Consumption of oranges decreases, consumption of apples increases.
e) We cannot tell; it depends on Harold's utility levels.

7.18
Correct: a)
Difficulty: 3
Page(s): 159–166
Scramble range: All
Topic: Marginal utility theory

7.18
Decreasing marginal utility is
a) an assumption of marginal utility theory.
b) an implication of marginal utility theory.
c) a prediction of marginal utility theory.
d) a result of the law of demand.
e) the law of demand.

7.19
Correct: b)
Difficulty: 4
Page(s): 166–167
Scramble range: All
Topic: Normal goods

7.19
As a consumer's income decreases, marginal utility theory predicts that
a) the price of normal goods will decrease.
b) the quantity demanded of normal goods will decrease.
c) the quantity demanded of all goods will decrease.
d) the quantity demanded of normal goods will increase.
e) utility will rise.

7.20
Correct: a)
Difficulty: 4
Page(s): 166–167
Scramble range: All
Topic: Marginal utility theory

7.20
Starting from a point of consumer equilibrium, marginal utility theory implies that a rise in income will
a) increase a consumer's total utility.
b) decrease marginal utility for all goods.
c) increase consumption for all goods.
d) increase consumption of inferior goods.
e) increase marginal utility of normal goods.

7.21
Correct: e)
Difficulty: 2
Page(s): 158
Scramble range: All
Topic: Preferences

7.21
An economist would define preferences as
a) a utility function.
b) an individual's choices of goods.
c) a characteristic similar to temperature.
d) the highest level of satisfaction attainable.
e) the likes and dislikes of an individual.

7.22
Correct: a)
Difficulty: 4
Page(s): 161–162
Scramble range: All
Topic: Consumer equilibrium

7.22
As seen from Table 7.2, Sam enjoys sailing and skiing equally well. Which of the following is *not* true?
a) Sam will consume the same number of hours of sailing and skiing regardless of the difference in price.
b) If the prices of sailing and skiing (per hour) are the same, Sam will spend the same number of hours at each activity.
c) The marginal utility of the 3rd hour of either sailing or skiing is 30.
d) The total utility of sailing for 3 hours and skiing for 2 hours is 210.
e) If the price of sailing is higher than the price of skiing, then Sam will spend more hours skiing than sailing.

Table 7.2

Hours spent	Utility from sailing	Utility from skiing
1	50	50
2	90	90
3	120	120
4	140	140

7.23
Correct: c)
Difficulty: 5
Page(s): 161–162
Scramble range: All
Topic: Consumer equilibrium

7.23
Consider Sam's utility from sailing and skiing reported in Table 7.2. If the price of sailing is $5 per hour and the price of skiing is $10 per hour, Sam will choose to spend
a) all his time sailing.
b) all his time skiing.
c) twice as much time sailing as skiing.
d) twice as much time skiing as sailing.
e) the same amount of time sailing and skiing, since they give the same amount of utility.

7.24
Correct: d)
Difficulty: 5
Page(s): 161–162
Scramble range: All
Topic: Consumer equilibrium

7.24
Consider Sam's utility from sailing and skiing as given by Table 7.2. The price of sailing is $5 per hour and the price of skiing is $10 per hour, while Sam's income to be spent on these activities is $40. In consumer equilibrium, Sam will sail for
a) 3 hours and ski for 2 hours.
b) 2 hours and ski for 4 hours.
c) 4 hours.
d) 4 hours and ski for 2 hours.
e) 8 hours.

7.25
Correct: b)
Difficulty: 5
Page(s): 161–162
Scramble range: All
Topic: Consumer equilibrium

7.25
Consider Sam's utility from sailing and skiing as given by Table 7.2. Suppose that the price of sailing is $5 per hour and the price of skiing is $10 per hour. If, in consumer equilibrium, Sam chooses to spend 2 hours sailing, we

a) know that he will spend 4 hours skiing and his income is $40.
b) know that he will spend 1 hour skiing and his income is $20.
c) know that he will spend 2 hours skiing and his income is $30.
d) cannot determine Sam's income or how long he will spend skiing.
e) know that he will spend zero hours skiing and his income is $10.

7.26
Correct: b)
Difficulty: 3
Page(s): 161–162
Scramble range: All
Topic: Consumer equilibrium

7.26
If income is fully spent and the marginal utility per dollar spent is equal for all goods, then

a) marginal utility is maximized.
b) total utility is maximized.
c) a consumer could not be better off even with greater income.
d) the proportion of income spent on each good must be equal.
e) the number of units of each good must be equal.

7.27
Correct: a)
Difficulty: 3
Page(s): 161–162
Scramble range: All
Topic: Consumer equilibrium

7.27
Which of the following is *not* true in consumer equilibrium?

a) The total utilities of all goods are equal.
b) The consumer is maximizing utility, given her income and the prices of goods and services.
c) The marginal utility per dollar spent is equal for all goods.
d) Given prices and her income, the consumer finds that any other possible choice of goods to consume would make her worse off.
e) The consumer will not change her choices, unless prices or income change.

7.28
Correct: b)
Difficulty: 4
Page(s): 161–162
Scramble range: All
Topic: Marginal utility theory

7.28
Billy likes candy bars and popcorn. Candy bars sell for 50 cents and popcorn sells for $1 a bag. Currently he is in consumer equilibrium with marginal utility per dollar spent on popcorn equal to 100. What is the marginal utility per dollar spent on candy bars?

a) 50.
b) 100.
c) 200.
d) 25.
e) 0.5.

7.29
Correct: e)
Difficulty: 5
Page(s): 161–165
Scramble range: All
Topic: Consumer equilibrium

7.29
Billy likes candy bars and popcorn. Candy bars sell for 50 cents and popcorn sells for $1 per bag. Currently he is in consumer equilibrium. Now the price of candy jumps to $1 per candy bar. Which statement is true in the new consumer equilibrium?

a) The marginal utility of popcorn will increase.
b) Marginal utility per dollar spent will be equal to 2.
c) Total utility will be higher.
d) The marginal utility of candy will decrease.
e) The marginal utility of candy will be equal to the marginal utility of popcorn.

7.30
Correct: d)
Difficulty: 4
Page(s): 161–162
Scramble range: All
Topic: Consumer equilibrium

7.30
Refer to Table 7.3. Henry is maximizing his utility by consuming 3 bags of popcorn and 3 bottles of soda. What must be the ratio of the price of popcorn to the price of soda?
a) 1/2.
b) 1.
c) 5/6.
d) 2.
e) 6/5.

Table 7.3

Bags of popcorn	Marginal utility	Bottles of soda	Marginal utility
1	100	1	60
2	80	2	50
3	60	3	30
4	50	4	20

7.31
Correct: a)
Difficulty: 4
Page(s): 158–160
Scramble range: All
Topic: Utility

7.31
Refer to Table 7.3. What is the total utility if 3 bags of popcorn and 2 bottles of soda are consumed?
a) 350.
b) 400.
c) 450.
d) 500.
e) 110.

7.32
Correct: d)
Difficulty: 3
Page(s): 161–162
Scramble range: All
Topic: Consumer equilibrium

7.32
Let MU_A and MU_B stand for the marginal utility of goods A and B, respectively. Let P_A and P_B stand for the price of goods A and B, respectively. Which statement must hold for consumer equilibrium?
a) $MU_A = MU_B$.
b) $MU_A = MU_B$ and $P_A = P_B$.
c) $MU_A/MU_B = P_B/P_A$.
d) $MU_A/MU_B = P_A/P_B$.
e) $MU_AP_A = MU_BP_B$.

7.33
Correct: e)
Difficulty: 3
Page(s): 161–162
Scramble range: All
Topic: Consumer equilibrium

7.33
To determine consumer equilibrium we need to know only
a) prices and income.
b) total utility and income.
c) marginal utility and income.
d) total utility and marginal utility.
e) prices and marginal utility.

7.34
Correct: a)
Difficulty: 4
Page(s): 161–162
Scramble range: All
Topic: Consumer equilibrium

7.34
Harold can consume either pens or milkshakes. Both pens and milkshakes sell for $1. Harold figures that when his income is spent, the marginal utility of pens will be 10 while his marginal utility of milkshakes will be 8. Harold could make himself better off by
a) consuming more pens and fewer milkshakes.
b) consuming more pens and more milkshakes.
c) consuming fewer pens and fewer milkshakes.
d) consuming fewer pens and more milkshakes.
e) continuing to consume the same number of pens and milkshakes.

7.35
Correct: b)
Difficulty: 2
Page(s): 162–163
Scramble range: All
Topic: Marginal utility theory

7.35
According to the marginal utility theory, consumers
a) maximize utility and minimize marginal utility.
b) maximize utility and equalize marginal utility per dollar spent across goods.
c) save part of their income for future consumption.
d) maximize utility by spending the most on the least expensive good.
e) maximize utility by spending the least on the least expensive good.

7.36
Correct: d)
Difficulty: 5
Page(s): 161–162
Scramble range: All
Topic: Consumer equilibrium

7.36
Sally derives utility from consuming apples and tacos as described in Table 7.4. Apples cost 50 cents each and tacos cost $1 each. What will be the combination that Sally chooses in consumer equilibrium if she has an income of $4.50?
a) 5 apples and 2 tacos.
b) 4 apples and 4 tacos.
c) 1 apple and 4 tacos.
d) 3 apples and 3 tacos.
e) 7 apples and 1 taco.

Table 7.4

Apples		Tacos	
Quantity	Utility	Quantity	Utility
1	40	1	100
2	75	2	180
3	105	3	240
4	130	4	280
5	150	5	300

7.37
Correct: b)
Difficulty: 2
Page(s): 159–160
Scramble range: All
Topic: Marginal utility theory

7.37
Which of the following is true for total utility and marginal utility as consumption of a good increases?
a) Total utility is increasing; marginal utility is increasing.
b) Total utility is increasing; marginal utility is decreasing.
c) Total utility is decreasing; marginal utility is increasing.
d) Total utility is decreasing; marginal utility is decreasing.
e) Total utility is decreasing; marginal utility is positive.

7.38
Correct: e)
Difficulty: 3
Page(s): 169
Scramble range: All
Topic: Utility paradox

7.38
Adam Smith's diamond–water paradox can be explained by
a) distinguishing between utility and price.
b) water having a high level of utility relative to diamonds.
c) water having a low price relative to diamonds.
d) the fact that utility can't be measured.
e) distinguishing between total utility and marginal utility.

7.39
Correct: d)
Difficulty: 2
Page(s): 166–167
Scramble range: All
Topic: Normal goods

7.39
When economists speak of normal goods they mean
a) manufactured goods with no defects.
b) goods people usually buy.
c) goods whose marginal utility decreases as consumption increases.
d) goods whose quantity demanded increases with rising incomes.
e) goods whose quantity demanded decreases as price rises.

7.40
Correct: b)
Difficulty: 1
Page(s): 168–169
Scramble range: All
Topic: Value

7.40
The maximum price a consumer is willing to pay for an item is known as
a) consumer surplus.
b) the value of a good.
c) individual demand.
d) law of highest return.
e) marginal utility of the good.

7.41
Correct: c)
Difficulty: 4
Page(s): 168–169
Scramble range: All
Topic: Consumer surplus

7.41
Currently Joe and Dan are consuming the same amount of strawberries, but Joe's demand curve is much more elastic than Dan's. Which statement is true?
a) Joe's consumer surplus exceeds Dan's.
b) Dan's consumer surplus equals Joe's.
c) Dan's consumer surplus exceeds Joe's.
d) No statement can be made comparing consumer surpluses.
e) Any comparison of consumer surplus depends on the price of strawberries.

7.42
Correct: c)
Difficulty: 3
Page(s): 168–169
Scramble range: All
Topic: Consumer surplus

7.42
Table 7.5 shows Arnold's demand for handkerchiefs. Suppose the price of handkerchiefs is $3 per item. What is Arnold's consumer surplus?
a) 1.
b) 2.
c) 3.
d) 4.
e) 5.

Table 7.5 Arnold's demand for handkerchiefs.

Price ($ per handkerchief)	Quantity demanded
5	1
4	2
3	3
2	4
1	5

7.43
Correct: b)
Difficulty: 5
Page(s): 168–169
Scramble range: All
Topic: Consumer surplus

7.43
Other things remaining constant, marginal utility theory implies that an increase in the price of a good will
a) increase the consumer surplus.
b) decrease the consumer surplus.
c) leave consumer surplus unchanged.
d) have an effect on consumer surplus that cannot be determined.
e) decrease consumer surplus by the amount equal to the total utility of all goods consumed before the increase but no longer after the increase.

7.44
Correct: a)
Difficulty: 4
Page(s): 168–169
Scramble range: All
Topic: Consumer surplus

7.44
Other things being equal, an increase in the supply of a good will
a) increase the consumer surplus.
b) decrease the consumer surplus.
c) leave consumer surplus unchanged.
d) have an effect on consumer surplus that cannot be determined.
e) have an effect on consumer surplus that depends on the source of the supply change.

7.45
Correct: a)
Difficulty: 3
Page(s): 168–169
Scramble range: All
Topic: Consumer surplus

7.45
Given two alternate demand curves for an individual that intersect at the prevailing price, which statement is true?
a) The more inelastic demand curve has the higher consumer surplus.
b) The more elastic demand curve has the higher consumer surplus.
c) The consumer surplus for the two demand curves is equal.
d) Consumer surplus cannot be compared.
e) A comparison of amount of consumer surplus for each demand curve depends on the level of the price.

7.46
Correct: a)
Difficulty: 1
Page(s): 168–169
Scramble range: All
Topic: Consumer surplus

7.46
The term "consumer surplus" refers to
a) the difference between the value of a purchase and the total paid for the purchase.
b) the total value that a consumer places upon a good.
c) the decreasing marginal utility that consumers receive from additional consumption of a good.
d) the area under the demand curve.
e) the total amount paid for the purchase.

7.47
Correct: d)
Difficulty: 3
Page(s): 159–164
Scramble range: All
Topic: Marginal utility theory

7.47
Which statement is *not* implied by marginal utility theory?
a) Demand curves are negatively sloped.
b) Consumer surplus is positive.
c) Marginal utility decreases as consumption increases.
d) Marginal utility across goods is equal at consumer equilibrium.
e) As income rises, the consumption of normal goods rises.

7.48
Correct: c)
Difficulty: 1
Page(s): 168–169
Scramble range: All
Topic: Consumer surplus

7.48
Consumer surplus is
a) the amount left over when consumption is complete.
b) the excess quantity demanded.
c) the difference between the value of a good and its price.
d) the highest price an individual is willing to pay.
e) the total value of consumption.

7.49
Correct: b)
Difficulty: 2
Page(s): 168
Scramble range: All
Topic: Consumer surplus

7.49
Consider the demand curve in Figure 7.1. What is the value of the first unit of the good?
a) $10.
b) $8.
c) $6.
d) $9.
e) We cannot tell unless we know the price of the good.

Figure 7.1

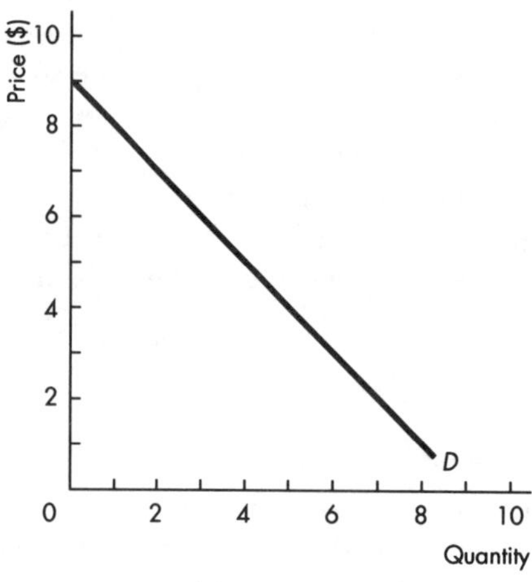

7.50
Correct: c)
Difficulty: 3
Page(s): 168–169
Scramble range: All
Topic: Consumer surplus

7.50
Consider the demand curve given in Figure 7.1. If the price is $4, what is the consumer surplus from the first unit of the good?
a) $8.
b) $6.
c) $4.
d) $2.
e) We cannot tell; it depends on the marginal utility of the good.

7.51
Correct: a)
Difficulty: 5
Page(s): 168–169
Scramble range: All
Topic: Consumer surplus

7.51
Consider the demand curve given in Figure 7.1. If the price of the good is $4, what is the total consumer surplus?
a) $10.
b) $15.
c) $20.
d) $30.
e) $39.

7.52
Correct: e)
Difficulty: 4
Page(s): 168–169
Scramble range: All
Topic: Consumer surplus

7.52
Other things being equal (including price), what happens to consumer surplus of a normal good as income increases?
a) It depends on whether the other good(s) is (are) normal or inferior.
b) It will decrease.
c) It will remain the same.
d) It cannot be determined.
e) It will increase.

7.53
Correct: c)
Difficulty: 3
Page(s): 168–169
Scramble range: All
Topic: Consumer surplus

7.53
Jim wants to go to a basketball game but it is sold out. He has a demand schedule as shown in Table 7.6. He then meets a ticket scalper who offers to sell him one ticket for $20 and a second ticket for $10. What is Jim's consumer surplus if he buys two tickets?
a) $10.
b) $20.
c) $0.
d) $30.
e) $34.

Table 7.6 Jim's demand for basketball tickets.

Price ($ per ticket)	Quantity demanded
20	1
10	2
3	3
1	4

7.54
Correct: d)
Difficulty: 3
Page(s): 168–169
Scramble range: All
Topic: Consumer surplus

7.54
From Table 7.6 we see that Jim values two basketball tickets at
a) $3.
b) $10.
c) $20.
d) $30.
e) $34.

7.55
Correct: b)
Difficulty: 2
Page(s): 157
Scramble range: All
Topic: Market demand

7.55
Market demand is
a) the sum of prices demanded by individuals at each quantity.
b) the sum of the quantities demanded by each individual at each price.
c) the sum of both prices and quantities demanded by all individuals.
d) the total amount of goods consumed.
e) the price one is willing to pay in equilibrium.

7.56
Correct: a)
Difficulty: 2
Page(s): 158–159
Scramble range: All
Topic: Total utility and consumption

7.56
As consumption of a good increases,
a) total utility increases.
b) total utility decreases.
c) total utility remains unchanged.
d) marginal utility increases.
e) marginal utility is zero.

7.57
Correct: c)
Difficulty: 2
Page(s): 159–160
Scramble range: All
Topic: Marginal utility

7.57
The fact that the fourth slice of pizza did not generate as much satisfaction as the third slice is an example of
a) consumer surplus.
b) diminishing total utility.
c) diminishing marginal utility.
d) the paradox of value.
e) the law of demand.

7.58
Correct: e)
Difficulty: 2
Page(s): 158–169
Scramble range: All
Topic: Utility and consumption

7.58
The benefit or satisfaction that a person receives from the consumption of a good is called
a) marginal utility.
b) consumer surplus.
c) consumer demand.
d) consumer equilibrium.
e) utility.

7.59
Correct: e)
Difficulty: 4
Page(s): 163–164
Scramble range: None
Topic: Price/ consumption changes

7.59
If the price of good *X* increases,
a) the marginal utility from the consumption of the last unit of *X* increases.
b) the total utility from the consumption of *X* increases.
c) the marginal utility per dollar spent on *X* increases.
d) the consumption of *X* decreases.
e) both a) and d).

7.60
Correct: c)
Difficulty: 5
Page(s): 159–160
Scramble range: All
Topic: Marginal utility

7.60
Refer to Table 7.7 for this question. The value for *B* should be
a) 38.
b) 48.
c) 53.
d) 63.
e) 58.

Table 7.7

Quantity	Utility	Marginal utility
0	0	0
1	20	20
2	*A*	18
3	*B*	15
4	63	*C*

7.61
Correct: e)
Difficulty: 5
Page(s): 156–160
Scramble range: All
Topic: Marginal utility

7.61
Refer to Table 7.7 for this question. The value for *C* should be
a) 0.
b) 13.
c) 15.
d) 22.
e) 10.

7.62 (SG 7.3)
Correct: a)
Difficulty: 3
Page(s): 161
Scramble range: None
Topic: Consumer equilibrium

7.62
If a consumer is in equilibrium, then
a) utility is maximized given the consumer's income and the prices of goods.
b) marginal utility is maximized given the consumer's income and the prices of goods.
c) the marginal utility of the last unit of each good will be the same.
d) both a) and c).
e) both b) and c).

7.63
Correct: d)
Difficulty: 4
Page(s): 161–162
Scramble range: All
Topic: Marginal utility/equilibrium prices

7.63
Sam consumes apples and bananas and is in consumer equilibrium. The marginal utility of the last apple is 10 and the marginal utility of the last banana is 5. If the price of an apple is 50 cents, we know that the price of a banana must be
a) 10 cents.
b) $1.00.
c) 50 cents.
d) 25 cents.
e) $2.00.

7.64
Correct: c)
Difficulty: 3
Page(s): 163–164
Scramble range: a)–d)
Topic: Marginal utility theory

7.64
Which of the following is not an assumption of marginal utility theory?
a) Consumers derive utility from consuming goods.
b) Marginal utility is positive.
c) Utility is maximized when the marginal utility per dollar spent is equal for all goods.
d) As consumption of a good increases, the marginal utility declines.
e) None of the above is an assumption of marginal utility theory.

7.65 (SG 7.13)
Correct: d)
Difficulty: 2
Page(s): 163–164
Scramble range: All
Topic: Marginal utility theory

7.65
Which of the following is not a prediction of marginal utility theory?
a) Other things being equal, the higher the price of a good, the lower is the quantity demanded.
b) Other things being equal, the higher the price of a good, the higher is the consumption of substitutes for that good.
c) The law of demand.
d) Decreasing marginal utility.
e) As income rises, consumption of inferior goods falls.

7.66
Correct: d)
Difficulty: 1
Page(s): 158
Scramble range: All
Topic: Marginal utility theory

7.66
The "inventor" of marginal utility theory is
a) Adam Smith.
b) Michael Edgeworth.
c) Milton Friedman.
d) Alfred Marshall.
e) Gary Becker.

7.67
Correct: a)
Difficulty: 3
Page(s): 162–163
Scramble range: All
Topic: Consumer disequilibrium

7.67
Suppose a consumer spends all of his income and his marginal utility per dollar spent on *X* is 4 and marginal utility per dollar spent on *Y* is 2, we know that
a) utility can be increased by increasing the consumption of *X* and decreasing the consumption of *Y*.
b) utility can be increased by decreasing the consumption of *X* and increasing the consumption of *Y*.
c) the price of *Y* must be twice the price of *X*.
d) utility is maximized.
e) the price of *Y* must be half the price of *X*.

7.68
Correct: e)
Difficulty: 4
Page(s): 162–163
Scramble range: All
Topic: Marginal utility

7.68
Refer to Table 7.8. The first $4 of income should be used to purchase
a) 2 units of good *X*.
b) 3 units of good *X*.
c) 4 units of good *Y*.
d) an amount of *X* and *Y* that cannot be determined from the table.
e) 2 units of good *Y* and 1 unit of *X*.

Table 7.8

Good *X* ($2 each)		Good *Y* ($1 each)	
Quantity	Utility	Quantity	Utility
1	20	1	14
2	32	2	24
3	42	3	32
4	48	4	37
5	52	5	40
6	54	6	42
7	55	7	43

7.69
Correct: c)
Difficulty: 5
Page(s): 161–162
Scramble range: All
Topic: Consumer equilibrium

7.69
Refer to Table 7.8. If income is $13, then utility is maximized with consumption of
a) 6 units of *X* and 1 unit of *Y*.
b) 5 units of *X* and 3 units of *Y*.
c) 4 units of *X* and 5 units of *Y*.
d) 3 units of *X* and 7 units of *Y*.
e) 2 units of *X* and 9 units of *Y*.

7.70 (SG 7.17)
Correct: d)
Difficulty: 2
Page(s): 168
Scramble range: All
Topic: Value theory

7.70
The value of a good is defined as
a) the price paid by an individual.
b) the average price paid by individuals in a market.
c) the cost of producing the good.
d) the highest price an individual is willing to pay.
e) the consumer surplus of the good.

7.71 (SG 7.18)
Correct: b)
Difficulty: 1
Page(s): 168–169
Scramble range: All
Topic: Consumer surplus

7.71
The difference between the value of a good and its price is known as
a) excess demand.
b) consumer surplus.
c) consumer excess.
d) marginal utility.
e) total utility.

7.72
Correct: a)
Difficulty: 3
Page(s): 167–168
Scramble range: All
Topic: Criticism marginal utility

7.72
One criticism of marginal utility theory is that in the real world people do not perform the calculations necessary to maximize utility. Choose the best rebuttal to this criticism.
a) The usefulness of a theory depends upon the accuracy of its predictions.
b) The usefulness of a theory depends upon the accuracy of its assumptions.
c) The usefulness of marginal utility theory depends upon the measurability of the utility function.
d) People actually do perform the calculations for consumer equilibrium.
e) We cannot observe utility anyway, so this criticism is irrelevant.

7.73
Correct: d)
Difficulty: 4
Page(s): 168–169
Scramble range: All
Topic: Consumer surplus

7.73
Refer to Table 7.9. If the actual price is $9, what is the total consumer surplus?
a) 0.
b) $3.
c) $6.
d) $10.
e) $12.

Table 7.9 Demand schedule for good X.

Price ($ per unit)	Quantity demanded
15	1
12	2
10	3
9	4
8	5

7.74 (SG 7.20)
Correct: d)
Difficulty: 3
Page(s): 169
Scramble range: All
Topic: Paradox of value

7.74
The high price of diamonds relative to the price of water reflects the fact that at typical levels of consumption
a) the total utility of water is much lower than the total utility of diamonds.
b) the marginal utility of water is high.
c) the demand for diamonds is upward sloping.
d) the marginal utility of diamonds is high.
e) water yields no utility.

7.75
Correct: e)
Difficulty: 1
Page(s): 157
Scramble range: All
Topic: Market demand

7.75
The sum of the quantities demanded by each individual at each price is
a) an individual's demand curve.
b) consumer surplus.
c) the market demand curve only for a public good.
d) the market supply curve.
e) the market demand curve.

7.76
Correct: d)
Difficulty: 3
Page(s): 160
Scramble range: All
Topic: Diminishing marginal utility

7.76
Diminishing marginal utility means
a) as consumption of one product increases, holding all else constant, total utility begins to decrease.
b) as consumption of one product increases, holding all else constant, total utility begins to increase.
c) that there will be no demand for the product.
d) that total utility is increasing at a decreasing rate.
e) as price goes down, consumption goes up at a decreasing rate.

7.77
Correct: e)
Difficulty: 2
Page(s): 168
Scramble range: All
Topic: Paradox of value

7.77
The paradox of value
a) is that values are the same for different people.
b) is that economists can calculate marginal utility, even though utility is unmeasurable.
c) is resolved by an appeal to the law of diminishing total utility.
d) remains unresolved by economists.
e) is resolved by an appeal to the difference between marginal utility and total utility.

7.78
Correct: d)
Difficulty: 2
Page(s): 160–161
Scramble range: All
Topic: Utility maximization

7.78
In order for the consumer to be maximizing utility out of a given income,
a) the marginal utility of each product must be maximized.
b) the total utility of each product must be maximized.
c) the marginal utilities of all goods and services consumed must be equal.
d) the marginal utilities of the last dollar's worth of all goods and services consumed must be equal.
e) the amount of each good consumed per dollar must be equal.

7.79
Correct: e)
Difficulty: 3
Page(s): 160–161
Scramble range: All
Topic: Utility maximization

7.79
Suppose that you are consuming hot dogs and cokes and believe you are receiving maximum total utility from the meal for entire budget of $6. The price of a hot dog is $1 and the price of a coke is $1. Which of the following can you conclude?
a) The total utility of hot dogs is maximized.
b) The marginal utilities of hot dogs and cokes divided by the quantity of each good must be equal.
c) The total utilities of hot dogs and cokes must be equal.
d) You are purchasing three hot dogs and three cokes.
e) The marginal utilities of hot dogs and cokes must be equal.

7.80
Correct: c)
Difficulty: 4
Page(s): 160
Scramble range: All
Topic: Utility maximization

7.80
Originally, you are consuming hot dogs and cokes and believe you are maximizing utility for your entire budget of $6, given that hot dogs and cokes each cost $1. Suppose now that the price of hot dogs rises to $2 and the price of cokes remains at $1. You adjust consumption of hot dogs and cokes and believe you are once again receiving maximum total utility from the meal. Which of the following can you conclude?
a) The total utility of hot dogs is maximized.
b) The marginal utilities of hot dogs and cokes must be equal.
c) The marginal utility of hot dogs must rise compared to the marginal utility of cokes.
d) You are purchasing 2 hot dogs and 2 cokes.
e) You are purchasing 1 hot dog and 4 cokes.

7.81
Correct: a)
Difficulty: 3
Page(s): 167–168
Scramble range: All
Topic: Consumer surplus

7.81
Consumer surplus is
a) the difference between the market price a consumer pays and the maximum price the consumer would have been willing to pay for all the units purchased.
b) the difference between the market price a consumer pays and the market price the sellers would have been willing to receive for all the units sold.
c) maximized when prices are at their highest.
d) the same as marginal utility.
e) maximized for a horizontal demand curve.

7.82
Correct: e)
Difficulty: 3
Page(s): 160
Scramble range: All
Topic: Utility maximization

7.82
Refer to Table 7.10. If both goods were free goods, how many of each should be consumed to maximize total utility?
a) 1 unit of *X* and 1 unit of *Y*.
b) 5 units of *X* and 8 units of *Y*.
c) 2 units of *X* and 2 units of *Y*.
d) 10 units of *X* and 10 units of *Y*.
e) 9 units of *X* and 8 units of *Y*.

Table 7.10

Units of *X*	Total utility (*X*)	Units of *Y*	Total utility (*Y*)
0	0	0	0
1	9	1	49
2	17	2	90
3	24	3	110
4	30	4	118
5	35	5	124
6	39	6	129
7	42	7	132
8	44	8	133
9	45	9	132
10	44	10	130

7.83
Correct: c)
Difficulty: 3
Page(s): 160
Scramble range: All
Topic: Utility maximization

7.83
Refer to Table 7.10. If both goods were free goods, and total utility is maximized, then
a) the marginal utility of *X* is maximized and the marginal utility of *Y* is maximized.
b) the marginal utility of *X* is minimized and the marginal utility of *Y* is minimized.
c) total utility equals 178.
d) the marginal utility of *X* does not equal the marginal utility of *Y*.
e) consumption of each good will be infinite.

7.84
Correct: c)
Difficulty: 4
Page(s): 160–162
Scramble range: All
Topic: Utility maximization

7.84
Refer to Table 7.10. Now suppose that the price of *X* is \$1 and the price of *Y* is \$1. How much of each should you purchase to maximize utility from a total expenditure of \$11?
a) 3 units of *X* and 9 units of *Y*.
b) 4 units of *X* and 7 units of *Y*.
c) 5 units of *X* and 6 units of *Y*.
d) 6 units of *X* and 5 units of *Y*.
e) 7 units of *X* and 4 units of *Y*.

7.85
Correct: b)
Difficulty: 5
Page(s): 158–168
Scramble range: All
Topic: Consumer choice

7.85
Consider a consumer deciding on the consumption of yogurt and chocolate-covered donuts. Pick the best statement.
a) Price is irrelevant, only utility matters.
b) If the price of donuts goes up, consumer surplus falls by an amount equal to the area to the left of the demand curve for donuts, between the old and the new prices.
c) A change in the price of yogurt will *always* affect the amount of donuts consumed.
d) As the amount of donuts consumed rises, the individual will always have the same marginal utility.
e) Equilibrium will occur when the utility of donuts per dollar spent on donuts equals the utility of yogurt per dollar spent on yogurt.

7.86
Correct: e)
Difficulty: 5
Page(s): 158–168
Scramble range: All
Topic: Consumer choice

7.86
Which one of the following statements is true?
a) Since consumers of a good consume this good until the price equals the value of the last unit, they clearly get no benefit from consuming this good.
b) Consumers choosing between goods *X* and *Y* will set $MU_X = MU_Y$.
c) The value of a good to a consumer is measured by the price.
d) Consumer surplus on a unit of a good will never be zero.
e) If the marginal utility per dollar of good *X* is less than the marginal utility per dollar of good *Y*, then the consumer should shift some spending from *X* to *Y*.

7.87
Correct: b)
Difficulty: 4
Page(s): 167–168
Scramble range: All
Topic: Consumer surplus

7.87
Consider Table 7.9. If price rises from $9 per unit to $12 per unit, then consumer surplus
a) rises from $9 to $12.
b) falls from $10 to $3.
c) stays the same.
d) falls from $6 to $3.
e) falls from $46 to $27.

7.88
Correct: c)
Difficulty: 4
Page(s): 161–162
Scramble range: All
Topic: Consumer equilibrium

7.88
Max enjoys windsurfing and snorkelling. His total utility from each activity is summarized by Table 7.11. Max has $35 to spend. Windsurfing equipment costs $10 per half-hour to rent, while snorkelling equipment costs $5 per half-hour. How long will Max choose to windsurf and to snorkel?
a) 1/2 hour windsurfing and 2 1/2 hours snorkelling.
b) 1 hour windsurfing and 1 1/2 hours snorkelling.
c) 1 1/2 hours windsurfing and 1/2 hour snorkelling.
d) 2 hours windsurfing and no hours snorkelling.
e) 1 hour windsurfing and 2 hours snorkelling.

7.89
Correct: d)
Difficulty: 5
Page(s): 161–162
Scramble range: All
Topic: Consumer equilibrium

8.89
Consider Max's utility of snorkelling and windsurfing in Table 7.11. Suppose that Max's total income is $55, and that equipment for windsurfing can be rented for $10 per half-hour, while snorkelling equipment rents for $5 per half-hour. What are Max's choices of time spent on the two activities?

a) 1/2 hour of windsurfing and 4 1/2 hours of snorkelling.
b) 1 hour of windsurfing and 3 1/2 hours of snorkelling.
c) 1 1/2 hours of windsurfing and 2 1/2 hours of snorkelling.
d) 2 hours of windsurfing and 1 1/2 hours of snorkelling.
e) 2 1/2 hours of windsurfing and 1/2 hour of snorkelling.

Table 7.11

Half-hours per month	Total utility from windsurfing	Total utility from snorkelling
1	60	20
2	110	38
3	150	53
4	180	64
5	200	70
6	210	70

Chapter 8 Possibilities, Preferences, and Choices

8.1 (SG 8.1)
Correct: b)
Difficulty: 2
Page(s): 175
Scramble range: All
Topic: Budget line

8.1
Which of the following statements best describes a consumer's budget line?
a) The amount of income a consumer can spend.
b) The limits to a consumer's consumption choices.
c) The desired level of consumption for a consumer.
d) The consumption choices made by a consumer.
e) The prices a consumer faces.

8.2
Correct: a)
Difficulty: 4
Page(s): 175
Scramble range: All
Topic: Budget line

8.2
In the construction of a budget line, we make all of the following assumptions *except*
a) prices of goods and services can be influenced by consumer bargaining.
b) prices of goods and services are fixed over time.
c) households have a limited amount of income to spend on the consumption of goods and services.
d) households are perfectly rational.
e) prices of goods and services are the same regardless of how many units are purchased.

8.3
Correct: a)
Difficulty: 2
Page(s): 175
Scramble range: All
Topic: Budget line

8.3
Choose the best answer: A household's consumption choices are limited by
a) its budget line.
b) its preferences.
c) income.
d) prices.
e) its ability to calculate.

8.4
Correct: e)
Difficulty: 2
Page(s): 175–176
Scramble range: All
Topic: Budget line

8.4
Guy has an income (I) of $50 with which he can purchase records (R) at $10 per album and compact discs (C) at $20 per disc. Which of the following best represents Guy's budget constraint?
a) $I = 10R + 20C$.
b) $50 = R + C$.
c) $I = 50 + R + C$.
d) $20I = R + 10C$.
e) $50 = 10R + 20C$.

8.5
Correct: c)
Difficulty: 3
Page(s): 176–177
Scramble range: All
Topic: Budget line

8.5
Sharon has an income of $500 with which she can purchase textbooks, groceries, and leisure activities. Textbooks cost $40 apiece, groceries cost $25 a purchase, and leisure costs $10 per hour. What is Sharon's real income in terms of an hour of leisure?
a) 12.5.
b) 20.
c) 50.
d) 35.
e) 6.67.

8.6
Correct: c)
Difficulty: 1
Page(s): 176
Scramble range: All
Topic: In/divisible goods

8.6
Which of the following would generally be considered an indivisible good?
a) Fuel oil.
b) Water.
c) Automobile.
d) Powdered sugar.
e) Electricity.

8.7
Correct: a)
Difficulty: 2
Page(s): 176
Scramble range: All
Topic: In/divisible goods

8.7
A divisible good is defined as a good
a) purchasable in any desired quantity.
b) manufacturable in any desired quantity.
c) manufactured in limited quantities.
d) both manufactured and purchased in any desired quantity.
e) that divides the household that owns it.

8.8
Correct: b)
Difficulty: 1
Page(s): 176
Scramble range: All
Topic: In/divisible goods

8.8
Electricity, telephone calls, and water would all be considered examples of
a) indivisible goods.
b) divisible goods.
c) limited goods.
d) inferior goods.
e) normal goods.

8.9
Correct: c)
Difficulty: 2
Page(s): 176
Scramble range: All
Topic: In/divisible goods

8.9
The budget line depicted in Figure 8.1 implicitly assumes that
a) apples cost the same as oranges.
b) a consumer will choose a point on the budget line.
c) apples and oranges are divisible goods.
d) the price of apples and oranges cannot change.
e) apples and oranges are complements.

Figure 8.1

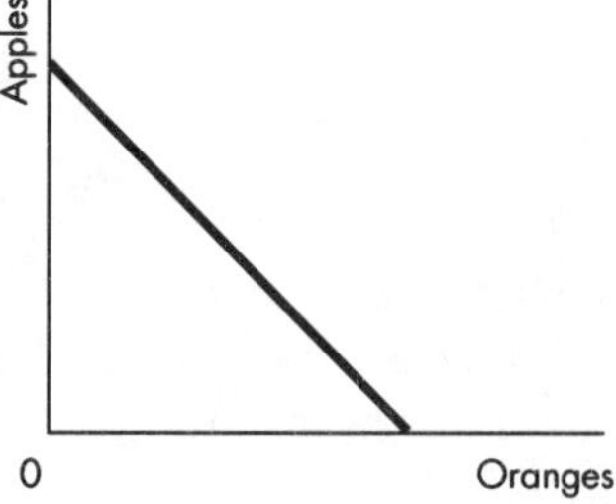

8.10
Correct: b)
Difficulty: 1
Page(s): 175–179
Scramble range: None
Topic: Budget line

8.10
Shelly's budget line is depicted in Figure 8.2. Which point(s) show unattainable consumption choices given her income and current prices?
a) *a.*
b) *b.*
c) *c.*
d) *d.*
e) *c* and *d.*

Figure 8.2

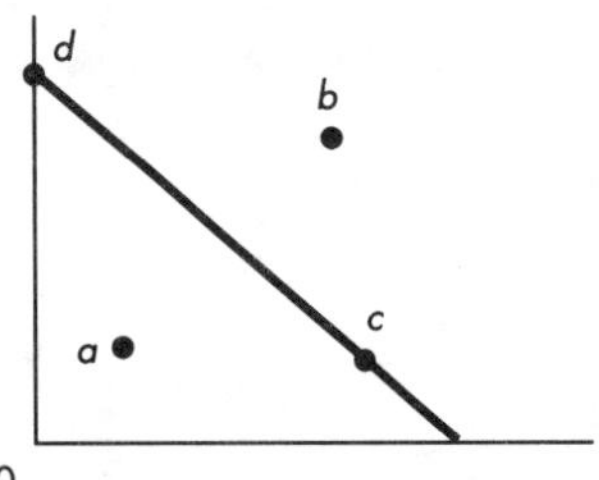

8.11
Correct: b)
Difficulty: 1
Page(s): 176
Scramble range: All
Topic: Budget line

8.11
The mathematical representation of the budget line is called the
a) budget surface.
b) budget equation.
c) affordable frontier.
d) budget isoquant.
e) production possibilities frontier.

8.12
Correct: a)
Difficulty: 1
Page(s): 176
Scramble range: All
Topic: Budget line

8.12
What is the relationship between the budget equation and the budget line?
a) The budget equation describes the budget line as a mathematical formula.
b) The budget line shows all possible consumption opportunities, while the budget equation gives the maximum possible consumption.
c) The budget line and budget equation both are determined by prices and income.
d) The budget line and budget equation both are determined by prices only.
e) There is no relationship.

8.13
Correct: b)
Difficulty: 2
Page(s): 176–177
Scramble range: All
Topic: Real income

8.13
David has an income of $30 with which he can buy movie tickets and bus tickets. If movie tickets cost $6 each and bus tickets cost $2 each, what is David's real income in terms of purchasable goods?
a) $30.
b) 5 movie tickets or 15 bus tickets.
c) $36.
d) $38.
e) $32.

8.14
Correct: e)
Difficulty: 2
Page(s): 177–179
Scramble range: All
Topic: Real income

8.14
Real income in terms of a good is defined as
a) income divided by the quantity consumed of a good.
b) the income of a producer of that good.
c) the budget equation.
d) dollar income unadjusted for inflation.
e) income divided by the price of a good.

8.15
Correct: d)
Difficulty: 3
Page(s): 177–179
Scramble range: All
Topic: Real income

8.15
Marie-Louise has an income of $10 and can buy either peanuts or popcorn. Peanuts cost $1 per bag and popcorn costs $2 per bag. What is Marie-Louise's real income in terms of popcorn?
a) 1/2 bag of popcorn.
b) 1 bag of popcorn.
c) 2 bags of popcorn.
d) 5 bags of popcorn.
e) 10 bags of popcorn.

8.16
Correct: c)
Difficulty: 3
Page(s): 177–179
Scramble range: All
Topic: Relative price

8.16
Lawrence has an income of $10 and can buy either peanuts or popcorn. Peanuts cost $1 per bag and popcorn costs $2 per bag. What is the relative price of peanuts in terms of popcorn?
a) 1 bag of popcorn.
b) 2 bags of popcorn.
c) 1/2 bag of popcorn.
d) 5 bags of popcorn.
e) $2.

8.17
Correct: b)
Difficulty: 1
Page(s): 177
Scramble range: All
Topic: Relative price

8.17
The price of one good divided by the price of another is called
a) an absolute price.
b) a relative price.
c) a marginal price.
d) a demand price.
e) a money price.

8.18
Correct: a)
Difficulty: 2
Page(s): 177
Scramble range: All
Topic: Relative price

8.18
Coffee sells for 25 cents a cup. Tea sells for 75 cents a cup. What is the price of tea relative to coffee?
a) 3.0.
b) 0.33.
c) 1.0.
d) 0.5.
e) 0.75.

8.19
Correct: a)
Difficulty: 3
Page(s): 177
Scramble range: All
Topic: Relative price

8.19
Choose the best response: The absolute value of the budget line slope is
a) the relative price of the good on the vertical axis.
b) the relative price of the good on the horizontal axis.
c) the absolute price of the good on the horizontal axis.
d) the real price of the good on the vertical axis.
e) the price of the good on the vertical axis.

8.20
Correct: a)
Difficulty: 5
Page(s): 177–179
Scramble range: All
Topic: Relative price

8.20
When speaking of the price of the good measured on the horizontal axis relative to the price of the good on the vertical axis, which statement is true?

a) The steeper the budget line slope, the more expensive the good on the horizontal axis.
b) The steeper the budget line slope, the less expensive the good on the horizontal axis.
c) The steeper the budget line slope, the more expensive the good on the vertical axis.
d) The slope of the budget line is independent of relative prices.
e) The flatter the budget line slope, the more expensive the good on the horizontal axis.

8.21
Correct: d)
Difficulty: 3
Page(s): 179
Scramble range: a)–d)
Topic: Preferences

8.21
Which of the following do economists *not* assume about preferences?

a) Preferences are not dependent upon the prices of goods.
b) Preferences are not dependent upon income.
c) More of any good is preferred to less of that good.
d) Preferences are unstable and change frequently.
e) Economists do not assume any of the above statements.

8.22
Correct: d)
Difficulty: 3
Page(s): 180–181
Scramble range: All
Topic: Indifference curve

8.22
Which of the indifference curves in Figure 8.3 violates the assumptions made about preferences?

a) (a).
b) (b) and (c).
c) (c).
d) (b).
e) (a) and (c).

Figure 8.3

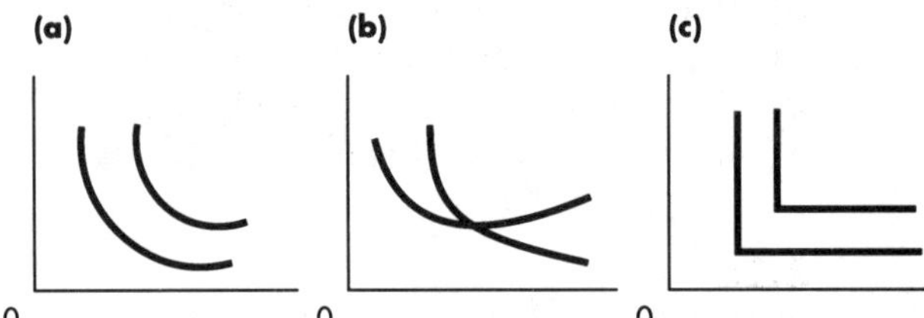

8.23
Correct: c)
Difficulty: 2
Page(s): 180
Scramble range: All
Topic: Indifference curve

8.23
An indifference curve is best defined as

a) a ranking of preferred consumption bundles.
b) a boundary line defining production possibilities.
c) the set of all bundles that the consumer enjoys equally well.
d) the level of consumption where a consumer is indifferent to receiving more consumption.
e) a boundary line between attainable and unattainable choices.

8.24
Correct: e)
Difficulty: 2
Page(s): 180
Scramble range: All
Topic: Preferences

8.24
A preference map is defined as
a) a series of points that represent levels of equal utility.
b) a single indifference curve.
c) the set of preferred indifference curves.
d) the marginal rate of substitution between goods.
e) a series of indifference curves.

8.25
Correct: b)
Difficulty: 2
Page(s): 181
Scramble range: All
Topic: Marginal rate of substitution

8.25
The marginal rate of substitution is defined as
a) the amount of good *Y* substituted for good *X* by a consumer.
b) the amount of good *Y* a consumer is willing to substitute for good *X* and stay at a given level of utility.
c) the feasible rate of substitution given prices.
d) the slope of the utility function.
e) the slope of the budget line.

8.26
Correct: d)
Difficulty: 5
Page(s): 181–182
Scramble range: All
Topic: Marginal rate of substitution

8.26
Which of the following statements is false?
a) If the indifference curve is steep, the marginal rate of substitution is high.
b) A low marginal rate of substitution implies a flat indifference curve.
c) A flat indifference curve implies a consumer must receive a large amount of good *X* to compensate for a small decrease in good *Y*.
d) A high rate of marginal substitution implies a consumer must receive a large amount of good *X* to compensate for a small decrease in good *Y*.
e) A high rate of marginal substitution implies a consumer must receive a small amount of good *X* to compensate for a large decrease in good *Y*.

8.27
Correct: a)
Difficulty: 1
Page(s): 181
Scramble range: All
Topic: Marginal rate of substitution

8.27
The slope of an indifference curve is defined as
a) the marginal rate of substitution.
b) the marginal rate of transformation.
c) the marginal propensity to consume.
d) the marginal propensity to substitute.
e) the relative price of good *Y*.

8.28
Correct: b)
Difficulty: 2
Page(s): 182
Scramble range: All
Topic: Marginal rate of substitution

8.28
The tendency for the marginal rate of substitution to decrease as a consumer moves along an indifference curve is known as
a) the law of demand.
b) the principle of diminishing marginal rate of substitution.
c) the principle of diminishing rates of substitution.
d) the income effect.
e) the principle of diminishing marginal utility.

8.29
Correct: e)
Difficulty: 2
Page(s): 183
Scramble range: All
Topic: Substitutes/ complements

8.29
Which of the diagrams in Figure 8.4 depicts perfect substitutes?
a) (a).
b) (c) and (d).
c) (c).
d) (d).
e) (b).

Figure 8.4

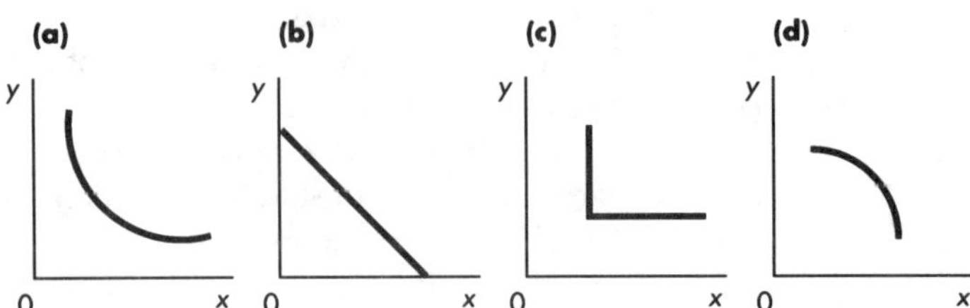

8.30
Correct: e)
Difficulty: 4
Page(s): 183
Scramble range: All
Topic: Substitutes

8.30
Which statement is true?
a) The closer two goods are to being substitutes, the smoother the indifference curve between the two goods.
b) The closer two goods are to being substitutes, the more L-shaped the indifference curve between the two goods.
c) Complements have a constant marginal rate of substitution.
d) Substitutes have a curved budget line.
e) The closer two goods are to being substitutes, the straighter the indifference curve between the two goods.

8.31
Correct: e)
Difficulty: 3
Page(s): 183
Scramble range: All
Topic: Substitutes

8.31
A constant marginal rate of substitution between two goods implies which of the following statements?
a) The goods are perfect complements.
b) The goods are imperfect substitutes.
c) The goods are both inferior.
d) One good is normal and one good is inferior.
e) The goods are perfect substitutes.

8.32
Correct: c)
Difficulty: 2
Page(s): 183
Scramble range: All
Topic: Substitutes/ complements

8.32
What is a distinguishing characteristic of complementary goods?
a) Straight-line indifference curves.
b) Perfectly smooth indifference curves.
c) L-shaped indifference curves.
d) Intersecting indifference curves.
e) Bowed-out indifference curves.

8.33
Correct: c)
Difficulty: 2
Page(s): 184
Scramble range: All
Topic: Consumer choice

8.33
A consumer's optimal consumption bundle will occur
a) inside the budget line.
b) outside the budget line.
c) on the budget line.
d) at a point that cannot be determined.
e) at a corner of the budget line, with only one good consumed.

8.34
Correct: d)
Difficulty: 2
Page(s): 184–185
Scramble range: All
Topic: Consumer choice

8.34
At the best affordable point, what is the relationship between the indifference curve and the budget line?
a) The level of the indifference curve equals the slope of the budget line.
b) The slope of the indifference curve exceeds the slope of the budget line.
c) The slope of the budget line exceeds the slope of the indifference curve.
d) The slope of the indifference curve equals the slope of the budget line.
e) The level of the indifference curve equals the level of the budget line.

8.35
Correct: c)
Difficulty: 3
Page(s): 184
Scramble range: None
Topic: Consumer choice

8.35
Which of the following is *not* an assumption of the model of consumer choice?
a) A household has a fixed income.
b) A household chooses its most preferred affordable combination of goods.
c) The slope of the indifference curve equals the slope of the budget line.
d) Indifference curves usually bow toward the origin.
e) Neither c) nor d).

8.36
Correct: a)
Difficulty: 3
Page(s): 184
Scramble range: None
Topic: Consumer choice

8.36
Jay has an income of $10 and can buy either peanuts or popcorn. Peanuts cost $1 per bag and popcorn costs $2 per bag. He chooses to consume 5 bags of peanuts and 2 bags of popcorn. What can we say about this consumption choice?
a) It in not optimal. He should consume more of either peanuts, popcorn, or both.
b) It is optimal and his marginal rate of substitution equals the slope of the budget line.
c) The consumption choice is on the budget line.
d) The consumption choice is beyond the budget line.
e) Both b) and c).

8.37
Correct: c)
Difficulty: 3
Page(s): 184
Scramble range: All
Topic: Consumer choice

8.37
Which of the following is true at the best affordable choice for a consumer?
a) Marginal rate of substitution exceeds the slope of the budget line.
b) Marginal rate of substitution is less than the ratio of prices.
c) Expenditures exhaust income.
d) The consumption choice is beyond the budget line.
e) Utility can be raised by altering the consumption bundle.

8.38
Correct: e)
Difficulty: 2
Page(s): 184
Scramble range: All
Topic: Consumer choice

8.38
What do all the different bundles represented by an indifference curve have in common?
a) The slope of the indifference curve equals the slope of the budget line.
b) The same quantity of both goods.
c) The same marginal rate of substitution.
d) Equal money expenditure.
e) The same level of utility.

8.39
Correct: b)
Difficulty: 3
Page(s): 184
Scramble range: All
Topic: Consumer choice

8.39
Which of the following is *not* an implication of the model of consumer choice?
a) The chosen consumption point is on the budget line.
b) Preferences do not change when prices and incomes change.
c) The chosen consumption point is on the highest affordable indifference curve.
d) At the chosen consumption point, the slope of the indifference curve equals the slope of the budget line.
e) A rise in income will raise the consumption of normal goods.

8.40
Correct: a)
Difficulty: 2
Page(s): 184
Scramble range: All
Topic: Consumer choice

8.40
At the best affordable point, which statement is true?
a) The slope of the indifference curve equals the slope of the budget line.
b) The marginal rate of substitution between two goods equals their absolute price.
c) The highest affordable indifference curve has the same intercept as the budget line.
d) The indifference curve maximizes marginal utility.
e) Some income is not spent.

8.41
Correct: b)
Difficulty: 1
Page(s): 187
Scramble range: All
Topic: Normal goods

8.41
Normal goods are defined as goods whose consumption
a) decreases as income increases.
b) increases as income increases.
c) decreases as prices increase.
d) increases as prices increase.
e) stays the same as income increases.

8.42
Correct: d)
Difficulty: 3
Page(s): 187
Scramble range: All
Topic: Normal goods

8.42
Peter's income increases and so does his consumption of both movies and pop, but his consumption of pop increases less than his consumption of movies. Which of the following statements is true?
a) Movies are inferior goods; pop is a normal good.
b) Movies are normal goods; pop is an inferior good.
c) Movies are inferior goods; pop is an inferior good.
d) Movies and pop are both normal goods.
e) Movies are normal goods, while we cannot tell about pop.

8.43
Correct: e)
Difficulty: 4
Page(s): 185–189
Scramble range: All
Topic: Normal goods

8.43
A consumer choosing between apples and oranges is at her best affordable point. Then the price of apples decreases. If both apples and oranges are normal goods, which of the following statements is true about her new best affordable point?
a) She will consume more apples and more oranges.
b) She will consume more apples and fewer oranges.
c) She will consume fewer apples and more oranges.
d) She will consume fewer apples and fewer oranges.
e) She will consume more apples, and we cannot tell for sure whether she will consume more or less oranges.

8.44
Correct: b)
Difficulty: 3
Page(s): 188
Scramble range: All
Topic: Normal goods

8.44
For a normal good, which statement is true?
a) The income effect dominates the substitution effect.
b) The income effect reinforces the substitution effect.
c) As income increases, consumption decreases.
d) As income increases, consumption remains constant.
e) As price decreases, we cannot tell whether consumption increases or decreases.

8.45
Correct: c)
Difficulty: 3
Page(s): 188–189
Scramble range: All
Topic: Inferior goods

8.45
For an inferior good, which statement is true?
a) The substitution effect is positive; as price increases, consumption increases.
b) The income effect is absent; as income increases, consumption remains constant.
c) The income effect moves in the opposite direction to the substitution effect.
d) The good has poor workmanship.
e) The substitution effect is negative; as price increases, consumption increases.

8.46
Correct: a)
Difficulty: 2
Page(s): 187
Scramble range: All
Topic: Inferior goods

8.46
Inferior goods are defined as goods whose consumption
a) decreases as income increases.
b) increases as income increases.
c) decreases as prices increase.
d) increases as prices increase.
e) is unchanged as prices increase.

8.47
Correct: a)
Difficulty: 1
Page(s): 187
Scramble range: All
Topic: Income effect

8.47
The change in consumption due to a change in income is known as the
a) income effect.
b) substitution effect.
c) normal effect.
d) inferior effect.
e) Giffen effect.

8.48
Correct: b)
Difficulty: 1
Page(s): 187
Scramble range: All
Topic: Income effect

8.48
The income effect is defined as the change in
a) consumption when prices change.
b) consumption when income changes.
c) prices when income changes.
d) utility when income changes.
e) utility when prices change.

8.49
Correct: b)
Difficulty: 2
Page(s): 187
Scramble range: a)–d)
Topic: Income effect

8.49
What is the relationship between goods and the income effect?
a) An inferior good has a positive income effect.
b) A normal good has a positive income effect.
c) An inferior good has a neutral income effect.
d) A normal good has a neutral income effect.
e) None of the above.

8.50
Correct: d)
Difficulty: 2
Page(s): 188–189
Scramble range: All
Topic: Income effect/ inferior goods

8.50
What is the distinguishing characteristic of inferior goods?
a) A negative substitution effect.
b) A positive income effect.
c) A positive substitution effect.
d) A negative income effect.
e) Upward sloping demand curves.

8.51
Correct: d)
Difficulty: 2
Page(s): 186–188
Scramble range: a)–d)
Topic: Income effect/ inferior goods

8.51
When Adil graduated from college and started working, his consumption of frozen zonkas (a meat substitute) went down. What kind of good is a zonka?
a) Normal.
b) Abnormal.
c) Superior.
d) Inferior.
e) None of the above.

8.52 (SG 8.16)
Correct: d)
Difficulty: 2
Page(s): 188–189
Scramble range: All
Topic: Substitution effect

8.52
The change in consumption due to a change in price, leaving utility unchanged, is known as the
a) income effect.
b) price effect.
c) marginal effect.
d) substitution effect.
e) Giffen effect.

8.53
Correct: e)
Difficulty: 3
Page(s): 188–189
Scramble range: All
Topic: Substitution effect

8.53
The substitution effect is defined as
a) the change in consumption when prices change.
b) the change in consumption when prices change, keeping income constant.
c) the decrease in consumption as prices decrease.
d) the increase in consumption as prices decrease.
e) the change in consumption when prices change, keeping utility constant.

8.54
Correct: a)
Difficulty: 2
Page(s): 189
Scramble range: All
Topic: Income/ substitution effect

8.54
A change in the price of a good will have what effect?
a) An income effect.
b) An increase in total utility.
c) A decrease in consumption.
d) An increase in marginal utility.
e) A Giffen effect.

8.55
Correct: c)
Difficulty: 2
Page(s): 189
Scramble range: All
Topic: Giffen good

8.55
A good whose quantity demanded increases as price increases is known as
a) an inverted good.
b) a perverse good.
c) a Giffen good.
d) a local good.
e) a normal good.

8.56
Correct: a)
Difficulty: 4
Page(s): 189
Scramble range: All
Topic: Income/ substitution effect

8.56
Suppose the price of potatoes falls and we see a decrease in the purchases of potatoes, what can we infer?
a) The income effect is negative and exceeds the substitution effect.
b) The income effect is negative and reinforces the substitution effect.
c) The income effect is positive and exceeds the substitution effect.
d) The income effect is positive and reinforces the substitution effect.
e) The income effect is negative and just offsets the substitution effect.

8.57
Correct: d)
Difficulty: 5
Page(s): 189
Scramble range: None
Topic: Income/ substitution effect

8.57
What is/are the implication(s) of a perfectly inelastic demand curve for a good?
a) The good is inferior.
b) The good is normal.
c) The income effect exactly offsets the substitution effect.
d) a) and c) only.
e) b) and c) only.

8.58
Correct: b)
Difficulty: 4
Page(s): 189
Scramble range: None
Topic: Income/ substitution effect

8.58
What is/are the implication(s) of a perfectly elastic demand curve for a good?
a) The good is inferior.
b) The good is normal.
c) The income effect exactly offsets the substitution effect.
d) a) and c) only.
e) b) and c) only.

8.59
Correct: e)
Difficulty: 2
Page(s): 189
Scramble range: All
Topic: Substitution effect

8.59
Which of the following is always true of the substitution effect?
a) It leads to a positive income effect.
b) It is positive.
c) It decreases consumption.
d) It leads to a negative income effect.
e) It is negative.

8.60
Correct: b)
Difficulty: 3
Page(s): 189
Scramble range: All
Topic: Income effect

8.60
When Denise graduated from college and started working, her consumption of xundas decreased sharply. What statement must be true about xundas?
a) They have a positive substitution effect.
b) They have a negative income effect.
c) They have a positive income effect.
d) They have a neutral substitution effect.
e) They are a normal good.

8.61
Correct: e)
Difficulty: 5
Page(s): 188–189
Scramble range: All
Topic: Income/ substitution effect

8.61
Refer to Figure 8.5. Initially Lucien, is consuming *X* at point *a*. Then the price of *X* increases and he moves to point *b*. Which statement is true?
a) *Y* is a normal good, *X* is an inferior good.
b) *X* is a normal good, *Y* is a Giffen good.
c) *X* is a normal good, *Y* is a normal good.
d) *Y* is a superior good, *X* is a normal good.
e) *X* is a normal good, *Y* could be either an inferior or a normal good, we cannot tell from the diagram.

Figure 8.5

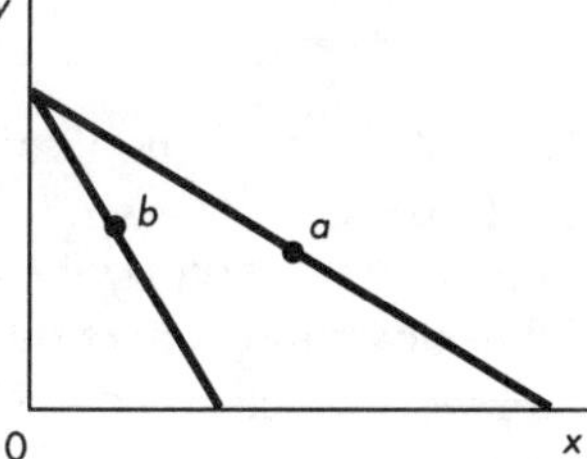

8.62
Correct: c)
Difficulty: 2
Page(s): 189
Scramble range: All
Topic: Substitution effect

8.62
The price of a good increases relative to other goods. Which of the following statements must be true?
a) The income effect is negative.
b) The income effect is positive.
c) The substitution effect is negative.
d) The substitution effect is positive.
e) The income effect is neutral.

8.63
Correct: a)
Difficulty: 4
Page(s): 189
Scramble range: All
Topic: Income/ substitution effect

8.63
Suppose all prices double and that income doubles. Which statement is true?
a) The best affordable point remains the same.
b) The slope of the budget line increases.
c) The slope of the budget line decreases.
d) The budget line moves away from the origin.
e) The consumption of normal goods will rise.

8.64
Correct: c)
Difficulty: 2
Page(s): 191
Scramble range: All
Topic: Labour supply

8.64
In determining labour supply, economists assign what price to an hour of leisure?
a) 10 percent of income.
b) 0.
c) The opportunity cost of leisure.
d) The marginal tax rate.
e) The value of time spent watching TV.

8.65
Correct: a)
Difficulty: 4
Page(s): 191
Scramble range: All
Topic: Labour supply

8.65
In determining labour supply, the highest possible indifference curve is attained by
a) equating the marginal rate of substitution between consumption and leisure and the wage rate relative to the prices of consumption goods.
b) equating the marginal rate of substitution between leisure and consumption and the wage rate.
c) equating the cost of labour and the wage rate.
d) equating the price of labour and the wage rate.
e) equating the cost of goods and the wage rate.

8.66
Correct: d)
Difficulty: 3
Page(s): 191
Scramble range: All
Topic: Labour supply

8.66
Which statement is always true?
a) The higher the wage rate, the less people will work.
b) The higher the wage rate, the lower is the price of leisure.
c) The higher the wage rate, the more people will work.
d) The higher the wage rate, the higher is the price of leisure.
e) The higher the wage rate, then the price of leisure can be higher or lower.

8.67
Correct: b)
Difficulty: 4
Page(s): 191
Scramble range: All
Topic: Labour supply

8.67
The economic explanation of a shorter modern work week (as compared with a nineteenth-century work week) is
a) the domination of the income effect by the substitution effect.
b) the domination of the substitution effect by the income effect.
c) people prefer shorter work weeks now.
d) labour is a normal good.
e) leisure is an inferior good.

8.68
Correct: d)
Difficulty: 5
Page(s): 191
Scramble range: All
Topic: Labour supply/ income effect

8.68
When the income effect in labour supply dominates the substitution effect, what is true of the supply curve for labour?
a) It is vertical.
b) It is positively sloped.
c) It is flat.
d) It is negatively sloped.
e) It can be either positively or negatively sloped.

8.69
Correct: c)
Difficulty: 3
Page(s): 195
Scramble range: All
Topic: Saving

8.69
In determining the allocation between current consumption and future consumption, what is the interpretation of the interest rate?
a) It is the absolute price of future consumption.
b) It is the absolute price of current consumption.
c) It is the relative price of current consumption versus future consumption.
d) It is the cost of future consumption.
e) It is the value of future consumption.

8.70
Correct: e)
Difficulty: 2
Page(s): 177–179
Scramble range: All
Topic: Opportunity cost

8.70
Henry has an income of $10 and can buy either peanuts or popcorn. Peanuts cost $1 per bag and popcorn costs $2 per bag. What is Henry's opportunity cost of a bag of popcorn?
a) 1 bag of peanuts.
b) $2.
c) 5 bags of peanuts.
d) 10 bags of peanuts.
e) 2 bags of peanuts.

8.71 (SG 8.2)
Correct: c)
Difficulty: 1
Page(s): 175
Scramble range: All
Topic: Budget line

8.71
The budget line depends on
a) income.
b) prices.
c) income and prices.
d) preferences.
e) preferences, income, and prices.

8.72
Correct: e)
Difficulty: 2
Page(s): 177
Scramble range: All
Topic: Budget equation

8.72
Let I = income, Q_X = quantity of good X and Q_Y = quantity of good Y, P_X = price of good X and P_Y = price of good Y. The budget equation is given by
a) $I = P_X/Q_X + P_Y/Q_Y$.
b) $I = Q_X + P_Y Q_Y/P_X$.
c) $Q_X = I + (P_X/P_Y)Q_Y$.
d) $Q_X = Q_Y + (P_X/P_Y)I$.
e) $I = P_X Q_X + P_Y Q_Y$.

8.73 (SG 8.4)
Correct: e)
Difficulty: 2
Page(s): 177–179
Scramble range: All
Topic: Budget line

8.73
If the price of the good measured on the vertical axis increases, the budget line will
a) become steeper.
b) swivel around the original consumption point.
c) shift inward but parallel to the original budget line.
d) shift outward but parallel to the original budget line.
e) become flatter.

8.74 (SG 8.5)
Correct: d)
Difficulty: 2
Page(s): 178–179
Scramble range: All
Topic: Budget line

8.74
If income increases, the budget line will
a) become steeper.
b) become flatter.
c) shift inward but parallel to the original budget line.
d) shift outward but parallel to the original budget line.
e) swivel around the original consumption point.

8.75 (SG 8.9)
Correct: e)
Difficulty: 3
Page(s): 177–179
Scramble range: All
Topic: Budget line

8.75
Bill consumes apples and bananas. Suppose Bill's income doubles and the prices of apples and bananas also double. Bill's budget line will
a) swivel around the original consumption point.
b) shift out but not change slope.
c) shift out and become steeper.
d) shift out and become flatter.
e) remain unchanged.

8.76 (SG 8.10)
Correct: c)
Difficulty: 2
Page(s): 180
Scramble range: All
Topic: Indifference curve

8.76
Which of the following statements is not true?
a) Indifference curves are negatively sloped.
b) A preference map consists of a series of nonintersecting indifference curves.
c) Indifference curves are bowed out.
d) The slope of an indifference curve is given by the marginal rate of substitution.
e) Indifference curves have the same level of utility all along them.

8.77
Correct: d)
Difficulty: 3
Page(s): 181
Scramble range: All
Topic: Indifference map

8.77
Figure 8.6 gives three indifference curves for Brenda. Which of the following is not true?
a) Brenda would be equally happy consuming at either point *b* or point *c*.
b) Brenda prefers consuming at point *b* to consuming at point *a*.
c) Brenda prefers consumption at point *d* to consumption at either point *b* or point *c*.
d) The marginal rate of substitution is higher at point *c* than at point *b*.
e) Brenda prefers consuming at point *d* to consuming at point *a*.

Figure 8.6

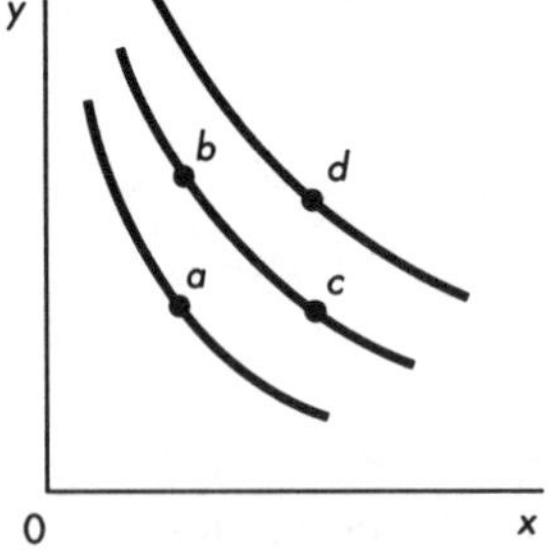

8.78 (SG 8.11)
Correct: c)
Difficulty: 3
Page(s): 181
Scramble range: All
Topic: Marginal rate of substitution

8.78

Suppose good *X* is measured on the horizontal axis and good *Y* on the vertical axis. The marginal rate of substitution is best defined as

a) the relative price of *X* in terms of good *Y*.
b) the relative price of *Y* in terms of good *X*.
c) the rate at which a consumer will give up good *Y* in order to obtain more of *X* and remain indifferent.
d) the rate at which a consumer will give up good *X* in order to obtain more of *Y* and remain indifferent.
e) the slope of the budget line.

8.79 (SG 8.12)
Correct: d)
Difficulty: 4
Page(s): 181
Scramble range: None
Topic: Marginal rate of substitution

8.79

In general, as a consumer moves along an indifference curve, increasing consumption of good *X* (measured on the horizontal axis),

a) more of *Y* must be given up for each additional unit of *X*.
b) less of *Y* must be given up for each additional unit of *X*.
c) the marginal rate of substitution declines.
d) both b) and c).
e) both a) and c).

8.80 (SG 8.13)
Correct: e)
Difficulty: 3
Page(s): 182–183
Scramble range: None
Topic: Substitutes

8.80

Which of the following statements is true of the indifference curves for two goods that are perfect substitutes?

a) The indifference curves are negatively sloped straight lines.
b) The indifference curves are L-shaped.
c) The marginal rate of substitution is constant.
d) The indifference curves have regular bowed-in shapes.
e) Both a) and c).

8.81
Correct: b)
Difficulty: 2
Page(s): 184–187
Scramble range: All
Topic: Income/ substitution effect

8.81

Which of the following statements is not a characteristic of the best affordable consumption point?

a) The point is on the budget line.
b) The income effect is equal to the substitution effect.
c) The marginal rate of substitution between the two goods is equal to their relative price.
d) The highest affordable indifference curve has the same slope as the budget line.
e) The consumer cannot improve his or her choice.

8.82
Correct: a)
Difficulty: 5
Page(s): 180
Scramble range: All
Topic: Budget line

8.82

Consider the budget line and indifference curve in Figure 8.7. If the price of good *X* is $1, then the price of good *Y* is

a) $0.75.
b) $1.
c) $1.25.
d) $2.
e) $1.33.

Figure 8.7

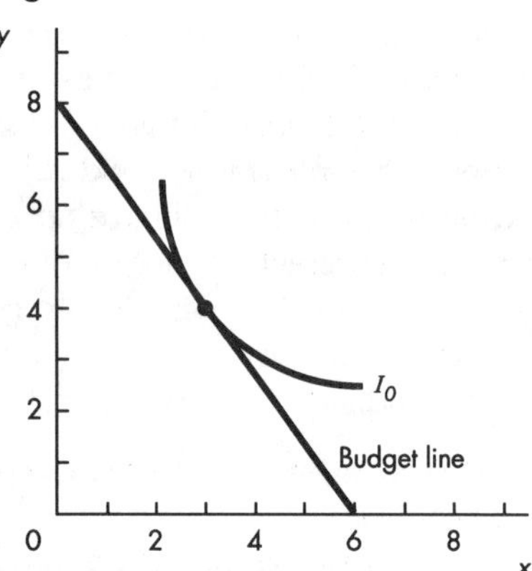

8.83
Correct: c)
Difficulty: 3
Page(s): 181–185
Scramble range: All
Topic: Marginal rate of substitution

8.83
Consider the budget line and indifference curve in Figure 8.7. At the best affordable point, the marginal rate of substitution is
a) 1/2.
b) 2.
c) 4/3.
d) 3/4.
e) 4.

8.84 (SG 8.16)
Correct: b)
Difficulty: 1
Page(s): 189
Scramble range: All
Topic: Substitution effect

8.84
When the price of a good changes, we call the change in consumption that leaves the consumer indifferent, the
a) utility effect.
b) substitution effect.
c) income effect.
d) price effect.
e) Giffen effect.

8.85 (SG 8.17)
Correct: d)
Difficulty: 4
Page(s): 189
Scramble range: All
Topic: Normal goods

8.85
If the price of a normal good rises, the income effect
a) will increase consumption of the good and the substitution effect will decrease consumption.
b) will decrease consumption of the good and the substitution effect will increase consumption.
c) and the substitution effect will both increase consumption of the good.
d) and the substitution effect will both decrease consumption of the good.
e) will increase consumption of the good, while the substitution effect will have an uncertain impact.

8.86 (SG 8.18)
Correct: c)
Difficulty: 4
Page(s): 189
Scramble range: All
Topic: Substitution effect

8.86
If the price of good *X* (measured on the horizontal axis) falls, the substitution effect is indicated by movement to a
a) higher indifference curve.
b) lower indifference curve.
c) flatter part of the same indifference curve.
d) steeper part of the same indifference curve.
e) lower part of the budget line.

8.87
Correct: b)
Difficulty: 2
Page(s): 190
Scramble range: All
Topic: Assumptions

8.87
Which of the following is not an assumption of the indifference curve model of consumer behaviour?
a) Consumers cannot influence the price of goods.
b) Consumers compute marginal rates of substitution.
c) A consumer has a given level of income to allocate among various goods.
d) A consumer chooses the most preferred affordable combination of goods.
e) A consumer can choose between different combinations of goods.

8.88
Correct: a)
Difficulty: 2
Page(s): 189
Scramble range: All
Topic: Price change/ budget line

8.88
Consider an initial budget line labelled *RS* in Figure 8.8. What would cause the budget line to shift to *RT*?
a) An increase in the price of good *X*.
b) A decrease in the price of good *X*.
c) An increase in the price of good *Y*.
d) A decrease in the price of good *Y*.
e) A decrease in income.

Figure 8.8

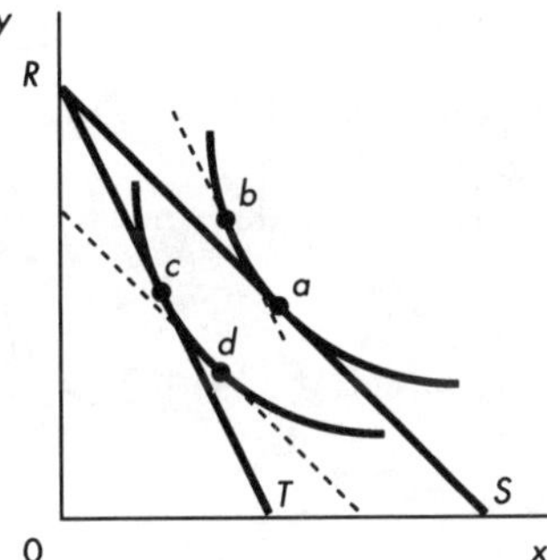

8.89
Correct: e)
Difficulty: 3
Page(s): 189
Scramble range: All
Topic: Substitution effect

8.89
Consider an initial budget line labelled *RS* in Figure 8.8. If the price of good *X* rises so that the budget line shifts to *RT*, the substitution effect is illustrated by the move from
a) *a* to *d*.
b) *b* to *c*.
c) *d* to *c*.
d) *a* to *c*.
e) *a* to *b*.

8.90
Correct: d)
Difficulty: 3
Page(s): 189
Scramble range: All
Topic: Income effect

8.90
Consider an initial budget line labelled *RS* in Figure 8.8. If the price of good *X* rises so that the budget line shifts to *RT*, the income effect is illustrated by the move from
a) *a* to *b*.
b) *b* to *d*.
c) *d* to *a*.
d) *b* to *c*.
e) *c* to *d*.

8.91
Correct: b)
Difficulty: 3
Page(s): 191
Scramble range: All
Topic: Labour supply

8.91
An increase in the quantity of labour supplied
a) will always be the result of an increase in wages.
b) is the same as an decrease in the quantity of leisure demanded.
c) is the result of the substitution effect of a decrease in wages.
d) cannot be explained using indifference curve analysis.
e) can always be explained as the result of an increase in nonwage income.

8.92 (SG 8.23)
Correct: d)
Difficulty: 3
Page(s): 195
Scramble range: All
Topic: Historical wages

8.92
Over the past hundred years, the quantity of labour supplied has fallen as wages have increased. This indicates that, as the wages have increased, the income effect
a) and the substitution effect have both operated to discourage leisure.
b) and the substitution effect have both operated to encourage leisure.
c) discouraging leisure has been dominated by the substitution effect encouraging leisure.
d) encouraging leisure has dominated the substitution effect discouraging leisure.
e) encouraging leisure has been dominated by the substitution effect discouraging leisure.

8.93
Correct: d)
Difficulty: 2
Page(s): 175
Scramble range: All
Topic: Budget line

8.93
The budget line for a household does not depend on
a) income.
b) price of food.
c) price of housing.
d) preferences.
e) income and prices.

8.94
Correct: a)
Difficulty: 3
Page(s): 176
Scramble range: All
Topic: Budget equation

8.94
Let $I = \$100$, Q_X = quantity of good X and Q_Y = quantity of good Y, $P_X = \$4$ and $P_Y = \$5$. The budget equation is given by
a) $100 = 4Q_X + 5Q_Y$.
b) $100 = Q_X + 4\ Q_Y/5$.
c) $Q_X = 100 + (4/5)Q_Y$.
d) $Q_X = Q_Y + (4/5)I$.
e) $Q_Y = Q_X + (4/5)I$.

8.95
Correct: c)
Difficulty: 2
Page(s): 177–179
Scramble range: All
Topic: Budget line

8.95
If income decreases, the budget line will
a) become steeper.
b) become flatter.
c) shift inward but parallel to the original budget line.
d) shift outward but parallel to the original budget line.
e) swivel around the original consumption point.

8.96
Correct: e)
Difficulty: 5
Page(s): 177
Scramble range: All
Topic: Budget line

8.96
Originally, Sarah Student has an income of $100, and purchases 5 rock tapes at $10 each and 10 pizzas at $5 each. Next, the government taxes pizzas and raises their price to $10 each. Simultaneously, they give Sarah a grant of $50 in income to make up for this. As a result, Sarah's budget line will

a) become steeper.
b) become flatter.
c) shift inward but parallel to the original budget line.
d) shift outward but parallel to the original budget line.
e) swivel around the original consumption choice.

8.97
Correct: e)
Difficulty: 4
Page(s): 175
Scramble range: All
Topic: Budget line

8.97
Bill consumes apples and bananas. Measure apples on the vertical axis and bananas on the horizontal axis. Suppose Bill's income doubles and the prices of apples doubles while the price of bananas triples. Bill's budget line will

a) remain unchanged.
b) shift out but not change slope.
c) shift out and become steeper.
d) shift out and become flatter.
e) shift in and become steeper.

8.98
Correct: d)
Difficulty: 2
Page(s): 180
Scramble range: All
Topic: Indifference curve

8.98
Which of the following statements is true?

a) Indifference curves are positively sloped.
b) A preference map consists of a series of intersecting indifference curves.
c) Indifference curves are bowed out.
d) The slope of an indifference curve is given by the marginal rate of substitution.
e) Indifference curves are always tangent to the budget line.

8.99
Correct: d)
Difficulty: 3
Page(s): 183
Scramble range: None
Topic: Substitutes

8.99
Which of the following statements is true of the indifference curves for two goods that are close but not perfect substitutes?

a) The indifference curves are negatively sloped straight lines.
b) The indifference curves are L-shaped.
c) The marginal rate of substitution is constant.
d) The marginal rate of substitution diminishes as substitution occurs.
e) Both a) and c).

8.100
Correct: d)
Difficulty: 2
Page(s): 189
Scramble range: All
Topic: Income/ substitution effect

8.100
Which of the following statements is a characteristic of the best affordable consumption point?

a) The point is to the right of the budget line.
b) The income effect is equal to the substitution effect.
c) The marginal rate of substitution between the two goods is equal to the difference between the relative prices.
d) The highest affordable indifference curve has the same slope as the budget line.
e) The point is to the left of the budget line.

8.101
Correct: e)
Difficulty: 5
Page(s): 187
Scramble range: All
Topic: Inferior goods

8.101
If the price of an inferior good rises, the income effect
a) will have an uncertain effect on consumption of the good and the substitution effect will decrease consumption.
b) will decrease consumption of the good and the substitution effect will decrease consumption.
c) and the substitution effects will both increase consumption of the good.
d) and the substitution effects will both decrease consumption of the good.
e) will increase consumption of the good and the substitution effect will decrease consumption.

8.102
Correct: d)
Difficulty: 4
Page(s): 189
Scramble range: All
Topic: Substitution effect

8.102
If the price of good *X* (measured on the horizontal axis) rises, the substitution effect is indicated by movement to a
a) higher indifference curve.
b) lower indifference curve.
c) flatter part of the same indifference curve.
d) steeper part of the same indifference curve.
e) different point on the budget line.

8.103
Correct: e)
Difficulty: 5
Page(s): 184–185
Scramble range: All
Topic: Consumer choice

8.103
Consider Fact 8.1. Marc's original marginal rate of substitution was
a) not calculable with the information given.
b) equal to 2 beer given up for each bag of chips gained.
c) equal to 1 beer given up for each bag of chips gained.
d) equal to 10 beer given up for each bag of chips gained.
e) equal to 1/2 beer given up for each bag of chips gained.

Fact 8.1
Marc has an income of $20. Beer costs $1 per can, and chips cost 50 cents a bag. Originally, Marc choose to consume 10 cans of beer and 20 bags of chips. Then prices change, such that the price of beer rises to $1.50 per can and the price of chips falls to 25 cents a bag.

8.104
Correct: e)
Difficulty: 5
Page(s): 175–179
Scramble range: All
Topic: Budget line

8.104
Consider Fact 8.1. In the new situation, Marc's budget line will
a) shift inwards, with the slope the same.
b) shift outwards, with the slope the same.
c) shift inwards, with a steeper slope.
d) shift inwards, with a flatter slope.
e) swivel around the original consumption point.

8.105
Correct: b)
Difficulty: 5
Page(s): 185–190
Scramble range: All
Topic: Consumer choice

8.105
Consider Fact 8.1. In the new situation, Marc
a) will consume more beer, more chips, and be better off.
b) will consume less beer, more chips, and be better off.
c) will consume less beer, more chips, and be worse off.
d) will consume less beer, less chips, and be worse off.
e) consume more beer, less chips, and be better off.

8.106
Correct: d)
Difficulty: 5
Page(s): 185–190
Scramble range: None
Topic: Consumer choice

8.106
Susy Sayles works in the Trendy Tools Store, where her salary consists solely of an income of $300 per week. The price of clothing is $10 per unit, and the price of tacos is $5 per week. Suzy initially consumes 10 units of clothing a week, and 40 units of food. Suzy then shifts jobs to the Coolchick Clothing Store, where she earns a salary of only $250 per week, but where the store gives her a discount on clothing, such that each unit she buys now costs only $5. Select the best statement.

a) Suzy will alter her combination of tacos and clothing purchased.
b) Suzy will not alter her combination of tacos and clothing purchased.
c) Suzy is better off.
d) Both a) and c).
e) Both b) and c).

8.107
Correct: d)
Difficulty: 4
Page(s): 175–179
Scramble range: All
Topic: Budget line

8.107
Points on a particular budget line

a) represent the various combinations of goods that could be purchased at various income levels.
b) represent various combinations of goods that could be purchased by a household as the prices of these goods vary.
c) represent various combinations of goods whose total cost is less than or equal to the household's income.
d) show the various combinations of goods that a household could purchase if it spends all of its income on these goods.
e) shows the various combinations of goods that have equal levels of utility.

Chapter 9 Organizing Production

9.1
Correct: b)
Difficulty: 1
Page(s): 209
Scramble range: All
Topic: Firms

9.1
An economist's generic name for a business organization is
a) a multinational.
b) a firm.
c) a corporation.
d) a partnership.
e) an organization.

9.2
Correct: d)
Difficulty: 1
Page(s): 209
Scramble range: All
Topic: Firms

9.2
Which of the following would an economist *not* consider to be a firm?
a) A multinational corporation.
b) A local fast-food restaurant.
c) A freelance photographer.
d) A state government.
e) A writer.

9.3
Correct: c)
Difficulty: 2
Page(s): 209
Scramble range: All
Topic: Firms

9.3
Revenue is defined as
a) the amount remaining after factor costs are paid.
b) the payments made to factors of production.
c) receipts from sales of goods and services.
d) the difference between receipts and payments.
e) the difference between costs and receipts.

9.4
Correct: d)
Difficulty: 1
Page(s): 209
Scramble range: All
Topic: Firms

9.4
The difference between a firm's revenue and payments is known as
a) receipts.
b) cost.
c) sales.
d) profits.
e) total revenue.

9.5
Correct: c)
Difficulty: 1
Page(s): 209
Scramble range: All
Topic: Firms

9.5
Which of the following statements best describes the problem of the firm?
a) To maximize revenues.
b) To maximize costs while minimizing revenues.
c) To maximize profits.
d) To minimize costs.
e) To minimize risk.

9.6
Correct: b)
Difficulty: 1
Page(s): 209
Scramble range: All
Topic: Firms

9.6
The payments made by a firm for its factors of production are called
a) revenues.
b) costs.
c) profits.
d) receipts.
e) losses.

9.7
Correct: c)
Difficulty: 1
Page(s): 209
Scramble range: a)–d)
Topic: Firms/ organization

9.7
Which of the following is *not* a main form of a business organization?
a) Proprietorships.
b) Partnerships.
c) Town councils.
d) Corporations.
e) All of the above are a main form of a business organization.

9.8
Correct: a)
Difficulty: 1
Page(s): 210
Scramble range: All
Topic: Firms/ organization

9.8
The most common type of firm is
a) proprietorship.
b) corporation.
c) partnership.
d) multinational.
e) not-for-profit organization.

9.9
Correct: b)
Difficulty: 1
Page(s): 210
Scramble range: All
Topic: Firms/ organization

9.9
A firm with a single owner with unlimited liability is known as
a) a corporation.
b) a proprietorship.
c) a limited partnership.
d) an unlimited partnership.
e) a cooperative.

9.10
Correct: c)
Difficulty: 2
Page(s): 210
Scramble range: All
Topic: Firms/ organization

9.10
The legal responsibility for liabilities incurred by a proprietorship falls upon
a) the shareholders.
b) the partners of the proprietorship.
c) the owner.
d) the creditors.
e) the managers.

9.11
Correct: e)
Difficulty: 2
Page(s): 210
Scramble range: All
Topic: Firms/ organization

9.11
The profits of a proprietorship are
a) taxed twice.
b) subject to a corporate tax.
c) not taxed.
d) exempt from taxation.
e) treated as personal income.

9.12
Correct: a)
Difficulty: 2
Page(s): 210
Scramble range: All
Topic: Firms/ organization

9.12
Typical examples of a partnership would include which of the following?
a) A law firm.
b) A corner drugstore.
c) An automobile manufacturer.
d) A bank.
e) A freelance writer.

9.13 (SG9.2)
Correct: a)
Difficulty: 2
Page(s): 210
Scramble range: All
Topic: Firms/ organization

9.13
A firm with two or more owners who have unlimited liability is known as a
a) partnership.
b) proprietorship.
c) corporation.
d) retail coop.
e) not-for-profit firm.

9.14
Correct: d)
Difficulty: 2
Page(s): 210
Scramble range: All
Topic: Firms/ organization

9.14
In a partnership, each partner is legally liable for
a) all the debts of the partnership.
b) the fraction of the debts corresponding to the fraction of ownership.
c) 50 percent of the debt.
d) all debts of the partnership up to the personal wealth of the partner.
e) an amount of debt limited to the amount of his or her investment in the partnership.

9.15
Correct: b)
Difficulty: 2
Page(s): 211
Scramble range: All
Topic: Firms/ organization

9.15
The vast majority of all business sales is accounted for by
a) partnerships.
b) corporations.
c) proprietorships.
d) not-for-profit organizations.
e) cooperatives.

9.16
Correct: c)
Difficulty: 4
Page(s): 211
Scramble range: All
Topic: Firms/ organization

9.16
Susan invests $1,000 to buy shares of TooNew stock. The company declares bankruptcy leaving many debts unpaid including Susan's $1,000 investment. Susan has a personal net worth of $50,000. What will be Susan's net worth if TooNew has total unpaid debts of $30,000?
a) $19,000.
b) $21,000.
c) $49,000.
d) $51,000.
e) $20,000.

9.17
Correct: b)
Difficulty: 1
Page(s): 210
Scramble range: All
Topic: Firms/ organization

9.17
A fraction of the stock of a corporation is known as a
a) piece.
b) share.
c) contract.
d) part.
e) dividend.

9.18
Correct: d)
Difficulty: 1
Page(s): 211
Scramble range: All
Topic: Firms/organization

9.18
Which of the following would *not* be considered a "not-for-profit" firm?
a) A university.
b) A mutual insurance company.
c) A church.
d) A grocery store.
e) A college.

9.19
Correct: e)
Difficulty: 3
Page(s): 210
Scramble range: All
Topic: Firms/organization

9.19
Hari has discovered a unique and efficient method of mowing lawns for large firms. However, he will need unskilled labour to implement his plan. What type of firm will Hari likely form?
a) A corporation.
b) A cooperative.
c) A partnership.
d) A not-for-profit.
e) A proprietorship.

9.20 (SG 9.7)
Correct: b)
Difficulty: 2
Page(s): 212
Scramble range: All
Topic: Business finance

9.20
The owner's stake in a business is called
a) a premium.
b) equity.
c) profit.
d) liability.
e) risk.

9.21
Correct: c)
Difficulty: 3
Page(s): 212
Scramble range: All
Topic: Business finance

9.21
Which of the following methods of raising funds are not generally available to nonincorporated firms?
a) Borrowing from a bank.
b) Borrowing on credit cards.
c) Issuing stock.
d) Deferred billing by input suppliers.
e) Borrowing from friends and relatives.

9.22
Correct: e)
Difficulty: 3
Page(s): 213
Scramble range: All
Topic: Business finance

9.22
A corporation selling a bond is analogous to
a) a bank loaning money to an individual.
b) a bank loaning money to a partnership.
c) buying stock on the stock market.
d) a fund-raising drive by a university.
e) an individual receiving money in exchange for an IOU.

9.23 (SG 9.8)
Correct: d)
Difficulty: 2
Page(s): 213
Scramble range: All
Topic: Business finance

9.23
A bond is defined as
a) a right to the profits of a corporation.
b) a stake in a partnership.
c) a portion of the stock of the firm.
d) an obligation to pay at some future date(s).
e) a right to some share of the profits of a corporation.

9.24
Correct: a)
Difficulty: 2
Page(s): 213
Scramble range: All
Topic: Business finance

9.24
The money paid to a bondholder between the date of issue and the redemption date is called the
a) coupon payment.
b) dividend.
c) profit.
d) redemption value.
e) liability.

9.25
Correct: d)
Difficulty: 3
Page(s): 214
Scramble range: All
Topic: Present value

9.25
Suppose the interest rate is 5 percent per year. What is the present value of $210 to be received 1 year from today?
a) $210.
b) $215.
c) $220.50.
d) $200.
e) $42.

9.26
Correct: e)
Difficulty: 4
Page(s): 214
Scramble range: All
Topic: Present value

9.26
The present value of $50 to be received next year is $40. What is the interest rate?
a) 10 percent.
b) 8 percent.
c) 20 percent.
d) 50 percent.
e) 25 percent.

9.27
Correct: b)
Difficulty: 2
Page(s): 214
Scramble range: All
Topic: Present value

9.27
What will be the value in 1 year of $25 invested today at an annual interest rate of 5 percent?
a) $25.
b) $26.25.
c) $27.50.
d) $30.
e) $23.81.

9.28
Correct: c)
Difficulty: 1
Page(s): 216
Scramble range: All
Topic: Present value

9.28
The total current value of a stream of payments is known as
a) current value.
b) future value.
c) net present value.
d) market value.
e) profits.

9.29
Correct: c)
Difficulty: 2
Page(s): 213
Scramble range: All
Topic: Business finance

9.29
Which of the following statements describes bondholders?
a) They have more control over the company than do stockholders.
b) They receive a greater share of the profit than do stockholders.
c) They get paid before stockholders.
d) They face greater risks in the event of bankruptcy than stockholders.
e) They bear unlimited liability.

9.30 (SG 9.13)
Correct: a)
Difficulty: 2
Page(s): 216
Scramble range: All
Topic: Business finance

9.30
Which type of stock gives the holder voting rights at stockholder meetings?
a) Common stock.
b) Deferred stock.
c) Preferred stock.
d) Convertible stock.
e) Equity stock.

9.31
Correct: c)
Difficulty: 1
Page(s): 216
Scramble range: All
Topic: Business finance

9.31
Which type of stock gives the holder no voting rights but gives prior claim on dividends at a fixed rate?
a) Common stock.
b) Deferred stock.
c) Preferred stock.
d) Convertible stock.
e) Equity stock.

9.32
Correct: e)
Difficulty: 3
Page(s): 217
Scramble range: All
Topic: Business finance

9.32
BadNews Inc. goes bankrupt. What is the order of the claimants on the remaining assets of the firm?
a) (1) common stockholders (2) bondholders (3) preferred stockholders.
b) (1) bondholders (2) common stockholders (3) preferred stockholders.
c) (1) preferred stockholders (2) common stockholders (3) bondholders.
d) (1) common stockholders (2) preferred stockholders (3) bondholders.
e) (1) bondholders (2) preferred stockholders (3) common stockholders.

9.33
Correct: d)
Difficulty: 2
Page(s): 217
Scramble range: All
Topic: Business finance/ convertible stock

9.33
A financial instrument that pays fixed coupon payments like a bond and offers the option of converting to a fixed number of stocks is known as
a) common stock.
b) preferred stock.
c) bonded stock.
d) convertible stock.
e) a convertible bond.

9.34
Correct: b)
Difficulty: 4
Page(s): 217
Scramble range: All
Topic: Stock price

9.34
Shortterm Inc. is a corporation that will cease to exist in three years. Shortterm will pay a dividend of $100 per share at the end of each of the three remaining years. No additional payments will ever be made. What is the value of a share of Shortterm stock if the annual interest rate is 5 percent?
a) $250.
b) $272.
c) $300.
d) $288.
e) $286.

9.35
Correct: d)
Difficulty: 4
Page(s): 217
Scramble range: None
Topic: Stock price

9.35
What is the most an investor would be willing to pay for a stock that will pay $210 next year and nothing before or after?
a) $200 regardless of the interest rate.
b) $200 if the interest rate is 5 percent per year.
c) $190.91 if the interest rate is 10 percent per year.
d) b) and c) only.
e) None of the above.

9.36
Correct: b)
Difficulty: 4
Page(s): 217
Scramble range: All
Topic: Stock price

9.36
A high price–earnings ratio can be interpreted to predict which of the following?
a) Prices and earnings are currently high relative to past values which means high potential for growth.
b) Prices are high relative to earnings so investors expect future earnings and dividends to grow quickly.
c) Earnings are high relative to share price so investors expect future earnings and dividends to grow quickly.
d) Future profits will grow slowly with a correspondingly low future dividend.
e) The stock is overpriced.

9.37
Correct: a)
Difficulty: 4
Page(s): 217–218
Scramble range: All
Topic: Stock price

9.37
If investors expected a share of common stock to pay exactly the same dividend as that guaranteed to a share of preferred stock, what will be the relationship between the share prices of the common and preferred stock?
a) The common stock will have the higher price.
b) The preferred stock will have the higher price.
c) They both will have the same share price.
d) The answer cannot be determined.
e) It depends on the rate of interest.

9.38
Correct: b)
Difficulty: 5
Page(s): 217
Scramble range: All
Topic: Stock price

9.38
Hansel and Gretel each had $1,000 with which to purchase stocks. Hansel chose a stock that paid dividends each year of $10 per share. Gretel instead chose a stock that paid dividends each year of $20 per share. At an annual interest rate of 10 percent, which of the following statements is true?
a) Hansel will purchase more shares and will receive a greater return than Gretel.
b) Hansel will purchase more shares and then receive a return equal to Gretel.
c) Gretel will purchase more shares and then receive a return equal to Hansel.
d) Gretel will purchase more shares and then receive a greater return than Hansel.
e) Hansel and Gretel will purchase the same number of shares, and Gretel will receive a greater return.

9.39
Correct: d)
Difficulty: 2
Page(s): 218–219
Scramble range: All
Topic: Costs

9.39
Historical costs value resources at the
a) value of all forgone opportunities.
b) value of the best forgone opportunity.
c) value of the goods at current prices.
d) value of the goods at the time of purchase.
e) net present value.

9.40
Correct: e)
Difficulty: 2
Page(s): 218–219
Scramble range: All
Topic: Costs

9.40
Surindar bought a hammer last year for $3. This year the same hammer sells for $4. Another hammer of a higher quality sold for $5 last year and now sells for $7. What is the historical cost of Surindar's hammer?
a) $2.
b) $7.
c) $4.
d) $5.
e) $3.

9.41
Correct: a)
Difficulty: 3
Page(s): 218–219
Scramble range: All
Topic: Costs

9.41
Which of the following is a likely source of differences between historical costs and opportunity costs?
a) Costs of durable factors of production.
b) Costs of electricity.
c) Raw materials.
d) Costs of unskilled labour.
e) Costs of heating.

9.42
Correct: b)
Difficulty: 2
Page(s): 218
Scramble range: All
Topic: Costs/durable goods

9.42
A good that is not consumed in a single period is known as
a) a long-term good.
b) a durable good.
c) a lump good.
d) an intermediate good.
e) a net present value.

9.43
Correct: e)
Difficulty: 2
Page(s): 219
Scramble range: All
Topic: Costs/durable goods

9.43
Which of the following is not an example of a durable good?
a) Buildings.
b) Automobiles.
c) Tractors.
d) Roads.
e) Gasoline.

9.44
Correct: c)
Difficulty: 3
Page(s): 219
Scramble range: All
Topic: Costs/historical

9.44
Quickstart Inc. just spent $50,000 out of profits to build a new building. If the depreciation rate is 15 percent per year, what would be the historical cost of the building at the end of the first year?
a) $50,000.
b) $42,500.
c) $7,500.
d) $0.
e) $43,478.

9.45
Correct: b)
Difficulty: 2
Page(s): 220
Scramble range: All
Topic: Costs/ opportunity

9.45
Which of the following statements about an implicit rent is true?
a) It is the total value of a durable good.
b) It is the price a company would be willing to pay if it had to rent.
c) It is equivalent to the notion of an explicit cost.
d) It is the amount paid for the use of land or buildings.
e) It is the net present value of a cost.

9.46
Correct: a)
Difficulty: 1
Page(s): 219
Scramble range: All
Topic: Costs/ depreciation

9.46
The difference in the price of a new car and the price of the car one year later is known as
a) economic depreciation.
b) physical depreciation.
c) economic deterioration.
d) physical deterioration.
e) present value.

9.47
Correct: c)
Difficulty: 2
Page(s): 219
Scramble range: All
Topic: Costs/ depreciation

9.47
Economic depreciation is defined as
a) the loss of physical productivity of an asset.
b) the increase in asset productivity of a durable good.
c) the change in the market price of an asset.
d) the deterioration of the physical appearance of an asset.
e) a change in prices.

9.48
Correct: b)
Difficulty: 3
Page(s): 219
Scramble range: All
Topic: Costs/ depreciation

9.48
Marc bought a new car last year for $10,000. He can now sell the car for $8,500. To buy this year's model of the same car he would have to pay $11,000. What is the one-year amount of economic depreciation?
a) $2,500.
b) $1,500.
c) $1,000.
d) $10,000.
e) $3,500.

9.49
Correct: e)
Difficulty: 3
Page(s): 219
Scramble range: All
Topic: Costs/ depreciation

9.49
Marc bought a new car last year for $10,000. He can now sell the car for $8,500. To buy this year's model of the same car he would have to pay $11,000. What is the imputed cost of using the car for one year at a 0 percent interest rate?
a) $2,500.
b) $3,500.
c) $1,000.
d) $10,000.
e) $1,500.

9.50
Correct: c)
Difficulty: 5
Page(s): 219–220
Scramble range: All
Topic: Costs/implicit

9.50
Marc bought a new car last year for $10,000. He can now sell the car for $8,500. To buy this year's model of the same car he would have to pay $11,000. Suppose also that Marc took out a $9,000 loan to buy the car, which had to be paid back in yearly instalments of $3,300 per year over three years. What is the imputed cost of the first year's use of the car?
a) $2,800.
b) $1,300.
c) $1,800.
d) $13,300.
e) $4,800.

9.51
Correct: a)
Difficulty: 2
Page(s): 219
Scramble range: All
Topic: Costs/implicit

9.51
The implicit cost to a firm of owning a building is defined as
a) the sum of depreciation costs and interest costs.
b) depreciation costs only.
c) interest costs only.
d) the cost of an alternative building.
e) the rent paid on the building.

9.52
Correct: b)
Difficulty: 2
Page(s): 220
Scramble range: All
Topic: Costs/inflation

9.52
What is true of the effect of inflation on the calculation of cost?
a) Inflation never affects opportunity cost calculations.
b) An increase in prices that leaves relative prices unchanged never affects opportunity cost calculations.
c) An increase in prices that changes relative prices will leave opportunity cost calculations unaffected.
d) Inflation always raises costs and reduces profits.
e) Inflation always lowers costs and increases profits.

9.53
Correct: a)
Difficulty: 4
Page(s): 220
Scramble range: All
Topic: Costs/sunk

9.53
The opportunity cost (in dollars) of using equipment that is functioning but has no resale value is
a) zero.
b) the cost of replacing the machine.
c) the original purchase price of the machine.
d) the original purchase price of the machine less accumulated depreciation.
e) the original purchase price of the machine plus accumulated depreciation.

9.54
Correct: a)
Difficulty: 3
Page(s): 220
Scramble range: All
Topic: Costs/sunk

9.54
A sunk cost is defined as
a) the historical cost of buying a good that currently has no resale value.
b) the cost of replacing a good.
c) the value of the best forgone alternative.
d) the amount of depreciation of a good.
e) the value of a destroyed good.

9.55
Correct: c)
Difficulty: 4
Page(s): 220
Scramble range: All
Topic: Costs/sunk

9.55
Several years ago Jones Inc. bought a copy machine which is still working but has no resale value. The cost of a new copier is $10,000 while the original cost of the machine was only $2,000. If the amount of depreciation recorded by the accountants is $1,500, what is the sunk cost of the machine?
a) $1,000.
b) $500.
c) $2,000.
d) $8,000.
e) $0.

9.56
Correct: c)
Difficulty: 2
Page(s): 220
Scramble range: All
Topic: Costs/inventories

9.56
Raw and semifinished materials held in temporary storage by a firm for use in production at a later date are known as
a) surplus goods.
b) excess goods.
c) inventory goods.
d) opportunity goods.
e) sunk goods.

9.57
Correct: e)
Difficulty: 3
Page(s): 219–220
Scramble range: All
Topic: Costs/inventories

9.57
For which of the following types of firms would the historical cost and opportunity cost probably differ substantially?
a) A local supermarket.
b) A fast-food restaurant.
c) An electrical power company.
d) A gasoline station.
e) A jewellery store.

9.58
Correct: b)
Difficulty: 3
Page(s): 220
Scramble range: All
Topic: Costs/inventories

9.58
If we assume no inflation, which of the following is the correct method of computing the opportunity cost of using an item in inventory?
a) The value of the newest item in the inventory.
b) The value of a replacement item.
c) The value of the oldest item in the inventory.
d) The value of the raw materials used to make the item.
e) The book value of the item.

9.59
Correct: c)
Difficulty: 4
Page(s): 220
Scramble range: All
Topic: Costs/opportunity

9.59
Big Truck, Inc., builds large diesel trucks. In building the final trucks, Big Truck draws upon an inventory of assembled engines. The total cost of raw materials used in each engine is constant at $500 but the price Big Truck pays for an engine varies. The purchase price of the oldest engine in inventory was $2,200 while the price of the newest was $3,000. The current price of an engine is $2,900. What is the opportunity cost of one engine in inventory?
a) $500.
b) $2,200.
c) $2,900.
d) $3,000.
e) $2,400.

9.60
Correct: b)
Difficulty: 3
Page(s): 219
Scramble range: All
Topic: Costs/opportunity

9.60
An expert electrician decides to quit his current job which pays $40,000 per year. He can then take a job with another firm for $45,000 per year or work for himself. What is the opportunity cost of working for himself?
a) $40,000.
b) $45,000.
c) $5,000.
d) $85,000.
e) Whatever profits he earns.

9.61
Correct: e)
Difficulty: 3
Page(s): 220–221
Scramble range: All
Topic: Costs/opportunity

9.61
Joe Smith and his son own a business called Smith's which has built a reputation for good service. Joe retires and his son changes the name to Sonny's. If the company was worth $100,000 before the name change and $95,000 immediately after the name change, what is the opportunity cost of the name "Smith's"?
a) $100,000.
b) $95,000
c) $90,000.
d) $195,000.
e) $5,000.

9.62
Correct: d)
Difficulty: 3
Page(s): 221
Scramble range: All
Topic: Costs/economic

9.62
In general, what is the relative value of economic profit versus historical profit?
a) Economic profit is higher since it includes more revenues.
b) Economic profit is higher since it includes the cost of inflation.
c) Economic profit is lower since it includes more revenues.
d) Economic profit is lower since it includes more costs.
e) Economic profit is lower sinces it includes the cost of depreciation.

9.63
Correct: c)
Difficulty: 2
Page(s): 221
Scramble range: All
Topic: Economic profit

9.63
Economic profit is defined as the difference between revenues and
a) historical costs of production.
b) interest costs of production.
c) opportunity costs of production.
d) excess costs of production.
e) explicit costs of production.

9.64
Correct: a)
Difficulty: 4
Page(s): 221
Scramble range: All
Topic: Economic profit

9.64
Gerald is a freelance writer who could work for a newspaper at $25,000 a year but instead works for himself for $40,000 a year. His only business expenses are $1,000 for writing materials and $12,000 for rent. What is Gerald's economic profit for working as a freelance writer?
a) $2,000.
b) $28,000.
c) $15,000.
d) $25,000.
e) $27,000.

9.65
Correct: d)
Difficulty: 4
Page(s): 225
Scramble range: All
Topic: Transaction costs

9.65
Which of the following is not generally a transaction cost?
a) The fee to a broker for buying stocks.
b) The cost of a lawyer who drafts a contract.
c) The cost of hiring someone to find you a supplier of raw materials.
d) The cost of the owner's time in a proprietorship.
e) The cost of phone calls made to find a buyer.

9.66
Correct: a)
Difficulty: 2
Page(s): 225
Scramble range: All
Topic: Economies of scale

9.66
When per-unit cost of a good decreases as the production rate increases, economists refer to this as
a) economies of scale.
b) economies of scope.
c) inverse production.
d) efficient production.
e) diminishing marginal rate of substitution.

9.67
Correct: d)
Difficulty: 3
Page(s): 225
Scramble range: All
Topic: Economies of scale

9.67
Which of the following would not likely be a firm with economies of scale?
a) An electrical production plant.
b) A steel mill.
c) A telephone company.
d) A firm that produces handmade cabinetry.
e) A multi-store photography firm.

9.68
Correct: a)
Difficulty: 3
Page(s): 225
Scramble range: All
Topic: Team production

9.68
A firm with a sales department, a production department, and a marketing department is an example of
a) team production.
b) joint production.
c) economies of scale.
d) economies of scope.
e) transactions costs.

9.69
Correct: b)
Difficulty: 2
Page(s): 225
Scramble range: All
Topic: Team production

9.69
Team production is defined as
a) a production process with decreasing costs per unit as production scale increases.
b) a production process with individuals specializing in mutually supportive tasks.
c) the production that results from market activity.
d) the cost of organizing an assembly line.
e) the lower costs resulting from organizing a firm versus using the market.

9.70
Correct: d)
Difficulty: 4
Page(s): 222–223
Scramble range: None
Topic: Efficiency

9.70
Firm *A* can produce a unit of output with 10 hours of labour and 5 units of material. Firm *B* can produce a unit of output with 5 hours of labour and 10 units of material. Firm *C* can produce a unit of output with 10 hours of labour and 10 units of material. If the prices of labour and material are $10 and $5, respectively, which firm(s) is (are) technologically efficient?
a) *A*.
b) *B*.
c) *C*.
d) *A* and *B* only.
e) *A* and *C* only.

9.71
Correct: d)
Difficulty: 3
Page(s): 209
Scramble range: All
Topic: Allocation of resources

9.71
Which of the following statements is *not* true of firms?
a) Firms are like markets since they are another institution for coordinating economic activity.
b) Firms organize factors of production in order to produce goods and services.
c) Firms sell goods and services.
d) Efficient firms can eliminate scarcity.
e) Firms can take advantage of economies of scale.

9.72 (SG 9.2)
Correct: b)
Difficulty: 1
Page(s): 209
Scramble range: All
Topic: Partnership

9.72
A firm with two or more owners with joint unlimited liability is a
a) proprietorship.
b) partnership.
c) conglomerate.
d) corporation.
e) multinational.

9.73 (SG 9.3)
Correct: c)
Difficulty: 1
Page(s): 210
Scramble range: a)–c)
Topic: Corporations

9.73
Which of the following types of firms issue(s) shares of stock?
a) Proprietorship.
b) Partnership.
c) Corporation.
d) All of the above.
e) None of the above.

9.74 (SG 9.4)
Correct: a)
Difficulty: 2
Page(s): 210
Scramble range: All
Topic: Stockholders

9.74
Which of the following is the residual claimant of a corporation?
a) Stockholders.
b) Bondholders.
c) Banks and other creditors.
d) Government taxing agencies.
e) Managers.

9.75 (SG 9.5)
Correct: e)
Difficulty: 3
Page(s): 211
Scramble range: All
Topic: Disadvantage of corporation

9.75
Which of the following is a *disadvantage* of a corporation relative to a proprietorship or partnership?
a) Owners have unlimited liability.
b) Corporations hire professional managers.
c) Difficult to raise money.
d) Perpetual life.
e) Profits are taxed as corporate profits and as dividend income to stockholders.

9.76 (SG 9.6)
Correct: a)
Difficulty: 1
Page(s): 210
Scramble range: All
Topic: Proprietorships

9.76
Most firms are
a) proprietorships.
b) partnerships.
c) corporations.
d) not-for-profit firms.
e) cooperatives.

9.77 (SG 9.7)
Correct: d)
Difficulty: 2
Page(s): 212
Scramble range: All
Topic: Equity capital

9.77
The owner's stake in a business is called
a) net worth.
b) redemption value.
c) total liabilities.
d) equity capital.
e) a transaction cost.

9.78 (SG 9.8)
Correct: c)
Difficulty: 2
Page(s): 213
Scramble range: All
Topic: Bonds

9.78
A bond
a) represents a right to share in the profits of a corporation.
b) allows the holder to vote for corporate directors.
c) is a promise by a corporation to pay given amounts of money on specified future dates.
d) pays dividends to the issuer.
e) is a residual claim.

9.79 (SG 9.9)
Correct: d)
Difficulty: 4
Page(s): 214
Scramble range: All
Topic: Present value

9.79
The present value of a future payment of money will be higher
a) the higher the interest rate or the further in the future the payment.
b) the lower the interest rate or the further in the future the payment.
c) the higher the interest rate or the nearer the date of the future payment.
d) the lower the interest rate or the nearer the date of the future payment.
e) the higher the interest rate, regardless of how near the date of the future payment.

9.80 (SG 9.10)
Correct: a)
Difficulty: 3
Page(s): 214
Scramble range: All
Topic: Present value

9.80
If the rate of interest is 10 percent per year, the present value of $100 in one year is
a) $90.91.
b) $95.45.
c) $100.00.
d) $110.00.
e) $90.00.

9.81 (SG 9.11)
Correct: b)
Difficulty: 3
Page(s): 214
Scramble range: All
Topic: Present value

9.81
If the interest rate is 10 percent per year, the present value of $100 in *two* years is
a) $80.00.
b) $82.64.
c) $90.91.
d) $120.00.
e) $121.00.

9.82 (SG 9.12)
Correct: e)
Difficulty: 3
Page(s): 214
Scramble range: All
Topic: Present value

9.82
If the present value of $500 in one year is $463, the interest rate is
a) 5 percent per year.
b) 7.4 percent per year.
c) 10 percent per year.
d) 12 percent per year.
e) 8 percent per year.

9.83 (SG 9.14)
Correct: c)
Difficulty: 4
Page(s): 217
Scramble range: All
Topic: Expected market price

9.83
XYZ Corporation is expected to pay a dividend of $5 a share every year into the indefinite future. If the interest rate is 5 percent per year, the market price of a share of XYZ stock will be
a) $5.
b) $50.
c) $100.
d) $1,000.
e) $10.

9.84 (SG 9.16)
Correct: e)
Difficulty: 4
Page(s): 219
Scramble range: All
Topic: Depreciation

9.84
A building cost $100,000 to build. The conventional depreciation allowance is 5 percent per year. At the end of the first year the market value of the building is $80,000. For the first year, the depreciation cost would be
a) $20,000 to an accountant or an economist.
b) $5,000 to an accountant or an economist.
c) $20,000 to an accountant but $5,000 to an economist.
d) $30,000 to an accountant but $5,000 to an economist.
e) $5,000 to an accountant but $20,000 to an economist.

9.85 (SG 9.17)
Correct: c)
Difficulty: 3
Page(s): 219
Scramble range: All
Topic: Opportunity cost

9.85
John operates a business and pays himself a salary of $20,000 per year. He was offered a job that paid $30,000 per year. The opportunity cost of John's time in the business is
a) $10,000.
b) $20,000.
c) $30,000.
d) $50,000.
e) $0.

9.86
Correct: b)
Difficulty: 3
Page(s): 219
Scramble range: All
Topic: Costs/historical

9.86
In general, historical costs include
a) implicit costs only.
b) explicit costs only.
c) both implicit and explicit costs.
d) both implicit and imputed costs.
e) sunk costs only.

9.87
Correct: d)
Difficulty: 3
Page(s): 219
Scramble range: All
Topic: Historical/accounting profit

9.87
"Historical" or accounting profit will generally be greater than economic profit because
a) accountants tend to overestimate revenue.
b) economists tend to overestimate cost.
c) accountants typically ignore explicit costs.
d) historical cost is generally less than opportunity cost.
e) accountants ignore depreciation.

9.88
Correct: a)
Difficulty: 3
Page(s): 223
Scramble range: All
Topic: Technical and economic efficiency

9.88
Which of the following statements is *not* true?
a) A production process is technologically efficient only if it is producing a given output at the lowest possible cost.
b) If a process is economically efficient, it must be technologically efficient as well.
c) Economic efficiency depends on the relative price of inputs, while technological efficiency does not.
d) Economically efficient firms will be more likely to survive than economically inefficient firms.
e) Technologically efficient firms are more likely to survive than technologically inefficient firms.

9.89
Correct: b)
Difficulty: 2
Page(s): 224
Scramble range: a)–d)
Topic: Firm efficiency

9.89
Which of the following is *not* a reason for firms frequently being more efficient than the market as a coordinator of economic activity?
a) Firms have lower transactions costs.
b) Firms have higher monitoring costs.
c) Firms have economies of scale.
d) Firms have economies of team production.
e) None of the above is a reason for firms frequently being more efficient than the market.

9.90 (SG 9.22)
Correct: c)
Difficulty: 3
Page(s): 225
Scramble range: All
Topic: Economies of scale

9.90
Economies of scale exist when
a) the cost of finding a trading partner is low.
b) a firm's decision to hire additional inputs does not result in an increase in the price of inputs.
c) the cost of producing a unit of output falls as the output rate increases.
d) the firm is too large and too diversified.
e) the firm is too small and too specialized.

9.91
Correct: e)
Difficulty: 3
Page(s): 209
Scramble range: All
Topic: Allocation of resources

9.91
Which of the following statements is true of firms?
a) Firms are markets in and of themselves.
b) Firms do not organize factors of production in order to produce goods and services.
c) Firms are buyers of goods and services.
d) Efficient firms can eliminate scarcity.
e) Firms decide on their organization and management structure.

9.92
Correct: c)
Difficulty: 2
Page(s): 211
Scramble range: a)–d)
Topic: Limited liability

9.92
Which of the following types of firms has limited liability?
a) Proprietorship.
b) Partnership.
c) Corporation.
d) Conglomerate.
e) None of the above.

9.93
Correct: d)
Difficulty: 3
Page(s): 211
Scramble range: All
Topic: Advantage of corporations

9.93
Which of the following is an advantage of a corporation relative to a proprietorship or partnership?
a) Owners have unlimited liability.
b) Profits are taxed as corporate profits and as dividend income to stockholders.
c) Difficult to raise money.
d) Perpetual life.
e) Complex management structure.

9.94
Correct: a)
Difficulty: 2
Page(s): 210
Scramble range: All
Topic: Proprietorships

9.94
Proprietorships
a) are the most common of all ways business firms organize.
b) are no different than partnerships.
c) always bring a higher return to owners than corporations.
d) are not-for-profit firms.
e) are typically the largest firms in terms of sales.

9.95
Correct: a)
Difficulty: 2
Page(s): 213
Scramble range: All
Topic: Equity capital

9.95
Equity capital is
a) the owner's stake in a business.
b) the same thing as net worth.
c) the same thing as redemption value.
d) always greater than 50 percent.
e) equivalent to bond capital.

9.96
Correct: e)
Difficulty: 3
Page(s): 217
Scramble range: All
Topic: Preferred stock

9.96
Preferred stock
a) gives the owner final residual claim.
b) allows the holder to vote for corporate directors.
c) is a promise by a corporation to pay given amounts of money on specified future dates.
d) pays dividends to the issuer.
e) represents a right to share in the profits of a corporation.

9.97
Correct: a)
Difficulty: 4
Page(s): 216
Scramble range: All
Topic: Present value

9.97
The present value of a future payment of money will be lower
a) the higher the interest rate or the further in the future the payment.
b) the lower the interest rate or the further in the future the payment.
c) the higher the interest rate or the nearer the date of the future payment.
d) the lower the interest rate or the nearer the date of the future payment.
e) the lower the interest rate, regardless of how near the date of the future payments is.

9.98
Correct: e)
Difficulty: 4
Page(s): 216
Scramble range: All
Topic: Present value

9.98
If the rate of interest is 15 percent per year, the present value of $200 in two years is
a) $170.00.
b) $185.00.
c) $173.91.
d) $264.50.
e) $151.23.

9.99
Correct: a)
Difficulty: 3
Page(s): 216
Scramble range: All
Topic: Present value

9.99
If the present value of $1,000 in one year is $800, the interest rate is
a) 25 percent per year.
b) 8 percent per year.
c) 10 percent per year.
d) 12 percent per year.
e) 125 percent per year.

9.100
Correct: e)
Difficulty: 4
Page(s): 218–222
Scramble range: All
Topic: Profits

9.100
Consider the decision of Michael Marvellous to leave his job as a buyer for a major department store (earning $67,000 per year), and start his own ritzy men's store in downtown Regina. He invests $280,000 of his own money (previously earning 11 percent interest per year in Canada Savings Bonds). In his first year of operation, the firm makes $1 million in revenue. The rent on the store plus costs of inventory plus worker's wages totals $940,000, and he keeps $40,000 as his own salary. Michael declares to his economist wife, Ethel Excellent, that he had had a profitable year, with positive profits. Ethel calculates his accounting and economic profits, and declares that he has earned __________ in accounting profits, and __________ in economic profits.
a) $20,000; –$7,000.
b) $20,000; –$7,000.
c) $60,000; –$7,000.
d) –$7,000; $20,000.
e) $20,000; –$37,800.

9.101
Correct: e)
Difficulty: 5
Page(s): 218–222
Scramble range: All
Topic: Profits

9.101
The ABC company purchases some computers, to be used in the production of CD players. Once used, the computers will be useless after one year. They pay $5 million for the computers, and it is *expected* that the computers (the only input) will produce $6 million worth of CD players. However, after they are purchased, the company finds that the computers are better than they originally thought — they are capable of producing $7 million worth of computers. In addition, this increased productivity is known to others, and therefore the resale value of the computers (unused) has risen to $8 million. Select the best statement.
a) The ABC company should produce the CD players, since the economic profits will be $1 million.
b) The ABC company should produce the CD players, since the economic profits will be $2 million.
c) The ABC company should produced the CD players, since the economic profits will be $3 million.
d) The ABC company should not produce the CD players, since the economic profits are actually losses of $2 million — they should sell the computers instead.
e) The ABC company should not produce the CD players, and instead should sell the computers because the economic profits are actually economic losses of $1 million.

9.102
Correct: d)
Difficulty: 5
Page(s): 218–222
Scramble range: None
Topic: Profits

9.102
Wendy Widget left her $18,000 per year job, and invested $300,000 of her own savings in a Balloon Greetings Firm which she proceeds to run. In the first year, she paid herself no salary and earned $52,000 in accounting profit. She expects this situation to continue. Select the best statement.

a) If the rate of interest is 10 percent, she earned negative economic profits.
b) If the rate of interest is 20 percent, she earned positive economic profits.
c) Even if being an entrepreneur gives her positive utility, Wendy should sell her firm and go back to work at her original job, if the rate of interest is 10 percent.
d) If being an entrepreneur gives Wendy neither positive nor negative utility, she should keep the firm going if the rate of interest is 10 percent.
e) Both a) and c).

9.103
Correct: e)
Difficulty: 4
Page(s): 222–224
Scramble range: None
Topic: Efficiency

9.103
Consider Fact 9.1. Which of the three production methods is technologically inefficient?

a) *A.*
b) *B.*
c) *C.*
d) All three methods are inefficient.
e) None of the three methods is inefficient.

Fact 9.1
Consider the following three methods of doing your tax return. Method *A* involves a personal computer (cost equal to $1,000) and 1 hour of your time. Method *B* involves a calculator (cost equal to $30) and 12 hours of your time. Method *C* involves pen and paper (cost equal to $1) and 2 days (16 hours) of your time.

9.104
Correct: d)
Difficulty: 5
Page(s): 222–224
Scramble range: a)–c)
Topic: Efficiency

9.104
Consider Fact 9.1. Choose the best statement.

a) When your wage rate is $5 per hour, the economically efficient method is method *C.*
b) When your wage rate is $50, the economically efficient method is method *B.*
c) When your wage rate is $500, the economically efficient method is method *A.*
d) All of the above.
e) None of the above.

Chapter 10 **Output and Costs**

10.1
Correct: b)
Difficulty: 2
Page(s): 231
Scramble range: All
Topic: Constraints/ market

10.1
A firm's market constraints are the conditions under which it can
a) convert inputs into output.
b) buy its inputs and sell its output.
c) issue stock market instruments.
d) produce salable products from the factors of production.
e) substitute between capital and labour.

10.2
Correct: c)
Difficulty: 2
Page(s): 231
Scramble range: All
Topic: Constraints/ technology

10.2
Any feasible way that inputs can be converted into output is called
a) economic efficiency.
b) a constraint.
c) a technique.
d) scarcity.
e) technological efficiency.

10.3
Correct: d)
Difficulty: 4
Page(s): 231–232
Scramble range: All
Topic: Constraints/ technology

10.3
A technique is
a) a way of converting output into profit.
b) the conversion of inputs into output in a way that maximizes total profit.
c) the conversion of inputs into output in a way that minimizes the average cost of production.
d) a feasible way of converting inputs into output.
e) a way of converting inputs into output that is economically efficient.

10.4
Correct: c)
Difficulty: 2
Page(s): 231
Scramble range: All
Topic: Constraints/ technology

10.4
Holding the level of output constant, a capital-intensive technique
a) is more economically efficient than a labour-intensive technique.
b) is more technologically efficient than a labour-intensive technique.
c) uses a relatively large amount of capital and a relatively small amount of labour.
d) uses a relatively large amount of labour and a relatively small amount of capital.
e) uses a relatively large amount of capital and a relatively large amount of labour.

10.5
Correct: a)
Difficulty: 2
Page(s): 231
Scramble range: All
Topic: Constraints/ technology

10.5
Suppose Swanky purchases a computer-controlled automated knitting machine which allows the firm to produce sweaters using a small amount of labour relative to capital. This method of production is an example of a(n)
a) capital-intensive technique.
b) labour-intensive technique.
c) technological efficiency.
d) economic efficiency.
e) market constraint.

10.6
Correct: c)
Difficulty: 2
Page(s): 231
Scramble range: All
Topic: Constraints/ technology

10.6
A capital-intensive technique is
a) an innovation.
b) more expensive than a labour-intensive technique.
c) a method of production that uses a relatively large amount of capital and a relatively small amount of labour to produce a given quantity of output.
d) a method of production that uses a relatively large amount of labour and a relatively small amount of capital to produce a given quantity of output.
e) a method of production that produces a relatively large amount of output using a relatively small amount of inputs.

10.7
Correct: d)
Difficulty: 2
Page(s): 232
Scramble range: All
Topic: Constraints/ short run

10.7
The short run is a period of time in which
a) the firm is not able to hire more workers.
b) the amount of output produced is fixed.
c) there is a shortage of most inputs.
d) the quantities of some inputs are fixed and others can be varied.
e) there is not enough time to make all of the decisions.

10.8
Correct: a)
Difficulty: 2
Page(s): 232
Scramble range: All
Topic: Constraints/ short run

10.8
The short run is a period of time
a) in which the quantity of some inputs is fixed and others can be varied.
b) in which the quantity of all inputs is fixed.
c) in which the quantity of all inputs can be varied.
d) that is less than one year.
e) that is less than one month.

10.9
Correct: e)
Difficulty: 2
Page(s): 232
Scramble range: All
Topic: Constraints/ long run

10.9
The long run is a period of time in which
a) the firm can hire all the workers that it wants to employ, but it does not have sufficient time to buy more equipment.
b) the firm is able to maximize total profit.
c) the firm may want to build a bigger plant, but cannot do so.
d) economic efficiency is achieved.
e) the quantities of all inputs can be varied.

10.10
Correct: c)
Difficulty: 2
Page(s): 232
Scramble range: All
Topic: Constraints/ short run

10.10
Fixed inputs are those inputs
a) that are too expensive for the firm to purchase.
b) that must be held in storage for at least one year.
c) whose quantity used cannot be changed in the short run.
d) in which the marginal product of the last unit of the input employed exceeds the marginal product of the previous unit.
e) which can be purchased only in fixed quantity lots (e.g., 200 at a time).

10.11
Correct: c)
Difficulty: 2
Page(s): 232
Scramble range: All
Topic: Constrain/ short/long run

10.11
Assume Swanky has a fixed amount of capital equipment in the form of knitting machines. Swanky can only vary its output by varying the quantity of labour. This is an example of
a) a market constraint.
b) horizontal run.
c) the short run.
d) the long run.
e) marginal product.

10.12
Correct: b)
Difficulty: 3
Page(s): 232
Scramble range: All
Topic: Short-run production

10.12
A firm's short-run production function describes
a) the minimum cost of producing a given amount of output.
b) how the maximum attainable output varies as the quantity of labour employed in a given production plant varies.
c) how the maximum attainable output varies as the size of the production plant varies, given the quantity of labour employed.
d) how the management of the firm makes decisions over short time periods.
e) how the amount of labour varies as the amount of output varies.

10.13
Correct: c)
Difficulty: 3
Page(s): 232
Scramble range: All
Topic: Short–run production

10.13
The total product curve is a graph of the
a) minimum cost of producing a given amount of output using different techniques.
b) maximum profit attainable for each unit of output sold.
c) maximum output attainable for each quantity of variable input employed.
d) minimum output attainable for each quantity of variable input employed.
e) change in total product for a change in marginal product.

10.14
Correct: d)
Difficulty: 3
Page(s): 232
Scramble range: All
Topic: Short–run production

10.14
See Figure 10.1, which illustrates Swanky's short-run production function. Which of the following statements is *false*?
a) All the points above the curve are unattainable.
b) All the points below the curve are attainable.
c) All the points below the curve are inefficient.
d) All the points on the curve involve equal cost to the firm.
e) All the points on the curve are attainable.

Figure 10.1

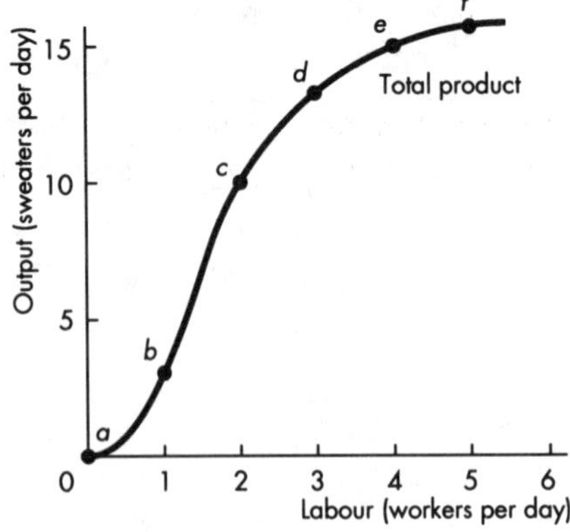

10.15
Correct: b)
Difficulty: 3
Page(s): 232–234
Scramble range: All
Topic: Short–run production

10.15
See Figure 10.1, which illustrates Swanky's short-run production function. Which of the following statements is *true*?
a) The points above the curve are attainable but they are inefficient.
b) The points below the curve are attainable but they are inefficient.
c) The points below the curve are efficient but they are unattainable.
d) The points on the curve are efficient but they are unattainable.
e) All the points on the curve have equal marginal product.

10.16
Correct: a)
Difficulty: 2
Page(s): 233
Scramble range: All
Topic: Short–run production/marginal product

10.16
The marginal product of labour is the change in total product caused by
a) a one-unit increase in the quantity of labour employed, holding the quantity of capital constant.
b) a one-unit increase in the quantity of capital employed, holding the quantity of labour constant.
c) a one-unit increase in both the quantity of labour and capital employed.
d) a change in the cost of labour.
e) a 1 percent change in the amount of labour used.

10.17
Correct: e)
Difficulty: 1
Page(s): 233
Scramble range: All
Topic: Short–run production

10.17
See Table 10.1, which represents Swanky's short-run production function. The total product that would be produced if the firm employed two workers is
a) 6.
b) 2.
c) 9.
d) 7.
e) 12.

Table 10.1

Labour (workers per day)	Output (sweaters per day)
0	0
1	3
2	12
3	19
4	23
5	25

10.18
Correct: d)
Difficulty: 1
Page(s): 233
Scramble range: All
Topic: Short–run/marginal product

10.18
See Table 10.1, which represents Swanky's short-run production function. The marginal product that would be produced if the firm employed the second worker is
a) 3.
b) 12.
c) 7.
d) 9.
e) 6.

10.19
Correct: b)
Difficulty: 1
Page(s): 235
Scramble range: All
Topic: Short–run production

10.19
See Table 10.1, which represents Swanky's short-run production function. The average product that would be produced if the firm employed the second worker is
a) 3.
b) 6.
c) 7.
e) 9.
e) 12.

10.20
Correct: d)
Difficulty: 1
Page(s): 233
Scramble range: All
Topic: Short–run production

10.20
See Table 10.2, which represents Swanky's short-run production function. The total product that would be produced if the firm employed four workers is
a) 2.
b) 8.
c) 12.
d) 15.
e) 3.75.

Table 10.2

Labour (workers per day)	Output (sweaters per day)
0	0
1	2
2	8
3	12
4	15
5	16

10.21
Correct: d)
Difficulty: 2
Page(s): 233
Scramble range: All
Topic: Short–run production/marginal product

10.21
See Table 10.2, which represents Swanky's short-run production function. The marginal product that would be produced if the firm employed the third worker is
a) 1.
b) 2.
c) 3.
d) 4.
e) 3.75.

10.22
Correct: d)
Difficulty: 2
Page(s): 235
Scramble range: All
Topic: Short–run production

10.22
See Table 10.2, which represents Swanky's short-run production function. The average product that would be produced if the firm employed the third worker is
a) 1.
b) 2.
c) 3.
d) 4.
e) 12.

10.23
Correct: d)
Difficulty: 2
Page(s): 233
Scramble range: All
Topic: Short–run production/marginal product

10.23
Suppose that a 1-unit rise in labour input, from 2 to 3 workers, increases output from 10 to 15 sweaters. The marginal product of the third worker is
a) 1.
b) 3.
c) 4.
d) 5.
e) 15.

10.24
Correct: d)
Difficulty: 2
Page(s): 233
Scramble range: All
Topic: Short–run production/marginal product

10.24
Suppose that when a firm increases the total units of labour employed from 5 to 6 workers, the firm's total output increases from 100 units to 400 units. The marginal product of the sixth worker is
a) 50.
b) 100.
c) 200.
d) 300.
e) 66.67.

10.25
Correct: e)
Difficulty: 3
Page(s): 234
Scramble range: All
Topic: Short–run production/marginal produc

10.25
The steeper the slope of the total product curve,
a) the higher is the level of output.
b) the lower is the level of the marginal product curve .
c) the higher is the level of the total cost curve.
d) the more efficient is the technology employed.
e) the higher is the level of the marginal product curve.

10.26
Correct: c)
Difficulty: 2
Page(s): 235
Scramble range: All
Topic: Short–run production

10.26
See Figure 10.2, which illustrates Swanky's total product curve. Average product can be measured as the
a) slope of the total product curve.
b) intercept of the total product curve.
c) slope of a line from the origin to a point on the total product curve.
d) peak of the total product curve.
e) average slope of the total product curve.

Figure 10.2

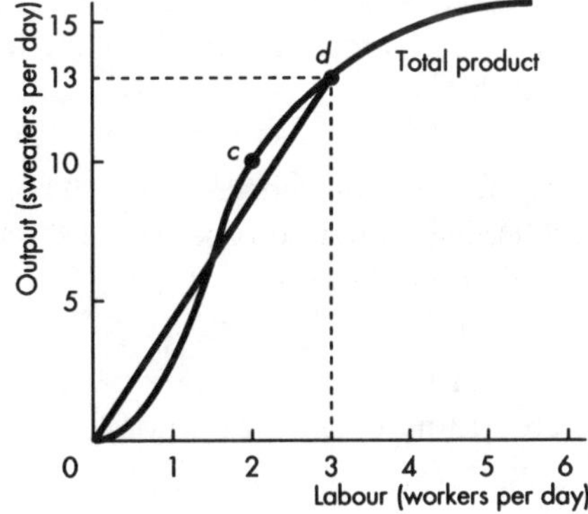

10.27
Correct: a)
Difficulty: 2
Page(s): 233
Scramble range: All
Topic: Short–run production/marginal product

10.27
See Figure 10.2, which illustrates Swanky's total product curve. Marginal product can be measured as the
a) slope of the total product curve.
b) intercept of the total product curve.
c) slope of a line from the origin to a point on the total product curve.
d) peak of the total product curve.
e) average slope of the total product curve.

10.28
Correct: b)
Difficulty: 2
Page(s): 235
Scramble range: All
Topic: Short–run production

10.28
See Figure 10.3, which illustrates Swanky's average product curve. The point of maximum average product is point
a) *b.*
b) *c.*
c) *d.*
d) *e.*
e) *f.*

Figure 10.3

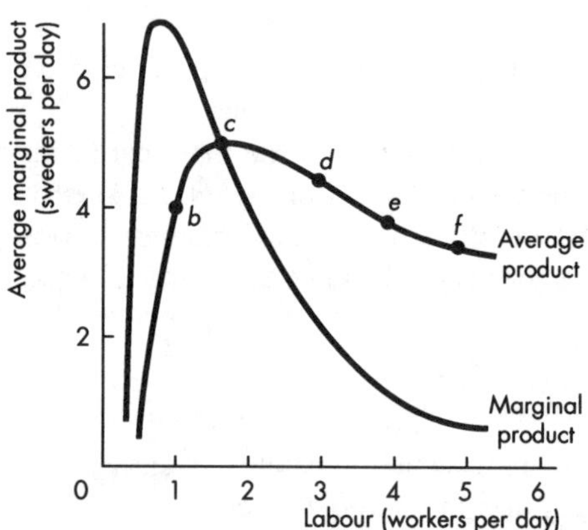

10.29
Correct: e)
Difficulty: 4
Page(s): 235
Scramble range: All
Topic: Short–run production/average, marginal product

10.29
Which one of the following statements is *true*?
a) The highest average product occurs where average product is above marginal product.
b) When the average product curve is rising, marginal product is below average product.
c) When the average product curve is falling, marginal product is above average product.
d) The maximum total product occurs at minimum marginal product.
e) The highest average product occurs where average and marginal product are equal to each other.

10.30
Correct: a)
Difficulty: 2
Page(s): 236
Scramble range: All
Topic: Short–run production

10.30
See Table 10.3, which represents Amy's test scores on the four exams that she took in an introductory course in economics. Her average score after taking the second exam was
a) 62.
b) 64.
c) 65.
d) 71.
e) 124.

Table 10.3

Test	Test score	Aggregate score
1	60	60
2	64	124
3	71	195
4	89	284

10.31
Correct: d)
Difficulty: 2
Page(s): 236
Scramble range: All
Topic: Short–run production/marginal product

10.31
See Table 10.3, which represents Amy's test scores on the four exams that she took in an introductory course in economics. Her marginal score on the third exam was
a) 62.
b) 64.
c) 65.
d) 71.
e) 195.

10.32
Correct: c)
Difficulty: 2
Page(s): 236
Scramble range: All
Topic: Short–run production

10.32
See Table 10.4, which represents Tema's test scores on the four exams that she took in an introductory course in biology. Her average score after taking the third exam was
a) 80.
b) 85.
c) 90.
d) 95.
e) 70.

Table 10.4

Test	Test score	Aggregate score
1	100	100
2	90	190
3	80	270
4	70	340

10.33
Correct: e)
Difficulty: 2
Page(s): 236
Scramble range: All
Topic: Short–run production/average, marginal product

10.33
See Table 10.4, which represents Tema's test scores on the four exams that she took in an introductory course in biology. Her marginal score on the third exam was
a) 90.
b) 70.
c) 71.
d) 62.
e) 80.

10.34
Correct: c)
Difficulty: 2
Page(s): 237
Scramble range: All
Topic: Short–run production/diminishing marginal return

10.34
Diminishing marginal return refers to a situation in which the __________ of the last worker hired falls short of the __________ of the previous worker.
a) marginal cost; marginal cost
b) average cost; average cost
c) marginal product; marginal product
d) average product; average product
e) marginal product; average product

10.35
Correct: c)
Difficulty: 2
Page(s): 237
Scramble range: All
Topic: Short–run production/diminishing marginal return

10.35
The law of diminishing returns states:
a) as the size of a plant increases, its marginal product eventually decreases.
b) as the size of a plant increases, its average cost eventually decreases.
c) as a firm uses more of a variable input, given the quantity of fixed inputs, its marginal product eventually decreases.
d) as a firm uses more of a variable input, given the quantity of fixed inputs, its average cost eventually decreases.
e) as a firm uses more of a fixed input, given the quantity of variable inputs, its marginal product eventually decreases.

10.36
Correct: d)
Difficulty: 2
Page(s): 237
Scramble range: All
Topic: Short–run production/diminishing marginal return

10.36
Law of diminishing marginal returns refers to the general tendency for __________ to eventually diminish as more of the variable input is employed, given the quantity of fixed inputs.
a) average total cost
b) marginal cost
c) capital
d) marginal product
e) average product

10.37
Correct: a)
Difficulty: 3
Page(s): 238
Scramble range: All
Topic: Short–run costs

10.37
See Table 10.5, which represents Swanky's short-run total cost schedule. The average fixed cost of producing 9 sweaters per day is
a) $2.22.
b) $1.25.
c) $10.00.
d) $1.11.
e) $1.54.

Table 10.5

		Cost ($)		
Labour (workers per day)	Output (sweaters per day)	Fixed *TFC*	Variable *TVC*	Total *TC*
0	0	20	0	20
1	4	20	25	45
2	9	20	50	70
3	13	20	75	95
4	16	20	100	120
5	18	20	125	145

10.38
Correct: d)
Difficulty: 4
Page(s): 238
Scramble range: All
Topic: Short–run costs

10.38
See Table 10.5, which represents Swanky's short-run total cost schedule. The average total cost of producing 16 sweaters per day is
a) $2.00.
b) $5.00.
c) $3.33.
d) $7.50.
e) $5.51.

10.39
Correct: e)
Difficulty: 4
Page(s): 238
Scramble range: All
Topic: Short–run costs

10.39
See Table 10.5, which represents Swanky's short-run total cost schedule. When output goes up from 4 to 9 sweaters, the marginal cost of one of those 5 sweaters is
a) $4.25.
b) $4.00.
c) $25.00.
d) $6.25.
e) $5.00.

10.40
Correct: a)
Difficulty: 4
Page(s): 238
Scramble range: All
Topic: Short–run costs

10.40
See Table 10.6, which represents Swanky's short-run total cost schedule. The average total cost of producing 14 sweaters is
a) $7.86.
b) $6.75.
c) $7.00.
d) $1.75.
e) $27.50.

Table 10.6

		Cost ($)		
Labour (workers per day)	Output (sweaters per day)	Fixed *TFC*	Variable *TVC*	Total *TC*
0	0	30	0	30
1	3	30	20	50
2	8	30	40	70
3	12	30	60	90
4	14	30	80	110
5	15	30	100	130

10.41
Correct: b)
Difficulty: 4
Page(s): 238
Scramble range: All
Topic: Short–run costs

10.41
See Table 10.6, which represents Swanky's short-run total cost schedule. When output goes up from 8 to 12 sweaters, the marginal cost of one of those 4 sweaters is
a) $20.00.
b) $5.00.
c) $1.00.
d) $6.67.
e) $2.00.

10.42
Correct: b)
Difficulty: 3
Page(s): 238
Scramble range: All
Topic: Short–run costs

10.42
If an increase in output from 5 to 10 sweaters causes the total cost of production to increase from $100 to $200, the marginal cost of one of those 5 sweaters is
a) $10.
b) $20.
c) $22.
d) $25.
e) dependent upon the amount of extra labour used.

10.43
Correct: b)
Difficulty: 1
Page(s): 237
Scramble range: All
Topic: Short–run costs

10.43
Marginal cost is calculated as
a) total cost divided by output.
b) the increase in total cost divided by the increase in output.
c) the increase in total cost divided by the increase in labour, given the amount of capital.
d) total variable cost minus total fixed cost.
e) the increase in total cost divided by the increase in variable cost.

10.44
Correct: d)
Difficulty: 3
Page(s): 237–239
Scramble range: All
Topic: Short–run costs

10.44
Which one of the following statements is *false*?
a) Average total cost is total cost per unit of output.
b) Average fixed cost plus average variable cost equals average total cost.
c) Marginal cost is the increase in total cost resulting from a unit increase in output.
d) Total cost equals fixed cost plus average cost.
e) Marginal cost depends on the amount of labour hired.

10.45
Correct: e)
Difficulty: 3
Page(s): 237–239
Scramble range: All
Topic: Short–run costs

10.45
Which one of the following statements concerning short-run costs is *false*?
a) Total variable cost is added to total fixed cost to calculate total cost.
b) Marginal cost is calculated as the change in total cost divided by the change in output.
c) Average total cost is calculated by dividing total cost by the level of output.
d) The average cost curve is U-shaped.
e) The total cost curve is U-shaped.

10.46
Correct: b)
Difficulty: 4
Page(s): 237–239
Scramble range: All
Topic: Short–run costs

10.46
Which one of the following statements concerning short-run costs is *false*?
a) Average total cost and average variable cost are U-shaped.
b) The gap between average total cost and average variable cost is marginal cost.
c) The gap between average total cost and average variable cost narrows as output increases.
d) Marginal cost cuts the average variable cost curve at its minimum point.
e) Marginal cost cuts the average total cost curve at its minimum point.

10.47
Correct: c)
Difficulty: 3
Page(s): 238
Scramble range: All
Topic: Short–run costs

10.47
See Figure 10.4, which illustrates short-run total cost curves.
Which one of the following statements is *false*?

a) Total fixed costs appears in the figure as curve *A*.
b) Total variable cost and total cost both increase with output.
c) The vertical gap between curves *B* and *C* is equal to total variable cost.
d) Marginal cost is represented by the slope of curve *C*.
e) Total fixed cost is constant.

Figure 10.4

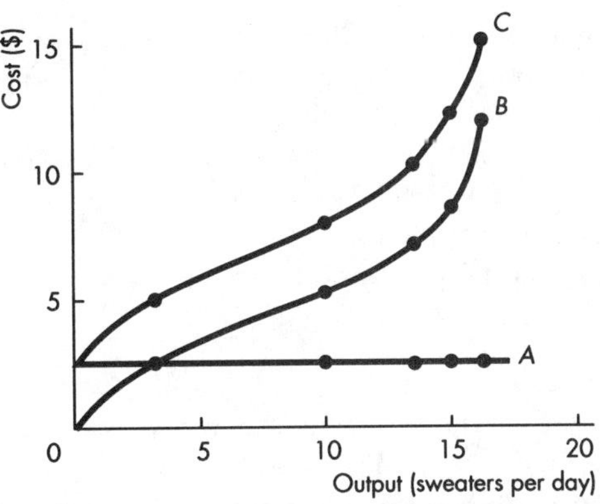

10.48
Correct: b)
Difficulty: 3
Page(s): 238
Scramble range: All
Topic: Short–run costs

10.48
See Figure 10.5, which illustrates short-run average cost curves. Which one of the following statements is *false*?

a) Average fixed cost decreases with output.
b) The vertical gap between curves *B* and *C* is equal to average variable cost.
c) Curve *B* comes closer to curve *C* as output increases because of a decrease in average fixed costs.
d) Curve *D* represents marginal cost.
e) The vertical gap between curves *B* and *C* is equal to average fixed cost.

Figure 10.5

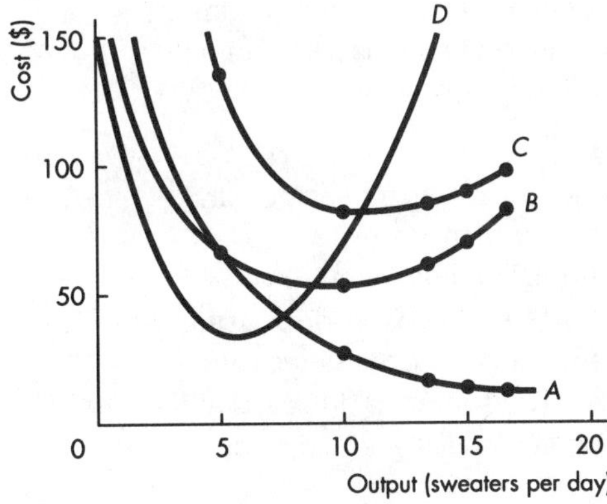

10.49
Correct: b)
Difficulty: 1
Page(s): 238
Scramble range: a)–d)
Topic: Short–run costs

10.49
See Figure 10.5, which illustrates the short-run average and marginal cost curves. The average variable cost curve is represented by the curve labelled
a) *A.*
b) *B.*
c) *C.*
d) *D.*
e) none of the above.

10.50
Correct: d)
Difficulty: 1
Page(s): 238
Scramble range: a)–d)
Topic: Short–run costs

10.50
See Figure 10.5, which illustrates the short-run average and marginal cost curves. The marginal cost curve is represented by the curve labelled
a) *A.*
b) *B.*
c) *C.*
d) *D.*
e) none of the above.

10.51
Correct: a)
Difficulty: 3
Page(s): 237–239
Scramble range: All
Topic: Short–run costs

10.51
Which one of the following statements concerning the short-run cost curves is *false?*
a) The marginal cost curve cuts the average variable and average total cost curves at their maximum points.
b) When marginal cost is above average variable cost, average variable cost is rising.
c) When marginal cost is above average total cost, average total cost is rising.
d) The average total cost curve is U-shaped.
e) The average fixed cost curve is always downward sloping.

10.52
Correct: a)
Difficulty: 2
Page(s): 237–239
Scramble range: All
Topic: Short–run costs

10.52
Average variable cost is at a minimum at the same output at which
a) average product is at a maximum.
b) marginal product is at a maximum.
c) average product is at a minimum.
d) marginal product is at a minimum.
e) average total cost is at a minimum.

10.53
Correct: e)
Difficulty: 4
Page(s): 237–239
Scramble range: All
Topic: Short–run costs

10.53
The range over which average variable cost is decreasing is the same as the range over which
a) marginal cost is increasing.
b) average fixed cost is decreasing.
c) marginal product is decreasing.
d) average product is decreasing.
e) average product is increasing.

10.54
Correct: d)
Difficulty: 3
Page(s): 241
Scramble range: All
Topic: Hydro/marginal costs

10.54
Which one of the following statements concerning Ontario Hydro is *false*?
a) The relationship between production and marginal cost is not exact because of maintenance scheduling.
b) The relationship between production and marginal cost is not exact because of uncontrollable factors such as plant breakdowns.
c) The marginal cost curve for electric power in Ontario rises steeply as output approaches the physical limits of the generating plant.
d) The marginal cost curve for electric power in Ontario reaches a maximum where average total cost is minimized.
e) Ontario Hydro uses its cheapest sources of power first.

10.55
Correct: c)
Difficulty: 4
Page(s): 241–242
Scramble range: All
Topic: Hydro/capacity

10.55
See Figure 10.6, which was used to illustrate Ontario Hydro's plant size choice. Though Ontario Hydro faces steeply increasing marginal costs, its average total costs decline up to the output Q_3. Between Q_3 and Q_4 average total cost rises. The capacity of Ontario Hydro's plant is
a) output Q_1.
b) output Q_2.
c) output Q_3.
d) output Q_4.
e) somewhere to the right of Q_4.

Figure 10.6

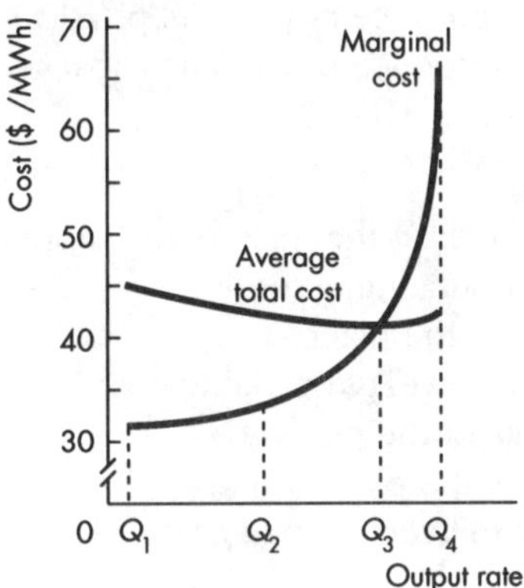

10.56
Correct: d)
Difficulty: 4
Page(s): 241–242
Scramble range: All
Topic: Hydro/physical limit

10.56
See Figure 10.6, which was used to illustrate Ontario Hydro's plant size choice. Which output is the physical limit of their plant?
a) Q_1.
b) Q_2.
c) Q_3.
d) Q_4.
e) A level to the right of Q_4.

10.57
Correct: b)
Difficulty: 2
Page(s): 242
Scramble range: All
Topic: Plant size/capacity

10.57
When the output rate is such that a plant's average total cost is at a minimum, the plant is said to be operating at
a) excess capacity.
b) capacity.
c) overutilized capacity.
d) neutral mode.
e) underutilized capacity.

10.58
Correct: a)
Difficulty: 1
Page(s): 242
Scramble range: All
Topic: Plant size/capacity

10.58
Capacity is the output rate at which a plant's
a) average total cost is a minimum.
b) marginal cost is a minimum.
c) average total cost is a maximum.
d) marginal cost is a maximum.
e) average variable cost is at a minimum.

10.59
Correct: e)
Difficulty: 3
Page(s): 242
Scramble range: All
Topic: Plant size/capacity

10.59
Which one of the following statements is *false*?
a) Overutilized capacity occurs when a plant produces more than the output at which average total cost is a minimum.
b) Excess capacity occurs when a plant produces less than the output at which average total cost is a minimum.
c) Physical limits refers to the maximum output that a plant can produce.
d) A plant cannot produce beyond its physical limits.
e) A plant cannot produce beyond its capacity.

10.60
Correct: a)
Difficulty: 2
Page(s): 242
Scramble range: All
Topic: Plant size/physical limit

10.60
When we want to refer to the maximum output that a plant can produce, the plant is said to be operating at the
a) physical limits of the plant.
b) plant's minimum average variable cost.
c) economic limits of the plant.
d) capacity limit of the plant.
e) plant's minimum average total cost.

10.61
Correct: d)
Difficulty: 2
Page(s): 243
Scramble range: All
Topic: Long–run production function

10.61
A long-run production function is the relationship between the maximum output attainable and the
a) price of output.
b) change in technology.
c) demand for output.
d) quantities of inputs used.
e) amount of labour used.

10.62
Correct: a)
Difficulty: 2
Page(s): 244
Scramble range: All
Topic: Long–run production function

10.62
See Figure 10.7, which illustrates the short-run total product curves for four different plant sizes as Swanky varies the quantities of knitting machines and workers per day. The curve that represents the plant using the largest number of knitting machines is

a) labelled plant *d.*
b) labelled plant *b.*
c) labelled plant *c.*
d) labelled plant *a.*
e) any of plants *a* to *d*, since they all use the same number of machines, just different amounts of labour.

Figure 10.7

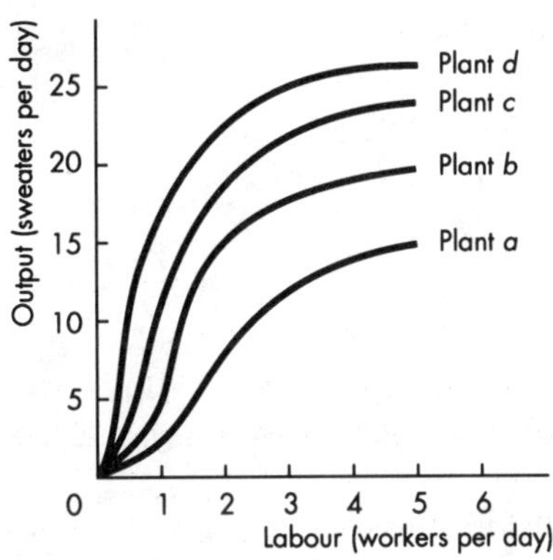

10.63
Correct: c)
Difficulty: 2
Page(s): 244
Scramble range: All
Topic: Long–run production/plant size

10.63
See Figure 10.7, which illustrates the short-run total product curves for four different plant sizes. One of the fundamental technological facts reflected in the shape of each of the total product curves is the

a) price of the inputs.
b) price of the output.
c) law of diminishing returns.
d) law of increasing returns.
e) fact that capital and labour cannot be substituted for each other.

10.64
Correct: b)
Difficulty: 2
Page(s): 244
Scramble range: All
Topic: Long–run production function

10.64
The marginal product of capital is the

a) change in total product resulting from a 1-unit increase in the quantity of labour employed, holding the quantity of the capital constant.
b) change in total product resulting from a 1-unit increase in the quantity of capital employed, holding the quantity of the labour constant.
c) total quantity of the product produced divided by the total quantity of capital employed, holding the quantity of the labour constant.
d) total quantity of the product produced divided by the total quantity of labour employed, holding the quantity of the capital constant.
e) change in the quantity of capital used resulting from a 1-unit change in total product, holding constant the quantity of labour.

10.65
Correct: e)
Difficulty: 1
Page(s): 244
Scramble range: All
Topic: Long–run production function

10.65
The marginal product of capital is the change in total _________ resulting from a 1-unit increase in the quantity of _________ employed, holding the quantity of other inputs constant.
a) profit; capital
b) profit; labour
c) output; both capital and labour
d) output; labour
e) output; capital

10.66
Correct: a)
Difficulty: 2
Page(s): 244–245
Scramble range: All
Topic: Returns to scale

10.66
Suppose General Motors could triple its production of Cavaliers by tripling its production facility for those cars. This is an example of
a) constant returns to scale.
b) increasing returns to scale.
c) decreasing returns to scale.
d) the law of diminishing returns.
e) economies of scale.

10.67
Correct: b)
Difficulty: 1
Page(s): 244–245
Scramble range: All
Topic: Returns to scale

10.67
Suppose a candy manufacturer could triple its production of fudge by doubling its production facility for making fudge. This is an example of
a) constant returns to scale.
b) increasing returns to scale.
c) decreasing returns to scale.
d) market contraints.
e) the law of diminishing returns.

10.68
Correct: c)
Difficulty: 2
Page(s): 245
Scramble range: All
Topic: Returns to scale

10.68
Decreasing returns to scale occur when the percentage rise in output is _________ the percentage rise in the scale of the inputs.
a) greater than
b) equal to
c) less than
d) unrelated to
e) greater than or equal to

10.69
Correct: a)
Difficulty: 2
Page(s): 245
Scramble range: All
Topic: Returns to scale

10.69
Increasing returns to scale (or economies of scale) are technological conditions under which the percentage change in a firm's output
a) exceeds the percentage change in its inputs.
b) is less than the percentage change in its inputs.
c) is increasing.
d) is decreasing.
e) is constant.

10.70
Correct: e)
Difficulty: 1
Page(s): 244
Scramble range: All
Topic: Long–run production function

10.70
See Table 10.7, which represents Swanky's production possibilities as the firm varies the quantities of knitting machines and workers per day. If the firm used 3 knitting machines and employed 5 workers, how many sweaters a day would it produce?

a) 17.
b) 25.
c) 22.
d) 23.
e) 26.

Table 10.7

Labour (workers per day)	Plant size (knitting machines) 1	2	3
1	5	11	14
2	11	16	19
3	14	19	23
4	16	21	25
5	17	22	26

10.71
Correct: c)
Difficulty: 4
Page(s): 244–245
Scramble range: All
Topic: Long–run production function

10.71
See Table 10.7, which represents Swanky's production possibilities as the firm varies the quantities of knitting machines and workers per day. If Swanky increased the number of knitting machines from 2 to 3 and increased the number of workers employed from 2 to 3, the factory would experience

a) economies of scale.
b) constant returns to scale.
c) diseconomies of scale.
d) constant marginal product.
e) increasing returns to scale.

10.72
Correct: d)
Difficulty: 1
Page(s): 246
Scramble range: All
Topic: Plant size/costs

10.72
See Figure 10.8, which illustrates the short-run average total cost curves for four different plant sizes. Which curve represents the average total cost for the largest of the four plant sizes?

a) ATC_a.
b) ATC_b.
c) ATC_c.
d) ATC_d.
e) Either ATC_c or ATC_d.

Figure 10.8

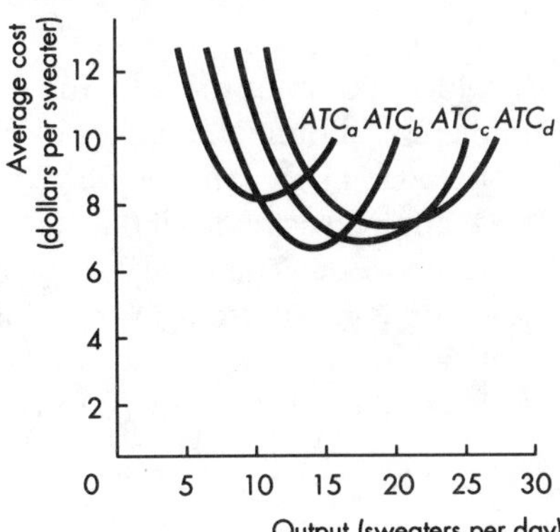

10.73
Correct: a)
Difficulty: 1
Page(s): 246
Scramble range: a)–d)
Topic: Plant size/costs

10.73
See Figure 10.8, which illustrates the short-run average total cost curves for four different plant sizes. Which plant has the lowest average total cost for an output rate of 5 sweaters a day?

a) Plant *a.*
b) Plant *b.*
c) Plant *c.*
d) Plant *d.*
e) None of the above.

10.74
Correct: b)
Difficulty: 2
Page(s): 248
Scramble range: All
Topic: Returns to scale

10.74
See Figure 10.9, which illustrates a firm's long-run average total cost of production. An increase in production from Q_1 to Q_2 sweaters per day results in

a) decreasing returns to scale.
b) increasing returns to scale.
c) diseconomies of scale.
d) constant total costs.
e) constant returns to scale.

Figure 10.9

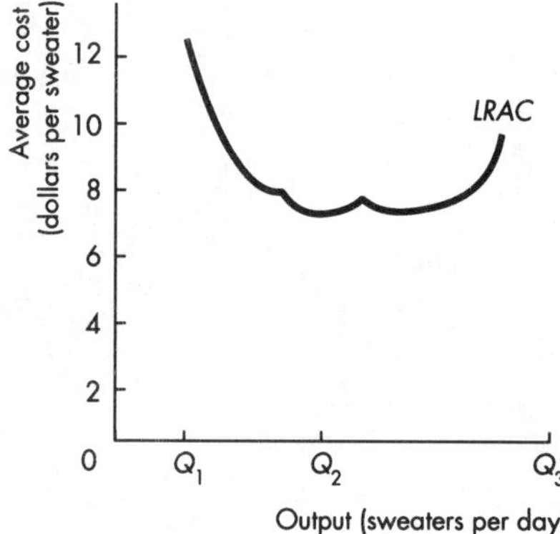

10.75
Correct: c)
Difficulty: 2
Page(s): 245–248
Scramble range: All
Topic: Returns to scale

10.75
There are decreasing returns to scale if an increase in production causes

a) diminishing returns.
b) market constraints.
c) an increase in long-run average cost.
d) a decrease in long-run average cost.
e) an increase in long-run total cost.

10.76
Correct: b)
Difficulty: 3
Page(s): 249
Scramble range: All
Topic: Returns to scale

10.76
See Figure 10.10, which illustrates the long-run average total cost of production when there is an infinite number of plant sizes and output ranges. Which one of the following statements is *false*?

a) Returns to scale are increasing from 0 to Q_0 units of output.
b) Returns to scale are decreasing from 0 to Q_1 units of output.
c) Returns to scale are constant from Q_1 to Q_2 units of output.
d) Returns to scale are decreasing after Q_2 units of output.
e) Returns to scale are increasing from Q_0 to Q_1 units of output.

Figure 10.10

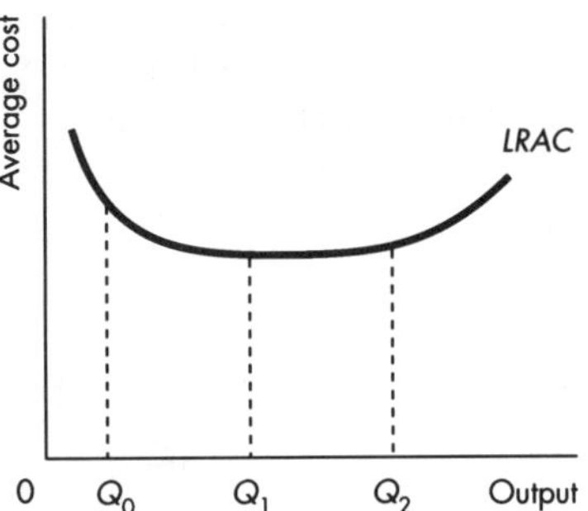

10.77
Correct: c)
Difficulty: 2
Page(s): 249
Scramble range: All
Topic: Returns to scale

10.77
See Figure 10.10, which illustrates the long-run average total cost of production when there is an infinite number of plant sizes and output ranges. Given an increase in output from Q_1 to Q_2,
a) returns to scale are increasing.
b) returns to scale are decreasing.
c) returns to scale are constant.
d) diminishing returns begins to occur.
e) there are diseconomies of scale.

10.78
Correct: a)
Difficulty: 2
Page(s): 249
Scramble range: All
Topic: Long–run costs/total

10.78
Long-run total cost is
a) the same as long-run total variable cost.
b) the same as long-run total fixed cost.
c) equal to long-run total fixed cost plus long-run variable cost.
d) equal to long-run total fixed cost minus long-run variable cost.
e) equal to short-run total cost.

10.79
Correct: e)
Difficulty: 2
Page(s): 249
Scramble range: All
Topic: Long–run costs/average, marginal

10.79
When long-run average cost is falling, long-run marginal cost is __________ long-run average cost.
a) first below and then above
b) above
c) equal to
d) indeterminate in its relationship to
e) below

10.80
Correct: b)
Difficulty: 3
Page(s): 247
Scramble range: All
Topic: Long–run costs/average, marginal

10.80
When long-run average cost is constant, long-run marginal cost is
a) zero.
b) equal to long-run average cost.
c) less than long-run average cost.
d) greater than long-run average cost.
e) falling.

10.81 (SG 10.1)
Correct: e)
Difficulty: 2
Page(s): 232
Scramble range: All
Topic: Short run

10.81
In economics, the *short run* refers to a time period
a) of one year or less.
b) in which all inputs are variable.
c) in which all inputs are fixed.
d) in which the firm's management is unable to react quickly.
e) in which there is at least one fixed input.

10.82 (SG 10.2)
Correct: b)
Difficulty: 2
Page(s): 231
Scramble range: All
Topic: Limit to profits

10.82
Which of the following does not limit the amount of profits a firm can make?
a) There is limited demand for every product.
b) There are always several ways to produce a product.
c) Suppliers of inputs are willing to supply additional quantities only at higher prices.
d) Many potential ways of converting inputs into output are not technically feasible.
e) A large firm can raise prices only if accepts that it will sell lower quantities.

10.83
Correct: c)
Difficulty: 2
Page(s): 232
Scramble range: All
Topic: Total product curve

10.83
The total product curve is
a) the sum of the average and marginal product curves.
b) the graph of the level of output that can be produced at a given quantity of a variable input at each price of the variable input.
c) the graph of the maximum output attainable for each quantity of a variable input, given the amount of other inputs.
d) the graph of total output divided by the amount of the fixed input.
e) the graph of the relationship between capital and labour used in producing a given level of output.

10.84
Correct: b)
Difficulty: 1
Page(s): 233
Scramble range: All
Topic: Marginal product

10.84
The change in total product resulting from a 1-unit increase in a variable input is called
a) average product.
b) marginal product.
c) average variable product.
d) total product.
e) labour product.

10.85 (SG 10.4)
Correct: a)
Difficulty: 2
Page(s): 233
Scramble range: All
Topic: Measuring average product graphically

10.85
The average product of labour can be measured
a) as the slope of a straight line from the origin to a point on the total product curve.
b) as the slope of the total product curve.
c) as the slope of the marginal product curve.
d) as the change in output divided by the change in labour input.
e) as the slope of a straight line from the origin to the peak of the total product curve.

10.86 (SG 10.6)
Correct: d)
Difficulty: 3
Page(s): 235
Scramble range: All
Topic: Marginal and average product

10.86
When the marginal product of labour is less than the average product of labour,
a) the average product of labour is increasing.
b) the marginal product of labour is increasing.
c) the total product curve is negatively sloped.
d) the firm is experiencing diminishing returns.
e) the average product curve is at its peak.

10.87
Correct: a)
Difficulty: 3
Page(s): 237
Scramble range: All
Topic: Diminishing marginal returns

10.87
When the seventh worker is hired, output increases from 100 units per week to 110 units per week. When the eighth worker is hired, output increases from 110 units to 118 units. This is an example of
a) diminishing marginal returns.
b) diminishing marginal cost.
c) decreasing returns to scale.
d) labour-intensive production.
e) increasing returns to scale.

10.88 (SG 10.8)
Correct: c)
Difficulty: 3
Page(s): 238
Scramble range: All
Topic: Total fixed cost

10.88
The vertical distance between the *TC* and *TVC* curves is
a) decreasing as output decreases.
b) equal to *AFC*.
c) equal to *TFC*.
d) equal to *MC*.
e) increasing as output decreases.

10.89 (SG 10.9)
Correct: d)
Difficulty: 3
Page(s): 238
Scramble range: All
Topic: Marginal and average cost curves

10.89
The marginal cost (*MC*) curve intersects the
a) *ATC*, *AVC*, and *AFC* curves at their minimum points.
b) *ATC* and *AFC* curves at their minimum points.
c) *AVC* and *AFC* curves at their minimum points.
d) *ATC* and *AVC* curves at their minimum points.
e) *ATC* curve at its minimum point.

10.90
Correct: a)
Difficulty: 4
Page(s): 238
Scramble range: All
Topic: Marginal and average variable cost

10.90
If the average variable cost of producing 10 units is $18 and the average variable cost of producing 11 units is $20, we know that, between 10 and 11 units of output,
a) marginal cost is increasing.
b) average total cost is increasing.
c) diminishing returns has not yet set in.
d) there is excess capacity.
e) there is increasing returns to scale.

10.91 (SG 10.14)
Correct: b)
Difficulty: 3
Page(s): 232
Scramble range: All
Topic: Long run

10.91
In the long run,
a) only the scale of plant is fixed.
b) all inputs are variable.
c) all inputs are fixed.
d) a firm must experience decreasing returns to scale.
e) a firm will not have excess capacity, because it can vary all the inputs.

10.92 (SG 10.15)
Correct: e)
Difficulty: 4
Page(s): 246
Scramble range: All
Topic: Long run firm problem

10.92
The problem of a firm in the long run is to
a) derive the long-run average cost curve.
b) choose the level of output that has minimum average cost of production, give the scale of the plant.
c) choose the amount of labour that has minimum average cost of producing the desired level of output, given the scale of plant.
d) produce the largest amount of output possible.
e) choose the scale of plant that has minimum average cost of producing the desired level of output.

10.93 (SG 10.16)
Correct: c)
Difficulty: 4
Page(s): 242
Scramble range: All
Topic: Capacity production

10.93
When a firm is producing at capacity, it is
a) maximizing profit.
b) producing at its physical limits.
c) producing at the level of output at which marginal cost equals average total cost.
d) producing on the upward sloping part of its long-run average cost curve.
e) producing on the downward sloping part of its average product curve.

10.94
Correct: a)
Difficulty: 2
Page(s): 243
Scramble range: All
Topic: Production function

10.94
The collection of all short-run production functions is called the
a) production function.
b) long-run total product curve.
c) returns to scale of a firm.
d) aggregate supply curve.
e) long-run average cost curve.

10.95 (SG 10.17)
Correct: d)
Difficulty: 3
Page(s): 245
Scramble range: All
Topic: Decrease return to scale

10.95
Output will increase by less than 10 percent when all inputs are increased by 10 percent if
a) marginal cost is decreasing.
b) the long-run average cost curve is negatively sloped.
c) increasing returns to scale are present.
d) decreasing returns to scale are present.
e) the long-run average fixed cost curve is negatively sloped.

10.96 (SG 10.18)
Correct: a)
Difficulty: 2
Page(s): 245
Scramble range: All
Topic: Marginal cost/diminishing returns

10.96
The reason for upward sloping marginal cost curves is the law of
a) diminishing returns.
b) diminishing marginal utility.
c) increasing returns to scale.
d) production.
e) supply.

10.97 (SG 10.19)
Correct: b)
Difficulty: 4
Page(s): 245
Scramble range: All
Topic: Constant returns to scale

10.97
Constant returns to scale means that, as all inputs are increased,
a) total output remains unchanged.
b) long-run average cost remains unchanged.
c) long-run average cost rises at the same rate as inputs.
d) marginal product is increasing.
e) average product is decreasing.

10.98 (SG 10.20)
Correct: e)
Difficulty: 3
Page(s): 246–247
Scramble range: All
Topic: Long–/short–run average cost

10.98
The long-run average cost curve
a) is the short-run average total cost curve with the lowest cost.
b) will shift up when fixed costs increase.
c) traces out the minimum points on all the short-run average total cost curves for each scale of plant.
d) traces out the minimum short-run average total cost for each input.
e) traces out the minimum short-run average total cost for each output level.

10.99 (SG 10.21)
Correct: b)
Difficulty: 3
Page(s): 250
Scramble range: All
Topic: Technical change/product curves

10.99
A technological advance will tend to shift
a) total, average, and marginal product curves up and total, average, and marginal cost curves up.
b) total, average and marginal product curves up and total, average, and marginal cost curves down.
c) total, average and marginal product curves down and total, average, and marginal cost curves up.
d) total, average, and marginal product curves down and total, average, and marginal cost curves down.
e) total, average and marginal product curves up, leaving the total, average and marginal cost curves unchanged.

10.100 (SG 10.22)
Correct: a)
Difficulty: 3
Page(s): 246–247
Scramble range: All
Topic: Long–run adjustment of firm

10.100
A firm will want to increase its scale of plant if
a) it is persistently producing on the upward-sloping part of its short-run average total cost curve.
b) it is persistently producing on the downward-sloping part of its short-run average total cost curve.
c) it is producing below capacity.
d) marginal cost is below average total cost.
e) marginal cost is increasing.

10.101 (SG 10.23)
Correct: c)
Difficulty: 4
Page(s): 246–247
Scramble range: All
Topic: Cost curve/input price change

10.101
The average variable cost curve will shift up if
a) there is an increase in fixed costs.
b) there is a technological advance.
c) the price of the variable input increases.
d) the price of output increases.
e) the average product curve shifts up.

10.102
Correct: b)
Difficulty: 2
Page(s): 232
Scramble range: All
Topic: Long run

10.102
In economics, the *long run* refers to a time period
a) of one year or less.
b) in which all inputs are variable.
c) in which all inputs are fixed.
d) in which there is at least one fixed input.
e) in which the firm can be more technologically efficient.

10.103
Correct: c)
Difficulty: 2
Page(s): 231
Scramble range: All
Topic: Limit to profits

10.103
Which of the following limits the amount of profits a firm can make?
a) There is unlimited demand for every product.
b) There are always several ways to produce a product.
c) Suppliers of inputs are willing to supply additional quantities only at higher prices.
d) An infinite number ways of converting inputs into output are technically feasible.
e) Many production choices are available.

10.104
Correct: e)
Difficulty: 2
Page(s): 233
Scramble range: All
Topic: Average product curve

10.104
The average product curve is
a) the sum of the average and marginal product curves.
b) the graph of the level of output that can be produced at a given quantity of a variable input at each price of the variable input.
c) the graph of the maximum output attainable for each quantity of a variable input, given the amount of other inputs.
d) the graph of total output divided by the amount of the fixed input.
e) the graph of total output divided by the amount of the variable input.

10.105
Correct: e)
Difficulty: 1
Page(s): 233
Scramble range: All
Topic: Total product

10.105
The graph of the maximum output attainable for each quantity of a variable input, given the amount of other inputs, is called
a) average product.
b) marginal product.
c) average variable product.
d) total fixed product.
e) total product.

10.106
Correct: e)
Difficulty: 3
Page(s): 233
Scramble range: None
Topic: Measuring marginal product graphically

10.106
The marginal product of labour can be measured
a) as the slope of a straight line from the origin to a point on the total product curve.
b) as the slope of the total product curve.
c) as the slope of the marginal product curve.
d) as the change in total product divided by the change in labour input.
e) both b) and d).

10.107
Correct: a)
Difficulty: 3
Page(s): 235
Scramble range: All
Topic: Marginal and average product

10.107
When the marginal product of labour is greater than the average product of labour,
a) the average product of labour is increasing.
b) the marginal product of labour is increasing.
c) the total product curve is negatively sloped.
d) the firm is experiencing diminishing returns.
e) the firm is experiencing constant returns.

10.108
Correct: b)
Difficulty: 4
Page(s): 235–238
Scramble range: All
Topic: Diminishing marginal cost

10.108
When the third worker is hired, output increases from 100 units per week to 110 units per week. When the fourth worker is hired, output increases from 110 units to 121 units. This is an example of
a) diminishing marginal returns.
b) diminishing marginal cost.
c) decreasing returns to scale.
d) labour-intensive production.
e) increasing average cost.

10.109
Correct: b)
Difficulty: 4
Page(s): 245–249
Scramble range: a)–c)
Topic: Average fixed cost

10.109
The short-run average cost curve is always greater than or equal to the long-run average cost curve because
a) the total cost of the firm will remain constant as output increases.
b) the firm's managers can select all the long-run choices in the short run, and therefore must be at least as well off.
c) labour supply is more flexible in the long run.
d) all of the above.
e) none of the above.

10.110
Correct: e)
Difficulty: 4
Page(s): 238–239
Scramble range: All
Topic: Marginal and average variable cost

10.110
If the average variable cost of producing 10 units is $18 and the average variable cost of producing 11 units is $17, we know that, between 10 and 11 units of output,
a) marginal cost is decreasing.
b) average total cost is increasing.
c) diminishing returns has not yet set in.
d) marginal cost is above average variable cost.
e) marginal cost is below average variable cost.

10.111
Correct: c)
Difficulty: 2
Page(s): 236–237
Scramble range: All
Topic: Returns to scale

10.111
Consider Table 10.8. The value of *A* in the table is
a) 1.75.
b) 2.
c) 3.
d) 7.
e) 4.

Table 10.8

Labour (persons per week)	Output (rubber boats per week)	Marginal product	Average product
1	1	1	1
2	2	1	1
3	4	2	*C*
4	7	*A*	*D*
5	11	4	2.2
6	14	*B*	*E*
7	16	2	2.28
8	17	1	2.13
9	18	1	2
10	18	0	1.8

10.112
Correct: d)
Difficulty: 3
Page(s): 232–237
Scramble range: All
Topic: Marginal/average product

10.112
Consider Table 10.8. The maximum value of marginal product occurs where output equals __________, while the maximum value of average product occurs where output equals __________.
a) 5; 6.
b) 6; 5.
c) 7; 14.
d) 11; 14.
e) 14; 11.

10.113
Correct: e)
Difficulty: 5
Page(s): 232–242
Scramble range: All
Topic: Cost curves

10.113
Consider Table 10.8. In this firm, the minimum of the average variable cost curve will occur at an __________, while the minimum of the marginal cost curve will occur at an __________.

a) output level of 18; output level of 18
b) output level that we cannot calculate without further data; output level that we cannot calculate without further data
c) output level of 5; output level of 6
d) output level of 11; output level of 14
e) output level of 14; output level of 11

10.114
Correct: a)
Difficulty: 5
Page(s): 232–242
Scramble range: All
Topic: Cost curves

10.114
Consider Table 10.8. When the amount of labour equals 10, then

a) both marginal cost and average total cost are equal to infinity.
b) both marginal cost and average total cost are equal to zero.
c) marginal cost equal zero and total cost equals 1.8.
d) we cannot tell the values of marginal cost and total cost without more information on variable costs.
e) the firm will be making its largest possible profits.

Chapter 11 Producing at Least Cost

11.1
Correct: a)
Difficulty: 3
Page(s): 261
Scramble range: All
Topic: Isoquant line

11.1
See Figure 11.1, which represents an isoquant. Which one of the following combinations of capital and labour would enable the firm to produce 30 sweaters a day?

a) 2 machines and 8 workers.
b) 4 machines and 2 workers.
c) 4 machines and 1 worker.
d) 2 machines and 2 workers.
e) 6 machines and 2 workers.

Figure 11.1

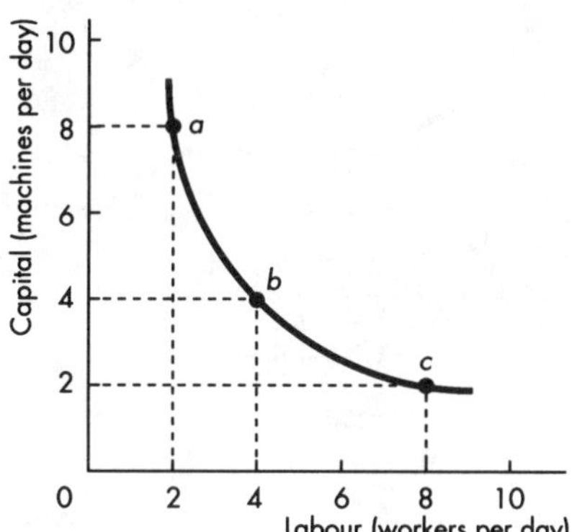

11.2
Correct: a)
Difficulty: 2
Page(s): 261
Scramble range: All
Topic: Isoquant line

11.2
The marginal rate of substitution is measured by the slope of an

a) isoquant line.
b) isocost line.
c) isoprofit line.
d) isoquant map.
e) average total cost curve.

11.3
Correct: d)
Difficulty: 3
Page(s): 261
Scramble range: All
Topic: Isoquant line

11.3
The marginal rate of substitution of capital for labour
a) measures the slope of the production function.
b) measures the the price of labour relative to the price of capital.
c) measures the increase in capital needed per unit increase in labour to keep output constant.
d) equals the ratio of the marginal product of labour to the marginal product of capital.
e) measures the decrease in capital needed per unit decrease in labour to keep output constant.

11.4
Correct: c)
Difficulty: 3
Page(s): 263
Scramble range: All
Topic: Isoquant line

11.4
See Figure 11.2, which shows the different ways of producing three levels of output a day. Which one of the following is *false*?
a) Point *a* uses 4 machines and 1 worker to produce 10 units of output.
b) Point *b* uses 2 machines and 2 workers to produce 10 units of output.
c) Point *c* uses 1 machine and 2 workers to produce 10 units of output.
d) Point *b* is attainable with current technology.
e) An output level of 16 units is unattainable with current technology.

Figure 11.2

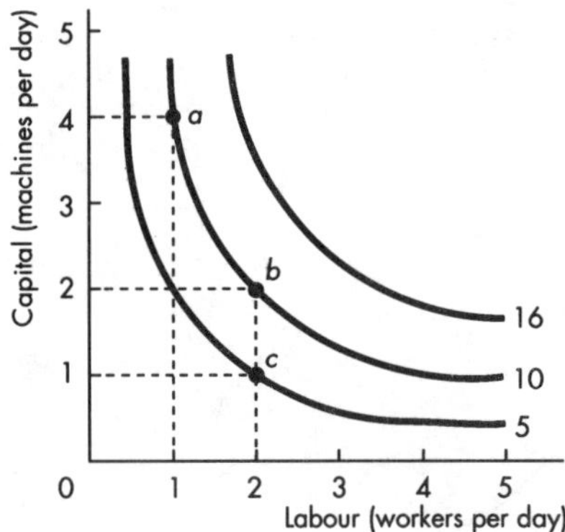

11.5
Correct: e)
Difficulty: 3
Page(s): 263
Scramble range: All
Topic: Isoquant line

11.5
See Figure 11.2, which shows the different ways of producing three levels of output a day. Which one of the following is *false*?
a) More capital is used at point *a* than at point *b*.
b) More output is produced at point *a* than at point *c*.
c) More output is produced at point *b* than at point *c*.
d) The same amount of labour is used at points *b* and *c*.
e) The same amount of capital is used at points *a* and *b*.

11.6
Correct: e)
Difficulty: 3
Page(s): 263
Scramble range: All
Topic: Isoquant line

11.6
See Figure 11.2, which shows the different ways of producing three levels of output a day. Which one of the following is *false*?
a) More capital is used in production at point *b* than at point *c*.
b) Less labour is used in production at point *a* than at point *b*.
c) The maximum output illustrated in the graph is 16 units.
d) Point *b* involves more output than point *c*.
e) More labour is used in production at point *a* than at point *b*.

11.7 (SG 11.1)
Correct: c)
Difficulty: 2
Page(s): 261
Scramble range: None
Topic: Isoquant line

11.7
The marginal rate of substitution of capital for labour is the
a) increase in capital needed per unit increase in labour to keep output constant.
b) increase in capital needed per unit increase in labour to increase output by one unit.
c) decrease in capital needed per unit increase in labour to keep output constant.
d) ratio of the price of capital to the price of labour.
e) both c) and d).

11.8
Correct: d)
Difficulty: 2
Page(s): 261–264
Scramble range: All
Topic: Isoquant line

11.8
As we lower the labour input and raise the capital input, we
a) decrease an isoquant line.
b) increase an isoquant line.
c) travel along an isocost line.
d) travel along an isoquant line.
e) raise output.

11.9
Correct: b)
Difficulty: 3
Page(s): 269
Scramble range: All
Topic: Isoquant line

11.9
If an isoquant illustrated in the text is steep, the capital input __________ relative to the rise in the labour input.
a) falls by a small amount
b) falls by a large amount
c) increases by a small amount
d) increases by a large amount
e) falls by about the same amount

11.10
Correct: a)
Difficulty: 3
Page(s): 269
Scramble range: All
Topic: Isoquant line

11.10
If an isoquant illustrated in the text has a gentle slope, the
a) fall in capital is small relative to the rise in labour.
b) fall in capital is large relative to the rise in labour.
c) marginal rate of substitution is constant.
d) marginal rate of substitution is large.
e) marginal rate of substitution is rising.

11.11
Correct: d)
Difficulty: 2
Page(s): 261
Scramble range: All
Topic: Isoquant line

11.11
The slope of the isoquant measures the
a) price of capital relative to the price of labour.
b) maximum amount of output that can be produced given the amount of inputs used in production.
c) minimum amount of output that can be produced given the amount of inputs used in production.
d) marginal rate of substitution.
e) marginal cost of capital relative to the marginal cost of labour.

11.12
Correct: e)
Difficulty: 2
Page(s): 263
Scramble range: All
Topic: Isoquant line

11.12
Isoquants for larger outputs are
a) closer to the origin.
b) equal to the origin.
c) single points instead of curves.
d) not related to the origin.
e) farther from the origin.

11.13
Correct: a)
Difficulty: 2
Page(s): 261
Scramble range: All
Topic: Isoquant line

11.13
An isoquant is a curve that shows the
a) different combinations of labour and capital required to produce a fixed amount of output.
b) different combinations of labour and capital required to produce an increasing amount of output.
c) marginal product of labour relative to the price of labour.
d) marginal product of capital relative to the price of labour.
e) different combinations of labour and output, given a fixed amount of capital.

11.14
Correct: d)
Difficulty: 2
Page(s): 261
Scramble range: All
Topic: Isoquant line

11.14
See Figure 11.3. Which technique(s) would not be capable of producing an output of 30 sweaters?
a) Technique *b.*
b) Technique *c.*
c) Technique *e.*
d) Technique *a.*
e) Technique *d.*

Figure 11.3

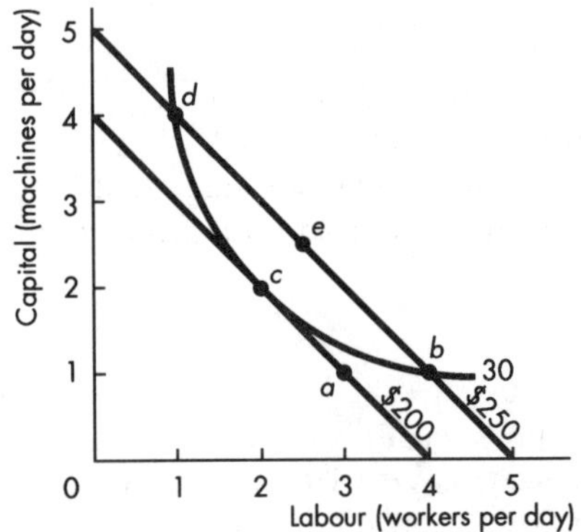

11.15
Correct: a)
Difficulty: 3
Page(s): 261
Scramble range: All
Topic: Isoquant line

11.15
See Figure 11.3. Which technique(s) would be capable of producing an output of more than 30 sweaters?
a) Technique *e.*
b) Technique *d.*
c) Technique *c.*
d) Technique *b.*
e) Technique *a.*

11.16
Correct: a)
Difficulty: 4
Page(s): 269
Scramble range: All
Topic: Isoquant line

11.16
If the inputs are very close substitutes for each other, the isoquants will be
a) almost straight lines and substitution will be large.
b) almost straight lines and large changes in input prices would lead to only small substitution effects.
c) curved very tightly and large changes in input prices would lead to only small substitution effects.
d) curved very tightly and large changes in input prices would lead to large substitution effects.
e) of average curvature, and substitution will be average.

11.17
Correct: b)
Difficulty: 2
Page(s): 261
Scramble range: All
Topic: Isoquant line

11.17
To remain on an isoquant,
a) the change in output must increase.
b) the change in output must be zero.
c) the change in output must decrease.
d) total cost of production must be minimized.
e) capital must increase.

11.18
Correct: c)
Difficulty: 2
Page(s): 261
Scramble range: All
Topic: Isoquant/marginal rate of substitution

11.18
The marginal rate of substitution of capital for labour measures the
a) slope of the long-run production function.
b) the price of labour relative to the price of capital.
c) decrease in capital needed per unit increase in labour to keep output constant.
d) increase in capital needed per unit increase in labour to keep output constant.
e) increase in capital needed per unit decrease in labour to keep output constant.

11.19
Correct: a)
Difficulty: 1
Page(s): 261
Scramble range: All
Topic: Isoquant line

11.19
An isoquant is a curve that shows the different combinations of inputs that can produce
a) a fixed amount of output.
b) an increasing amount of output.
c) a decreasing amount of output.
d) a given amount of output at minimum average cost.
e) a given amount of output for a given amount of capital and a varying amount of labour.

11.20
Correct: a)
Difficulty: 2
Page(s): 272
Scramble range: All
Topic: Isoquant line

11.20
The slope of the isoquant is
a) $MRS = MP_L/MP_K$.
b) $K = TC/P_K - (P_L/P_K)L$.
c) $P_L L + P_K K$.
d) $P_L K + P_K L$.
e) $MRS = MP_K/MP_L$.

11.21
Correct: d)
Difficulty: 2
Page(s): 263
Scramble range: All
Topic: Isoquant map

11.21
An isoquant map is a map that shows a series of
a) isocost lines, each for a different total cost.
b) isoquant lines, each for a different total cost.
c) isocost lines, each for a different quantity of output.
d) isoquant lines, each for a different quantity of output.
e) both isoquant and isocost lines, for differing amounts of costs and output.

11.22
Correct: e)
Difficulty: 3
Page(s): 261
Scramble range: All
Topic: Isoquant line

11.22
The law of diminishing marginal rate of substitution is a law stating that the marginal rate of substitution of

a) capital for labour falls as the amount of capital and the amount of labour both decrease.
b) capital for labour increases as the amount of capital decreases and the amount of labour increases.
c) capital for labour falls as the amount of both capital and labour increases.
d) the price of labour for the price of capital falls as the quantity of capital employed increases relative to the quantity of labour.
e) capital for labour falls as the amount of capital decreases and the amount of labour increases.

11.23
Correct: c)
Difficulty: 2
Page(s): 264
Scramble range: All
Topic: Isocost line

11.23
The equation of an isocost line is

a) $Q = TC/P_K - (P_L/P_K)L$.
b) $TC = TC/P_K - (P_L/P_K)L$.
c) $K = TC/P_K - (P_L/P_K)L$.
d) $P_L L + P_K K$.
e) $MRS = MP_L/MP_K$.

11.24
Correct: c)
Difficulty: 2
Page(s): 264
Scramble range: All
Topic: Isocost line

11.24
The slope of the isocost line is

a) $MRS = MP_L/MP_K$.
b) $K = TC/P_K - (P_L/P_K)L$.
c) P_L/P_K.
d) $P_L L + P_K K$.
e) P_K/P_L.

11.25
Correct: a)
Difficulty: 2
Page(s): 263
Scramble range: All
Topic: Isocost line

11.25
An isocost line shows the combinations of capital and labour that can be bought

a) for a given total cost.
b) to produce a given quantity of output.
c) to produce an increasing quantity of output.
d) to maximize total profit.
e) to minimize costs.

11.26
Correct: e)
Difficulty: 3
Page(s): 263–265
Scramble range: All
Topic: Isocost line

11.26
The slopes of the lines in an isocost map are determined by the

a) absolute price of the two inputs.
b) price of labour divided by the price of the finished output.
c) price of the output relative to the inputs.
d) selling price of the final product.
e) relative price of the two inputs.

11.27
Correct: c)
Difficulty: 2
Page(s): 266
Scramble range: All
Topic: Isocost map

11.27
An isocost map shows a series of

a) average total cost curves.
b) marginal cost curves.
c) isocost lines, each for a different level of total cost.
d) isocost lines, each for a different level of total output.
e) isocost lines, each for a different isoquant.

11.28
Correct: b)
Difficulty: 2
Page(s): 263–265
Scramble range: All
Topic: Isocost line

11.28
The slope of an isocost line is the ratio of the
a) price of inputs to the price of the output.
b) price of labour to the price of capital.
c) average cost curve to the marginal cost curve.
d) total cost of production to total profit.
e) marginal product of labour to the marginal product of capital.

11.29
Correct: b)
Difficulty: 2
Page(s): 263–265
Scramble range: All
Topic: Isocost line

11.29
Total cost equals
a) the price of labour multiplied by the quantity of output plus the price of capital multiplied by the quantity of output.
b) the price of labour multiplied by the quantity of labour employed plus the price of capital multiplied by the quantity of capital employed.
c) the marginal rate of substitution multiplied by the quantity of output.
d) all the alternative combinations of capital and labour that can produce a given level of output.
e) the marginal product of labour multiplied by the quantity of labour plus the marginal product of capital multiplied by the amount of capital.

11.30
Correct: c)
Difficulty: 2
Page(s): 263–265
Scramble range: All
Topic: Isocost map

11.30
See Figure 11.2, which shows the different ways of producing three levels of output a day. The figure represents
a) isocost lines.
b) isoprofit lines.
c) an isoquant map.
d) an isocost map.
e) a production function table.

11.31
Correct: d)
Difficulty: 2
Page(s): 264
Scramble range: All
Topic: Isocost line

11.31
If labour and capital each cost $30 a day, for a total cost of $150 Swanky can employ which combination of capital and labour?
a) 1 machine and 1 worker.
b) 2 machines and 1 worker.
c) 3 machines and 1 worker.
d) 3 machines and 2 workers.
e) 3 machines and 3 workers.

11.32
Correct: e)
Difficulty: 3
Page(s): 264
Scramble range: All
Topic: Isocost line

11.32
If labour costs $50 a day and capital costs $100 a day, for a total cost of $900 Swanky can employ which combination of capital and labour?
a) 1 machine and 4 workers.
b) 2 machines and 7 workers.
c) 2 machines and 8 workers.
d) 3 machines and 8 workers.
e) 4 machines and 10 workers.

11.33
Correct: a)
Difficulty: 2
Page(s): 265
Scramble range: All
Topic: Isocost line

11.33
The slope of the isocost line depends on
a) the relative input prices.
b) the price of the output relative to the input prices.
c) the price of the output relative to the prices of other goods produced for sale in the market.
d) the nature of production technology.
e) the ease with which capital and labour can be substituted for each other.

11.34
Correct: c)
Difficulty: 1
Page(s): 263–265
Scramble range: All
Topic: Isocost line

11.34
An isocost map shows a series of
a) isoprofit lines.
b) isocost lines.
c) isoquants, each for a different level of output.
d) short-run production functions.
e) isoproduction lines.

11.35
Correct: b)
Difficulty: 2
Page(s): 264
Scramble range: All
Topic: Isocost line

11.35
An isocost line is a line that shows all the combinations of capital
a) and labour that can be bought to produce the same level of output.
b) and labour that can be bought for the same total cost.
c) that can be bought for the same total cost of labour.
d) that can be bought for the same total cost of capital.
e) that can be produced for a given amount of labour.

11.36
Correct: c)
Difficulty: 2
Page(s): 263–265
Scramble range: All
Topic: Isocost line

11.36
An isocost map is a map that shows a series of
a) isocost lines, each for a different quantity of output.
b) isoquant lines, each for a different total cost.
c) isocost lines, each for a different total cost.
d) isoquant lines, each for a different quantity of output.
e) isocost and isoquant lines.

11.37
Correct: c)
Difficulty: 3
Page(s): 265
Scramble range: All
Topic: Isocost line

11.37
When the inputs each have the same price, the isocost line has a slope
a) of 0.
b) of 1/2.
c) of 1.
d) of 2.
e) equal to the price.

11.38
Correct: d)
Difficulty: 4
Page(s): 265
Scramble range: All
Topic: Isocost line

11.38
See Figure 11.4. The line labelled *A* shows the isocost line for a total cost of $200 when capital and labour each cost $50 a unit. If the price of capital increased to $200 and the price of labour stayed at $50, the new isocost line would be
a) line *A*.
b) line *B*.
c) line *C*.
d) line *D*.
e) above line *A*.

Figure 11.4

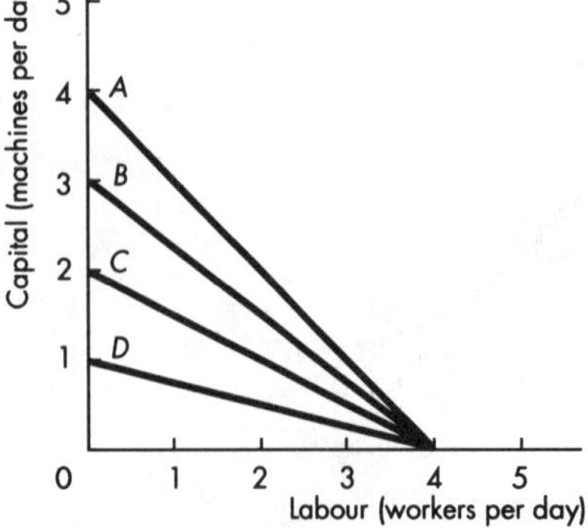

11.39
Correct: a)
Difficulty: 3
Page(s): 264
Scramble range: All
Topic: Isocost line

11.39
See Figure 11.4. Which isocost line has a slope of –1?
a) Line *A*.
b) Line *B*.
c) Line *C*.
d) Line *D*.
e) All of the lines.

11.40
Correct: b)
Difficulty: 3
Page(s): 265
Scramble range: All
Topic: Isocost line

11.40
See Figure 11.5. The shift in the curve from *X* to *Y* represents
a) an innovation.
b) an increase in the price of labour.
c) an increase in the price of capital.
d) a change in technology.
e) an increase in the price of both capital and labour.

Figure 11.5

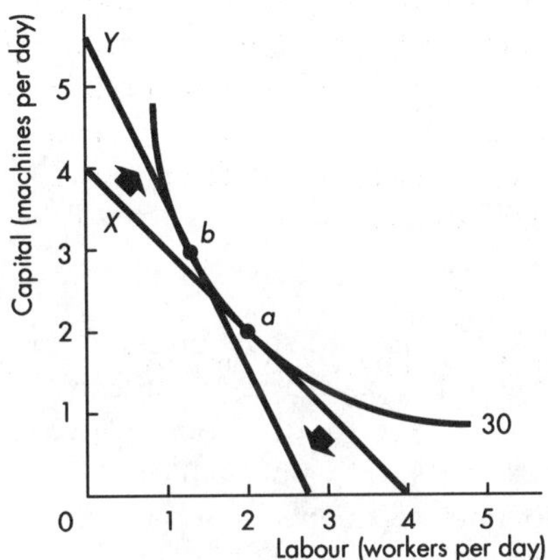

11.41
Correct: d)
Difficulty: 3
Page(s): 265
Scramble range: All
Topic: Isocost line

11.41
See Figure 11.6. The shift in the curve from *X* to *Y* represents
a) an increase in the production of the product.
b) an increase in the price of labour.
c) an increase in the use of capital.
d) a decrease in the price of labour.
e) a decrease in the price of both capital and labour.

Figure 11.6

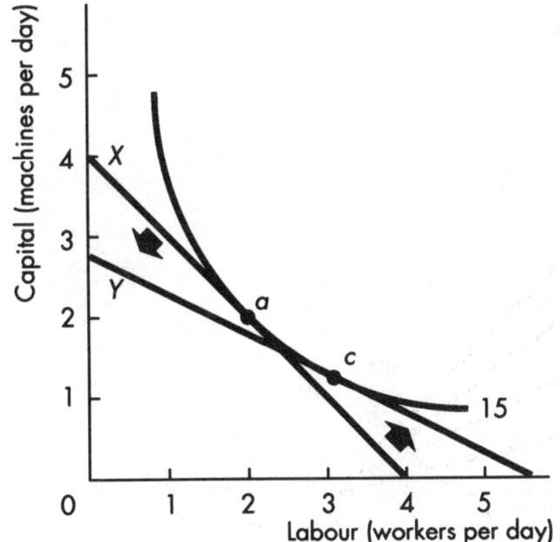

11.42
Correct: d)
Difficulty: 3
Page(s): 265
Scramble range: All
Topic: Isocost map

11.42
See Figure 11.7. For each isocost line, the prices of capital and labour are
a) $10 each.
b) $20 each.
c) $30 each.
d) $40 each.
e) $20 for capital and $40 for labour.

Figure 11.7

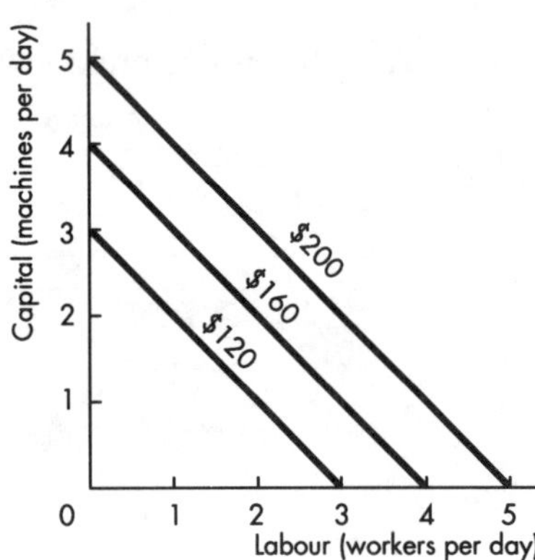

11.43
Correct: d)
Difficulty: 3
Page(s): 266
Scramble range: All
Topic: Isocost map

11.43
See Figure 11.7. The upward shifts in the isocost lines represent
a) an increase in the price of capital relative to labour.
b) an increase in the price of labour relative to capital.
c) an increase in the prices of both capital and labour.
d) increased amounts of spending on both capital and labour.
e) a decrease in the prices of both capital and labour.

11.44
Correct: c)
Difficulty: 4
Page(s): 267
Scramble range: All
Topic: Least-cost production/measure

11.44
See Figure 11.3. The least-cost technique of producing 30 sweaters occurs at
a) point *a*.
b) point *b*.
c) point *c*.
d) point *d*.
e) point *e*.

11.45
Correct: c)
Difficulty: 2
Page(s): 267
Scramble range: All
Topic: Least-cost production

11.45
See Figure 11.3. The total cost of producing an output of 30 sweaters using the least-cost technique is
a) $0.
b) $30.
c) $200.
d) $250.
e) $100.

11.46
Correct: b)
Difficulty: 4
Page(s): 267
Scramble range: All
Topic: Least-cost production

11.46
See Figure 11.3. Which technique(s) would produce an output of 30 sweaters at a total cost of $250?
a) Technique *a.*
b) Technique *b.*
c) Technique *c.*
d) Technique *e.*
e) Techniques *b* and *e.*

11.47
Correct: e)
Difficulty: 3
Page(s): 267
Scramble range: All
Topic: Least-cost production/measure

11.47
The least-cost of production occurs when
a) the marginal rate of substitution equals the marginal cost of production.
b) the slope of isoquant exceeds the slope of isocost line.
c) the isoquant cuts through the isocost line.
d) the marginal cost curve is at a minimum.
e) the marginal rate of substitution equals the relative price of the inputs.

11.48
Correct: b)
Difficulty: 4
Page(s): 267
Scramble range: All
Topic: Least-cost production/measure

11.48
If the isoquant cuts the isocost line
a) the least-cost technique has been found.
b) the least-cost technique has not been found.
c) the marginal rate of substitution equals the relative price of the inputs.
d) the slope of the isoquant equals the slope of the isocost line.
e) the firm needs to spend more to produce that level of output.

11.49
Correct: d)
Difficulty: 2
Page(s): 267
Scramble range: All
Topic: Least-cost of production

11.49
The least-cost technique of production measures the
a) minimum price of labour to the minimum price of capital.
b) minimum price of inputs to the price of the output.
c) quantity of capital used in production relative to the minimum quantity of labour.
d) least-expensive combination of inputs that produces a given output.
e) only technologically efficient method of production.

11.50
Correct: e)
Difficulty: 2
Page(s): 267
Scramble range: All
Topic: Least-cost production/measure

11.50
The least-cost technique of producing a given output occurs where
a) an isocost line is greater than the isoquant.
b) an isocost line is at its minimum point.
c) an isoquant line is at its maximum point.
d) the price of capital equals the price of labour.
e) an isocost line is tangential to the isoquant.

11.51
Correct: b)
Difficulty: 3
Page(s): 267
Scramble range: All
Topic: Least-cost production/measure

11.51
With the least-cost technique, the marginal rate of substitution of capital for labour equals the
a) ratio of the quantity of labour used relative to the quantity of capital used.
b) ratio of the price of labour to the price of capital.
c) minimum point on the isoquant line.
d) marginal cost of capital.
e) ratio of the marginal cost of capital to the marginal cost of labour.

11.52
Correct: e)
Difficulty: 2
Page(s): 267
Scramble range: All
Topic: Least-cost production

11.52
A change in input prices changes the
a) technology.
b) isocost line.
c) production function.
d) total product curve.
e) isoquant line.

11.53
Correct: a)
Difficulty: 3
Page(s): 268
Scramble range: All
Topic: Least-cost production

11.53
The higher the relative price of an input, the
a) smaller is the quantity of that input used in the least-cost technique.
b) greater is the quantity of that input used in the least-cost technique.
c) lower the amount of output that can be produced.
d) steeper the slope of the total product curve.
e) steeper the slope of the isoquant.

11.54
Correct: a)
Difficulty: 3
Page(s): 268
Scramble range: All
Topic: Least-cost production

11.54
See Figure 11.5. Suppose that the least-cost method of producing 30 sweaters a day changes from *a* to *b*. This indicates that the technique used is
a) more capital intensive.
b) more labour intensive.
c) capable of producing more than 30 sweaters.
d) capable of producing beyond plant capacity.
e) both more capital and more labour intensive.

11.55
Correct: b)
Difficulty: 3
Page(s): 268
Scramble range: All
Topic: Least-cost production

11.55
See Figure 11.6. Suppose that the least-cost method of producing 15 sweaters a day changes from *a* to *c*. This indicates that the technique used is
a) more capital intensive.
b) more labour intensive.
c) no longer capable of producing 15 sweaters.
d) capable of producing beyond plant capacity.
e) less expensive.

11.56
Correct: b)
Difficulty: 3
Page(s): 268
Scramble range: All
Topic: Least-cost production/measure

11.56
When total cost is minimized, the ratio of the marginal product of labour to the marginal product of capital
a) exceeds the ratio of the price of labour to the price of capital by the maximum amount.
b) equals the ratio of the price of labour to the price of capital.
c) is at a maximum.
d) is at a minimum.
e) equals the ratio of the price of capital to the price of labour.

11.57
Correct: b)
Difficulty: 3
Page(s): 271
Scramble range: All
Topic: Least-cost production/measure

11.57
When the least-cost technique of production is used, the marginal product of labour per dollar spent on labour is equal to the
a) average product of labour per dollar spent on labour.
b) marginal product of capital per dollar spent on capital.
c) the price of labour divided by the price of capital.
d) minumum average cost of production.
e) the slope of the isocost line.

11.58
Correct: e)
Difficulty: 2
Page(s): 266
Scramble range: All
Topic: Least-cost production

11.58
The least-cost technique is
a) represented by the isoquant line.
b) represented by the isocost line.
c) the combination of inputs that minimizes marginal cost.
d) the combination of inputs that maximizes total output.
e) the combination of inputs that minimizes total cost.

11.59
Correct: d)
Difficulty: 4
Page(s): 268
Scramble range: All
Topic: Least-cost production/measure

1.59
The firm cannot be using the least-cost technique when the
a) slopes of the isoquant and the isocost line are the same.
b) marginal product per dollar spent on labour equals the marginal product per dollar spent on capital.
c) the extra output from the last dollar spent on capital equals the extra output from the last dollar spent on labour.
d) marginal product of a purchased output equals zero.
e) the firm is economically efficient.

11.60
Correct: a)
Difficulty: 4
Page(s): 268
Scramble range: a)–d)
Topic: Least-cost production/measure

11.60
If the extra output from the last dollar spent on capital exceeded the extra output from the last dollar spent on labour it would pay the firm to use
a) less labour and more capital.
b) less capital and more labour.
c) more labour and more capital.
d) less labour and less capital.
e) none of the above.

11.61
Correct: a)
Difficulty: 2
Page(s): 272
Scramble range: All
Topic: Least-cost production/measure

11.61
When the least-cost technique is employed,
a) $MP_L/MP_K = P_L/P_K$.
b) $P_L = P_K$.
c) $MP_L = MP_K$.
d) $L = K$.
e) $MP_L/P_K = MP_K/P_L$.

11.62
Correct: a)
Difficulty: 4
Page(s): 268
Scramble range: a)–d)
Topic: Least-cost production/measure

11.62
If the extra output from the last dollar spent on labour exceeded the extra output from the last dollar spent on capital, it would pay the firm to use
a) less capital and more labour.
b) more capital and more labour.
c) less capital and less labour.
d) more capital and less labour.
e) none of the above.

11.63
Correct: e)
Difficulty: 3
Page(s): 268
Scramble range: All
Topic: Least-cost production/measure

11.63
A firm achieves the least-cost technique of production only when the extra output from the last dollar spent on all the inputs is
a) greater than 1.
b) equal to 1.
c) less than 1.
d) equal to the total cost of production.
e) the same.

11.64
Correct: a)
Difficulty: 2
Page(s): 266
Scramble range: All
Topic: Least-cost production/measure

11.64
The total cost of production is described by the expression:
a) $P_L L + P_K K$.
b) $P_L K + P_K L$.
c) $P_L/L + P_K/K$.
d) $P_L/K + P_K/L$.
e) $MP_L/MP_K = P_L/P_K$.

11.65
Correct: b)
Difficulty: 4
Page(s): 272
Scramble range: None
Topic: Least-cost production

11.65
Select the best statement.
a) The firm will generally be at the minimum of its average cost curve.
b) The firm will minimize costs for a given output level.
c) The firm will select capital and labour such that the average product per dollar spend on each input is equalized.
d) All of the above.
e) Both b) and c).

11.66
Correct: a)
Difficulty: 3
Page(s): 268
Scramble range: None
Topic: Least-cost production/measure

11.66
Total cost is minimized when
a) the marginal product per dollar spent on labour equals the marginal product per dollar spent on capital.
b) the total product per dollar spent on labour equals the total product per dollar spent on capital.
c) total cost with fixed capital and a change in labour input equals total cost with fixed labour and a change in capital input.
d) both a) and b).
e) both a) and c).

11.67
Correct: b)
Difficulty: 4
Page(s): 272
Scramble range: All
Topic: Least-cost production/measure

11.67
Total cost of a given level of output is minimized when
a) total cost with fixed capital and a change in labour input equals total cost with fixed labour and a change in capital input.
b) marginal cost with fixed capital and a change in labour input equals marginal cost with fixed labour and a change in capital input.
c) $K = TC/P_K - (P_L/P_K)L$.
d) marginal cost is mimimized.
e) the marginal product of capital equals the marginal product of labour.

11.68
Correct: a)
Difficulty: 3
Page(s): 272
Scramble range: All
Topic: Least-cost production/measure

11.68
Total cost of producing a given level of output is minimized when the
a) marginal product per dollar spent on labour equals the marginal product per dollar spent on capital.
b) marginal product per dollar spent on labour exceeds the marginal product per dollar spent on capital by the maximum amount.
c) total product per dollar spent on labour equals the total product per dollar spent on capital.
d) total product curve is at a maximum.
e) ratio of the marginal product of labour to the marginal product of capital equals one.

11.69
Correct: e)
Difficulty: 2
Page(s): 267
Scramble range: All
Topic: Least-cost production/measure

11.69
At the least-cost point, the marginal rate of substitution equals the
a) marginal productivity of capital.
b) slope of the average fixed cost curve.
c) slope of the average total cost curve.
d) slope of the total cost curve.
e) relative price of the inputs.

11.70
Correct: e)
Difficulty: 2
Page(s): 267
Scramble range: All
Topic: Least-cost production/measure

11.70
At the least-cost point, the slope of an isoquant equals
a) the slope of the marginal cost curve.
b) 1.
c) less than 1.
d) more than 1.
e) the slope of an isocost line.

11.71
Correct: b)
Difficulty: 2
Page(s): 271
Scramble range: All
Topic: Least-cost production/measure

11.71
Only when all inputs have the __________ impact on marginal cost has the firm achieved the minimum cost method of production.
a) minimum
b) same
c) maximum
d) average
e) marginal

11.72
Correct: a)
Difficulty: 4
Page(s): 271
Scramble range: All
Topic: Marginal product

11.72
Holding labour input constant, the marginal product of each additional unit of
a) capital diminishes as the capital input increases.
b) capital diminishes as the capital input decreases.
c) labour diminishes as the capital input increases.
d) capital remains constant as capital input increases or decreases.
e) input diminishes as the input increases.

11.73
Correct: a)
Difficulty: 3
Page(s): 271–272
Scramble range: All
Topic: Marginal product

11.73
If output rises because one more unit of labour is employed,
a) total cost rises by the cost of the extra labour.
b) output rises by the average product of the labour.
c) the firm is producing at minimum cost.
d) the firm is on a new production function.
e) total cost rises by the cost of the extra labour, plus the cost of the capital that extra labour uses.

11.74
Correct: c)
Difficulty: 3
Page(s): 272–273
Scramble range: a)–d)
Topic: Marginal product

11.74
The price of labour divided by the marginal product of labour is
a) marginal cost when the labour input is held constant.
b) average cost when the labour input is held constant.
c) marginal cost when the capital input is held constant.
d) average cost when the capital input is held constant.
e) none of the above.

11.75
Correct: c)
Difficulty: 3
Page(s): 271–272
Scramble range: All
Topic: Marginal product

11.75
Marginal cost is the price of labour
a) multiplied by the marginal product of labour.
b) plus the marginal product of labour.
c) divided by the marginal product of labour.
d) multiplied by the total number of workers employed.
e) divided by the price of capital.

11.76
Correct: d)
Difficulty: 3
Page(s): 268
Scramble range: All
Topic: Choice of technology/product

11.76
The long-run production function describes the
a) ratio of capital to labour.
b) price of capital relative to the price of labour.
c) isoquant curve.
d) output produced by different combinations of capital and labour.
e) the marginal product of capital relative to the marginal product of labour.

11.77
Correct: d)
Difficulty: 4
Page(s): 269
Scramble range: All
Topic: Choice of technology/industry variations

11.77
Which of the following does *not* cause variations in capital intensity across industries?
a) Differences in production functions between industries.
b) Some industries have isoquants that lead them to choose a capital-intensive technique as the least-cost technique of production.
c) Differences in wages between industries.
d) Failure of average fixed cost to decline as output increases.
e) Differences in the price of capital between industries.

11.78
Correct: c)
Difficulty: 3
Page(s): 269
Scramble range: All
Topic: Choice of technology/cross-country

11.78
Firms in a high-wage country use __________ techniques while those in low-wage countries adopt __________ techniques.
a) more costly; less costly
b) less costly; more costly
c) capital-intensive; labour-intensive
d) labour-intensive; capital-intensive
e) capital intensive; more costly

11.79
Correct: d)
Difficulty: 4
Page(s): 269
Scramble range: All
Topic: Choice of technology/industry variations

11.79
Variations in capital intensity across industries in a given country arise from the fact that
a) there are differences in world prices of inputs.
b) all firms buy their inputs in common markets, so they have to pay similar input prices.
c) firms face similar isocost lines.
d) the isoquants that describe their technologies differ.
e) there are differences in wage rates.

11.80
Correct: c)
Difficulty: 4
Page(s): 269
Scramble range: All
Topic: Choice of technology/industry variations

11.80
Over the industrial economic history of Canada, there has been a steady increase in the relative price of labour. As wages have increased,
a) the isocost line has shifted inward and become flatter.
b) the isocost line has shifted outward.
c) firms have chosen a more capital-intensive technique.
d) firms have increased the labour intensity of production in the long run.
e) the isocost line has shifted outward and become flatter.

11.81
Correct: b)
Difficulty: 4
Page(s): 268–272
Scramble range: All
Topic: Least-cost production

11.81
Suppose we have a firm that is initially in long-run cost-minimizing equilibrium. Suppose that the price of capital rises, all else being equal.
a) The firm will not change any of its decisions, since capital is a fixed cost that the firm cannot change.
b) The firm will use more labour, and less capital, as now labour yields a higher return per dollar expended.
c) The firm will substitute towards using more capital, since clearly it is now more productive.
d) The firm will probably close down, since the higher costs will drive it out of business.
e) The firm can never get back in long-run cost-minimizing equilibrium, as it cannot stay on the same isoquant.

11.82 (SG 11.2)
Correct: d)
Difficulty: 4
Page(s): 261
Scramble range: All
Topic: Diminishing marginal rate of substitution

11.82
Which of the following reflects the law of diminishing marginal rate of substitution? As we continually increase labour one unit at a time,
a) the addition to output will become larger, if capital is held constant.
b) the addition to output will become smaller, if capital is held constant.
c) larger reductions in capital will be required to keep output constant.
d) smaller reductions in capital will be required to keep output constant.
e) larger increases in labour will be required to keep output constant.

11.83 (SG 11.3)
Correct: e)
Difficulty: 3
Page(s): 261
Scramble range: All
Topic: Isoquant

11.83
Figure 11.8 shows a series of isoquants. Which of the following is *not* a combination of labour and capital required to produce 20 units of output?
a) 8 units of labour and 1 unit of capital.
b) 5 units of labour and 2 units of capital.
c) 3 units of labour and 3 units of capital
d) 2 units of labour and 4 units of capital.
e) 7 units of labour and 2 units of capital.

Figure 11.8

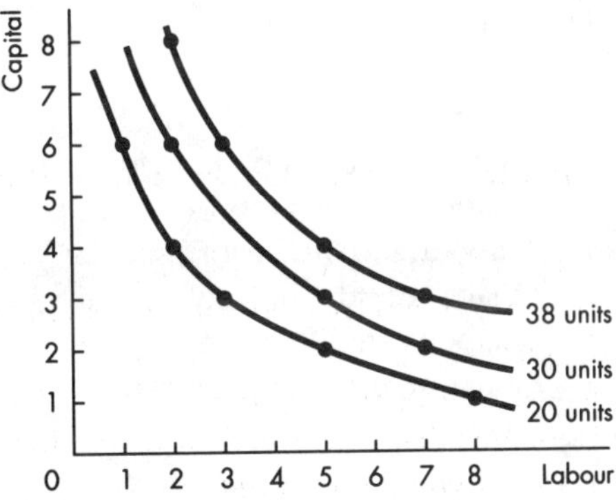

11.84 (SG 11.4)
Correct: c)
Difficulty: 4
Page(s): 260–261
Scramble range: All
Topic: Marginal rate of substitution

11.84
Refer to Figure 11.8. What is the marginal rate of substitution of capital for labour as labour is increased from 2 to 3 units if output is being kept constant at 38 units?
a) 1/2.
b) 1.
c) 2.
d) 3.
e) 6.

11.85 (SG 11.5)
Correct: e)
Difficulty: 4
Page(s): 261
Scramble range: All
Topic: Marginal product

11.85
Refer to Figure 11.8. Suppose 6 units of capital and 2 units of labour are currently in use. What is the marginal product of an additional unit of labour?
a) 2.
b) 18.
c) 10.
d) 1.5.
e) 8.

11.86 (SG 11.6)
Correct: b)
Difficulty: 3
Page(s): 261
Scramble range: All
Topic: Diminishing marginal rate of substitution

11.86
Refer to Figure 11.8. What characteristic of these isoquants reflects the law of diminishing marginal rate of substitution?
a) The isoquants are negatively sloped.
b) The isoquants become flatter as labour input increases.
c) The isoquants farther to the right correspond to larger output.
d) Output increases by a smaller amount as we continually shift to the right.
e) The isoquants become steeper as labour input increases.

11.87 (SG 11.7)
Correct: a)
Difficulty: 1
Page(s): 261
Scramble range: All
Topic: Isoquant map

11.87
Figure 11.8 is an example of
a) an isoquant map.
b) an isocost map.
c) a shifting production function.
d) the least-cost technique.
e) the production decision of the firm.

11.88 (SG 11.8)
Correct: c)
Difficulty: 3
Page(s): 265
Scramble range: All
Topic: Ratio marginal product and slope

11.88
The (absolute value of the) slope of an isocost line (with labour measured on the horizontal axis) is the ratio of
a) the marginal product of labour to the marginal product of capital.
b) the marginal product of capital to the marginal product of labour.
c) the price of labour to the price of capital.
d) the price of capital to the price of labour.
e) the marginal product of labour to the price of labour.

11.89 (SG 11.9)
Correct: e)
Difficulty: 2
Page(s): 264
Scramble range: All
Topic: Isocost line

11.89
Figure 11.9 shows an isocost line. Which of the following is *not* a combination of capital and labour that can be bought for $240?
a) 0 units of labour and 6 units of capital.
b) 1 unit of labour and 5 units of capital.
c) 5 units of labour and 2 units of capital.
d) 8 units of labour and 0 units of capital.
e) 4 units of labour and 4 units of capital.

Figure 11.9

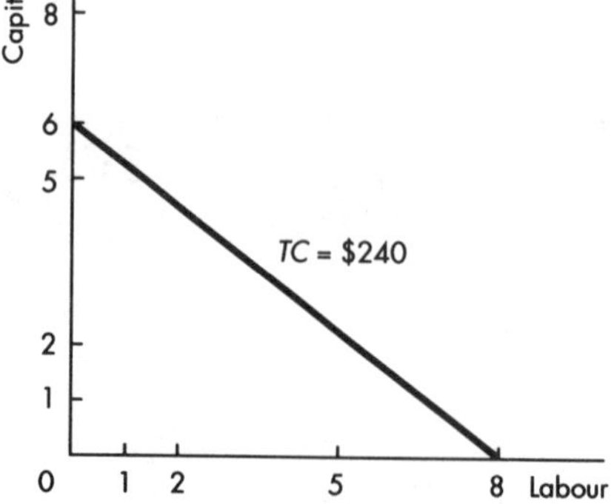

11.90 (SG 11.10)
Correct: d)
Difficulty: 3
Page(s): 264
Scramble range: All
Topic: Isocost and input prices

11.90
Refer to Figure 11.9. What is the price of a unit of capital?
a) $10.
b) $20.
c) $30.
d) $40.
e) $6.

11.91 (SG 11.11)
Correct: a)
Difficulty: 3
Page(s): 265
Scramble range: All
Topic: Isocost line

11.91
Refer to Figure 11.9. If the price of labour rises, the isocost line will
a) become steeper.
b) become flatter.
c) shift to the right but retain the same slope.
d) shift to the left but retain the same slope.
e) shift to the right but become steeper.

11.92 (SG 11.12)
Correct: d)
Difficulty: 4
Page(s): 266–267
Scramble range: All
Topic: Least-cost production

11.92
Which of the following is *not* a characteristic of the least-cost technique of production?
a) The marginal rate of substitution of capital for labour equals the ratio of the price of labour to the price of capital.
b) The slope of the isoquant equals the slope of the isocost line.
c) The isocost line is tangent to the isoquant.
d) The marginal product of labour equals the marginal product of capital.
e) Total cost is minimized given the output level.

11.93 (SG 11.13)
Correct: b)
Difficulty: 4
Page(s): 267
Scramble range: All
Topic: Least-cost production

11.93
Figure 11.10 gives isoquants and isocost lines for a firm. What combination of labour and capital give the least-cost technique of producing 20 units?
a) 1 unit of labour and 8 units of capital.
b) 3 1/2 units of labour and 3 1/2 units of capital.
c) 4 units of labour and 5 units of capital.
d) 6 units of labour and 2 units of capital.
e) 2 units of labour and 7 units of capital.

Figure 11.10

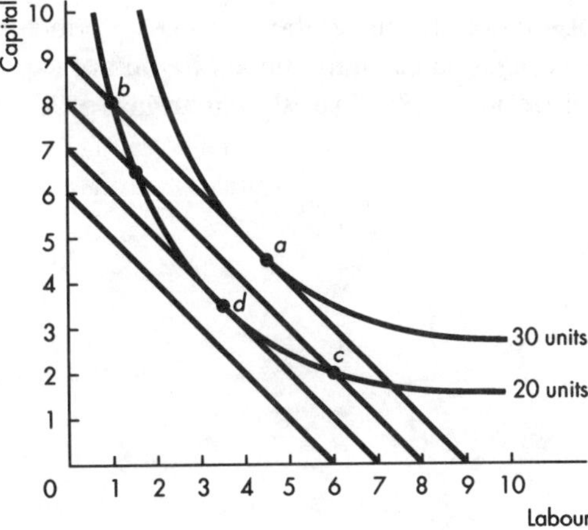

11.94 (SG 11.14)
Correct: b)
Difficulty: 3
Page(s): 267
Scramble range: All
Topic: Marginal rate of substitution

11.94
Refer to Figure 11.10. At point *a*, the marginal rate of substitution of capital for labour
a) is 1/2.
b) is 1.
c) is 2.
d) is 3/4.
e) cannot be determined without further data.

11.95 (SG 11.15)
Correct: a)
Difficulty: 5
Page(s): 267
Scramble range: All
Topic: Least-cost production

11.95
Refer to Figure 11.10. If the price of a unit of capital is $20, what is the least cost required to produce 30 units of output?
a) $180.
b) $150.
c) $100.
d) $80.
e) $90.

11.96 (SG 11.16)
Correct: e)
Difficulty: 5
Page(s): 266–268
Scramble range: All
Topic: Firm equilibrium

11.96
Refer to Figure 11.10. Which of the following is true at point *c*?
a) Total cost is the same as at point *b*.
b) Total cost is less than at point *d*.
c) The marginal rate of substitution of capital for labour is greater than one.
d) Total cost is the same as at point *d*.
e) The cost of producing 20 units of output can be reduced by decreasing labour and increasing capital.

11.97 (SG 11.17)
Correct: e)
Difficulty: 3
Page(s): 268
Scramble range: All
Topic: Slope isocost/input price

11.97
Suppose the price of capital falls. If capital is measured on the vertical axis, the isocost curve will become
a) steeper and production will become more labour intensive.
b) steeper and production will become less capital intensive.
c) flatter and production will become more capital intensive.
d) flatter and production will become less capital intensive.
e) steeper and production will become more capital intensive.

11.98 (SG 11.18)
Correct: b)
Difficulty: 4
Page(s): 271
Scramble range: All
Topic: Least-cost production

11.98
We observe a firm using the least-cost production technique. The marginal product of capital is 5, the price of a unit of capital is $20, and the price of a unit of labour is $8. What is the marginal product of labour?
a) 1.
b) 2.
c) 1/2.
d) 8.
e) 4.

11.99 (SG 11.19)
Correct: d)
Difficulty: 5
Page(s): 266–271
Scramble range: All
Topic: Firm equilibrium

11.99
A firm finds that, for its current production technique, the ratio of the marginal product of labour to the marginal product of capital is greater than the ratio of the price of labour to the price of capital. The firm can
a) produce more only if it is willing to increase total cost.
b) produce more at the same total cost only if the price of capital falls.
c) produce the same amount at lower cost if it decreases labour and increases capital.
d) produce the same amount at lower cost if it increases labour and decreases capital.
e) produce the same amount at lower cost if it increases labour and capital.

11.100 (SG 11.20)
Correct: c)
Difficulty: 3
Page(s): 269–271
Scramble range: All
Topic: Differences in production function

11.100
The main reason for variations in capital intensity across different industries in a single country is differences in
a) the price of labour.
b) the slope of isocost lines.
c) production functions.
d) access to technology.
e) the price of capital.

11.101
Correct: a)
Difficulty: 2
Page(s): 260
Scramble range: All
Topic: Marginal rate of substitution

11.101
The decrease in capital per unit increase in labour to keep output constant is called
a) the marginal rate of substitution of capital for labour.
b) the marginal rate of substitution of labour for capital.
c) decreasing returns to scale.
d) increasing returns to scale.
e) the law of diminishing marginal rate of substitution.

11.102
Correct: d)
Difficulty: 2
Page(s): 261
Scramble range: All
Topic: Diminishing marginal rate of substitution

11.102
As we continually increase labour one unit at a time, smaller reductions in capital will be required to keep output constant. This statement reflects
a) the law of diminishing returns.
b) the law of increasing costs.
c) the law of decreasing marginal returns.
d) diminishing marginal rate of substitution.
e) the law of supply.

11.103
Correct: e)
Difficulty: 5
Page(s): 267
Scramble range: All
Topic: Least-cost production

11.103
The owner of the Burning Belly Taco Stand has hired you as an economist to evaluate her choice of inputs. She has two workers, the only inputs in the production process, Carol Cook and Walter Waiter. You calculate W.W.'s marginal product as 40 tacos per hour of work, and C.C.'s marginal product as 60 tacos per hour of work. Walter gets paid $5 per hour (plus he earns an average of $3 per hour in tips because customers love his rudeness), while Carol earns $12 per hour. Your recommendation to the firm will be

a) that the Taco Stand is operating with economic efficiency, and no changes should be made.
b) that both workers are working too little given their marginal product, and that they should both get more hours.
c) that both workers are working too much given their marginal product, and that they both should work less hours.
d) that Walter is working too many hours, and should work less and Carol should work more hours.
e) that Walter is working too few hours, and that he should work more hours and Carol should work less hours.

11.104
Correct: b)
Difficulty: 1
Page(s): 261
Scramble range: All
Topic: Isoquant

11.104
A curve showing all the different combinations of producing a given level of output in a technically efficient way is called

a) an isocost.
b) an isoquant.
c) a production function.
d) an indifference curve.
e) a marginal cost curve.

11.105
Correct: b)
Difficulty: 3
Page(s): 266
Scramble range: All
Topic: Ratio of marginal product and slope

11.105
With labour measured on the horizontal axis, the ratio of the price of labour to the price of capital is equal to

a) the slope of the isoquant line.
b) the marginal product of labour to the marginal product of capital.
c) the marginal product of capital to the marginal product of labour.
d) the absolute value of the slope of an isoquant line.
e) the marginal cost of labour.

11.106
Correct: b)
Difficulty: 5
Page(s): 265
Scramble range: All
Topic: Isocost line

11.106
Consider an isocost line graphed with labour on the vertical axis and capital on the horizontal axis. As the price of labour rises, the isocost line will

a) become steeper.
b) become flatter.
c) shift to the right but retain the same slope.
d) shift to the left but retain the same slope.
e) shift to the right but become flatter.

11.107
Correct: e)
Difficulty: 3
Page(s): 267
Scramble range: All
Topic: Least-cost production

11.107
Which of the following is a characteristic of the least-cost technique of production?

a) The ratio of the marginal product of capital to the marginal product of labour equals the ratio of the price of labour to the price of capital.
b) The marginal product of labour equals the price of labour.
c) The isocost line is steeper than the isoquant.
d) The marginal product of labour equals the marginal product of capital.
e) The slope of the isoquant equals the slope of the isocost line.

11.108
Correct: d)
Difficulty: 4
Page(s): 268
Scramble range: All
Topic: Slope isocost/input price

11.108
Suppose the price of capital rises. If capital is measured on the vertical axis, the isocost curve will become
a) steeper and production will become more capital intensive.
b) steeper and production will become less capital intensive.
c) flatter and production will become more capital intensive.
d) flatter and production will become less capital intensive.
e) flatter and production will become less labour intensive.

11.109
Correct: e)
Difficulty: 5
Page(s): 272
Scramble range: All
Topic: Least-cost production

11.109
We observe a firm using the least-cost production technique. The marginal product of capital is 10, the price of a unit of capital is $40, and the price of a unit of labour is $16. What is the marginal product of labour?
a) 1/4.
b) 8.
c) 2.
d) 1.
e) 4.

11.110
Correct: c)
Difficulty: 4
Page(s): 266–268
Scramble range: All
Topic: Firm equilibrium

11.110
A firm finds that, for its current production technique, the ratio of the marginal product of labour to the marginal product of capital is less than the ratio of the price of labour to the price of capital. The firm can produce
a) more only if it is willing to increase total cost.
b) more at the same total cost only if the price of capital falls.
c) the same amount at lower cost if it decreases labour and increases capital.
d) the same amount at lower cost if it increases labour and decreases capital.
e) the same amount at lower cost if it increases labour and capital.

11.111
Correct: d)
Difficulty: 4
Page(s): 260
Scramble range: All
Topic: Marginal rate of substitution

11.111
Consider Fact 11.1. If the firm switches the method of production from 1 unit of labour and 3 units of capital to 2 units of each, then the marginal rate of substitution of capital for labour is
a) 90.
b) 1/2.
c) 2.
d) 1.
e) not calculable because the firm does not remain on the same isoquant.

Fact 11.1 The following table shows the output per hour of a doughnut producer using alternative combinations of capital and labour:

Units of capital	Units of labour 1	2	3
3	280	430	490
2	190	280	320
1	100	160	190

11.112
Correct: d)
Difficulty: 5
Page(s): 266–268
Scramble range: All
Topic: Least-cost production

11.112
Consider Fact 11.1. Suppose now that the doughnut producer finds that labour costs $10 an hour and capital rents for $15 an hour. If she decides to produce 190 doughnuts per hour, *in whole units* what are her optimal amounts of labour and capital?

a) 1 unit of capital and 1 unit of labour.
b) 1 unit of capital and 2 units of labour.
c) 1 unit of capital and 3 units of labour.
d) 2 units of capital and 1 unit of labour.
e) 2 units of capital and 2 units of labour.

11.113
Correct: e)
Difficulty: 4
Page(s): 266–268
Scramble range: None
Topic: Least-cost production

11.113
Consider Table 11.1, which gives information on the firm of Economics 101:

a) This "firm" is above its least-cost production level.
b) The head of this firm should have Prof. Meany work fewer months, and have Prof. Softy work more months.
c) The head of this firm should have Prof. Meany work more months, and have Prof. Softy work fewer months.
d) Both a) and b).
e) Both a) and c).

Table 11.1

	Prof. Meany	Prof. Softy
Wage rate	$2,500/month	$5,000/month
Marginal product (tough exams)	50/month	60/month

Chapter 12 Competition

12.1
Correct: a)
Difficulty: 1
Page(s): 283
Scramble range: All
Topic: Perfect competition

12.1
Perfect competition occurs in a market where there are many firms each selling a(n)
a) identical product.
b) similiar product.
c) unique product.
d) capital-intensive product.
e) competitive product.

12.2
Correct: c)
Difficulty: 2
Page(s): 283
Scramble range: All
Topic: Perfect competition

12.2
Which one of the following does *not* occur in perfect competition?
a) No single firm can exert a significant influence on the market price of the good.
b) There are many buyers.
c) There are significant restrictions on entry into the industry.
d) Firms and buyers are completely informed about the prices of the products of each firm in the industry.
e) Firms already in the industry have no advantage over potential new entrants.

12.3
Correct: d)
Difficulty: 2
Page(s): 285
Scramble range: All
Topic: Perfect competition

12.3
Which one of the following is *not* one of the key decisions a perfectly competitive firm has to make?
a) Whether to stay in the industry or leave it.
b) If the decision is to stay in the industry, whether to produce or temporarily shut down.
c) If the decision is to produce, how much to produce.
d) After the decision is made to produce a certain amount of output, what price to charge for the product.
e) Whether to exit or enter the industry.

12.4
Correct: d)
Difficulty: 2
Page(s): 284–286
Scramble range: All
Topic: Revenue/firm's demand

12.4
A price-taking firm faces a
a) downward sloping average revenue curve.
b) downward sloping marginal revenue curve.
c) downward sloping supply curve.
d) demand curve that is perfectly elastic.
e) downward sloping demand curve.

12.5
Correct: b)
Difficulty: 2
Page(s): 285
Scramble range: All
Topic: Revenue/average

12.5
Under perfect competition, a firm's average revenue is
a) total revenue divided by the total cost.
b) equal to price.
c) the revenue received by the firm per unit of labour hired.
d) price times quantity sold.
e) marginal revenue divided by price.

12.6
Correct: e)
Difficulty: 3
Page(s): 285
Scramble range: None
Topic: Revenue/marginal

12.6
In perfect competition, a firm's marginal revenue equals its
a) price.
b) total revenue.
c) supply curve.
d) average revenue.
e) both a) and d).

12.7
Correct: b)
Difficulty: 3
Page(s): 285
Scramble range: All
Topic: Revenue/marginal

12.7
Marginal revenue is the
a) change in total quantity resulting from a 1-unit increase in the price of the product sold.
b) change in total revenue resulting from a 1-unit increase in the quantity sold.
c) total revenue divided by a 1-unit increase in the quantity sold.
d) increase in profit divided by a 1-unit increase in the quantity sold.
e) change in price resulting from a 1-unit increase in the quantity sold.

12.8
Correct: d)
Difficulty: 3
Page(s): 285–286
Scramble range: All
Topic: Revenue/marginal

12.8
Which one of the following is *not* true in the case of the perfectly competitive firm?
a) The price remains constant when the quantity sold changes.
b) The change in total revenue is equal to price multiplied by the change in quantity.
c) Marginal revenue equals price.
d) Marginal revenue is generally less than average revenue.
e) Average revenue equals price.

12.9
Correct: d)
Difficulty: 3
Page(s): 286
Scramble range: All
Topic: Revenue/total

12.9
See Figure 12.1, which represents a cost or revenue curve for a perfectly competitive firm. Curve *A* represents the firm's
a) total fixed cost.
b) average fixed cost.
c) average variable cost.
d) total revenue.
e) marginal revenue.

Figure 12.1

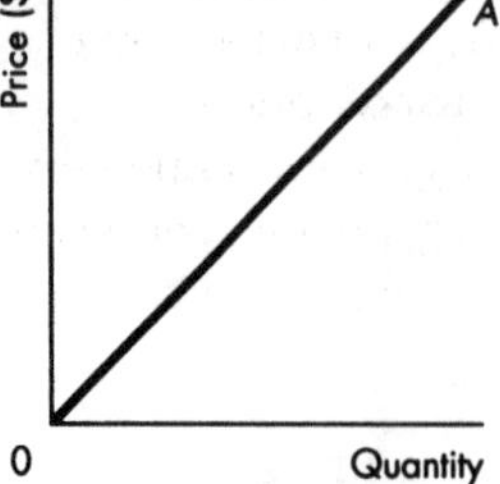

12.10
Correct: a)
Difficulty: 4
Page(s): 286
Scramble range: All
Topic: Revenue/total

12.10
See Figure 12.1, which represents a cost or revenue curve for a perfectly competitive firm. Curve *A* is straight because the firm
a) is a price taker.
b) faces constant returns to scale.
c) wants to maximize profits.
d) has perfect information.
e) has constant fixed cost.

12.11
Correct: c)
Difficulty: 3
Page(s): 285
Scramble range: All
Topic: Revenue/total

12.11
See Table 12.1, which represents the revenue schedule for a perfectly competitive firm. If the firm sells 5 units of output, total revenue is
a) $15.
b) $30.
c) $75.
d) $90.
e) $105.

Table 12.1

Quantity sold, *Q*	Price, *P* ($)
5	15
6	15
7	15

12.12
Correct: a)
Difficulty: 3
Page(s): 285
Scramble range: All
Topic: Revenue/average

12.12
See Table 12.1, which represents the revenue schedule for a perfectly competitive firm. If the firm sells 6 units of output, average revenue is
a) $15.
b) $30.
c) $75.
d) $90.
e) $105.

12.13
Correct: a)
Difficulty: 3
Page(s): 285
Scramble range: All
Topic: Revenue/marginal

12.13
See Table 12.1, which represents the revenue schedule for a perfectly competitive firm. If the quantity sold by the firm rises from 5 to 6, marginal revenue is
a) $15.
b) $30.
c) $75.
d) $90.
e) $105.

12.14
Correct: d)
Difficulty: 3
Page(s): 283–286
Scramble range: All
Topic: Revenue/firm's demand

12.14
The perfectly competitive firm's demand curve is *not*
a) perfectly elastic at the market price.
b) the same as the firm's average revenue curve.
c) the same as the firm's marginal revenue curve.
d) downward sloping to the right.
e) horizontal.

12.15
Correct: e)
Difficulty: 3
Page(s): 285
Scramble range: All
Topic: Revenue/price

12.15
See Table 12.2, which represents the total revenue and cost schedule of a perfectly competitive firm. The short-run equilibrium price of the product is
a) $ 3.
b) $10.
c) $15.
d) $25.
e) $30.

Table 12.2

Output *O*	Total revenue *TR*	Total cost *TC*
0	0	25
1	30	49
2	60	69
3	90	86
4	120	100
5	150	114
6	180	128

12.16
Correct: e)
Difficulty: 3
Page(s): 285
Scramble range: All
Topic: Revenue/ marginal

12.16
See Table 12.2, which represents the total revenue and cost schedule of a perfectly competitive firm. The marginal revenue received from the sale of the fourth unit of output is
a) $ 3.
b) $15.
c) $10.
d) $120.
e) $30.

12.17
Correct: a)
Difficulty: 3
Page(s): 288
Scramble range: All
Topic: Costs/marginal

12.17
See Table 12.2, which represents the total revenue and cost schedule of a perfectly competitive firm. The marginal cost of the production of the fifth unit of output is
a) $ 14.
b) $128.
c) $100.
d) $25.
e) $30.

12.18
Correct: b)
Difficulty: 3
Page(s): 290
Scramble range: All
Topic: Production decision

12.18
It pays a firm to shut down production if price is
a) above minimum average variable cost.
b) below minimum average variable cost.
c) above minimum average fixed cost.
d) below minimum average revenue.
e) below average total cost.

12.19
Correct: d)
Difficulty: 4
Page(s): 290
Scramble range: All
Topic: Production decision

12.19
See Table 12.3, which shows the hourly costs for Chip's Pizza Palace, a perfectly competitive firm. If pizzas sell for $6, what is Chip's profit-maximizing output per hour?
a) 0.
b) 1.
c) 2.
d) 3.
e) 4.

Table 12.3

Output (pizzas per hour)	Total cost (dollars per hour)
0	10
1	12
2	16
3	22
4	30
5	40

12.20
Correct: b)
Difficulty: 3
Page(s): 290
Scramble range: All
Topic: Production decision

12.20
See Table 12.3, which shows the hourly costs for Chip's Pizza Palace, a perfectly competitive firm. If Chip were to shut down in the short run, his total cost would be
a) $ 0.
b) $10.
c) $12.
d) $22.
e) $40.

12.21
Correct: b)
Difficulty: 2
Page(s): 291
Scramble range: All
Topic: Costs/fixed

12.21
See Table 12.4, which shows the hourly costs for Brenda's Balloon Shop, a perfectly competitive firm. The total fixed cost of production is
a) $ 3.00.
b) $ 4.00.
c) $ 7.00.
d) $29.00.
e) not determinable from the data.

Table 12.4

Output (balloons per hour)	Total cost (dollars per hour)
0	4.00
1	7.00
2	8.00
3	12.50
4	17.20
5	22.00
6	29.00

12.22
Correct: d)
Difficulty: 3
Page(s): 291
Scramble range: All
Topic: Costs/marginal

12.22
See Table 12.4, which shows the hourly costs for Brenda's Balloon Shop, a perfectly competitive firm. The marginal cost of producing the fifth unit of output is
a) $1.00.
b) $4.50.
c) $4.70.
d) $4.80.
e) $4.40.

12.23
Correct: e)
Difficulty: 4
Page(s): 291
Scramble range: All
Topic: Costs/average

12.23
See Table 12.4, which shows the hourly costs for Brenda's Balloon Shop, a perfectly competitive firm. The average fixed cost of producing the fourth unit of output is
a) $4.30.
b) $4.80.
c) $4.70.
d) $4.50.
e) $1.00.

12.24
Correct: e)
Difficulty: 5
Page(s): 291
Scramble range: All
Topic: Costs/average

12.24
See Table 12.4, which shows the hourly costs for Brenda's Balloon Shop, a perfectly competitive firm. The average variable cost of producing the first unit of output is
a) $1.00.
b) $4.00.
c) $2.00.
d) $4.80.
e) $3.00.

12.25
Correct: c)
Difficulty: 3
Page(s): 290
Scramble range: All
Topic: Economic profit/breakeven point

12.25
When Swanky makes zero economic profit, then Sidney, its owner,
a) is taking a loss.
b) will shut down in the short run.
c) is making an income in the form of compensation that Swanky pays him for the time and capital that Sidney supplied.
d) is suffering economic hardship.
e) will exit in the long run.

12.26
Correct: c)
Difficulty: 3
Page(s): 290
Scramble range: All
Topic: Economic profit/breakeven point

12.26
When Swanky makes zero economic profit, then Sidney, its owner, is
a) going to go out of business in the long run.
b) taking a loss in the short run.
c) making an income equal to the opportunity cost of the resources he owns.
d) suffering economic hardship.
e) going to hire a new manager.

12.27
Correct: a)
Difficulty: 4
Page(s): 290
Scramble range: All
Topic: Economic profit

12.27
Economic profit is
a) the difference between revenue and cost when all opportunity costs are taken into account.
b) the difference between revenue and cost excluding all opportunity costs.
c) zero when opportunity costs just begin to increase.
d) zero when opportunity costs just begin to decrease.
e) always zero due to entry and exit.

12.28
Correct: a)
Difficulty: 3
Page(s): 290
Scramble range: All
Topic: Economic profit/measurement

12.28
See Figure 12.2, which represents the short-run production decision of a perfectly competitive firm. Given the market price of P_1, the firm is
a) making economic profit
b) taking a loss.
c) breaking even.
d) failing to cover its opportunity costs.
e) going to close down temporarily.

Figure 12.2

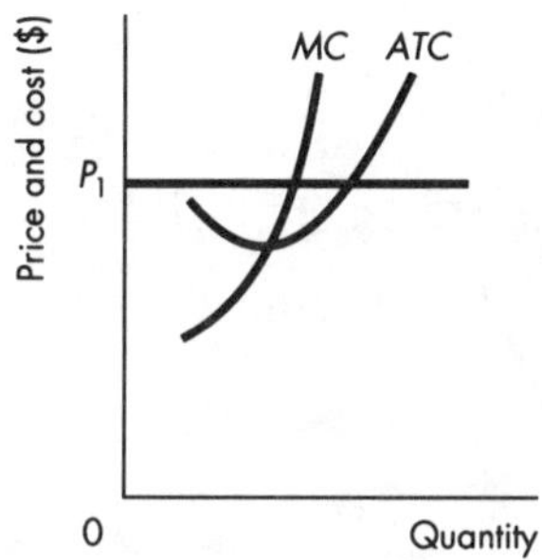

12.29
Correct: c)
Difficulty: 3
Page(s): 290–291
Scramble range: All
Topic: Economic loss/measurement

12.29
See Table 12.2, which represents the total revenue and cost schedule of a perfectly competitive firm. If the firm produces 2 units of output, it will make an economic
a) profit of $ 9.
b) profit of $60.
c) loss of $ 9.
d) loss of $60.
e) loss of $69.

12.30
Correct: a)
Difficulty: 3
Page(s): 290–291
Scramble range: All
Topic: Economic profit/measurement

12.30
See Table 12.2, which represents the total revenue and cost schedule of a perfectly competitive firm. If the firm produces 3 units of output, it will
a) make an economic profit of $ 4.
b) make an economic profit of $90.
c) make an economic loss of $ 4.
d) break even.
e) make an economic loss of $86.

12.31
Correct: b)
Difficulty: 3
Page(s): 288–291
Scramble range: a)–d)
Topic: Production decision

12.31
A firm will shut down temporarily when the price is so low that total revenue is not even enough to cover the total
a) cost of production.
b) variable costs of production.
c) fixed costs of production.
d) fixed plus variable costs of production.
e) none of the above.

12.32
Correct: e)
Difficulty: 4
Page(s): 290–291
Scramble range: All
Topic: Economic loss/measurement

12.32
See Figure 12.3, which represents the curves necessary for a perfectly competitive firm to make its production decision in the short run. Given the market price of the product is $8, the firm will produce _________ units of output and make an economic _________
a) 10; loss of $40.
b) 10; loss of $80.
c) less than 10; loss of $120.
d) 10; profit of $40.
e) less than 10; loss of less than $40, but greater than $0.

Figure 12.3

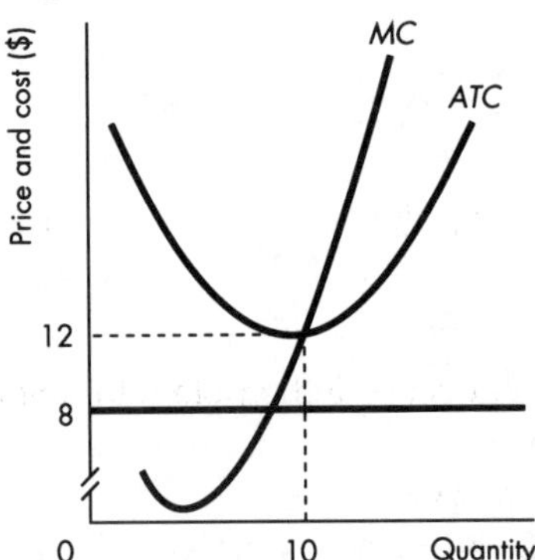

12.33
Correct: d)
Difficulty: 3
Page(s): 291
Scramble range: All
Topic: Production decision

12.33
See Figure 12.3, which represents the curves necessary for a perfectly competitive firm to make its production decision. Given the market price of the product is $8, in the short run the firm will
a) exit from the industry.
b) break even.
c) make economic profit.
d) incur economic losses.
e) close down.

12.34
Correct: a)
Difficulty: 2
Page(s): 290–291
Scramble range: All
Topic: Costs/fixed

12.34
The costs incurred even at a zero output are called
a) fixed costs.
b) variable costs.
c) decreasing costs.
d) marginal costs.
e) total costs.

12.35
Correct: a)
Difficulty: 2
Page(s): 290
Scramble range: All
Topic: Production decision

12.35
A firm that shuts down and produces no output makes a loss equal to its
a) fixed costs.
b) variable costs.
c) marginal costs.
d) marginal revenue.
e) average costs.

12.36
Correct: b)
Difficulty: 4
Page(s): 290–292
Scramble range: All
Topic: Production decision

12.36
Suppose that a firm is trying to decide whether or not to shut down in order to minimize its total loss. If the price just equals the average variable cost of production, then
a) total revenue equals total fixed cost and the loss equals total variable cost.
b) total revenue equals total variable cost and the loss equals total fixed cost.
c) total fixed cost is zero.
d) total variable cost equals total fixed cost.
e) total cost equals total fixed cost.

12.37
Correct: d)
Difficulty: 2
Page(s): 290
Scramble range: All
Topic: Production decision

12.37
The minimum quantity that a firm will produce in the short run is called its
a) point of cost retainment.
b) breakeven point.
c) resolution point.
d) shutdown point.
e) average variable point.

12.38
Correct: b)
Difficulty: 2
Page(s): 290
Scramble range: All
Topic: Production decision

12.38
The shutdown point occurs at the point of minimum
a) marginal cost.
b) average variable cost.
c) average fixed cost.
d) total cost.
e) average total cost.

12.39
Correct: a)
Difficulty: 2
Page(s): 290
Scramble range: a)–d)
Topic: Production decision

12.39
A firm maximizes profit by producing the output at which marginal cost equals
a) marginal revenue.
b) average total cost.
c) average variable cost.
d) average fixed cost.
e) none of the above.

12.40
Correct: e)
Difficulty: 3
Page(s): 290
Scramble range: All
Topic: Production decision

12.40
The lowest output a firm will produce is that at which
a) average total cost is at a minimum.
b) average fixed cost is at a minimum.
c) marginal cost is at a minimum.
d) total cost is at a minimum.
e) average variable cost is at a minimum.

12.41
Correct: c)
Difficulty: 3
Page(s): 291
Scramble range: All
Topic: Production decision

12.41
If price falls below the minimum of average variable cost, the best a firm can do is
a) step up production and make a loss equal to its total variable cost.
b) step up production and make a loss equal to its total fixed cost.
c) stop production and make a loss equal to its total fixed cost.
d) stop production and make a loss equal to its total variable cost.
e) stay at the same production level and make a loss equal to the difference between total cost and total revenue.

12.42
Correct: d)
Difficulty: 3
Page(s): 291
Scramble range: All
Topic: Economic profit/breakeven point

12.42
The breakeven point occurs at an output rate at which
a) total revenue equals total cost.
b) economic profit is positive.
c) a firm is taking a loss.
d) average total cost is minimized.
e) economic profit is negative.

12.43
Correct: d)
Difficulty: 4
Page(s): 288–289
Scramble range: All
Topic: Economic profit/measurement

12.43
See Figure 12.4, which graphs a perfectly competitive firm's total revenue and total cost curves. Which one of the following statements is *false*?
a) Total profit is seen as the vertical distance by which the total revenue curve exceeds the total cost curve.
b) At an output of Q_1 units a day, the firm makes zero economic profit.
c) At an output above Q_3 units a day, the firm makes an economic loss.
d) At an output of Q_2 units a day, the firm suffers economic losses.
e) At an output less than Q_1 units a day, the firm makes economic losses.

Figure 12.4

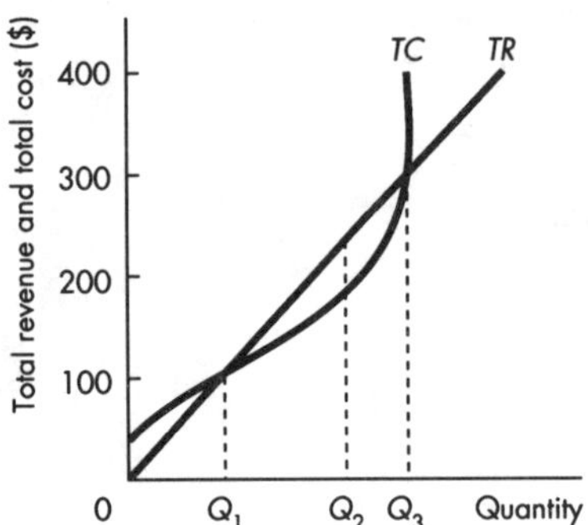

12.44
Correct: a)
Difficulty: 3
Page(s): 288–289
Scramble range: All
Topic: Economic loss/measurement

12.44
See Figure 12.5, which graphs a perfectly competitive firm's total profit curve. The firm is taking a loss at
a) point *a*.
b) point *b*.
c) point *c*.
d) point *d*.
e) points *b* and *d*.

Figure 12.5

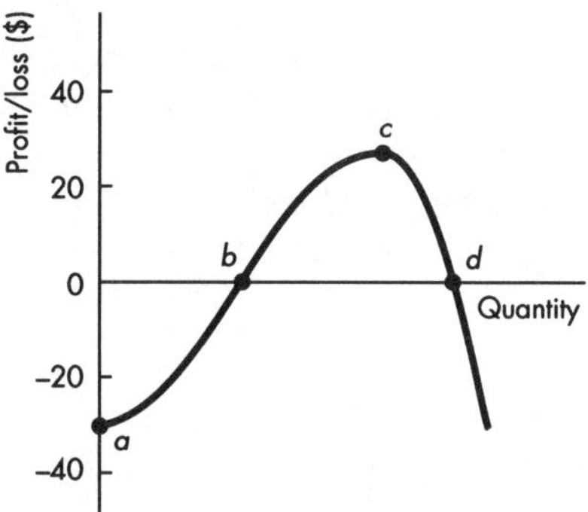

12.45
Correct: b)
Difficulty: 3
Page(s): 288–289
Scramble range: All
Topic: Economic profit/measurement

12.45
See Figure 12.5, which graphs a perfectly competitive firm's total profit curve. The firm is breaking even at points

a) *a* and *c*.
b) *b* and *d*.
c) *c* and *d*.
d) *a* and *d*.
e) *b* and *c*.

12.46
Correct: b)
Difficulty: 3
Page(s): 288–289
Scramble range: All
Topic: Economic loss/measurement

12.46
See Figure 12.6, which represents the short-run production decision of a perfectly competitive firm. Given the market price of P_1, the firm is

a) making economic profit.
b) taking a loss.
c) breaking even.
d) meeting all opportunity costs.
e) going to close down for sure.

Figure 12.6

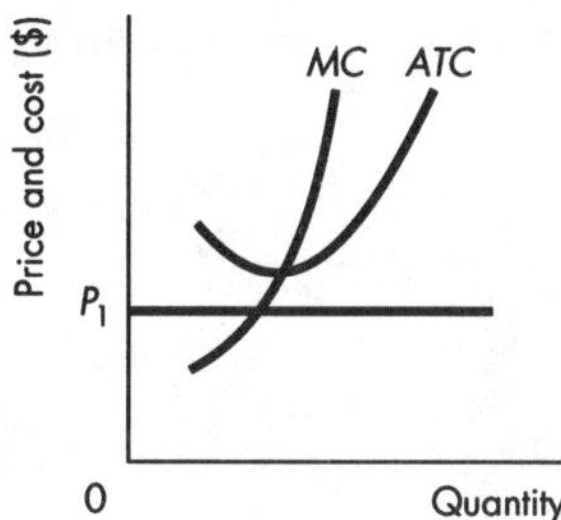

12.47
Correct: d)
Difficulty: 3
Page(s): 293
Scramble range: All
Topic: Perfect competition

12.47
A perfectly competitive firm's supply curve is made up of its marginal cost curve at all points above the minimum

a) average total cost curve.
b) average fixed cost curve.
c) average price.
d) average variable cost curve.
e) marginal cost curve.

12.48
Correct: e)
Difficulty: 3
Page(s): 293
Scramble range: All
Topic: Perfect competition

12.48
Industry supply is the sum of the
a) marginal costs of all the individual firms.
b) average variable costs of all the individual firms.
c) average total costs of all of the firms.
d) average fixed costs of all the firms.
e) supplies of all the individual firms.

12.49
Correct: e)
Difficulty: 3
Page(s): 293
Scramble range: All
Topic: Perfect competition

12.49
The firm's supply curve is the upward-sloping part of its
a) average variable curve, at all points above the point of minimum average variable cost.
b) marginal cost curve, at all points above the point of minimum average fixed cost.
c) marginal revenue curve, at all points above the point of minimum average revenue.
d) marginal revenue curve, at all points above the point of minimum average total cost.
e) marginal cost curve, at all points above the point of minimum average variable cost.

12.50
Correct: a)
Difficulty: 4
Page(s): 296
Scramble range: All
Topic: Long-run/exit

12.50
If firms exit an industry, the
a) industry supply curve shifts to the left.
b) price of the product falls.
c) profits of the remaining firms decrease.
d) output of the industry increases.
e) profits of the remaining firms stay the same.

12.51
Correct: a)
Difficulty: 3
Page(s): 296
Scramble range: None
Topic: Long-run/equilibrium

12.51
Long-run equilibrium occurs in a competitive industry when economic profits are
a) zero.
b) equal to the opportunity cost of the firm's owner.
c) negative.
d) positive.
e) both a) and b).

12.52
Correct: c)
Difficulty: 4
Page(s): 296
Scramble range: All
Topic: Long-run/entry

12.52
Which one of the following does *not* occur in the long run when an industry makes economic profits?
a) Firms enter the industry.
b) The supply curve shifts to the right.
c) The market price increases.
d) Profits decrease.
e) The market price decreases.

12.53
Correct: d)
Difficulty: 4
Page(s): 296
Scramble range: All
Topic: Long-run/exit

12.53
Firms will stop exiting only when
a) marginal revenue equals average revenue.
b) marginal revenue equals marginal cost.
c) economic profits are again present.
d) zero economic profits are being made.
e) marginal revenue equals average fixed cost.

12.54
Correct: c)
Difficulty: 3
Page(s): 297
Scramble range: All
Topic: Long-run/ equilibrium

12.54
See Figure 12.7, which represents a perfectly competitive firm's short-run and long-run cost curves. Given the price of a unit of output of P_1, the firm will want to

a) reduce its plant size in order to lower its average costs and make a bigger profit.
b) retain the same plant size in order to maximize its total profit.
c) expand its plant size in order to lower its average costs and make a bigger profit.
d) expand its plant size in order to lower its price to avoid taking a loss.
e) reduce its plant size in order to raise its price and make a bigger profit.

Figure 12.7

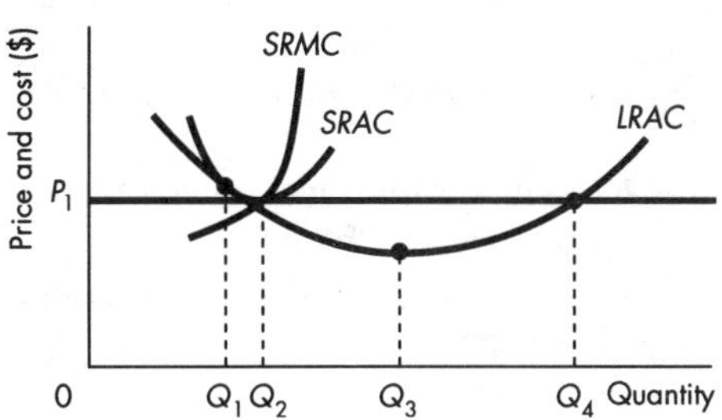

12.55
Correct: c)
Difficulty: 3
Page(s): 297
Scramble range: a)–d)
Topic: Long-run/ equilibrium

12.55
See Figure 12.7, which represents a perfectly competitive firm's short-run and long-run cost curves. What amount of output will the firm produce when the firm has reached its long-run equilibrium position?

a) Q_1.
b) Q_2.
c) Q_3.
d) Q_4.
e) None of the above.

12.56
Correct: d)
Difficulty: 4
Page(s): 294–296
Scramble range: All
Topic: Long-run/ equilibrium

12.56
See Figure 12.6, which represents the short-run production decision of a perfectly competitive firm. Given the market price of P_1, in the long run, market

a) demand will increase.
b) demand will decrease.
c) supply will increase.
d) supply will decrease.
e) both demand and supply will increase.

12.57
Correct: a)
Difficulty: 5
Page(s): 294–296
Scramble range: All
Topic: Long-run/ equilibrium

12.57
See Figure 12.6, which represents the short-run production decision of a perfectly competitive firm. Given the market price of P_1, in the long run

a) firms that remain in the market will expand production.
b) market demand will increase.
c) firms will adopt labour-saving technology.
d) industry output will remain constant.
e) firms will enter.

12.58
Correct: c)
Difficulty: 4
Page(s): 294–296
Scramble range: All
Topic: Long-run/ equilibrium

12.58
See Figure 12.6, which represents the short-run production decision of a perfectly competitive firm. Given the market price of P_1, firms are making economic

a) profit, and some firms will leave the industry, causing industry supply curve to decrease.
b) profit, and some firms will enter the industry, causing industry supply curve to increase.
c) loss, and some firms will leave the industry, causing industry supply curve to decrease.
d) loss, and some firms will enter the industry, causing industry supply curve to increase.
e) loss, but since they are covering average variable cost, no one will exit the industry in the long run.

12.59
Correct: c)
Difficulty: 4
Page(s): 294–296
Scramble range: All
Topic: Long-run/ equilibrium

12.59
See Figure 12.2, which represents the short-run production decision of a perfectly competitive firm. Given the market price of P_1, in the long run, market

a) demand will increase.
b) demand will decrease.
c) supply will increase.
d) supply will decrease.
e) both supply and demand will decrease.

12.60
Correct: e)
Difficulty: 4
Page(s): 294–296
Scramble range: All
Topic: Long-run/equilibrium

12.60
See Figure 12.2, which represents the short-run production decision of a perfectly competitive firm. Given the market price of P_1, in the long run

a) firms that remain in the market will expand production.
b) market demand will increase.
c) market supply will decrease.
d) firms will exit the market.
e) firms that remain in the market will reduce production.

12.61
Correct: c)
Difficulty: 4
Page(s): 301–302
Scramble range: All
Topic: Long-run/ equilibrium

12.61
Assuming long-run external diseconomies, when demand increases in a perfectly competitive market, price

a) remains constant and the quantity traded increases.
b) remains constant and the quantity traded decreases.
c) increases and the quantity traded increases.
d) decreases and the quantity traded decreases.
e) will rise and the quantity traded stays the same.

12.62
Correct: d)
Difficulty: 4
Page(s): 301–302
Scramble range: All
Topic: Long-run/ equilibrium

12.62
Assuming long-run external economies, when demand increases in a perfectly competitive market, price

a) remains constant and the quantity traded increases.
b) remains constant and the quantity traded decreases.
c) increases and the quantity traded decreases.
d) decreases and the quantity traded increases.
e) decreases and the quantity traded stays the same.

12.63
Correct: d)
Difficulty: 4
Page(s): 294–302
Scramble range: All
Topic: Long-run/ equilibrium

12.63
Long-run competitive equilibrium *cannot* exist if
a) each firm maximizes its short-run profit.
b) economic profit is zero, so that there is no entry or exit.
c) each firm produces at the point of minimum long-run average cost, so it has no incentive to change its plant size.
d) positive economic profits exist.
e) there are external economies or diseconomies.

12.64
Correct: e)
Difficulty: 4
Page(s): 294–302
Scramble range: All
Topic: Long-run/ equilibrium

12.64
In a perfectly competitive market, if there are no external economies or diseconomies in the face of an increase in demand, the
a) market price increases in the long run.
b) average cost decreases in the long run.
c) market price decreases in the long run.
d) average cost increases in the long run.
e) market price remains constant in the long run.

12.65
Correct: a)
Difficulty: 4
Page(s): 294–302
Scramble range: All
Topic: Long-run/ equilibrium

12.65
If there are external economies, as demand rises
a) price falls.
b) price increases.
c) firms exit from the industry.
d) output decreases.
e) average cost increases.

12.66
Correct: b)
Difficulty: 4
Page(s): 303
Scramble range: All
Topic: Long-run/ equilibrium

12.66
New technology increases the industry supply. Which of the following effects will *not* occur?
a) The market price falls and quantity traded rises.
b) The number of firms in the industry falls.
c) Firms that are slow to change to the new technology will make losses and eventually will go out of business.
d) Firms that are quick to adopt to the new technology will make economic profits initially, but in the long run they will make zero economic profit.
e) Average cost falls for those who adopt the new technology.

12.67
Correct: a)
Difficulty: 3
Page(s): 306
Scramble range: All
Topic: Costs/fixed

12.67
The farm problem of the 1980s has one central feature that can be understood using the model of perfect competition. Which one of the following is that central feature? A large increase in
a) interest rates increased farms' fixed costs.
b) interest rates increased farms' variable costs.
c) gasoline prices increased farms' fixed costs.
d) gasoline prices increased farms' variable costs.
e) food prices increased farms' revenues.

12.68
Correct: c)
Difficulty: 4
Page(s): 301–302
Scramble range: All
Topic: Costs/external economies

12.68
External economies are factors beyond the control of an individual firm which
a) lower its average revenue as industry output rises.
b) raises its costs as industry output rises.
c) lower its costs as industry output rises.
d) lower its profit as industry output rises.
e) raise its profit as industry output rises.

12.69
Correct: c)
Difficulty: 4
Page(s): 301–302
Scramble range: All
Topic: Costs/external diseconomy

12.69
Which of the following is an example of an external cost?
a) The price that a consumer pays to buy a new car.
b) The price a firm pays for consulting advice.
c) Pollution.
d) The damage created by a tornado.
e) Taxes.

12.70
Correct: b)
Difficulty: 3
Page(s): 301–302
Scramble range: All
Topic: Costs/external diseconomy

12.70
Congestion is an example of
a) external economies.
b) external diseconomies.
c) internal economies.
d) internal diseconomies.
e) internal costs.

12.71
Correct: b)
Difficulty: 2
Page(s): 301–302
Scramble range: a)–d)
Topic: Costs/external diseconomy

12.71
See Figure 12.8. Given the increase in market demand from D_0 to D_1, the graph represents
a) a constant cost industry.
b) an increasing cost industry.
c) a decreasing cost industry.
d) a monopolized industry.
e) none of the above.

Figure 12.8

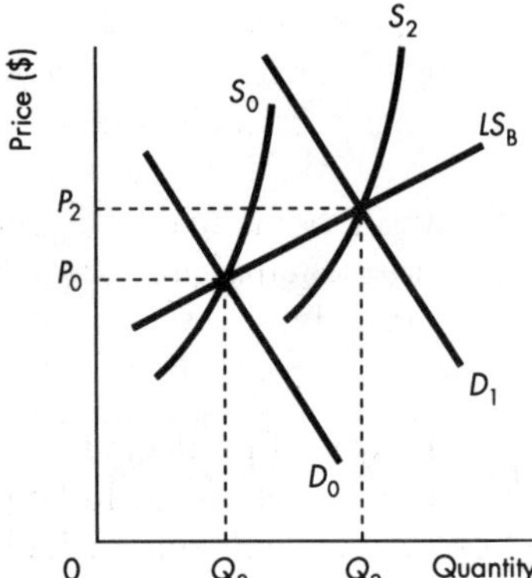

12.72
Correct: c)
Difficulty: 4
Page(s): 303
Scramble range: All
Topic: Production decision

12.72
It pays a firm to scrap even a relatively new plant (embodying the old technology) in favour of a plant with the new technology once
a) marginal cost cannot be covered by marginal revenue.
b) average revenue just equals average cost.
c) average variable cost cannot be covered by average revenue.
d) average fixed cost cannot be covered by average revenue.
e) average total cost cannot be covered by average revenue.

12.73
Correct: e)
Difficulty: 3
Page(s): 307
Scramble range: All
Topic: Efficiency/ allocative

12.73
Which the following need not be satisfied to achieve allocative efficiency?
a) Economic efficiency.
b) Consumer efficiency.
c) Marginal social cost equals marginal social benefit.
d) Technological efficiency.
e) Only high-quality goods are produced.

12.74
Correct: a)
Difficulty: 3
Page(s): 307
Scramble range: All
Topic: Efficiency/ economic

12.74
Economic efficiency involves
a) producing a given output at minimum cost.
b) using the newest available technology.
c) increasing market demand.
d) sacrificing environmental quality.
e) external economies.

12.75
Correct: c)
Difficulty: 3
Page(s): 307
Scramble range: All
Topic: Efficiency/ economic

12.75
Economic efficiency involves
a) the maximum expansion of output by all firms in an industry.
b) producing the maximum possible output.
c) using inputs in their cost-minimizing proportions.
d) reducing the quality of life.
e) equality of marginal social benefit and marginal social cost.

12.76
Correct: c)
Difficulty: 3
Page(s): 308
Scramble range: All
Topic: Efficiency/ consumer

12.76
Consumer efficiency occurs when
a) marginal revenue equals average cost.
b) price equals average revenue.
c) consumers cannot make themselves better off by reallocating their budget.
d) the quantity bought is a point below the demand curve.
e) marginal social cost equals marginal social benefit.

12.77
Correct: e)
Difficulty: 2
Page(s): 308
Scramble range: All
Topic: Costs/marginal social

12.77
Marginal social cost is the cost of producing
a) one additional unit of output, not including external costs.
b) one additional unit of consumption, including any external benefits.
c) output for export to other nations.
d) below minimum average variable cost.
e) one additional unit of output, including external costs.

12.78
Correct: c)
Difficulty: 3
Page(s): 308
Scramble range: All
Topic: Efficiency/allocative

12.78
Allocative efficiency occurs when
a) marginal revenue equals minimum average variable cost.
b) average revenue equals minimum average fixed cost.
c) marginal social cost equals marginal social benefit.
d) marginal revenue equals marginal social benefit.
e) marginal cost equals price.

12.79
Correct: a)
Difficulty: 2
Page(s): 309
Scramble range: All
Topic: Efficiency/allocative

12.79
Which one of the following is *not* a main obstacle to allocative efficiency?
a) Marginal costs.
b) External costs and benefits.
c) Monopoly.
d) External benefits.
e) External costs.

12.80
Correct: b)
Difficulty: 4
Page(s): 308
Scramble range: All
Topic: Costs/external diseconomy

12.80
The production of some goods impose high external costs. Perfect competition will result in
a) an underproduction of such goods.
b) an overproduction of such goods.
c) the product of such goods in an amount that maximizes the total satisfaction of society.
d) an elimination of external costs.
e) too high a price of such goods.

12.81 (SG 12.1)
Correct: e)
Difficulty: 2
Page(s): 283
Scramble range: All
Topic: Characteristics of competitive markets

12.81
Which of the following is *not* a characteristic of a perfectly competitive market?
a) There are many firms.
b) There are many buyers.
c) There are no restrictions on entry into the industry.
d) Firms in the industry have no advantage over potential new entrants.
e) Each firm produces a slightly different product.

12.82
Correct: c)
Difficulty: 2
Page(s): 283
Scramble range: All
Topic: Firm as price taker

12.82
A price taker is a firm that
a) must lower its price if it wants to sell more output.
b) must accept the price set by a monopoly.
c) cannot influence the price of its product.
d) is experiencing economic losses.
e) can raise its price if it lowers output.

12.83 (SG 12.2)
Correct: d)
Difficulty: 3
Page(s): 285–288
Scramble range: All
Topic: Price equals marginal cost

12.83
If a firm faces a perfectly elastic demand for its product, then
a) it is not a price taker.
b) it will want to lower its price to increase sales.
c) it will want to raise its price to increase total revenue.
d) its marginal cost curve is equal to the price of the product.
e) its average revenue is greater than its marginal revenue.

12.84 (SG 12.3)
Correct: a)
Difficulty: 4
Page(s): 288
Scramble range: All
Topic: Profit maximization

12.84
A perfectly competitive firm is maximizing profit if
a) marginal cost equals price and price is above minimum average variable cost.
b) marginal cost equals price and price is above minimum average fixed cost.
c) total revenue is a maximum.
d) average variable cost is a minimum.
e) marginal cost equals marginal revenue and price is above minimum average total cost.

12.85
Correct: c)
Difficulty: 3
Page(s): 286
Scramble range: All
Topic: Average and marginal revenue

12.85
For a perfectly competitive firm, the average revenue curve
a) is the same as the firm's demand curve and the marginal revenue curve lies below the firm's demand curve.
b) lies above the firm's demand curve and the marginal revenue curve lies below the firm's demand curve.
c) and the marginal revenue curve are both the same as the firm's demand curve.
d) lies above the firm's demand curve and the marginal revenue curve is the same as the firm's demand curve.
e) is always negatively sloped.

12.86
Correct: b)
Difficulty: 3
Page(s): 290
Scramble range: All
Topic: Breaking even

12.86
If a competitive firm is producing an output at which price is equal to average total cost, the firm
a) should shut down.
b) is breaking even.
c) is still making a positive *economic* profit.
d) is experiencing economic losses.
e) is still making a positive *accounting* profit.

12.87
Correct: c)
Difficulty: 3
Page(s): 289
Scramble range: All
Topic: Profit maximization

12.87
If a profit-maximizing firm's marginal revenue is less than its marginal cost, the firm
a) must be experiencing economic losses.
b) must be making economic profits.
c) should decrease its output.
d) should increase its output.
e) must have its average revenue less than its marginal revenue.

12.88 (SG 12.6)
Correct: e)
Difficulty: 3
Page(s): 290
Scramble range: All
Topic: Maximum economic loss

12.88
The maximum loss a firm will experience in the short run is
a) zero.
b) its total liability.
c) its total variable costs.
d) its total costs.
e) its total fixed costs.

12.89
Correct: a)
Difficulty: 3
Page(s): 290
Scramble range: All
Topic: Shut–down point

12.89
If, in the short run, the price falls below minimum average variable cost, a firm
a) should produce no output.
b) will be making a loss but should still continue producing in the short run.
c) should produce the output for which marginal cost is equal to price.
d) is not necessarily experiencing economic losses.
e) should exit the industry.

12.90
Correct: e)
Difficulty: 3
Page(s): 293
Scramble range: All
Topic: Firm's supply curve

12.90
In the price range above minimum average variable cost, a perfectly competitive firm's supply curve is
a) horizontal at the market price.
b) vertical at zero output.
c) the same as its average total cost curve.
d) the same as its average variable cost curve.
e) the same as its marginal cost curve.

12.91 (SG 12.7)
Correct: b)
Difficulty: 3
Page(s): 293
Scramble range: All
Topic: Firm's supply curve

12.91
In the price range below minimum average variable cost, a perfectly competitive firm's supply curve is
a) horizontal at the market price.
b) vertical at zero output.
c) the same as its average total cost curve.
d) the same as its average variable cost curve.
e) the same as its marginal cost curve.

12.92 (SG 12.8)
Correct: a)
Difficulty: 3
Page(s): 294
Scramble range: All
Topic: Industry supply curve

12.92
The short-run industry supply curve is
a) constructed as the horizontal sum of the supply curves of the individual firms.
b) constructed as the vertical sum of the supply curves of the individual firms.
c) vertical at the total level of output being produced by all firms.
d) horizontal at the current market price.
e) negatively or positively sloped depending on whether or not there are external economies or diseconomies.

12.93 (SG 12.9)
Correct: d)
Difficulty: 4
Page(s): 294–297
Scramble range: All
Topic: Long-run adjustment in a competitive industry

12.93
If profits are being made by firms in a competitive industry, new firms will enter. This will
a) shift the industry demand curve to the left, causing market price to fall.
b) shift the industry demand curve to the right, causing market price to rise.
c) shift the industry supply curve to the left, causing market price to rise.
d) shift the industry supply curve to the right, causing market price to fall.
e) shift both the industry demand and supply curves to the right, causing market price to be unchanged.

12.94 (SG 12.17)
Correct: a)
Difficulty: 3
Page(s): 296–297
Scramble range: All
Topic: Long-run/ equilibrium

12.94
The maximum loss a firm will experience in long-run equilibrium is
a) zero.
b) its total cost.
c) its total variable cost.
d) its average variable cost.
e) its liability.

12.95
Correct: c)
Difficulty: 3
Page(s): 297–298
Scramble range: All
Topic: Short–run equilibrium

12.95
Figure 12.7 illustrates the cost curves for a perfectly competitive firm. In the short run, the price is P_1 and the firm has the scale of plant associated with *SRAC*. How much will the firm produce in short-run equilibrium?
a) 0.
b) Q_1.
c) Q_2.
d) Q_3.
e) Q_4.

12.96
Correct: a)
Difficulty: 5
Page(s): 298–299
Scramble range: All
Topic: Long-run adjustment

12.96
Figure 12.7 illustrates the cost curves for a perfectly competitive firm. Suppose the current price is P_1 and that the firm has the scale of plant associated with *SRAC*. Over time, this firm will
a) increase its scale of plant, and other firms will exit from the industry.
b) retain its current scale of plant, and other firms will enter the industry.
c) increase its scale of plant, and other firms will enter the industry.
d) decrease its scale of plant, and other firms will enter the industry.
e) retain its current scale of plant, and other firms will exit the industry.

12.97
Correct: e)
Difficulty: 4
Page(s): 296–298
Scramble range: All
Topic: Long-run/ equilibrium

12.97
Figure 12.7 illustrates the cost curves for a perfectly competitive firm. In long-run equilibrium, the market price will be
a) zero.
b) greater than P_1.
c) P_1.
d) less than P_1.
e) minimum long run average cost.

12.98
Correct: d)
Difficulty: 4
Page(s): 297–298
Scramble range: All
Topic: Long-run/equilibrium

12.98
Figure 12.7 illustrates the cost curves for a perfectly competitive firm. In long-run equilibrium, how many units of output will the firm produce?
a) 0.
b) Q_1.
c) Q_2.
d) Q_3.
e) Q_4.

12.99 (SG 12.21)
Correct: b)
Difficulty: 3
Page(s): 301–302
Scramble range: All
Topic: Long-run industry supply curve

12.99
The long-run competitive industry supply curve will be positively sloped if
a) there are external economies.
b) there are external diseconomies.
c) there are no external economies or diseconomies.
d) the external economies equal the external diseconomies.
e) price rises.

12.100 (SG 12.22)
Correct: c)
Difficulty: 4
Page(s): 301–302
Scramble range: All
Topic: Long-run/ equilibrium

12.100
Which of the following is *not* true of a new long-run equilibrium which is the result of a new technology in a perfectly competitive industry?
a) Price will be lower.
b) Industry output will be greater.
c) Firm profits will be greater.
d) All firms in the industry will be using the new technology.
e) Firms will adopt the new technology at different times.

12.101
Correct: a)
Difficulty: 5
Page(s): 298
Scramble range: All
Topic: Long-run/ equilibrium

12.101
A perfectly competitive industry is in long-run equilibrium when there is an increase in total variable costs facing each firm. Why does the short-run industry supply curve shift to the left?
a) Each firm's marginal cost curve shifts to the left, *and* firms will exit.
b) Firms will exit, but there is no change in each firm's marginal cost curve.
c) Each firm's marginal cost curve shifts left, although firms will *not* exit.
d) Each firm's average total cost curve will shift upward.
e) Each firm's marginal cost curve shifts to the left, *and* average total cost rises.

12.102 (SG 12.4)
Correct: d)
Difficulty: 4
Page(s): 308
Scramble range: All
Topic: Allocative efficiency

12.102
Under which of the following circumstances would a long-run equilibrium in a perfectly competitive industry *not* be allocatively efficient?
a) Firms are price takers.
b) There are new technologies developed.
c) There are external economies or external diseconomies.
d) There are external costs or external benefits.
e) Demand rises.

12.103
Correct: e)
Difficulty: 3
Page(s): 308
Scramble range: All
Topic: Monopoly/ allocative efficiency

12.103
Which of the following is an important obstacle to allocative efficiency?
a) External diseconomies.
b) The objective of firms to maximize profit.
c) The invisible hand.
d) Prices.
e) The existence of monopoly.

12.104
Correct: d)
Difficulty: 3
Page(s): 283
Scramble range: All
Topic: Characteristics of competitive markets

12.104
Which of the following is a characteristic of a perfectly competitive market?
a) There are 1,000 firms in the industry.
b) Each firm produces a slightly different product.
c) There is limited entry into the industry.
d) Firms in the industry have no advantage over potential new entrants.
e) Firms can effect prices.

12.105
Correct: d)
Difficulty: 3
Page(s): 283
Scramble range: All
Topic: Firm as price taker

12.105
Perfectly competitive firms
a) are price setters.
b) must lower their prices when demand increases if they wish to sell the same amount of output as before.
c) must accept the price set by a monopoly.
d) cannot influence the price of their product.
e) must raise their prices when demand decreases if they wish to make profits.

12.106
Correct: d)
Difficulty: 2
Page(s): 283
Scramble range: All
Topic: Price setters

12.106
If a firm faces a negatively sloped demand curve for its product, then
a) it is a price taker.
b) it will want to lower its price to increase total revenue.
c) it will want to raise its price to increase total revenue.
d) it is not a price taker.
e) it is a perfectively competitive firm.

12.107
Correct: e)
Difficulty: 3
Page(s): 287
Scramble range: All
Topic: Profit maximization

12.107
A perfectly competitive firm is not maximizing profit if
a) marginal cost equals price and price is above minimum average variable cost.
b) marginal cost equals average revenue.
c) total cost is a minimum.
d) marginal cost equals marginal revenue.
e) total revenue is at a maximum.

12.108
Correct: c)
Difficulty: 4
Page(s): 286
Scramble range: All
Topic: Average and marginal revenue

12.108
For a perfectly competitive firm, the marginal revenue curve
a) is the same as the firm's demand curve and the average revenue curve lies below the firm's demand curve.
b) lies above the firm's demand curve and the average revenue curve lies below the firm's demand curve.
c) and the average revenue curve are both the same as the firm's demand curve.
d) lies above the firm's demand curve and the average revenue curve is the same as the firm's demand curve.
e) lies below the average revenue curve, and the average revenue curve is the firm's demand curve.

12.109
Correct: e)
Difficulty: 3
Page(s): 290
Scramble range: All
Topic: Shutdown point

12.109
If a competitive firm is producing an output at which price is less than average total cost, the firm
a) should shut down.
b) is breaking even.
c) is still making a positive economic profit.
d) is experiencing economic losses but should continue to operate as long as price is above minimum average fixed cost.
e) is experiencing economic losses but should continue to operate as long as price is above minimum average variable cost.

12.110
Correct: d)
Difficulty: 3
Page(s): 289
Scramble range: All
Topic: Profit maximization

12.110
If a profit-maximizing firm's marginal revenue is greater than its marginal cost, the firm
a) must be experiencing economic losses.
b) must be making economic profits.
c) should decrease its output.
d) should increase its output.
e) should close down.

12.111
Correct: b)
Difficulty: 3
Page(s): 290
Scramble range: All
Topic: Shutdown point

12.111
If, in the short run, the price falls below minimum average total cost, a firm
a) should produce no output.
b) will be making a loss but could possibly still continue producing in the short run.
c) should abandon the marginal cost equals marginal revenue rule.
d) is not necessarily experiencing economic losses.
e) will raise output.

12.112
Correct: c)
Difficulty: 3
Page(s): 298–299
Scramble range: All
Topic: Long-run adjustment in a competitive industry

12.112
If losses are being made by firms in a competitive industry, then this will
a) shift the industry demand curve to the left causing market price to fall.
b) shift the industry demand curve to the right causing market price to rise.
c) shift the industry supply curve to the left causing market price to rise.
d) shift the industry supply curve to the right causing market price to fall.
e) shift the industry supply curve to the left, but not alter price due to the presence of external diseconomies.

12.113
Correct: d)
Difficulty: 4
Page(s): 294–298
Scramble range: All
Topic: Long-run/ equilibrium

12.113
The long-run equilibrium for a firm in a perfectly competitive industry is best represented by which one of the following choices?
a) $P = MR = SATC$.
b) P is greater than MR, but $MR = MC = LRATC$.
c) $MR = MC = SATC$.
d) $P = MC = LRATC$, where $LRATC$ is at a minimum.
e) $MR = MC = LRATC$.

12.114
Correct: b)
Difficulty: 5
Page(s): 298–307
Scramble range: All
Topic: Long-run/ equilibrium

12.114
Consider the perfectly competitive market for widgets. There are no external economies or diseconomies. A news story is released, arguing that consumption of widgets helps fight cancer. As a result,
a) in the short run both price and quantity will rise, while in the long run quantity will rise and price will end up being lower.
b) in the short run both price and quantity will rise, while in the long run price will come back to the original level and quantity will be higher.
c) in the short run price will remain constant while quantity rises, and in the long run both price and quantity will be higher.
d) in the short run price and quantity rise, while in the long run both price and quantity will be higher than the original values.
e) in the short run both price and quantity will be unchanged, while in the long run price and quantity will be higher.

12.115
Correct: e)
Difficulty: 5
Page(s): 298–307
Scramble range: All
Topic: Short–run/ equilibrium

12.115
Consider Fact 12.1. In this industry, price is __________ and quantity traded is __________
a) $7.75; 370,000.
b) $8.75; 360,000.
c) $11.75; 330,000.
d) $10.75; 340,000.
e) $9.75; 350,000.

12.116
Correct: b)
Difficulty: 5
Page(s): 298–307
Scramble range: All
Topic: Short–run/ equilibrium

12.116
Consider Fact 12.1. In equilibrium, the output of each firm is
a) 250 albums.
b) 350 albums.
c) 300 albums.
d) 450 albums.
e) 400 albums.

Fact 12.1 The market demand schedule for record albums is as follows:

Price (dollars per album)	Quantity demanded (albums per week)
4.75	400,000
5.75	390,000
6.75	380,000
7.75	370,000
8.75	360,000
9.75	350,000
10.75	340,000
11.75	330,000
12.75	320,000

The market is perfectly competitive, and each firm has the cost structure described by the following table:

Output (albums per week)	Marginal cost (dollars per album)	Average variable cost (dollars (per album)	Average total cost (dollars (per album)
150	4.82	8.80	15.47
200	4.09	7.69	12.69
250	4.63	7.00	11.00
300	6.75	6.75	10.07
350	9.75	6.91	9.75
400	13.95	7.50	10.00
450	19.62	8.52	10.74
500	26.57	9.97	11.97

There are 1,000 firms in the industry.

12.117
Correct: e)
Difficulty: 5
Page(s): 298–307
Scramble range: All
Topic: Economic profit

12.117
Consider Fact 12.1. In equilibrium, the economic profit of each firm is
a) a loss of $312.50.
b) $312.50.
c) a loss of $96.00.
d) $96.00.
e) zero.

12.118
Correct: b)
Difficulty: 4
Page(s): 293–295
Scramble range: All
Topic: Shutdown point

12.118
Consider Fact 12.1. The shutdown point for each firm is
a) dependent on the price.
b) $6.75.
c) $9.75.
d) $4.09.
e) any price lower than $9.75.

Chapter 13 **Monopoly**

13.1
Correct: b)
Difficulty: 1
Page(s): 317
Scramble range: All
Topic: Monopoly

13.1
A market that is monopolized has
a) no barriers to the entry of rival firms.
b) only one firm.
c) many rival markets in which close substitutes may be bought or sold.
d) only one buyer.
e) a few large firms.

13.2
Correct: d)
Difficulty: 2
Page(s): 317
Scramble range: All
Topic: Monopoly

13.2
Barriers to entry characterize markets
a) that are perfectly competitive.
b) that set price equal to minimum average variable cost.
c) in which economic profit must be zero.
d) that may be dominated by a monopoly.
e) with many buyers, making it difficult for new firms.

13.3
Correct: c)
Difficulty: 3
Page(s): 317
Scramble range: All
Topic: Maintain monopoly power

13.3
Markets that are monopolized
a) promote allocative efficiency.
b) promote production at minimum long-run average cost.
c) are supported by barriers to entry of rivals.
d) have prices below marginal costs of production.
e) are technologically inefficient.

13.4
Correct: c)
Difficulty: 2
Page(s): 317
Scramble range: All
Topic: Monopoly

13.4
If a firm has no rival competitors that produce a close substitute, then
a) the firm must earn only zero profit in the long run.
b) the product must be an inferior good.
c) the firm enjoys a degree of market power.
d) the firm should exit the industry after the depreciation of its capital.
e) the market probably cannot support any firms, and the firm will eventually go broke.

13.5
Correct: b)
Difficulty: 2
Page(s): 317
Scramble range: All
Topic: Monopoly barriers entry

13.5
Barriers to entry may include
a) union pickets.
b) patents.
c) other firms selling close substitutes.
d) fair pricing laws.
e) too many customers.

13.6
Correct: d)
Difficulty: 2
Page(s): 317
Scramble range: All
Topic: Barriers to entry

13.6
Barriers to entry do not include
a) patents.
b) copyrights.
c) a government franchise.
d) union pickets.
e) economies of scale.

13.7
Correct: b)
Difficulty: 2
Page(s): 317
Scramble range: All
Topic: Barriers to entry

13.7
The right under the law to make use of a specific resource or sell a particular product is
a) a licence.
b) a patent.
c) a characteristic only of government establishments.
d) the essential characteristic of natural monopoly.
e) economies of scale.

13.8
Correct: c)
Difficulty: 2
Page(s): 317
Scramble range: All
Topic: Market power

13.8
Market power refers to
a) the production of a high-quality product that few buyers will be able to resist.
b) the incentive to maximize the profit of the firm.
c) the ability to set the price.
d) the ability to meet production quotas.
e) the ability to control a market.

13.9
Correct: a)
Difficulty: 3
Page(s): 318
Scramble range: All
Topic: Monopoly pricing

13.9
The ability to maximize profit by setting the price is
a) an essential characteristic of monopoly.
b) an essential characteristic of competitive markets.
c) reserved exclusively for government franchises.
d) possible only if the firm holds a patent on the product it sells.
e) possible only if the firm has a natural monopoly.

13.10
Correct: c)
Difficulty: 3
Page(s): 319-320
Scramble range: All
Topic: Monopoly/ demand elastic

13.10
In a market that is monopolized
a) the monopolist always faces a perfectly elastic demand.
b) the monopolist always faces a perfectly inelastic demand.
c) the market demand may be elastic or inelastic.
d) the law of demand is violated.
e) the price is always at the highest possible level.

13.11
Correct: c)
Difficulty: 3
Page(s): 318-319
Scramble range: All
Topic: Monopoly/ demand elastic

13.11
If a firm faces a perfectly elastic demand for its product,
a) it holds a patent on the product it wishes to sell.
b) it must lower its price in order to expand its market share.
c) it cannot be a monopoly seller.
d) its price-setting power is limited but not absent.
e) it cannot make positive economic profits.

13.12
Correct: a)
Difficulty: 3
Page(s): 318-319
Scramble range: All
Topic: Marginal revenue

13.12
The marginal revenue of the monopolist is
a) the change in total revenue for the sale of an additional unit of output.
b) the price the monopolist charges for the product.
c) the profit the monopolist earns in excess of the profit earned by a firm in a competitive industry.
d) usually greater than the price charged.
e) usually greater than marginal cost.

13.13
Correct: e)
Difficulty: 3
Page(s): 319
Scramble range: All
Topic: Monopolist marginal revenue

13.13
For a monopolist, the change in total revenue for a change in the number of units sold per market period is always
a) equal to the price received for the product.
b) equal to the average total cost of production.
c) greater than the price received for the product.
d) greater than the marginal cost.
e) less than the price received for the product.

13.14
Correct: c)
Difficulty: 4
Page(s): 318-319
Scramble range: All
Topic: Marginal revenue

13.14
Suppose that a monopolist can sell 5 units of output per day for a price of $3, and 6 units of output per day for $2.50 each. The marginal revenue for the sixth unit sold is equal to
a) $2.50.
b) $3.00.
c) zero.
d) $0.50.
e) uncertain, as not enough information is given to compute the marginal revenue.

13.15
Correct: b)
Difficulty: 4
Page(s): 318-319
Scramble range: All
Topic: Marginal revenue

13.15
Suppose that a monopolist can sell 20 units of output per day for a price of $10 each, and 21 units of output per day for $9.80 each. The marginal revenue for the 21st unit sold is equal to
a) zero.
b) $5.80.
c) $9.80.
d) $0.20.
e) uncertain, as not enough information is given to compute the marginal revenue.

13.16
Correct: e)
Difficulty: 4
Page(s): 318-319
Scramble range: All
Topic: Marginal revenue

13.16
Suppose that a monopolist can sell 50 units of output per day for a price of $20 each, and 51 units of output per day for $19 each. The marginal revenue for the 51st unit sold is equal to
a) zero.
b) $1.00.
c) $19.00.
d) uncertain, as not enough information is given to compute the marginal revenue.
e) –$31.00.

13.17
Correct: d)
Difficulty: 2
Page(s): 321
Scramble range: All
Topic: Goals of the monopolist

13.17
The behaviour of the monopolist is assumed to be motivated by the desire to
a) minimize the average cost of production.
b) minimize the marginal cost of production.
c) maximize the difference between the marginal cost and the price charged.
d) maximize the difference between total revenue and total cost.
e) minimize the effort of running the firm.

13.18
Correct: c)
Difficulty: 1
Page(s): 322
Scramble range: All
Topic: Goals of the firm

13.18
Profit-maximizing behaviour
a) characterizes monopoly markets only.
b) is represented only in competitive markets.
c) is assumed for both competitive markets and monopolized markets.
d) is assumed only for firms which enjoy a government franchise.
e) is not relevant in the case of a natural monopoly.

13.19
Correct: d)
Difficulty: 3
Page(s): 323
Scramble range: All
Topic: Monopoly shutdown

13.19
A monopolist will shut down the firm when
a) the price charged does not cover the marginal revenue.
b) the price charged does not cover the average total cost of production.
c) the profit is less than normal profit.
d) the price charged does not cover the average variable cost of production.
e) price is less than marginal cost.

13.20
Correct: d)
Difficulty: 3
Page(s): 323
Scramble range: All
Topic: Price, cost, and profit

13.20
When the monopolist's price exceeds minimum average variable cost, then the firm
a) will shut down in the long run.
b) will earn positive economic profit.
c) cannot cover its fixed costs of production.
d) may be earning positive economic profit.
e) will be earning negative economic profit.

13.21
Correct: a)
Difficulty: 3
Page(s): 323
Scramble range: All
Topic: Price, cost, and profit

13.21
When the monopolist's price does not exceed the minimum average variable cost, then the firm
a) will shut down in the long run.
b) will earn positive economic profit.
c) cannot cover its fixed costs of production.
d) may be earning positive economic profit.
e) will be earning zero economic profit.

13.22
Correct: b)
Difficulty: 3
Page(s): 320-322
Scramble range: All
Topic: Price and marginal revenue

13.22
For the monopolist facing a downward sloping demand, the marginal revenue never exceeds the price because
a) the producers of substitutes keep the price low.
b) the monopolist must lower the price in order to sell more during any given period of time.
c) the monopoly will be a large corporation with high fixed costs.
d) the monopolist must accept the marginal revenue set by the market as a whole.
e) the monopolist has low marginal cost relative to a competitive firm.

13.23
Correct: a)
Difficulty: 3
Page(s): 320-323
Scramble range: All
Topic: Monopoly profit

13.23
The monopolist will maximize the profit of the firm by
a) producing the quantity at which the marginal revenue equals the marginal cost, and then selling that output for as high a price as the market can bear.
b) producing the quantity at which the marginal cost equals the price charged.
c) setting the price equal to the marginal cost of production.
d) charging a price that is as high as the market can bear.
e) producing the quantity at which marginal revenue equals price.

13.24
Correct: e)
Difficulty: 3
Page(s): 320-323
Scramble range: All
Topic: Monopoly profit

13.24
Assuming an upward sloping marginal cost curve, if a monopolist produces the output level at which the marginal cost equals the marginal revenue, then
a) economic profit must be zero.
b) economic profit must be positive.
c) the price must less than the marginal cost.
d) the price must equal the marginal cost.
e) economic profit must be maximized.

13.25
Correct: a)
Difficulty: 4
Page(s): 317-322
Scramble range: All
Topic: Price-setting power

13.25
Price setting by the monopolist means that
a) the monopolist, and only the monopolist, has any influence over the market price.
b) consumers will pay unfair prices.
c) average costs will always be covered by the chosen price.
d) consumers will pay the highest price that any consumers are willing and able to pay.
e) quantity will be too high compared to a competitive market.

13.26
Correct: d)
Difficulty: 3
Page(s): 320
Scramble range: All
Topic: Price-taking behaviour

13.26
Price-taking behaviour
a) describes the pricing strategy of a monopolist.
b) represents an unrealistic assumption about the behaviour of monopolies.
c) does not describe the behaviour of competitive firms.
d) implies that the market cannot be monopolized.
e) describes the behaviour of consumers faced by a monopoly firm.

13.27
Correct: e)
Difficulty: 2
Page(s): 321
Scramble range: All
Topic: Monopoly profit

13.27
Refer to Figure 13.1. What is the profit-maximizing output level for this monopolist?
a) 8 units per day.
b) 4 units per day.
c) 1 units per day.
d) 6 units per day.
e) 2 units per day.

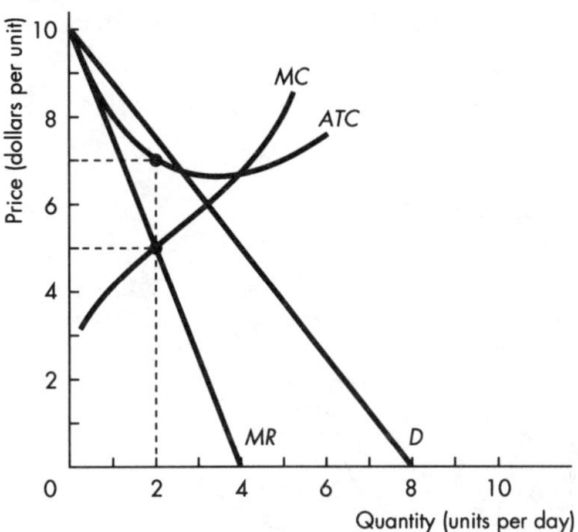

13.28
Correct: d)
Difficulty: 2
Page(s): 321
Scramble range: All
Topic: Monopoly pricing

13.28
Refer to Figure 13.1. What price will the monopolist charge in order to maximize profit?
a) $2.
b) $5.
c) $7.
d) $7.50.
e) $10.

13.29
Correct: d)
Difficulty: 3
Page(s): 321
Scramble range: All
Topic: Monopoly total revenue

13.29
Refer to Figure 13.1. At the profit-maximizing price and output, the total revenue is
a) $9.
b) $25.
c) $18.
d) $15.
e) $7.50.

13.30
Correct: b)
Difficulty: 3
Page(s): 321-322
Scramble range: All
Topic: Monopoly total cost

13.30
Refer to Figure 13.1. At the profit-maximizing price and output, the total cost is
a) $8.
b) $14.
c) $18.
d) $15.
e) $7.

13.31
Correct: e)
Difficulty: 4
Page(s): 320-322
Scramble range: All
Topic: Monopoly profit

13.31
Refer to Figure 13.1. The total profit for this monopolist is
a) zero.
b) $5.
c) $4.
d) impossible to compute without more information concerning the fixed costs.
e) $1.

13.32
Correct: c)
Difficulty: 2
Page(s): 320-322
Scramble range: All
Topic: Monopoly profit

13.32
Refer to Figure 13.2. What is the profit-maximizing output level for this monopolist?
a) 1 unit per day.
b) 2 units per day.
c) 3 units per day.
d) 4 units per day.
e) 5 units per day.

Figure 13.2

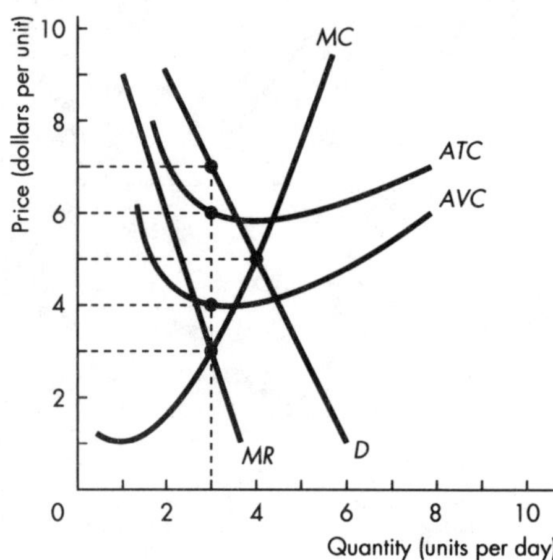

13.33
Correct: e)
Difficulty: 3
Page(s): 320-322
Scramble range: All
Topic: Monopoly pricing

13.33
Refer to Figure 13.2. What price will the monopolist charge in order to maximize profit?
a) \$3.
b) \$5.
c) \$10.
d) \$4.
e) \$7.

13.34
Correct: d)
Difficulty: 4
Page(s): 320-322
Scramble range: All
Topic: Monopoly total revenue

13.34
Refer to Figure 13.2. At the profit-maximizing price and output, the total revenue is
a) \$10.
b) \$16.
c) \$18.
d) \$21.
e) \$7.

13.35
Correct: e)
Difficulty: 4
Page(s): 320-322
Scramble range: All
Topic: Monopoly total cost

13.35
Refer to Figure 13.2. At the profit-maximizing price and output, the total cost is
a) \$8.
b) \$14.
c) \$6.
d) \$22.
e) \$18.

13.36
Correct: e)
Difficulty: 4
Page(s): 320-322
Scramble range: All
Topic: Monopoly profit

13.36
Refer to Figure 13.2. The total profit for this monopolist is
a) zero.
b) \$1.
c) \$9.
d) impossible to compute without more information concerning the fixed costs.
e) \$3.

13.37
Correct: c)
Difficulty: 2
Page(s): 323
Scramble range: All
Topic: Shutdown price

13.37
Refer to Figure 13.2. The monopolist would not shut down the firm since at the profit-maximizing output, the price is greater than the
a) marginal revenue.
b) marginal cost.
c) average variable cost.
d) average fixed cost.
e) average total cost.

13.38
Correct: c)
Difficulty: 4
Page(s): 333
Scramble range: All
Topic: Allocative efficiency

13.38
Refer to Figure 13.2. At the profit-maximizing output level
a) the resource allocation is efficient in the economy since the price is less than the highest price some buyers would be willing to pay.
b) the resource allocation is efficient in the economy since the marginal revenue equals the marginal cost.
c) the resource allocation is inefficient in the economy since the price exceeds the marginal cost.
d) the efficiency of the resource allocation is assured since profit is maximized.
e) the efficiency of the resource allocation is assured since cost is minimized.

13.39
Correct: b)
Difficulty: 2
Page(s): 320-322
Scramble range: All
Topic: Monopoly profit

13.39
Refer to Figure 13.3. What is the profit-maximizing output level for this monopolist?
a) 15 units per day.
b) 20 units per day.
c) 25 units per day.
d) 40 units per day.
e) zero units per day.

Figure 13.3

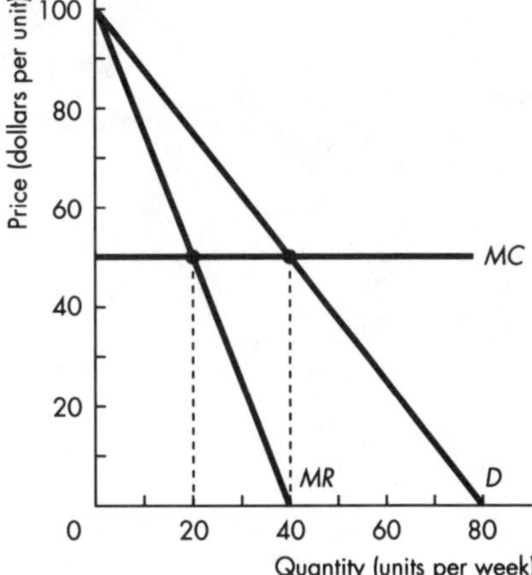

13.40
Correct: c)
Difficulty: 3
Page(s): 320-322
Scramble range: All
Topic: Monopoly pricing

13.40
Refer to Figure 13.3. What price will the monopolist charge in order to maximize profit?
a) $25.
b) $50.
c) $75.
d) $100.
e) $20.

13.41
Correct: a)
Difficulty: 3
Page(s): 320-322
Scramble range: All
Topic: Monopoly total revenue

13.41
Refer to Figure 13.3. At the profit-maximizing price and output, the total revenue is
a) $1,500.
b) $1,000.
c) $100.
d) $2,000.
e) $75.

13.42
Correct: d)
Difficulty: 5
Page(s): 320-322
Scramble range: All
Topic: Monopoly total cost

13.42
Refer to Figure 13.3. Assuming the monopolist has total fixed costs equal to $100, at the profit-maximizing price and output, the total cost of production is
a) $200.
b) $500.
c) $1,000.
d) $1,100.
e) not calculable with the given information.

13.43
Correct: d)
Difficulty: 4
Page(s): 320-322
Scramble range: All
Topic: Monopoly profit

13.43
Refer to Figure 13.3. The total profit for this monopolist is
a) zero.
b) $200.
c) $400.
d) impossible to compute without more information concerning the fixed costs.
e) $500.

13.44
Correct: c)
Difficulty: 5
Page(s): 322
Scramble range: All
Topic: Shutdown price

13.44
Refer to Figure 13.3. Assuming the fixed costs are $100, the monopolist would not shut down the firm since at the profit-maximizing output
a) the price is greater than the marginal revenue.
b) the price is greater than the marginal cost.
c) the economic profit is positive.
d) price equals average total cost.
e) the economic profit would be zero.

13.45
Correct: c)
Difficulty: 4
Page(s): 333
Scramble range: All
Topic: Allocative efficiency

13.45
Refer to Figure 13.3. At the profit-maximizing output level
a) the resource allocation is efficient in the economy since the price is less than the highest price some buyers would be willing to pay.
b) the resource allocation is efficient in the economy since the marginal revenue equals the marginal cost.
c) the resource allocation is inefficient in the economy since the price exceeds the marginal cost.
d) the efficiency of the resource allocation is assured since profit is maximized.
e) the efficiency of the reousrce allocation is assured since cost is minimized.

13.46
Correct: e)
Difficulty: 5
Page(s): 322
Scramble range: All
Topic: Marginal cost and monopoly

13.46
Refer to Figure 13.3. Since the marginal cost of production is constant at $50,
a) this diagram cannot represent the case of a monopolist.
b) this diagram must represent a market that is perfectly competitive.
c) average total cost must also equal $50.
d) the price would never exceed $50.
e) it nevertheless may represent the case of a monopolist.

13.47
Correct: a)
Difficulty: 3
Page(s): 332-334
Scramble range: All
Topic: Monopoly and competition

13.47
Refer to Figure 13.3. If this market were perfectly competitive, the output level would exceed the monopoly output level by
a) 20 units.
b) 40 units.
c) an amount impossible to determine without more information.
d) zero. They would be the same since marginal cost is constant.
e) 30 units.

13.48
Correct: b)
Difficulty: 3
Page(s): 334
Scramble range: All
Topic: Allocative efficiency

13.48
Refer to Figure 13.3. For the resource allocation to be efficient, the output level must be
a) 20 units.
b) 40 units.
c) 60 units.
d) 80 units.
e) zero units.

13.49
Correct: d)
Difficulty: 4
Page(s): 334
Scramble range: All
Topic: Allocative efficiency

13.49
Refer to Figure 13.3. Assuming this market is monopolized, at the profit-maximizing output level
a) the resource allocation is efficient since the monopolist is maximizing profit.
b) the price is equal to the marginal cost and therefore the efficiency of the resource allocation is assured.
c) the price is less than the marginal cost, leading to gains in consumer surplus.
d) the price is greater than the marginal cost and therefore the resource allocation is inefficient.
e) the resource allocation is inefficient since the monopolist has too high costs.

13.50
Correct: a)
Difficulty: 4
Page(s): 334
Scramble range: All
Topic: Allocative efficiency

13.50
Refer to Figure 13.3. The resource allocation is efficient if
a) the price consumers must pay is equal to the marginal cost of production.
b) the price consumers must pay is equal to the average cost of production.
c) the price consumers must pay exceeds minimum average variable cost.
d) the output level of 80 units is produced.
e) the output level of 20 units is produced.

13.51
Correct: c)
Difficulty: 3
Page(s): 317
Scramble range: All
Topic: Natural monopoly

13.51
A natural monopoly exists when
a) the firm uses large amounts of a scarce natural resource.
b) the firms controls access to a critical input.
c) the marginal cost of production decreases as the output level increases.
d) the firm faces a downward sloping demand curve and no other firm produces a close substitute.
e) the average total cost curve is upward sloping.

13.52
Correct: d)
Difficulty: 2
Page(s): 317
Scramble range: All
Topic: Natural monopoly

13.52
A natural monopoly exists when
a) the government protects the firm by granting an exclusive franchise.
b) production can take place with constant returns to scale.
c) there are no rivals in the market.
d) one firm can supply the entire market and be the most efficient plant size.
e) the average total cost curve is upward sloping.

13.53
Correct: a)
Difficulty: 3
Page(s): 317
Scramble range: All
Topic: Natural monopoly and *LRAC*

13.53
For a natural monopoly, the average total cost curve
a) declines in the relevant range of output levels.
b) is constant in the relevant range of output levels.
c) increases in the relevant range of output levels.
d) may be either increasing or decreasing in the relevant range of output levels.
e) is less than the marginal cost curve.

13.54
Correct: d)
Difficulty: 2
Page(s): 317
Scramble range: All
Topic: *LRAC* and returns to scale

13.54
A natural monopoly produces subject to
a) decreasing returns to scale and increasing *LRAC.*
b) constant returns to scale and decreasing *LRAC.*
c) increasing returns to scale and constant *LRAC.*
d) increasing returns to scale and decreasing *LRAC.*
e) decreasing returns to scale and decreasing *LRAC.*

13.55
Correct: a)
Difficulty: 3
Page(s): 317
Scramble range: All
Topic: Natural monopoly

13.55
Refer to Figure 13.4. This figure represents a natural monopoly since
a) the average and marginal costs decline throughout the relevant range of demand.
b) the demand faced by the firm is downward sloping.
c) the sellers of electricity can price discriminate between residential users of electricity and business users of electricity.
d) positive profits will be made.
e) this cost and demand structure could not possibly lead to the rise of a natural monopoly.

Figure 13.4

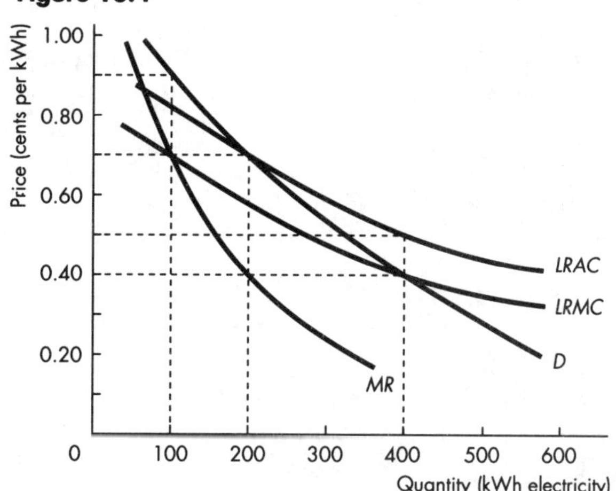

13.56
Correct: a)
Difficulty: 4
Page(s): 317-322
Scramble range: All
Topic: Unregulated natural monopoly

13.56
Refer to Figure 13.4. The profit-maximizing output of electricity is
a) 100 kWh.
b) 200 kWh.
c) 300 kWh.
d) 400 kWh.
e) 500 kWh.

13.57
Correct: a)
Difficulty: 4
Page(s): 320-322
Scramble range: All
Topic: Price/unregulated natural monopoly

13.57
Refer to Figure 13.4. The profit-maximizing price charged would be
a) $0.90.
b) $0.70.
c) $0.60.
d) $0.50.
e) $0.40.

13.58
Correct: d)
Difficulty: 4
Page(s): 334
Scramble range: All
Topic: Regulation of natural monopoly

13.58
Refer to Figure 13.4. The output of electricity that would be allocatively efficient is
a) 100 kWh.
b) 200 kWh.
c) 300 kWh.
d) 400 kWh.
e) 500 kWh.

13.59
Correct: a)
Difficulty: 5
Page(s): 322
Scramble range: All
Topic: Monopoly profits

13.59
Consider a single-price monopoly firm currently at its profit-maximizing choice. Suppose that the cost of inputs falls, creating a change in its marginal and average cost curves. As a result,
a) the firm sells its goods at a lower price, sells a higher quantity, and makes a higher profit than originally.
b) the firm sells its goods at a lower price, sells a higher quantity, and makes a lower profit than originally.
c) the firm sells its goods at the same price, sells a higher quantity, and makes a higher profit than originally.
d) the firm sells its goods at a higher price, sells a lower quantity, and makes a higher profit than originally.
e) the firm sells its goods at the same price, sells the same quantity, but makes a higher profit than originally.

13.60
Correct: e)
Difficulty: 3
Page(s): 320-322
Scramble range: a)-d)
Topic: Monopoly pricing

13.60
Refer to Figure 13.5. Assuming that this firm is a monopolist that charges a single price, what is the profit-maximizing price to charge for the tickets?
a) $5.00.
b) $4.00.
c) $3.00.
d) $2.00.
e) None of the above.

Figure 13.5

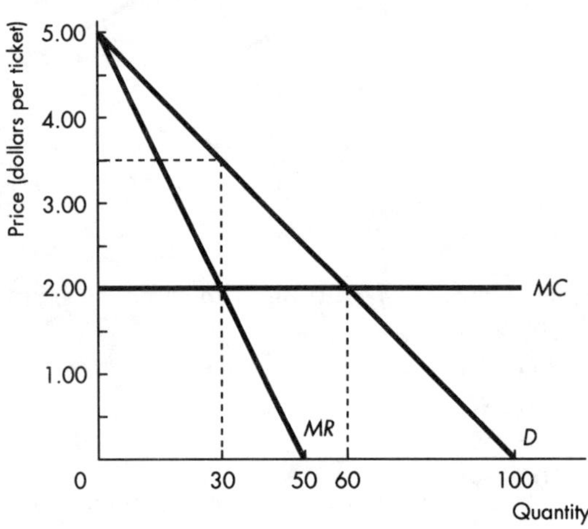

13.61
Correct: b)
Difficulty: 3
Page(s): 320-322
Scramble range: All
Topic: Monopoly output

13.61
Refer to Figure 13.5. Assuming no price discrimination, how many tickets should this monopolist sell in order to maximize total profit?
a) 20 tickets.
b) 30 tickets.
c) 50 tickets.
d) 60 tickets.
e) 100 tickets.

13.62
Correct: d)
Difficulty: 5
Page(s): 320-322
Scramble range: All
Topic: Monopoly total cost

13.62
Refer to Figure 13.5. Assuming that there are fixed costs of $20, the total cost of the one-price monopolist is
a) $140.00.
b) $30.00.
c) $40.00.
d) $80.00.
e) impossible to determine without more information.

13.63
Correct: c)
Difficulty: 5
Page(s): 320-322
Scramble range: All
Topic: Monopoly profit

13.63
Refer to Figure 13.5. Assuming that there are fixed costs of $20, the total profit of the one-price monopolist is
a) a loss of $15.00.
b) zero.
c) $25.00.
d) $50.00.
e) impossible to determine without more information.

13.64
Correct: c)
Difficulty: 4
Page(s): 326
Scramble range: All
Topic: Price discrimination

13.64
Refer to Figure 13.5. Assume that this monopolist can practise perfect price discrimination. This means that
a) only white, Anglo-Saxon Protestants will be allowed to purchase tickets.
b) one price can be charged to young people and a different price can be charged to older people.
c) a different price can be charged to each buyer.
d) prices will go up to all the buyers of tickets.
e) quantity sold will go down compared to the case of no price discrimination.

13.65
Correct: e)
Difficulty: 4
Page(s): 331
Scramble range: All
Topic: Perfect price discrimination

13.65
Refer to Figure 13.5. Assume that this monopolist can practise perfect price discrimination. What is the lowest price that will be charged for tickets in order to maximize profit?
a) zero.
b) $1.00.
c) $3.50.
d) $3.00.
e) $2.00.

13.66
Correct: b)
Difficulty: 4
Page(s): 331
Scramble range: All
Topic: Perfect price discrimination

13.66
Refer to Figure 13.5. Assume that this monopolist can practise perfect price discrimination. How many tickets will be sold in order to maximize profit?
a) 20 tickets.
b) 60 tickets.
c) 40 tickets.
d) 100 tickets.
e) 80 tickets.

13.67
Correct: b)
Difficulty: 5
Page(s): 331
Scramble range: All
Topic: Perfect price discrimination

13.67
Refer to Figure 13.5. Assume that this monopolist can practise perfect price discrimination. How much total revenue is earned by the monopolist?
a) $110.
b) $210.
c) $310.
d) $120.
e) Impossible to determine without more information.

13.68
Correct: c)
Difficulty: 5
Page(s): 331
Scramble range: All
Topic: Profit in price discrimination

13.68
Refer to Figure 13.5. Assume that this monopolist can practise perfect price discrimination, and that total fixed costs are $20. How much is profit increased by the ability to practise perfect price discrimination?
a) Zero.
b) $25.00.
c) $55.00.
d) Impossible to compute without more information.
e) $70.00.

13.69
Correct: a)
Difficulty: 4
Page(s): 326
Scramble range: All
Topic: Price discrimination

13.69
In order for a monopolist to be able to practise price discrimination,
a) the monopolist must be able to segment the market according to the different prices the consumers are willing to pay.
b) the monopolist must be a price taker.
c) the monopolist must have different marginal costs of production for different output levels.
d) the monopolist must have declining average variables costs of production.
e) the monopolist must be able to shrink output.

13.70
Correct: b)
Difficulty: 4
Page(s): 327, 330
Scramble range: All
Topic: Price discrimination

13.70
Perfect price discrimination can be profitable because
a) the price can be set lower for buyers with inelastic demand.
b) the price can be set lower for buyers with elastic demand.
c) the demand is perfectly elastic for the product.
d) the seller can charge higher prices for those buyers with elastic demand.
e) price and total revenue go up.

13.71
Correct: b)
Difficulty: 3
Page(s): 331
Scramble range: None
Topic: Price discrimination

13.71
For price discrimination to be possible, it is necessary to
a) practicse price-taking behaviour.
b) prevent resale of the product or service.
c) charge a higher price for goods that cost less to produce.
d) be able to identify different groups of buyers with different elasticities of demand.
e) both b) and d).

13.72
Correct: d)
Difficulty: 4
Page(s): 320-322
Scramble range: All
Topic: Fixed cost

13.72
Suppose that the fixed costs of a monopolist double. This would lead to
a) a doubling of the profit-maximizing price charged by the monopolist.
b) profit that is only half of the amount that the monopolist earned before the cost increase.
c) the likely shutdown of the plant if the price did not change accordingly.
d) no change in the profit-maximizing price charged by the monopolist.
e) a fall in price as the monopolist attempts to raise total revenue.

13.73
Correct: d)
Difficulty: 4
Page(s): 320-322
Scramble range: All
Topic: Fixed cost

13.73
When fixed cost rises for a monopolist,
a) the increase will be passed on to the consumers directly in the form of a higher price.
b) the monopolist will decrease output until the fixed cost is reduced to the original level.
c) the monopolist will increase output to make up for the increase in fixed cost.
d) the monopolist will not change output or price, and only the profit will be affected.
e) the monopolist will react by lowering price and attempting to raise quantity in order to lower average fixed costs.

13.74
Correct: c)
Difficulty: 3
Page(s): 320-322
Scramble range: All
Topic: Monopoly profit

13.74
Monopolies often earn positive economic profit since
a) they typically receive government subsidies.
b) the ability to set the market price guarantees a positive economic profit.
c) barriers to entry prevent the price from declining.
d) taking on monopoly risk ensures economic profit.
e) they always have lower costs than competitive firms.

13.75
Correct: b)
Difficulty: 4
Page(s): 320-322
Scramble range: All
Topic: Monopoly pricing

13.75
A monopolist will lower the profit-maximizing price when
a) fixed costs are decreased.
b) marginal costs are decreased.
c) the market demand increases.
d) average total costs are decreased.
e) average fixed costs are decreased.

13.76
Correct: b)
Difficulty: 3
Page(s): 320-322
Scramble range: All
Topic: Monopoly pricing

13.76
A monopolist will not tend to produce the output level at which marginal cost equals the price because
a) profit would be zero in that case.
b) profit would not be maximized in that case.
c) entry into the industry keeps the price lower than that level.
d) the monopolist always charges the highest price the market will bear.
e) total costs are too high at this point.

13.77
Correct: d)
Difficulty: 3
Page(s): 317
Scramble range: a)-c)
Topic: Monopoly

13.77
In order for monopoly to arise there must be
a) a single supplier of a good in the industry.
b) no close substitutes for the good.
c) barriers preventing entry of other firms.
d) all of the above.
e) none of the above.

13.78 (SG 13.1)
Correct: b)
Difficulty: 2
Page(s): 317
Scramble range: All
Topic: Barriers to entry

13.78
Which of the following is an example of a possible natural barrier to the entry of new firms in an industry?
a) Licensing of professions.
b) Economies of scale.
c) Issuing a patent.
d) A public franchise.
e) Diseconomies of scope.

13.79
Correct: b)
Difficulty: 2
Page(s): 318
Scramble range: All
Topic: Monopoly demand

13.79
Which of the following is *not* true of a single-price monopoly?
a) Since there is a single firm, the firm demand is the industry demand.
b) Demand is inelastic since there are no good substitutes for the good.
c) The average revenue curve is the demand curve.
d) Marginal revenue is less than price.
e) It is possible that the monopoly is a natural monopoly.

13.80
Correct: a)
Difficulty: 3
Page(s): 320-322
Scramble range: All
Topic: Monopoly pricing

13.80
In order to sell an additional unit, a single-price monopoly must reduce the price, not only on the additional unit but on all units. This explains why
a) marginal revenue is less than average revenue.
b) a monopoly will never lower price.
c) a monopoly will not be able to maximize profits.
d) the marginal cost curve is positively sloped.
e) price is less than marginal revenue.

13.81 (SG 13.3)
Correct: e)
Difficulty: 4
Page(s): 320
Scramble range: All
Topic: Monopoly marginal revenue

13.81
If marginal revenue is negative at a particular output, then
a) price must be negative.
b) a profit-maximizing monopoly should increase output.
c) the elasticity of demand is greater than one at that output.
d) demand must be elastic at that output.
e) a profit-maximizing monopoly should decrease output.

13.82 (SG 13.5)
Correct: d)
Difficulty: 3
Page(s): 320-322
Scramble range: All
Topic: Monopoly profit

13.82
A profit-maximizing monopoly will never produce at an output level
a) at which it would make economic losses.
b) where marginal revenue is less than price.
c) at which average cost is greater than marginal cost.
d) in the inelastic range of its demand curve.
e) in the elastic range of its demand curve.

13.83 (SG 13.7)
Correct: a)
Difficulty: 3
Page(s): 320-322
Scramble range: All
Topic: Monopoly profit

13.83
If a profit-maximizing monopoly is producing at an output at which marginal cost exceeds marginal revenue, it
a) should raise price and lower output.
b) should lower price and raise output.
c) is making losses.
d) is maximizing profit.
e) has marginal revenue greater than price.

13.84 (SG 13.8)
Correct: c)
Difficulty: 4
Page(s): 323
Scramble range: All
Topic: Monopoly shutdown

13.84
A monopoly will go out of business in the short run if
a) it is making an economic loss.
b) it cannot maximize profit due to government regulation.
c) price is less than average variable cost.
d) the profit-maximizing level of output is in the elastic range of the demand curve.
e) the profit-maximizing level of output is in the inelastic range of the demand curve.

13.85 (SG13.11)
Correct: d)
Difficulty: 2
Page(s): 324
Scramble range: All
Topic: Monopoly supply

13.85
The supply curve for a monopoly
a) is the marginal cost curve above average total cost.
b) is the marginal cost curve above average variable cost.
c) is the positively sloped portion of the marginal revenue curve.
d) does not exist.
e) is horizontal.

13.86 (SG 13.12)
Correct: e)
Difficulty: 3
Page(s): 321
Scramble range: All
Topic: Profit maximization

13.86
For the monopoly depicted in Figure 13.6, when profit is maximized,
a) quantity will be 3 and price will be $3.
b) quantity will be 3 and price will be $4.
c) quantity will be 4 and price will be $4.
d) quantity will be 4 and price will be $5.
e) quantity will be 3 and price will be $6.

Figure 13.6

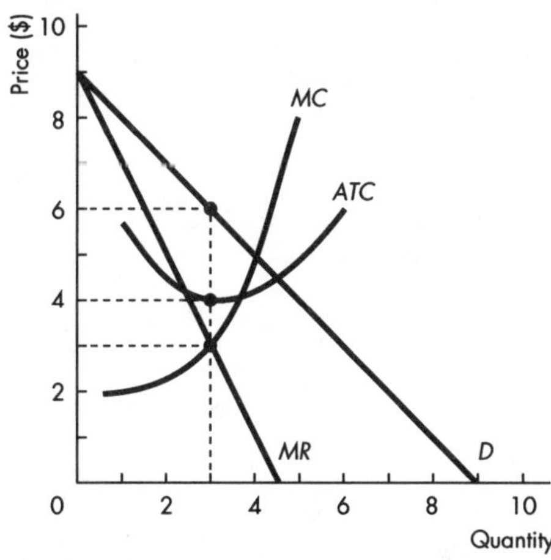

13.87 (SG 13.13)
Correct: c)
Difficulty: 4
Page(s): 322
Scramble range: All
Topic: Monopoly profit

13.87
If the monopoly depicted in Figure 13.6 is maximizing profit, total profit will be
a) $3.
b) $4.
c) $6.
d) $9.
e) $18.

13.88
Correct: a)
Difficulty: 4
Page(s): 323-331
Scramble range: All
Topic: Price discrimination

13.88
If a price discriminating monopoly charges a lower price to students, it is likely that the firm
a) believes that student demand is relatively elastic.
b) believes that student demand is relatively inelastic.
c) wants to shift student demand.
d) cares about the well-being of students.
e) is out to exploit students.

13.89
Correct: e)
Difficulty: 4
Page(s): 323-331
Scramble range: All
Topic: Price discrimination

13.89
If a firm practises perfect price discrimination,
a) its average revenue curve is its demand.
b) it will maximize revenue.
c) it is assured of making a profit.
d) it will produce the quantity at which price intersects the average total cost curve.
e) it will produce the quantity at which marginal cost intersects the demand curve.

13.90
Correct: d)
Difficulty: 4
Page(s): 323-331
Scramble range: All
Topic: Price discrimination

13.90
If a perfect price discriminating monopoly faces the demand relation given in Table 13.1 and if marginal cost is constant at $3, output will be
a) 2.
b) 3.
c) 4.
d) 5.
e) 6.

Table 13.1

Price ($)	Quantity demanded
8	0
7	1
6	2
5	3
4	4
3	5
2	6
1	7

13.91
Correct: e)
Difficulty: 5
Page(s): 323-331
Scramble range: All
Topic: Price discrimination

13.91
Table 13.1 gives the demand schedule faced by a monopoly. If the monopoly is a perfect price discriminator, the marginal revenue from the sale of the third unit of output is
a) $2.
b) $6.
c) $4.
d) $3.
e) $5.

13.92
Correct: d)
Difficulty: 5
Page(s): 323-331
Scramble range: All
Topic: Price discrimination

13.92
Table 13.1 gives the demand schedule faced by a perfect price discriminating monopoly. If 3 units are sold, total revenue is
a) $15.
b) $16.
c) $17.
d) $18.
e) $5.

13.93 (SG 13.17)
Correct: b)
Difficulty: 3
Page(s): 323-331
Scramble range: All
Topic: Price discrimination

13.93
A (not perfect) price discriminating monopoly will produce
a) less than a single-price monopoly.
b) more than a single-price monopoly but less than a perfectly competitive industry.
c) the same amount as a perfectly competitive industry.
d) more than a perfectly competitive industry.
e) more than a perfectly discriminating monopoly.

13.94 (SG 13.18)
Correct: c)
Difficulty: 4
Page(s): 334
Scramble range: All
Topic: Producer surplus

13.94
Table 13.2 gives information on the marginal cost for the XYZ firm. If XYZ sells 3 units at a price of $6 each, what is its producer surplus?
a) $2.
b) $6.
c) $9.
d) $12.
e) $18.

Table 13.2

Quantity	Marginal cost ($)
1	2
2	3
3	4
4	5

13.95
Correct: b)
Difficulty: 4
Page(s): 334
Scramble range: All
Topic: Deadweight loss

13.95
Consider the industry demand curve in Figure 13.7. Which area in the diagram indicates the deadweight loss from a single-price monopoly?
a) *iacg.*
b) *acd.*
c) *iabh.*
d) *iadcg.*
e) The deadweight loss is zero.

Figure 13.7

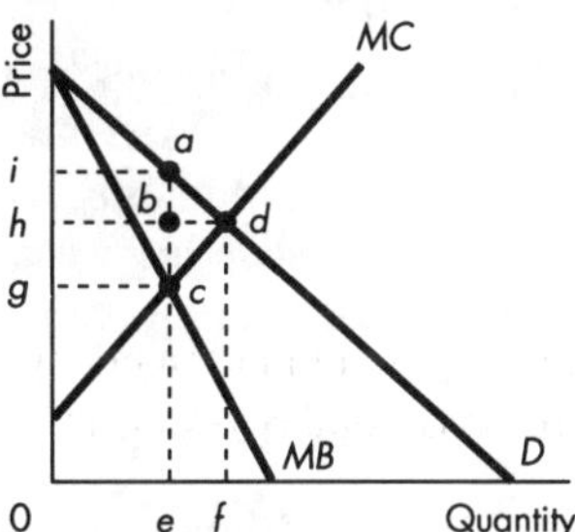

13.96 (SG 13.23)
Correct: a)
Difficulty: 2
Page(s): 335
Scramble range: All
Topic: Rent seeking

13.96
Activity with the purpose of creating monopoly is
a) called rent seeking.
b) illegal in Canada.
c) known as price discrimination.
d) called legal monopoly.
e) called a natural monopoly.

13.97 (SG 13.24)
Correct: c)
Difficulty: 3
Page(s): 336
Scramble range: All
Topic: Economies of scope

13.97
A monopoly has economies of scope if
a) average total cost declines as output increases.
b) total profit declines as output increases.
c) average total cost declines as the number of different goods produced increases.
d) total profit declines as the number of different goods produced increases.
e) price declines as the number of different goods produced increases.

13.98
Correct: d)
Difficulty: 2
Page(s): 317
Scramble range: All
Topic: Monopoly

13.98
In order to prevent monopoly from arising there must be
a) a single supplier of a good in the industry.
b) no close substitutes for the good.
c) barriers preventing entry of other firms.
d) freedom of entry into the industry.
e) economies of scale.

13.99
Correct: b)
Difficulty: 3
Page(s): 317
Scramble range: All
Topic: Barriers to entry

13.99
Which of the following is not an example of a possible natural barrier to the entry of new firms in an industry?
a) Licensing of professions.
b) A high wage rate of labour.
c) Issuing a patent.
d) A public franchise.
e) Economies of scope.

13.100
Correct: c)
Difficulty: 2
Page(s): 318
Scramble range: All
Topic: Monopoly demand

13.100
Which of the following is true of a single-price monopoly?
a) Since there is a single firm, the firm demand is less than the industry demand.
b) Demand is inelastic since there are no good substitutes for the good.
c) The average revenue curve is the demand curve.
d) Marginal revenue is equal to the price.
e) Marginal revenue is equal to average revenue.

13.101
Correct: e)
Difficulty: 4
Page(s): 331
Scramble range: All
Topic: Monopoly pricing

13.101
A perfect price discriminating monopoly will produce
a) less than a single-price monopoly.
b) more than a single-price monopoly but less than a perfectly competitive industry.
c) less than a (not perfectly) discriminating monopolist.
d) more than a perfectly competitive industry.
e) the same amount as a perfectly competitive industry.

13.102
Correct: c)
Difficulty: 4
Page(s): 318-319
Scramble range: All
Topic: Monopoly marginal revenue

13.102
If marginal revenue is positive at a particular output, then
a) price must be negative.
b) a profit-maximizing monopoly should decrease output.
c) the elasticity of demand is greater than one at that output.
d) demand must be inelastic at that output.
e) a profit-maximizing firm should increase output.

13.103
Correct: d)
Difficulty: 3
Page(s): 320-322
Scramble range: All
Topic: Monopoly profit

13.103
A profit-maximizing monopoly will always produce at an output level
a) at which it would make positive economic profit.
b) where marginal revenue is greater than price.
c) at which average cost is greater than marginal cost.
d) in the elastic range of its demand curve.
e) at which average cost is less than marginal cost.

13.104
Correct: b)
Difficulty: 3
Page(s): 320-322
Scramble range: All
Topic: Monopoly profit

13.104
If a profit-maximizing monopoly is producing at an output at which marginal cost is less than marginal revenue, it
a) should raise price and lower output.
b) should lower price and raise output.
c) is making losses.
d) is maximizing profit.
e) has marginal revenue greater than price.

13.105
Correct: e)
Difficulty: 3
Page(s): 330
Scramble range: All
Topic: Price discrimination

13.105
If a price discriminating monopoly charges a higher price to businesses, it is likely that the monopoly
a) believes that business demand is relatively elastic.
b) wants to exploit businesses.
c) wants to shift business demand.
d) cares about the well-being of business people.
e) believes that business demand is relatively inelastic.

13.106
Correct: e)
Difficulty: 3
Page(s): 331
Scramble range: All
Topic: Price discrimination

13.106
If a firm practises perfect price discrimination,
a) its demand is the average revenue curve.
b) it will minimize total costs.
c) it is assured of making a zero profit.
d) it will produce the quantity at which price equals average total cost.
e) it will produce the quantity at which marginal cost equals the lowest price charged.

13.107
Correct: e)
Difficulty: 5
Page(s): 330-334
Scramble range: All
Topic: Perfect price discrimination

13.107
A perfect price discriminating monopoly will be
a) less allocatively efficient than a single-price monopoly.
b) more allocatively efficient than a single-price monopoly but less allocatively efficient than a perfectly competitive industry.
c) as allocatively efficient as a single-price monopoly.
d) more allocatively efficient than a perfectly competitive industry.
e) as allocatively efficient as a perfectly competitive industry.

13.108
Correct: a)
Difficulty: 5
Page(s): 320-322
Scramble range: All
Topic: Monopoly profit

13.108
Consider Fact 13.1. If Barbara charges all the customers the same price for a meal, that price will be __________, and Barbara will make a total profit of __________
a) \$3.00; \$160.
b) \$3.50; \$150.
c) \$2.50; \$150.
d) \$2.00; \$120.
e) \$4.00; \$120.

Fact 13.1 Barbara runs a truck stop on the Prairies. She has a monopoly and faces the following demand schedule for meals:

Price (dollars per meal)	Quantity demanded (meals per week)
1.00	160
1.50	140
2.00	120
2.50	100
3.00	80
3.50	60
4.00	40
4.50	35
5.00	30
5.50	25

Barbara's marginal cost and average total cost are a constant $1 per meal.

13.109
Correct: a)
Difficulty: 5
Page(s): 334
Scramble range: All
Topic: Deadweight loss

13.109
Consider Fact 13.1. Barbara is operating as a single-price monopolist, and has made her profit-maximizing choice. This results in a deadweight loss of
a) $80.
b) $100.
c) $160.
d) $60.
e) $90.

13.110
Correct: e)
Difficulty: 5
Page(s): 326-331
Scramble range: All
Topic: Discriminating monopoly

13.110
Consider Fact 13.2. Barbara decides to operate as a two-price discriminating monopolist. She charges the truck-drivers __________ and charges the tourists __________
a) $2.50; $4.00.
b) $3.50; $3.00.
c) $3.00; $3.50.
d) $2.00; $4.00.
e) $4.00; $2.50.

Fact 13.2 Barbara runs a truck stop on the Prairies. She has a constant marginal and average cost equal to $1. She has a monopoly and discovers that there are two different groups of people stopping for meals at her truck stop. She estimates the demand schedules for the two groups are:

Price (dollars per week)	Quantity demanded (meals per week)	
	Truck drivers	Tourists
1.00	70	90
1.50	65	75
2.00	60	60
2.50	55	45
3.00	50	30
3.50	45	15
4.00	40	0
4.50	35	0
5.00	30	0
5.50	25	0

13.111
Correct: b)
Difficulty: 4
Page(s): 334
Scramble range: All
Topic: Consumer/ producer surplus

13.111

Consider Figure 13.8. Suppose we have a market with a single-price monopolist. If the slanted barred area shows the consumer surplus, and the vertical barred area shows the producer surplus, which of the graphs correctly represents this market?

a) (a).
b) (b).
c) (c).
d) (d).
e) (b) and (c).

Figure 13.8

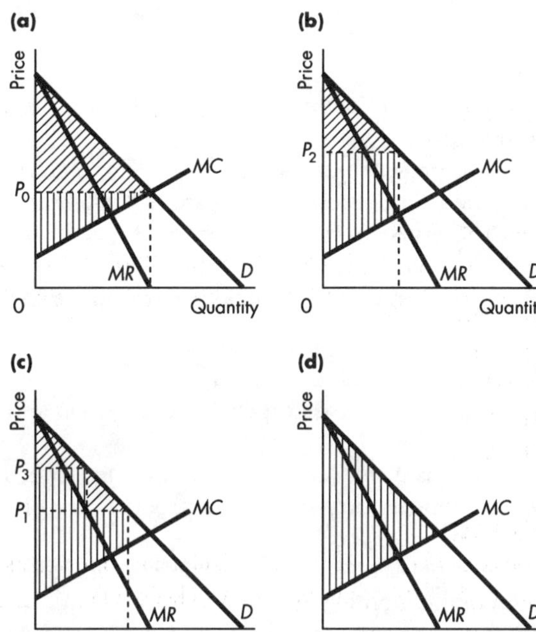

13.112
Correct: c)
Difficulty: 5
Page(s): 334
Scramble range: All
Topic: Consumer/ producer surplus

13.112

Consider Figure 13.8. Suppose we have a market with a two-price monopolist. If the slanted barred area shows the consumer surplus and the vertical barred area shows the producer surplus, which of the graphs correctly represents this market?

a) (a).
b) (b).
c) (c).
d) (d).
e) (b) and (d).

Chapter 14 Monopolistic Competition and Oligopoly

14.1
Correct: c)
Difficulty: 2
Page(s): 347
Scramble range: All
Topic: Monopolistic competition

14.1
Which of the following describes an industry that is monopolistically competitive?
a) The presence of significant barriers to entry.
b) The products of the firms are not differentiated.
c) The firms are mutually dependent.
d) There is a small number of large firms.
e) Each firm faces a horizontal demand curve.

14.2
Correct: d)
Difficulty: 2
Page(s): 347
Scramble range: All
Topic: Monopolistic competition

14.2
One difference between perfect competition and monopolistic competition is that
a) there is a smaller number of firms in perfectly competitive industries.
b) in perfect competition, the products are slightly differentiated between firms.
c) monopolistic competition has barriers to entry, whereas perfect competition has none.
d) firms in monopolistic competition have some degree of market power.
e) there is a smaller number of firms in monopolistically competitive industries.

14.3
Correct: d)
Difficulty: 2
Page(s): 347
Scramble range: All
Topic: Monopolistic competition

14.3
One difference between oligopoly and monopolistic competition is that
a) there is a smaller number of firms in monopolistically competitive industries than in oligopolies.
b) in oligopolies the products are slightly differentiated between firms, whereas in monopolistic competition the products are identical.
c) monopolistic competition has barriers to entry, whereas oligopoly has none.
d) fewer firms compete in oligopolies than in monopolistic competition.
e) in oligopolies, firms are typically smaller in size.

14.4
Correct: d)
Difficulty: 2
Page(s): 347
Scramble range: All
Topic: Monopolistic competition

14.4
A good example of an industry that is monopolistically competitive is the
a) wheat market.
b) foreign exchange market.
c) stocks on the Toronto Stock Exchange.
d) restaurant industry.
e) telephone industry.

14.5
Correct: c)
Difficulty: 3
Page(s): 347
Scramble range: All
Topic: Product differentiation

14.5
Firms in monopolistic competition can achieve product differentiation by
a) expanding the plant size.
b) exploiting economies of scale in production.
c) explaining special characteristics in their advertisements.
d) setting their price equal to their marginal cost.
e) exploiting economies of scope in production, and producing several different goods.

14.6
Correct: c)
Difficulty: 3
Page(s): 347
Scramble range: All
Topic: Product differentiation

14.6
Firms in monopolistic competition can differentiate their products by
a) pricing according to the elasticity of demand.
b) having a sale every Monday morning.
c) creating a unique product design.
d) paying their labourers more than the going market wage rate.
e) lowering the price.

14.7
Correct: a)
Difficulty: 3
Page(s): 347
Scramble range: All
Topic: Product differentiation

14.7
Product differentiation can be achieved by
a) offering guarantees of product quality and reliability which exceed that of the competition.
b) conducting a sale on the day following Thanksgiving Day.
c) printing the name of the product on the label.
d) creating barriers to the entry of potential rivals.
e) taking advantage of economies of scale.

14.8
Correct: c)
Difficulty: 3
Page(s): 347
Scramble range: All
Topic: Product differentiation

14.8
Price differences among firms
a) cannot exist in monopolistic competition.
b) most often exist in markets which are perfectly competitive.
c) are caused by the differences in product quality and the willingness of consumers to pay more for added quality.
d) cannot be maintained for long in industries that are monopolistically competitive.
e) are a result of cost differences among firms.

14.9
Correct: e)
Difficulty: 3
Page(s): 347
Scramble range: All
Topic: Price differentiation/ imperfect competition

14.9
Price differences among firms
a) can exist in perfect competition but not in monopolistic competition.
b) most often exist in markets that are monopolies.
c) are due to perfect substitution between differing firms' products.
d) cannot be maintained for long in industries that are monopolistically competitive since perfect substitutes are readily available.
e) are made possible by the existence of demand that is not perfectly elastic.

14.10
Correct: d)
Difficulty: 3
Page(s): 347
Scramble range: All
Topic: Product differentiation

14.10
To achieve more market power, firms can
a) lobby the government to eliminate barriers to entry.
b) reduce their costs of production.
c) advertise that they charge low prices.
d) differentiate their products from the products of their rivals.
e) raise their markups on prices.

14.11
Correct: d)
Difficulty: 3
Page(s): 347
Scramble range: All
Topic: Elastic and monopolistic competition

14.11
One difference between perfect competition and monopolistic competition is
a) that the firms in perfect competition face a demand that is less elastic than firms in monopolistic competition.
b) products are highly differentiated in perfect competition but identical in monopolistic competition.
c) monopolistically competitive firms face a demand curve that is perfectly elastic.
d) monopolistically competitive firms face demand curves that are less elastic than those faced by perfectly competitive firms.
e) that cost curves differ.

14.12
Correct: b)
Difficulty: 3
Page(s): 347
Scramble range: All
Topic: Profit in monopolistic competition

14.12
Normal economic profit in monopolistically competitive industries can be caused by
a) failure to accept worthwhile risks.
b) the lack of significant barriers to the entry of rival firms.
c) the existence of excess capacity.
d) the fact that they must pay for expensive advertisements on television if their rivals do the same.
e) barriers to entry.

14.13
Correct: b)
Difficulty: 3
Page(s): 349
Scramble range: All
Topic: Profit in monopolistic competition

14.13
Firms in monopolistically competitive industries may earn only normal economic profit in the long run since
a) their costs rise as the capital stock grows older.
b) the demand that they face will be decreased as rival firms offer slightly differentiated products for sale in the same market.
c) their marginal cost curve slopes upward.
d) the market eventually becomes perfectly competitive.
e) costs always rise over time.

14.14
Correct: e)
Difficulty: 4
Page(s): 349
Scramble range: All
Topic: Pricing in monopolistic competition

14.14
If firms in monopolistic competition have some degree of price-setting power, then
a) all firms will earn positive economic profit.
b) the price will be set equal to marginal cost in order to achieve maximum profit.
c) price will be lower than under perfect competition.
d) production will always take place at minimum average total cost.
e) the price will always be set above the marginal cost of production.

14.15
Correct: a)
Difficulty: 3
Page(s): 349
Scramble range: All
Topic: Pricing in monopolistic competition

14.15
Firms in monopolistic competition must have some degree of price-setting power since
a) they must lower their price in order to sell a greater quantity.
b) they can never earn less than normal economic profit.
c) the price they charge is never more than the marginal cost of production.
d) they offer identical products and can therefore underbid their competitors.
e) they earn at best normal economic profit.

14.16
Correct: c)
Difficulty: 3
Page(s): 349
Scramble range: All
Topic: Economic profit and rival entry

14.16
If some firms in the industry earn positive economic profit, then
a) the industry cannot be perfectly competitive.
b) the industry must be monopolistically competitive.
c) rival firms will enter if there are no barriers to entry.
d) their product must have been differentiated from that of their rivals.
e) the industry must be oligopolistic.

14.17
Correct: a)
Difficulty: 3
Page(s): 349
Scramble range: All
Topic: Economic profit/short-run production

14.17
For a monopolistically competitive firm to be earning positive economic profit,
a) the production period must be the short run.
b) the production period must be the long run.
c) rival firms must not exist.
d) their rivals must also be earning positive economic profit.
e) barriers to entry must exist.

14.18
Correct: c)
Difficulty: 4
Page(s): 347
Scramble range: All
Topic: Product differentiation

14.18
The purpose of product differentiation is to
a) make the demand less inelastic.
b) make the demand more elastic.
c) increase demand for the product and make the demand less elastic.
d) lower the average cost of production and therefore increase profit.
e) lower the marginal cost of production and therefore to be able to lower price.

14.19
Correct: b)
Difficulty: 3
Page(s): 349
Scramble range: All
Topic: Profit and entry/exit industry

14.19
When the economic profit is negative in an industry that is monopolistically competitive, then
a) firms will enter the industry and produce better products.
b) firms will exit the industry, and the demand will increase for the products of the firms that remain.
c) firms will exit the industry, and the demand will decrease for those firms that remain in the industry.
d) firms will enter the industry and the demand will become more elastic for those firms that were originally in the industry.
e) the industry will eventually disappear.

14.20
Correct: d)
Difficulty: 3
Page(s): 349
Scramble range: All
Topic: Profit and entry/exit industry

14.20
When the economic profit is positive in an industry that is monopolistically competitive, then
a) firms will enter the industry, thereby increasing the demand for the product of the firms originally in the market.
b) firms will exit the industry and the demand will increase for the products of the firms that remain.
c) firms will exit the industry and the demand will decrease for those firms that remain in the industry.
d) firms will enter the industry and the demand will become more elastic for those firms that were originally in the industry.
e) eventually it will become monopolized.

14.21
Correct: e)
Difficulty: 4
Page(s): 349
Scramble range: All
Topic: Interaction of firms

14.21
Firms in monopolistic competition have rivals that
a) will always match their price increases.
b) will always match their price decreases but not their price increases.
c) all agree on a common price.
d) set their price where the demand curve is tangent to the average cost curve.
e) set their price according to the demand they face.

14.22
Correct: a)
Difficulty: 3
Page(s): 347–349
Scramble range: All
Topic: Profit maximization

14.22
Refer to Figure 14.1. If this firm is in monopolistic competition, then it will produce an output level
a) of 40 units.
b) of 60 units.
c) of 80 units.
d) that is impossible to determine without information concerning the rival firms.
e) that is lower than 40 units.

Figure 14.1

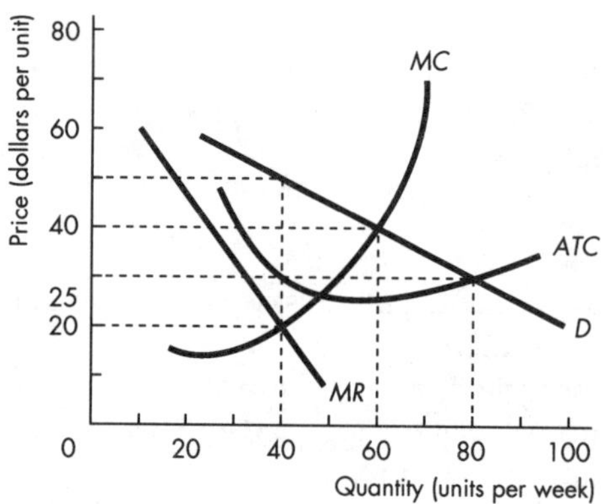

14.23
Correct: b)
Difficulty: 3
Page(s): 349
Scramble range: All
Topic: Pricing in monopolistic competition

14.23
Refer to Figure 14.1. If this firm is in monopolistic competition, then it will charge a price
a) of $20.
b) of $50.
c) of $40.
d) of $30.
e) that is impossible to determine without information concerning the behaviour of the rival firms.

14.24
Correct: a)
Difficulty: 3
Page(s): 349
Scramble range: All
Topic: Profit in monopolistic competition

14.24
Refer to Figure 14.1. This firm in monopolistic competition will earn
a) positive economic profit.
b) zero economic profit.
c) negative economic profit.
d) economic profit that is impossible to determine without information concerning the behaviour of the rival firms.
e) either a zero or a positive profit.

14.25
Correct: a)
Difficulty: 3
Page(s): 349
Scramble range: All
Topic: Profit maximization

14.25
Refer to Figure 14.1. If this firm in monopolistic competition faces the demand pictured in Figure 14.1, then
a) rival firms will enter the industry.
b) some firms will exit the industry.
c) economic profit will be zero.
d) 60 units of output will be produced in order to maximize profit.
e) the firm's profits can be expected to rise over time.

14.26
Correct: e)
Difficulty: 3
Page(s): 349
Scramble range: All
Topic: Profit maximization

14.26
Refer to Figure 14.2. In order to maximize profit, this firm in monopolistic competition will charge a price of
a) $10.
b) $25.
c) $20.
d) greater than $30.
e) $30.

Figure 14.2

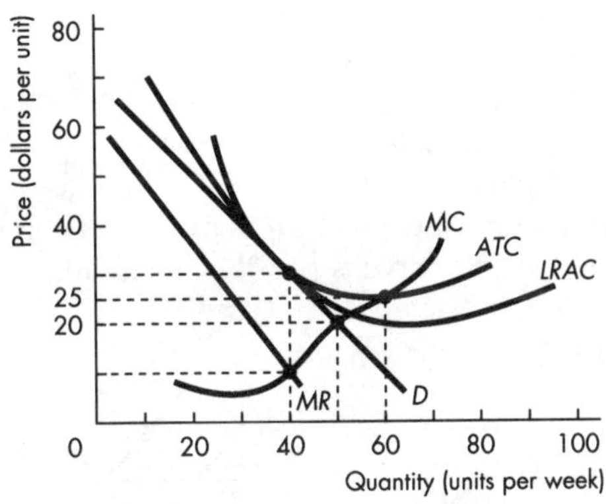

14.27
Correct: a)
Difficulty: 3
Page(s): 349
Scramble range: All
Topic: Output in monopolistic competition

14.27
Refer to Figure 14.2. In order to maximize profit, this firm in monopolistic competition will produce an output
a) of 40 units.
b) of 50 units.
c) of 60 units.
d) that cannot be determined with information concerning rival firms.
e) that is less than 40 units.

14.28
Correct: b)
Difficulty: 3
Page(s): 349
Scramble range: All
Topic: Economic profit

14.28
Refer to Figure 14.2. Economic profit earned by this firm is
a) negative.
b) zero.
c) positive.
d) impossible to determine with information concerning the price charged by the rival firms.
e) zero and will rise over time.

14.29
Correct: e)
Difficulty: 3
Page(s): 350
Scramble range: a)–d)
Topic: Efficient resource allocation

14.29
Refer to Figure 14.2. Assuming this firm in monopolistic competition is maximizing profit,
a) there would be entry of rival firms into the industry.
b) rival firms would exit the industry.
c) this firm's profits will rise over time.
d) this firm would exit the industry in the long run.
e) none of the above.

14.30
Correct: b)
Difficulty: 3
Page(s): 350
Scramble range: All
Topic: Efficient resource allocation

14.30
Refer to Figure 14.2. For the resource allocation to be efficient, the firm's output must be equal to
a) 40 units.
b) 50 units.
c) 60 units.
d) zero, as the firm should shut down.
e) greater than 60 units.

14.31
Correct: b)
Difficulty: 3
Page(s): 349
Scramble range: All
Topic: Demand in monopolistic competition

14.31
Refer to Figure 14.3. Which demand curve must this monopolistically competitive firm face in the long run?
a) Demand curve D_1.
b) Demand curve D_2.
c) Either demand curve D_1 or D_2.
d) Neither demand curve D_1 nor demand curve D_2.
e) Any demand curve is possible, including D_1 or D_2.

Figure 14.3

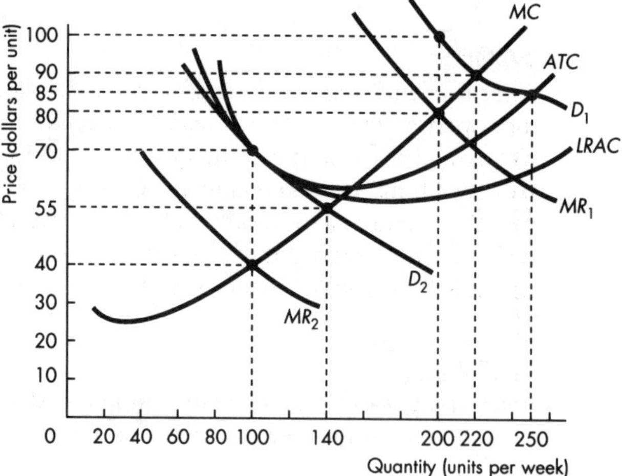

14.32
Correct: a)
Difficulty: 3
Page(s): 349
Scramble range: All
Topic: Profit maximization

14.32
Refer to Figure 14.3. Assume this firm faces demand curve D_1. In order to maximize profit, this firm in monopolistic competition will charge a price of
a) $100.
b) $90.
c) $80.
d) $70.
e) $55.

14.33
Correct: c)
Difficulty: 3
Page(s): 349
Scramble range: All
Topic: Monopolistic competition

14.33
Refer to Figure 14.3. Assume this firm faces demand curve *D*1. In order to maximize profit, this firm in monopolistic competition will produce an output of

a) 100 units.
b) 220 units.
c) 200 units.
d) 260 units.
e) 140 units.

14.34
Correct: c)
Difficulty: 3
Page(s): 349
Scramble range: All
Topic: Economic profit

14.34
Refer to Figure 14.3. Assume this firm faces demand curve D_1. At the profit-maximizing output level, the economic profit earned by this firm is

a) negative.
b) zero.
c) positive.
d) impossible to determine with information concerning the price charged by the rival firms.
e) lower than the profit earned by firms in perfect competition.

14.35
Correct: a)
Difficulty: 3
Page(s): 349
Scramble range: All
Topic: Economic profit and rival entry

14.35
Refer to Figure 14.3. Assume this firm faces demand curve D_1. If this firm in monopolistic competition is maximizing profit,

a) there would be entry of rival firms into the industry.
b) rival firms would exit the industry.
c) the resource allocation would be efficient.
d) this firm would exit the industry in the long run.
e) this firm's profits will rise over time.

14.36
Correct: c)
Difficulty: 3
Page(s): 350
Scramble range: All
Topic: Efficient resource allocation

14.36
Refer to Figure 14.3. Assume this firm faces demand curve D_1. If this firm in monopolistic competition is maximizing profit,

a) rival firms would exit the industry.
b) rival firms would contract their product lines.
c) the resource allocation would be inefficient.
d) this firm would exit the industry in the long run.
e) this firm would expand output in the long run.

14.37
Correct: b)
Difficulty: 4
Page(s): 350
Scramble range: All
Topic: Efficient resource allocation

14.37
Refer to Figure 14.3. Assume this firm faces demand curve D_1. For the resource allocation to be efficient, the firm's output must be equal to

a) 100 units.
b) 220 units.
c) 200 units.
d) 260 units.
e) 140 units.

14.38
Correct: e)
Difficulty: 3
Page(s): 349
Scramble range: All
Topic: Profit maximization

14.38
Refer to Figure 14.3. Assume this firm faces demand curve D_2. In order to maximize profit, this firm in monopolistic competition will charge a price of
a) $40.
b) $90.
c) $80.
d) $55.
e) $70.

14.39
Correct: a)
Difficulty: 3
Page(s): 349
Scramble range: All
Topic: Output in monopolistic competition

14.39
Refer to Figure 14.3. Assume this firm faces demand curve D_2. In order to maximize profit, this firm in monopolistic competition will produce an output of
a) 100 units.
b) 220 units.
c) 260 units.
d) 200 units.
e) 140 units.

14.40
Correct: b)
Difficulty: 3
Page(s): 349
Scramble range: All
Topic: Economic profit

14.40
Refer to Figure 14.3. Assume this firm faces demand curve D_2. At the profit-maximizing output level, the economic profit earned by this firm is
a) negative.
b) zero.
c) positive.
d) impossible to determine without information concerning the price charged by the rival firms.
e) zero and will fall over time.

14.41
Correct: d)
Difficulty: 3
Page(s): 349
Scramble range: All
Topic: Economic profit and rival entry

14.41
Refer to Figure 14.3. Assume this firm faces demand curve D_2. If this firm in monopolistic competition is maximizing profit,
a) there would be entry of rival firms into the industry.
b) rival firms would exit the industry.
c) the resource allocation would be efficient.
d) the number of firms in the industry would remain constant.
e) profits will fall over time.

14.42
Correct: c)
Difficulty: 3
Page(s): 349
Scramble range: All
Topic: Efficient resource allocation

14.42
Refer to Figure 14.3. Assume this firm faces demand curve D_2. If this firm in monopolistic competition is maximizing profit,
a) rival firms would exit the industry.
b) rival firms would contract their product lines.
c) the resource allocation would be inefficient.
d) this firm would exit the industry in the long run.
e) this firm's profits will rise over time.

14.43
Correct: b)
Difficulty: 4
Page(s): 350
Scramble range: All
Topic: Efficient resource allocation

14.43
Refer to Figure 14.3. Assume this firm faces demand curve D_2. For the resource allocation to be efficient, the firm's output must be equal to
a) 100 units.
b) 140 units.
c) 200 units.
d) 220 units.
e) 260 units.

14.44
Correct: c)
Difficulty: 4
Page(s): 350
Scramble range: All
Topic: Efficient resource allocation

14.44
Refer to Figure 14.3. Assume this firm faces demand curve D_2. For the resource allocation to be efficient, the firm's profit must be
a) positive.
b) zero.
c) negative.
d) impossible to determine without more information concerning the behaviour of rival firms.
e) zero and falling over time.

14.45
Correct: e)
Difficulty: 3
Page(s): 349
Scramble range: All
Topic: Long–run profit

14.45
In the long run, all firms in an industry that is monopolistically competitive earn
a) accounting profit that is negative.
b) accounting profit that is zero.
c) economic profit that is negative.
d) economic profit that is positive.
e) economic profit that is zero.

14.46
Correct: c)
Difficulty: 3
Page(s): 349
Scramble range: All
Topic: Degree of market power

14.46
In monopolistically competitive industries,
a) competition is weak at best.
b) there is little range of choice over the products.
c) firms are sensitive to changes in consumer demand.
d) all firms produce where marginal cost is equal to the marginal benefit to the consumers.
e) all firms produce where the demand curve is tangent to the average cost curve.

14.47
Correct: a)
Difficulty: 3
Page(s): 349
Scramble range: All
Topic: Nonprice competition

14.47
In monopolistically competitive industries,
a) nonprice competition is vigorous.
b) the range of choice over products is the same as in perfectly competitive industries.
c) firms are insensitive to changes in consumer demand.
d) all firms produce where marginal cost is greater than the marginal benefit to the consumers.
e) all firms make positive profits.

14.48
Correct: e)
Difficulty: 3
Page(s): 350
Scramble range: All
Topic: Value of advertising

14.48
Advertising by firms in monopolistic competition
a) does not provide consumers with useful information.
b) increases the marginal cost of production.
c) is allocatively inefficient.
d) is a waste of valuable resources since firms are forced by the entry of rival firms to be price takers.
e) generates the perception among consumers that product differentiation exists.

14.49
Correct: a)
Difficulty: 3
Page(s): 350
Scramble range: All
Topic: Excess capacity

14.49
Excess capacity in monopolistically competitive firms is caused by
a) the fact that each firm faces a demand that is not perfectly elastic.
b) the fact that each firm attempts to maximize profit.
c) the waste associated with many slightly differentiated products serving almost the same purpose.
d) the fact that rival firms will enter the industry and reduce the demand for the products of the firms already in the industry.
e) cost curves being higher than they are under perfect competition.

14.50
Correct: d)
Difficulty: 3
Page(s): 350
Scramble range: All
Topic: Excess capacity

14.50
Excess capacity in monopolistically competitive firms is described by the fact that
a) each firm faces a demand that is perfectly elastic.
b) each firm builds a huge plant.
c) the existence of slightly differentiated products serving almost the same purpose causes a waste of precious natural resources.
d) firms produce at an output that is less than the output associated with their minimum average total cost.
e) marginal cost is too high.

14.51
Correct: c)
Difficulty: 2
Page(s): 347
Scramble range: All
Topic: Oligopoly markets

14.51
Which of the following industries is the best example of an oligopoly?
a) The market for wheat.
b) The fast-food industry.
c) The automobile industry.
d) The clothing industry.
e) The restaurant industry.

14.52
Correct: a)
Difficulty: 2
Page(s): 347
Scramble range: All
Topic: Oligopoly markets

14.52
Which of the following industries is the best example of an oligopoly?
a) The steel industry.
b) The foreign exchange market.
c) The footwear industry.
d) The cosmetics industry.
e) The power industry.

14.53
Correct: c)
Difficulty: 2
Page(s): 347
Scramble range: All
Topic: Characteristics of oligopoly

14.53
Which of the following characteristics applies to oligopolistic markets?
a) There is a large number of firms.
b) The absence of barriers to entry of firms.
c) Firms are large relative to the size of the market.
d) All firms are price takers.
e) Firms produce differentiated products.

14.54
Correct: d)
Difficulty: 2
Page(s): 351
Scramble range: All
Topic: Characteristics of oligopoly

14.54
Which of the following characteristics applies to oligopolistic markets?
a) There is perfectly free entry of rival firms.
b) Firms are so large relative to the market that they do not have to consider the behaviour of rival firms.
c) Firms are mutually dependent because there are so few firms in the industry.
d) Firms do have to consider the behaviour of their rivals since their rivals are also large relative to the size of the industry as a whole.
e) Economic profits equal zero.

14.55
Correct: b)
Difficulty: 2
Page(s): 351
Scramble range: All
Topic: Oligopoly

14.55
Why might only a few firms dominate an oligopolistic industry?
a) Decreasing returns to scale makes small scale inefficient.
b) Increasing returns to scale makes only larger size firms efficient.
c) Collusion among firms is difficult to detect and prosecute.
d) The production of the firms may be subject to constant returns to scale.
e) Product differentiation.

14.56
Correct: a)
Difficulty: 2
Page(s): 351
Scramble range: All
Topic: Oligopoly

14.56
Why might only a few firms dominate an oligopolistic industry?
a) Entry into the industry may be limited due to patents.
b) Perfectly elastic demand makes small-scale operation economically inefficient.
c) Decreasing returns to scale may make small-scale more advantageous.
d) Inelastic market demand leads to the domination of the industry by a few firms.
e) Due to the outcome of the prisoner's dilemma.

14.57
Correct: e)
Difficulty: 4
Page(s): 351
Scramble range: All
Topic: Oligopoly interdependence

14.57
If firm *X* is producing in an oligopolistically industry, when it increases its price
a) then rival firm *Y* will always increase its price.
b) then rival firm *Y* will increase its market share if firm *Y* increases its price.
c) then the behaviour of rival firm *Y* will have no impact on the market share of firm *X*.
d) the market as a whole will become less profitable.
e) the rival firm *Y* will increase its market share if firm *Y* keeps a constant price.

14.58
Correct: c)
Difficulty: 3
Page(s): 351
Scramble range: All
Topic: Interdependent oligopoly markets

14.58
If Ford lowers the price of its cars and General Motors follows this action, then
a) the relative market share will increase for General Motors.
b) the relative market share will increase for Ford.
c) relative market shares will not change, but both firms will increase their sales.
d) relative market shares will not change, but both firms will lose sales as customers will shift to rival firms, such as Chrysler Corporation.
e) relative market shares will fall as both firms' sales rise.

14.59
Correct: a)
Difficulty: 3
Page(s): 351–359
Scramble range: All
Topic: Price reduction oligopoly

14.59
In an oligopoly, when all firms lower prices
a) then all firms will find their profits reduced.
b) then all firms will find their profits unchanged.
c) then all firms will find their sales reduced but their profit increased.
d) the efficiency of the resource allocation will be reduced.
e) the efficiency of the resource allocation will be unchanged.

14.60
Correct: e)
Difficulty: 4
Page(s): 351
Scramble range: All
Topic: Interdependent firms oligopoly

14.60
Price competition in oligopoly will
a) result in higher average costs of production.
b) hurt consumers.
c) damage technical efficiency.
d) increase industry profit if demand is inelastic.
e) result in lower industry profit.

14.61
Correct: a)
Difficulty: 4
Page(s): 355
Scramble range: All
Topic: Prisoner's dilemma

14.61
In the language of game theory, the case of "prisoner's dilemma" describes a case in which
a) collusion of the participants leads to the best solution from their point of view.
b) competition among a large number of rivals leads to lower overall profit.
c) one prisoner has no chance to be acquitted since there is no other prisoner to support his testimony.
d) a prisoner has no incentive to confess to his crime, and hence stands a greater chance of not going to prison.
e) competition of the participants leads to the best solution from their point of view.

14.62
Correct: c)
Difficulty: 5
Page(s): 355
Scramble range: All
Topic: Prisoner's dilemma

14.62
Refer to Table 14.1. This table includes the sentences that Bob and Joe may receive if convicted. They have been apprehended by the police under the suspicion of committing armed robbery. The two are immediately separated and questioned about the case. Which of the following observations is correct?
a) Bob would be smart to confess no matter what Joe does.
b) Joe would be smart to not confess no matter what Bob does.
c) Both Bob and Joe would be better off by not confessing if they both do not confess.
d) Both Bob and Joe would be better off by "coming clean" and confessing to their crime.
e) Both Bob and Joe have a dominant strategy of not confessing.

Table 14.1

		Bob	
		Confess	Don't confess
Joe	Confess	B: 10 years J: 10 years	B: 20 years J: 1 year
	Don't confess	B: 1 year J: 20 years	B: Go free J: Go free

14.63
Correct: b)
Difficulty: 5
Page(s): 355
Scramble range: All
Topic: Prisoner's dilemma

14.63
Refer to Table 14.1. This table includes the sentences that Bob and Joe may receive if convicted. They have been apprehended by the police under the suspicion of committing armed robbery. The two are immediately separated and questioned about the case. Which of the following observations is correct?

a) If Joe confesses, Bob would be better off by not confessing.
b) If Bob confesses, Joe would be better off by confessing.
c) The outcome of the game, assuming Joe and Bob cannot collude, is that they will both go free.
d) If Joe does not confess, Bob would be better off by confessing.
e) The outcome of the game, assuming Joe and Bob cannot collude, is that they will both confess.

14.64
Correct: d)
Difficulty: 5
Page(s): 355
Scramble range: All
Topic: Prisoner's dilemma

14.64
Refer to Table 14.2. Sears and Eaton's must decide whether or not to lower their prices. The elements in the table are the dollar profits earned by Sears and Eaton's. Which of the following observations is correct?

a) This is not a game described as a prisoner's dilemma.
b) If Sears lowers its prices and Eaton's does not, Sears will earn a $20 profit.
c) If Eaton's chooses to lower its prices, then Sears will be better off by staying with unchanged prices.
d) Both Sears and Eaton's would be better off if they could collude and agree to not lower prices.
e) Both Sears and Eaton's have a dominant strategy of lowering their prices.

Table 14.2

		Sears	
		Lower prices	Don't lower prices
Eaton's	Lower prices	S: $5 E: $5	S: $1 E: $10
	Don't lower prices	S: $10 E: $1	S: $20 E: $20

14.65
Correct: b)
Difficulty: 5
Page(s): 355
Scramble range: All
Topic: Prisoner's dilemma

14.65
Refer to Table 14.2. Sears and Eaton's must decide whether or not to lower their prices. The elements in the table are the dollar profits earned by Sears and Eaton's. Which of the following observations is correct?

a) The solution to this game is not a Nash equilibrium.
b) This game has no dominant strategies.
c) This game does have a Nash equilibrium, and it is for both Sears and Eaton's to not lower prices.
d) This game does have dominant strategies for Sears and Eaton's, and that strategy is to lower prices.
e) This is not a prisoner's dilemma.

14.66
Correct: b)
Difficulty: 5
Page(s): 355
Scramble range: All
Topic: Game theory

14.66
Refer to Table 14.3. The marketers of Budweiser Light beer and Miller Lite beer must decide whether or not to offer new advertising campaigns promoting their products. The elements in the table are the dollar profits earned by Bud and Miller. Which of the following observations is correct?

a) This is not a game described as a prisoner's dilemma.
b) If Bud offers a new advertising campaign and Miller does not, Bud will earn a $200 profit.
c) If Miller offers a new advertising campaign, then Bud will be better off by not offering a new advertising campaign.
d) Both Bud and Miller would be better off if they could collude and agree to coordinate their new advertising campaigns.
e) Both Bud and Miller will be better off if they both offer a new advertising campaign.

Table 14.3

		Bud Light	
		Offer new ads	Don't offer new ads
Miller Lite	Offer new ads	B: $100 M: $100	B: $50 M: $200
	Don't offer new ads	B: $200 M: $50	B: $120 M: $120

14.67
Correct: a)
Difficulty: 4
Page(s): 355
Scramble range: All
Topic: Game theory

14.67
Refer to Table 14.3. The marketers of Budweiser Light beer and Miller Lite beer must decide whether or not to offer new advertising campaigns promoting their products. The elements in the table are the dollar profits earned by Bud and Miller. Which of the following observations is correct?

a) This is a game described as a prisoner's dilemma.
b) If Bud offers a new advertising campaign and Miller does not, Bud will earn a $100 profit.
c) If Bud offers a new advertising campaign, then Miller will be better off by not offering a new advertising campaign.
d) Both Bud and Miller would be better off if they could collude and agree to coordinate their new advertising campaigns.
e) If Miller does not offer a new advertising campaign, then Bud is better off if it doesn't offer a new advertising campaign.

14.68
Correct: e)
Difficulty: 4
Page(s): 355
Scramble range: All
Topic: Game theory

14.68
Refer to Table 14.3. The marketers of Budweiser Light beer and Miller Lite beer must decide whether or not to offer new advertising campaigns promoting their products. The elements in the table are the dollar profits earned by Bud and Miller. Which of the following observations is correct?

a) This game has no dominant strategies.
b) This game has no Nash equilibrium.
c) This game has no connection with the prisoner's dilemma.
d) Both Bud and Miller would be better off if they could collude and agree to coordinate their new advertising campaigns.
e) This game has dominant strategies.

14.69
Correct: e)
Difficulty: 4
Page(s): 355
Scramble range: All
Topic: Game theory

14.69
Refer to Table 14.3. The marketers of Budweiser Light beer and Miller Lite beer must decide whether or not to offer new advertising campaigns promoting their products. The elements in the table are the dollar profits earned by Bud and Miller. Which of the following observations is correct?
a) This game has no dominant strategies.
b) Bud will conduct a new advertising campaign, but Miller will not.
c) This game is not properly conceived as there are more than two firms in the brewing industry.
d) Neither Bud and nor Miller will conduct a new advertising campaign.
e) This game has a Nash equilibrium.

14.70
Correct: a)
Difficulty: 4
Page(s): 355
Scramble range: All
Topic: Game theory

14.70
Refer to Table 14.3. The marketers of Budweiser Light beer and Miller Lite beer must decide whether or not to offer new advertising campaigns promoting their products. The elements in the table are the dollar profits earned by Bud and Miller. Which of the following observations is correct?
a) The equilibrium of the game is that both firms will conduct new advertising campaigns.
b) The equilibrium of the game is that neither firm will conduct a new advertising campaign.
c) The equilibrium solution has Bud conducting a new advertising campaign, but not Miller.
d) The equilibrium solution has Miller conducting a new advertising campaign, but not Bud.
e) There is not equilibrium to this game — the industry will have alternating cycles of advertising and no advertising.

14.71
Correct: e)
Difficulty: 3
Page(s): 351
Scramble range: All
Topic: Game theory

14.71
Game theory focuses on three aspects of a competitive struggle between rivals. They are
a) costs, prices, and profits.
b) revenues, elasticity, and profits.
c) rules, strategies, and profits.
d) patents, copyrights, and barriers to entry.
e) rules, strategies, and payoffs.

14.72
Correct: d)
Difficulty: 3
Page(s): 359
Scramble range: All
Topic: Cartels

14.72
For a cartel to succeed
a) it must have cooperation of a majority of firms in the industry.
b) there must be free entry of rival firms.
c) consumers must have alternative products available to satisfy the same need.
d) no major producer must remain outside the agreement of the cartel.
e) the industry must have an elastic demand curve.

14.73
Correct: a)
Difficulty: 2
Page(s): 359
Scramble range: All
Topic: Cartels

14.73
Without barriers to the entry of new firms,
a) cartels will fail to achieve monopoly profit.
b) cartels members would shut down their operations.
c) the profit of the cartel will be greater than if there were barriers to entry.
d) supply will be decreased and monopoly profit will be earned.
e) firms will produce at the minimum efficient scale.

14.74
Correct: c)
Difficulty: 3
Page(s): 359
Scramble range: All
Topic: Cartels

14.74
With barriers to the entry of new firms,
a) cartels are guaranteed to earn monopoly profit.
b) cartels members have no incentive to cheat.
c) the profit of the cartel will be greater than if there were not significant barriers to entry.
d) industry supply will expand nevertheless, and profit will be decreased.
e) cartel members can safely cheat and get away with it.

14.75
Correct: b)
Difficulty: 3
Page(s): 359
Scramble range: All
Topic: Cartels

14.75
Once a cartel determines the profit-maximizing price,
a) all members of the cartel have a strong incentive to abide by the agreed-upon price.
b) each member will face the temptation to cheat on the cartel price in order to increase its sales and profit.
c) changes in the output of any member firms will have no impact on the market price.
d) entry into the industry of rival firms will have no impact on the profit of the cartel.
e) entry into the industry of rival firms will raise profits as long as they join the cartel.

14.76
Correct: c)
Difficulty: 3
Page(s): 361
Scramble range: All
Topic: Cartels

14.76
In a cartel the incentive to cheat is significant since
a) each individual member has the incentive to restrict its own output to maximize profit.
b) the marginal cost is equal to the cartel price at the profit-maximizing output level.
c) each firm has the incentive to lower its price to sell more than its allotted amount.
d) each firm has the incentive to cheat by raising its price to maximize its profit.
e) price is less than marginal cost to each member of the cartel.

14.77
Correct: d)
Difficulty: 4
Page(s): 361
Scramble range: All
Topic: Cartels

14.77
In a cartel the incentive to cheat is significant since
a) each individual member has the incentive to restrict its own output to maximize profit.
b) the marginal cost is greater than the cartel price at the profit-maximizing output level.
c) each firm has the incentive to raise its price to reap monopoly rewards.
d) each firm has the incentive to expand output to increase its profit.
e) each firm has the incentive to expand output to increase its price.

14.78
Correct: b)
Difficulty: 2
Page(s): 355
Scramble range: All
Topic: Duopoly

14.78
A duopoly is
a) a market in which three dominant firms collude to decide the profit-maximizing price.
b) a market in which two firms compete for profit and market share.
c) the same as a monopoly.
d) the same as oligopoly.
e) a market with two distinct products.

14.79
Correct: d)
Difficulty: 3
Page(s): 361
Scramble range: All
Topic: Duopoly

14.79
If there is a collusive agreement in a duopoly to maximize profit, then
a) the industry price will equal the marginal cost of production.
b) the industry price will equal the average cost of production.
c) the price will be the same as the competitive price.
d) the price will be the monopoly price.
e) the industry marginal revenue will equal industry average cost of production.

14.80
Correct: b)
Difficulty: 3
Page(s): 361
Scramble range: All
Topic: Duopoly

14.80
If a duopoly collusive agreement is made that maximizes joint profit,
a) each of the duopolists has no incentive to cheat on the agreement.
b) each duopolist has the incentive to cheat on the duopoly agreement by lowering the price.
c) each duopolist has the incentive to cheat on the agreement by increasing the price to earn monopoly profit.
d) there is no concern over the entrance of potential rivals since they cannot decrease the duopolists' profit.
e) the dominant strategy is to collude.

14.81 (SG14.1)
Correct: b)
Difficulty: 2
Page(s): 346
Scramble range: All
Topic: Concentration ratio

14.81
The four-firm concentration ratio is the percentage of the value accounted for by the largest four firms in terms of industry
a) profit.
b) sales.
c) cost.
d) capital.
e) quantity.

14.82 (SG14.2)
Correct: d)
Difficulty: 3
Page(s): 346–347
Scramble range: All
Topic: Concentration ratio

14.82
Which of the following is *not* a problem with concentration ratios as a measure of industry competitiveness?
a) Concentration ratios are national measures, but firms in some industries operate in regional markets.
b) Concentration ratios are national measures, but firms in some industries operate in international markets.
c) Concentration ratios tell us nothing about the severity of barriers to entry in the industry.
d) Concentration ratios tell us nothing about how cost varies among firms in the industry.
e) Concentration ratios cannot deal with diversified, multi-market firms.

14.83
Correct: a)
Difficulty: 3
Page(s): 348
Scramble range: All
Topic: Monopolistic competition

14.83
The following are all characteristics of a monopoly. Which of them is *not* also a characteristic of a monopolistically competitive industry?
a) There are barriers to entry.
b) The firm is a profit-maximizer.
c) The firm faces a downward-sloping demand curve.
d) The product produced by the firm is different from products produced by other firms.
e) The firm selects output where marginal cost equals marginal revenue.

14.84
Correct: e)
Difficulty: 3
Page(s): 347–348
Scramble range: All
Topic: Monopolistic competition

14.84
The following are all characteristics of a competitive industry. Which of them is *not* also a characteristic of monopolistic competition?
a) There is a large number of firms in the industry.
b) Firms select output where marginal cost equals marginal revenue.
c) Firms are profit-maximizers.
d) There is free entry.
e) Products produced by firms in the industry are identical.

14.85 (SG14.5)
Correct: e)
Difficulty: 3
Page(s): 349
Scramble range: All
Topic: Monopolistic competition

14.85
Figure 14.4 represents a monopolistically competitive firm in the short run. The firm's level of output will be
a) Q_4.
b) zero.
c) Q_1.
d) Q_3.
e) Q_2.

Figure 14.4

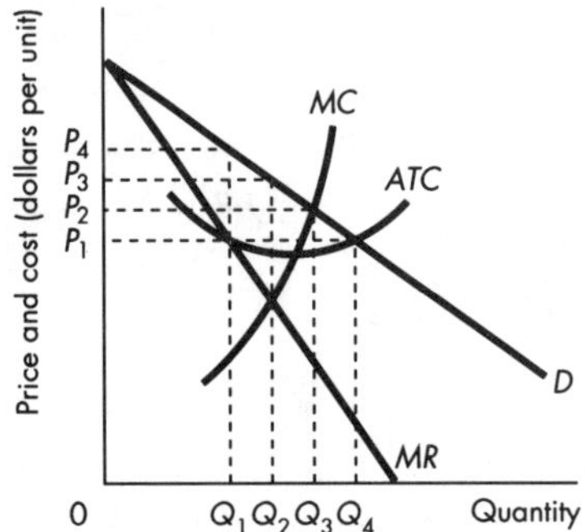

14.86 (SG14.6)
Correct: d)
Difficulty: 3
Page(s): 349
Scramble range: All
Topic: Monopolistic competition

14.86
The price charged by the monopolistic competitor of Figure 14.4 will be
a) P_2.
b) P_1.
c) P_4.
d) P_3.
e) less than P_1.

14.87 (SG14.7)
Correct: a)
Difficulty: 3
Page(s): 349
Scramble range: All
Topic: Monopolistic competition

14.87
Refer to the short-run situation illustrated in Figure 14.4. We know that in the long run,
a) there will be entry of new firms and each existing firm's demand will shift to the left.
b) there will be entry of new firms and each existing firm's demand will shift to the right.
c) existing firms will leave and each remaining firm's demand will shift to the left.
d) existing firms will leave and each remaining firm's demand will shift to the right.
e) the entry of firms will bid up wages and raise costs.

14.88 (SG14.8)
Correct: d)
Difficulty: 2
Page(s): 349
Scramble range: a)–d)
Topic: Monopolistic competition

14.88
In the long run, a monopolistically competitive firm will produce the output at which price equals
a) marginal cost.
b) marginal revenue.
c) average variable cost.
d) average total cost.
e) none of the above.

14.89
Correct: c)
Difficulty: 3
Page(s): 351
Scramble range: All
Topic: Monopolistic competition

14.89
Each of the following is a characteristic of monopolistic competition. Which of them is *not* also a characteristic of oligopoly?
a) Each firm faces a downward-sloping demand curve.
b) Firms are profit-maximizers.
c) The sales of one firm will not have a significant effect on other firms.
d) There is more than one firm in the industry.
e) Firms set marginal cost equal to marginal revenue.

14.90 (SG14.14)
Correct: e)
Difficulty: 2
Page(s): 351
Scramble range: All
Topic: Game theory

14.90
Which of the following is *not* an aspect common to all games?
a) Rules.
b) Payoffs.
c) Strategies.
d) Score.
e) Collusion.

14.91 (SG14.15)
Correct: d)
Difficulty: 3
Page(s): 355
Scramble range: None
Topic: Prisoner's dilemma

14.91
In the prisoner's dilemma, each "player" (prisoner) would be best off if
a) he confesses and the other denies.
b) he denies and the other confesses.
c) both confess.
d) both deny.
e) either c) or d).

14.92 (SG14.16)
Correct: a)
Difficulty: 3
Page(s): 355
Scramble range: All
Topic: Prisoner's dilemma

14.92
In the prisoner's dilemma, the dominant strategy equilibrium is
a) both prisoners confess.
b) neither prisoner confesses.
c) one denies and the other confesses.
d) indeterminate.
e) dependent on who the player is.

14.93 (SG14.17)
Correct: c)
Difficulty: 4
Page(s): 361
Scramble range: All
Topic: Duopoly

14.93
Consider a duopoly with collusion. If the duopoly maximizes profit,
a) each firm will produce the same amount.
b) each firm will produce its maximum output possible.
c) industry marginal revenue will equal industry marginal cost at the level of total output.
d) total output will be greater than before collusion.
e) each firm will set their own marginal cost equal to marginal revenue.

14.94 (SG14.18)
Correct: e)
Difficulty: 4
Page(s): 363
Scramble range: All
Topic: Game theory

14.94
Consider a cartel consisting of two firms in collusion to maximize profit. If this game is nonrepeated, the dominant strategy equilibrium is
a) dependent on who the player is.
b) both firms adhere to the agreement.
c) one firm cheats while the other adheres to the agreement.
d) indeterminate.
e) both firms cheat on the agreement.

14.95 (SG14.19)
Correct: b)
Difficulty: 4
Page(s): 364
Scramble range: All
Topic: Game theory

14.95
Consider a cartel consisting of two firms in collusion to maximize profit. However, the game is repeated indefinitely and each player employs a tit-for-tat strategy. The equilibrium is
a) dependent on who the player is.
b) both firms adhere to the agreement.
c) one firm cheats while the other adheres to the agreement.
d) indeterminate.
e) both firms cheat on the agreement.

14.96 (SG14.20)
Correct: d)
Difficulty: 3
Page(s): 364
Scramble range: All
Topic: Game theory

14.96
Consider a "prisoner's dilemma" game consisting of two firms in collusion to maximize profit. However, the game is repeated indefinitely and each player employs a tit-for-tat strategy. The equilibrium described here is called a
a) credible strategy equilibrium.
b) dominant player equilibrium.
c) duopoly equilibrium.
d) trigger strategy equilibrium.
e) collusive equilibrium.

14.97 (SG14.21)
Correct: c)
Difficulty: 3
Page(s): 363
Scramble range: All
Topic: Game theory

14.97
Table 14.4 gives the payoff matrix in terms of profit for firms *A* and *B* when there are two strategies facing each firm: (1) charge a low price or (2) charge a high price. The equilibrium in this game (played once) will be dominant strategy equilibrium since
a) firm *B* will reduce profit by more than *A* if both charge a lower price.
b) firm *B* is the dominant firm.
c) the best strategy for each firm does not depend on the strategy chosen by the other.
d) there is no credible threat by either firm to "punish" the other if it breaks the agreement.
e) firm *B* always does better than firm *A*.

Table 14.4

		Firm *B*	
		Low price	High price
Firm *A*	Low price	*A*: \$2 *B*: \$5	*A*: \$20 *B*: −\$10
	High price	*A*: −\$10 *B*: \$25	*A*: \$10 *B*: \$20

14.98 (SG14.22)
Correct: b)
Difficulty: 3
Page(s): 364
Scramble range: All
Topic: Duopoly

14.98
Refer to the duopoly in Table 14.4. In equilibrium, firm *A* will make a profit of
a) –$10.
b) $2.
c) $10.
d) $20.
e) $25.

14.99
Correct: d)
Difficulty: 3
Page(s): 361
Scramble range: All
Topic: Cartels

14.99
Consider a cartel consisting of several firms which is maximizing total profit. If one firm cheats on the cartel agreement by cutting its price and increasing its output, the best response of the other firms is to
a) cancel the cheating firm's membership in the cartel.
b) continue to sell at the agreed-upon price.
c) raise their price in order to recapture lost profit.
d) cut their prices as well.
e) cut output to keep total cartel output at its original level.

14.100
Correct: e)
Difficulty: 2
Page(s): 361
Scramble range: All
Topic: Cartels

14.100
It is difficult to maintain a cartel for a long period of time. Which of the following is the most important reason?
a) Each firm has an incentive to collude.
b) Other firms will enter the industry.
c) Firms in the cartel will want to drop out and stop colluding.
d) Consumers will eventually decide not to buy the cartel's output.
e) Each firm has an incentive to cheat.

14.101
Correct: d)
Difficulty: 2
Page(s): 346
Scramble range: All
Topic: Concentration ratio

14.101
The four-firm concentration ratio is the percentage of the value accounted for by the largest four firms in terms of the industry
a) per unit revenue.
b) per unit profit.
c) per unit cost.
d) sales.
e) output.

14.102
Correct: a)
Difficulty: 3
Page(s): 347
Scramble range: All
Topic: Monopolistic competition

14.102
None of the following are characteristics of a monopoly. Which of them is a characteristic of a monopolistically competitive industry?
a) There are no barriers to entry.
b) The firm is a sales-maximizer.
c) The firm is a cost-minimizer.
d) The product produced by the firm is identical to the products produced by other firms.
e) The firm faces a horizontal demand curve.

14.103
Correct: b)
Difficulty: 3
Page(s): 347
Scramble range: All
Topic: Monopolistic competition

14.103
None of the following are characteristics of a competitive industry. Which of them is a characteristic of monopolistic competition?
a) There is a small number of firms in the industry.
b) Products produced by firms in the industry are differentiated.
c) Firms are sales-maximizers.
d) There is no free entry.
e) There are barriers to entry.

14.104 (SG14.8)
Correct: d)
Difficulty: 3
Page(s): 349
Scramble range: All
Topic: Monopolistic competition

14.104
In the long run, a monopolistically competitive firm will produce the output at which
a) average cost equals marginal cost.
b) marginal revenue equals price.
c) average variable cost is minimized.
d) price equals average total cost.
e) price equals marginal cost.

14.105
Correct: c)
Difficulty: 3
Page(s): 351
Scramble range: All
Topic: Monopolistic competition

14.105
Each of the following is *not* a characteristic of monopolistic competition. Which of them is a characteristic of oligopoly?
a) Each firm faces a horizontal demand curve.
b) Firms are sales-maximizers.
c) The sales of one firm will have a significant effect on other firms.
d) There is no more than one firm in the industry.
e) If firms raise their output, profits always rise.

14.106
Correct: a)
Difficulty: 2
Page(s): 351
Scramble range: All
Topic: Game theory

14.106
Which of the following is an aspect common to all games?
a) Rules.
b) Collusion.
c) Strongholds.
d) Style.
e) Cheating.

14.107
Correct: e)
Difficulty: 4
Page(s): 361
Scramble range: None
Topic: Cartels

14.107
Consider a cartel of widget makers. Which of the following statements is true?
a) The cartel will set prices so as to maximize the revenue of the widget makers.
b) If the cartel was working and if all the widget makers are identical, then they would all make positive economic profits.
c) The cartel would have to restrict entry into the industry to make the cartel work.
d) Since the widget makers understand their industry best, clearly society is better off with the cartel.
e) Both b) and c).

14.108
Correct: e)
Difficulty: 4
Page(s): 363
Scramble range: All
Topic: Game theory

14.108
Consider the economic game in Table 14.5, based on potential gas prices between two competitors. The dollar values reflect the profits of the firms. The most likely outcome is
a) a cycle of first \$0.35/litre and then \$0.55/litre, etc.
b) Hare sets her prices at \$0.55/litre, while Turtle sets his at \$0.35/litre.
c) Hare sets her prices at \$0.35/litre, while Turtle sets his at \$0.55/litre.
d) both set their prices at \$0.55/litre.
e) both set their prices at \$0.35/litre.

Table 14.5

		Hare Gas Bar's choices	
		$0.55/litre	$0.35/litre
Turtle Gas Bar's choices	$0.55/litre	H: $500 T: $500	H: $1,000 T: $50
	$0.35/litre	H: $50 T: $1,000	H: $200 T: $200

14.109
Correct: c)
Difficulty: 3
Page(s): 360–361
Scramble range: All
Topic: Cartels

14.109
Consider a cartel consisting of several firms which is maximizing total profit. If one firm cheats on the cartel agreement by cutting its price and increasing its output, the best response of the other firms is to
a) expand membership in the cartel.
b) sell at the cartel price.
c) decrease price to increase profit.
d) increase prices.
e) decrease output to try and undercut the cheater.

14.110
Correct: c)
Difficulty: 3
Page(s): 360–361
Scramble range: All
Topic: Cartels

14.110
It is difficult to maintain a cartel for a long period of time. Which of the following is the most important reason?
a) No firm has an incentive to cheat.
b) Other firms will enjoy barriers to entry.
c) Firms in the cartel will want to cheat.
d) Consumers will deplete inventories of the cartel.
e) Demand will rise over time.

14.111
Correct: d)
Difficulty: 3
Page(s): 366
Scramble range: All
Topic: Oligopoly/competition

14.111
Oligopolies compete
a) only by cheating within a cartel.
b) only by offering lower prices than their competitors.
c) only by raising the quality of their goods.
d) by lowering prices, raising quality, product differentiation, advertising, research and development.
e) by altering quantity and therefore price.

14.112
Correct: d)
Difficulty: 5
Page(s): 347–350
Scramble range: All
Topic: Monopolistic competition

14.112
Consider a monopolistically competitive industry in long-run equilibrium. Suppose that demand for the industry's product rises. What happens to each firm in the short and the long run?

a) In the short run, price will rise as quantity demanded falls, while in the long run entry will guarantee even higher prices and higher quantity demanded.
b) In the short run, price and quantity will rise, while in the long run entry will guarantee even higher quantity demanded and the same prices as in the short run.
c) In the short run, price will rise as quantity demanded rises, while in the long run barriers to entry guarantee that prices and quantity demanded stay the same as in the short run.
d) In the short run, price and quantity demanded will rise, while in the long run entry will drive down both price and quantity demanded.
e) In the short run, price and quantity demanded will rise, while in the long run price will fall due to entry, but quantity demanded will stay the same as in the short run.

14.113
Correct: e)
Difficulty: 5
Page(s): 347–350
Scramble range: All
Topic: Monopolistic competition

14.113
Consider a monopolistically competitive industry in long-run equilibrium. Suppose there is a large increase in wages that raises the costs of all firms. What happens within each firm in the short run?

a) They will each be forced to close down due to the excess costs.
b) They will each continue producing as before, cushioned by their previous excess profits.
c) They will expand output to try to make up for lost profits.
d) They will lower prices to try to steal customers away from their rivals.
e) They will constrict quantity to produce where marginal revenue equals the new (higher) marginal cost curves; this means a rise in price.

Chapter 15 Pricing and Allocating Factors of Production

15.1
Correct: c)
Difficulty: 2
Page(s): 381–384
Scramble range: All
Topic: Resource markets

15.1
Firms buy resources because
a) they are limited in availability.
b) they can sell the resources to consumers.
c) consumers may be willing to buy the goods and services that the resources can produce.
d) it is only in the very long run that resources will no longer be scarce.
e) they wish to hoard them against higher future prices.

15.2
Correct: c)
Difficulty: 1
Page(s): 381–384
Scramble range: All
Topic: Resource markets

15.2
Resources can be divided into three main categories. These categories are
a) productive resources, neutral resources, and nonproductive resources.
b) men, women, and children.
c) labour, capital, and land.
d) machines, factories, and farms.
e) labour, money, and land.

15.3
Correct: b)
Difficulty: 1
Page(s): 384
Scramble range: All
Topic: Resource markets

15.3
The demand for productive resources is called
a) a determined demand.
b) a derived demand.
c) a kinked demand.
d) an insatiable demand.
e) a desperate demand.

15.4
Correct: e)
Difficulty: 1
Page(s): 384
Scramble range: All
Topic: Resource markets

15.4
The demand for productive resources is referred to as
a) a marginal demand.
b) a detrimental demand.
c) a circular demand.
d) comparable demand.
e) a derived demand.

15.5
Correct: b)
Difficulty: 2
Page(s): 384, 391
Scramble range: All
Topic: Resource and product markets

15.5
Which of the following is true concerning the circular flows in an economy?
a) Firms are buyers in product markets and sellers in resource markets.
b) Households are buyers in product markets and sellers in resource markets.
c) Households are sellers in product markets and firms are buyers in product markets.
d) Firms are sellers in resource markets and households are sellers in resource markets.
e) Firms are buyers in product markets and households are buyers in product markets.

15.6
Correct: c)
Difficulty: 1
Page(s): 381
Scramble range: All
Topic: Payments to labour

15.6
Wages to labour may include any of the following except
a) salaries.
b) commissions.
c) rents.
d) bonuses.
e) fringe benefits such as free life insurance.

15.7
Correct: a)
Difficulty: 3
Page(s): 384
Scramble range: All
Topic: Resource markets

15.7
Resources are of value to firms because
a) the products they produce are valuable to consumers.
b) the supply of resources is limited.
c) the demand for resources is limited.
d) they earn money directly for firms.
e) they can produce goods.

15.8
Correct: d)
Difficulty: 2
Page(s): 393
Scramble range: All
Topic: Perfectly competitive labour markets

15.8
For firms hiring labour in perfectly competitive labour markets,
a) they must pay a greater wage if they wish to hire more labour.
b) they will be willing to pay a lower wage to attract more skilled workers.
c) the demand for labour is perfectly elastic at the going market wage rate.
d) the supply of labour is perfectly elastic at the going market wage rate.
e) they can use their market power to lower the wages they have to pay.

15.9
Correct: d)
Difficulty: 2
Page(s): 393
Scramble range: All
Topic: Perfectly competitive labour markets

15.9
For firms hiring labour in perfectly competitive labour markets,
a) they must pay a lower wage than the market wage rate in order to increase profit.
b) they must pay a lower wage to attract more workers.
c) the demand for labour is completely inelastic at the going market wage rate.
d) they can hire all the workers they care to at the going market wage rate.
e) they must pay a higher wage to make up for the fact they are less attractive than noncompetitive firms.

15.10
Correct: d)
Difficulty: 2
Page(s): 393
Scramble range: All
Topic: Perfectly competitive labour markets

15.10
For firms hiring labour in perfectly competitive labour markets,
a) they must charge a lower price in order to sell more output.
b) they may charge a higher price to increase profit.
c) they can sell more output only by lowering the wage they pay to labour.
d) there is no need to offer a higher wage rate in order to hire more labour.
e) they must increase output in order to be able to afford the higher wages they have to pay.

15.11
Correct: c)
Difficulty: 2
Page(s): 386
Scramble range: All
Topic: Employment motivation

15.11
Western economists generally assume that firms hire labour
a) in order to minimize the average cost of employment of labour.
b) in order to exploit them.
c) in order to maximize their profit.
d) because capital is more expensive.
e) in order to minimize their costs.

15.12
Correct: e)
Difficulty: 3
Page(s): 386
Scramble range: All
Topic: Optimal labour employment

15.12
For a firm wishing to maximize profit, labour should be hired until
a) there is no more available at the market wage rate.
b) they can sell that labour for no more than what they paid for it.
c) the wage rate paid to the labour equals the marginal cost of production.
d) the additional benefit of hiring the labour is equal to the additional revenue the labour generates.
e) the additional cost of hiring the labour is equal to the additional revenue the labour generates.

15.13
Correct: c)
Difficulty: 3
Page(s): 384
Scramble range: All
Topic: Optimal labour employment

15.13
In order to maximize profit, the firm must equate
a) the wage rate to the product price.
b) the wage rate to the marginal product of the labour.
c) the marginal revenue product to the marginal factor cost.
d) the marginal factor cost to the price of the output.
e) the marginal cost of the factor to the marginal product of the factor.

15.14
Correct: c)
Difficulty: 2
Page(s): 384
Scramble range: All
Topic: Marginal revenue product

15.14
The marginal revenue product of labour is the extra revenue
a) generated by selling an additional unit of the output.
b) needed to hire an additional unit of labour.
c) generated by the employment of an additional unit of labour.
d) needed to cover the cost of producing an additional unit of output.
e) generated to cover the cost of hiring an extra unit of labour.

15.15
Correct: a)
Difficulty: 2
Page(s): 384
Scramble range: All
Topic: Marginal revenue product

15.15
Marginal revenue is the extra revenue
a) generated by selling an additional unit of the output.
b) needed to hire an additional unit of labour.
c) generated by the employment of an additional unit of labour.
d) needed to cover the cost of producing an additional unit of output.
e) generated to cover the cost of hiring an extra unit of labour.

15.16
Correct: d)
Difficulty: 2
Page(s): 384
Scramble range: All
Topic: Marginal factor cost

15.16
Marginal factor cost is defined as
a) the wage rate that must be paid to labour.
b) the wage rate of labour plus the value of fringe benefits.
c) the average labour cost for each level of output.
d) the additional labour costs that are associated with hiring an additional unit of labour.
e) the additional fixed costs that are associated with hiring an additional unit of labour.

15.17
Correct: b)
Difficulty: 3
Page(s): 384
Scramble range: All
Topic: Marginal factor cost

15.17
Assume that a firm can hire labour in a competitive labour market. This implies that the marginal factor cost will equal the
a) marginal cost of the output.
b) market wage rate.
c) minimum average variable cost of production.
d) minimum average total cost of production.
e) marginal revenue.

15.18
Correct: b)
Difficulty: 4
Page(s): 393
Scramble range: All
Topic: Marginal factor cost

15.18
If the firm faces an upward-sloping supply curve of labour, then the marginal factor cost
a) will be less than the wage rate.
b) will be greater than the wage rate.
c) will be equal to the wage rate.
d) is constant as additional units of labour are hired.
e) declines as additional units of labour are hired.

15.19
Correct: d)
Difficulty: 4
Page(s): 393
Scramble range: All
Topic: Marginal factor cost

15.19
If the wage rate is less than the marginal factor cost, then
a) the firm must be able to hire labour in a perfectly competitive labour market.
b) the firm must face a supply curve of labour that is backward bending.
c) the supply of labour must be perfectly elastic.
d) the firm faces an upward-sloping supply curve of labour.
e) the firm faces a downward-sloping supply curve of labour.

15.20
Correct: a)
Difficulty: 3
Page(s): 386
Scramble range: All
Topic: Marginal revenue product

15.20
If a firm sells its output in a competitive market, then the marginal revenue product of labour diminishes as more labour is hired due to
a) diminishing marginal product of labour.
b) increasing marginal product of labour.
c) the necessity to lower the price in order to sell more output.
d) the necessary contraction of the capital stock as more money is spent on labour.
e) the fact that marginal revenue is always less than price.

15.21
Correct: b)
Difficulty: 3
Page(s): 386
Scramble range: All
Topic: Diminishing marginal returns of labour

15.21
Refer to Table 15.1. Based on the production function in this table, it can be concluded that
a) production is subject to constant marginal returns to the variable factor.
b) production is subject to eventually diminishing marginal returns to the variable factor.
c) production is independent of the amount of labour hired.
d) the firm would never hire more than four units of labour during any production period.
e) production is subject to constant average returns to the variable factor.

Table 15.1

Units of labour	Units of output
0	0
1	5
2	11
3	18
4	26
5	32
6	37
7	41
8	44
9	46
10	47

15.22
Correct: e)
Difficulty: 3
Page(s): 386
Scramble range: All
Topic: Diminishing marginal returns of labour

15.22
Refer to Table 15.1. The marginal product of labour increases for
a) none of the units of labour.
b) units of labour 5 through 10.
c) units of labour 1 through 6.
d) units of labour 7 through 10.
e) units of labour 1 through 4.

15.23
Correct: b)
Difficulty: 3
Page(s): 386
Scramble range: All
Topic: Diminishing marginal returns of labour

15.23
Refer to Table 15.1. The marginal product of labour decreases for _______ units of labour?
a) 1 through 4.
b) 5 through 10.
c) 1 through 6.
d) 1 through 10.
e) 8 through 10.

15.24
Correct: c)
Difficulty: 3
Page(s): 386
Scramble range: All
Topic: Marginal product of labour

15.24
Refer to Table 15.1. The marginal product of labour reaches a maximum with which unit of labour?
a) The 3rd unit.
b) The 1st unit.
c) The 4th unit.
d) The 10th unit.
e) The 5th unit.

15.25
Correct: b)
Difficulty: 3
Page(s): 386
Scramble range: All
Topic: Diminishing marginal product

15.25
Why would a firm ever want to hire labour beyond the level at which the marginal product is maximized?
a) It would never wish to.
b) It may wish to if the marginal product is positive.
c) Negative marginal products can save the firm money in the long run.
d) More information concerning the production function must be given in order to answer this question.
e) It wants to produce up to the point where the average product of labour is maximized.

15.26
Correct: c)
Difficulty: 3
Page(s): 385–386
Scramble range: All
Topic: Marginal revenue product

15.26
Refer to Table 15.1. If the firm can sell all the output it wants to for the price of $5, what is the marginal revenue product of the 6th unit of labour?
a) Without the wage rate this cannot be determined.
b) 0.
c) $25.
d) $40.
e) $185.

15.27
Correct: d)
Difficulty: 4
Page(s): 387
Scramble range: All
Topic: Profit maximization

15.27
Refer to Table 15.1. If the firm can sell all the output it wants to for the price of $4, what is the profit-maximizing employment level of labour if the firm can hire all the labourers it wishes to for a wage rate of $12?
a) At that wage rate the firm would not want to hire any labour.
b) At that wage rate the firm would hire all 10 units of labour.
c) At that wage rate the firm would hire 4 labourers.
d) At that wage rate the firm would hire 8 labourers.
e) At that wage rate the firm would hire 6 labourers.

15.28
Correct: d)
Difficulty: 5
Page(s): 387–388
Scramble range: All
Topic: Profit maximization

15.28
Refer to Table 15.1. If the firm can sell all the output it wants to for the price of $4, and hire all of the labour it wants for a wage rate of $12, what is the total profit of the firm? Assume that fixed costs are equal to $20.
a) This cannot be determined by the information given.
b) The firm will earn only normal economic profit.
c) $36.
d) $60.
e) $48.

15.29
Correct: c)
Difficulty: 4
Page(s): 387–388
Scramble range: All
Topic: Profit maximization

15.29
Refer to Table 15.1. If the firm can sell all the output it wants to for the price of $5, what is the profit-maximizing employment level if it can hire all the labourers it wants to for a wage of $30?
a) It will hire only 1 unit of labour.
b) It will hire 4 units of labour.
c) It will hire 5 units of labour.
d) It will hire 6 units of labour.
e) It will hire 7 units of labour.

15.30
Correct: d)
Difficulty: 4
Page(s): 387–388
Scramble range: All
Topic: profit maximization

15.30
Refer to Table 15.1. If the firm can sell all the output it wants to for the price of $10, what is the profit-maximizing employment level if it can hire all the labourers it wants to for a wage of $30?
a) It will hire only 1 unit of labour.
b) It will hire 5 units of labour.
c) It will hire 7 units of labour.
d) It will hire 8 units of labour.
e) It will hire 9 units of labour.

15.31
Correct: d)
Difficulty: 3
Page(s): 388
Scramble range: All
Topic: Market structure

15.31
Refer to Table 15.2. It contains the production function that relates the level of employment to the level of output and the demand schedule that relates the level of sales to the price of the output. Which of the following observations may correctly be made?
a) The firm is a monopsonist.
b) The firm hires labour in a competitive labour market.
c) The firm can sell its output in a perfectly competitive output market.
d) The firm has some degree of market power in the output market.
e) The firm has some degree of market power in the labour market.

Table 15.2

Units of labour	Units of output	Price ($)
0	0	—
1	5	10
2	11	9
3	18	8
4	26	7
5	32	6
6	37	5
7	41	4
8	44	3
9	46	2
10	47	1

15.32
Correct: a)
Difficulty: 5
Page(s): 388
Scramble range: All
Topic: Marginal revenue product

15.32
Refer to Table 15.2. It contains the production function that relates the level of employment to the level of output and the demand schedule that relates the level of sales to the price of the output. For which unit of labour is the marginal revenue product maximized?
a) The 1st unit.
b) The 2nd unit.
c) The 5th unit.
d) The 8th unit.
e) The 10th unit.

15.33
Correct: c)
Difficulty: 5
Page(s): 388
Scramble range: All
Topic: Marginal revenue product

15.33
Refer to Table 15.2. It contains the production function that relates the level of employment to the level of output and the demand schedule that relates the level of sales to the price of the output. As long as this profit-maximizing firm must pay a positive wage for the labour it hires, it is certain that the firm will never hire more than
a) 1 unit of labour.
b) 3 units of labour.
c) 5 units of labour.
d) 7 units of labour.
e) 10 units of labour.

15.34
Correct: c)
Difficulty: 5
Page(s): 388
Scramble range: All
Topic: Profit maximization

15.34
Refer to Table 15.2. It contains the production function that relates the level of employment to the level of output and the demand schedule that relates the level of sales to the price of the output. If this profit-maximizing firm can hire all the labour it wishes at a wage rate of $5 per unit, how many units will it hire?
a) 3 units.
b) 1 unit.
c) 5 units.
d) None, as it would shut down under these circumstances.
e) 4 units.

15.35
Correct: c)
Difficulty: 5
Page(s): 388
Scramble range: All
Topic: Profit maximization

15.35
Refer to Table 15.2. It contains the production function that relates the level of employment to the level of output and the demand schedule that relates the level of sales to the price of the output. If this profit-maximizing firm can hire all the labour it wishes at a wage rate of $5 per unit, what is the maximum level of profit? Assume that total fixed costs are $20.
a) $79.
b) $27.
c) $147.
d) It cannot be determined with the information given.
e) $142.

15.36
Correct: a)
Difficulty: 5
Page(s): 388
Scramble range: All
Topic: Profit maximization

15.36
Refer to Table 15.2. It contains the production function that relates the level of employment to the level of output and the demand schedule that relates the level of sales to the price of the output. If this profit-maximizing firm can hire all the labour it wishes at a wage rate of $25 per unit, how many units will it hire?
a) 4 units.
b) 2 units.
c) None, as it would shut down under these circumstances.
d) 6 units.
e) 8 units.

15.37
Correct: b)
Difficulty: 5
Page(s): 388
Scramble range: All
Topic: Profit maximization

15.37
Refer to Table 15.2. It contains the production function that relates the level of employment to the level of output and the demand schedule that relates the level of sales to the price of the output. If this profit-maximizing firm can hire all the labour it wishes at a wage rate of $25 per unit, what is the maximum level of profit? Assume that total fixed costs are $20.
a) $26.
b) $62.
c) $102.
d) It cannot be determined with the information given.
e) Losses of $88.

15.38
Correct: a)
Difficulty: 5
Page(s): 388
Scramble range: All
Topic: Profit maximization

15.38
Refer to Table 15.2. It contains the production function that relates the level of employment to the level of output and the demand schedule that relates the level of sales to the price of the output. If this profit-maximizing firm can hire all the labour it wishes at a wage rate of $40 per unit, how many units will it hire?
a) 3 units.
b) 1 unit.
c) 5 units.
d) None, as it would shut down under these circumstances.
e) 7 units.

15.39
Correct: a)
Difficulty: 5
Page(s): 388
Scramble range: All
Topic: Profit maximization

15.39
Refer to Table 15.2. It contains the production function that relates the level of employment to the level of output and the demand schedule that relates the level of sales to the price of the output. If this profit-maximizing firm can hire all the labour it wishes at a wage rate of $40 per unit, what is the maximum level of profit? Assume that total fixed costs are $20.
a) $4.
b) $44.
c) $40.
d) It would shut down under these circumstances, therefore suffering a loss of $20.
e) $24.

15.40
Correct: a)
Difficulty: 5
Page(s): 388
Scramble range: All
Topic: Market structure

15.40
Refer to Table 15.3. It contains the production function, relating the level of employment to the level of output; the demand schedule, relating the level of sales to the price of the output; and the labour supply schedule, relating the amount of labour available at different wage rates. Which of the following observations is correct?
a) The firm has some degree of market power in the labour market.
b) The firm hires labour in a competitive labour market.
c) The firm can sell its output in a perfectly competitive output market.
d) The firm is in perfect competition in the output market and a monopsonist in the labour market.
e) The firm has some degree of market power in the output market, and hires labour in a competitive labour market.

Table 15.3

Wage rate	Units of labour	Units of output	Price ($)
—	0	0	—
1	1	5	10
2	2	11	9
3	3	18	8
4	4	26	7
5	5	32	6
6	6	37	5
7	7	41	4
8	8	44	3
9	9	46	2
10	10	47	1

15.41
Correct: e)
Difficulty: 5
Page(s): 388
Scramble range: All
Topic: Optimal input decisions

15.41
Refer to Table 15.3. It contains the production function, relating the level of employment to the level of output; the demand schedule, relating the level of sales to the price of the output; and the labour supply schedule, relating the amount of labour available at different wage rates. Which of the following observations is incorrect?
a) The firm has some degree of market power in the labour market.
b) The marginal factor cost is always greater than or equal to the wage rate.
c) The marginal revenue is always less than or equal to the price of the output.
d) The firm would never want to hire more than 5 units of labour.
e) The firm would never want to hire any labour.

15.42
Correct: e)
Difficulty: 5
Page(s): 385–388
Scramble range: All
Topic: Marginal factor cost

15.42
Refer to Table 15.3. It contains the production function, relating the level of employment to the level of output; the demand schedule, relating the level of sales to the price of the output; and the labour supply schedule, relating the amount of labour available at different wage rates. How much is the marginal factor cost of hiring the seventh unit of labour?
a) $7.
b) $10.
c) This cannot be determined without knowledge of the marginal cost curve.
d) $4.
e) $13.

15.43
Correct: d)
Difficulty: 5
Page(s): 384–388
Scramble range: All
Topic: Profit maximization

15.43
Refer to Table 15.3. It contains the production function, relating the level of employment to the level of output; the demand schedule, relating the level of sales to the price of the output; and the labour supply schedule, relating the amount of labour available at different wage rates. What is the profit-maximizing employment level?
a) 2 units of labour.
b) 3 units of labour.
c) 4 units of labour.
d) 5 units of labour.
e) 6 units of labour.

15.44
Correct: c)
Difficulty: 5
Page(s): 384–388
Scramble range: All
Topic: Profit maximization

15.44
Refer to Table 15.3. It contains the production function, relating the level of employment to the level of output; the demand schedule, relating the level of sales to the price of the output; and the labour supply schedule, relating the amount of labour available at different wage rates. What is the profit-maximizing price the firm should charge for its output?
a) $8.
b) $7.
c) $6.
d) $5.
e) $4.

15.45
Correct: d)
Difficulty: 5
Page(s): 384–388
Scramble range: All
Topic: Profit maximization

15.45
Refer to Table 15.3. It contains the production function, relating the level of employment to the level of output; the demand schedule, relating the level of sales to the price of the output; and the labour supply schedule, relating the amount of labour available at different wage rates. What is the maximum level of profit? Assume total fixed costs are $20.
a) 0.
b) $47.
c) $74.
d) $147.
e) $135.

15.46
Correct: b)
Difficulty: 2
Page(s): 387
Scramble range: All
Topic: Diminishing marginal returns

15.46
Refer to Table 15.4. It contains the production function, relating inputs of labour to the level of output. At what level of employment does the marginal product of labour begin to diminish?
a) The 3rd unit.
b) The 5th unit.
c) The 7th unit.
d) The 9th unit.
e) The 19th unit.

Table 15.4

Units of labour	Units of output
0	0
2	60
4	140
6	200
8	240
10	260
12	270
14	276
16	280
18	282
20	282

15.47
Correct: c)
Difficulty: 4
Page(s): 387
Scramble range: All
Topic: Profit maximization

15.47
Refer to Table 15.4. It contains the production function, relating inputs of labour to the level of output. Assume that this profit-maximizing firm can sell all the output it cares to for a price of $2. How many units of labour would it hire if it could hire all the labour it wished to for a wage rate of $5?
a) None, as it would shut down in this case.
b) 10 units of labour.
c) 14 units of labour.
d) 18 units of labour.
e) 20 units of labour.

15.48
Correct: c)
Difficulty: 5
Page(s): 387
Scramble range: All
Topic: Profit maximization

15.48
Refer to Table 15.4. It contains the production function, relating inputs of labour to the level of output. Assume that this profit-maximizing firm can sell all the output it cares to for a price of $2. Also assume that it can hire all the labour it wishes to for a wage rate of $5. What is the maximum level of profit for the firm? Assume total fixed costs are $20.
a) $62.
b) $450.
c) $462.
d) $454.
e) $444.

15.49
Correct: d)
Difficulty: 4
Page(s): 387
Scramble range: All
Topic: Profit maximization

15.49
Refer to Table 15.5. It contains the production function that relates inputs of labour to the level of output and the demand schedule for the firm's output. If the firm can hire all the labour it wishes to for a wage rate of $10, how much labour should be hired to maximize profit?
a) 2 units.
b) 4 units.
c) 6 units.
d) 8 units.
e) 10 units.

Table 15.5

Units of labour	Units of output	Price ($)
2	60	10
4	140	9
6	200	8
8	240	7
10	260	6
12	270	5
14	276	4
16	280	3
18	282	2
20	282	1

15.50
Correct: c)
Difficulty: 4
Page(s): 387
Scramble range: All
Topic: Profit maximization

15.50
Refer to Table 15.5. It contains the production function that relates inputs of labour to the level of output and the demand schedule for the firm's output. If the firm can hire all the labour it wishes to for a wage rate of $100, how much labour should be hired in order to maximize profit?
a) 2 units.
b) 4 units.
c) 6 units.
d) 8 units.
e) 10 units.

15.51
Correct: b)
Difficulty: 5
Page(s): 384–388
Scramble range: All
Topic: Profit maximization

15.51
Refer to Table 15.6. It contains the production function that relates inputs of labour to the level of output; the demand schedule for the firm's output; and the supply schedule of labour which the firm faces. How many units of labour should be hired to maximize profit?
a) 6 units.
b) 8 units.
c) 10 units.
d) It cannot be determined without more information.
e) 0 units.

Table 15.6

Wage rate	Units of labour	Units of output	Price ($)
1	2	60	10
2	4	140	9
3	6	200	8
4	8	240	7
5	10	260	6
6	12	270	5
7	14	276	4
8	16	280	3
9	18	282	2
10	20	282	1

15.52
Correct: e)
Difficulty: 5
Page(s): 384–388
Scramble range: All
Topic: Profit maximization

15.52
Refer to Table 15.6. It contains the production function, relating inputs of labour to the level of output; the demand schedule for the firm's output; and the supply schedule of labour which the firm faces. What price should the firm charge in order to maximize profit?
a) $8.
b) $10.
c) $4.
d) $5.
e) $7.

15.53
Correct: a)
Difficulty: 2
Page(s): 386–387
Scramble range: All
Topic: Demand for labour

15.53
The firm's demand curve for labour is
a) the downward-sloping portion of the marginal revenue product curve.
b) the downward-sloping portion of the marginal product curve.
c) perfectly elastic if it can sell its output in a perfectly competitive market.
d) inelastic if it is a monopsonist.
e) the downward-sloping portion of the average revenue product curve.

15.54
Correct: c)
Difficulty: 3
Page(s): 388
Scramble range: All
Topic: Changes in demand for labour

15.54
A change in a firm's demand curve for labour can be caused by a change in the
a) wage rate of labour.
b) opportunity costs of labour.
c) price of the output.
d) working-age population.
e) marginal cost of labour.

15.55
Correct: d)
Difficulty: 3
Page(s): 388
Scramble range: All
Topic: Changes in demand for labour

15.55
A change in a firm's demand curve for labour can be caused by each of the following *except* a change in the
a) price of inputs other than labour.
b) technology.
c) price of the output.
d) wage rate.
e) marginal product of labour.

15.56
Correct: b)
Difficulty: 3
Page(s): 389
Scramble range: a)–d)
Topic: Elasticity of demand for labour

15.56
The short-run elasticity of demand for labour depends on all of the following *except*
a) the short-run price elasticity of demand for the product that the labour produces.
b) the supply of labour.
c) the labour intensity in production.
d) the slope of the marginal product of labour curve.
e) it does not depend on any of the above.

15.57
Correct: e)
Difficulty: 3
Page(s): 390
Scramble range: All
Topic: Elasticity of demand for labour

15.57
The long-run elasticity of demand for labour depends on all of the following *except*
a) the long-run price elasticity of demand for the product which the labour produces.
b) the slope of the marginal product of labour curve.
c) the labour intensity in production.
d) the substitutability of other factors of production for labour.
e) the supply of labour.

15.58
Correct: b)
Difficulty: 2
Page(s): 391
Scramble range: All
Topic: Labour supply

15.58
The supply of labour depends on
a) the technology.
b) the value of nonmarket activities that the labourer could pursue.
c) the substitutability of other factors of production for labour.
d) whether or not the firm is a monopsonist.
e) the value of the output produced by the labour.

15.59
Correct: e)
Difficulty: 2
Page(s): 391
Scramble range: All
Topic: Reservation wage rate

15.59
The reservation wage of labour is
a) the wage below which the labourer will be willing to work.
b) the wage above which the worker would be willing to retire.
c) the wage rate for which the firm would find it profitable to hire labour.
d) the wage rate which makes it better for the firm to shut down rather than to pay such a wage to labour.
e) the wage above which the worker would be willing to supply labour to the market.

15.60
Correct: e)
Difficulty: 2
Page(s): 391
Scramble range: All
Topic: Labour supply

15.60
The substitution effect on the labour supply refers to
a) the degree to which the firm can substitute other factors of production for labour.
b) the degree to which buyers can substitute other products for the products which are made by organized labour.
c) the degree to which labour is willing to substitute nonlabour income for wages.
d) the degree to which labour prefers to substitute nonmonetary payments for money wages.
e) the degree to which labour is willing to substitute work for other nonmarket activities.

15.61
Correct: b)
Difficulty: 3
Page(s): 391
Scramble range: All
Topic: Income effect

15.61
The income effect on the labour supply refers to
a) the fact that at higher wages the worker earns more income.
b) the fact that as the wage increases and income increases, labourers demand more of all normal goods, including leisure activities.
c) the increase in the income of firms which is necessary to pay higher wages.
d) the fact that as workers become more productive, they earn more income.
e) the fact that as the wages increases and income increases, labourers demand more of all normal goods, including labour.

15.62
Correct: b)
Difficulty: 3
Page(s): 391
Scramble range: All
Topic: Backward–bending supply

15.62
The labour supply may eventually become "backward bending" at high wages because
a) the income effect of the higher wage is dominated by the substitution effect.
b) the income effect of the higher wage dominates the substitution effect of the higher wage.
c) firms will demand added productivity from the workers as the wage reaches very high levels.
d) firms will demand longer hours in trade for the higher wages.
e) people get tired of working so many hours and refuse to increase their labour supply.

15.63
Correct: a)
Difficulty: 2
Page(s): 393
Scramble range: All
Topic: The supply of capital

15.63
The supply of capital depends on all of the following *except*
a) the marginal productivity of capital.
b) the expected future income of households.
c) the current income of households.
d) expected future income versus current income of households.
e) the interest rate.

15.64
Correct: c)
Difficulty: 2
Page(s): 396
Scramble range: All
Topic: Change in the labour market

15.64
Assume that the labour supply curve slopes upward but is not backward bending. Also assume that the demand for labour is downward sloping. If there is an increase in the demand for the output that labour produces, then the wage of labour will
a) increase as employment of labour decreases.
b) decrease as employment of labour increases.
c) increase as the employment of labour also increases.
d) decrease as the employment of labour decreases as well.
e) increase, but the change in employment is uncertain.

15.65
Correct: d)
Difficulty: 2
Page(s): 396
Scramble range: All
Topic: Change in the labour market

15.65
Assume that the labour supply curve slopes upward but is not backward bending. Also assume that the demand for labour is downward sloping. If there is a decrease in the demand the output that labour produces, then the wage of labour will

a) increase as employment of labour decreases.
b) decrease as employment of labour increases.
c) increase as the employment of labour also increases.
d) decrease as the employment of labour decreases as well.
e) decrease, and the change in employment is uncertain.

15.66
Correct: d)
Difficulty: 2
Page(s): 395
Scramble range: All
Topic: Supply of land

15.66
In the short run the market supply of land is

a) relatively elastic.
b) relatively inelastic.
c) perfectly elastic.
d) completely inelastic.
e) either elastic or inelastic depending on the productivity of the land.

15.67
Correct: a)
Difficulty: 2
Page(s): 395
Scramble range: All
Topic: The land market

15.67
In the short run in the market for land

a) the supply of land determines the amount sold and the marginal productivity of the land determines the rent on the land.
b) the demand for land determines the amount sold and the supply of the land determines the rent on the land.
c) the marginal productivity of land determines both the rent on the land and the amount sold.
d) the supply of land determines both the rent on the land and the amount of land sold.
e) both the demand and supply of land determine both the price and the amount of land sold.

15.68
Correct: e)
Difficulty: 2
Page(s): 398–399
Scramble range: All
Topic: Transfer earnings

15.68
Transfer earnings are

a) the payments that must be made to state and local governments out of earned wages.
b) the payments that must be made to the federal government only out of earned income.
c) transfers from parents to children.
d) payments that are a surplus value to the capitalists.
e) the income that must be paid to factors of production in order to keep them in their present employment.

15.69
Correct: e)
Difficulty: 2
Page(s): 398–399
Scramble range: All
Topic: Economic rent

15.69
Economic rent is

a) the payments that must be made to state and local governments out of earned wages for the use of government services.
b) the payments that must be made to the federal government for the use of government services.
c) the income that must be paid to factors of production in order to keep them in their present employment.
d) the return to land.
e) payments to factors of production in excess of what would keep them from changing employment.

15.70
Correct: b)
Difficulty: 2
Page(s): 398–399
Scramble range: All
Topic: Economic rent

15.70
In the market for land in the short run, all payments to the land are
a) transfer earnings.
b) economic rent.
c) mostly transfer earnings but with some economic rent.
d) mostly economic rent but with some transfer earnings.
e) returns to the marginal productivity of land.

15.71
Correct: a)
Difficulty: 2
Page(s): 399
Scramble range: All
Topic: Transfer earnings

15.71
In a labour market in which the labour supply is perfectly elastic,
a) all payments to labour are transfer earnings.
b) all payments to labour are economic rent.
c) most of the payments to labour are transfer earnings.
d) most of the payments to labour are economic rent.
e) no one will work here, since they are indifferent between this job and those in other markets.

15.72
Correct: a)
Difficulty: 2
Page(s): 398–399
Scramble range: All
Topic: Economic rent

15.72
Economic rent is the payment that is
a) in excess of the opportunity cost of the resource.
b) compensation for the opportunity costs of the resource.
c) directly related to the size of the housing available.
d) usually made to state and local government in the form of property taxes.
e) made to use land.

15.73
Correct: b)
Difficulty: 3
Page(s): 398–399
Scramble range: All
Topic: Economic rent

15.73
In a resource market in which the supply is completely inelastic, an increase in demand for the resource will
a) increase only the transfer earnings of the resource.
b) increase only the economic rent received by the resource.
c) increase both the transfer earnings and the economic rent received by the resource.
d) decrease the economic rent but increase the transfer earnings of the resource.
e) decrease both the transfer earnings and the economic rent received by the resource.

15.74
Correct: a)
Difficulty: 3
Page(s): 398–399
Scramble range: All
Topic: Economic rent

15.74
In a resource market in which the supply is perfectly elastic, an increase in demand for the resource will
a) increase only the transfer earnings of the resource.
b) increase only the economic rent received by the resource.
c) increase both the transfer earnings and the economic rent received by the resource.
d) decrease the economic rent but increase the transfer earnings of the resource.
e) raise the price and therefore the economic rent.

15.75
Correct: a)
Difficulty: 5
Page(s): 400
Scramble range: All
Topic: Price and marginal revenue product

15.75
If a firm sells its output in a monopolistically competitive market and hires resources in competitive markets, then
a) the price of the output will overstate the added value of the marginal product of the resources.
b) the price of the output will understate the added value of the marginal product of the resources.
c) it has monopsonistic market power by virtue of its monopolistic market power.
d) the wage it must pay always underestimates the marginal factor cost of the resources it hires.
e) the price of the output will reflect the added value of the marginal product of the resources.

15.76
Correct: e)
Difficulty: 4
Page(s): 384
Scramble range: All
Topic: Marginal factor cost

15.76
If a firm can hire 80 workers at a wage of $6 each but must pay $7 each to hire 81 workers, the marginal factor cost of the 81st worker is equal to
a) $27.
b) $7.
c) $57.
d) $567.
e) $87.

15.77
Correct: c)
Difficulty: 4
Page(s): 388
Scramble range: All
Topic: Monopsonist labour market

15.77
If a firm enjoys market power in the resource market,
a) it can hire all the workers it chooses for any wage rate it chooses.
b) it can hire all the workers it chooses at the market wage rate.
c) it must pay a higher wage to increase employment.
d) it can force workers to work longer hours for lower wages.
e) it will always make positive economic profits.

15.78
Correct: d)
Difficulty: 4
Page(s): 388
Scramble range: All
Topic: Market power/ labour market

15.78
Compared with a firm without market power, a firm that enjoys market power in the labour market will
a) employ more labour and pay higher wages.
b) restrict employment but pay higher wages.
c) pay lower wages but employ more workers.
d) pay lower wages and restrict employment.
e) pay lower wages but hire the same number of people.

15.79
Correct: d)
Difficulty: 4
Page(s): 389
Scramble range: All
Topic: Elastic demand in labour market

15.79
The demand for a particular type of labour will be more elastic
a) the more difficult it is to substitute other factors of production for the labour.
b) the younger are the labourers.
c) the more highly skilled are the labourers.
d) the easier it is to substitute other factors of production for the labour.
e) the higher the price of the labour.

15.80
Correct: e)
Difficulty: 3
Page(s): 393
Scramble range: All
Topic: Labour supply elasticity

15.80
Which labour market's supply is most likely to be most elastic in the short run?
a) Brain surgeons.
b) Atomic engineers.
c) Economists.
d) Policemen.
e) Fast-food restaurant workers.

15.81 (SG 15.1)
Correct: c)
Difficulty: 2
Page(s): 381
Scramble range: All
Topic: Factor payments

15.81
The income received by owners of factors of production are wages paid for labour,
a) profit paid for capital, and interest paid for money.
b) dividends paid for capital, and interest paid for money.
c) interest paid for capital, and rent paid for land.
d) profit paid for capital, and rent paid for land.
e) dividends paid for capital and rent paid for land.

15.82 (SG 15.2)
Correct: a)
Difficulty: 2
Page(s): 383
Scramble range: All
Topic: Factor supply and adjustment

15.82
Suppose that the supply of a factor of production is very elastic. Then an increase in the demand for that factor will result in
a) a large increase in the quantity of the factor demanded and a small increase in its price.
b) a small increase in the quantity of the factor demanded and a large increase in its price.
c) a large increase in both quantity of the factor demanded and its price.
d) a small increase in both quantity of the factor demanded and its price.
e) no change in price, and a large increase in the quantity of the factor demanded.

15.83 (SG 15.3)
Correct: b)
Difficulty: 2
Page(s): 383
Scramble range: All
Topic: Supply and factor income

15.83
An increase in the supply of a factor of production will
a) increase income of the factor of production if the elasticity of demand is less than 1.
b) decrease income of the factor of production if the elasticity of demand is less than 1.
c) always increase income of the factor.
d) always decrease income of the factor.
e) never increase income of the factor in perfect competition.

15.84 (SG 15.4)
Correct: e)
Difficulty: 3
Page(s): 384
Scramble range: All
Topic: Derived demand

15.84
An example of derived demand is the demand for
a) sweaters derived by an economics student.
b) sweaters produced by labour and capital.
c) exams produced by economics professors.
d) sweater brushes.
e) labour used in the production of sweaters.

15.85 (SG 15.5)
Correct: e)
Difficulty: 2
Page(s): 384
Scramble range: All
Topic: Revenue to capital

15.85
The change in total revenue resulting from employing an additional unit of capital is the
a) marginal product of capital.
b) marginal revenue of capital.
c) marginal revenue cost of capital.
d) average revenue product of capital.
e) marginal revenue product of capital.

15.86 (SG 15.6)
Correct: a)
Difficulty: 3
Page(s): 387
Scramble range: All
Topic: Equilibrium in factor markets

15.86
Which of the following will *not* be true in profit-maximizing equilibrium?
a) Marginal revenue equals marginal product.
b) Marginal revenue equals marginal cost.
c) Marginal revenue times marginal product of a factor equals marginal cost of the factor.
d) Marginal revenue product of a factor equals marginal cost of the factor.
e) Marginal revenue product of labour equals the wage rate, in a competitive setting.

15.87 (SG 15.9)
Correct: c)
Difficulty: 2
Page(s): 387
Scramble range: All
Topic: Labour market

15.87
Suppose a profit-maximizing firm hires labour in a competitive labour market. If the marginal revenue product of labour is greater than the wage, the firm should
a) increase the wage rate.
b) decrease the wage rate.
c) increase the quantity of labour it hires.
d) decrease the quantity of labour it hires.
e) raise wages so it can raise the quantity of labour it hires.

15.88
Correct: a)
Difficulty: 2
Page(s): 387
Scramble range: All
Topic: Demand for labour

15.88
Which of the following will *not* shift the firm's demand curve for labour?
a) The wage rate.
b) The price of the firm's output.
c) The price of other inputs.
d) Technology.
e) Marginal product of other inputs.

15.89
Correct: e)
Difficulty: 3
Page(s): 384
Scramble range: All
Topic: Derived demand

15.89
An increase in the price of a competitive firm's output will cause
a) the supply of labour to increase.
b) a decline in the quantity of inputs hired.
c) an increase in marginal product.
d) the wage rate of the labour used to rise, so that the firm can attract more labour.
e) an increase in marginal revenue product.

15.90 (SG 15.12)
Correct: b)
Difficulty: 1
Page(s): 388
Scramble range: a)–d)
Topic: Changing demand for labour

15.90
A technological change that causes an increase in the marginal product of labour will shift the labour
a) demand curve to the left.
b) demand curve to the right.
c) supply curve to the left.
d) supply curve to the right.
e) none of the above.

15.91 (SG 15.13)
Correct: a)
Difficulty: 3
Page(s): 389
Scramble range: All
Topic: Costs of labour

15.91
Other things being equal, the larger the proportion of total cost coming from labour,
a) the more elastic is the demand for labour.
b) the less elastic is the demand for labour.
c) the more elastic is the supply of labour.
d) the less elastic is the supply of labour.
e) the more or less elastic is the demand for labour, it depends on the size of the total cost of labour, not just the proportion.

15.92 (SG 15.15)
Correct: c)
Difficulty: 3
Page(s): 391
Scramble range: All
Topic: Substitution effect

15.92
If the wage rate increases, the substitution effect will give a household an incentive to
a) raise its reservation wage.
b) increase its nonmarket activity and decrease its market activity.
c) increase its market activity and decrease its nonmarket activity.
d) increase both market and nonmarket activity.
e) lower its reservation wage.

15.93 (SG 15.16)
Correct: b)
Difficulty: 3
Page(s): 391
Scramble range: All
Topic: Income effect

15.93
If the wage rate increases, the income effect will give a household an incentive to
a) raise its reservation wage.
b) increase the amount of leisure it consumes.
c) decrease the amount of leisure it consumes.
d) increase the amount of work it offers.
e) lower its reservation wage.

15.94 (SG 15.17)
Correct: d)
Difficulty: 4
Page(s): 391
Scramble range: All
Topic: Backward-bending supply

15.94
As the wage rate continues to rise, a household will have a backward-bending supply of labour curve if
a) the income effect is in the same direction as the substitution effect.
b) the wage rate rises above the reservation wage.
c) the substitution effect dominates the income effect.
d) the income effect dominates the substitution effect.
e) the amount of labour supply passes 48 hours a week, and the firm must pay overtime.

15.95 (SG 15.18)
Correct: e)
Difficulty: 3
Page(s): 393–394
Scramble range: All
Topic: Saving

15.95
Households will increase the amount they save if there is
a) either a decrease in current income compared with expected future income or an increase in the interest rate.
b) either a decrease in current income compared with expected future income or a decrease in the interest rate.
c) a decrease in current income compared with expected future income *combined* with an increase in the interest rate.
d) either an increase in current income compared with expected future income or a decrease in the interest rate.
e) either an increase in current compared with expected future income or an increase in the interest rate.

15.96 (SG 15.19)
Correct: a)
Difficulty: 3
Page(s): 394
Scramble range: All
Topic: Life-cycle hypothesis

15.96
The main factor influencing whether a household's current income is high or low compared with expected future income is
a) the stage of the life cycle the household is in.
b) whether the household is rich or poor.
c) whether interest rates are high or low.
d) the weather.
e) the marginal product of the household's labour.

15.97 (SG 15.20)
Correct: b)
Difficulty: 2
Page(s): 394
Scramble range: All
Topic: Supply of capital

15.97
In the short run, a firm faces a supply of capital that is
a) perfectly elastic.
b) perfectly inelastic.
c) positively sloped.
d) negatively sloped (i.e., backward bending).
e) somewhat inelastic.

15.98 (SG 15.21)
Correct: a)
Difficulty: 3
Page(s): 392–393
Scramble range: All
Topic: Leisure

15.98
If the desire for leisure increased,
a) the wage rate would rise and the quantity of labour hired would fall.
b) the wage rate would rise and the quantity of labour hired would rise.
c) the wage rate would fall and the quantity of labour hired would fall.
d) the wage rate would fall and the quantity of labour hired would rise.
e) the wage rate would be unchanged and the quantity of labour hired would rise.

15.99 (SG 15.22)
Correct: a)
Difficulty: 4
Page(s): 394
Scramble range: All
Topic: Interest rates and capital

15.99
If the interest rate on capital in industry *A* is lower than the interest rate on capital in industry *B*,
a) the supply of capital in industry *A* will gradually decrease and the supply of capital in industry *B* will gradually increase until the interest rates are equal.
b) the supply of capital in industry *A* will gradually increase and the supply of capital in industry *B* will gradually decrease until the interest rates are equal.
c) the supply of capital in industry *A* must be more elastic than the supply of capital in industry *B*.
d) the supply of capital in industry *A* must be less elastic than the supply of capital in industry *B*.
e) the demand for capital in industry *A* will gradually decrease and the demand for capital in industry *B* will gradually increase until the interest rates are equal.

15.100 (SG 15.23)
Correct: d)
Difficulty: 2
Page(s): 398–399
Scramble range: All
Topic: Economic rent

15.100
Economic rent is
a) the price paid for the use of a hectare of land.
b) the price paid for the use of a unit of capital.
c) the income required to induce a given quantity of a factor of production to be supplied.
d) the income received which is above the amount required to induce a given quantity of a factor of production to be supplied.
e) consumer surplus.

15.101 (SG 15.24)
Correct: e)
Difficulty: 5
Page(s): 398–399
Scramble range: All
Topic: Transfer earnings

15.101
Consider the supply schedule of a factor of production given in Table 15.7. If 4 units of the factor are supplied at a price of $8 per unit, transfer earnings are

a) $8.
b) $12.
c) $32.
d) $16.
e) $20.

Table 15.7

Price of a factor ($)	Quantity of factor supplied
2	1
4	2
6	3
8	4
10	5

15.102 (SG 15.25)
Correct: b)
Difficulty: 5
Page(s): 398–399
Scramble range: All
Topic: Economic rent

15.102
Consider the supply schedule of a factor of production given in Table 15.7. If 4 units of the factor are supplied at a price of $8 per unit, economic rent is

a) $8.
b) $12.
c) $20.
d) $32.
e) $16.

15.103
Correct: e)
Difficulty: 1
Page(s): 381
Scramble range: All
Topic: Factor payments

15.103
The income received by owners of factors of production are interest paid for capital,

a) profit paid for capital, and rent paid for money.
b) dividends paid for capital, and interest paid for money.
c) wages of labour, and interest paid for land.
d) wages paid for the use of capital, and rent paid for land.
e) wages of labour, and rent paid for land.

15.104
Correct: b)
Difficulty: 2
Page(s): 382
Scramble range: All
Topic: Factor supply and adjustment

15.104
Suppose that the supply of a factor of production is very inelastic. Then an increase in the demand for that factor will result in

a) a large increase in the quantity of the factor demanded and a small increase in its price.
b) a small increase in the quantity of the factor demanded and a large increase in its price.
c) a large increase in both quantity of the factor demanded and its price.
d) a small increase in both quantity of the factor demanded and its price.
e) no change in the quantity of the factor demanded and a large increase in its price.

15.105
Correct: a)
Difficulty: 2
Page(s): 382
Scramble range: All
Topic: Supply and factor income

15.105
A decrease in the supply of a factor of production will
a) increase income of the factor of production if the elasticity of demand is less than 1.
b) decrease income of the factor of production if the elasticity of demand is less than 1.
c) always increase income of the factor.
d) always decrease income of the factor.
e) never change income of the factor in perfect competition.

15.106
Correct: e)
Difficulty: 2
Page(s): 384
Scramble range: All
Topic: Derived demand

15.106
An example of derived demand is the demand for
a) paint brushes used by an economics student.
b) paint brushes produced by labour and capital.
c) televisions by households.
d) apples.
e) raw materials used in the production of paint brushes.

15.107
Correct: d)
Difficulty: 1
Page(s): 384
Scramble range: All
Topic: Revenue of labour

15.107
The change in total revenue resulting from employing an additional unit of labour is the
a) marginal product of labour.
b) marginal revenue of labour.
c) marginal revenue cost of labour.
d) marginal revenue product of labour.
e) average revenue product of labour.

15.108
Correct: e)
Difficulty: 4
Page(s): 387
Scramble range: All
Topic: Equilibrium in factor markets

15.108
Which of the following will be true in profit-maximizing equilibrium?
a) Marginal revenue equals marginal product.
b) Marginal revenue exceeds marginal cost.
c) Marginal revenue times marginal product of a factor will exceed the marginal cost of the factor.
d) Marginal product of a factor will exceed the marginal cost of the factor.
e) Average revenue product exceeds the marginal revenue product.

15.109
Correct: d)
Difficulty: 2
Page(s): 387
Scramble range: All
Topic: Labour market

15.109
Suppose a profit-maximizing firm hires labour in a competitive labour market. If the marginal revenue product of labour is less than the wage, the firm should
a) increase the wage rate.
b) decrease the wage rate.
c) increase the quantity of labour it hires.
d) decrease the quantity of labour it hires.
e) lower the wage rate so it can lower the quantity of labour hired.

15.110
Correct: e)
Difficulty: 3
Page(s): 384
Scramble range: All
Topic: Derived demand

15.110
A decrease in the price of a competitive firm's output will cause
a) the supply of labour to decrease.
b) a rise in the quantity of inputs hired.
c) an increase in marginal revenue product.
d) the wage of the labour used by this firm to fall as the quantity of labour hired falls.
e) a decrease in marginal revenue product.

15.111
Correct: c)
Difficulty: 1
Page(s): 388
Scramble range: a)–d)
Topic: Changing demand for labour

15.111
A technological change that causes a decrease in the marginal product of labour will shift
a) the labour supply curve to the left.
b) the labour demand curve to the right.
c) the labour demand curve to the left.
d) the labour supply curve to the right.
e) none of the above.

15.112
Correct: b)
Difficulty: 4
Page(s): 389
Scramble range: All
Topic: Costs of labour

15.112
Other things being equal, the smaller the proportion of total cost coming from labour,
a) the more elastic is the demand for labour.
b) the less elastic is the demand for labour.
c) the more elastic is the supply of labour.
d) the less elastic is the supply of labour.
e) the more or less elastic is the demand for labour; it depends on the size of the total cost, not just its proportion.

15.113
Correct: e)
Difficulty: 3
Page(s): 392
Scramble range: All
Topic: Market supply of labour

15.113
Consider the market for labour. Select the best statement.
a) The supply of labour is always in the backward-bending portion for each individual in the market.
b) The market supply of labour is less elastic than the individual supply of labour.
c) The market supply of labour is usually in the backward-bending portion.
d) The supply of labour is never in the backward-bending portion for any individual.
e) The market supply of labour is more elastic than the individual supply of labour.

15.114
Correct: e)
Difficulty: 4
Page(s): 395
Scramble range: All
Topic: Supply of land

15.114
Consider the market for land. Suppose that the demand for land rises, then
a) the quantity supplied of land will rise as it is used more intensively.
b) the quantity supplied of land will rise as it is used less intensively.
c) the transfer payments to the owners of land will rise.
d) the price of land will rise, leading to a rise in the quantity of land in the long run, although there will be no rise in the short run.
e) the economic rent received by landowners will rise, and the land will be used more intensively.

15.115
Correct: c)
Difficulty: 4
Page(s): 399
Scramble range: All
Topic: Economic rent

15.115
Wayne Gretzky is the highest paid hockey player in the NHL. For the purposes of this question, suppose Mr. Gretzky receives $2 million per year. Mr. Gretzky's best alternative employment is as a actor in Los Angeles, and he would receive $500,000 per year doing this. Suppose the average NHLer receives a salary of $200,000 for the purpose of this question, and his best alternative employment is as a televison sports announcer, earning $30,000 per year. From this, we can calculate that
a) Mr. Gretzky gets paid too much.
b) Mr. Gretzky gets paid too little.
c) Mr. Gretzky's economic rent is $1,500,000 per year.
d) Mr. Gretzky's economic rent is $1,800,000 per year.
e) Mr. Gretzky's economic rent is $1,970,000 per year.

15.116
Correct: d)
Difficulty: 3
Page(s): 384–391
Scramble range: All
Topic: Marginal revenue product

15.116
Consider Table 15.8. Suppose that the apples can be sold for $0.50 per kilogram. Then, the marginal revenue product of the fifth student is
a) $0.50.
b) $72.50.
c) $14.50.
d) $12.50.
e) $10.00.

Table 15.8 Wendy owns an apple orchard and she employs students to pick the apples. In an hour they can pick the following amounts:

Number of students	Quantity of apples (kg)
1	20
2	50
3	90
4	120
5	145
6	165
7	180
8	190

15.117
Correct: e)
Difficulty: 3
Page(s): 384–391
Scramble range: All
Topic: Labour market equilibrium

15.117
Consider Table 15.8. Suppose that the apples can be sold for $0.50 per kilogram, and that apple pickers receive $7.50 per hour in the competitive apple pickers' market. Then the number of pickers that Wendy will hire is
a) 3.
b) 4.
c) 5.
d) 6.
e) 7.

15.118
Correct: c)
Difficulty: 2
Page(s): 395–398
Scramble range: All
Topic: Competitive equilibrium

15.118
Consider Table 15.9. In competitive equilibrium, the wage rate will be
a) $4.
b) $5.
c) $6.
d) $7.
e) $8.

Table 15.9 The labour market in an isolated town in northern Quebec. Everyone works for logging companies, but there are many logging companies in the area. The market for logging workers is competitive. The local supply and demand for labour is as follows:

Wage rate (dollars/hour)	Quantity of labour supplied (hours)	Quantity of labour demanded (hours)
2	120	440
3	160	400
4	200	360
5	240	320
6	280	280
7	320	240
8	360	200

15.119
Correct: d)
Difficulty: 5
Page(s): 398–400
Scramble range: All
Topic: Economic rent

15.119
Consider Table 15.9. In competitive equilibrium, economic rent will be _________ and transfer earnings will be _________

a) $960; $720.
b) $1,680; 0.
c) 0; $1,680.
d) $720; $960.
e) $840; $840.

Chapter 16 Labour Markets

16.1
Correct: b)
Difficulty: 1
Page(s): 406
Scramble range: All
Topic: Return to human capital

16.1
A 22-year-old college graduate, on the average, earns how much more than a 22-year-old noncollege graduate?
a) Zero, as they earn the same income on average.
b) 30 percent more.
c) 60 percent more.
d) 300 percent more.
e) 3 percent more.

16.2
Correct: c)
Difficulty: 1
Page(s): 406
Scramble range: All
Topic: Return to human capital

16.2
A middle-aged college graduate, on the average, earns how much more than a middle-aged noncollege graduate?
a) Zero, as they earn the same income on average.
b) 500 percent more.
c) 50 percent more.
d) 30 percent more.
e) 5 percent more.

16.3
Correct: d)
Difficulty: 1
Page(s): 406
Scramble range: All
Topic: Return to human capital

16.3
In middle age, a college graduate, on the average, earns how much more than someone who attended elementary school only?
a) Zero, as they earn the same income on average.
b) 20 percent more.
c) 2 percent more.
d) 200 percent more.
e) 30 percent more.

16.4
Correct: a)
Difficulty: 3
Page(s): 407
Scramble range: All
Topic: Wages and skill levels

16.4
Compared with unskilled workers, skilled workers can
a) perform more complex tasks with higher marginal revenue products.
b) usually earn more income for less difficult work.
c) perform the same tasks yet earn more money.
d) perform less complex tasks with lower marginal revenue products.
e) work more hours and earn more money.

16.5
Correct: e)
Difficulty: 2
Page(s): 407
Scramble range: All
Topic: Demand for skilled labour

16.5
The demand for skilled labour is derived from the
a) exploitation of the less skilled workers.
b) marginal cost of production.
c) lower wage of the labour.
d) supply of the skilled labourers.
e) marginal revenue product of the labour.

16.6
Correct: e)
Difficulty: 2
Page(s): 407
Scramble range: All
Topic: Demand for unskilled labour

16.6
The demand for unskilled labour is derived from the
a) work left undone by the skilled workers.
b) marginal cost of production.
c) lower wage rate of the labour.
d) supply of the skilled labourers.
e) marginal revenue product of the labour.

16.7
Correct: b)
Difficulty: 2
Page(s): 407–408
Scramble range: All
Topic: Demand for labour

16.7
The greater the marginal revenue product of labour,
a) the greater will be the supply of those labourers.
b) the greater will be the demand for those labourers.
c) the greater will be the marginal cost of production.
d) the greater will be the employment of those labourers.
e) the lower will be the wage rate of those labourers.

16.8
Correct: b)
Difficulty: 3
Page(s): 407–408
Scramble range: All
Topic: Change in the demand for labour

16.8
Assuming that the supply of labour is upward sloping but not vertical, if the marginal revenue product of labour increases,
a) the supply of those labourers will increase.
b) the wage rate of those labourers will increase.
c) the marginal cost of production will increase.
d) the exploitation of those labourers will decrease.
e) the employment of those labourers will be unchanged.

16.9
Correct: d)
Difficulty: 3
Page(s): 407–408
Scramble range: All
Topic: Change in the demand for labour

16.9
Assuming that the supply of labour is upward sloping but not vertical, if the marginal revenue product of labour increases,
a) the supply of those labourers will increase.
b) the wage rate of those labourers will decrease.
c) the marginal cost of production will increase.
d) the employment of those labourers will increase.
e) profit per labourer will fall.

16.10
Correct: b)
Difficulty: 4
Page(s): 408
Scramble range: All
Topic: Un/skilled labour wages

16.10
Refer to Figure 16.1. For any given employment level
a) skilled labourers will receive a lower wage than unskilled labourers.
b) skilled labourers will receive a higher wage than unskilled labourers.
c) skilled labourers and unskilled labourers will receive the same wage.
d) no conclusion can be reached concerning the wage rates without more information.
e) the wage rate depends on the relative supply curves.

Figure 16.1

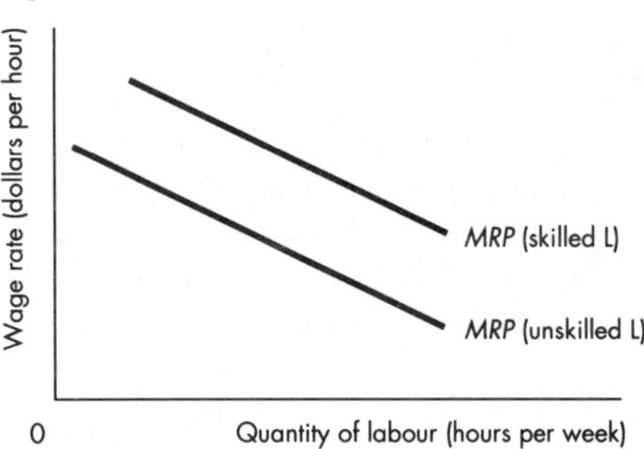

16.11
Correct: a)
Difficulty: 3
Page(s): 408
Scramble range: All
Topic: Un/skilled labour employment

16.11
Refer to Figure 16.1. For any given wage rate,
a) more skilled workers will be hired than unskilled workers.
b) more unskilled workers will be hired than skilled workers.
c) the employment of skilled workers and unskilled workers will be the same.
d) no conclusion can be reached concerning employment without more information.
e) the amount of employment of skilled workers and unskilled workers will be dependent on their relative supply curves.

16.12
Correct: a)
Difficulty: 2
Page(s): 409
Scramble range: All
Topic: Wage differentials

16.12
Refer to Figure 16.1. For any given employment level, the difference between the wage rate of the skilled and unskilled workers
a) is equal to the difference in the marginal revenue product of the workers.
b) is equal to the difference in the average revenue product of the workers.
c) is caused by discrimination against minorities.
d) is caused by discrimination against women.
e) equals the cost of acquiring the skills.

16.13
Correct: c)
Difficulty: 2
Page(s): 408
Scramble range: All
Topic: Wages and skill levels

16.13
Refer to Figure 16.2. At an employment level of 20 hours per week, firms are willing to pay
a) a wage rate of $7 to unskilled workers.
b) a maximum of $5 to skilled workers.
c) up to $7 for skilled workers.
d) the same for skilled workers as for unskilled workers.
e) a differential of $3 higher for skilled workers.

Figure 16.2

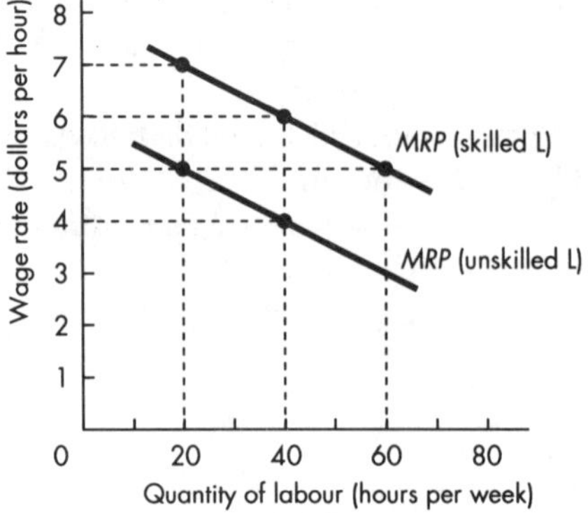

16.14
Correct: b)
Difficulty: 3
Page(s): 408
Scramble range: All
Topic: Wages and skill levels

16.14
Refer to Figure 16.2. At an employment level of 20 hours per week, firms are willing to pay
a) a wage rate of $7 to unskilled workers.
b) a maximum of $5 to unskilled workers.
c) up to $8 for skilled workers.
d) the same for skilled workers as for unskilled workers.
e) a differential of $3 higher for skilled workers.

16.15
Correct: b)
Difficulty: 2
Page(s): 407–410
Scramble range: All
Topic: Productivity differential

16.15
Refer to Figure 16.2. At an employment level of 40 hours per week, the difference in the marginal revenue product of skilled workers and unskilled workers is
a) zero.
b) $2.
c) $6.
d) $4.
e) $3.

16.16
Correct: d)
Difficulty: 3
Page(s): 408
Scramble range: All
Topic: Wages and employment

16.16
Refer to Figure 16.2. For a wage rate of $5, an employer would hire
a) the same amount of skilled workers as unskilled workers.
b) 20 hours of unskilled labour and 40 hours of skilled labour.
c) 60 hours of unskilled labour and 20 hours of skilled labour.
d) 60 hours of skilled labour and 20 hours of unskilled labour.
e) 40 hours of unskilled labour and 60 hours of skilled labour.

16.17
Correct: c)
Difficulty: 3
Page(s): 408
Scramble range: All
Topic: Wages and employment

16.17
Refer to Figure 16.2. For the employer to hire 40 hours per week of both skilled and unskilled labour,
a) skilled workers would have to earn a wage rate that is twice that of the unskilled workers.
b) skilled workers would have to earn a wage rate that is less than that of the skilled workers.
c) skilled workers would have to earn a wage that is $2 more than the wage paid to unskilled workers.
d) unskilled workers would have to earn a wage that is $2 more than the wage paid to skilled workers.
e) skilled workers need to earn a wage that is between 0 and $2 more than that of unskilled workers.

16.18
Correct: e)
Difficulty: 2
Page(s): 407
Scramble range: All
Topic: Acquiring human capital

16.18
Paying to acquire the skills necessary to join the ranks of skilled labour can be considered as
a) a consumption expenditure.
b) an investment in physical capital.
c) a free good.
d) unnecessary to earning the wage of skilled workers.
e) an investment in human capital.

16.19
Correct: c)
Difficulty: 2
Page(s): 407
Scramble range: All
Topic: Human capital

16.19
By "human capital" economists mean
a) machines that can replace humans on an assembly line.
b) machines skilled enough to perform tasks even more delicate than can be accomplished by human labour.
c) accumulated skill and knowledge of humans.
d) humans performing repetitive tasks on an assembly line for so long that they become dehumanized.
e) formal education in university or college.

16.20
Correct: d)
Difficulty: 2
Page(s): 407
Scramble range: All
Topic: Payments to human capital

16.20
The value of acquired human capital to a worker is
a) the cost of tuition, books, and miscellaneous expenditures of attending university.
b) the money that could have been earned had the worker chosen not to attend university.
c) the added salary received in the first job compared to what unskilled workers earn.
d) the present value of the extra earnings received over a lifetime as a result of the skills acquired.
e) the life skills learned in university.

16.21
Correct: d)
Difficulty: 3
Page(s): 408
Scramble range: All
Topic: Cost of acquiring human capital

16.21
The cost of acquiring human capital must include all of the following *except*
a) the money spent directly on training, such as tuition expenditures.
b) the interest payments on loans taken to finance a university education.
c) the forgone income that could have been earned had the worker become employed instead of attending school.
d) the finance charges on the new suit purchased while attending university.
e) the cost of books and equipment.

16.22
Correct: a)
Difficulty: 3
Page(s): 408
Scramble range: All
Topic: Acquiring human capital

16.22
For a worker undergoing on-the-job training,
a) the wage is usually reduced compared with the worker who does not require on-the-job training.
b) the wage is usually greater compared with the worker who does not require on-the-job training.
c) the wage is usually equal to that of the worker who does not require on-the-job training.
d) there is no cost to acquiring human capital.
e) the firm pays all of the costs of the training.

16.23
Correct: d)
Difficulty: 3
Page(s): 408
Scramble range: All
Topic: Un/skilled labour supply

16.23
Refer to Figure 16.3. For any given level of employment for skilled and unskilled workers, the vertical distance between the two supply curves
a) disappears over time.
b) is created by the greater productivity of skilled workers.
c) is created by discrimination against unskilled workers by some employers.
d) is the compensation required for the cost of acquiring the skills.
e) equals the difference in marginal revenue product between skilled and unskilled workers.

Figure 16.3

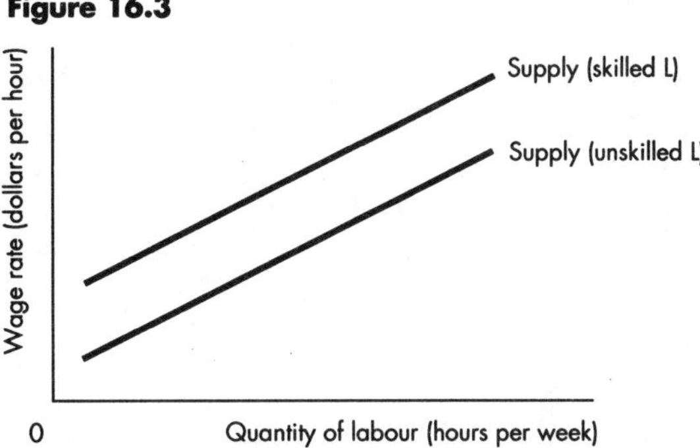

16.24
Correct: c)
Difficulty: 3
Page(s): 408
Scramble range: All
Topic: Un/skilled labour supply

16.24
Refer to Figure 16.3. For any given wage rate,

a) the same number of unskilled workers will be supplied as skilled workers.
b) there will be a greater number of skilled workers supplied than unskilled workers.
c) there will be a greater number of unskilled workers supplied than skilled workers.
d) no conclusion can be drawn about the amount of labour supplied without more information concerning the marginal productivity of the workers.
e) the amount of skilled versus unskilled labour depends on the relative amounts of demand for the two types.

16.25
Correct: b)
Difficulty: 2
Page(s): 408
Scramble range: All
Topic: Wages and skill levels

16.25
Refer to Figure 16.4. Given in the figure are the labour supply curves for skilled and unskilled workers. For an employment level of 20 hours per week, firms must be willing to pay

a) a wage rate of $7 to unskilled workers.
b) a minimum of $6 to skilled workers.
c) up to $8 for skilled workers.
d) the same for skilled workers as for unskilled workers.
e) a differential of $3 more for skilled workers versus unskilled workers.

Figure 16.4

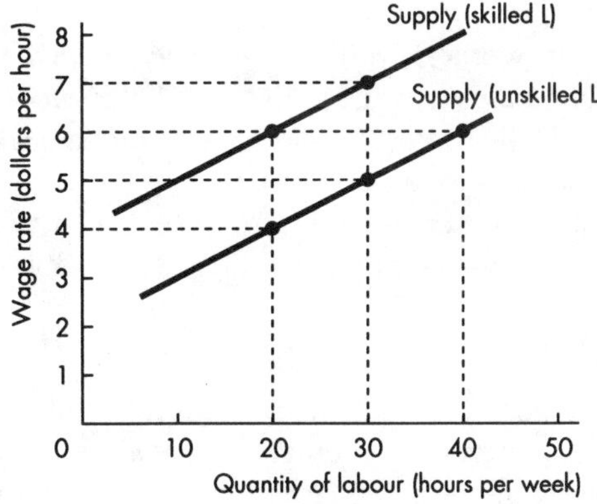

16.26
Correct: e)
Difficulty: 2
Page(s): 408
Scramble range: All
Topic: Wages and skill levels

16.26
Refer to Figure 16.4. At an employment level of 20 hours per week, firms must be willing to pay
a) a wage rate of $7 to unskilled workers.
b) a minimum of $5 to unskilled workers.
c) up to $8 for skilled workers.
d) the same for skilled workers as for unskilled workers.
e) a minimum of $4 to unskilled workers.

16.27
Correct: b)
Difficulty: 2
Page(s): 408
Scramble range: All
Topic: Wage differentials

16.27
Refer to Figure 16.4. At an employment level of 40 hours per week, the difference in the compensation required for the acquired skills of the skilled workers
a) is zero.
b) is $2.
c) is $4.
d) is $6.
e) cannot be determined.

16.28
Correct: d)
Difficulty: 3
Page(s): 408
Scramble range: All
Topic: Wages and labour supply

16.28
Refer to Figure 16.4. For a wage rate of $6, an employer could hire
a) the same amount of skilled labour as unskilled labour.
b) a maximum of 20 hours of unskilled labour and 40 hours of skilled labour.
c) a maximum of 60 hours of unskilled labour and 20 hours of skilled labour.
d) a maximum of 40 hours of unskilled labour and a maximum of 20 hours of skilled labour.
e) a maximum of 20 hours of unskilled labour and a maximum of 30 hours of unskilled labour.

16.29
Correct: c)
Difficulty: 3
Page(s): 408
Scramble range: All
Topic: Wages and labour supply

16.29
Refer to Figure 16.4. In order for the employer to hire a maximum of 40 hours per week of both skilled and unskilled labour,
a) skilled workers would have to be paid a wage rate that is twice that of the unskilled workers.
b) skilled workers would have to be paid a wage rate that is less than that of the skilled workers.
c) skilled workers would have to be paid a wage that is a minimum of $2 more than the wage paid to unskilled workers.
d) unskilled workers would have to be paid a wage that is $2 more than the wage paid to skilled workers.
e) skilled workers would have to be paid a wage rate that is between 0 and $2 more than that received by unskilled workers.

16.30
Correct: e)
Difficulty: 4
Page(s): 408
Scramble range: All
Topic: Labour market equilibrium

16.30
Refer to Figure 16.5. This figure shows the labour supply curves for skilled and unskilled workers and the marginal revenue product curves for skilled and unskilled workers. If the labour markets are competitive, then the equilibrium wage rate for unskilled workers will be
a) $3.
b) $7.
c) $6.
d) $5.
e) $4.

Figure 16.5

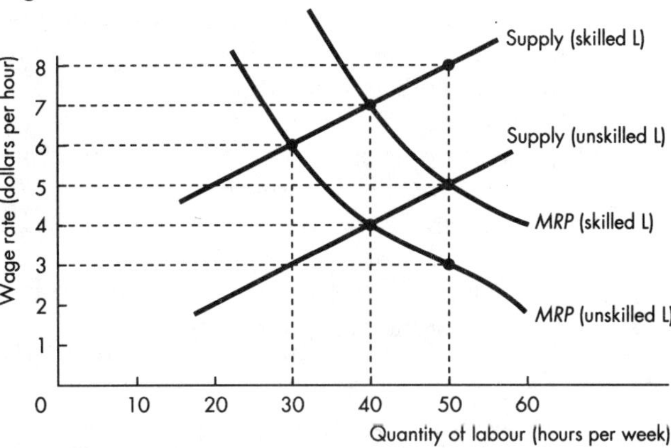

16.31
Correct: b)
Difficulty: 4
Page(s): 408
Scramble range: All
Topic: Labour market equilibrium

16.31
Refer to Figure 16.5. This figure shows the labour supply curves for skilled and unskilled workers and the marginal revenue product curves for skilled and unskilled workers. If the labour markets are competitive, then the equilibrium employment level for unskilled workers will be
a) 30 hours per week.
b) 40 hours per week.
c) 50 hours per week.
d) 70 hours per week.
e) dependent on the wage rate.

16.32
Correct: e)
Difficulty: 4
Page(s): 408
Scramble range: All
Topic: Labour market equilibrium

16.32
Refer to Figure 16.5. This figure shows the labour supply curves for skilled and unskilled workers and the marginal revenue product curves for skilled and unskilled workers. If the labour markets are competitive, then the equilibrium wage rate for skilled workers will be
a) $5.
b) $4.
c) $6.
d) $8.
e) $7.

16.33
Correct: b)
Difficulty: 4
Page(s): 408
Scramble range: All
Topic: Labour market equilibrium

16.33
Refer to Figure 16.5. This figure shows the labour supply curves for skilled and unskilled workers and the marginal revenue product curves for skilled and unskilled workers. If the labour markets are competitive, then the equilibrium employment level for skilled workers will be
a) 30 hours per week.
b) 40 hours per week.
c) 50 hours per week.
d) 70 hours per week.
e) dependent on the wage rate.

16.34
Correct: c)
Difficulty: 4
Page(s): 407–410
Scramble range: All
Topic: Compensate human capital

16.34
Refer to Figure 16.5. This figure shows the labour supply curves for skilled and unskilled workers and the marginal revenue product curves for skilled and unskilled workers. If the labour markets are competitive, then for the standard 40-hour work week, skilled workers must be paid

a) $3 to compensate for the cost of acquiring their human capital and for their enhanced productivity.
b) an extra $20 to compensate for the cost of acquiring their human capital and for their enhanced productivity.
c) an extra $120 to compensate for the cost of acquiring their human capital and for their enhanced productivity.
d) an extra $300 to compensate for the cost of acquiring their human capital and for their enhanced productivity.
e) an extra $180 to compensate for the cost of acquiring their human capital and for their enhanced productivity.

16.35
Correct: a)
Difficulty: 5
Page(s): 408
Scramble range: All
Topic: Wages and productivity growth

16.35
Refer to Figure 16.5. This figure shows the labour supply curves for skilled and unskilled workers, and the marginal revenue product curves for skilled and unskilled workers. Assume that labour markets are competitive. If employers purchased more advanced machinery which increased the marginal revenue product of the unskilled workers to the level of the skilled workers, then

a) wages paid to unskilled workers would rise to $5.
b) wages paid to unskilled workers would rise to $4.
c) wages paid to unskilled workers would rise to $7.
d) wages paid to unskilled workers would rise to $6.
e) there would be no change in the wages of unskilled workers since the added capital is the cause of the productivity increase of labour.

16.36
Correct: d)
Difficulty: 4
Page(s): 408
Scramble range: All
Topic: Employment and productivity growth

16.36
Refer to Figure 16.5. This figure shows the labour supply curves for skilled and unskilled workers and the marginal revenue product curves for skilled and unskilled workers. Assume that the labour markets are competitive. If employers purchased more advanced machinery which increased the marginal revenue product of the unskilled workers to the level of the skilled workers, then employment of

a) unskilled workers would remain the same.
b) unskilled workers would decrease as fewer labourers are needed in order to produce the same output.
c) unskilled labour would increase to 40 hours per week.
d) unskilled labour would increase to 50 hours per week.
e) unskilled labour would increase to the same level as that of skilled labour.

16.37
Correct: b)
Difficulty: 4
Page(s): 408
Scramble range: All
Topic: Wages and labour supply

16.37
Refer to Figure 16.5. This figure shows the labour supply curves for skilled and unskilled workers and the marginal revenue product curves for skilled and unskilled workers. Assume that the labour markets are competitive. If there is an increase in the supply of skilled workers so that the supply of skilled workers in now equal to the supply of unskilled workers, then

a) wages paid to skilled workers would fall to $4.
b) wages paid to skilled workers would fall to $5.
c) wages paid to skilled workers would fall to $6.
d) there would be no change in the wages of skilled workers since the added supply is irrelevant.
e) there would be no change in the wages of skilled workers, since their marginal revenue product is unchanged.

16.38
Correct: d)
Difficulty: 4
Page(s): 408
Scramble range: All
Topic: Employment and productivity growth

16.38
Refer to Figure 16.5. This figure shows the labour supply curves for skilled and unskilled workers, and the marginal revenue product curves for skilled and unskilled workers. Assume that the labour markets are competitive. If there is an increase in the supply of skilled workers so that the supply of skilled workers in now equal to the supply of unskilled workers, then employment of skilled labour would

a) remain the same.
b) decrease.
c) increase to 40 hours per week.
d) increase to 50 hours per week.
e) increase to the same level as that of unskilled labour.

16.39
Correct: e)
Difficulty: 2
Page(s): 409
Scramble range: All
Topic: Source of earnings differentials

16.39
One important source of earnings differentials is the

a) style of dress of the employee.
b) hair colour level of the employee.
c) type of car driven by the employee.
d) number of years it takes the employee to graduate from college.
e) education level of the employee.

16.40
Correct: a)
Difficulty: 2
Page(s): 409
Scramble range: All
Topic: Source of earnings differentials

16.40
One important source of earnings differentials is the

a) age of the employee.
b) type of music the employee enjoys.
c) attractiveness of the spouse of the employee.
d) number of years it takes the employee to graduate from college.
e) neatness of the employee.

16.41
Correct: c)
Difficulty: 2
Page(s): 410
Scramble range: All
Topic: Labour unions

16.41
A labour union is

a) an illegal conspiracy of workers formed in order to strike against employers.
b) a legal organization of workers whose goal is to overthrow the capitalist class.
c) an organized group that attempts to increase wages and influence other employment conditions.
d) an organized group of crime syndicates.
e) a union in which members work in the same industry, but in different jobs.

16.42
Correct: b)
Difficulty: 2
Page(s): 410
Scramble range: All
Topic: Labour unions

16.42
A labour union attempts to

a) increase the number of workers that enjoy the same job skills.
b) exert market power in the labour market in a way analogous to the way monopolists exert their power in product markets.
c) restrain wage increases in order to fight inflation.
d) act like a monopsonist in the labour market.
e) increase employment.

16.43
Correct: c)
Difficulty: 2
Page(s): 410
Scramble range: All
Topic: Craft unions

16.43
A craft union is
a) a group of workers with identical skills employed in the same factory.
b) a group of workers with similar skills employed in different factories owned by the same corporation.
c) a group of workers with similar skills employed in different industries and regions.
d) the same as an industrial union.
e) a union that acts as the voice of labour in media and political arenas.

16.44
Correct: c)
Difficulty: 2
Page(s): 410
Scramble range: All
Topic: Craft unions

16.44
An example of a craft union is the
a) Canadian Auto Workers.
b) United Steel Workers.
c) carpenters' union.
d) Saskatchewan Federation of Labour.
e) Sherwood Credit Union.

16.45
Correct: e)
Difficulty: 2
Page(s): 410
Scramble range: All
Topic: Industrial unions

16.45
An industrial union is
a) a group of workers with identical skills employed in the same factory.
b) a group of workers with similar skills employed in different factories owned by the same corporation.
c) a union that acts as the voice of labour in media and political arenas.
d) the same as a craft union.
e) a group of workers with varying skills employed in the same firm or industry.

16.46
Correct: b)
Difficulty: 2
Page(s): 410
Scramble range: All
Topic: Industrial unions

16.46
Examples of industrial unions include all of the following *except* the
a) International Ladies Garment Union.
b) carpenters' union.
c) Canadian Auto Workers.
d) Ontario Teachers' Association.
e) Teamsters' Union.

16.47
Correct: d)
Difficulty: 2
Page(s): 410
Scramble range: All
Topic: Canadian Labour Congress

16.47
To the nearest decade, the Canadian Labour Congress was founded in
a) 1783.
b) 1883.
c) 1940.
d) 1956.
e) 1986.

16.48
Correct: b)
Difficulty: 2
Page(s): 410
Scramble range: All
Topic: Canadian Congress of Labour

16.48
The Canadian Congress of Labour (CCL) was formed to
a) organize craft unions.
b) organize industrial unions.
c) limit Irish immigration.
d) fight for the rights of women in the workplace.
e) fight for employment in the Great Depression of the 1930s.

16.49
Correct: a)
Difficulty: 2
Page(s): 410
Scramble range: All
Topic: Labour unions

16.49
At the peak of the strength of labour unions in Canada, what percentage of the labour force belonged to a union?
a) 40 percent.
b) 20 percent.
c) 5 percent.
d) 60 percent.
e) 50 percent.

16.50
Correct: e)
Difficulty: 2
Page(s): 410
Scramble range: All
Topic: Decline in labour union participation

16.50
Labour union membership in Canada has
a) declined since the 1880s.
b) declined since the 1930s.
c) declined the 1970s.
d) risen since the 1970s.
e) been roughly constant since the early 1980s.

16.51
Correct: d)
Difficulty: 2
Page(s): 410
Scramble range: All
Topic: Union participation in the 1980s

16.51
Labour union participation in Canada in the late 1980s was
a) less than 5 percent of the labour force.
b) less than 10 percent but greater than 5 percent of the labour force.
c) less than 20 percent of the labour force.
d) greater than 20 percent but less than 50 percent of the labour force.
e) greater than 50 percent of the labour force.

16.52
Correct: c)
Difficulty: 2
Page(s): 410
Scramble range: All
Topic: Union growth in the 1980s

16.52
One union that has grown in membership and strength in the 1980s is the
a) Sherwood Credit Union.
b) United Steel Workers.
c) union of government employees.
d) United Mine Workers.
e) shipbuilders' union.

16.53
Correct: d)
Difficulty: 2
Page(s): 410
Scramble range: All
Topic: Open shops

16.53
An open shop is
a) a union that accepts any members who wish to join.
b) a union that works for safer conditions on the job.
c) a business in which all workers belong to the same union.
d) an arrangement in which workers may be employed without belonging to a union.
e) a union where anyone can quit whenever they wish.

16.54
Correct: c)
Difficulty: 2
Page(s): 410
Scramble range: All
Topic: Closed shops

16.54
A closed shop is
a) a union that does not accept any members who wish to join.
b) a union that works for safer conditions on the job.
c) a business in which all workers must belong to the same union in order to remain employed.
d) an arrangement in which workers may be employed without belonging to a union.
e) a union where one cannot quit whenever one wishes to.

16.55
Correct: e)
Difficulty: 2
Page(s): 410
Scramble range: All
Topic: Rand Formula

16.55
The Rand Formula (1945) makes
a) closed shops legal.
b) closed shops illegal.
c) open shops illegal.
d) labour unions pay a special tax in order to be incorporated.
e) it compulsory for all workers to contribute to the union whether or not they belong to the union.

16.56
Correct: e)
Difficulty: 2
Page(s): 411
Scramble range: All
Topic: Unions

16.56
The largest union in Canada is the
a) Canadian Auto Workers.
b) United Steelworkers of America.
c) Teamsters.
d) United Food and Commercial Workers.
e) Canadian Union of Public Employees (CUPE).

16.57
Correct: e)
Difficulty: 2
Page(s): 411
Scramble range: All
Topic: Unions

16.57
The unions with the largest memberships in Canada are the
a) automobile worker unions.
b) Teamsters and food workers.
c) natural resources sector unions (e.g., logging unions).
d) teachers' unions.
e) public service workers' unions.

16.58
Correct: c)
Difficulty: 2
Page(s): 411
Scramble range: All
Topic: Collective bargaining

16.58
Collective bargaining means that
a) each member of the firm must bargain with the union in contract disputes.
b) only the chief executive officer of the corporation can bargain with union employees in contract disputes.
c) unions can elect representatives to bargain for the entire union in contract disputes or wage negotiations.
d) firms that agree to hire all the members of one union will receive wage concessions from the union.
e) all the firms in an industry band together and bargain collectively with all the workers.

16.59
Correct: a)
Difficulty: 2
Page(s): 411
Scramble range: All
Topic: Lockouts and strikes

16.59
The power of a union is derived from the threat of
a) strikes.
b) lobbying for stronger industrial relations boards.
c) lobbying for more costly environmental regulations.
d) lobbying for more costly safety regulations.
e) destroying the firm's production.

16.60
Correct: a)
Difficulty: 2
Page(s): 411
Scramble range: All
Topic: Lockouts and strikes

16.60
A firm can check the power of a union by the use of, or threats of the use of,
a) a lockout.
b) a strike.
c) a retraining program.
d) nothing, as there is no check on union power.
e) the threat of firing all the workers.

16.61
Correct: b)
Difficulty: 2
Page(s): 411
Scramble range: All
Topic: Lockouts and strikes

16.61
A lockout is
a) a work slowdown by unions.
b) a firm's refusal to operate a factory and employ its union employees.
c) an attempt by one labour union to displace another in a factory.
d) an abandonment of operations by a craft union.
e) a walkout from the bargaining process by the firm.

16.62
Correct: c)
Difficulty: 2
Page(s): 411
Scramble range: All
Topic: Binding arbitration

16.62
Binding arbitration is a process in which
a) guarantees of higher wages must be accepted by union members.
b) guarantees of improved working conditions must be accepted by the operators of the factory.
c) a third party mediates disputes between labour and management in order to determine wages and other working conditions.
d) limitations on union members must be relaxed or else a strike will take place.
e) the government legislates the end to a strike or lockout.

16.63
Correct: b)
Difficulty: 2
Page(s): 411
Scramble range: All
Topic: Goals of unions

16.63
All of the following are objectives of unions except
a) improving working conditions.
b) maximizing the number of employees on the job.
c) improving compensation.
d) improving retirement pay.
e) improving fringe benefits.

16.64
Correct: d)
Difficulty: 3
Page(s): 411
Scramble range: All
Topic: Union effectiveness

16.64
A union will be more effective the greater the
a) number of unskilled workers belonging to the union.
b) extent of the market.
c) import penetration in the market.
d) percentage of the workforce controlled by the union.
e) percentage of skilled workers belonging to the union.

16.65
Correct: a)
Difficulty: 3
Page(s): 411
Scramble range: All
Topic: Union effectiveness

16.65
A constraint on union effectiveness is
a) the downward-sloping nature of the labour demand curve by businesses.
b) the minimum wage law.
c) the Fair Labour Standards Practices Act.
d) increasing export competitiveness.
e) the competition of other unions.

16.66
Correct: d)
Difficulty: 3
Page(s): 411–412
Scramble range: All
Topic: Union actions

16.66
In order to increase the demand for union labour, or to make that demand more inelastic, unions do all of the following *except* support
a) increases in the minimum wage.
b) increases in import restrictions.
c) immigration restrictions.
d) decreases in demand for the firm's products.
e) increases in the marginal product of labour.

16.67
Correct: a)
Difficulty: 3
Page(s): 412
Scramble range: All
Topic: Wages in competitive labour markets

16.67
Figure 16.6 shows a labour market with a nonunion supply curve of labour and a union supply curve. The marginal revenue product of labour, both union and nonunion, is also presented in the figure. If there is no labour union, then the equilibrium wage rate will be
a) $7.
b) $6.
c) $12.
d) $10.
e) $5.

Figure 16.6

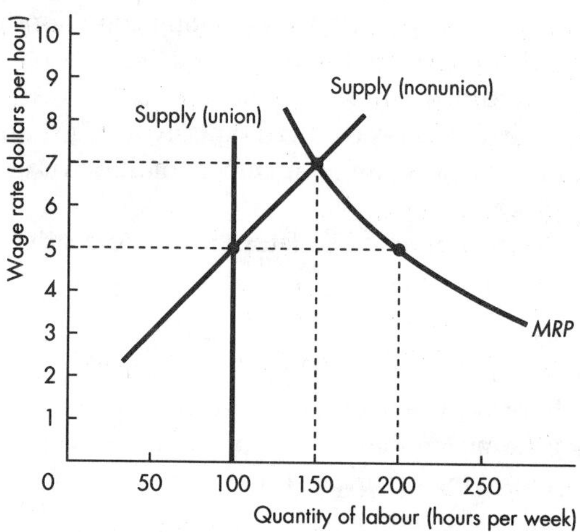

16.68
Correct: b)
Difficulty: 3
Page(s): 412
Scramble range: All
Topic: Employment in competitive labour markets

16.68
Figure 16.6 shows a labour market with a nonunion supply curve of labour and a union supply curve. The marginal revenue product of labour, both union and nonunion, is also presented in the figure. If there is no labour union, then the employment level of labour will be
a) zero, as no workers will be hired without the union.
b) 150 labour hours per day.
c) 100 labour hours per day.
d) 50 labour hours per day.
e) 200 labour hours per day.

16.69
Correct: e)
Difficulty: 3
Page(s): 412
Scramble range: All
Topic: Employment in union labour markets

16.69
Figure 16.6 shows a labour market with a nonunion supply curve of labour and a union supply curve. The marginal revenue product of labour, both union and nonunion, is also presented in the figure. If there is a restriction on employment to only union members, then employment will be
a) zero, as no workers will be hired with the union.
b) 200 labour hours per day.
c) 150 labour hours per day.
d) 50 labour hours per day.
e) 100 labour hours per day.

16.70
Correct: e)
Difficulty: 3
Page(s): 412
Scramble range: All
Topic: Wages in union labour markets

16.70
Figure 16.6 shows a labour market with a nonunion supply curve of labour and a union supply curve. The marginal revenue product of labour, both union and nonunion, is also presented in the figure. If there is a restriction on employment to only union members, then the union wage rate will be
a) $5.
b) $6.
c) $7.
d) $8.
e) greater than $8.

16.71
Correct: e)
Difficulty: 3
Page(s): 412
Scramble range: All
Topic: Non/union labour wages

16.71
Figure 16.6 shows a labour market with a nonunion supply curve of labour and a union supply curve. The marginal revenue product of labour, both union and nonunion, is also presented in the figure. If employment were not restricted to union members, how many labour hours would be supplied at the union wage rate?
a) zero hours per day.
b) 50 labour hours per day.
c) 100 labour hours per day.
d) 150 labour hours per day.
e) greater than 150 labour hours per day.

16.72
Correct: d)
Difficulty: 2
Page(s): 413
Scramble range: All
Topic: Monopsony

16.72
A monopsony is a
a) resource market in which a single seller dominates the market.
b) product market in which a single buyer dominates the market.
c) resource market in which a single seller controls the entire market.
d) resource market in which a single buyer controls the entire market.
e) product market in which a single seller controls the entire market.

16.73
Correct: c)
Difficulty: 3
Page(s): 413
Scramble range: All
Topic: Wages in competitive labour markets

16.73
Figure 16.7 gives the marginal revenue product of labour, the labour supply curve, and the marginal cost of labour curve. If this labour market were competitive, the wage rate would be
a) $4.
b) $5.
c) $6.
d) $7.
e) greater than $7.

Figure 16.7

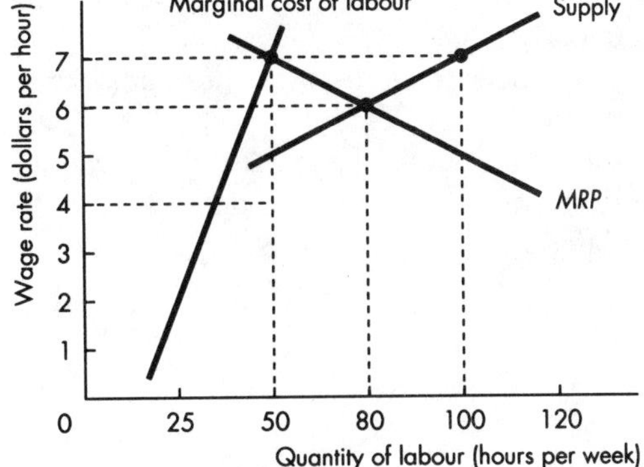

16.74
Correct: c)
Difficulty: 3
Page(s): 413
Scramble range: All
Topic: Employment in competitive labour markets

16.74
Figure 16.7 gives the marginal revenue product of labour, the labour supply curve, and the marginal cost of labour curve. If this labour market were competitive, the employment level of labour would be
a) 30 hours per week.
b) 50 hours per week.
c) 80 hours per week.
d) 100 hours per week.
e) greater than 100 hours per week.

16.75
Correct: d)
Difficulty: 4
Page(s): 413
Scramble range: All
Topic: Monopsony

16.75
Figure 16.7 gives the marginal revenue product of labour, the labour supply curve, and the marginal cost of labour curve. If this labour market were controlled by a monopsony, then wages would be
a) \$7.
b) \$6.
c) \$4.
d) \$5.
e) zero, as the market would be shut down.

16.76
Correct: b)
Difficulty: 4
Page(s): 413
Scramble range: All
Topic: Monopsony

16.76
Figure 16.7 gives the marginal revenue product of labour, the labour supply curve, and the marginal cost of labour curve. If this labour market were controlled by a monopsony, then the monopsonist would employ
a) zero, as the market would be shut down.
b) 50 labour hours per week.
c) 80 labour hours per week.
d) 100 labour hours per week.
e) greater than 100 labour hours per week.

16.77
Correct: c)
Difficulty: 4
Page(s): 413
Scramble range: All
Topic: Monopsony

16.77
Figure 16.7 gives the marginal revenue product of labour, the labour supply curve, and the marginal cost of labour curve. If this labour market were controlled by a monopsony, then the monopsonist would
a) pay a wage rate that is greater than the marginal revenue product of labour.
b) pay a wage rate exactly equal to the marginal revenue product of labour.
c) pay a wage rate that is less than the marginal revenue product of labour.
d) employ more labour hours per week than in a competitive labour market.
e) pay a wage equal to the marginal cost of labour.

16.78
Correct: a)
Difficulty: 3
Page(s): 418
Scramble range: All
Topic: Wage differentials

16.78
Differences in wages between the sexes and the races can be attributed to all of the following *except*
a) differences in attitudes toward authority.
b) discrimination.
c) differences in the degree of specialization.
d) differences in human capital.
e) differences in job choices.

16.79
Correct: c)
Difficulty: 2
Page(s): 424
Scramble range: All
Topic: Comparable worth

16.79
Advocates of comparable-worth laws believe that such laws are needed to ensure that all people
a) of the same age receive the same wage.
b) doing the same job receive the same pay.
c) doing jobs with similar characteristics should receive equal pay.
d) doing productive work will receive a "living wage."
e) receive the same wage.

16.80
Correct: d)
Difficulty: 2
Page(s). 425
Scramble range: All
Topic: Compensation alternatives

16.80
Compensation rules which are alternatives to time-related compensation include all of the following *except*
a) commissions and royalties.
b) piece rates.
c) profit-sharing.
d) sales of assets.
e) team performance rules.

16.81 (SG 16.1)
Correct: a)
Difficulty: 3
Page(s): 407
Scramble range: All
Topic: Labour markets

16.81
Which of the following is *not* a reason why the wage of skilled workers exceeds the wage of unskilled workers?
a) The market for skilled workers is more competitive than the market for unskilled labour.
b) The marginal revenue product of skilled workers is greater than that of unskilled workers.
c) The cost of training skilled workers is greater than the cost of training unskilled workers.
d) Skilled workers have acquired more human capital than unskilled workers.
e) Skilled workers are more productive than unskilled workers.

16.82 (SG 16.2)
Correct: e)
Difficulty: 3
Page(s): 407–408
Scramble range: All
Topic: Productivity

16.82
Other things remaining the same, if education costs rise substantially, we would expect to see
a) a decrease in the marginal revenue product of skilled workers.
b) a decrease in the supply of unskilled workers.
c) an increase in the wage of unskilled workers.
d) an increase in the number of skilled workers employed.
e) an increase in the wage received by skilled workers.

16.83 (SG 16.3)
Correct: d)
Difficulty: 3
Page(s): 407
Scramble range: All
Topic: Human capital

16.83
The economic value of the increase in human capital due to additional education is the
a) money cost of the additional education.
b) money cost of the additional education plus forgone earnings.
c) present value of all expected future earnings.
d) present value of all extra expected future earnings which are the result of the additional education.
e) opportunity cost of the additional education.

16.84 (SG 16.4)
Correct: a)
Difficulty: 2
Page(s): 410
Scramble range: All
Topic: Unions

16.84
A union working arrangement in which all workers must be members of the union before they can be hired by the firm is called
a) a closed shop.
b) an open shop.
c) a union shop.
d) a craft shop.
e) a Rand shop.

16.85 (SG 16.5)
Correct: a)
Difficulty: 2
Page(s): 410
Scramble range: All
Topic: Unions

16.85
A union that organizes workers with a similar skill regardless of the firm or industry that employs them is
a) a craft union.
b) an industrial union.
c) a local union.
d) a national union.
e) a skills union.

16.86 (SG 16.6)
Correct: e)
Difficulty: 3
Page(s): 411
Scramble range: All
Topic: Unions

16.86
Which of the following would unions be *least* likely to support?
a) An increase in the legal minimum wage.
b) Immigration restrictions.
c) Increasing the marginal product of their workers.
d) Increasing demand for the goods their workers produce.
e) Reducing barriers to imports.

16.87 (SG 16.8)
Correct: a)
Difficulty: 4
Page(s): 412–413
Scramble range: All
Topic: Monopsony

16.87
When compared to a competitive labour market with the same marginal revenue product and labour supply curves, a monopsonist labour market will pay a
a) lower wage and employ fewer workers.
b) lower wage and employ more workers.
c) higher wage and employ fewer workers.
d) higher wage and employ more workers.
e) lower wage and employ the same amount of workers.

16.88 (SG 16.9)
Correct: b)
Difficulty: 3
Page(s): 413
Scramble range: All
Topic: Monopsony

16.88
Figure 16.8 illustrates a monopsonist in the labour market (*MCL* = marginal cost of labour). The profit-maximizing wage rate and quantity of labour hired will be
a) \$4 per hour and 800 hours of labour.
b) \$4 per hour and 400 hours of labour.
c) \$7 per hour and 600 hours of labour.
d) \$9 per hour and 400 hours of labour.
e) \$4 per hour and 600 hours of labour.

Figure 16.8

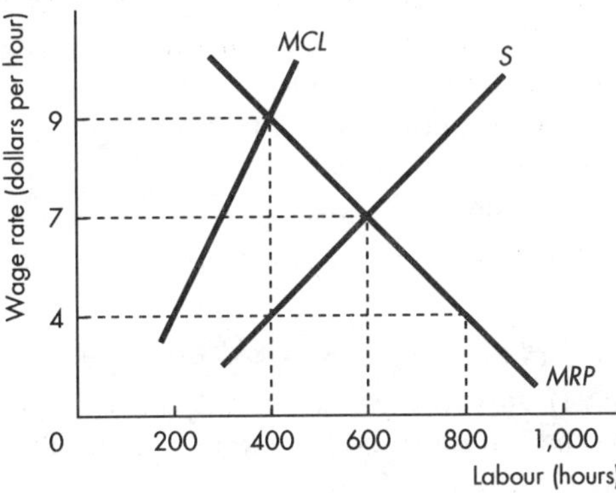

16.89 (SG 16.10)
Correct: c)
Difficulty: 3
Page(s): 413
Scramble range: All
Topic: Labour markets

16.89
If the labour market illustrated in Figure 16.8 became competitive, the equilibrium wage rate and quantity of labour hired will be

a) $4 per hour and 800 hours of labour.
b) $4 per hour and 400 hours of labour.
c) $7 per hour and 600 hours of labour.
d) $9 per hour and 400 hours of labour.
e) $4 per hour and 600 hours of labour.

16.90 (SG 16.13)
Correct: d)
Difficulty: 5
Page(s): 424
Scramble range: All
Topic: Comparable growth

16.90
Consider two types of workers: *A* and *B*. In competitive labour markets, the wage paid to type *A* workers is substantially higher than the wage paid to type *B* workers. Suppose that a comparable-worth law is enacted and type *A* and *B* workers are judged to be comparable. Furthermore, assume that to equalize wages, the wage rate for type *B* workers rises and the wage rate for type *A* workers falls. We can conclude that

a) employment of type *A* workers will rise, while employment of type *B* workers will fall.
b) employment of type *A* workers will fall, while employment of type *B* workers will rise.
c) employment of both types of workers will rise.
d) employment of both types of workers will fall.
e) we cannot tell the impact on employment without knowing the supply response.

16.91 (SG 16.14)
Correct: c)
Difficulty: 2
Page(s): 425
Scramble range: All
Topic: Compensation rules

16.91
Frank is a barber who gets paid $5 for every haircut he gives. This compensation rule is an example of

a) a commission.
b) a time rate.
c) a piece rate.
d) profit-sharing.
e) team performance compensation.

16.92 (SG 16.16)
Correct: a)
Difficulty: 2
Page(s): 425
Scramble range: All
Topic: Compensation rules

16.92
The model we use to study compensation rules is called the
a) principal–agent model.
b) efficient compensation model.
c) performance compensation model.
d) monitoring cost model.
e) union model.

16.93
Correct: e)
Difficulty: 3
Page(s): 409
Scramble range: All
Topic: Labour markets

16.93
Which of the following is a reason for the wage of skilled workers to exceed the wage of unskilled workers?
a) The market for skilled workers is more discriminatory than the market for unskilled labour.
b) The average revenue product of skilled workers is greater than that of unskilled workers.
c) The cost of training skilled workers is less than the cost of training unskilled workers.
d) Skilled workers have better unions than unskilled workers.
e) Skilled workers have acquired more human capital than unskilled workers.

16.94
Correct: c)
Difficulty: 3
Page(s): 409
Scramble range: All
Topic: Productivity

16.94
Other things remaining the same, if education costs decrease substantially, we would expect to see
a) an increase in the marginal revenue product of skilled workers.
b) an increase in the supply of unskilled workers.
c) a decrease in the wage received by skilled workers.
d) a decrease in the number of skilled workers employed.
e) a decrease in the wage of unskilled workers.

16.95
Correct: d)
Difficulty: 3
Page(s): 409
Scramble range: All
Topic: Human capital

16.95
The economic value of the increase in human capital due to additional education is the
a) real money cost of the marginal education.
b) money cost of the forgone earnings.
c) present value of current income.
d) present value of all extra expected future earnings which are the result of the additional education.
e) value of the time spent receiving the education.

16.96
Correct: a)
Difficulty: 2
Page(s): 410
Scramble range: All
Topic: Unions

16.96
A union working arrangement in which all workers do not have to be members of the union before they can be hired by the firm is called
a) an open shop.
b) a closed shop.
c) a union shop.
d) a craft shop.
e) a Rand shop.

16.97
Correct: e)
Difficulty: 2
Page(s): 410
Scramble range: All
Topic: Unions

16.97
A union that organizes workers with different skills regardless of the firm or industry that employs them, could be
a) a guild.
b) a craft union.
c) a fragmented union.
d) a skills union.
e) an industrial union.

16.98
Correct: a)
Difficulty: 3
Page(s): 411
Scramble range: All
Topic: Unions

16.98
Which of the following would unions be most likely to support?
a) Increased barriers to imports.
b) Eased immigration restrictions.
c) A decrease in the legal minimum wage.
d) Decreasing demand for the goods their workers produce.
e) Decreasing the marginal product of its workers.

16.99
Correct: d)
Difficulty: 3
Page(s): 412–413
Scramble range: All
Topic: Monopsony

16.99
When compared to a monopsonist with the same marginal revenue product and labour supply curves, a perfectly competitive labour market will pay a
a) lower wage and employ fewer workers.
b) lower wage and employ more workers.
c) higher wage and employ fewer workers.
d) higher wage and employ more workers.
e) higher wage and employ the same amount of workers.

16.100
Correct: b)
Difficulty: 4
Page(s): 424
Scramble range: All
Topic: Comparable worth

16.100
Consider two types of workers: *A* and *B*. In competitive labour markets the wage paid to type *A* workers is substantially higher than the wage paid to type *B* workers. Suppose that a comparable-worth law is enacted and type *A* and *B* workers are judged to be comparable. Furthermore, assume that to equalize wages, the wage rate for type *B* workers rises and the wage rate for type *A* workers falls. We can conclude that
a) workers will be attracted to employment type *A*.
b) workers will be attracted to employment type *B*.
c) it will have no impact on the relative attractiveness of the employment types.
d) it will have the same impact on both types of employment.
e) we cannot tell the employment response without knowing the demand responses.

16.101
Correct: b)
Difficulty: 3
Page(s): 425
Scramble range: All
Topic: Compensation rules

16.101
Bill is a butcher who gets paid $20 for every hour he works. This compensation rule is an example of
a) a commission.
b) a time rate.
c) a piece rate.
d) profit-sharing.
e) team performance compensation.

16.102
Correct: a)
Difficulty: 5
Page(s): 410–424
Scramble range: All
Topic: Unions, monoposony

16.102
Select the best statement.
a) If an industry has either a monopoly union or a monopsony firm, then in both cases there is a similar effect on employment.
b) If an industry has either a monopoly union or a monoposony firm, then it has the same effect on the workers and the firm.
c) In a industry with a monoposony, the introduction of a union always leads to an improvement in employment.
d) With the introduction of a union, all workers in an industry gain.
e) With the introduction of pay equity, all workers in an industry gain.

16.103
Correct: e)
Difficulty: 4
Page(s): 416
Scramble range: All
Topic: Monopsony/ minimum wages

16.103
Consider Figure 16.8. (*MCL* = marginal cost of labour.) Suppose this industry is initially in a monopsony situation and then the government introduces a minimum wage of $8 per hour.
a) Then, wages will rise, but employment will fall.
b) Then, wages will rise, but employment will stay the same.
c) Then, wages will rise to $8 per hour, and employment will rise to 800 hours.
d) Then, wages will rise to $8 per hour, and employment will rise to 600 hours.
e) Then, wages will rise to $8 per hour, and employment will rise to somewhere between 400 and 600 hours.

16.104
Correct: e)
Difficulty: 4
Page(s): 419
Scramble range: All
Topic: Discrimination

16.104
Consider a legal market where men and women have exactly equal levels of productivity and, if there was no discrimination, they would receive the same wages and there would be an equal number of female and male lawyers. However, due to prejudice, customers in this market are not as willing to pay as much for the legal advice of female lawyers. As a result, compared to the nondiscrimination outcome,
a) the wages of female lawyers will be lower than that of male lawyers, and there will be more female lawyers than male lawyers.
b) the wages of female lawyers will be the same as those of male lawyers, but there will be less female lawyers than male lawyers.
c) the wages of female lawyers will be less than those of male lawyers, but there will be as many female lawyers as male lawyers.
d) there will be as many female lawyers as male lawyers, and they will receive the same wage rate.
e) there will be less female lawyers than male lawyers, and they will receive a lower wage.

16.105
Correct: c)
Difficulty: 2
Page(s): 425
Scramble range: All
Topic: Principal

16.105
In economic terms, a principal is
a) the person in charge of a school.
b) the person hired by an agent to perform various tasks.
c) an employer who sets a compensation rule to motivate an agent.
d) an inducement to an agent to behave in a particular way.
e) the observation of an agent's actions.

16.106
Correct: a)
Difficulty: 4
Page(s): 425–426
Scramble range: All
Topic: Optimal compensation

16.106
A principal must design an optimal compensation scheme because
a) it is difficult to monitor an agent's effort.
b) an agent will always cheat you.
c) an agent is always lazy.
d) it is difficult to monitor an agent's skills.
e) a time payment scheme pays too little.

16.107 (SG 16.19)
Correct: e)
Difficulty: 3
Page(s): 427
Scramble range: None
Topic: Compensation rule

16.107
Which of the following is a characteristic of an efficient compensation rule?
a) The rule delivers a maximum efficient profit for the principal.
b) The rule minimizes risk for the agent.
c) The rule minimizes effort for the agent.
d) The rule is acceptable to the agent.
e) Both a) and d).

16.108
Correct: d)
Difficulty: 5
Page(s): 427–430
Scramble range: All
Topic: Compensation schemes

16.108
Ali is about to set up his own firm, producing and selling a new product he has invented, the Magic Hairgrowing Lotion. Ali is about to hire several salespersons to sell his product door-to-door around the country. Ali has asked you for advice on the compensation scheme he should employ for his salespersons. Your advice is that
a) the best thing to do is pay them by the hour and spend time monitoring them.
b) the best thing is to pay them with a piece rate equal to 100 percent of the price of the lotion.
c) the best thing is to pay them with a rank-order scheme where the best salesperson receives a huge bonus and the rest receive nothing.
d) the best thing is to pay them a base amount, plus a piece rate less than 100 percent — the actual amounts dependent upon the value of shirking and the return to the principal.
e) the best thing is to give each agent a percentage of the profits of the company based on their total sales and then to monitor their effort.

16.109
Correct: b)
Difficulty: 4
Page(s): 429
Scramble range: All
Topic: Rank–tournament rule

16.109
A rank-tournament compensation rule is one in which
a) the payment to the principal depends on his or her rank in the tournament.
b) the payment to the agent depends on his or her rank in the tournament.
c) the principal monitors the agent and pays him or her based on his or her observed effort level.
d) the agent receives a fixed percentage of his or her total sales.
e) the principal maximizes profits by forcing the agent to compete with other agents.

Chapter 17 Capital and Natural Resource Markets

17.1
Correct: d)
Difficulty: 2
Page(s): 439
Scramble range: All
Topic: Assets

17.1
An asset is
a) the value of what is owed to a household by borrowers.
b) anything of value that a firm owes to the state or local government.
c) anything of value that the government has paid to a household or firm.
d) anything of value that a household, firm, or government owns.
e) any physical thing, such as a building.

17.2
Correct: d)
Difficulty: 2
Page(s): 439
Scramble range: All
Topic: Liability

17.2
A liability is
a) the value of what is owed to a household by borrowers.
b) anything of value that a firm owes to the state or local government.
c) anything of value that the government has paid to a household or firm.
d) anything of value that a household, firm, or government owes.
e) a claim against another household or business.

17.3
Correct: d)
Difficulty: 1
Page(s): 439
Scramble range: All
Topic: Balance sheet

17.3
A balance sheet is a
a) list of assets.
b) list of liabilities.
c) list of net assets and net liabilities.
d) list of total assets and total liabilities.
e) measurement of net worth.

17.4
Correct: b)
Difficulty: 2
Page(s): 439
Scramble range: All
Topic: Net worth

17.4
The net worth or wealth of a household or firm is
a) the sum of their assets and liabilities.
b) the difference between the assets and liabilities of a firm, household, or government.
c) the total physical stock of capital in the possession of a firm.
d) the total tax payments owed to the government by firms and households.
e) the total physical and financial assets owned by the firm.

17.5
Correct: e)
Difficulty: 2
Page(s): 439
Scramble range: All
Topic: Types of assets

17.5
Assets are of two types. They are
a) real assets and artificial assets.
b) productive assets and nonproductive assets.
c) real assets and capital assets.
d) household assets and firm assets.
e) real assets and financial assets.

17.6
Correct: c)
Difficulty: 2
Page(s): 439
Scramble range: All
Topic: Financial assets

17.6
Financial assets include
a) office buildings.
b) banks and savings and loans.
c) claims against another firm, household, or government.
d) statements of account.
e) inventories.

17.7
Correct: c)
Difficulty: 2
Page(s): 439
Scramble range: All
Topic: Net financial assets

17.7
The difference between financial assets of a firm and the financial liabilities of a firm is the
a) total value of the firm.
b) net present value of the firm.
c) net financial assets of the firm.
d) total indebtedness of the firm.
e) net worth of the firm.

17.8
Correct: c)
Difficulty: 2
Page(s): 439
Scramble range: All
Topic: Real assets

17.8
Real assets include all of the following *except*
a) buildings.
b) inventories.
c) bank balances.
d) machine capital.
e) consumer durables.

17.9
Correct: a)
Difficulty: 2
Page(s): 439–440
Scramble range: All
Topic: Capital

17.9
Capital is
a) the real assets of a firm, household, or government.
b) the financial assets of a firm, household, or government.
c) the real assets of a foreign government lent to Canada.
d) the present discounted value of the liquidity of a household, firm, or government.
e) the net worth of a firm.

17.10
Correct: c)
Difficulty: 2
Page(s): 440
Scramble range: All
Topic: Net worth

17.10
Capital plus net financial assets equals the
a) net liabilities of a firm.
b) net assets of a firm.
c) net worth of a firm.
d) total present value of the firm.
e) profits of a firm.

17.11
Correct: b)
Difficulty: 2
Page(s): 440
Scramble range: All
Topic: Stock markets

17.11
A stock variable or quantity is
a) one that is measured over time.
b) one that is measured for a particular period of time.
c) one that is measured using the interest rate as a discounting figure.
d) one that is measured in different currencies.
e) one sold on the New York Stock Exchange or the Toronto Stock Exchange.

17.12
Correct: e)
Difficulty: 3
Page(s): 440
Scramble range: All
Topic: Stock markets

17.12
An example of a stock variable is
a) the gross national product of Canada.
b) the income of General Motors.
c) your income.
d) the value of a day's business on the Toronto Stock Exchange.
e) the capital of a firm.

17.13
Correct: a)
Difficulty: 2
Page(s): 440
Scramble range: All
Topic: Flow variables

17.13
A flow variable is one that is
a) measured over time.
b) measured for a particular period of time.
c) measured using the interest rate as a discounting figure.
d) measured in different currencies.
e) sold on the New York Stock Exchange or the Toronto Stock Exchange.

17.14
Correct: a)
Difficulty: 3
Page(s): 440
Scramble range: All
Topic: Flow variables

17.14
An example of a flow variable is
a) your income.
b) the number of cars on the highway.
c) the number of students in your economics class.
d) the price of your economics textbook.
e) the capital of a firm.

17.15
Correct: a)
Difficulty: 3
Page(s): 440
Scramble range: a)–d)
Topic: Investment as a flow

17.15
Investment is
a) a flow variable since it adds to the capital stock.
b) a stock variable since it adds to the capital stock.
c) a flow variable since it adds to the capital flows.
d) a stock variable since it adds to the capital flows.
e) none of the above.

17.16
Correct: b)
Difficulty: 2
Page(s): 440
Scramble range: All
Topic: Depreciation

17.16
Depreciation is the
a) increase in the value of the capital stock over time.
b) decrease in the value of the capital stock over time.
c) increase in the value of the capital flows over time.
d) decrease in the value of the capital flows over time.
e) decrease in the value of investment over time.

17.17
Correct: d)
Difficulty: 2
Page(s): 440
Scramble range: All
Topic: Depreciation

17.17
Anything that lowers the value of the capital stock over time is
a) a net loss to the firm.
b) a tax liability of the firm.
c) destructive of net value.
d) depreciation.
e) investment.

17.18
Correct: c)
Difficulty: 3
Page(s): 440
Scramble range: All
Topic: Gross investment

17.18
Gross investment is
a) investment in assets that produce goods of no redeeming social value.
b) investment in assets that produce goods for export only.
c) investment in new capital equipment regardless of the type of products produced by the capital.
d) always greater than depreciation.
e) net investment minus depreciation.

17.19
Correct: b)
Difficulty: 2
Page(s): 440
Scramble range: All
Topic: Net investment

17.19
Net investment is
a) total gross investment times depreciation of assets.
b) total gross investment minus depreciation.
c) total gross investment plus depreciation.
d) total gross investment as a percentage of depreciation.
e) investment in new capital equipment regardless of the type of products produced by the capital.

17.20
Correct: e)
Difficulty: 2
Page(s): 440
Scramble range: All
Topic: Capital accumulation

17.20
Capital accumulates in an economy because individuals
a) spend money on consumption.
b) work extra hard.
c) borrow money.
d) pay taxes to the government.
e) save money.

17.21
Correct: a)
Difficulty: 1
Page(s): 440
Scramble range: All
Topic: Saving

17.21
Saving is
a) income minus consumption expenditures.
b) consumption minus investment expenditures.
c) income minus tax payments.
d) taxes plus consumption expenditures.
e) portfolio choice.

17.22
Correct: e)
Difficulty: 3
Page(s): 440
Scramble range: All
Topic: Household net wealth

17.22
A household's net wealth is equal to the
a) flow of saving.
b) stock of saving accumulated over time.
c) stock of saving accumulated over time minus inheritance.
d) stock of saving accumulated over time plus inheritance minus tax payments.
e) stock of saving accumulated over time plus inheritance.

17.23
Correct: a)
Difficulty: 2
Page(s): 440
Scramble range: All
Topic: Portfolio choices

17.23
A household's choice of how much to hold in assets and how much to owe in liabilities is called a(n)
a) portfolio choice.
b) autonomous choice.
c) exogenous choice.
d) induced choice.
e) investment.

17.24
Correct: b)
Difficulty: 3
Page(s): 442
Scramble range: All
Topic: Capital markets

17.24
Capital markets are markets in which
a) agricultural goods are exchanged.
b) saving is directed into investment.
c) saving is directed into consumption.
d) investment is directed into saving.
e) firms buy capital goods such as buildings or equipment.

17.25
Correct: d)
Difficulty: 3
Page(s): 442
Scramble range: All
Topic: Investment

17.25
Investment takes place in all of the following ways *except*
a) households buying capital.
b) firms buying capital financed by selling stocks or bonds.
c) firms buying capital financed by loans.
d) households buying consumer nondurables.
e) households buying consumer durables.

17.26
Correct: a)
Difficulty: 3
Page(s): 442
Scramble range: All
Topic: Uses of savings

17.26
Households can employ savings in all of the following ways *except*
a) buying consumer nondurables.
b) buying firms.
c) buying stocks and bonds.
d) placing deposits in banks.
e) buying consumer durables.

17.27
Correct: c)
Difficulty: 2
Page(s): 442
Scramble range: All
Topic: Financial intermediaries

17.27
Firms that take deposits, make loans, and buy securities are called
a) insurance companies.
b) government agencies.
c) financial intermediaries.
d) financial planning institutions.
e) banks.

17.28
Correct: e)
Difficulty: 4
Page(s): 443
Scramble range: All
Topic: Household net worth

17.28
It is frequently noted in the newspapers that Canadians owe billions of dollars in financial liabilities. For example, in 1988 households had total financial liabilities of $300 billion. Select the best statement.
a) Things look bad for Canadians because of these high levels of debt.
b) This is good for Canada, as all the people who own the households' liabilities will be wealthy.
c) The high levels of debt are irrelevant; what matters is the amount of net financial worth for households.
d) This is bad for Canada; these households will be in big trouble if they lose their jobs as they will be unable to pay off their debts.
e) This is neither good nor bad; it depends on the net worth of the households, which includes financial assets and liabilities and real assets, and this net worth is very high.

17.29
Correct: c)
Difficulty: 2
Page(s): 442
Scramble range: All
Topic: Chartered banks

17.29
Chartered banks
a) take out loans.
b) make deposits in credit unions.
c) make loans and accept deposits.
d) can neither borrow or lend money on their own.
e) deal mainly with households in the form of mortgages.

17.30
Correct: e)
Difficulty: 3
Page(s): 442
Scramble range: All
Topic: Investment banks

17.30
Trust companies
a) can invest money in chartered banks.
b) can help firms raise money to buy new capital.
c) can help firms raise money by selling old capital.
d) are prohibited by law from helping firms raise capital.
e) mainly loan to households for mortgages.

17.31
Correct: b)
Difficulty: 3
Page(s): 442
Scramble range: All
Topic: Other financial intermediaries

17.31
Insurance companies
a) are prohibited from loaning money to the public, but not to the government.
b) are another form of financial intermediary.
c) are prohibited from loaning money to the government, but not to the public.
d) are not considered to be related to the financial sector of the economy because of the many restrictions placed on their operations by the government.
e) mainly loan to households for mortgages.

17.32
Correct: c)
Difficulty: 2
Page(s): 443
Scramble range: All
Topic: Stock markets

17.32
A market in which the equities of firms are traded is called a
a) fiduciary market.
b) nonpecuniary market.
c) stock market.
d) flow market.
e) bond market.

17.33
Correct: e)
Difficulty: 2
Page(s): 443
Scramble range: All
Topic: Direct ownership of capital

17.33
The riskiest portfolio choice for a household is the
a) financial futures market.
b) foreign exchange market.
c) stock market.
d) government bond market.
e) direct ownership of capital in one firm.

17.34
Correct: b)
Difficulty: 2
Page(s): 443
Scramble range: All
Topic: Raising money

17.34
The government raises money by
a) buying bonds.
b) selling bonds.
c) selling stocks.
d) buying stocks.
e) borrowing directly from banks and trust companies.

17.35
Correct: c)
Difficulty: 2
Page(s): 445
Scramble range: All
Topic: Toronto Stock Exchange

17.35
On an average day in 1987, the daily volume of stocks traded on the Toronto Stock Exchange was
a) 2 million shares.
b) 230 million shares.
c) 23 million shares.
d) 2.3 billion shares.
e) 64 million shares.

17.36
Correct: b)
Difficulty: 4
Page(s): 445
Scramble range: All
Topic: Profit maximization

17.36
The profit-maximizing firm will increase its capital stock until
a) there is no more money remaining in the capital account.
b) the additional revenue generated from an additional unit of capital is equal to the additional cost of that unit of capital.
c) the total revenue generated from the capital stock is just equal to the total cost of acquiring that capital.
d) the present value of the total revenue generated from the capital is maximized.
e) the present value of the total cost generated from the capital is minimized.

17.37
Correct: a)
Difficulty: 2
Page(s): 445
Scramble range: All
Topic: Present value

17.37
A present value
a) converts a stream of future payments into a dollar value in the present.
b) expresses the total value of the capital stock in nominal dollars, as opposed to real dollars.
c) expresses the total value of the capital stock in real dollars, as opposed to nominal dollars.
d) measures the value of the capital stock today minus what it would cost to replace it at a given time in the future.
e) measures the current net worth of a firm.

17.38
Correct: c)
Difficulty: 3
Page(s): 446
Scramble range: All
Topic: Net worth

17.38
The net worth of a firm is the
a) firm's accounting profit.
b) firm's economic profit.
c) present value of the firm's expected future profit.
d) present value of the firm's assets.
e) sum of the firm's expected future profit.

17.39
Correct: e)
Difficulty: 3
Page(s): 447
Scramble range: All
Topic: Demand for capital

17.39
The demand for capital will depend on
a) the supply of capital.
b) the inflow of funds from abroad.
c) net investment.
d) the capital stock minus the capital flows.
e) the interest rate.

17.40
Correct: a)
Difficulty: 3
Page(s): 447
Scramble range: All
Topic: Demand for capital

17.40
The demand for capital will depend on the interest rate since
a) the net present value of the marginal revenue product of the capital depends on the interest rate.
b) the Bank of Canada has control over the interest rate.
c) the supply of capital depends on the interest rate.
d) interest rates determine the productivity of capital.
e) the higher the interest rate, the higher the demand for capital.

17.41
Correct: b)
Difficulty: 2
Page(s): 447
Scramble range: All
Topic: Demand for capital

17.41
A firm's demand curve for capital expresses the relationship between
a) the price level and the productivity of capital.
b) the interest rate and the quantity of capital demanded.
c) the net present value of the interest rate and the productivity of capital.
d) the net present value of the interest rate and the productivity of capital, discounted over the lifetime of the capital.
e) the productivity of capital and the net present value of the capital.

17.42
Correct: d)
Difficulty: 3
Page(s): 448
Scramble range: All
Topic: Change in demand for capital

17.42
Changes in the demand for capital can be caused by changes in
a) the supply of capital.
b) the interest rate.
c) the net present value of the firm.
d) the productivity of capital.
e) current household income.

17.43
Correct: a)
Difficulty: 3
Page(s): 448
Scramble range: All
Topic: Change in demand for capital

17.43
Advances in the technology of desktop computers
a) has led to a decrease in demand for typewriters.
b) has led to an increase in demand for typewriters.
c) has led to a decrease in supply of this type of capital.
d) has caused an increase in the interest rate on capital.
e) has lowered the marginal productivity of this type of capital.

17.44
Correct: c)
Difficulty: 2
Page(s): 447–448
Scramble range: All
Topic: Marginal revenue product of capital

17.44
The marginal revenue product of capital
a) increases as more and more capital is employed.
b) is constant as the capital stock expands.
c) decreases as the capital stock expands.
d) is not related to the demand for capital.
e) is related to the supply of labour.

17.45
Correct: d)
Difficulty: 3
Page(s): 448
Scramble range: All
Topic: Slope of demand curve for capital

17.45
If the marginal revenue product of capital decreases as more capital is employed, then the
a) supply of capital will be upward sloping.
b) supply of capital will be downward sloping.
c) demand for capital will be horizontal.
d) demand for capital will be downward sloping.
e) demand for capital will be upward sloping.

17.46
Correct: e)
Difficulty: 4
Page(s): 448
Scramble range: All
Topic: Optimal employment of capital

17.46
Capital will be demanded up to the point at which
a) the price of the capital equals the cost of the capital to the firm.
b) the interest rate is equal to the present value of the future marginal revenue products generated by the capital.
c) the interest rate is equal to the opportunity cost of the capital.
d) the last unit of capital no longer generates a positive marginal revenue product.
e) the present value of the future marginal revenue products generated by the capital equals the price of the capital.

17.47
Correct: d)
Difficulty: 2
Page(s): 449
Scramble range: All
Topic: The supply of capital

17.47
The supply of capital depends on the
a) productivity of the capital.
b) the marginal revenue product generated by that capital.
c) the present value of the future marginal revenue products generated by the capital.
d) the savings decisions of households.
e) the savings decisions of governments.

17.48
Correct: a)
Difficulty: 2
Page(s): 449
Scramble range: All
Topic: The supply of capital

17.48
Household saving is determined by all of the following *except*
a) the productivity of household capital.
b) the current household income.
c) the expected future income of the household.
d) the interest rate.
e) the household's stage in the life-cycle.

17.49
Correct: b)
Difficulty: 3
Page(s): 449
Scramble range: All
Topic: Consumption smoothing

17.49
By "consumption smoothing" economists mean
a) consumption spending changes little over time.
b) when income is relatively high the household will save, and when income is relatively low the household will dissave.
c) when the number of household members increases, consumption will increase.
d) when the number of household members increases, saving will increase and consumption will decrease.
e) when income is relatively high the household will spend lots and save little, and when income is relatively low the household will spend little and save lots.

17.50
Correct: b)
Difficulty: 3
Page(s): 449
Scramble range: All
Topic: Substitution effect on saving

17.50
The substitution effect on saving means
a) saving decreases as interest rates rise.
b) as the interest rate rises, the opportunity cost of consumption increases, leading to increased saving.
c) as the interest rate rises, the opportunity cost of consumption decreases, leading to decreased saving.
d) as interest rates rise, households feel wealthier and therefore save more.
e) as interest rates rise, households feel wealthier and therefore save less.

17.51
Correct: d)
Difficulty: 3
Page(s): 449
Scramble range: All
Topic: Income effect on saving

17.51
The income effect on saving means
a) saving decreases as income rise.
b) as the interest rate rises, the opportunity cost of consumption increases, leading to increased saving.
c) as the interest rate rises, the opportunity cost of consumption decreases, leading to decreased saving.
d) as interest rates rise, households feel wealthier and therefore save more.
e) as interest rates rise, households feel wealthier and therefore save less.

17.52
Correct: c)
Difficulty: 3
Page(s): 449–450
Scramble range: All
Topic: Supply of capital

17.52
The supply curve of capital
a) depends on the marginal productivity of the capital.
b) depends on the opportunity cost of labour as well as capital.
c) is the total stock of accumulated savings of households.
d) is the total value of the accumulated consumption expenditures of households.
e) is the net worth of households.

17.53
Correct: c)
Difficulty: 3
Page(s): 450
Scramble range: All
Topic: Change in supply of capital

17.53
The supply of capital may change with changes in all of the following *except* the
a) age distribution of the population.
b) population.
c) productivity of capital.
d) average income level.
e) proportion of young people in the population.

17.54
Correct: a)
Difficulty: 2
Page(s): 450
Scramble range: All
Topic: Change in supply of capital

17.54
If the average income level increases,
a) this will increase the supply of capital.
b) the capital supply will remain constant.
c) the capital supply will decrease.
d) the demand for capital will decrease.
e) the demand for capital will increase.

17.55
Correct: b)
Difficulty: 3
Page(s): 450
Scramble range: All
Topic: Portfolio choices

17.55
Portfolio choices of households depend on the
a) average age of the members of the household.
b) relative degrees of risk for the various financial assets.
c) relative prices of goods that they may consume.
d) supply of capital.
e) average level of the interest rate.

17.56
Correct: b)
Difficulty: 3
Page(s): 450
Scramble range: All
Topic: Portfolio choices

17.56
Portfolio choices of households depend on the
a) average age of the members of the household.
b) relative interest rates for the various financial assets.
c) relative prices of goods that they may consume.
d) supply of capital.
e) average level of risk.

17.57
Correct: d)
Difficulty: 2
Page(s): 450
Scramble range: All
Topic: Portfolio choices

17.57
If the interest rates on equities and bonds are equal, then, other things being equal, households will
a) invest in bonds.
b) invest in equities.
c) invest in neither since neither gives an advantage.
d) be indifferent to the two types of portfolio choices.
e) invest in equities because it is more exciting.

17.58
Correct: e)
Difficulty: 3
Page(s): 450
Scramble range: All
Topic: Bond price/interest rate

17.58
If a bond earns a guaranteed dollar yield, then
a) the interest rate on that bond is fixed as well.
b) the interest rate has nothing to do with the bond yield.
c) you cannot lose money on the bond, although you may gain an extra yield.
d) it is not a risky portfolio choice.
e) the market price of the bond may change, thereby changing the interest rate earned by the bond.

17.59
Correct: a)
Difficulty: 3
Page(s): 450
Scramble range: All
Topic: Return on share of stock

17.59
A stock yield may vary because of a change in the
a) market price of the share of the stock.
b) interest rate.
c) profitability of the firm that issues the stock.
d) stock market index.
e) yield on bonds.

17.60
Correct: a)
Difficulty: 3
Page(s): 450
Scramble range: All
Topic: Return on share of stock

17.60
A stock yield may vary because of
a) a change in the dividend paid on the stock.
b) an increase in the interest rate.
c) a reduction in the profitability of the firm that issues the stock.
d) a change in the price level.
e) a change in the yield on bonds.

17.61
Correct: c)
Difficulty: 3
Page(s): 451
Scramble range: All
Topic: Interest rates

17.61
Actual interest rates will be distributed around the average market equilibrium interest rate due to
a) imperfect information.
b) transactions costs.
c) differences in risk.
d) differences in attitudes toward risk.
e) difference in the markets firms sell their products in.

17.62
Correct: e)
Difficulty: 2
Page(s): 453
Scramble range: All
Topic: Rational expectations

17.62
A rational expectation is
a) the expectation that the future will be similar to the present.
b) the expectation that the future will be quite different than the present.
c) the cost-minimizing forecast.
d) that values will continue to increase at the rate of inflation.
e) the best forecast based on all available and relevant information.

17.63
Correct: b)
Difficulty: 3
Page(s): 453
Scramble range: All
Topic: Price–earnings ratio

17.63
A price–earnings ratio measures
a) the stock price divided by the average rate of industry-wide profit in the previous year.
b) the stock price divided by the previous year's profit per share.
c) the expected future price divided by the most recent dividend paid on the stock.
d) the average of the stock price and other stock prices representing the same industry, divided by the most recent dividend paid on the stock.
e) the value of a firm.

17.64
Correct: d)
Difficulty: 3
Page(s): 453
Scramble range: All
Topic: Share prices

17.64
The share price of a stock is determined by the
a) profit per share in the previous period.
b) profit per share in the current period.
c) expected future profit of the firm.
d) present value of the expected future profit of the firm.
e) interest rate.

17.65
Correct: c)
Difficulty: 4
Page(s): 453
Scramble range: All
Topic: Stock markets

17.65
Large volume in the stock market is an indication of
a) trouble.
b) prosperity.
c) large amounts of disagreements concerning the expected future profit of the firms represented in the exchange.
d) a growing economy.
e) changing expectations.

17.66
Correct: d)
Difficulty: 3
Page(s): 454
Scramble range: All
Topic: Mergers and takeovers

17.66
A takeover occurs when
a) the market share of one firm begins to exceed that of its rival.
b) the share price of the stock of one firm begins to exceed the share price of its rival firm.
c) the government rescues a firm that has fallen into receivership.
d) one firm purchases a majority of the stock of another firm.
e) the price of a firm rises.

17.67
Correct: c)
Difficulty: 2
Page(s): 454
Scramble range: All
Topic: Mergers and takeovers

17.67
The combining of the assets of two firms to form a single new firm is called
a) formation of a trust.
b) collusion.
c) a merger.
d) formation of a cartel.
e) a takeover.

17.68
Correct: a)
Difficulty: 3
Page(s): 454
Scramble range: All
Topic: Mergers and takeovers

17.68
When the stock market value of a firm is lower than the present value of the expected future profit,
a) mergers or takeovers are likely to occur.
b) the firm will make positive profits.
c) the firm will need to recapitalize.
d) the firm will recall its previous dividend.
e) its stock market value will fall.

17.69
Correct: b)
Difficulty: 2
Page(s): 455
Scramble range: All
Topic: Natural resources

17.69
Natural resources that deplete as they are used
a) should not be used.
b) are exhaustible natural resources.
c) should be used for only highly valued uses.
d) should be conserved for future generations.
e) are nonexhaustible natural resources.

17.70
Correct: e)
Difficulty: 3
Page(s): 455
Scramble range: All
Topic: Exhaustible resources

17.70
Examples of exhaustible resources include all of the following *except*
a) oil.
b) coal.
c) potash.
d) natural gas.
e) timber.

17.71
Correct: e)
Difficulty: 3
Page(s): 455
Scramble range: All
Topic: Nonexhaustible resources

17.71
Examples of nonexhaustible resources include all of the following *except*
a) rivers.
b) cattle.
c) lakes.
d) wheat.
e) coal.

17.72
Correct: c)
Difficulty: 3
Page(s): 455
Scramble range: All
Topic: Equilibrium in natural resource markets

17.72
Equilibrium occurs in the market for a stock of a natural resource when
a) the price of the resource equals the interest rate.
b) the increase in the price of the resource equals the expected increase in the interest rate.
c) the expected increase in the price of the resource over time is equal to the interest rate.
d) the stock of the natural resource is eventually depleted.
e) the price today equals the expected future price.

17.73
Correct: b)
Difficulty: 3
Page(s): 455
Scramble range: All
Topic: Hotelling Principle

17.73
The Hotelling Principle states that
a) hotels will tend to be built next to major highways.
b) equilibrium in natural resource markets occurs when the expected increase in the price of the resource over time is equal to the interest rate.
c) the stock of a resource will be depleted at a rate equal to the rate of interest.
d) natural resources should be depleted only for the production of goods that would help maintain environmental quality.
e) we should use only nonexhaustible natural resources and conserve exhaustible natural resources.

17.74
Correct: a)
Difficulty: 3
Page(s): 458–459
Scramble range: All
Topic: Natural resource usage

17.74
When the expected increase in the price of the resource over time is greater than the interest rate, then
a) the natural resource will remain unused.
b) all the natural resource will be extracted.
c) the market for that natural resource will be in equilibrium.
d) the resource will be exploited to the fullest extent possible.
e) some of the natural resource will be extracted.

17.75
Correct: b)
Difficulty: 4
Page(s): 458–459
Scramble range: All
Topic: Natural resource usage

17.75
When the expected increase in the price of the resource over time is less than the interest rate, then
a) the natural resource will remain unused.
b) the natural resource will be extracted.
c) the market for that natural resource will be in equilibrium.
d) the resource will be conserved to the fullest extent possible.
e) people will shift to substitutes for this resource.

17.76
Correct: d)
Difficulty: 3
Page(s): 458–459
Scramble range: All
Topic: Future expected changes in price

17.76
The market for a stock of a resource
a) determines the current level of the price of the resource.
b) determines the interest rate.
c) is dominated by the market for the flow of the resource.
d) determines the future expected rate of change in the price.
e) determines the price of a flow of the resource.

17.77
Correct: c)
Difficulty: 3
Page(s): 459
Scramble range: All
Topic: Choke price

17.77
The choke price of a flow of natural resources
a) is that price at which the resource will begin to be extracted.
b) is the price that is high enough to ensure the depletion of the resource.
c) is the price that is high enough to ensure that the resource will not be used.
d) is the price at which the resource will be used as a substitute for other scarce resources.
e) is the price at which the price of the resource will start to fall.

17.78
Correct: e)
Difficulty: 3
Page(s): 460
Scramble range: All
Topic: Prices of resources

17.78
The resources that are actually used are
a) those for which there are plenty of substitutes.
b) the most valuable resources available.
c) always those that are exhaustible.
d) those for which there are no substitutes.
e) the least expensive resources available.

17.79
Correct: d)
Difficulty: 3
Page(s): 460
Scramble range: All
Topic: Resource prices

17.79
The equilibrium price and flow of a natural resource depend on all of the following *except* the
a) interest rate.
b) demand for the flow of the resource.
c) stock of the resource remaining.
d) degree to which the resource is exhaustible.
e) marginal revenue product of the resource.

17.80
Correct: a)
Difficulty: 4
Page(s): 461
Scramble range: a)–d)
Topic: Resource prices

17.80
Sudden and large changes in the relative price of a resource can be caused by
a) new information about the stock of the resource available.
b) a rise in inflation.
c) unchanging expectations about future prices.
d) changes in the political party in control of the Senate.
e) all of the above.

17.81
Correct: b)
Difficulty: 3
Page(s): 463
Scramble range: All
Topic: Depletion of natural resources

17.81
The market economy handles the depleting stock of exhaustible resources by
a) enforcing government regulations limiting the rate of extraction of the resources.
b) causing the price to rise as it becomes depleted, motivating the substitution of other resources for the resource rising in price.
c) using up the resource quickly so political debates do not rage for long.
d) imposing price ceilings on the resource which would ensure its conservation.
e) allowing the resource to be depleted too quickly.

17.82
Correct: a)
Difficulty: 2
Page(s): 439
Scramble range: All
Topic: Net worth

17.82
The net worth of a household or firm is
a) total assets minus total liabilities.
b) total financial assets minus total real assets.
c) financial assets minus financial liabilities.
d) income minus consumption.
e) savings.

17.83 (SG 17.2)
Correct: e)
Difficulty: 3
Page(s): 439–444
Scramble range: All
Topic: Stock markets

17.83
Which of the following is an example of a stock?
a) Investment.
b) Depreciation.
c) Savings.
d) Income.
e) Capital.

17.84 (SG 17.3)
Correct: d)
Difficulty: 2
Page(s): 440
Scramble range: All
Topic: Investment

17.84
The decline in the value of capital resulting from its use over time is given by
a) the level of saving.
b) investment.
c) net investment.
d) gross investment minus net investment.
e) net investment minus gross investment.

17.85 (SG 17.4)
Correct: e)
Difficulty: 2
Page(s): 440
Scramble range: All
Topic: Net worth

17.85
Household determination of how net worth is held and financed is called
a) investment.
b) balance sheet decision making.
c) capital choice.
d) the price–earnings problem.
e) portfolio choice.

17.86 (SG 17.5)
Correct: b)
Difficulty: 2
Page(s): 442
Scramble range: All
Topic: Financial intermediaries

17.86
Firms that are primarily engaged in taking deposits, making loans, and buying securities are called
a) brokers.
b) financial intermediaries.
c) insurance companies.
d) monopsonists.
e) banks.

17.87 (SG 17.6)
Correct: a)
Difficulty: 3
Page(s): 445
Scramble range: All
Topic: Profit maximization

17.87
A profit-maximizing firm will choose to buy an extra unit of capital whenever
a) its net present value is greater than zero.
b) its net marginal revenue product is greater than zero.
c) the present value of expected future profit is greater than zero.
d) the present value of expected future profit exceeds the market rate of interest.
e) the present value of expected future profits are greater than current profits.

17.88 (SG 17.7)
Correct: e)
Difficulty: 4
Page(s): 445
Scramble range: All
Topic: Interest rate/present value

17.88
The higher the rate of interest,
a) the higher is the net present value of an investment.
b) the lower is the quantity supplied of capital.
c) the greater is the quantity of capital demanded.
d) the greater is the marginal revenue product of capital.
e) the lower is the present value of the stream of marginal revenue products of an investment.

17.89 (SG 17.8)
Correct: d)
Difficulty: 3
Page(s): 449
Scramble range: All
Topic: Substitution effect

17.89
If the interest rate increases, the
a) substitution effect encourages more saving only if the household is a net borrower.
b) substitution effect encourages more saving only if the household is a net lender.
c) income effect encourages more saving only if the household is a net borrower.
d) income effect encourages more saving only if the household is a net lender.
e) income effect always raises savings.

17.90 (SG 17.9)
Correct: e)
Difficulty: 4
Page(s): 449
Scramble range: All
Topic: Supply of capital

17.90
Which of the following would cause the supply of capital curve to shift to the right?
a) An increase in the proportion of young households in the population.
b) An increase in the interest rate.
c) A decrease in the proportion of older households.
d) An increase in the marginal revenue product of capital.
e) An increase in average household income.

17.91 (SG 17.11)
Correct: a)
Difficulty: 5
Page(s): 446
Scramble range: All
Topic: Net present value

17.91
A machine that costs $2,000 will generate marginal revenue product of $1,100 at the end of one year and the same amount at the end of two years. What is the net present value of the machine, if the interest rate is 10 percent?
a) –$90.91.
b) –$49.90.
c) $0.
d) $90.91.
e) $181.81.

17.92 (SG 17.12)
Correct: d)
Difficulty: 4
Page(s): 451
Scramble range: a)–d)
Topic: Stock markets

17.92
The yield on a stock will rise if
a) either the dividend increases or the share price of the stock increases.
b) either the dividend decreases or the share price of the stock decreases.
c) either the dividend decreases or the share price of the stock increases.
d) either the dividend increases or the share price of the stock decreases.
e) none of the above.

17.93 (SG 17.10)
Correct: a)
Difficulty: 3
Page(s): 451
Scramble range: All
Topic: Bonds and risk

17.93
Bond *A* is more risky than bond *B*. Then, in equilibrium,
a) the interest rate on *A* must be higher than that on *B*.
b) the interest rate on *A* must be lower than that on *B*.
c) no one will want to buy *A*.
d) only those who prefer risk will buy *A*.
e) *A* will sell less than *B*, but at the same interest rate.

17.94 (SG 17.13)
Correct: d)
Difficulty: 4
Page(s): 451–452
Scramble range: All
Topic: Interest rates

17.94
A firm is expected to pay an $8 dividend per share of stock each year into the indefinite future. If the market rate of interest is 8 percent, the price of a share of stock in this firm will be
a) $8.
b) $64.
c) $80.
d) $100.
e) $1,000.

17.95 (SG 17.14)
Correct: b)
Difficulty: 4
Page(s): 451–452
Scramble range: All
Topic: Stock markets

17.95
The price of a share of XYZ Corporation's stock is $80 and the current dividend payment is $4. The stock yield is
a) 4 percent.
b) 5 percent.
c) 8 percent.
d) 20 percent.
e) 50 percent.

17.96 (SG 17.15)
Correct: d)
Difficulty: 4
Page(s): 452
Scramble range: All
Topic: Bond yield

17.96
A newly issued bond promises to pay $100 at the end of one year plus a $10 interest payment. If the price of the bond today is $98, what is its yield?
a) 2 percent.
b) 8 percent.
c) 11 percent.
d) 12 percent.
e) 15 percent.

17.97 (SG 17.16)
Correct: c)
Difficulty: 4
Page(s): 452
Scramble range: All
Topic: Stock markets

17.97
An event occurs which almost everyone agrees will cause a decline in the future profit of the XYZ Corporation. Immediately after the event becomes known, what would we expect to observe with regard to XYZ stock?
a) The stock price will fluctuate up and down with a high volume of trading.
b) The stock price will fall gradually with a high volume of trading.
c) The stock price will fall quickly with a low volume of trading.
d) The stock price will fall quickly with a high volume of trading.
e) The stock price will fall gradually with a low volume of trading.

17.98 (SG 17.17)
Correct: b)
Difficulty: 3
Page(s): 456
Scramble range: All
Topic: Mergers and takeovers

17.98
A takeover of a firm is likely to occur when
a) the stock market value of the firm is higher than expected future profit from operating the firm.
b) the stock market value of the firm is lower than expected future profit from operating the firm.
c) current firm profit is higher than expected future profit from operating the firm.
d) current firm profit is lower than expected future profit from operating the firm.
e) interest rates are high.

17.99 (SG 17.18)
Correct: a)
Difficulty: 2
Page(s): 455
Scramble range: All
Topic: Exhaustible resources

17.99
Which of the following is an exhaustible natural resource?
a) Coal.
b) Land.
c) Water.
d) Trees.
e) Cattle.

17.100 (SG 17.19)
Correct: d)
Difficulty: 2
Page(s): 445
Scramble range: All
Topic: Yield on stock of natural resources

17.100
The yield on a stock of a natural resource is
a) the rate of interest on the loan used to buy the resource.
b) the marginal revenue product of the resource divided by its price.
c) the marginal revenue product of the resource multiplied by the market interest rate.
d) the rate of change in the price of the resource.
e) the price divided by the interest rate.

17.101 (SG 17.20)
Correct: a)
Difficulty: 2
Page(s): 460–461
Scramble range: All
Topic: Resource prices

17.101
If the market for a stock of a natural resource is in equilibrium, then it must be that the price of the resource is
a) expected to rise at a rate equal to the rate of interest.
b) equal to the choke price of the resource.
c) equal to the marginal revenue product of the resource.
d) equal to the Hotelling price of the resource.
e) expected to decrease at a rate equal to the depreciation rate.

17.102 (SG 17.21)
Correct: c)
Difficulty: 4
Page(s): 460–461
Scramble range: All
Topic: Natural resource pricing

17.102
The current price of a natural resource is higher, the
a) lower its marginal revenue product.
b) larger the stock of the resource remaining.
c) lower the interest rate.
d) lower the choke price.
e) lower the future price.

17.103
Correct: d)
Difficulty: 2
Page(s): 439
Scramble range: All
Topic: Net worth

17.103
The net worth of a household or firm is
a) total assets plus total liabilities.
b) total financial assets plus total real assets.
c) financial assets plus financial liabilities.
d) total assets minus total liabilities.
e) income minus consumption expenditure.

17.104
Correct: e)
Difficulty: 3
Page(s): 439–440
Scramble range: All
Topic: Stock markets

17.104
Which of the following is an example of a stock variable?
a) Saving.
b) Consumption.
c) Federal government budget deficit.
d) Depreciation.
e) Federal government debt.

17.105
Correct: e)
Difficulty: 2
Page(s): 440
Scramble range: All
Topic: Investment

17.105
The decline in the value of capital resulting from its use over time is given by
a) the level of saving.
b) net investment minus gross investment.
c) net consumption minus investment.
d) gross investment by the government.
e) gross investment minus net investment.

17.106 (SG 17.5)
Correct: d)
Difficulty: 2
Page(s): 442
Scramble range: All
Topic: Financial intermediaries

17.106
Firms that are primarily engaged in taking deposits, making loans, and buying securities are called
a) stock and bond brokers.
b) fiduciary intermediates.
c) banks.
d) financial intermediaries.
e) trust companies.

17.107
Correct: a)
Difficulty: 4
Page(s): 445
Scramble range: All
Topic: Profit maximization

17.107
A profit-maximizing firm will choose *not* to buy an extra unit of capital whenever
a) its net present value is less than zero.
b) its net marginal revenue product is greater than zero.
c) the present value of expected future profit is greater than zero.
d) the present value of expected future profit exceeds the market rate of interest.
e) the marginal revenue product of capital is less than the interest rate.

17.108
Correct: b)
Difficulty: 3
Page(s): 446
Scramble range: All
Topic: Interest rate/present value

17.108
The lower the rate of interest,
a) the lower is the net present value of an investment.
b) the higher is the present value of the stream of marginal revenue products of an investment.
c) the lower is the quantity of capital demanded.
d) the lower is the marginal revenue product of capital.
e) the higher is the marginal revenue product of capital.

17.109
Correct: c)
Difficulty: 4
Page(s): 449
Scramble range: All
Topic: Supply of capital

17.109
Which of the following would cause the supply of capital curve to shift to the left?
a) A decrease in the proportion of young households in the population.
b) A decrease in the interest rate.
c) A decrease in average household income.
d) A decrease in the marginal revenue product of capital.
e) A rise in the proportion of older households.

17.110
Correct: e)
Difficulty: 5
Page(s): 446
Scramble range: All
Topic: Net present value

17.110
A machine that costs $4,000 will generate marginal revenue product of $2,200 at the end of one year and the same amount at the end of the second year. What is the net present value of the machine if the interest rate is 10 percent?
a) –$90.91.
b) –$49.90.
c) $0.
d) $90.91.
e) –$181.81.

17.111
Correct: b)
Difficulty: 4
Page(s): 451
Scramble range: a)–d)
Topic: Stock markets

17.111
The yield on a stock will fall if either the dividend
a) decreases or the share price of the stock decreases.
b) decreases or the share price of the stock increases.
c) increases or the share price of the stock decreases.
d) increases or the share price of the stock increases.
e) none of the above.

17.112
Correct: a)
Difficulty: 4
Page(s): 451
Scramble range: All
Topic: Bonds and risk

17.112
Bond *A* is less risky than bond *B*. Then, in equilibrium,
a) the interest rate on *A* must be lower than that on *B*.
b) the interest rate on *A* must be higher than that on *B*.
c) no one will want to buy *B*.
d) only those who prefer risk will buy *A*.
e) *A* will sell more, but at the same interest rate.

17.113
Correct: e)
Difficulty: 4
Page(s): 451–452
Scramble range: All
Topic: Interest rates

17.113
A firm is expected to pay a $4 dividend per share of stock each year into the indefinite future. If the market rate of interest is 8 percent, the price of a share of stock in this firm will be
a) $4.
b) $5.
c) $100.
d) $80.
e) $50.

17.114
Correct: c)
Difficulty: 5
Page(s): 445–451
Scramble range: All
Topic: Capital

17.114
In the next 20 years in Canada, the so-called “baby-boomers” will be aging. This means that the proportion of older people in the population will be rising. As a result, we would expect
a) the demand for capital to rise, the supply of capital to be unchanged, and the interest rate to rise.
b) the demand for capital to fall, the supply of capital to be unchanged, and the interest rate to fall.
c) the demand for capital to be unchanged, the supply of capital to rise, and the interest rate to fall.
d) the demand for capital to remain unchanged, the supply of capital to fall, and the interest rate to rise.
e) this to have no impact on the demand or supply of capital, and therefore no impact on the interest rate.

17.115
Correct: d)
Difficulty: 5
Page(s): 448–451
Scramble range: All
Topic: Risk and interest rates

17.115
Suppose there are only two bonds in the world, *A* and *B*, which are initially identical in all aspects. Suppose that suddenly bond *B* becomes riskier than it initially was. As a result, the interest rate on bond *A* will __________, and the interest rate on bond *B* will __________

a) rise; be unchanged.
b) fall; fall.
c) be unchanged; rise.
d) fall; rise.
e) be unchanged; be unchanged.

17.116
Correct: e)
Difficulty: 5
Page(s): 439–441
Scramble range: All
Topic: Capital stock

17.116
Consider Fact 17.1. What is the value of the firm's stock of capital at the end of 1990?

a) $1,000,000.
b) $900,000.
c) $1,250,000.
d) $1,125,000.
e) $1,150,000.

Fact 17.1
At the end of 1989, a firm had a production plant worth $1,000,000. During 1990, its plant depreciated by 10 percent. During the same year, the firm bought new capital equipment for $250,000.

17.117
Correct: d)
Difficulty: 4
Page(s): 439–441
Scramble range: All
Topic: Net investment

17.117
Consider Fact 17.1. What is the firm's net investment over the year 1990?

a) $100,000.
b) $250,000.
c) $125,000.
d) $150,000.
e) 0.

17.118
Correct: d)
Difficulty: 3
Page(s): 439–441
Scramble range: All
Topic: Wealth

17.118
You earn $10,000 per year for three years, and you spend $8,000 each year. What is the change in your wealth over this time period? (Assume that the interest rate is zero over this time period.)

a) +$30,000.
b) –$6,000.
c) +$24,000.
d) +$6,000.
e) 0.

17.119
Correct: c)
Difficulty: 5
Page(s): 445–448
Scramble range: All
Topic: Present value

17.119
A firm is considering buying a new machine. It is estimated that the marginal revenue product of the machine will be $1,000 a year for five years. The machine will have a scrap value at the end of five years of $1,000. The interest rate is 10 percent per year. What is the maximum price that the firm will pay for the machine?
a) $6,000.
b) $3,791.
c) $4,412.
d) $4,545.
e) $5,454.

17.120
Correct: e)
Difficulty: 4
Page(s): 457–462
Scramble range: All
Topic: Exhaustible resource price

17.120
Suppose that a new supply of an exhaustible natural resource is discovered. This will result in the current price of the resource __________ and the future price of the resource __________
a) falling; being unchanged.
b) falling; rising.
c) rising; falling.
d) being unchanged; falling.
e) falling; falling.

Chapter 18 The Distribution of Income and Wealth

18.1
Correct: b)
Difficulty: 2
Page(s): 467
Scramble range: All
Topic: Net assets of the poor

18.1
According to the text, the poorest 40 percent of families own what percentage of the nation's net assets?
a) 0 percent.
b) 1 percent.
c) 10 percent.
d) 15 percent.
e) 25 percent.

18.2
Correct: b)
Difficulty: 2
Page(s): 467
Scramble range: All
Topic: Income of the poor

18.2
According to the text, the poorest 20 percent of families earn what percentage of the nation's income?
a) 15 percent.
b) 5 percent.
c) 40 percent.
d) 20 percent.
e) 1 percent.

18.3
Correct: c)
Difficulty: 2
Page(s): 467
Scramble range: All
Topic: Median income

18.3
The median family income
a) is the average family income.
b) is defined as the poverty level.
c) is that income level at which 50 percent of households earn a higher income and 50 percent earn a lower income.
d) is the income that a majority of families earn.
e) is the mean family income.

18.4
Correct: c)
Difficulty: 2
Page(s): 467
Scramble range: All
Topic: Median income

18.4
In 1989, the median household income in Canada was approximately
a) $3,000.
b) $15,000.
c) $20,000.
d) $40,000.
e) $55,000.

18.5
Correct: d)
Difficulty: 2
Page(s): 467
Scramble range: All
Topic: Share of income of the rich

18.5
In 1988, the 20 percent of the households with the highest incomes received what percentage of the total income?
a) 14 percent.
b) 4 percent.
c) 71 percent.
d) 43 percent.
e) 55 percent.

18.6
Correct: e)
Difficulty: 2
Page(s): 466
Scramble range: All
Topic: Share of income

18.6
The top 1 percent of Canadian families have an average income that exceeds
a) $400,000.
b) $100,000.
c) $55,000.
d) $150,000.
e) $200,000.

18.7
Correct: b)
Difficulty: 3
Page(s): 467
Scramble range: All
Topic: Income distribution

18.7
The distribution of income among families and individuals depends on the
a) prices of related goods and services.
b) quantities of resources these families or individuals supply to the market.
c) income effect in production.
d) substitution effect in production.
e) time they have available.

18.8
Correct: c)
Difficulty: 3
Page(s): 467
Scramble range: All
Topic: Income distribution

18.8
The distribution of income among families and individuals depends on all the following *except* the
a) prices of the labour they supply.
b) interest rates in the market.
c) income effect in production.
d) dividend rates.
e) rental rates.

18.9
Correct: a)
Difficulty: 3
Page(s): 468
Scramble range: All
Topic: Lorenz curve

18.9
A Lorenz curve measures
a) the distribution of income or wealth among households ranked from the poorest to the richest.
b) the income or wealth among households ranked from the poorest to richest.
c) the income or wealth among households ranked from the richest to the poorest.
d) the factor prices earned by the rich compared with the poor.
e) the shares of wealth or income among households ranked from the richest to the poorest.

18.10
Correct: c)
Difficulty: 2
Page(s): 468
Scramble range: All
Topic: Income distribution

18.10
If each family or household unit had equal levels of income, then the Lorenz curve would be
a) not defined, since it measures income inequality rather than equality.
b) the line of poverty.
c) the line of equality.
d) a right angle.
e) perfectly flat.

18.11
Correct: d)
Difficulty: 3
Page(s): 470–471
Scramble range: All
Topic: Equity and efficiency

18.11
Economic efficiency and economic equity have what relation?
a) Redistribution of income reduces economic equality while it increases economic efficiency.
b) Income is equitably distributed in free market systems without intervention by government.
c) There is a no tradeoff between the two.
d) There is a tradeoff between equality and efficiency.
e) More equality is generally more efficient.

18.12
Correct: a)
Difficulty: 3
Page(s): 484
Scramble range: All
Topic: Discrimination

18.12
According to Nozick's process view of distributive justice, discrimination-reducing employment of qualified individuals is
a) inefficient and inequitable.
b) efficient and inequitable.
c) equitable and inefficient.
d) efficient and equitable.
e) acceptable if it is inefficient.

18.13
Correct: b)
Difficulty: 3
Page(s): 479
Scramble range: All
Topic: Labour income

18.13
The percentage of individual income earned from the sale of labour resources is approximately
a) 95 percent.
b) 75 percent.
c) 50 percent.
d) 20 percent.
e) 10 percent.

18.14
Correct: d)
Difficulty: 3
Page(s): 472
Scramble range: All
Topic: Welfare

18.14
Government transfer payments, such as welfare payments, redistribute income and also
a) increase the incentive to work.
b) improve economic efficiency.
c) increase tax receipts.
d) decrease the incentive to work.
e) push the Lorenz curve further away from the line of equality.

18.15
Correct: b)
Difficulty: 4
Page(s): 479
Scramble range: All
Topic: Labour income

18.15
Labour income is underreported in the national accounts since
a) the income of firms is really the return to labour.
b) nonmarket labour is not reported.
c) capitalists inaccurately report earned income.
d) income from wealth matters only for the rich.
e) the national accounts estimates individuals' labour supply at too high a level.

18.16
Correct: b)
Difficulty: 3
Page(s): 468
Scramble range: All
Topic: Middle-income group

18.16
In 1988, the middle 20 percent of families received what percent of total Canadian income?
a) 4 percent.
b) 18 percent.
c) 25 percent.
d) 43 percent.
e) 52 percent.

18.17
Correct: e)
Difficulty: 2
Page(s): 468
Scramble range: All
Topic: Lorenz curve

18.17
Refer to Figure 18.1. The poorest 20 percent of households receive what share of total income?
a) 40 percent.
b) 60 percent.
c) 20 percent.
d) 5 percent.
e) 10 percent.

Figure 18.1

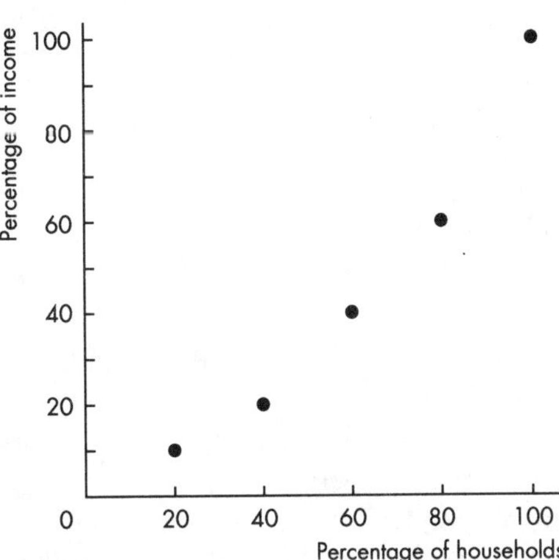

18.18
Correct: c)
Difficulty: 3
Page(s): 468
Scramble range: All
Topic: Lorenz curve

18.18
Refer to Figure 18.1. The richest 20 percent of households receive what share of total income?
a) 10 percent.
b) 30 percent.
c) 40 percent.
d) 60 percent.
e) 100 percent.

18.19
Correct: a)
Difficulty: 3
Page(s): 468
Scramble range: All
Topic: Lorenz curve

18.19
Refer to Figure 18.1. The middle 20 percent of households receive what share of total income?
a) 20 percent.
b) 25 percent.
c) 35 percent.
d) 15 percent.
e) 60 percent.

18.20
Correct: a)
Difficulty: 3
Page(s): 468
Scramble range: All
Topic: Lorenz curve

18.20
A Lorenz curve illustrates the distribution of income by graphing the
a) cumulative percentage of income received and the cumulative percentage of households.
b) chance of a family earning a specific income.
c) percentage of income received by a given percentage of households.
d) cumulative frequency of specific incomes.
e) percentage change in income for a percentage change in population.

18.21
Correct: e)
Difficulty: 4
Page(s): 468
Scramble range: a)–d)
Topic: Lorenz curve

18.21
The larger the gap between the Lorenz curve and the diagonal,
a) the greater is the equality in the income distribution.
b) the less is the inequality in the income distribution.
c) the poorer are the top 50 percent of households.
d) the richer are the lowest 50 percent of households.
e) none of the above.

18.22
Correct: e)
Difficulty: 3
Page(s): 471
Scramble range: All
Topic: Income distribution

18.22
The single most important factor (of those listed) determining the relative position in the income distribution is
a) race.
b) sex.
c) participation in the labour force.
d) geography.
e) marital status.

18.23
Correct: c)
Difficulty: 4
Page(s): 470
Scramble range: All
Topic: Marital status and income

18.23
Marital status is important in determining the position in the income distribution since
a) marriage means two mouths to feed and lowers the relative position in the income distribution.
b) married couples on average earn 50 percent more than do single people.
c) married couples on average are 1/5 as likely to be poor as single female parents.
d) employers generally discriminate against single females in the workplace.
e) married couples are twice as likely as a single male parent to be poor.

18.24
Correct: d)
Difficulty: 3
Page(s): 471
Scramble range: All
Topic: Determination of income distribution

18.24
Determinants of the relative position of a household in the income distribution include all of the following *except*
a) household size.
b) race.
c) age.
d) height.
e) sex.

18.25
Correct: b)
Difficulty: 2
Page(s): 470
Scramble range: All
Topic: Poverty

18.25
Poverty is defined by the
a) church.
b) government.
c) market.
d) banks.
e) National Anti-Poverty Organization.

18.26
Correct: c)
Difficulty: 2
Page(s): 470
Scramble range: All
Topic: Poverty

18.26
The poverty level is defined as
a) an income level below the national average income.
b) an income level below the national median income.
c) an income which is less than that needed to afford a minimum standard of living.
d) the income earned by the poorest 20 percent of households.
e) receiving transfer payments from the government.

18.27
Correct: d)
Difficulty: 3
Page(s): 470
Scramble range: All
Topic: Income redistribution

18.27
There are two main efforts through which the government redistributes income. They are
a) sales taxes and user fees.
b) sales taxes and income taxes.
c) user fees and welfare programs.
d) income taxes and social security programs.
e) welfare programs and social security programs.

18.28
Correct: b)
Difficulty: 2
Page(s): 470
Scramble range: All
Topic: Progressive income tax

18.28
A progressive income tax
a) taxes lower incomes by a larger percentage than higher incomes.
b) taxes lower incomes by a smaller percentage than higher incomes.
c) receives more from rich people, but taxes them at the same rate as poor people.
d) taxes everyone at the same rate.
e) taxes everyone at a constant rate.

18.29
Correct: d)
Difficulty: 2
Page(s): 470
Scramble range: All
Topic: Proportional income tax

18.29
A proportional income tax
a) taxes lower incomes by a larger percentage than higher incomes.
b) taxes lower incomes by a smaller percentage than higher incomes.
c) receives more from rich people, but taxes them at the same rate as poor people.
d) taxes everyone at the same rate.
e) taxes income at a marginal rate that falls with rises in income.

18.30
Correct: a)
Difficulty: 2
Page(s): 470
Scramble range: All
Topic: Regressive income tax

18.30
A regressive income tax
a) taxes lower incomes by a larger percentage than higher incomes.
b) taxes lower incomes by a smaller percentage than higher incomes.
c) receives more from rich people, but taxes them at the same rate as poor people.
d) taxes everyone at the same rate.
e) taxes income at a marginal rate that rises with rises in income.

18.31
Correct: d)
Difficulty: 3
Page(s): 470
Scramble range: All
Topic: Income distribution and equity

18.31
A constant income distribution over time means that
a) each individual has the same income as before.
b) the income of the average family in each group is constant.
c) inequality will have changed significantly, and living standards will be reduced.
d) equality will be unchanged, but some poor people may have become rich people.
e) poverty has been conquered.

18.32
Correct: e)
Difficulty: 4
Page(s): 472–474
Scramble range: All
Topic: Poverty

18.32
One difficulty with a standard of poverty includes the fact that
a) the poverty standard cannot involve a moving income level adjusting for changes in household size and changes in prices.
b) once an absolute poverty level is established, government can determine what it will cost to eliminate poverty.
c) a poverty level that is too high will cause assistance to underestimate the minimum standard of living.
d) fixing the poverty level at too few dollars would be a disincentive to working.
e) wealthy people often have a low labour income.

18.33
Correct: a)
Difficulty: 3
Page(s): 470
Scramble range: All
Topic: Provincial taxes

18.33
The most heavily taxed Canadians live in
a) Quebec.
b) Manitoba.
c) Alberta.
d) Ontario.
e) British Columbia.

18.34
Correct: e)
Difficulty: 3
Page(s): 470
Scramble range: All
Topic: Marginal tax rates

18.34
Most Canadians paid taxes at a marginal rate around
a) 8 percent.
b) 15 percent.
c) 60 percent.
d) 40 percent.
e) 25 percent.

18.35
Correct: e)
Page(s): 471
Scramble range: All
Topic: Marginal tax rates

18.35
For incomes above $60,000 per year, the marginal tax rate is around
a) 5 percent.
b) 15 percent.
c) 25 percent.
d) 35 percent.
e) 50 percent.

18.36
Correct: d)
Difficulty: 3
Page(s): 470
Scramble range: All
Topic: Poverty

18.36
The low-income cutoff level is
a) a level of housing and food provided by the government.
b) a fixed real income used to determine whether or not a household may qualify for welfare.
c) a moving level of wealth which varies for households with different characteristics.
d) a moving level of income which varies for households with different characteristics.
e) a level of income below which starvation occurs.

18.37
Correct: e)
Difficulty: 2
Page(s): 471
Scramble range: All
Topic: Origin of welfare programs

18.37
Federal social security benefits include all of the following progams except
a) senior citizens' benefits.
b) family allowances.
c) child tax credits.
d) unemployment insurance.
e) the minimum wage.

18.38
Correct: e)
Difficulty: 3
Page(s): 472–473
Scramble range: All
Topic: Senior citizens' programs

18.38
Considering the programs to aid senior citizens, and the taxes they pay, senior citizens
a) are treated no differently than any other group in society with respect to redistribution.
b) are generally wealthier than other groups, and hence are taxed more and receive less benefits.
c) receive benefits only if their income is less than $12,000.
d) receive benefits if their income is less than $22,000, and pay no taxes if their income is above $22,000.
e) receive benefits if their income is below $22,000, and pay taxes if their income is above $22,000.

18.39
Correct: c)
Difficulty: 3
Page(s): 472
Scramble range: All
Topic: Social security

18.39
One criticism of the social security programs such as the Guaranteed Income Supplement is that often
a) they promote efficiency rather than equity.
b) they hurt both efficiency and equity.
c) they take benefits away at a high marginal rate as the household earns more income.
d) they take benefits away at a low marginal rate as the household earns more income.
e) often provincial programs counter their effects.

18.40
Correct: b)
Difficulty: 3
Page(s): 472
Scramble range: All
Topic: Welfare

18.40
One criticism of social security programs such as the Guaranteed Income Supplement is that
a) it promotes efficiency rather than equity.
b) it helps equity but hurts efficiency.
c) there is an implicit negative income tax.
d) it gives too much money to the poor.
e) it gives too much money to the rich.

18.41
Correct: b)
Difficulty: 3
Page(s): 473
Scramble range: All
Topic: Negative income tax

18.41
A negative income tax
a) means that the rich would pay less taxes than with a positive tax.
b) means that the marginal tax rate would be kept below 100 percent.
c) means that rates could not be progressive.
d) more employees would be needed to administer the tax than are employed to administer the welfare programs.
e) means that the government gives people money instead of taxing them.

18.42
Correct: d)
Difficulty: 2
Page(s): 472
Scramble range: All
Topic: Redistribution policies

18.42
Other policies that result in a redistribution of income toward the poor include all of the following *except* public
a) provision of elementary education.
b) provision of high school education.
c) provision of health care services.
d) excise taxes.
e) provision of subsidized university education.

18.43
Correct: a)
Difficulty: 2
Page(s): 474
Scramble range: All
Topic: Market income distribution

18.43
In the absence of government policies to redistribute income, the income distribution will be the
a) market distribution.
b) unfair distribution.
c) capitalist distribution.
d) efficient distribution.
e) line of equality.

18.44
Correct: b)
Difficulty: 3
Page(s): 474
Scramble range: All
Topic: Income distribution and source

18.44
The richest 20 percent of the income distribution
a) receive the largest percentage of the transfer payments.
b) receive a large portion of their income from interest and dividends from financial assets.
c) pay a marginal tax rate of only 15 percent.
d) pay a marginal tax rate of 72 percent.
e) receive almost all of their income from labour income.

18.45
Correct: b)
Difficulty: 4
Page(s): 474
Scramble range: All
Topic: Source of income

18.45
The individuals and households not in the top 80 percent of the income distribution
a) earn no income from interest and dividends on financial assets.
b) on the average, earn a small amount of their income from interest and dividends.
c) on the average, earn a fair amount of their income from interest and dividends.
d) on the average, earn a large amount of their income from interest and dividends.
e) on the average, earn almost all of their income from interest and dividends.

18.46
Correct: b)
Difficulty: 3
Page(s): 474
Scramble range: All
Topic: Income and wealth

18.46
From an examination of data on income and wealth, it can be concluded that
a) wealth distribution is more equitable than income distribution.
b) income distribution is more equitable than wealth distribution.
c) the wealth distribution is equal to the income distribution.
d) income and wealth are the same.
e) income and wealth are unrelated.

18.47
Correct: a)
Difficulty: 3
Page(s): 474
Scramble range: All
Topic: Efficient/equity tradeoff

18.47
Which of the following statements is true?
a) Equality sometimes hurts efficiency.
b) Economics explains what is a fair income distribution.
c) A market can increase efficiency only by reducing equity.
d) Government can act without facing the equity and efficiency tradeoff.
e) To most governments, only efficiency is important.

18.48
Correct: c)
Difficulty: 3
Page(s): 470–471
Scramble range: All
Topic: Characteristics of the poor

18.48
Which of the descriptions of the poor given below is true?
a) They are mostly middle-aged individuals.
b) The youngest individuals are not often poor, since those under 18 years of age are generally the richest but not the wealthiest.
c) A high incidence of poverty in the 1980s occurred in female-headed households.
d) From 1951 to 1985, the incidence of poverty among households was greatly increased.
e) They are usually in their 30s.

18.49
Correct: d)
Difficulty: 3
Page(s): 471
Scramble range: a)–c)
Topic: Poverty

18.49
The poorest people are likely
a) to have a household head who is less than 25 years old.
b) to live in Quebec.
c) to have a female as the household head.
d) all of the above.
e) none of the above.

18.50
Correct: c)
Difficulty: 3
Page(s): 472
Scramble range: All
Topic: Poverty

18.50
Which of the following statements is true?
a) Most of the poor people have graduated from high school.
b) People with at least one year of college are never in poverty.
c) Low education and poverty tend to reinforce each other.
d) High education levels are not concentrated in the upper income levels.
e) Poor people are more likely than rich people to be employed (the so-called working poor).

18.51
Correct: a)
Difficulty: 3
Page(s): 475
Scramble range: All
Topic: Discrimination

18.51
Which idea below illustrates economic discrimination?
a) An employer who will hire only female bookkeepers, but would never accept a female supervisor.
b) An employer who permits employees to choose retirement age.
c) An employer who chooses the stronger workers for the projects using heavy manual labour.
d) An employer who hires only qualified individuals for jobs in sales.
e) An employer who will only hire people if they have a university degree.

18.52
Correct: b)
Difficulty: 3
Page(s): 476
Scramble range: All
Topic: Economic discrimination

18.52
For the economy as a whole, economic discrimination
a) is never efficient but always equitable.
b) is both inefficient and inequitable.
c) is efficient but equitable.
d) inefficient but equitable.
e) always inequitable, sometimes inefficient.

18.53
Correct: a)
Difficulty: 2
Page(s): 471–472
Scramble range: All
Topic: Welfare

18.53
Social security programs do not include which of the following?
a) Regressive income taxes.
b) Cash transfer payments.
c) In-kind transfers of income.
d) Income supplements.
e) Tax credits.

18.54
Correct: d)
Difficulty: 3
Page(s): 472
Scramble range: All
Topic: Negative income tax

18.54
With a negative income tax,
a) every household would receive a tax refund.
b) households with very low incomes would pay income taxes in the usual manner.
c) rich households would pay a negative tax.
d) households with below-poverty income would receive a negative tax or a subsidy to their income.
e) your marginal tax rate falls as income rises.

18.55
Correct: b)
Difficulty: 2
Page(s): 472
Scramble range: a)–d)
Topic: Break–even income

18.55
Refer to Table 18.1. The break-even level of income for this hypothetical tax system is
a) $8,000.
b) $14,000.
c) $20,000.
d) $26,000.
e) none of the above.

Table 18.1 Hypothetical tax system

Earned income	Tax payment	Disposable income
$ 8,000	–$2000	$10,000
$14,000	0	$14,000
$20,000	$1000	$19,000
$26,000	$2000	$24,000

18.56
Correct: d)
Difficulty: 3
Page(s): 472
Scramble range: All
Topic: Income tax of the poor

18.56
Refer to Table 18.1. For an individual with an income of $8,000, which of the following is true?
a) They are so poor that they unaffected by the tax system.
b) They are poor but still pay $2,000 in income tax.
c) They earn an income, so they pay a tax equal to $1,000.
d) They pay a "negative tax" of $2,000, which means they receive $2,000 from the government.
e) They are made worse off by the tax system.

18.57
Correct: c)
Difficulty: 4
Page(s): 472
Scramble range: All
Topic: Compute marginal tax rate

18.57
Refer to Table 18.1. The implicit marginal tax rate on each dollar earned between $8,000 and $14,000 is
a) impossible to determine without more information on tax rates.
b) 3 percent.
c) 33 percent.
d) 100 percent.
e) –33 percent.

18.58
Correct: c)
Difficulty: 4
Page(s): 472
Scramble range: All
Topic: Compute marginal tax rate

18.58
Refer to Table 18.1. The implicit marginal tax rate on each dollar earned between $14,000 and $20,000 is
a) impossible to determine without more information on tax rates.
b) 1.66 percent.
c) 16.66 percent.
d) 100 percent.
e) 83.33 percent.

18.59
Correct: c)
Difficulty: 2
Page(s): 474
Scramble range: All
Topic: Wealth

18.59
Wealth is the
a) large income earned by the rich.
b) large stock of income available to rich people.
c) stock of assets owned by an individual.
d) flow of assets to an individual in any fiscal year from labour income.
e) flow of assets to an individual in any fiscal year from capital.

18.60
Correct: a)
Difficulty: 3
Page(s): 474
Scramble range: All
Topic: Income

18.60
Income is the
a) flow of payments from a stock of wealth.
b) large stock of wealth available to rich people.
c) stock of assets owned by an individual.
d) flow of wealth to an individual in any fiscal year.
e) flow payments from a stock of human capital.

18.61
Correct: d)
Difficulty: 3
Page(s): 474
Scramble range: All
Topic: Wealth and human capital

18.61
Measured wealth distributions that do not consider the distribution of human capital
a) overstate the equality of the income distribution.
b) understate the inequality of the income distribution.
c) are correct nevertheless since human capital is difficult to accurately measure.
d) overstate the inequality of the income distribution.
e) are correct nevertheless because the distribution of human capital is about the same as the distribution of nonhuman wealth.

18.62
Correct: c)
Difficulty: 3
Page(s): 476
Scramble range: All
Topic: Income and wealth

18.62
Comparing income and wealth across households
a) is analytically impossible since it implies interpersonal comparisons of utility.
b) has no analytical difficulties since there is never any conflict between the two.
c) is tricky since different households may be at different stages in the life cycle.
d) involves comparing flows with flows, so it is correct.
e) involves comparing flows with stocks, so it can never be done.

18.63
Correct: a)
Difficulty: 4
Page(s): 479
Scramble range: All
Topic: Distribution of resources

18.63
The distribution of income depends on the
a) distribution of the endowment of resources.
b) home province of the workers.
c) age of the workers.
d) flows of wealth between different generations in the same household.
e) height of the workers.

18.64
Correct: e)
Difficulty: 2
Page(s): 480
Scramble range: All
Topic: Resource endowments

18.64
By the "distribution of endowments" economists mean who
a) gets what share of the economic pie.
b) earns what share of the national income.
c) earns what returns on their endowments.
d) buys the most resources.
e) owns what share of the productive resources.

18.65
Correct: e)
Difficulty: 3
Page(s): 480
Scramble range: All
Topic: Resource markets

18.65
Individuals in competitive resource markets
a) determine how much and at what price to sell their resources.
b) determine the price at which their resources sell, but the market determines the quantity they will sell.
c) have no control over price of the resources, but select how much of the resources to sell within a limited scope.
d) have no control over the price of the resources or the amount they will sell.
e) determine how much of the resources to sell at prices set by the market.

18.66
Correct: a)
Difficulty: 3
Page(s): 481
Scramble range: All
Topic: Wage differences

18.66
Workers with similar skills may be paid different wages because
a) their marginal revenue products are different.
b) their marginal revenue products are the same.
c) pay-equity laws are enforced.
d) pay-equity laws are not enforced.
e) their supply of endowments is different.

18.67
Correct: c)
Difficulty: 2
Page(s): 481
Scramble range: All
Topic: Bequests

18.67
A bequest is
a) a mistake.
b) an inheritance.
c) a gift from one generation to the next.
d) an incentive for future generations to work harder.
e) a gift of schooling.

18.68
Correct: b)
Difficulty: 2
Page(s): 482
Scramble range: All
Topic: Saving and income distribution

18.68
Savings do not have to represent an inequality in the distribution of income since
a) wealth is increased when saving increases.
b) savings may redistribute uneven income over the life cycle.
c) they can be left to future generations.
d) the interest payments on savings plans are too small.
e) debts cannot be bequeathed.

18.69
Correct: b)
Difficulty: 2
Page(s): 482
Scramble range: All
Topic: Bequests

18.69
A generation that is "lucky" or wealthy and makes a bequest to another generation that is "unlucky" or not wealthy
a) increases the inequality of the income distribution.
b) decreases the inequality of the income distribution.
c) does not change the distribution of income.
d) proves that inheritance taxes are needed.
e) is improving efficiency.

18.70
Correct: a)
Difficulty: 2
Page(s): 483
Scramble range: All
Topic: Minimum bequests

18.70
What is the minimum bequest one generation can leave to another?
a) Zero.
b) \$2,000, the amount of the standard deduction.
c) \$2,000 for each member of the family.
d) There is no minimum as millions of dollars of debt can be left behind by dearly-departed debtors.
e) An amount of debt equal to the net wealth of the recipient.

18.71
Correct: b)
Difficulty: 3
Page(s): 483
Scramble range: All
Topic: Bequests

18.71
Bequests of assets
a) normally will make the distribution of income more equal.
b) normally will make the distribution of income no less unequal.
c) are limited since the government taxes this type of bequest at a very high marginal tax rate.
d) are one of the main causes of social unrest.
e) distort life-cycle inequality effects.

18.72
Correct: d)
Difficulty: 3
Page(s): 484
Scramble range: All
Topic: Assortative mating

18.72
Assortative mating
a) tends to breakdown barriers between the social classes.
b) tends to increase the equality of the income distribution.
c) tends to increase the equality of the distribution of wealth.
d) tends to keep the income and wealth distributions from becoming more equal.
e) occurs rarely these days due to changes in social values.

18.73
Correct: d)
Difficulty: 2
Page(s): 484
Scramble range: All
Topic: Assortative mating

18.73
Assortative mating means that
a) rich men tend to marry poor women.
b) rich women tend to marry poor younger men.
c) rich men tend to marry poor younger women.
d) rich men tend to marry rich women.
e) "opposites attract."

18.74
Correct: e)
Difficulty: 3
Page(s): 482
Scramble range: All
Topic: Distributive justice

18.74
Distributive justice refers to
a) who gets what share of the economic pie.
b) who does the majority of the work to produce the economic pie.
c) examining efficiency versus equity.
d) who gets convicted and if they belong to a minority group.
e) the judgement as to which distributions of income are more fair than others.

18.75
Correct: a)
Difficulty: 2
Page(s): 483–484
Scramble range: All
Topic: Process theory/distributive justice

18.75
The belief that everyone should get an even opportunity to earn wealth is
a) a process theory of distributive justice.
b) part of affirmative action programs.
c) an end-state theory of distributive justice.
d) a steady-state theory of distributive justice.
e) unfair, according to both end-state and process theories of distributive justice.

18.76
Correct: e)
Difficulty: 3
Page(s): 483–484
Scramble range: All
Topic: End-state theory/distributive justice

18.76
"Everyone should earn the same income and enjoy the same wealth." This is a statement from
a) a process theory of distributive justice.
b) part of the Hegelian dialectic.
c) Nozick's theories of distributive justice.
d) a steady-state theory of distributive justice.
e) an end-state theory of distributive justice.

18.77
Correct: c)
Difficulty: 3
Page(s): 484
Scramble range: All
Topic: Utilitarian theory of distributive justice

18.77
The utilitarian theory of justice states
a) whatever leads to happiness is just.
b) whatever leads to happiness for one group will lead to happiness for another.
c) that an outcome is just if it leads to maximum utility for the society as a whole.
d) that an outcome is unjust if it leads to some groups achieving greater utility than others.
e) that an outcome is just if it maximizes the increase in the utility of the worse-off group in society.

18.78
Correct: e)
Difficulty: 4
Page(s): 484
Scramble range: All
Topic: Utilitarian theory of justice

18.78
The utilitarian theory of justice states that a distribution of income is just if
a) the utility of each individual is the same.
b) the utility is the same for each member of the same age category.
c) all individuals receive the same level of income.
d) by redistributing income from rich to poor the loss in utility was not too large.
e) the marginal utility of income is equal for all individuals.

18.79
Correct: b)
Difficulty: 4
Page(s): 484
Scramble range: All
Topic: Rawls' theory of justice

18.79
The Rawlsian theory of justice states that
a) all individuals should have the same income for distributive justice to be ensured.
b) the fairest income distribution is that which gives the poorest individuals the maximum possible income.
c) all individuals should receive the income they earn, but no more so.
d) all individuals should be subject to a proportional income tax, but not a progressive one.
e) the fairest income distribution maximizes the total utility of society.

18.80
Correct: d)
Difficulty: 3
Page(s): 484
Scramble range: All
Topic: Libertarian distributive

18.80
Robert Nozick argues in *Anarchy, State, and Utopia* that
a) there is no such thing as distributive justice.
b) there is validity to end-state theories of distributive justice.
c) there is no validity to process theories of distributive justice.
d) there is no validity to end-state theories of distributive justice.
e) there is no validity to either end-state or process theories of distributive justice.

18.81 (SG 18.1)
Correct: e)
Difficulty: 2
Page(s): 484
Scramble range: All
Topic: Labour earnings

18.81
Which of the following statements is true?
a) Labour earns the largest share of total income and that share has decreased over the last 50 years.
b) Labour earns the largest share of total income and that share has increased drastically over the last 50 years.
c) Owners of capital earn the largest share of total income and that share has decreased over the last 50 years.
d) Owners of capital earn the largest share of total income and that share has increased over the last 50 years.
e) Labour earns the largest share of total income and that share has increased slightly over the last 50 years.

18.82 (SG 18.2)
Correct: c)
Difficulty: 3
Page(s): 469
Scramble range: All
Topic: Wage differences

18.82
For the most part, differences in the wage rates received by different individuals reflect differences in
a) inherited wealth.
b) holdings of financial wealth.
c) marginal product of labour.
d) the quantity of labour offered.
e) discrimination.

18.83 (SG 18.3)
Correct: d)
Difficulty: 4
Page(s): 467–471
Scramble range: All
Topic: Wealth distribution

18.83
The inequality in the distribution of wealth is
a) less than the inequality in the distribution of income.
b) decreased by the existence of assortative mating.
c) a better measure of the inequality in the distribution of economic resources than is the inequality in the distribution of income.
d) even greater if we look at the distribution of wealth among the richest 1 percent of all families.
e) even greater if we look at the distribution of wealth among the poorest 20 percent of all families.

18.84
Correct: e)
Difficulty: 2
Page(s): 468
Scramble range: All
Topic: Wealth distribution

18.84
The wealthiest 10 percent of Canadian families own approximately
a) 72 percent of the wealth.
b) 21 percent of the wealth.
c) 95 percent of the wealth.
d) 85 percent of the wealth.
e) 57 percent of the wealth.

18.85 (SG 18.6)
Correct: a)
Difficulty: 2
Page(s): 469
Scramble range: All
Topic: Lorenz curve

18.85
The diagram used by economists to illustrate the distribution of income or wealth is the
a) Lorenz curve.
b) normal distribution.
c) Rawls curve.
d) Okun tradeoff curve.
e) utility tradeoff curve.

18.86
Correct: e)
Difficulty: 2
Page(s): 469
Scramble range: All
Topic: Lorenz curve

18.86
Consider the Lorenz curves in Figure 18.2. Which Lorenz curve corresponds to the greatest income inequality?
a) *A*.
b) *B*.
c) *C*.
d) *D*.
e) One to the right of *D*.

Figure 18.2

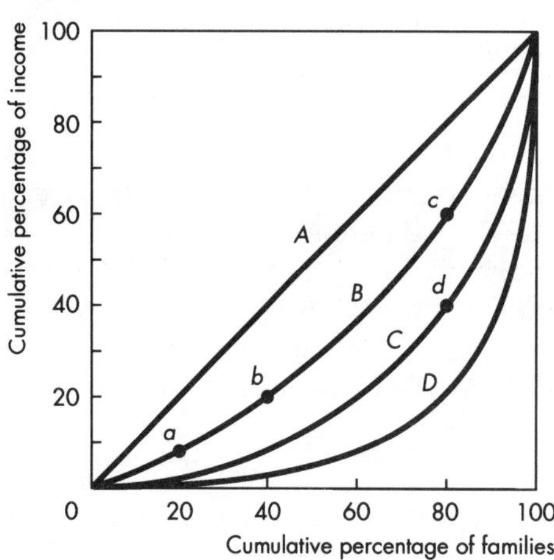

18.87
Correct: b)
Difficulty: 2
Page(s): 469
Scramble range: All
Topic: Line of equality

18.87
In Figure 18.2, curve *A* (a straight line) is called the
a) market distribution line.
b) line of equality.
c) fairness line.
d) Okun tradeoff curve.
e) line of Rawlsian equity.

18.88 (SG 18.12)
Correct: c)
Difficulty: 4
Page(s): 469
Scramble range: a)–d)
Topic: Lorenz curve

18.88
Which point in Figure 18.2 indicates that the richest 20 percent of families earn 40 percent of the income?
a) *a*.
b) *b*.
c) *c*.
d) *d*.
e) None of the above.

18.89
Correct: d)
Difficulty: 2
Page(s): 470
Scramble range: All
Topic: Poverty

18.89
In Canada, the low-income cutoff level for a family was when approximately __________ percent of income was spent on food, shelter and clothing.
a) 30 percent.
b) 40 percent.
c) 50 percent.
d) 60 percent.
e) 70 percent.

18.90 (SG 18.8)
Correct: a)
Difficulty: 2
Page(s): 470
Scramble range: All
Topic: Tax system

18.90
If the marginal tax rate increases as income increases, the income tax is
a) progressive.
b) proportional.
c) negative.
d) regressive.
e) utilitarian.

18.91 (SG 18.9)
Correct: c)
Difficulty: 3
Page(s): 476
Scramble range: All
Topic: Income distribution

18.91
The distribution of annual income
a) understates the degree of inequality because it does not take into account the family's stage in its life cycle.
b) understates the degree of inequality because it does not take into account the distribution of human capital.
c) overstates the degree of inequality because it does not take into account the family's stage in its life cycle.
d) overstates the degree of inequality because it does not take into account the distribution of human capital.
e) overstates the degree of inequality because it does not take into account the distribution of wealth.

18.92 (SG 18.14)
Correct: d)
Difficulty: 4
Page(s): 472–473
Scramble range: All
Topic: Implicit marginal tax rate

18.92
Suppose that if a family earns zero income, it receives a monthly transfer payment of $1,000 from the government. If the family earns $400 in a month, the government payment drops to $700. What is the marginal tax rate in this case?
a) 40 percent.
b) 10 percent.
c) 50 percent.
d) 75 percent.
e) 70 percent.

18.93 (SG 18.15)
Correct: a)
Difficulty: 3
Page(s): 480
Scramble range: All
Topic: Income distribution

18.93
Even if the distribution of wages is symmetric, the distribution of income will be skewed because
a) individuals tend to supply more labour at higher wages.
b) of the uneven distribution of welfare among different groups in society.
c) more people will have incomes that are larger than average.
d) so many rich individuals will be unwilling to work.
e) abilities are distributed symmetrically.

18.94 (SG 18.16)
Correct: a)
Difficulty: 3
Page(s): 467–478
Scramble range: All
Topic: Income and wealth

18.94
Which of the following reduces the inequality of income or wealth relative to the market distribution?
a) Government payments to the poor.
b) A regressive income tax.
c) Large bequests.
d) Assortative mating.
e) The distribution of wealth.

18.95 (SG 18.17)
Correct: d)
Difficulty: 3
Page(s): 484
Scramble range: All
Topic: Distributive justice

18.95
A theory of distributive justice that emphasizes the mechanism by which distribution takes place is
a) a utilitarian theory.
b) an end-state theory.
c) a Rawlsian theory.
d) a process theory.
e) an unfair theory.

18.96 (SG 18.18)
Correct: e)
Difficulty: 4
Page(s): 484
Scramble range: All
Topic: Rawlsian theory

18.96
According to the Rawlsian theory, income should be redistributed if the
a) average person can be made better off.
b) marginal utility is not the same for all individuals.
c) richest person can be made worse off.
d) wage rate is not equal to the marginal product of labour.
e) poorest person can be made better off.

18.97 (SG 18.19)
Correct: e)
Difficulty: 3
Page(s): 483–484
Scramble range: All
Topic: Distributive justice

18.97
Which of the following is an example of an end-state theory of distributive justice?
a) Marginal product theory.
b) The theory of Robert Nozick.
c) The theory of Arthur Okun.
d) The process theory.
e) The utilitarian theory.

18.98 (SG 18.20)
Correct: a)
Difficulty: 3
Page(s): 483
Scramble range: All
Topic: The big tradeoff

18.98
Redistribution of income from the rich to the poor will lead to a reduction in total output. This is known as
a) the big tradeoff.
b) the process theory of distributive justice.
c) market distribution.
d) the capitalist dilemma.
e) Rawlsian justice.

18.99
Correct: e)
Difficulty: 4
Page(s): 484
Scramble range: None
Topic: Labour earnings

18.99
Which of the following statements is *not* true?
a) Labour earns the largest share of total income and that share has increased over the last 50 years.
b) Labour earns the smallest of total income and that share has increased over the last 50 years.
c) Owners of capital earn the smallest share of total income and that share has decreased over the last 50 years.
d) Owners of capital earn the largest share of total income and that share has decreased over the last 50 years.
e) Neither b) nor d) is true.

18.100
Correct: d)
Difficulty: 3
Page(s): 467–478
Scramble range: All
Topic: Wage differences

18.100
For the most part, differences in the wage rates received by different individuals are associated with
a) wealth and assets.
b) holdings of wealth.
c) the elasticity of the output demand function.
d) differences in the marginal productivity of the individuals.
e) differences in the labour supply of the individuals.

18.101
Correct: e)
Difficulty: 4
Page(s): 469
Scramble range: All
Topic: Wealth distribution

18.101
The equality in the distribution of wealth is
a) less than the inequality in the distribution of income.
b) increased by the existence of assortative mating.
c) a better measure of the equality in the distribution of economic resources than is the inequality in the distribution of income.
d) more if we look at the distribution of wealth among the richest 1 percent of all families.
e) more if we look at the distribution of wealth among the poorest 20 percent of all families.

18.102
Correct: e)
Difficulty: 4
Page(s): 474–478
Scramble range: a)–d)
Topic: Distributive justice

18.102
Consider Fact 18.1. A Rawlsian would say that
a) income should be redistributed to Pierre.
b) income should be redistributed to Luigi.
c) wealth should be redistributed to Luigi.
d) wealth should be redistributed to Pierre.
e) none of the above.

Fact 18.1
There are only two people in the world. Pierre has $500,000 in nonhuman wealth, which earns a return of 10 percent, as well as $25,000 in labour income. Luigi has nonhuman wealth of $50,000, which also earns a return of 10 percent per year, as well as a labour income of $70,000 per year.

18.103
Correct: e)
Difficulty: 4
Page(s): 482–484
Scramble range: All
Topic: Distributive justice

18.103
Consider Fact 18.1. A utilitarian would say that
a) income should be redistributed toward Luigi.
b) income should be redistributed toward Pierre.
c) wealth should be redistributed toward Luigi.
d) redistribution depends on the fairness of the process that yielded the distributions of wealth and income.
e) redistribution depends on the marginal utility of the last dollar spend by Pierre versus Luigi.

18.104
Correct: d)
Difficulty: 2
Page(s): 470
Scramble range: All
Topic: Tax system

18.104
If the marginal tax rate decreases as income increases, the income tax is
a) progressive.
b) proportional.
c) negative.
d) regressive.
e) Rawlsian.

18.105
Correct: a)
Difficulty: 4
Page(s): 472–473
Scramble range: All
Topic: Implicit marginal tax rate

18.105
Suppose that if a family earns zero income, it receives a monthly transfer payment of $1,000 from the government. If the family earns $200 in a month, the government payment drops to $800. What is the marginal tax rate in this case?
a) 100 percent.
b) 40 percent.
c) 50 percent.
d) 10 percent.
e) Zero percent.

18.106
Correct: a)
Difficulty: 3
Page(s): 467–478
Scramble range: All
Topic: Income and wealth

18.106
Which of the following increases the inequality of income or wealth relative to the market distribution?
a) Decreases in government payments to the poor.
b) A progressive income tax.
c) Elimination of bequests.
d) Distributive mating.
e) A constant marginal income tax.

18.107
Correct: a)
Difficulty: 4
Page(s): 483–484
Scramble range: All
Topic: Distributive justice

18.107
A theory of distributive justice that emphasizes the satisfaction generated by the income distribution is
a) a utilitarian theory.
b) an end-state theory.
c) a Rawlsian theory.
d) a process theory.
e) a Nozickian theory.

18.108
Correct: b)
Difficulty: 4
Page(s): 483–484
Scramble range: All
Topic: Rawlsian theory

18.108
According to the Rawlsian theory, income should *not* be redistributed if the
a) average person cannot be made better off.
b) poorest person cannot be made better off.
c) richest person cannot be made worse off.
d) wage rate is equal to the marginal product of labour.
e) marginal utility is the same for all individuals.

18.109
Correct: e)
Difficulty: 4
Page(s): 482–484
Scramble range: All
Topic: Distributive justice

18.109
Consider Fact 18.1. A Nozickian would say that
a) income should be redistributed towards Pierre.
b) income should be redistributed towards Luigi.
c) wealth should be redistributed towards Luigi.
d) redistribution depends on whether the marginal utility of the last dollar spend is equal for Pierre and Luigi.
e) it depends on whether the process that generated the income and wealth distributions is fair or not.

Chapter 19 **Market Failure**

19.1
Correct: b)
Difficulty: 2
Page(s): 495
Scramble range: All
Topic: The scope of government

19.1
The government consists of many separate organizations. To the nearest factor of ten, the Canadian government consists of
a) 400 separate organizations.
b) 4,000 separate organizations.
c) 40,000 separate organizations.
d) 400,000 separate organizations.
e) 4 million separate organizations.

19.2
Correct: c)
Difficulty: 2
Page(s): 495
Scramble range: All
Topic: Size of government

19.2
The government, including the sum of federal, provincial, and local government, in the year 1990, accounts for what share of national income (to the nearest 1 percent)?
a) 3 percent.
b) 13 percent.
c) 33 percent.
d) 43 percent.
e) 53 percent.

19.3
Correct: b)
Difficulty: 2
Page(s): 495
Scramble range: All
Topic: Size of government

19.3
The government, including the sum of federal, provincial, and local government, in the year 1940, accounted for what share of national income (to the nearest 10 percent)?
a) 5 percent.
b) 20 percent.
c) 30 percent.
d) 40 percent.
e) 50 percent.

19.4
Correct: d)
Difficulty: 2
Page(s): 495
Scramble range: All
Topic: Size of government

19.4
Government employment at the end of the 1980s was about
a) 2,500,000.
b) 1,000,000.
c) 500,000.
d) 250,000.
e) 50,000.

19.5
Correct: a)
Difficulty: 3
Page(s): 496
Scramble range: All
Topic: Market failure

19.5
Market failure arises due to all of the following reasons *except*
a) an unfair distribution of resources.
b) some goods and services are necessarily in common.
c) external costs are present in production.
d) external benefits are present in production.
e) production of some goods is restricted by monopolies and cartels.

19.6
Correct: e)
Difficulty: 3
Page(s): 496
Scramble range: None
Topic: Redistribution

19.6
Governments redistribute wealth and income because
a) of a desire for distributive justice.
b) of positive economics.
c) of rent-seeking behaviour.
d) both a) and b).
e) both a) and c).

19.7
Correct: b)
Difficulty: 3
Page(s): 495
Scramble range: All
Topic: Positive analysis of government

19.7
Positive analysis of government
a) stresses the good that the government creates.
b) explains the reasons for and the effects of government choices.
c) evaluates the desirability of government action.
d) seeks to gain support for future growth in the size of government.
e) predicts that government action will take place to achieve efficiency.

19.8
Correct: b)
Difficulty: 3
Page(s): 496
Scramble range: All
Topic: Positive analysis of government

19.8
Explaining the reasons for and the effects of government is
a) normative analysis of government.
b) positive analysis of government.
c) both positive and normative analysis.
d) neither positive nor normative analysis.
e) a public interest theory of government.

19.9
Correct: c)
Difficulty: 3
Page(s): 496
Scramble range: All
Topic: Normative analysis of government

19.9
Normative analysis of government
a) stresses the good that the government creates.
b) explains the reasons for and the effects of government choices.
c) evaluates the desirability of government action.
d) seeks to gain support for future growth in the size of government.
e) is a public choice theory of government.

19.10
Correct: b)
Difficulty: 3
Page(s): 496
Scramble range: All
Topic: Positive analysis of government

19.10
Explaining the consequences of government actions is
a) normative analysis of government.
b) positive analysis of government.
c) both positive and normative analysis of government.
d) neither positive nor normative analysis of government.
e) public interest theory.

19.11
Correct: a)
Difficulty: 3
Page(s): 496
Scramble range: All
Topic: Normative analysis of government

19.11
Evaluating the desirability of government action is a part of
a) normative analysis of government.
b) positive analysis of government.
c) both positive and normative analysis of government.
d) neither positive nor normative analysis of government.
e) public choice theory.

19.12
Correct: a)
Difficulty: 3
Page(s): 496
Scramble range: All
Topic: Normative analysis of government

19.12
Arguing for or against a proposal of government is a part of
a) normative analysis of government.
b) positive analysis of government.
c) both positive and normative analysis of government.
d) neither positive nor normative analysis of government.
e) public interest theory.

19.13
Correct: a)
Difficulty: 2
Page(s): 496
Scramble range: All
Topic: Normative analysis of government

19.13
"The government should increase taxes to reduce the federal budget deficit." This is an example of
a) normative analysis of government.
b) positive analysis of government.
c) both positive and normative analysis of government.
d) neither positive nor normative analysis of government.
e) public interest analysis of government.

19.14
Correct: e)
Difficulty: 2
Page(s): 496
Scramble range: All
Topic: Government economic action

19.14
Much government economic action originates from what aspect of economic life?
a) Natural disasters.
b) Stock market crashes.
c) Inflation.
d) Unionization of industry.
e) Market failure.

19.15
Correct: a)
Difficulty: 2
Page(s): 496
Scramble range: All
Topic: Government economic action

19.15
Much government economic action originates from what aspect of economic life?
a) Redistribution of income.
b) Stock market crashes.
c) Unemployment.
d) Education.
e) The will of the people.

19.16
Correct: e)
Difficulty: 3
Page(s): 496
Scramble range: All
Topic: Market failure

19.16
Which of the following refers to what economists call market failure?
a) The low quality of many mass-produced goods.
b) An unfair wealth distribution due to inheritances.
c) The rising cost of living.
d) Persistent unemployment.
e) The provision of goods and services that we consume in common with everyone else.

19.17
Correct: c)
Difficulty: 3
Page(s): 496
Scramble range: All
Topic: Market failure

19.17
Which of the following refers to what economists call market failure?
a) The high cost of many mass-produced goods.
b) The rising frequency of bank failures.
c) The production of goods or services where external costs or benefits are present.
d) Discrimination again women in many types of employment.
e) High interest rates.

19.18
Correct: e)
Difficulty: 2
Page(s): 496
Scramble range: All
Topic: Market failure

19.18
Which of the following refers to what economists call market failure?
a) The number of people below the poverty line.
b) Quotas on imported Japanese automobiles.
c) The lack of low-cost, yet safe, urban housing.
d) The growing number of crimes involving the purchase of hand guns.
e) The restriction of output by monopolies.

19.19
Correct: d)
Difficulty: 3
Page(s): 496
Scramble range: All
Topic: Market failure

19.19
Which of the following refers to what economists call market failure?
a) The growing threat of foreign investment in Canada.
b) The huge federal budget deficit that seems impossible to reduce.
c) Laws concerning bankruptcy.
d) The formation of cartels that act like monopolies.
e) The minimum wage.

19.20
Correct: a)
Difficulty: 2
Page(s): 496
Scramble range: All
Topic: Market failure

19.20
In the case of market failure, unregulated markets will
a) fail to achieve an efficient allocation of resources.
b) will guarantee an efficient allocation of resources.
c) result in rising cost of production.
d) keep prices low.
e) do better than if the government intervenes.

19.21
Correct: b)
Difficulty: 3
Page(s): 496
Scramble range: All
Topic: Market failure

19.21
In the case of market failure, unregulated markets will
a) fail to achieve an inefficient allocation of resources.
b) produce an output level for which the marginal social cost does not equal the marginal social benefit.
c) result in decreasing cost of production.
d) produce too little output.
e) produce too much output.

19.22
Correct: b)
Difficulty: 2
Page(s): 496
Scramble range: All
Topic: Redistribution of income

19.22
Redistribution of income or wealth concerns
a) commutative justice.
b) distributive justice.
c) pollution regulations.
d) public transit systems charging low prices.
e) governments more than market failure does.

19.23
Correct: b)
Difficulty: 3
Page(s): 496
Scramble range: All
Topic: Income redistribution

19.23
When governments redistribute income or wealth

a) they create wealth and income.
b) they reduce income and wealth for some people and increase the income and wealth for other people.
c) income and wealth is reduced for all people, except those people who work for the government.
d) they increase income and wealth for all the people who are citizens of the country.
e) they create market failures.

19.24
Correct: e)
Difficulty: 2
Page(s): 496
Scramble range: All
Topic: Positive and normative statements

19.24
Many people feel that an unregulated market system will result in an unfair distribution of income and wealth. This statement is a(n)

a) example of market failure.
b) positive statement.
c) neither a positive nor normative statement.
d) both a positive and a normative statement.
e) normative statement.

19.25
Correct: e)
Difficulty: 2
Page(s): 496
Scramble range: All
Topic: Positive and normative statements

19.25
Many people feel that a regulated market system will result in an unfair distribution of income and wealth. This statement is a(n)

a) example of market failure.
b) positive statement.
c) neither a positive nor normative statement.
d) both a positive and a normative statement.
e) normative statement.

19.26
Correct: a)
Difficulty: 2
Page(s): 496
Scramble range: All
Topic: Positive and normative statements

19.26
Government ought to redistribute income and wealth since some people are too rich and other people are too poor. This statement is a(n)

a) normative statement.
b) positive statement.
c) neither a positive nor normative statement.
d) both a positive and a normative statement.
e) example of public choice theory in action.

19.27
Correct: d)
Difficulty: 2
Page(s): 496
Scramble range: All
Topic: Types of economic theory of government

19.27
One economic theory of government is the

a) positive theory.
b) private interest theory.
c) private choice theory.
d) public choice theory.
e) multinational theory of government.

19.28
Correct: b)
Difficulty: 2
Page(s): 496
Scramble range: All
Topic: Types of economic theory of government

19.28
One economic theory of government is the
a) private choice theory.
b) public interest theory.
c) theory of the leisure class.
d) national theory of government.
e) normative theory of government.

19.29
Correct: c)
Difficulty: 2
Page(s): 496
Scramble range: All
Topic: Public interest theory of government

19.29
The public interest theory of government argues that government officials act to
a) maximize the likelihood of their re-election.
b) maximize the amount of their campaign contributions.
c) eliminate waste and promote an efficient allocation of resources.
d) maximize the exchange value of their office.
e) promote the redistribution of wealth and income.

19.30
Correct: e)
Difficulty: 2
Page(s): 496
Scramble range: All
Topic: Public interest theory of government

19.30
Public choice theory explains that government officials
a) act to promote the redistribution of wealth and income.
b) act to maximize the amount of their campaign contributions.
c) act to eliminate waste and promote an efficient allocation of resources.
d) act to maximize the exchange value of their office.
e) sell their services in a political marketplace.

19.31
Correct: d)
Difficulty: 2
Page(s): 497
Scramble range: All
Topic: Rivalrous consumption

19.31
Private goods are those for which consumption is
a) nonrivalrous.
b) nonexcludable.
c) regulated.
d) rivalrous.
e) unregulated.

19.32
Correct: d)
Difficulty: 2
Page(s): 497
Scramble range: All
Topic: Public goods

19.32
When consumption is nonrivalrous and nonexclusive, the product is a
a) publicly provided good.
b) private good.
c) mixed good.
d) public good.
e) service.

19.33
Correct: d)
Difficulty: 2
Page(s): 497
Scramble range: All
Topic: Private goods

19.33
When consumption is rivalrous and exclusive, the product is a
a) publicly provided good.
b) public good.
c) mixed good.
d) private good.
e) service.

19.34
Correct: e)
Difficulty: 2
Page(s): 497
Scramble range: All
Topic: Private goods

19.34
Travel on a limited-access toll road is an example of a
a) public good.
b) publicly provided good.
c) mixed good.
d) service.
e) private good.

19.35
Correct: d)
Difficulty: 2
Page(s): 497
Scramble range: All
Topic: Rivalrous consumption

19.35
Public goods are those for which consumption is
a) excludable.
b) rivalrous.
c) regulated.
d) nonrivalrous.
e) unregulated.

19.36
Correct: b)
Difficulty: 2
Page(s): 497
Scramble range: All
Topic: Nonexcludability

19.36
Public goods are those for which
a) those people who do not pay can be excluded from the consumption.
b) those people who do not pay cannot be excluded from the consumption.
c) consumers generally must pay a high price.
d) consumers generally must pay a low price.
e) production is carried out by the government.

19.37
Correct: b)
Difficulty: 2
Page(s): 497
Scramble range: All
Topic: Free riding

19.37
Free riding
a) is possible if the consumption of the good or service is characterized by excludability.
b) is possible if the consumption of the good or service is characterized by nonexcludability.
c) is a characteristic of pure private goods.
d) is due to consumers paying excessively high prices for goods and services provided by the government.
e) is due to the government providing the good for nothing.

19.38
Correct: a)
Difficulty: 2
Page(s): 499
Scramble range: All
Topic: Demand for public goods

19.38
The market demand for a public good is derived by
a) adding the marginal benefits for all the consumers for given amounts of consumption of the good.
b) adding the quantities demanded for all the consumers for given prices charged.
c) surveying consumers and asking how much they use a certain good or service.
d) adding the total benefits for all the consumers for given amounts of consumption of the good.
e) adding up all the prices of the good.

19.39
Correct: d)
Difficulty: 3
Page(s): 501
Scramble range: All
Topic: Private provision of public goods

19.39
Private provision of public goods
a) fails because the private firm will always go broke.
b) succeeds because public provision is often more costly.
c) succeeds if consumers expect to obtain marginal benefits from the consumption of the public good.
d) fails because of the free-rider problem.
e) fails because private firms generally charge higher prices than public firms, and therefore lose customers.

19.40
Correct: c)
Difficulty: 3
Page(s): 501
Scramble range: All
Topic: Private provision of public goods

19.40
Private provision of public goods
a) fails because of rivalry.
b) succeeds because public provision is often less costly.
c) fails because of the inability to collect a price from the consumers of the product.
d) fails because private firms generally have higher production costs than public operations.
e) succeeds if consumers expect to obtain marginal benefits from the consumption of the public good.

19.41
Correct: a)
Difficulty: 3
Page(s): 505
Scramble range: None
Topic: Externalities

19.41
An example of a negative externality is
a) a chemical factory dumping waste in a river upstream from a popular fishing spot.
b) a chemical factory producing fertilizers that do not, in fact, help plants grow.
c) a chemical factory producing fertilizers that kill plants, rather than help them as advertised.
d) a chemical factory that enters a town and bids up wages and therefore the costs of other firms.
e) both a) and d).

19.42
Correct: b)
Difficulty: 2
Page(s): 505
Scramble range: All
Topic: Externalities

19.42
Immunizations from communicable diseases generates
a) negative externalities.
b) positive externalities.
c) market failures.
d) the provision of public goods.
e) too much output.

19.43
Correct: b)
Difficulty: 2
Page(s): 505
Scramble range: All
Topic: Externalities

19.43
Beautification of the national highways through the planting of shrubs and wildflowers
a) would be profitable for a private landscaping company.
b) would bestow benefits even to people who do not help pay for the shrubs and flowers.
c) would provide a flow of services that would involve rivalrous consumption.
d) would provide a flow of services that would involve exclusive consumption.
e) should be provided by the government.

19.44
Correct: a)
Difficulty: 2
Page(s): 505
Scramble range: None
Topic: Externalities

19.44
Positive externalities are
a) benefits received by those who do not pay the price of the product.
b) costs imposed on those who do not pay the price of the product.
c) benefits received by those who do pay for the product.
d) costs imposed on those who do pay the price of the product.
e) both a) and b).

19.45
Correct: b)
Difficulty: 2
Page(s): 505
Scramble range: None
Topic: Externalities

19.45
Negative externalities are
a) benefits received by those who do not pay the price of the product.
b) costs imposed on those who do not receive the revenues from the sale of the product.
c) benefits received by those who do pay for the product.
d) costs imposed on those who do pay the price of the product.
e) both b) and d).

19.46
Correct: e)
Difficulty: 3
Page(s): 505–507
Scramble range: All
Topic: Private property rights

19.46
One way to solve externality problems is to
a) organize a limited boycott of the products.
b) tax the positive externalities and subsidize the negative externalities.
c) establish and enforce property rights in common.
d) petition for redress of grievances.
e) establish and enforce private property rights.

19.47
Correct: d)
Difficulty: 3
Page(s): 505–507
Scramble range: All
Topic: Externalities

19.47
Refer to Figure 19.1. Given in this figure are the private and social marginal cost functions and the market demand function. If the market is unregulated, then the output will be
a) zero.
b) Q_1.
c) Q_2.
d) Q_3.
e) too low.

Figure 19.1

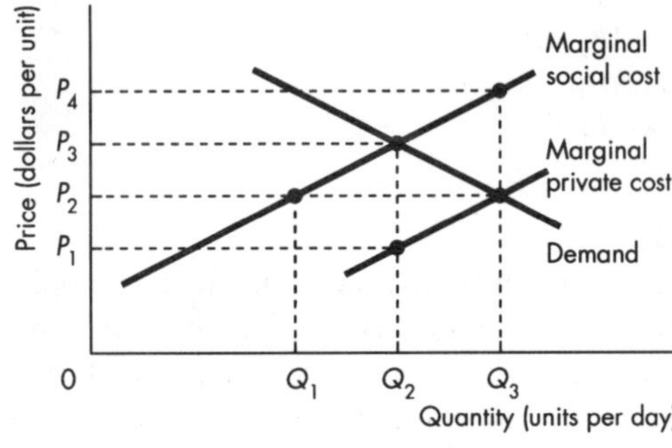

19.48
Correct: d)
Difficulty: 3
Page(s): 505–507
Scramble range: All
Topic: Externalities

19.48
Refer to Figure 19.1. Given in this figure are the private and social marginal cost functions and the market demand function. If the market is unregulated, then the price will be
a) P_1.
b) P_4.
c) below P_1.
d) P_2.
e) P_3.

19.49
Correct: b)
Difficulty: 3
Page(s): 505–507
Scramble range: All
Topic: Externalities

19.49
Refer to Figure 19.1. Given in this figure are the private and social marginal cost functions and the market demand function. If the market is unregulated, then at the equilibrium output level the marginal social cost of production is
a) less than the marginal benefit to consumers.
b) greater than the marginal benefit to consumers.
c) equal to the marginal benefit to consumers.
d) equal to the marginal private cost of production.
e) less than the marginal private cost of production.

19.50
Correct: c)
Difficulty: 4
Page(s): 505–507
Scramble range: All
Topic: Externalities

19.50
Refer to Figure 19.1. Given in this figure are the private and social marginal cost functions and the market demand function. If the market is unregulated, then
a) the level of output is correct, but price is too low.
b) too little output will be produced.
c) too much output will be produced.
d) the allocation of resources will be minimized.
e) the allocation of resources will be efficient.

19.51
Correct: c)
Difficulty: 5
Page(s): 505–507
Scramble range: All
Topic: Externalities

19.51
Refer to Figure 19.1. Given in this figure are the private and social marginal cost functions and the market demand function. In order to promote an efficient allocation of resources, the government could impose an excise tax equal to
a) zero.
b) P_1.
c) $P_3 - P_1$.
d) $P_4 - P_1$.
e) $P_3 - P_2$.

19.52
Correct: c)
Difficulty: 4
Page(s): 505–507
Scramble range: All
Topic: Externalities

19.52
Refer to Figure 19.1. Given in this figure are the private and social marginal cost functions and the market demand function. If an excise tax is imposed which generates an efficient allocation of resources, then the output level will be
a) zero, as the industry will be shut down.
b) Q_1.
c) Q_2.
d) Q_3.
e) greater than Q_3.

19.53
Correct: d)
Difficulty: 5
Page(s): 505–507
Scramble range: All
Topic: Externalities

19.53
Refer to Figure 19.1. Given in this figure are the private and social marginal cost functions and the market demand function. If an excise tax is imposed which generates an efficient allocation of resources, then consumers will pay a price of
a) zero, as the industry will be shut down.
b) P_1.
c) P_2.
d) P_3.
e) P_4.

19.54
Correct: e)
Difficulty: 5
Page(s): 505–507
Scramble range: All
Topic: Externalities

19.54
Refer to Figure 19.1. Given in this figure are the private and social marginal cost functions and the market demand function. If an excise tax is imposed which generates an efficient allocation of resources, then producers will receive a price of
a) zero, as the industry will be shut down.
b) P_4.
c) P_3.
d) P_2.
e) P_1.

19.55
Correct: c)
Difficulty: 3
Page(s): 505–507
Scramble range: All
Topic: Externalities

19.55
Refer to Figure 19.2. Given in this figure are the marginal private benefit and marginal social benefit functions and the market supply function. If the market is unregulated, then the output will be
a) zero.
b) Q_1.
c) Q_2.
d) Q_3.
e) between 0 and Q_1.

Figure 19.2

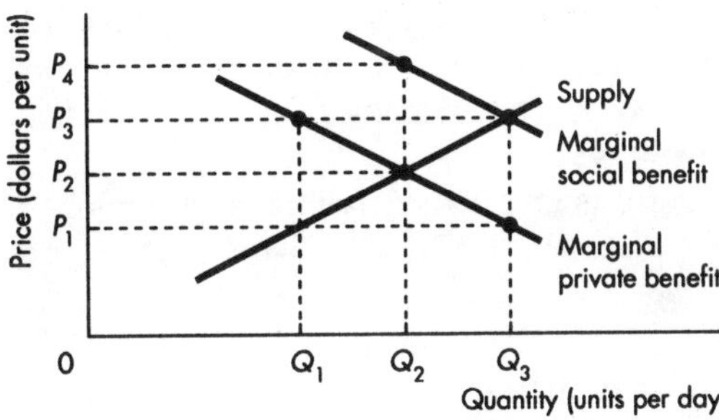

19.56
Correct: c)
Difficulty: 3
Page(s): 505–507
Scramble range: All
Topic: Externalities

19.56
Refer to Figure 19.2. Given in this figure are the marginal private benefit and marginal social benefit functions and the market supply function. If the market is unregulated, then the price will be
a) P_1.
b) P_3.
c) P_2.
d) greater than P_4.
e) P_4.

19.57
Correct: e)
Difficulty: 4
Page(s): 505–507
Scramble range: All
Topic: Externalities

19.57
Refer to Figure 19.2. Given in this figure are the marginal private benefit and marginal social benefit functions and the market supply function. If the market is unregulated, then at the equilibrium output level the marginal social benefit from consumption is
a) less than the marginal cost to producers.
b) less than the marginal social cost of production.
c) equal to the marginal cost to producers.
d) equal to the marginal private benefit from consumption.
e) greater than the marginal cost to producers.

19.58
Correct: e)
Difficulty: 4
Page(s): 505–507
Scramble range: None
Topic: Externalities

19.58
Refer to Figure 19.2. Given in this figure are the marginal private benefit and marginal social benefit functions and the market supply function. If the market is unregulated, then
a) too much output will be produced.
b) too little output will be produced.
c) the allocation of resources will be inefficient.
d) the allocation of resources will be minimized.
e) both b) and c).

19.59
Correct: c)
Difficulty: 5
Page(s): 505–507
Scramble range: All
Topic: Externalities

19.59
Refer to Figure 19.2. Given in this figure are the marginal private benefit and marginal social benefit functions and the market supply function. In order to promote an efficient allocation of resources the government could grant a subsidy equal to
a) zero.
b) P_1.
c) $P_3 - P_1$.
d) $P_4 - P_1$.
e) $P_2 - P_1$.

19.60
Correct: d)
Difficulty: 4
Page(s): 505–507
Scramble range: All
Topic: Externalities

19.60
Refer to Figure 19.2. Given in this figure are the marginal private benefit and marginal social benefit functions and the market supply function. If a subsidy is granted which generates an efficient allocation of resources, then the output level will be
a) zero, as the industry will be shut down.
b) Q_1.
c) Q_2.
d) Q_3.
e) greater than Q_3.

19.61
Correct: b)
Difficulty: 5
Page(s): 505–507
Scramble range: All
Topic: Externalities

19.61
Refer to Figure 19.2. Given in this figure are the marginal private benefit and marginal social benefit functions and the market supply function. If a subsidy is granted to consumers which generates an efficient allocation of resources, then consumers will pay a net price of
a) zero, as the industry will be shut down.
b) P_1.
c) P_2.
d) P_3.
e) P_4.

19.62
Correct: d)
Difficulty: 5
Page(s): 505–507
Scramble range: All
Topic: Externalities

19.62
Refer to Figure 19.2. Given in this figure are the marginal private benefit and marginal social benefit functions and the market supply function. If a consumption subsidy is granted to consumers which generates an efficient allocation of resources, then producers will receive a price of
a) zero, as the industry will be shut down.
b) P_1.
c) P_2.
d) P_3.
e) P_4.

19.63
Correct: a)
Difficulty: 2
Page(s): 498
Scramble range: All
Topic: Public goods

19.63
An example of a pure public good is
a) national defence services.
b) a Ford truck.
c) a loaf of bread.
d) a home computer.
e) a television.

19.64
Correct: a)
Difficulty: 2
Page(s): 505
Scramble range: All
Topic: Externalities

19.64
An example of an activity that generates positive externalities is
a) primary school education.
b) waste water poured into a stream by a factory.
c) an old truck that produces black exhaust.
d) eating an apple.
e) decorating your living room in a style you like.

19.65
Correct: a)
Difficulty: 2
Page(s): 505
Scramble range: All
Topic: Externalities

19.65
An example of an activity that generates negative externalities is
a) a laundry dumping dirty soap suds into a river where fishermen fish.
b) national defence services.
c) planting flowers along the interstate highway.
d) eating an apple.
e) decorating your living room in a style you like.

19.66
Correct: c)
Difficulty: 4
Page(s): 505–507
Scramble range: All
Topic: Externalities

19.66
The efficient level of pollution in the environment is
a) zero.
b) zero if the cleanup costs are less than $1 billion.
c) the level at which the marginal cost of cleanup equals the marginal benefit of the cleanup.
d) that which preserves all species for future generations.
e) whatever level the free market decides.

19.67
Correct: b)
Difficulty: 3
Page(s): 505
Scramble range: All
Topic: Externalities

19.67
Effective strategies for addressing the problem of pollution and externalities include
a) taxing the profit of polluting companies at twice the rate of nonpolluting companies.
b) imposing taxes on the activity that generates the pollution.
c) stressing the use of renewable resources.
d) imposing recycling laws.
e) closing down a polluting industry.

19.68
Correct: c)
Difficulty: 4
Page(s): 497
Scramble range: All
Topic: Public choice

19.68
Government could "fail" according to public choice theory because
a) government officials do not listen to the pleading of special interest groups.
b) lobbyists would write legislation instead of the elected officials.
c) government officials would more likely consider the interests of the special interest groups than the national interest.
d) the benefits of the government action would be greater than the costs.
e) government cannot calculate the levels of externalities since there is no market for them.

19.69
Correct: d)
Difficulty: 3
Page(s): 505–507
Scramble range: All
Topic: Profit maximization

19.69
Refer to Table 19.1. Given in the table are the marginal private benefits and costs for the production of chemical fertilizer. If there are no externalities in the production and consumption of fertilizer and if the market is perfectly competitive, then the output level of fertilizer will be
a) 1 unit.
b) 2 units.
c) 3 units.
d) 4 units.
e) 5 units.

Table 19.1

Output	Marginal private benefit	Marginal private cost
0	80	0
1	70	10
2	60	20
3	50	30
4	40	40
5	30	50
6	20	60

19.70
Correct: d)
Difficulty: 3
Page(s): 505–507
Scramble range: All
Topic: Profit maximization

19.70
Refer to Table 19.1. Given in the table are the marginal private benefits and costs for the production of chemical fertilizer. If there are no externalities in the production and consumption of fertilizer and if the market is perfectly competitive, then the price of fertilizer will be
a) $70.
b) $60.
c) $50.
d) $40.
e) $30.

19.71
Correct: e)
Difficulty: 3
Page(s): 505–507
Scramble range: All
Topic: Externalities

19.71
Refer to Table 19.2. Given in the table are the marginal private and social costs for the production of chemical fertilizer and the marginal private benefit from the consumption of fertilizer. Under these circumstances,

a) there are positive externalities associated with this market.
b) there are negative externalities associated with this market, equal to $10 per unit.
c) there are no externalities associated with this market.
d) not enough information is provided to determine whether or not there are externalities.
e) there are negative externalities associated with this market, equal to $20 per unit.

Table 19.2

Output	Marginal private benefit	Marginal private cost	Marginal social cost
0	80	0	20
1	70	10	30
2	60	20	40
3	50	30	50
4	40	40	60
5	30	50	70
6	20	60	80

19.72
Correct: d)
Difficulty: 3
Page(s): 505–507
Scramble range: All
Topic: Profit maximization

19.72
Refer to Table 19.2. Given in the table are the marginal private and social costs for the production of chemical fertilizer and the marginal private benefit from the consumption of fertilizer. Assume the market is perfectly competitive. Under these circumstances, the output level of fertilizer will be

a) 1 unit.
b) 2 units.
c) 3 units.
d) 4 units.
e) 5 units.

19.73
Correct: d)
Difficulty: 3
Page(s): 505–507
Scramble range: All
Topic: Profit maximization

19.73
Refer to Table 19.2. Given in the table are the marginal private and social costs for the production of chemical fertilizer and the marginal private benefit from the consumption of fertilizer. Assume the market is perfectly competitive. At the profit-maximizing output level, the market price will be

a) $10.
b) $20.
c) $30.
d) $40.
e) $50.

19.74
Correct: c)
Difficulty: 5
Page(s): 505–507
Scramble range: All
Topic: Externalities

19.74
Refer to Table 19.2. Given in the table are the marginal private and social costs for the production of chemical fertilizer and the marginal private benefit from the consumption of fertilizer. Assume the market is perfectly competitive. At the profit-maximizing output level, the marginal

a) social cost equals the marginal private benefit.
b) private cost is less than the marginal private benefit.
c) private cost equals the marginal private benefit.
d) social cost is equal to the marginal private benefit.
e) private cost is greater than marginal private benefit.

19.75
Correct: b)
Difficulty: 3
Page(s): 505–507
Scramble range: All
Topic: Externalities

19.75
Refer to Table 19.2. Given in the table are the marginal private and social costs for the production of chemical fertilizer and the marginal private benefit from the consumption of fertilizer. Assume the market is perfectly competitive. At the profit-maximizing output level,

a) the resource allocation is efficient.
b) the resource allocation is inefficient.
c) too few units of fertilizer are produced.
d) consumers must pay too high a price for their fertilizer.
e) production is technologically inefficient.

19.76
Correct: a)
Difficulty: 3
Page(s): 505–507
Scramble range: All
Topic: Externalities

19.76
Refer to Table 19.3. Given in the table are the marginal private and social benefits for the consumption of chemical fertilizer and the marginal private cost of the production fertilizer. Under these circumstances,

a) there are positive externalities of $20 associated with this market.
b) there are negative externalities associated with this market.
c) there are no externalities associated with this market.
d) not enough information is provided to determine whether or not there are externalities.
e) there are positive externalities of $10 associated with this market.

Table 19.3

Output	Marginal private benefit	Marginal private cost	Marginal social benefit
0	80	20	100
1	70	30	90
2	60	40	80
3	50	50	70
4	40	60	60
5	30	70	50
6	20	80	40

19.77
Correct: c)
Difficulty: 3
Page(s): 505–507
Scramble range: All
Topic: Profit maximization

19.77
Refer to Table 19.3. Given in the table are the marginal private and social benefits for the consumption of chemical fertilizer and the marginal private cost of the production fertilizer. If the market is competitive, the output level of fertilizer will be
a) 1 unit.
b) 2 units.
c) 3 units.
d) 4 units.
e) 5 units.

19.78
Correct: c)
Difficulty: 3
Page(s): 505–507
Scramble range: All
Topic: Profit maximization

19.78
Refer to Table 19.3. Given in the table are the marginal private and social benefits for the consumption of chemical fertilizer and the marginal private cost of the production fertilizer. If the market is competitive, at the profit-maximizing output level the market price will be
a) $70.
b) $60.
c) $50.
d) $40.
e) $30.

19.79
Correct: a)
Difficulty: 4
Page(s): 505–507
Scramble range: All
Topic: Externalities

19.79
Refer to Table 19.3. Given in the table are the marginal private and social benefits for the consumption of chemical fertilizer and the marginal private cost of the production fertilizer. If the market is competitive, at the profit-maximizing output level marginal
a) private cost equals the marginal private benefit.
b) private cost is less than the marginal private benefit.
c) social cost is less than the marginal private benefit.
d) social cost is greater than the marginal private benefit.
e) social benefit is less than marginal private benefit.

19.80
Correct: e)
Difficulty: 4
Page(s): 505–507
Scramble range: All
Topic: Externalities

19.80
Refer to Table 19.3. Given in the table are the marginal private and social benefits for the consumption of chemical fertilizer and the marginal private cost of the production fertilizer. If the market is competitive, at the profit-maximizing output level
a) resource allocation is efficient.
b) an excise tax should be imposed.
c) too many units of fertilizer are produced.
d) consumers must pay too low a price for their fertilizer.
e) resource allocation is inefficient.

19.81
Correct: c)
Difficulty: 3
Page(s): 495
Scramble range: All
Topic: Size of government

19.81
Which of the following is *not* a true statement about the Canadian government?
a) Since 1940, the share of total government spending has risen from less than a fifth to about a third of all spending.
b) The three levels of government are federal, provincial, and local.
c) The government provides all security services.
d) At all levels, government employs about 250,000 workers.
e) The Fraser Institute thinks that government is too big in Canada.

19.82
Correct: c)
Difficulty: 4
Page(s): 497
Scramble range: All
Topic: Federal government employment

19.82
Which of the following is an example of how public interest theory thinks government works?
a) Building a dam to please your constituents.
b) Selecting which shipyard gets to build a warship due to political pressure.
c) Building a lighthouse, because the private market cannot do it due to free-riding problems.
d) Subsidizing a failing industry to save jobs.
e) Building up a large bureaucracy.

19.83 (SG 19.3)
Correct: e)
Difficulty: 3
Page(s): 496
Scramble range: All
Topic: Welfare judgements

19.83
If, in an unregulated economy, it is possible for someone to be made better off without making anyone worse off, then
a) income is distributed unfairly.
b) total benefit is at a maximum.
c) allocative efficiency has been achieved.
d) net benefit is at a maximum.
e) we have market failure.

19.84 (SG 19.4)
Correct: c)
Difficulty: 3
Page(s): 496
Scramble range: All
Topic: Market failure

19.84
In the production of which of the following are we *least* likely to experience market failure?
a) Education.
b) National defence.
c) Bread.
d) Chemical fertilizer.
e) Immunization treatment.

19.85
Correct: d)
Difficulty: 3
Page(s): 496
Scramble range: All
Topic: Market failure

19.85
Which of the following is *not* a situation in which market failure rises?
a) When there are public goods.
b) When cartels collude to restrict output.
c) When externalities exist.
d) When competition is very strong.
e) When there is pollution.

19.86 (SG 19.5)
Correct: c)
Difficulty: 3
Page(s): 496
Scramble range: All
Topic: Market failure

19.86
When market failure occurs, the government will act to reduce the level of inefficiency. This is a prediction of
a) an end-state theory of government behaviour.
b) a process theory of government behaviour.
c) a public interest theory of government behaviour.
d) a public choice theory of government behaviour.
e) maximizing behaviour.

19.87 (SG 19.7)
Correct: a)
Difficulty: 2
Page(s): 497
Scramble range: All
Topic: Public and private goods

19.87
A good that exhibits both rivalry and excludability is a
a) private good.
b) public good.
c) government good.
d) mixed good.
e) free-rider good.

19.88 (SG 19.8)
Correct: e)
Difficulty: 2
Page(s): 497
Scramble range: All
Topic: Public goods

19.88
Governments provide pure public goods like national defence because
a) governments are more efficient than private firms at producing goods.
b) of the free-rider problem which results in over production by private markets.
c) people do not value national defence very highly.
d) of the potential that private firms will make excess profits.
e) of the free-rider problem which results in under production by private markets.

19.89 (SG 19.9)
Correct: c)
Difficulty: 3
Page(s): 497
Scramble range: All
Topic: Public goods

19.89
Which of the following goods has the nonexcludability feature?
a) A city bus.
b) A bridge that charges a toll.
c) National defence.
d) An art museum.
e) A television.

19.90 (SG 19.10)
Correct: c)
Difficulty: 2
Page(s): 497
Scramble range: All
Topic: Market demand for private goods

19.90
The market demand curve for a private good is obtained by summing the individual
a) marginal cost curves horizontally.
b) marginal cost curves vertically.
c) marginal benefit curves horizontally.
d) marginal benefit curves vertically.
e) total benefit curves horizontally.

19.91 (SG 19.11)
Correct: d)
Difficulty: 3
Page(s): 497–503
Scramble range: All
Topic: Demand for public goods

19.91
The economy's total demand curve for a public good is obtained by summing the individual
a) marginal cost curves horizontally.
b) marginal cost curves vertically.
c) marginal benefit curves horizontally.
d) marginal benefit curves vertically.
e) total benefit curves vertically.

19.92 (SG 19.12)
Correct: a)
Difficulty: 3
Page(s): 497
Scramble range: All
Topic: Public goods

19.92
The total benefit of a given level of provision of a public good can be obtained by
a) adding the marginal benefit of each level of provision up to the given level.
b) adding the marginal benefit of each level of provision and then subtracting the marginal cost of each level of provision.
c) adding the net benefit of each level of provision up to the given level.
d) multiplying net benefit by the quantity of the public good provided.
e) multiplying marginal benefit by the quantity of the public good provided.

19.93 (SG 19.13)
Correct: b)
Difficulty: 2
Page(s): 501
Scramble range: All
Topic: Externalities

19.93
An externality is
a) the effect of government regulation on market price and output.
b) a cost or benefit that arises from a decision but is not borne by the decision maker.
c) the amount by which price exceeds marginal cost.
d) someone who consumes a good without paying for it.
e) a good which people cannot be excluded from consuming.

19.94 (SG 19.14)
Correct: d)
Difficulty: 2
Page(s): 501
Scramble range: All
Topic: External costs

19.94
Which of the following illustrates the concept of external cost?
a) Bad weather reduces the size of the wheat crop.
b) A reduction in the size of the wheat crop causes the income of wheat farmers to fall.
c) Smoking harms the health of the smoker.
d) Smoking harms the health of nonsmokers who are nearby.
e) Immunization prevents the spread of disease.

19.95 (SG 19.15)
Correct: a)
Difficulty: 3
Page(s): 505–507
Scramble range: All
Topic: Externalities

19.95
Figure 19.3 depicts the demand for good *A* as well as the marginal private cost (*MPC*) and marginal social cost (*MSC*) associated with the production of good *A*. Production of the sixth unit of output generates an external
a) cost of $2.50.
b) cost of $6.
c) benefit of $2.50.
d) benefit of $6.
e) cost of $3.50.

Figure 19.3

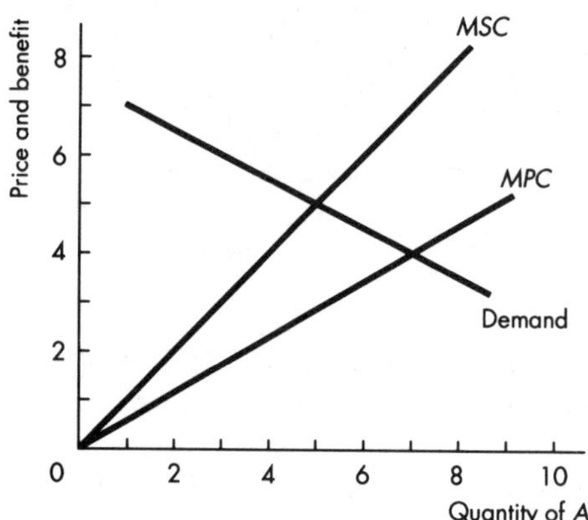

19.96 (SG 19.16)
Correct: e)
Difficulty: 3
Page(s): 505–507
Scramble range: All
Topic: Externalities

19.96
Refer to Figure 19.3. How many units of good *A* will be produced in an unregulated market?
a) 5 units.
b) 0 units.
c) 6 units.
d) 8 units.
e) 7 units.

19.97 (SG 19.17)
Correct: a)
Difficulty: 4
Page(s): 505–507
Scramble range: All
Topic: Externalities

19.97
Refer to Figure 19.3. What is the allocatively efficient quantity of good *A*?
a) 5 units.
b) 0 units.
c) 6 units.
d) 8 units.
e) 7 units.

19.98 (SG 19.18)
Correct: c)
Difficulty: 3
Page(s): 505–507
Scramble range: All
Topic: Externalities

19.98
Figure 19.4 depicts the demand curve for good *B* as well as the marginal social benefit (*MSB*) and marginal cost (*MC*) curves. How many units of good *B* will be produced and consumed in an unregulated market?
a) 0 units.
b) 5 units.
c) 3 units.
d) 7 units.
e) 2 units.

Figure 19.4

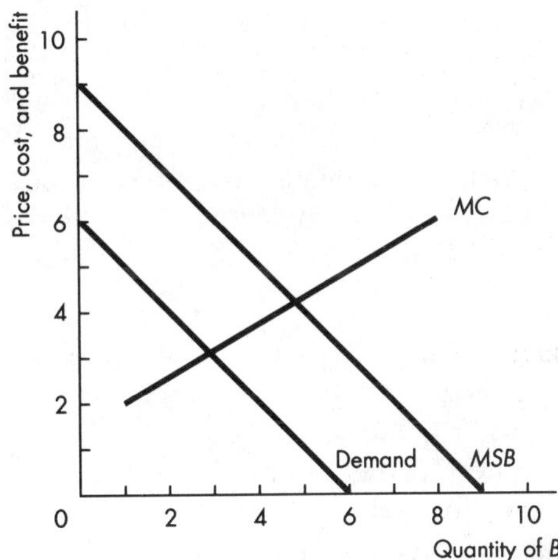

19.99 (SG 19.19)
Correct: b)
Difficulty: 4
Page(s): 505–507
Scramble range: All
Topic: Externalities

19.99
Refer to Figure 19.4. What is the allocatively efficient quantity of good *B*?
a) 0 units.
b) 5 units.
c) 3 units.
d) 7 units.
e) 2 units.

19.100 (SG 19.20)
Correct: e)
Difficulty: 4
Page(s): 505–507
Scramble range: All
Topic: Externalities

19.100
Refer to Figure 19.4. Which of the following government policies would induce the market to achieve allocative efficiency?
a) Tax the production of *B* in the amount of $3 per unit.
b) Tax the production of *B* in the amount of $4 per unit.
c) Require output to equal to 5 units.
d) Subsidize the consumption of *B* in the amount of $4 per unit.
e) Subsidize the consumption of *B* in the amount of $3 per unit.

19.101
Correct: d)
Difficulty: 4
Page(s): 505–507
Scramble range: a)–d)
Topic: Externalities

19.101
Suppose we have a market with external costs and external benefits. Then, under perfect competition, output
a) must be too high.
b) must be too low.
c) must be just correct.
d) can be just correct.
e) none of the above.

19.102
Correct: d)
Difficulty: 3
Page(s): 495–497
Scramble range: a)–d)
Topic: Government role

19.102
"The government should never interfere in a private market." This statement is
a) true.
b) false.
c) positive.
d) normative.
e) none of the above.

19.103
Correct: c)
Difficulty: 4
Page(s): 496
Scramble range: All
Topic: Welfare judgements

19.103
In an unregulated economy, if it is not possible for someone to be made better off without making anyone worse off, then
a) income is distributed fairly.
b) market failure is endemic.
c) allocative efficiency has been achieved.
d) net benefit is at a minimum.
e) total benefit is at a maximum.

19.104
Correct: b)
Difficulty: 2
Page(s): 496
Scramble range: All
Topic: Market failure

19.104
Market failure is most likely to be found in which of the following activities?
a) Eating pizza at the local pizza parlour.
b) The production of a lighthouse.
c) Eating fresh oranges from the local food store.
d) Cleaning the leaves from your private swimming pool.
e) Television production.

19.105
Correct: e)
Difficulty: 3
Page(s): 496
Scramble range: None
Topic: Market failure

19.105
Which of the following is a situation in which market failure arises?
a) When there is no problem of public goods.
b) When cartels collude but do not restrict output.
c) When externalities exist.
d) When monopolies are very strong.
e) Both c) and d).

19.106
Correct: e)
Difficulty: 3
Page(s): 496
Scramble range: All
Topic: Market failure

19.106
When market failure occurs and the government does not act to reduce the level of economic inefficiency, then it is
a) violating an end-state theory of government behaviour.
b) not following a process theory of government behaviour.
c) violating the public interest theory of government behaviour.
d) exhibiting rent-seeking behaviour.
e) possibly taking into account the high costs of creating and enforcing such regulations.

19.107
Correct: a)
Difficulty: 2
Page(s): 497
Scramble range: All
Topic: Public and private goods

19.107
A good that exhibits neither rivalry nor excludability cannot be a
a) pure private good.
b) pure public good.
c) government good.
d) mixed good.
e) merit good.

19.108
Correct: b)
Difficulty: 3
Page(s): 497
Scramble range: All
Topic: Public goods

19.108
Public goods are provided by government since
a) governments are more efficient than private firms at producing private goods.
b) free-rider problems result in an underproduction by private markets.
c) people value national defence very highly.
d) private firms will make positive economic profits.
e) private firms do not take into account the impact of external costs.

19.109
Correct: e)
Difficulty: 3
Page(s): 497
Scramble range: All
Topic: Public goods

19.109
Which of the following goods most exhibits the nonexcludability feature?
a) A cheeseburger.
b) Roads.
c) Rides on the U.S. Space Shuttle.
d) A national park.
e) A lighthouse.

19.110
Correct: c)
Difficulty: 2
Page(s): 501
Scramble range: All
Topic: External costs

19.110
Which of the following best illustrates the concept of an external cost?
a) A drought in U.S. wheat lands increases profit in Canadian wheat production.
b) An increase in wheat production causes the price of wheat to decrease.
c) Storage of hazardous waste gets delayed in parliament while radioactive waste contaminates land in Quebec.
d) Nonsmokers are denied access to handicapped parking.
e) Immunization reduces the probability of disease spreading.

19.111
Correct: e)
Difficulty: 4
Page(s): 497–501
Scramble range: All
Topic: Public goods

19.111
Consider Fact 19.1. What is the capacity that achieves maximum net benefit?
a) 1.
b) 5.
c) 4.
d) 2.
e) 3.

Fact 19.1
A city of 1 million people has the following facts about its potential sewage disposal system:

Capacity (thousands of litres a day)	Marginal private benefit to one person (dollars)	Total cost (millions of dollars a day)
0	—	0
1	50	5
2	40	15
3	30	30
4	10	50
5	5	75

19.112
Correct: a)
Difficulty: 5
Page(s): 497–501
Scramble range: All
Topic: Public goods

19.112
Consider Fact 19.1. How much will each person have to pay in taxes in order to pay for the efficient capacity?
a) $30.
b) $50.
c) $75.
d) $15.
e) $5.

19.113
Correct: a)
Difficulty: 5
Page(s): 497–501
Scramble range: All
Topic: Public goods

19.113
Consider Fact 19.1. At the efficient capacity, what is the level of net benefits?
a) $90 million.
b) $80 million.
c) $60 million.
d) $45 million.
e) $30 million.

19.114
Correct: c)
Difficulty: 3
Page(s): 497
Scramble range: All
Topic: Public goods

19.114
Which of the following is the best example of a pure public good?
a) A television.
b) A government-provided university education.
c) A lighthouse.
d) A private security system in a rich neighbourhood.
e) A beautifully kept yard.

19.115
Correct: b)
Difficulty: 3
Page(s): 501–507
Scramble range: None
Topic: Externalities

19.115
Total net benefit to society is maximized when
a) the difference between marginal benefit and marginal cost is at its highest.
b) social marginal benefit equals social marginal cost.
c) individuals in a perfectly competitive market are able to make free choices, uninhibited by government action.
d) both a) and b).
e) both a) and c).

Chapter 20 **Public Choice**

20.1
Correct: d)
Difficulty: 2
Page(s): 512
Scramble range: All
Topic: Public policy goals

20.1
Over the last 40 years,
a) both the Liberals and the Conservatives have cut taxes and spending.
b) the Liberals have cut taxes and spending, while the Conservatives have not.
c) the Conservatives have cut taxes and spending, while the Liberals have not.
d) neither the Conservatives nor the Liberals have cut taxes and spending.
e) political parties such as the Liberals and the Conservatives have carried out very different policies while in power.

20.2
Correct: e)
Difficulty: 2
Page(s): 512
Scramble range: All
Topic: Policy results

20.2
In the last 40 years, government has
a) grown only under the Conservatives.
b) grown only under the Liberals.
c) grown only in the provinces.
d) shrunk under all parties and levels.
e) grown under all parties and levels.

20.3
Correct: e)
Difficulty: 2
Page(s): 512
Scramble range: a)–d)
Topic: Government presence

20.3
Government is present at all of the following occasions *except*
a) birth.
b) working.
c) death.
d) education.
e) It is present at all of the above.

20.4
Correct: e)
Difficulty: 2
Page(s): 512
Scramble range: a)–d)
Topic: Government presence

20.4
The government is present at all of the following occasions *except*
a) unemployment.
b) retirement.
c) illness.
d) drug consumption.
e) It is present at all of the above.

20.5
Correct: b)
Difficulty: 3
Page(s): 512–513
Scramble range: All
Topic: Politicians

20.5
Which of the following statements about politicians best illustrates reality?
a) They are all liars.
b) They take very different views on issues beforehand, but implement very similar policies.
c) They are only interested in what's best for society.
d) They take very similar views on issues beforehand, but implement very different policies.
e) They take very different views on issues beforehand, and implement very different policies.

20.6
Correct: c)
Difficulty: 1
Page(s): 513
Scramble range: All
Topic: Political actors

20.6
The three types of actors in the political marketplace are
a) lobbyists, voters, and politicians.
b) government unions, bureaucrats, and voters.
c) bureaucrats, voters, and politicians.
d) bureaucrats, lobbyists, and politicians.
e) bureaucrats, politicians, and government unions.

20.7
Correct: c)
Difficulty: 2
Page(s): 512
Scramble range: All
Topic: Growth of government

20.7
In the last 40 years the size of government spending at the federal, provincial, and local levels, as a percentage of national income, has
a) decreased.
b) remained the same.
c) increased.
d) tripled.
e) quadrupled.

20.8
Correct: c)
Difficulty: 2
Page(s): 513
Scramble range: All
Topic: Public choice

20.8
Public choice theory assumes that government actions are determined by the behaviour of
a) public-minded citizens.
b) public-interested bureaucrats.
c) elected officials and bureaucrats pursuing their own economic objectives.
d) the federal government in the public interest, but the provinces in the private interests of special interest groups.
e) the provinces in the public interest, but the federal government in the private interests of special interest groups.

20.9
Correct: c)
Difficulty: 2
Page(s): 516
Scramble range: All
Topic: Public choice

20.9
The assumption that elected officials and bureaucrats pursue their own economic objectives is
a) unpatriotic.
b) unrealistic.
c) a basic tenet of public choice theory.
d) a basic tenet of Keynesian economics.
e) a basic tenet of public interest theory.

20.10
Correct: a)
Difficulty: 2
Page(s): 516
Scramble range: All
Topic: Political marketplace

20.10
According to public choice theory, the main actors in the political marketplace include all of the following *except*
a) the clergy.
b) the voters.
c) the bureaucrats.
d) the politicians.
e) the lobbyists.

20.11
Correct: a)
Difficulty: 2
Page(s): 516
Scramble range: All
Topic: Public choice

20.11
Politicians, bureaucrats, and voters are
a) the main actors in political economy, according to public choice theory.
b) the main actors in conducting Keynesian countercyclical fiscal policy.
c) always working at cross-purposes, thereby reaching a political equilibrium.
d) never working at cross-purposes, thereby failing to reach a political equilibrium.
e) never working at cross-purposes, thereby reaching a political equilibrium.

20.12
Correct: d)
Difficulty: 2
Page(s): 516
Scramble range: All
Topic: Political marketplace

20.12
Voters can express their demands in the political marketplace by doing all of the following *except*
a) voting.
b) contributing money to a campaign.
c) not voting.
d) saving more money.
e) lobbying.

20.13
Correct: c)
Difficulty: 2
Page(s): 516
Scramble range: All
Topic: Political marketplace

20.13
Voters can express their demands in the political marketplace by doing all of the following *except*
a) lobbying members of parliament.
b) contributing money to a campaign.
c) spending more money.
d) organizing an election boycott.
e) voting a party out of power.

20.14
Correct: c)
Difficulty: 2
Page(s): 516
Scramble range: All
Topic: Bureaucrats

20.14
Bureaucrats are
a) private sector lobbyists of parliament.
b) public sector lobbyists of the prime minister.
c) appointed officials working at various levels of government.
d) not as numerous as members of parliament.
e) lobbyists for their unions.

20.15
Correct: b)
Difficulty: 2
Page(s): 516
Scramble range: All
Topic: Constraints on bureaucrats

20.15
Bureaucrats are constrained in the pursuit of their own private interests by
a) big labour unions.
b) politicians.
c) bankers.
d) import/export companies.
e) lobbyists.

20.16
Correct: b)
Difficulty: 3
Page(s): 516
Scramble range: All
Topic: Constraints on politicians

20.16
Politicians are constrained in the pursuit of their own private interests by
a) nonvoting small family farmers.
b) voters and bureaucrats.
c) nonvoting industrialists.
d) voters but not the bureaucrats.
e) bureaucrats but not voters.

20.17
Correct: d)
Difficulty: 3
Page(s): 516
Scramble range: All
Topic: Constraints on politicians

20.17
Politicians are constrained in the pursuit of their own private interests by all the following *except*
a) voters.
b) bureaucrats.
c) technology.
d) their ability to calculate the optimal policy.
e) lobbyists.

20.18
Correct: c)
Difficulty: 3
Page(s): 516
Scramble range: All
Topic: Political marketplace

20.18
When politicians, bureaucrats, and voters interact in such a way that no group wants to alter its behaviour, the situation is described by public choice theory as
a) deplorable.
b) sustainable.
c) political equilibrium.
d) political corruption.
e) political disequilibrium.

20.19
Correct: c)
Difficulty: 3
Page(s): 516
Scramble range: All
Topic: Public choice

20.19
Economic models of public choice assume that politicians
a) always act in the public interest.
b) always act in their own private interest.
c) always act to maximize the likelihood of their election and subsequent re-election.
d) never look past the last election.
e) wish to maximize the size of the bureaucracy.

20.20
Correct: b)
Difficulty: 3
Page(s): 516
Scramble range: All
Topic: Public choice

20.20
Economic models of public choice assume that voters always vote
a) in the public interest.
b) in their own private interest.
c) on controversial issues, even if they are not directly affected by the outcome.
d) based on reality, not perceptions.
e) based on lobbyists' viewpoints.

20.21
Correct: d)
Difficulty: 3
Page(s): 516
Scramble range: All
Topic: Party platform/ public choice

20.21
Political programs that make all groups better off
a) don't exist.
b) seldom appear in any political platform.
c) will appear in one party platform, but never in all platforms.
d) will appear in the platforms of all parties.
e) are never achieved in political equilibrium.

20.22
Correct: c)
Difficulty: 3
Page(s): 516
Scramble range: All
Topic: Party platform/ public choice

20.22
Political programs that make one group better off at the expense of another group
a) don't exist.
b) seldom appear in any political platform.
c) will appear in one party platform, but in all platforms only rarely.
d) will appear in the platforms of all parties.
e) are never achieved in political equilibrium.

20.23
Correct: b)
Difficulty: 3
Page(s): 516
Scramble range: All
Topic: Party platform/ public choice

20.23
Competition among political parties produces a platform which
a) minimizes the perceived tax payments by voters.
b) maximizes the perceived net benefits accruing to voters.
c) minimizes the perceived net benefits accruing to voters.
d) minimizes the net cost of administering the programs included in the platform.
e) maximizes the perceived total benefits accruing to voters.

20.24
Correct: e)
Difficulty: 4
Page(s): 516
Scramble range: All
Topic: Environmental policy

20.24
If all voters do not share the same attitudes toward the optimal sacrifice to reduce externalities, then politicians will
a) not propose any environmental legislation.
b) propose the degree of environmental controls which minimize the perceived net benefit to the environmentalists.
c) propose the degree of environmental controls which maximize the perceived net benefit to the voters.
d) propose the degree of environmental controls which maximize the perceived net benefit to the environmentalists.
e) propose the degree of environmental controls which maximize the perceived net benefit to the median voter.

20.25
Correct: b)
Difficulty: 3
Page(s): 516–517
Scramble range: All
Topic: Public choice

20.25
With a diversity of opinion among voters the political parties
a) will attempt to appeal to all tastes.
b) cannot appeal to all the tastes.
c) will ignore the tastes of voters.
d) will collude to divide the interest groups into equal parts.
e) will alternate keeping first one group and then another group happy.

20.26
Correct: d)
Difficulty: 3
Page(s): 516
Scramble range: All
Topic: Public choice

20.26
To attract a majority of voters, a political party will
a) aim its message to the most enthusiastic groups.
b) aim its message to a small but loyal following.
c) present a political package aimed at making a majority of voters better off, as the politicians perceive it.
d) present a political package aimed at making a majority of voters better off, as the voters perceive it.
e) respond strongest to the most vigorous lobbyists.

20.27
Correct: c)
Difficulty: 3
Page(s): 518
Scramble range: All
Topic: Minimum differentiation

20.27
The idea that the platforms of the political parties will tend to become similar over time is
a) not a reflection of reality.
b) not an implication of public choice theory.
c) called the principle of minimum differentiation.
d) called the principle of minimal political confrontation.
e) the result of intense lobbying pressure.

20.28
Correct: c)
Difficulty: 3
Page(s): 518
Scramble range: All
Topic: Minimum differentiation

20.28
Minimum differentiation among the political parties suggests that
a) the parties will have few ideas in common on their platforms.
b) the parties will offer few ideas on minimizing the size and scope of government.
c) the platforms of the parties will tend to become similar as they try to appeal to a majority of voters.
d) the platforms of the parties will tend to become dissimilar as they try to appeal to a loyal majority of voters.
e) the platforms of the parties will tend to have few, if any, new ideas.

20.29
Correct: b)
Difficulty: 3
Page(s): 518–519
Scramble range: All
Topic: Location decisions

20.29
Refer to Figure 20.1. Assume that hot dog buyers are evenly distributed along the beach between Seller #1 and Seller #2. Where should a third seller locate in order to maximize sales?
a) Position *A*.
b) Position *B*.
c) Position *C*.
d) Right next to Seller #1.
e) Right next to Seller #2.

Figure 20.1 The location of two hot dog sellers on a long, straight beach.
Positions A, B, and C are available new spots for potential rivals to the first two sellers.

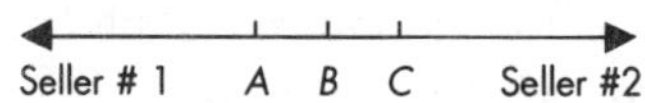

20.30
Correct: e)
Difficulty: 4
Page(s): 518–519
Scramble range: All
Topic: Location theory

20.30
Refer to Figure 20.1. Assume that hot dog buyers are evenly distributed along the beach between Seller #1 and Seller #2. If the third seller located at position *A*, then
a) the third seller would receive the most business.
b) Seller #1 and the third seller would both receive the most business.
c) Seller #1 would receive the most business.
d) they would all have the same volume of business.
e) Seller #2 would receive the most business.

20.31
Correct: d)
Difficulty: 4
Page(s): 518–519
Scramble range: All
Topic: Location theory

20.31
Refer to Figure 20.1. Assume that hot dog buyers are evenly distributed along the beach between Seller #1 and Seller #2. If the third seller located at position *B*, then
a) the third seller would receive the most business.
b) Seller #2 would receive the most business.
c) Seller #1 would receive the most business.
d) they would all have the same volume of business.
e) Sellers #1 and #2 would each receive the most business.

20.32
Correct: c)
Difficulty: 4
Page(s): 518–519
Scramble range: All
Topic: Location theory

20.32
Refer to Figure 20.1. Assume that hot dog buyers are evenly distributed along the beach between Seller #1 and Seller #2. If the third seller located at position *C*, then

a) the third seller would receive the most business.
b) Seller #2 would receive the most business.
c) Seller #1 would receive the most business.
d) they would all have the same volume of business.
e) Seller #2 and the third seller would receive the most business.

20.33
Correct: a)
Difficulty: 3
Page(s): 519
Scramble range: All
Topic: Median voter theorem

20.33
The median voter theory suggests that

a) politicians will aim their platform at the median voter.
b) policies will be adopted that first keep half the voters happy, and then the other half happy.
c) politicians will aim their platform at a loyal following with unusual preferences.
d) voters will aim their preferences at the median politician in the election.
e) politicians believe all voters are average individuals.

20.34
Correct: c)
Difficulty: 3
Page(s): 519
Scramble range: All
Topic: Median voter theorem

20.34
Refer to Figure 20.2. Which tax on gasoline should a politician favour to receive a maximum of votes on this single issue?

a) $0.00.
b) $0.20.
c) $0.30.
d) $0.40.
e) $0.60.

Figure 20.2 Frequency distribution of voter opinions on the question of the optimal tax on each litre of gasoline.

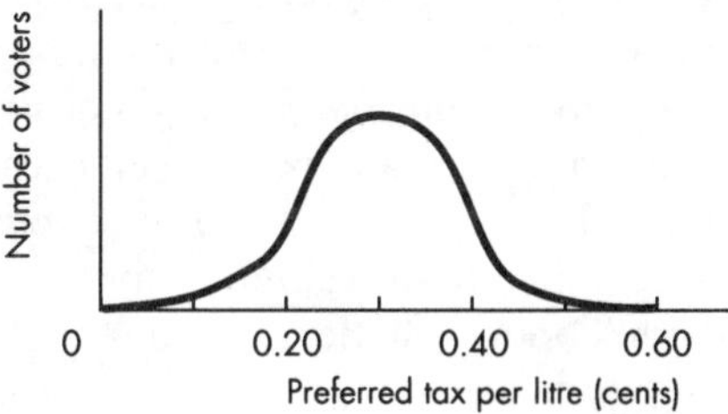

20.35
Correct: d)
Difficulty: 4
Page(s): 519
Scramble range: All
Topic: Median voter theorem

20.35
Refer to Figure 20.2. If politician #1 states that his political platform consists of a proposal to impose a gasoline tax of $0.50 per litre, what tax should his opponent favour to maximize votes received on this single issue?

a) Anything greater than $0.50.
b) A $0.30 tax.
c) A zero tax.
d) A $0.49 tax.
e) A $0.40 tax.

20.36
Correct: c)
Difficulty: 4
Page(s): 519
Scramble range: All
Topic: Median voter theorem

20.36
Refer to Figure 20.2. If politician #1 states that his political platform consists of a proposal to impose no gasoline tax, what tax should his opponent favour in order to maximize votes received on this single issue?
a) Anything greater than zero.
b) A zero tax.
c) A $0.01 tax.
d) A $0.20 tax.
e) A $0.30 tax.

20.37
Correct: c)
Difficulty: 4
Page(s): 519
Scramble range: All
Topic: Median voter theorem

20.37
Refer to Figure 20.2. If politician #1 states that his political platform consists of a proposal to impose a gasoline tax of $0.30 per litre, what tax should his opponent favour in order to maximize votes received on this single issue?
a) Anything greater than $0.30.
b) A zero tax.
c) A $0.30 tax.
d) Anything less than $0.30.
e) A $0.31 tax.

20.38
Correct: a)
Difficulty: 3
Page(s): 519
Scramble range: All
Topic: Median voter theorem

20.38
Refer to Figure 20.2. The median voter theorem suggests that both politicians would favour a
a) $0.30 tax.
b) zero tax.
c) tax greater than $0.50.
d) $0.49 tax.
e) $0.60 tax.

20.39
Correct: b)
Difficulty: 3
Page(s): 519
Scramble range: All
Topic: Changing tastes of voters

20.39
If the distribution of voter preferences changes over time,
a) politicians who remain successful will never change their policies.
b) politicians who remain successful will change their platforms accordingly to aim at the new median voter preferences.
c) there may well be a cyclical majority of voting.
d) the political equilibrium will not change.
e) political equilibrium will never occur.

20.40
Correct: a)
Difficulty: 3
Page(s): 519
Scramble range: a)–d)
Topic: Median voter theorem

20.40
Many U.S. analysts suggest that Ronald Reagan's conservative policy proposals did not change significantly from 1964 to 1984, yet Reagan's party lost in a landslide in 1964 and won in a landslide in 1984. What is one explanation for this observation?
a) The preferences of the median voter moved towards Reagan's more conservative agenda.
b) The preferences of the median voter stayed the same as well as Reagan's proposals.
c) The preferences of the median voters became more liberal in those 20 years.
d) The presence of a third party significantly hurt Reagan's opponent.
e) None of the above.

20.41
Correct: c)
Difficulty: 2
Page(s): 519
Scramble range: All
Topic: Median voter theorem

20.41
According to the median voter theorem, all politicians will propose ideas that are intended to
a) tax the rich and give it to the poor.
b) tax the poor and give it to the rich.
c) increase the income the median voter expects to receive.
d) decrease the size and scope of government.
e) increase the size of the bureaucracy.

20.42
Correct: a)
Difficulty: 2
Page(s): 522
Scramble range: All
Topic: Bureaucrats

20.42
According to William Niskanen, bureaucrats aim to
a) maximize the budget of their bureau.
b) minimize the chance of being fired.
c) minimize their expenditures of effort.
d) minimize the budget of their bureau.
e) please the median voter.

20.43
Correct: b)
Difficulty: 3
Page(s): 522
Scramble range: All
Topic: Bureaus and budgets

20.43
According to public choice theory, the larger the budget for a bureau, the
a) larger is the chance of mismanagement and waste.
b) larger is the prestige of the bureau chief.
c) fewer are the opportunities for promotion down the bureaucratic ladder.
d) greater is the chance that the bureau will discriminate against women and minorities.
e) the better off are the politicians in charge of it.

20.44
Correct: e)
Difficulty: 3
Page(s): 522
Scramble range: All
Topic: Bureaus and budgets

20.44
According to public choice theory, the larger the budget for a bureau, the
a) lower is the chance of mismanagement and waste.
b) lower is the prestige of the bureau chief.
c) better off are the lobbyists in this area.
d) lower is the chance that the bureau will discriminate against women and minorities.
e) greater are the opportunities for promotion down the bureaucratic ladder.

20.45
Correct: e)
Difficulty: 3
Page(s): 522
Scramble range: None
Topic: Bureaucratic constraints

20.45
The constraint on maximizing the size of the bureaucrat's budget is
a) the number of voters in the districts.
b) the implications for the politicians of the budget.
c) the number of employees in the bureau.
d) the amount of taxes the politicians levy.
e) both b) and d).

20.46
Correct: a)
Difficulty: 2
Page(s): 522–523
Scramble range: All
Topic: Bureaucratic strategy

20.46
Bureaucrats in particular agencies will try to convince politicians that the politicians will win more votes by
a) allocating additional money to their own agency rather than a rival agency.
b) spreading the funds evenly throughout all agencies or departments.
c) promising austerity.
d) giving funds to rival bureaucracies.
e) appealing to the median voter.

20.47
Correct: b)
Difficulty: 2
Page(s): 522–523
Scramble range: All
Topic: Public choice

20.47
The budget maximization strategy results in campaigns to
a) reduce taxes.
b) convince voters that they need such spending programs.
c) clean up waste in government.
d) eliminate fraud in government.
e) appeal to the median voter.

20.48
Correct: b)
Difficulty: 3
Page(s): 524
Scramble range: All
Topic: Rational ignorance

20.48
Rational ignorance suggests that
a) all voters are ignorant.
b) all voters will be ignorant on issues that do not have special interest to them.
c) all voters will pursue information about each issue before voting.
d) low voter turnout is due to a lack of understanding of the importance of the political platforms.
e) it is easier to aim at the median voter because it is a less costly strategy for the politicians.

20.49
Correct: d)
Difficulty: 3
Page(s): 524
Scramble range: All
Topic: Rational ignorance

20.49
Rational ignorance suggests that a voter should stop acquiring more information about an issue when
a) the total cost of acquiring the information exceeds the total benefits of acquiring the information.
b) the total cost of acquiring the information is minimized.
c) the total benefit from acquiring the information is maximized.
d) the marginal cost of acquiring the information is equal to the marginal benefit derived from the information.
e) the marginal cost of acquiring the information is greater than zero.

20.50
Correct: d)
Difficulty: 2
Page(s): 524
Scramble range: All
Topic: Rational ignorance

20.50
Rational ignorance suggests that voters will
a) understand defence technology before voting for defence policy.
b) understand the auditing procedures of National Revenue before voting for tax reform.
c) understand the chemistry of the atmosphere before voting for a clean air act.
d) vote without complete information on many issues.
e) vote based on their complete trust of politicians and bureaucrats.

20.51
Correct: c)
Difficulty: 2
Page(s): 524
Scramble range: All
Topic: Federal revenue

20.51
The bulk of the tax revenues in Canada are derived from
a) cigarette taxes.
b) alcohol taxes.
c) personal income taxes.
d) gasoline taxes.
e) corporate taxes.

20.52
Correct: c)
Difficulty: 2
Page(s): 525
Scramble range: All
Topic: Nonincome tax revenues

20.52
Tax revenue from excise and ad valorem taxes on cigarettes, alcohol, gasoline, and similar goods account for about what percentage of total tax revenues?
a) 1 percent.
b) 5 percent.
c) 17 percent.
d) 25 percent.
e) 50 percent.

20.53
Correct: a)
Difficulty: 2
Page(s): 525
Scramble range: All
Topic: Excise tax

20.53
An excise tax is a tax on
a) the purchases of goods and services.
b) the purchase of imported goods only.
c) income earned over $100,000 per year.
d) income earned over $1,000,000 per year.
e) the sale of exported goods.

20.54
Correct: c)
Difficulty: 2
Page(s): 525
Scramble range: All
Topic: *Ad valorem* tax

20.54
An *ad valorem* tax is
a) computed as a certain amount of money per unit purchased.
b) a lump-sum tax.
c) computed as a percentage of the value of the purchased products.
d) not like a sales tax.
e) computed as a percentage of your income.

20.55
Correct: a)
Difficulty: 2
Page(s): 525
Scramble range: All
Topic: Price determination

20.55
Refer to Figure 20.3. Without any taxes on gasoline, the equilibrium price of gasoline will be
a) $1.00.
b) $1.50.
c) $2.00.
d) $0.50.
e) $2.50.

Figure 20.3 The competitive market for gasoline

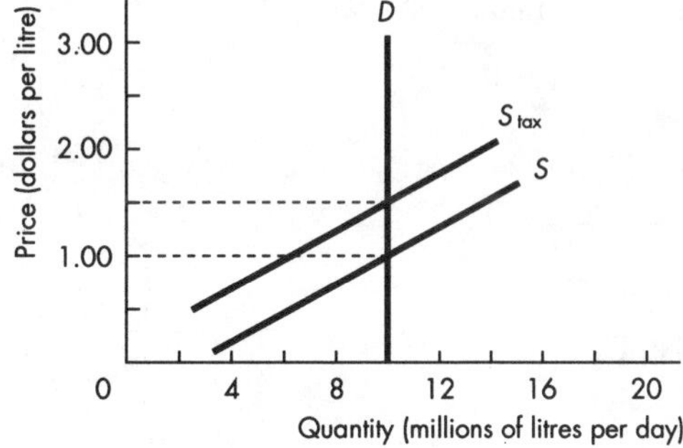

20.56
Correct: c)
Difficulty: 2
Page(s): 525
Scramble range: All
Topic: Equilibrium output

20.56
Refer to Figure 20.3. Without any taxes on gasoline, the equilibrium quantity of gasoline bought and sold will be
a) 6 million litres per day.
b) 8 million litres per day.
c) 10 million litres per day.
d) 12 million litres per day.
e) 14 million litres per day.

20.57
Correct: b)
Difficulty: 3
Page(s): 525
Scramble range: All
Topic: Tax distortion

20.57
Refer to Figure 20.3. Suppose the government imposes an excise tax of $0.50 per litre of gasoline. From the perspective of the buyers of gasoline, what will change on the supply side of the market?
a) It will appear that the supply of gasoline is increased.
b) It will appear that the supply of gasoline is decreased.
c) There will be no apparent change in supply.
d) More information is needed to answer this question.
e) It will appear that the price of gasoline has fallen.

20.58
Correct: a)
Difficulty: 3
Page(s): 525
Scramble range: All
Topic: Tax distortion

20.58
Refer to Figure 20.3. Suppose the government imposes an excise tax of $0.50 per litre of gasoline. The new price to the buyers will be
a) $1.50.
b) $1.00.
c) $2.00.
d) $3.00.
e) $0.50.

20.59
Correct: c)
Difficulty: 3
Page(s): 525
Scramble range: All
Topic: Equilibrium output with a tax

20.59
Refer to Figure 20.3. Suppose the government imposes an excise tax of $0.50 per litre of gasoline. The new quantity of gasoline bought and sold will be
a) 6 million litres per day.
b) 8 million litres per day.
c) 10 million litres per day.
d) 12 million litres per day.
e) 14 million litres per day.

20.60
Correct: a)
Difficulty: 4
Page(s): 525
Scramble range: All
Topic: Tax distortion

20.60
Refer to Figure 20.3. Suppose the government imposes an excise tax of $0.50 per litre of gasoline. The new price received by the sellers, net of the tax, will be
a) $1.00.
b) $1.50.
c) $2.00.
d) $3.00.
e) $0.50.

20.61
Correct: e)
Difficulty: 4
Page(s): 525
Scramble range: All
Topic: Tax incidence

20.61
Refer to Figure 20.3. Suppose the government imposes an excise tax of $0.50 per litre of gasoline. Who pays the tax in this case?
a) The seller pays the tax.
b) The buyer pays all the tax in this case and every other possible case.
c) The seller pays most of the tax.
d) The buyer pays most of the tax.
e) The buyer pays the tax in this case.

20.62
Correct: b)
Difficulty: 4
Page(s): 525
Scramble range: All
Topic: Tax revenue

20.62
Refer to Figure 20.3. Suppose the government imposes an excise tax of $0.50 per litre of gasoline. What is the total tax revenue to the government in this case?
a) $1 million per day.
b) $5 million per day.
c) $10 million per day.
d) $15 million per day.
e) Impossible to compute without more information.

20.63
Correct: e)
Difficulty: 2
Page(s): 525
Scramble range: All
Topic: Price determination

20.63
Refer to Figure 20.4. Without any taxes on gasoline, the equilibrium price of gasoline will be
a) $1.50.
b) $2.00.
c) 0.
d) $0.50.
e) $1.00.

Figure 20.4 The competitive market for gasoline

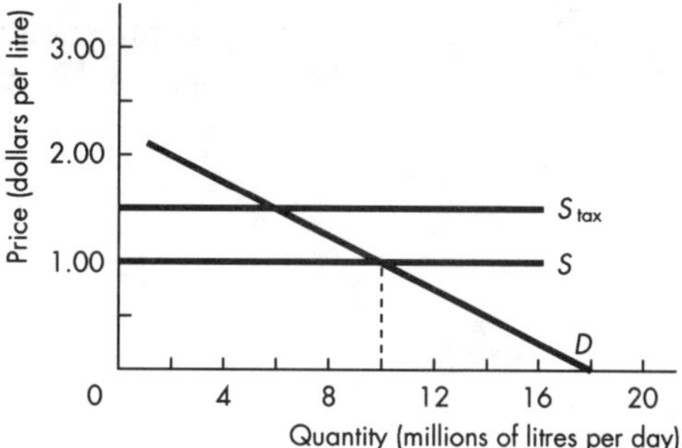

20.64
Correct: c)
Difficulty: 2
Page(s): 525
Scramble range: All
Topic: Equilibrium output

20.64
Refer to Figure 20.4. Without any taxes on gasoline, the equilibrium quantity of gasoline bought and sold will be
a) 6 million litres per day.
b) 8 million litres per day.
c) 10 million litres per day.
d) 12 million litres per day.
e) 14 million litres per day.

20.65
Correct: b)
Difficulty: 3
Page(s): 525
Scramble range: All
Topic: Tax distortion

20.65
Refer to Figure 20.4. Suppose the government imposes an excise tax of $0.50 per litre of gasoline. From the perspective of the buyers of gasoline, what will change on the supply side of the market?
a) It will appear that there is an increase in the supply of gasoline.
b) It will appear that there is a decrease in the supply of gasoline.
c) There will be no apparent change in supply.
d) More information is needed to answer this question.
e) It will appear that there is a fall in the price of gasoline.

20.66
Correct: b)
Difficulty: 3
Page(s): 525
Scramble range: All
Topic: Tax distortion

20.66
Refer to Figure 20.4. Suppose the government imposes an excise tax of $0.50 per litre of gasoline. The new price to the buyers will be
a) $1.00.
b) $1.50.
c) $2.00.
d) $2.50.
e) $3.00.

20.67
Correct: a)
Difficulty: 3
Page(s): 525
Scramble range: All
Topic: Equilibrium output with a tax

20.67
Refer to Figure 20.4. Suppose the government imposes an excise tax of $0.50 per litre of gasoline. The new quantity of gasoline bought and sold will be
a) 6 million litres per day.
b) 8 million litres per day.
c) 10 million litres per day.
d) 12 million litres per day.
e) 14 million litres per day.

20.68
Correct: a)
Difficulty: 3
Page(s): 525
Scramble range: All
Topic: Tax distortion

20.68
Refer to Figure 20.4. Suppose the government imposes an excise tax of $0.50 per litre of gasoline. The new price received by the sellers, net of the tax, will be
a) $1.00.
b) $1.50.
c) $2.00.
d) $2.50.
e) $3.00.

20.69
Correct: e)
Difficulty: 4
Page(s): 525
Scramble range: All
Topic: Tax incidence

20.69
Refer to Figure 20.4. Suppose the government imposes an excise tax of $0.50 per litre of gasoline. Who pays the tax in this case?
a) The seller pays the tax.
b) The buyer pays all the tax in this case and every other possible case.
c) The buyer pays most of the tax.
d) The seller pays most of the tax.
e) The buyer pays the tax in this case.

20.70
Correct: b)
Difficulty: 4
Page(s): 525
Scramble range: All
Topic: Tax revenue

20.70
Refer to Figure 20.4. Suppose the government imposes an excise tax of $0.50 per litre of gasoline. What is the total tax revenue to the government in this case?
a) $1 million per day.
b) $3 million per day.
c) $5 million per day.
d) $6 million per day.
e) Impossible to compute without more information.

20.71
Correct: a)
Difficulty. 5
Page(s): 525
Scramble range: All
Topic: Lost surplus

20.71
Refer to Figure 20.4. Suppose the government imposes an excise tax of $0.50 per litre of gasoline. What is the deadweight loss of consumer surplus from the tax?
a) $1 million per day.
b) $2 million per day.
c) $4 million per day.
d) Zero.
e) Impossible to compute without more information.

20.72
Correct: d)
Difficulty: 5
Page(s): 525
Scramble range: All
Topic: Lost surplus

20.72
Refer to Figure 20.4. Suppose the government imposes an excise tax of $0.50 per litre of gasoline. What is the deadweight loss of producer surplus from the tax?
a) $1 million per day.
b) $6 million per day.
c) $4 million per day.
d) Zero.
e) $2 million per day.

20.73
Correct: d)
Difficulty: 4
Page(s): 526
Scramble range: All
Topic: Incidence of a tax

20.73
With the imposition of an excise tax, the price to the buyer will be unchanged if
a) the supply is elastic.
b) the demand is elastic.
c) the supply is perfectly elastic.
d) the supply is completely inelastic.
e) the demand is inelastic.

20.74
Correct: d)
Difficulty: 4
Page(s): 526
Scramble range: All
Topic: Incidence of a tax

20.74
With the imposition of an excise tax, the price to the seller will be unchanged if
a) the supply is elastic.
b) the demand is elastic.
c) the demand is perfectly elastic.
d) the demand is completely inelastic.
e) the supply is perfectly inelastic.

20.75
Correct: b)
Difficulty: 3
Page(s): 526
Scramble range: All
Topic: Tax distortion

20.75
Refer to Figure 20.5. Suppose the government imposes an excise tax of $1.00 per litre of gasoline. The new price to the buyers will be
a) $1.00.
b) $1.50.
c) $0.50.
d) $3.00.
e) $2.00.

Figure 20.5 The competitive market for gasoline

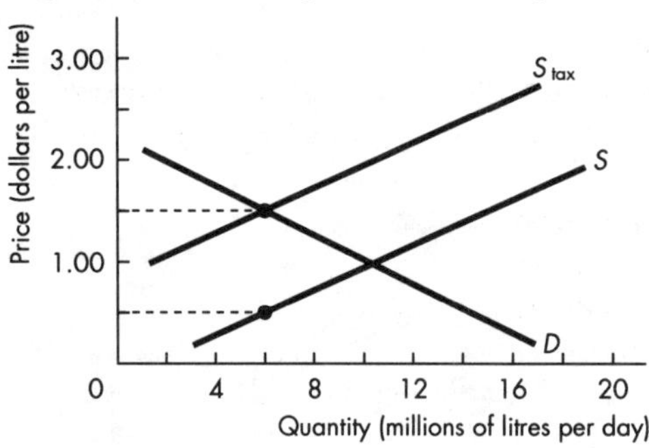

20.76
Correct: a)
Difficulty: 3
Page(s): 526
Scramble range: All
Topic: Equilibrium output with a tax

20.76
Refer to Figure 20.5. Suppose the government imposes an excise tax of $1.00 per litre of gasoline. The new quantity of gasoline bought and sold will be
a) 6 million litres per day.
b) 8 million litres per day.
c) 10 million litres per day.
d) 12 million litres per day.
e) 14 million litres per day.

20.77
Correct: a)
Difficulty: 4
Page(s): 526
Scramble range: All
Topic: Tax distortion

20.77
Refer to Figure 20.5. Suppose the government imposes an excise tax of $1.00 per litre of gasoline. The new price received by the sellers, net of the tax, will be
a) $0.50.
b) $1.00.
c) $1.50.
d) $2.00.
e) $2.50.

20.78
Correct: d)
Difficulty: 5
Page(s): 526
Scramble range: All
Topic: Tax incidence

20.78
Refer to Figure 20.5. Suppose the government imposes an excise tax of $1.00 per litre of gasoline. Who pays the tax in this case?
a) The seller pays the tax.
b) The buyer pays all the tax in this case.
c) The buyer pays most of the tax in this case.
d) The buyer and the seller share the tax equally.
e) The seller pays most of the tax in this case.

20.79
Correct: a)
Difficulty: 5
Page(s): 526
Scramble range: All
Topic: Lost surplus

20.79
Refer to Figure 20.5. Suppose the government imposes an excise tax of $1.00 per litre of gasoline. What is the deadweight loss of consumer surplus from the tax?
a) $1 million per day.
b) $4 million per day.
c) $2 million per day.
d) $3.5 million per day.
e) Zero.

20.80
Correct: a)
Difficulty: 5
Page(s): 526
Scramble range: All
Topic: Lost surplus

20.80
Refer to Figure 20.5. Suppose the government imposes an excise tax of $1.00 per litre of gasoline. What is the deadweight loss of producer surplus from the tax?
a) $1 million per day.
b) $4 million per day.
c) $2 million per day.
d) Zero.
e) $3.5 million per day.

20.81 (SG 20.1)
Correct: e)
Difficulty: 3
Page(s): 513
Scramble range: All
Topic: Public choice

20.81
Public choice theory
a) argues that government has a tendency to conduct policies that help the economy toward allocative efficiency.
b) argues that politicians and bureaucrats tend to be more concerned about the public interest than individuals in the private sector.
c) argues that government spending is carried out in response to bureaucrats trying to increase their department size.
d) applies the tools of political analysis to the analysis of economic markets.
e) applies the economic tools used to analyse markets to the analysis of government behaviour.

20.82 (SG 20.2)
Correct: a)
Difficulty: 2
Page(s): 513
Scramble range: All
Topic: Public choice theory/candidate preference

20.82
According to public choice theory, a voter will favour a candidate whose political program is
a) perceived by the voter to offer the greatest personal benefit.
b) best for the majority of the people.
c) closest to allocative efficiency.
d) favoured by the median voter.
e) favoured by lobbyists.

20.83
Correct: b)
Difficulty: 3
Page(s): 515
Scramble range: All
Topic: Nobel Prize in economic science

20.83
Who was awarded the Nobel Prize in economic science for his fundamental contributions to public choice theory?
a) Anthony Downs.
b) James Buchanan.
c) William Niskanen.
d) Milton Friedman.
e) Gordon Tullock.

20.84 (SG 20.3)
Correct: a)
Difficulty: 2
Page(s): 516
Scramble range: All
Topic: Political motivation

20.84
Public choice theory assumes that those involved in the political process are generally motivated by
a) self-interest.
b) the desire to achieve allocative efficiency.
c) dishonesty.
d) public spirit.
e) the desire to increase the size of the bureaucracy.

20.85 (SG 20.4)
Correct: d)
Difficulty: 3
Page(s): 519
Scramble range: All
Topic: Median voter

20.85
If voters have similar views and are well informed, the quantity of national defence provided by the government will tend to be
a) greater than the allocatively efficient quantity.
b) less than the allocatively efficient quantity.
c) the least costly quantity.
d) the quantity that maximizes net benefit.
e) the quantity that maximizes total benefits.

20.86 (SG 20.5)
Correct: b)
Difficulty: 3
Page(s): 519
Scramble range: All
Topic: Political marketplace

20.86
Competition between two political parties will cause those parties to
a) produce quite different policy proposals.
b) have very similar policy proposals.
c) find ways to clearly distinguish themselves in order to give voters a clear choice.
d) propose policies which have the effect of reducing the well-being of middle income families and increasing the well-being of the rich and the poor.
e) select "niches" among voters.

20.87 (SG 20.6)
Correct: d)
Difficulty: 3
Page(s): 519
Scramble range: All
Topic: Median voter behaviour

20.87
On any given spending issue subject to a vote, the median voter is the one who
a) opposes spending uniformly.
b) favours the most spending.
c) favours the efficient level of spending.
d) favours more spending than half of the voters and less spending than half of the voters.
e) favours spending half the amount of the voter who favours the maximum amount of spending.

20.88 (SG 20.7)
Correct: d)
Difficulty: 3
Page(s): 519
Scramble range: All
Topic: Voting and welfare

20.88
Voters are asked to vote for either proposition *A* or proposition *B*. Proposition *A* will win if it
a) is closer to allocative efficiency.
b) is supported by bureaucrats.
c) it generates greater social benefit than social cost.
d) is preferred by the median voter.
e) receives the most lobbying.

20.89 (SG 20.8)
Correct: e)
Difficulty: 4
Page(s): 520
Scramble range: All
Topic: Redistribution policies

20.89
The tendency for redistribution policies to be stable for long periods of time is best explained by
a) cycles in voting.
b) the range of differences among voters.
c) the principle of minimum differentiation.
d) lobbying.
e) the tradeoff between redistribution and the average level of income.

20.90 (SG 20.9)
Correct: e)
Difficulty: 4
Page(s): 522
Scramble range: All
Topic: Bureaucratic motivation

20.90
The claim that bureaucrats will attempt to maximize the budget of their agency follows from the assumption that bureaucrats
a) have a superior understanding of the public interest.
b) have an inferior understanding of the public interest.
c) do not face any constraints on their behaviour.
d) are less honest than individuals in the private sector.
e) are motivated by the same forces of self-interest that motivate individuals in the private sector.

20.91 (SG 20.11)
Correct: b)
Difficulty: 4
Page(s): 522
Scramble range: All
Topic: Bureaucrats

20.91
The budget of a government bureau is likely to increase beyond the quantity that maximizes net benefit of the economy if
a) voters are well informed.
b) there is rational voter ignorance combined with special interest lobbying.
c) it is allocatively efficient to do so.
d) bureaucrats are rationally ignorant.
e) bureaucrats are overly influenced by lobbyists.

20.92 (SG 20.12)
Correct: d)
Difficulty: 3
Page(s): 523
Scramble range: All
Topic: Well-informed voters

20.92
A voter will tend to be well informed if the issue in question
a) is complicated and difficult to understand.
b) affects everyone a little.
c) is of special interest to a small group to which the voter does not belong.
d) has a large direct effect on the voter.
e) is dominated by large lobby groups.

20.93 (SG 20.13)
Correct: d)
Difficulty: 2
Page(s): 525
Scramble range: All
Topic: Sales tax

20.93
A sales tax that collects 5 percent of the amount of a purchase is an example of
a) a specific tax.
b) a proportional income tax.
c) a flat tax.
d) an *ad valorem* tax.
e) a capital gains tax.

20.94 (SG 20.14)
Correct: b)
Difficulty: 4
Page(s): 525
Scramble range: All
Topic: Excise tax

20.94
In general, a tax of $3 per unit of good *A* will
a) shift the supply curve for *A* up by $3 and increase the price of *A* by $3.
b) shift the supply curve for *A* up by $3 and increase the price of *A* by less than $3.
c) shift the supply curve for *A* up by more than $3 and increase the price of *A* by $3.
d) shift the supply curve for *A* up by less than $3 and increase the price of *A* by less than $3.
e) shift the demand curve for *A* down by more than $3 and increase the price of *A* by $3.

20.95 (SG 20.15)
Correct: e)
Difficulty: 3
Page(s): 526
Scramble range: All
Topic: Deadweight loss

20.95
The deadweight loss from a price increase resulting from a tax is
a) the loss of consumer surplus.
b) the loss of producer surplus.
c) the total benefit of the lost output.
d) the loss of consumer surplus minus the loss of producer surplus.
e) the loss of consumer surplus plus the loss of producer surplus.

20.96 (SG 20.16)
Correct: e)
Difficulty: 4
Page(s): 525
Scramble range: None
Topic: Deadweight loss

20.96
The deadweight loss created by a new tax is zero if
a) the supply curve is perfectly inelastic.
b) the demand curve is perfectly inelastic.
c) the demand curve is more elastic than the supply curve.
d) the demand curve is less elastic than the supply curve.
e) both a) and b).

20.97 (SG 20.17)
Correct: e)
Difficulty: 4
Page(s): 525
Scramble range: All
Topic: Import tariff

20.97
Figure 20.6 gives the demand and supply for imported cheese. Suppose that the government imposes a $3 tax per kilogram of imported cheese. What will happen to the price?
a) It will increase by $3 to $7.
b) It will increase by $3 to $6.
c) It will increase by $1 to $5.
d) It will increase by $2 to $5.
e) It will increase by $2 to $6.

Figure 20.6

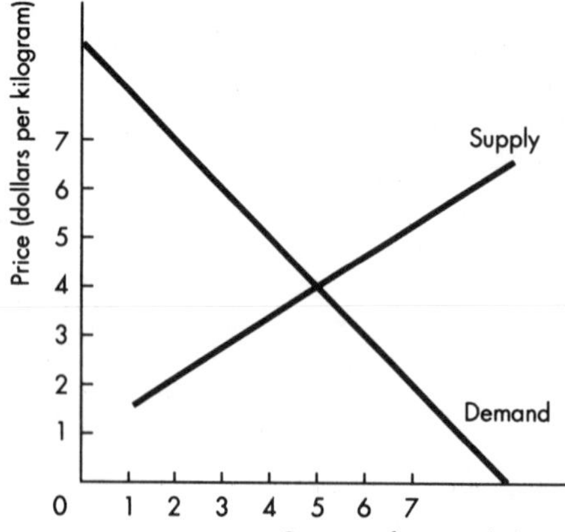

20.98 (SG 20.18)
Correct: d)
Difficulty: 5
Page(s): 526
Scramble range: All
Topic: Tax burden

20.98
Consider the $3 per kilogram tax imposed on the market for cheese shown in Figure 20.6. How is the burden of the tax shared between consumers and producers?
a) The entire $3 is borne by consumers in the form of a higher price.
b) The entire $3 is borne by producers in the form of lower sales.
c) $2 is borne by producers in the form of lower receipts per unit and $1 is borne by consumers in the form of a higher price.
d) $2 is borne by consumers in the form of a higher price and $1 is borne by producers in the form of lower receipts per unit.
e) $1 is borne by consumers in the form of a higher price and $1 is borne by producers in the form of lower receipts per unit.

20.99 (SG 20.20)
Correct: a)
Difficulty: 4
Page(s): 532
Scramble range: All
Topic: Government subsidies

20.99
If the government subsidizes a good, its
a) supply curve will shift downward, price will fall, and quantity traded will increase.
b) supply curve will shift upward, price will rise, and quantity traded will increase.
c) demand curve will shift upward, price will rise, and quantity traded will decrease.
d) demand curve will shift downward, price will fall, and quantity traded will decrease.
e) demand curve will shift downward, price will fall, and quantity traded will rise.

20.100 (SG 20.1)
Correct: e)
Difficulty: 4
Page(s): 513
Scramble range: All
Topic: Public choice

20.100
Public choice theory
a) argues that government has a tendency to conduct policies that do not move the economy away from allocative efficiency.
b) argues that politicians and bureaucrats tend to be less concerned about the private interests than in the public interest.
c) argues economies will always be allocatively efficient if in political equilibrium.
d) applies politics more than economics to evaluate government policy.
e) uses market analysis to evaluate government behaviour.

20.101 (SG 20.2)
Correct: d)
Difficulty: 3
Page(s): 513
Scramble range: All
Topic: Public choice theory/candidate preference

20.101
According to public choice theory, a voter will not favour a candidate whose political program is
a) perceived by the voter to offer great personal benefit.
b) opposed by the median voter.
c) opposed to promoting allocative efficiency.
d) perceived by the voter to offer the greatest personal cost.
e) perceived by the voter to lead to a larger bureaucracy.

20.102
Correct: b)
Difficulty: 2
Page(s): 514
Scramble range: All
Topic: Nobel Prize in economic science

20.102
Who has *not* been awarded the Nobel Prize in economics among the following list of candidates?
a) George Stigler.
b) John Kenneth Galbraith.
c) Milton Friedman.
d) Frederic Hayek.
e) Kenneth Arrow.

20.103
Correct: e)
Difficulty: 2
Page(s): 516
Scramble range: All
Topic: Political motivation

20.103
Public choice theory assumes that those involved in the political process are *not* generally motivated by
a) the desire for a large bureaucracy.
b) the desire to achieve allocative efficiency.
c) honesty.
d) potential private gain.
e) the public interest.

20.104
Correct: d)
Difficulty: 3
Page(s): 519
Scramble range: All
Topic: Median voter

20.104
If voters have similar views and are well informed, the quantity of public education provided by the government will tend to be
a) less than the allocatively efficient quantity.
b) greater than the allocatively efficient quantity.
c) the least costly quantity.
d) the quantity that maximizes net benefit.
e) the quantity that maximizes total benefit.

20.105
Correct: d)
Difficulty: 5
Page(s): 528
Scramble range: All
Topic: Subsidy

20.105
Recently, the province of Saskatchewan removed a large subsidy it used to pay to homeowners to help pay for home renovations. This means
a) that homeowners suffer, but renovating firms are indifferent because they never received the subsidy.
b) that renovating firms suffer, but homeowners are indifferent because the firms really got all the subsidy.
c) both the firms and the homeowners suffer, with the amount of the suffering depending on the relative levels of their respective incomes.
d) both the firms and the homeowners suffer, with the amount of the suffering depending on the relative levels of their respective elasticities.
e) both the firms and the homeowners suffer, with the amount of the suffering depending on the relative levels of taxes each previously paid.

20.106 (SG 20.6)
Correct: d)
Difficulty: 3
Page(s): 519
Scramble range: All
Topic: Median voter behaviour

20.106
When asked about a spending issue that is about to be subject to a vote, the median voter is the one who
a) opposes spending the same this year as was spent last year.
b) favours the least spending.
c) favours the inefficient level of spending.
d) favours spending more than half of the voters and spending less than half of the voters.
e) favours more spending half the time and less spending half the time.

20.107
Correct: e)
Difficulty: 3
Page(s): 520
Scramble range: All
Topic: Voting and welfare

20.107
Voters are asked to vote for either proposition *A* or proposition *B*. Proposition *B* will win if it
a) is closer to economic efficiency.
b) is opposed by the bureaucrats.
c) is not preferred by the median voter.
d) generates maximum net social benefit.
e) generates maximum net social benefit for the median voter.

20.108
Correct: b)
Difficulty: 5
Page(s): 530
Scramble range: All
Topic: Net benefits

20.108
Consider the case of a certain good, say a trailer park, that has been constructed but not yet lived in. A tornado comes along and wipes out the entire trailer park. The total loss to society of this event is
a) the total cost of producing the trailer park.
b) the total benefits that could have been realized from consuming the park.
c) the lost consumer surplus that could have been realized from the park.
d) the lost producer surplus that could have been gained from the park.
e) the total net benefits that could have been gained from consuming the park.

20.109
Correct: b)
Difficulty: 3
Page(s): 522
Scramble range: All
Topic: Bureaucrats

20.109
The budget of a government bureau will not be likely to increase beyond the quantity that maximizes net benefit of the economy if
a) voters are not well informed.
b) there is not rational voter ignorance combined with effective special interest lobbying.
c) it is allocatively inefficient to do so.
d) bureaucrats are not rationally ignorant.
e) bureaucrats are selfish maximizers.

20.110
Correct: e)
Difficulty: 4
Page(s): 525
Scramble range: All
Topic: Taxes

20.110
The Goods and Services Tax is an excise tax that is placed on the sale price of new homes *only*. As a result of this, the price of new houses will __________ while the price of old houses will __________
a) rise; stay the same.
b) stay the same; rise.
c) rise; fall.
d) fall ; rise.
e) rise; rise.

20.111
Correct: e)
Difficulty: 4
Page(s): 522
Scramble range: All
Topic: Median voter

20.111
A community of 9 people, identified by letters A through I, have strong but differing views about a local factory that is polluting the atmosphere. Some of them work at the factory and don't want the government to take any action against it, while others want to see the imposition of a huge tax based on the scale of pollution. The preferences of each person concerning the scale of the tax that should be imposed are given in Table 20.1 . Suppose there are two political parties competing for office in this community. What tax rate would the parties propose?
a) Zero.
b) 80 percent.
c) 70 percent.
d) 90 percent.
e) 60 percent.

Table 20.1

	Individual								
	A	B	C	D	E	F	G	H	I
Tax rate (% of firm's profits)	100	90	80	70	60	0	0	0	0

Chapter 21 Competition Policy

21.1
Correct: e)
Difficulty: 2
Page(s): 538
Scramble range: All
Topic: Airline deregulation

21.1
The deregulation of the airline industry began in
a) 1962 with the creation of the CBC.
b) 1978 with the elimination of the Canadian Transport Commission.
c) 1981 with the deregulation of crude oil prices.
d) 1986 with the tax reform law.
e) 1984 with government changes in the regulatory process.

21.2
Correct: c)
Difficulty: 2
Page(s): 538
Scramble range: All
Topic: Airline deregulation

21.2
With the "completion" of airline deregulation in the 1980s, all
a) government involvement with airlines ended.
b) government controls over airports continued.
c) safety regulations on airlines continued.
d) minimum fuel efficiency standards continued.
e) regulation of airline routes still continued.

21.3
Correct: c)
Difficulty: 2
Page(s): 538
Scramble range: All
Topic: Airline deregulation

21.3
Airline deregulation in the 1980s completed the partial deregulation of
a) airline fares but not airline routes.
b) airline routes but not airline fares.
c) both airline fares and airline routes.
d) neither airline routes nor fares.
e) airline fares, routes, and safety.

21.4
Correct: d)
Difficulty: 3
Page(s): 538
Scramble range: All
Topic: Airline deregulation

21.4
The short-run effect of U.S. airline deregulation included all of the following *except*
a) a reduction in airline fares.
b) an initial increase in the number of competitors in the industry.
c) total passenger miles flown by the airlines increased.
d) the deregulation of airports.
e) a long-run decrease in the number of competitors in certain cities.

21.5
Correct: d)
Difficulty: 2
Page(s): 538–539
Scramble range: All
Topic: Deregulated industries

21.5
Industries deregulated in the late 1970s and 1980s include all of the following *except* the
a) oil industry.
b) banking and insurance industry.
c) airlines industry.
d) steel industry.
e) domestic gas industry.

21.6
Correct: c)
Difficulty: 3
Page(s): 539
Scramble range: All
Topic: Anti-combine law

21.6
Anti-combine laws attempt to
a) support prices.
b) establish minimum wages.
c) prevent monopolies or collusion.
d) establish fair trade laws.
e) regulate monopolies.

21.7
Correct: b)
Difficulty: 3
Page(s): 557
Scramble range: All
Topic: Anti-combine law

21.7
The breakup of AT&T in the mid-1980s resulted in
a) the bankruptcy of AT&T.
b) more competition in long-distance telephone service.
c) less competition in long-distance telephone service.
d) less competition in local telephone service.
e) lower consumer benefits.

21.8
Correct: e)
Difficulty: 3
Page(s): 539
Scramble range: All
Topic: Anti-combine law

21.8
When Bell Canada was ordered in 1980 to permit its customers to buy equipment from any supplier,
a) this lead to the merger of Bell Canada and Northern Telecom.
b) this meant lower prices for long-distance telephone service.
c) this meant less competition in telephone markets.
d) this meant higher prices for long-distance telephone service.
e) this meant a rise in the variety and quality of equipment.

21.9
Correct: c)
Difficulty: 3
Page(s): 539
Scramble range: All
Topic: Economic regulation

21.9
Economic regulation includes all of the following *except*
a) commissions to set prices.
b) imposition of product standards and types.
c) limits on the maximum incomes of firms.
d) regulations on the nature of barriers of entry into the industry.
e) regulations on the levels of profits.

21.10
Correct: a)
Difficulty: 2
Page(s): 539
Scramble range: All
Topic: First economic regulation

21.10
The first economic regulatory authority in Canada was carried out under the auspices of the
a) Railway Act.
b) Federal Trade Commission.
c) Canadian Transport Commission.
d) National Revenue Department.
e) Canadian Radio-television and Telecommunications Commission.

21.11
Correct: a)
Difficulty: 2
Page(s): 539
Scramble range: All
Topic: First economic regulation

21.11
The first economic regulation occurred in the
a) 1880s.
b) 1930s.
c) 1960s.
d) 1970s.
e) 1980s.

21.12
Correct: d)
Difficulty: 2
Page(s): 539
Scramble range: All
Topic: Peak of economic regulation

21.12
Since the initial economic regulation by the federal government, economic regulation peaked in the
a) 1960s.
b) 1930s.
c) 1970s.
d) 1980s.
e) 1880s.

21.13
Correct: d)
Difficulty: 2
Page(s): 539
Scramble range: All
Topic: Economic regulation

21.13
Into the early 1970s, economic regulation was extended to all of the following *except*
a) airlines and buses.
b) trucking.
c) railroads.
d) nuclear waste disposal.
e) agricultural products.

21.14
Correct: c)
Difficulty: 3
Page(s): 539
Scramble range: All
Topic: Anti-combine law

21.14
Anti-combine law is enacted by
a) the courts and enforced by provincial legislatures.
b) Parliament and enforced by the Cabinet.
c) Parliament and enforced by the judicial system.
d) the Cabinet and enforced by the Cabinet.
e) the provincial legislatures and enforced by the federal government.

21.15
Correct: e)
Difficulty: 2
Page(s): 539
Scramble range: All
Topic: Market intervention

21.15
The three main ways the government intervenes in the market are
a) crown corporations, privatization, and regulation.
b) nationalization, legislation, and privatization.
c) nationalization, regulation, and privatization.
d) legislation, regulation, and privatization.
e) legislation, regulation, and nationalization.

21.16
Correct: a)
Difficulty: 2
Page(s): 539
Scramble range: All
Topic: Purpose of anti-combine law

21.16
The main purpose of anti-combine law is to
a) minimize monopoly pricing.
b) enforce pollution regulations on big business.
c) encourage the formation of cartels.
d) regulate the stock and bond markets.
e) increase safety factors in dangerous industries.

21.17
Correct: b)
Difficulty: 2
Page(s): 539
Scramble range: All
Topic: Crown corporations

21.17
All of the following are Crown corporations *except*
a) Ontario Hydro.
b) Bell Canada.
c) Petro-Canada.
d) VIA Rail.
e) the Canadian Broadcasting Corporation.

21.18
Correct: a)
Difficulty: 2
Page(s): 540
Scramble range: All
Topic: Consumer/ producer surplus

21.18
The gains and losses created by government economic regulation are called
a) consumer and producer surplus.
b) consumer and producer opportunity cost.
c) accounting costs.
d) economic costs.
e) the gains from trade to consumers.

21.19
Correct: c)
Difficulty: 2
Page(s): 540
Scramble range: All
Topic: Consumer surplus

21.19
Consumer surplus is
a) a value that is wasted on consumers.
b) a value extracted unfairly from producers by consumers.
c) the gain from trade for the consumer.
d) increased only when producer revenue decreases.
e) the difference between the opportunity costs of consumption and the price.

21.20
Correct: c)
Difficulty: 2
Page(s): 540
Scramble range: All
Topic: Producer surplus

21.20
Producer surplus is
a) a value that is wasted on producers.
b) a value extracted unfairly from consumers by producers.
c) the gains from trade for the producer.
d) increased only when consumer expenditure increases.
e) the difference between what the producer is willing to pay and the amount they actually receive.

21.21
Correct: a)
Difficulty: 2
Page(s): 540
Scramble range: All
Topic: Total surplus

21.21
Total surplus is
a) the total of consumer surplus and producer surplus.
b) consumer surplus minus producer surplus.
c) producer surplus minus consumer surplus.
d) consumer surplus divided by producer surplus.
e) maximized when marginal cost equals marginal revenue.

21.22
Correct: b)
Difficulty: 3
Page(s): 540
Scramble range: All
Topic: Maximum producer surplus

21.22
The maximum possible producer surplus value occurs whenever the price is
a) driven by competition to equal the marginal cost.
b) equal to the monopoly price.
c) equal to the competitive equilibrium price.
d) equal to minimum long-run average cost.
e) equal to the highest possible value.

21.23
Correct: a)
Difficulty: 3
Page(s): 540
Scramble range: All
Topic: Maximum total surplus

21.23
The maximum total surplus occurs whenever the price is
a) driven by competition to equal the marginal cost.
b) equal to the monopoly price.
c) equal to the competitive equilibrium price.
d) equal to minimum long-run average cost.
e) equal to the highest possible value.

21.24
Correct: a)
Difficulty: 3
Page(s): 540
Scramble range: All
Topic: Conflict in goals

21.24
There is always a conflict between
a) regulation aimed at the maximum total surplus and regulation aimed at the maximum producer surplus.
b) regulation forbidding monopoly and regulation encouraging the maximization of the total surplus.
c) allocative efficiency and maximizing the total surplus.
d) allocative efficiency and antitrust policy.
e) the regulatory agency and the producer.

21.25
Correct: b)
Difficulty: 2
Page(s): 540
Scramble range: All
Topic: Public interest theory

21.25
The public interest theory of economic regulation reasons that government
a) regulations should promote the interests of the public officials.
b) economic regulation attempts to maximize the total surplus.
c) economic regulation attempts to maximize the producer surplus.
d) economic regulations promote marcoeconomic stability.
e) economic regulation attempts to maximize the consumer surplus.

21.26
Correct: c)
Difficulty: 3
Page(s): 540
Scramble range: All
Topic: Economic theory

21.26
The economic theory of regulation reasons that government
a) regulations promote only the interests of the public officials.
b) economic regulation attempts to maximize the total surplus.
c) economic regulation attempts to maximize the producer surplus.
d) economic regulations promote macroeconomic stability.
e) economic regulation attempts to maximize the consumer surplus.

21.27
Correct: c)
Difficulty: 2
Page(s): 540
Scramble range: All
Topic: Demand for regulation

21.27
The demand for regulations, according to the economic theory of regulation, comes from all of the following *except*
a) consumers.
b) producers.
c) government officials.
d) bankers.
e) air travellers.

21.28
Correct: e)
Difficulty: 2
Page(s): 540
Scramble range: All
Topic: Lobbying efforts

21.28
Lobbying by the groups that demand regulations
a) is illegal.
b) is unprofitable.
c) is costless.
d) is altruistic.
e) raises their surplus.

21.29
Correct: b)
Difficulty: 3
Page(s): 540
Scramble range: All
Topic: Motives of lobbyists

21.29
Since lobbying is costly, the demanders of regulations must expect
a) society to gain from the regulations.
b) themselves to gain from the regulations.
c) competition to be enhanced by the regulations.
d) government not to gain anything in return.
e) surplus to fall as lobbying rises.

21.30
Correct: d)
Difficulty: 3
Page(s): 540
Scramble range: All
Topic: Demand for regulation

21.30
Main factors influencing the demand for regulations include all of the following *except* the
a) number of firms in the industry.
b) producer surplus per firm.
c) number of buyers in the market.
d) number of government officials involved.
e) consumer surplus per buyer.

21.31
Correct: b)
Difficulty: 3
Page(s): 540
Scramble range: All
Topic: Demand for regulation

21.31
The larger the surplus gained per capita from the economic regulation, the
a) more likely it will be that the government will return to regulation.
b) greater the demand for the regulation will be.
c) lower would be the number of demanders for regulation.
d) lower will be the price paid for the regulations.
e) greater will be the number of producers demanding to be regulated.

21.32
Correct: d)
Difficulty: 3
Page(s): 540
Scramble range: All
Topic: Demand for regulation

21.32
The larger the number of firms in the potentially affected industry, the
a) more likely it will be that the government will return to regulation.
b) greater the demand for the regulation will be.
c) lower would be the number of demanders for regulation.
d) lower will be the price paid for the regulations.
e) the greater will be the number of consumers demanding to be regulated.

21.33
Correct: b)
Difficulty: 3
Page(s): 540
Scramble range: All
Topic: Economic theory of regulation

21.33
For a given size of the surplus,
a) the greater the number of households who will share the surplus, the greater demand there will be for the regulation.
b) the lower the number of households who will share the surplus, the greater demand there will be for the regulation.
c) the greater the number of firms who will share the surplus, the greater demand there will be for the regulation.
d) the lower the number of firms who will share the surplus, the lower demand there will be for the regulation.
e) the greater the number of bureaucrats affected, the lower demand there will be for the regulation.

21.34
Correct: c)
Difficulty: 2
Page(s): 540–541
Scramble range: All
Topic: Supply of economic regulations

21.34
The supply of economic regulations originates with
a) monopolists.
b) labour unions and heavy industry.
c) politicians and bureaucrats.
d) fair trade associations.
e) producers and consumers.

21.35
Correct: d)
Difficulty: 2
Page(s): 540–541
Scramble range: All
Topic: Supply of economic regulations

21.35
The supply of economic regulations depends on
a) consumer surplus per seller.
b) producer surplus per buyer.
c) consumer surplus per bureaucrat.
d) consumer surplus per buyer.
e) producer surplus per bureaucrat.

21.36
Correct: b)
Difficulty: 2
Page(s): 540–541
Scramble range: All
Topic: Supply of economic regulations

21.36
The supply of economic regulations depends on
a) consumer surplus per seller.
b) producer surplus per seller.
c) consumer surplus per politician.
d) producer surplus per buyer.
e) consumer surplus per bureaucrat.

21.37
Correct: b)
Difficulty: 2
Page(s): 540–541
Scramble range: All
Topic: Supply of economic regulations

21.37
The supply of economic regulations depends on
a) the age of the politicians.
b) the number of persons affected by the regulations.
c) actions of Parliament.
d) actions of the Bank of Canada's board of governors.
e) the amount of producer surplus per buyer.

21.38
Correct: d)
Difficulty: 3
Page(s): 540–541
Scramble range: None
Topic: Supply of economic regulations

21.38
The tendency to supply economic regulations will be greater whenever
a) consumer surplus per buyer decreases.
b) producer surplus per seller decreases.
c) the number of affected persons decreases.
d) consumer surplus per buyer increases.
e) both a) and b).

21.39
Correct: b)
Difficulty: 3
Page(s): 540–541
Scramble range: None
Topic: Supply of economic regulations

21.39
The tendency to supply economic regulations will be greater whenever
a) consumer surplus per buyer decreases.
b) producer surplus per seller increases.
c) the number of affected persons decreases.
d) consumer surplus per seller increases.
e) both b) and d).

21.40
Correct: c)
Difficulty: 3
Page(s): 540–541
Scramble range: None
Topic: Supply of economic regulations

21.40
The tendency to supply economic regulations will be greater whenever
a) consumer surplus per buyer decreases.
b) producer surplus per seller decreases.
c) the number of affected persons increases.
d) producer surplus per buyer increases.
e) both a) and b).

21.41
Correct: b)
Difficulty: 3
Page(s): 541
Scramble range: All
Topic: Equilibrium in economic regulation

21.41
When there is no interest group that wishes to spend more on influencing economic regulations, and no politicians offering different regulations, then
a) corruption is eliminated.
b) equilibrium is achieved in the market for economic regulations.
c) regulations will be in oversupply.
d) regulations will be at their socially optimal level.
e) there will be no regulation.

21.42
Correct: a)
Difficulty: 3
Page(s): 541
Scramble range: All
Topic: Equilibrium in economic regulation

21.42
When there is no interest group that wishes to spend more on influencing economic regulations, and no politicians offering different regulations, then
a) everyone is not necessarily in agreement about the economic regulations.
b) the economic regulations make all groups better off.
c) regulations will no longer be demanded.
d) regulations will no longer be supplied.
e) there will be no regulation.

21.43
Correct: d)
Difficulty: 3
Page(s): 541
Scramble range: All
Topic: Economic regulation

21.43
When there is no interest group that wishes to spend more on influencing economic regulations, and no politicians offering different regulations, then
a) all political parties will agree about the economic regulations.
b) the economic regulations will no longer be instituted.
c) no resources will be devoted to maintaining existing regulations.
d) no group will want to change the policy proposals they are making.
e) all participants in the regulatory process will agree about the economic regulations.

21.44
Correct: e)
Difficulty: 2
Page(s): 541
Scramble range: All
Topic: Public interest theory

21.44
The public interest theory of regulation assumes that
a) all participants in the regulatory process are interested only in their own surplus.
b) regulations promote the attainment of monopoly profit in the economy.
c) public officials are public spirited, but consumers and producers are not.
d) public officials and private individuals are seeking their own gain through regulation.
e) regulations promote the attainment of allocative efficiency in the economy.

21.45
Correct: e)
Difficulty: 2
Page(s): 541
Scramble range: All
Topic: Public interest theory

21.45
The public interest theory of regulation assumes that
a) regulations promote the attainment of maximum deadweight loss in the economy.
b) regulations promote the attainment of monopoly in the economy.
c) producer surplus will be maximized by the regulatory process.
d) public officials are seeking gain for their constituents through regulation.
e) public officials are motivated to minimize the deadweight loss in the economy.

21.46
Correct: b)
Difficulty: 2
Page(s): 541
Scramble range: All
Topic: Public interest theory

21.46
The public interest theory of regulation assumes that
a) regulations promote the exploitation of labour by capital.
b) regulations promote the attainment of competitive output and prices in the economy.
c) public officials are motivated to minimize the likelihood of incumbancy.
d) public officials are seeking gain for the constituents of rivals through regulation.
e) bureaucrats operate to raise the size of their bureaucracy.

21.47
Correct: b)
Difficulty: 2
Page(s): 541
Scramble range: All
Topic: Capture theory of regulation

21.47
The capture theory of economic regulation assumes that
a) regulations promote the attainment of allocative efficiency in the economy.
b) regulations promote the attainment of monopoly profit in the economy.
c) public officials are public spirited, but consumers and producers are not.
d) public officials and private individuals are seeking their own gain through regulation.
e) bureaucrats operate to maximize the size of their bureaucracy.

21.48
Correct: c)
Difficulty: 2
Page(s): 541
Scramble range: All
Topic: Capture theory of regulation

21.48
The capture theory of regulation assumes that
a) regulations promote the exploitation of capital by labour.
b) regulations promote the attainment of competitive output and prices in the economy.
c) public officials are motivated to maximize producer surplus.
d) public officials are seeking gain for the constituents of rivals through regulation.
e) public officials are motivated to maximize total surplus.

21.49
Correct: e)
Difficulty: 4
Page(s): 541
Scramble range: All
Topic: Capture theory of regulation

21.49
One critical idea of the capture theory of regulation is that the cost of regulation is
a) low and regulation will therefore occur on a wide range of issues.
b) high and regulation will therefore occur on a wide range of issues.
c) high and regulation will therefore occur only when it benefits large, identifiable groups.
d) high and regulation will therefore occur only when it benefits large, unidentifiable groups.
e) high and regulation will therefore occur only when it benefits small, identifiable groups.

21.50
Correct: e)
Difficulty: 4
Page(s): 541
Scramble range: All
Topic: Capture theory of regulation

21.50
According to the capture theory of regulation, regulations
a) will be imposed only when the benefits are received by disinterested parties.
b) will not be imposed unless external costs are generated.
c) will not be imposed if net benefits are not positive.
d) will not be imposed if external costs result.
e) may be imposed even if external costs are imposed on disinterested parties.

21.51
Correct: b)
Difficulty: 3
Page(s): 541
Scramble range: All
Topic: Capture theory of regulation

21.51
According to the capture theory, regulation occurs because a
a) small group of losers from such regulations loses a great deal on a per capita basis.
b) small group of winners from such regulations gains a great deal on a per capita basis.
c) small group of winners from such regulations gains only a small amount on a per capita basis.
d) large group of winners from such regulations gains a great deal on a per capita basis.
e) large group of losers from such regulations loses a great deal on a per capita basis.

21.52
Correct: a)
Difficulty: 4
Page(s): 541
Scramble range: All
Topic: Capture theory of regulation

21.52
According to the capture theory, regulation occurs because
a) losers from such regulations would have to pay more per capita to organize an opposition and lobby than the regulations cost per capita.
b) losers from such regulations would have to pay less per capita to organize an opposition and lobby than the regulations cost per capita.
c) winners from such regulations deserve such regulations.
d) winners gain less in total than the losers gain from such regulations.
e) winners gain less in total than the losers pay in the costs of such regulation.

21.53
Correct: b)
Difficulty: 3
Page(s): 541
Scramble range: All
Topic: Capture theory of regulation

21.53
According to the capture theory,
a) regulators impose only those regulations which do not impose costs on others.
b) regulators award regulations to the highest bidder for those regulations.
c) in order to cut government budget deficits, regulators award regulations only in those cases in which government tax receipts would increase.
d) regulators accept the lowest bid, like they do on most government contracts.
e) regulators tend to award regulations to areas where bureaucratic size is maximized.

21.54
Correct: a)
Difficulty: 3
Page(s): 541
Scramble range: All
Topic: Capture theory of regulation

21.54
According to the capture theory, the demander of regulations offers a price through all of the following means *except*
a) campaign promises.
b) votes.
c) campaign contributions.
d) employment opportunities after government service.
e) a large bureaucracy.

21.55
Correct: e)
Difficulty: 2
Page(s): 542
Scramble range: All
Topic: Regulated sectors

21.55
The predominant sectors that are regulated federally in Canada include all of the following *except*
a) agriculture.
b) energy.
c) transport.
d) telecommunications.
e) sales.

21.56
Correct: e)
Difficulty: 2
Page(s): 542
Scramble range: All
Topic: Regulatory agencies

21.56
Which of the following is *not* a federal regulatory agency?
a) Canadian Dairy Commission.
b) Canadian Transport Commission.
c) Canadian Wheat Board.
d) National Energy Board.
e) National Anti-Poverty Coalition.

21.57
Correct: d)
Difficulty: 4
Page(s): 543–544
Scramble range: All
Topic: Natural monopolies

21.57
Consider Figure 21.1. Suppose that this agency was run by the regulatory body as a breakeven proposition. As a result, the price would be __________, the quantity __________, and the resulting equilibrium __________.
a) P_4; Q_1; efficient
b) P_3; Q_1; inefficient
c) P_2; Q_3; efficient
d) P_2; Q_2; inefficient
e) P_1; Q_3; efficient

Figure 21.1

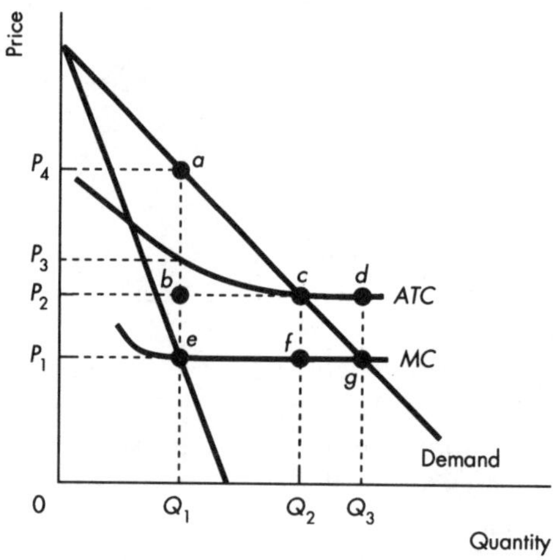

21.58
Correct: b)
Difficulty: 4
Page(s): 543
Scramble range: a)–d)
Topic: Natural monopoly

21.58
Consider Figure 21.1. Suppose this market is unregulated by the government. Select the best statement.
a) The monopolist in this market will not be able to make positive profits, since the marginal cost curve is always below the average cost curve.
b) The monopolist will choose to produce at Q_1.
c) The monopolist will choose to produce at Q_2.
d) The consumers in this market are better off if the monopolist does not produce since, if she produces, she will raise prices so high as to take all the consumer surplus away.
e) None of the above.

21.59
Correct: d)
Difficulty: 4
Page(s): 543–544
Scramble range: All
Topic: Economic regulation

21.59
Consider Figure 21.1. Suppose that this market is regulated by the government. Select the best statement.
a) The government can achieve the socially optimal level of output if it uses marginal cost pricing.
b) The government can achieve the socially optimal level of output by using average cost pricing.
c) The government can never achieve the social equilibrium in this market, since the marginal cost curve is always below the average cost curve.
d) The government cannot achieve the socially optimal level of output unless it subsidizes the monopoly and forces it to produce at Q_3.
e) The best choice of the government is to shut down the industry, even though we lose some net benefits by doing this, since the firm can never produce at a nonnegative profit.

21.60
Correct: d)
Difficulty: 2
Page(s): 543
Scramble range: All
Topic: Regulatory process

21.60
The regulatory process involves the decisions of all of the following *except*
a) senior bureaucrats appointed by the government.
b) bureaucrats who are experts in matters of concern to the industry under consideration.
c) members of parliament.
d) members of the judicial system.
e) the appointed members of the regulatory agency.

21.61
Correct: a)
Difficulty: 2
Page(s): 543
Scramble range: All
Topic: Economic regulation

21.61
The regulatory agency can decide all of the following *except* the
a) technology the firm will use.
b) total output produced by the firm.
c) level of prices charged by the firm.
d) markets served by the firm.
e) *structure* of prices charged by the firm.

21.62
Correct: c)
Difficulty: 2
Page(s): 545
Scramble range: All
Topic: Rate of return regulation

21.62
Rate of return regulation is typically imposed in what type of market structure?
a) Monopolistic competition.
b) Oligopoly.
c) Natural monopoly.
d) Perfect competition.
e) Cartels.

21.63
Correct: c)
Difficulty: 3
Page(s): 545
Scramble range: All
Topic: Rate of return regulation

21.63
Rate of return regulation can generate greater than normal profit if
a) there is a great demand for the product.
b) there is a competitive struggle to determine which firms will supply the market.
c) the regulated firm overstates its costs of production.
d) price is set at average total cost of production.
e) the rate is set too low.

21.64
Correct: c)
Difficulty: 3
Page(s): 546
Scramble range: All
Topic: Cartels

21.64
A cartel is
a) an arrangement to flood the market and eliminate competition.
b) an arrangement to steal secret industrial processes from rival firms.
c) an arrangement among firms to reduce output and raise price.
d) usually a stable organization, with no threat from cheaters on the cartel arrangements.
e) an arrangement among firms to capture the regulator.

21.65
Correct: b)
Difficulty: 2
Page(s): 544
Scramble range: All
Topic: Economic regulation

21.65
As communications technology improves, economic regulations may decrease if
a) the benefits from regulations to producers continue to increase.
b) there is a reduction in the cost of organizing consumers to protest regulations.
c) Canada imposed tariffs on Japanese goods.
d) the cost of opposing the regulations goes up.
e) the benefits of regulation rise as a result.

21.66
Correct: d)
Difficulty: 2
Page(s): 551
Scramble range: All
Topic: Crown corporations

21.66
The total number of Crown corporations in Canada is about
a) 25.
b) 35.
c) 90.
d) 125.
e) 1250.

21.67
Correct: e)
Difficulty: 2
Page(s): 551
Scramble range: All
Topic: Crown corporations

21.67
Crown corporations are
a) corporations that are regulated by the Crown.
b) corporations that are owned by the federal government.
c) corporations that are owned by the provincial governments.
d) operated to maximize the profits of the owners.
e) owned by the provinces or the federal government.

21.68
Correct: a)
Difficulty: 3
Page(s): 551
Scramble range: All
Topic: Crown corporations

21.68
To be efficient, a Crown corporation will obey the rule of producing at an output level
a) where price equals marginal cost.
b) where price equals zero.
c) that maximizes the number of votes for the governing party.
d) where price equals average cost.
e) that maximizes the budget of the Crown, subject to the constraints imposed on it by Parliament.

21.69
Correct: d)
Difficulty: 2
Page(s): 552
Scramble range: All
Topic: Crown corporations

21.69
Consider Figure 21.1. Suppose that this is the case of a Crown corporation. If this Crown was run to be efficient, then output would be
a) zero.
b) Q_1.
c) Q_2.
d) Q_3.
e) where the demand curve crosses the horizontal axis.

21.70
Correct: e)
Difficulty: 4
Page(s): 552
Scramble range: All
Topic: Crown corporations

21.70
Consider Figure 21.1. Suppose this firm was a Crown corporation where the managers have the goal of budget maximization, subject to a constraint of marginal cost pricing. As a result, output would be

a) Q_1, but price would be only P_3.
b) Q_2, with price equal to P_2, but average costs would rise to extract all available consumer surplus.
c) Q_3, price would be P_2, and average costs would rise to extract all consumer surplus.
d) Q_3, price would be P_1, but average costs would rise to extract all available producer surplus.
e) Q_3, price would be P_1, and average costs would rise to extract all available consumer surplus.

21.71
Correct: d)
Difficulty: 5
Page(s): 552
Scramble range: All
Topic: Crown corporations

21.71
Consider Figure 21.1. Suppose that this diagram represented a Crown corporation. If this firm was run by its managers to maximize their budget, subject to a constraint of zero price, then output would be

a) Q_1, while price would be zero, and average costs would equal P_3.
b) Q_2, while price would be zero, and average costs would rise to extract all available consumer surplus.
c) Q_3, while price would be zero, and average costs would rise to extract all available consumer surplus.
d) where the demand curve crosses the horizontal axis, price would be zero, and average costs would rise to extract all available consumer surplus.
e) where the demand curve crosses the horizontal axis, price would be zero, and average costs would rise to extract all available producer surplus.

21.72
Correct: e)
Difficulty: 4
Page(s): 553
Scramble range: All
Topic: Crown corporations

21.72
The theories used to examine Crown corporations predict that in reality we will find Crown corporations

a) operating at the allocatively efficient level of output, with average costs minimized for that level.
b) producing too little output at too high a price and cost.
c) producing the allocatively efficient level of output, but with costs too high compared to a profit-maximizing firm.
d) totally ignoring the consumers' interest.
e) producing too much output, with its average costs too high compared to a profit-maximizing firm.

21.73
Correct: c)
Difficulty: 3
Page(s): 553
Scramble range: None
Topic: Crown corporations

21.73
Studies comparing publicly owned enterprises to privately owned enterprises have found

a) that publicly owned enterprises are always more allocatively efficient.
b) that privately owned enterprises are always more allocatively efficient.
c) that publicly owned enterprises usually have a higher cost structure.
d) both b) and c).
e) both a) and c).

21.74 (SG 21.5)
Correct: a)
Difficulty: 2
Page(s): 540
Scramble range: All
Topic: Producer surplus in monopoly

21.74
In a monopoly industry, producer surplus is maximized when
a) marginal revenue equals marginal cost.
b) marginal cost equals average total cost.
c) price equals marginal cost.
d) price equals average total cost.
e) price equals marginal revenue.

21.75 (SG 21.6)
Correct: d)
Difficulty: 3
Page(s): 540
Scramble range: All
Topic: Regulation

21.75
Which of the following means a large demand for regulation by producers? Regulation results in
a) small consumer surplus per buyer.
b) large consumer surplus per buyer.
c) small producer surplus per buyer.
d) large producer surplus per buyer.
e) large consumer surplus per seller.

21.76 (SG 21.7)
Correct: b)
Difficulty: 3
Page(s): 541
Scramble range: All
Topic: Political equilibrium

21.76
In a political equilibrium,
a) allocative efficiency must be achieved.
b) no one wants to change their proposals.
c) firms will be making zero economic profit.
d) all parties will agree that the appropriate level of regulation has been achieved.
e) producer surplus must be at a maximum.

21.77 (SG 21.8)
Correct: a)
Difficulty: 3
Page(s): 541
Scramble range: All
Topic: Public interest theory

21.77
Which of the following is consistent with the public interest theory of regulation?
a) Regulation of a natural monopolist by setting price equal to marginal cost.
b) Regulation of a competitive industry to increase output.
c) Regulation of the airline industry by establishing minimum airfares.
d) Regulation of agriculture by establishing barriers to exit from the industry.
e) Regulation of agriculture by lowering the price faced by consumers.

21.78 (SG 21.9)
Correct: c)
Difficulty: 3
Page(s): 541
Scramble range: All
Topic: Capture theory of regulation

21.78
Which of the following is consistent with the capture theory of regulation?
a) Regulation of a natural monopolist by setting price equal to marginal cost.
b) Regulation of a competitive industry to increase output.
c) Regulation of the airline industry by establishing minimum airfares.
d) Regulation of agriculture by establishing barriers to exit from the industry.
e) Regulation of agriculture by lowering the price faced by consumers.

21.79 (SG 21.10)
Correct: d)
Difficulty: 2
Page(s): 544
Scramble range: All
Topic: Natural monopoly

21.79
Which of the following is least likely to be a natural monopoly?
a) Local subway services.
b) Local electric utilities.
c) Local water and sewer services.
d) Local taxicab service.
e) Local cable television services.

21.80 (SG 21.11)
Correct: a)
Difficulty: 2
Page(s): 544
Scramble range: All
Topic: Natural monopoly

21.80
Figure 21.1 gives the revenue and cost curves for an industry. This industry will become a natural monopoly because
a) one firm can supply the entire market at a lower price than two or more firms could.
b) the *MC* curve is negatively sloped when it intersects the demand curve.
c) there are diseconomies of scale over the entire range of demand.
d) even a single firm will be unable to earn a positive profit in this industry.
e) marginal cost is always below average cost, for all levels of output.

21.81 (SG 21.14)
Correct: d)
Difficulty: 4
Page(s): 544
Scramble range: All
Topic: Natural monopoly

21.81
Consider the natural monopoly depicted in Figure 21.1. Total surplus is a maximum when quantity is
a) Q_1 and price is P_3.
b) Q_1 and price is P_4.
c) Q_2 and price is P_2.
d) Q_3 and price is P_1.
e) where the demand curve crosses the horizontal axis.

21.82 (SG 21.15)
Correct: b)
Difficulty: 4
Page(s): 544
Scramble range: All
Topic: Natural monopoly

21.82
Consider the natural monopoly depicted in Figure 21.1. Producer surplus is a maximum when quantity is
a) Q_1 and price is P_3.
b) Q_1 and price is P_4.
c) Q_2 and price is P_2.
d) Q_3 and price is P_1.
e) where the demand curve crosses the horizontal axis.

21.83 (SG 21.16)
Correct: d)
Difficulty: 4
Page(s): 544
Scramble range: a)–d)
Topic: Natural monopoly

21.83
Consider the natural monopoly depicted in Figure 21.1. If a regulator uses a marginal cost pricing rule, what line segment gives the amount of subsidy (per unit of output) that will be required to assure that the monopolist will remain in business?
a) *ba*.
b) *ea*.
c) *fc*.
d) *gd*.
e) None of the above.

21.84 (SG 21.17)
Correct: e)
Difficulty: 5
Page(s): 544
Scramble range: All
Topic: Natural monopoly

21.84
Consider the natural monopoly depicted in Figure 21.1. What region in the graph represents the deadweight loss arising from an average cost pricing rule?
a) P_1P_2cf.
b) *cdg*.
c) P_1P_2dg.
d) *aeg*.
e) *cfg*.

21.85 (SG 21.18)
Correct: a)
Difficulty: 4
Page(s): 545
Scramble range: All
Topic: Monopoly regulation

21.85
A monopolist under rate of return regulation has an incentive to
a) inflate costs.
b) produce more than the efficient quantity of output.
c) charge a price equal to marginal cost.
d) maximize consumer surplus.
e) cut output.

21.86
Correct: a)
Difficulty: 2
Page(s): 554
Scramble range: All
Topic: Anti-combine law

21.86
Canada's anti-combine law dates back to the
a) 1890s.
b) 1910s.
c) 1930s.
d) 1960s.
e) 1980s.

21.87
Correct: e)
Difficulty: 2
Page(s): 555
Scramble range: All
Topic: Anti-combine law

21.87
Canada's anti-combine law is enforced by
a) Parliament.
b) the criminal courts.
c) the civil courts.
d) the Economic Council of Canada.
e) a quasi-judicial tribunal.

21.88
Correct: c)
Difficulty: 3
Page(s): 555
Scramble range: All
Topic: Competition Act

21.88
Under the Competition Act of 1986, the Tribunal may do all of the following *except*
a) prohibit one or more persons from completely controlling a class of business.
b) prohibit one or more persons from engaging in anti-competitive acts.
c) force firms to lower their prices.
d) dissolve mergers.
e) prevent mergers.

21.89
Correct: e)
Difficulty: 4
Page(s): 557
Scramble range: All
Topic: Anti-combine law

21.89
Various cases under Canada's anti-combine law have established that
a) the word "unduly" in the law currently means a complete monopoly across Canada.
b) as long as there are potential entrants into the market, it does not matter if one firm currently controls the market and deters entry.
c) only regional aspects of monopoly power matters.
d) the government always wins whenever they prosecute.
e) a firm can have a regional monopoly, but this does not matter if there is competition from elsewhere in Canada.

21.90
Correct: c)
Difficulty: 4
Page(s): 557
Scramble range: All
Topic: Public/private interest

21.90
Select the best statement about regulation and anti-combine law.
a) Regulation and anti-combine law both seem to operate mostly in the public interest.
b) Regulation and anti-combine law both seem to operate mostly in the interests of the bureaucrats and the producers.
c) Regulation seems to operate mostly in the interest of the bureaucrats and the producers, while anti-combine law seems to operate mostly in the public interest.
d) Regulation seems to operate mostly in the public interest, while anti-combine law seems to operate mostly in the interest of the bureaucrats and the producers.
e) Both regulation and anti-combine law will usually achieve allocative efficiency.

21.91
Correct: c)
Difficulty: 3
Page(s): 540
Scramble range: All
Topic: Regulation

21.91
Which situation would increase the demand for regulation by producers?
a) An increase in consumer surplus per buyer.
b) A decrease in consumer surplus per buyer.
c) An increase in producer surplus per buyer.
d) A decrease in producer surplus per buyer.
e) A increase in the cost of lobbying.

21.92 (SG 21.7)
Correct: e)
Difficulty: 4
Page(s): 541
Scramble range: All
Topic: Political equilibrium

21.92
In a political equilibrium,
a) allocative efficiency cannot be the goal.
b) consumer surplus must be maximized.
c) firms will be making positive economic profit.
d) no parties will agree that the appropriate level of regulation has been achieved.
e) no interest group changes their lobbying position.

21.93 (SG 21.9)
Correct: c)
Difficulty: 3
Page(s): 541
Scramble range: All
Topic: Capture theory of regulation

21.93
Which of the following is consistent with the capture theory of regulation?
a) Regulation of a natural monopolist by setting price equal to marginal revenue.
b) Regulation of a monopoly industry in order to reduce output.
c) Regulation of the airline industry by establishing minimum airfares.
d) Regulation of agriculture by establishing price ceilings.
e) Regulation of the airline industry to establish certain mandatory regional routes.

21.94
Correct: e)
Difficulty: 2
Page(s): 544
Scramble range: All
Topic: Natural monopoly

21.94
Which of the following is most likely to be a natural monopoly?
a) Local sandwich shops.
b) Local printing services.
c) Local welding services.
d) Local automotive service.
e) Local electric utilities.

21.95
Correct: a)
Difficulty: 3
Page(s): 545
Scramble range: All
Topic: Monopoly regulation

21.95
A monopolist under rate of return regulation has no incentive to
a) underestimate costs.
b) produce less than the efficient quantity of output.
c) charge a price less than marginal cost.
d) maximize consumer surplus.
e) raise output.

21.96
Correct: b)
Difficulty: 4
Page(s): 544
Scramble range: All
Topic: Natural monopoly

21.96
Consider Fact 21.1. Suppose the industry is unregulated. In this case, output would be
a) 400,000 bottles per day.
b) 500,000 bottles per day.
c) 600,000 bottles per day.
d) 700,000 bottles per day.
e) 800,000 bottles per day.

Fact 21.1
Cascade Springs Inc. is a natural monopoly that bottles water from a spring high in the Rocky Mountains. The total fixed cost it incurs is $80,000, and its marginal cost is 10 cents a bottle. The demand for Cascade Springs bottled water is

Price (cents per bottle)	Quantity demanded (thousands of bottles per year)
100	0
90	100
80	200
70	300
60	400
50	500
40	600
30	700
20	800
10	900
0	1,000

21.97
Correct: d)
Difficulty: 4
Page(s): 544
Scramble range: All
Topic: Natural monopoly

21.97
Consider Fact 21.1. Suppose the industry is not regulated, and the firm is at its optimal choice. In this case, the deadweight loss to society is
a) zero.
b) $250,000 per day.
c) $90,000 per day.
d) $80,000 per day.
e) $160,000 per day.

21.98
Correct: d)
Difficulty: 4
Page(s): 545
Scramble range: All
Topic: Marginal cost pricing

21.98
Consider Fact 21.1. Suppose the firm is regulated by the government, who imposes marginal cost pricing. The price of a bottle of water is
a) zero.
b) 50 cents per bottle.
c) 30 cents per bottle.
d) 10 cents per bottle.
e) 20 cents per bottle.

21.99
Correct: a)
Difficulty: 5
Page(s): 545
Scramble range: All
Topic: Marginal cost pricing

21.99
Consider Fact 21.1. The government regulates the firm, and imposes marginal cost pricing. What will the firm's profits be in equilbrium, if they are not subsidized?
a) –$80,000.
b) $90,000.
c) $120,000.
d) $60,000.
e) Zero.

21.100
Correct: e)
Difficulty: 5
Page(s): 545
Scramble range: All
Topic: Average cost pricing

21.100
Consider Fact 21.1. Suppose that the government regulates the firm with average cost pricing. What will the price be?
a) Zero.
b) $0.50.
c) $0.30.
d) $0.10.
e) $0.20.

Chapter 22 Inflation, Unemployment, Cycles, and Deficits

22.1
Correct: b)
Difficulty: 2
Page(s): 562
Scramble range: All
Topic: Distinguishing macro/micro

22.1
Macroeconomics is the branch of economics that attempts to
a) explain changes in the mix of goods and services produced in an economy.
b) study output, employment, and inflation in the economy as a whole.
c) study the distribution of income between employees in differing industries across an economy.
d) explain why certain firms are less efficient than others.
e) explain government policy with respect to unemployment and inflation.

22.2
Correct: a)
Difficulty: 2
Page(s): 562
Scramble range: All
Topic: Distinguishing macro/micro

22.2
Explaining why the average price of consumer goods and services increased almost twofold from 1980 to 1990 would require
a) using macroeconomic analysis to study changes in the general price level.
b) using microeconomic analysis to study changes in relative prices.
c) more appropriate data to be available.
d) the use of normative economics only.
e) an analysis using the demand and supply of various goods.

22.3
Correct: b)
Difficulty: 2
Page(s): 562
Scramble range: All
Topic: Distinguishing macro/micro

22.3
Macroeconomists are distinguished from microeconomists in that macroeconomists are more interested in
a) the total sales of a major corporation than the total sales of the corner grocery store.
b) the unemployment rate for the Canadian economy than the unemployment rate in the Canadian steel industry.
c) the demand for coal than the demand for labour in Canada.
d) the relative price of food products than the general price level.
e) the total sales of an industry than the total sales of a major corporation.

22.4
Correct: d)
Difficulty: 2
Page(s): 563
Scramble range: All
Topic: Recent inflation record

22.4
Since 1955 the
a) inflation rate has always decreased.
b) price level has increased at times and decreased at other times.
c) inflation rate has always increased.
d) inflation rate has gone up and down.
e) price level has increased at an ever-increasing rate.

22.5
Correct: b)
Difficulty: 2
Page(s): 564
Scramble range: All
Topic: Inflation/value of money

22.5
The value of money varies
a) directly with the inflation rate.
b) inversely with the inflation rate.
c) is unrelated to the inflation rate.
d) as the supply of gold varies.
e) directly with the unemployment rate.

22.6
Correct: e)
Difficulty: 4
Page(s): 564
Scramble range: All
Topic: Inflation/value of money

22.6
Lucie receives a pension of $10,000 a year. Suppose that when she first began receiving the $10,000 pension eight years ago, prices were half what they are today. One may conclude that the purchasing power of her pension
a) has risen.
b) has stayed the same.
c) has fallen by less than the price level has risen.
d) is worth twice as much as when she first started receiving it.
e) is worth half as much as when she first started receiving it.

22.7
Correct: c)
Difficulty: 3
Page(s): 564
Scramble range: All
Topic: Inflation

22.7
Which of the following statements is false?
a) The inflation rate is positive when there is an increase in the general level of prices.
b) When the inflation rate is positive, the purchasing power of money decreases.
c) When the inflation rate is positive, lenders always gain more from the borrower than was anticipated.
d) Inflation that is unanticipated redistributes income.
e) Inflation that is anticipated imposes an opportunity cost on money.

22.8
Correct: c)
Difficulty: 3
Page(s): 564
Scramble range: All
Topic: Inflation

22.8
According to economic theory, when the actual rate of inflation is greater than the rate anticipated by decision makers, then income will be redistributed from
a) the federal government to local governments.
b) borrowers to lenders.
c) lenders to borrowers.
d) retail business firms to customers.
e) people who do not hold money to those who do hold money.

22.9
Correct: a)
Difficulty: 4
Page(s): 567
Scramble range: All
Topic: Inflation and borrowers/lenders

22.9
Suppose that Tom borrows $100 from Pat for one semester. They agree upon a 5 percent rate of interest per semester and neither anticipates any inflation during the period.
a) If there is a 5 percent inflation, then income is redistributed from Pat to Tom as a result.
b) If there is a 5 percent inflation, then Tom must pay Pat $110 at the end of the semester.
c) If there is a 5 percent inflation, then income is redistributed from Tom to Pat as a result.
d) If there is a 5 percent inflation, then Tom need pay Pat only $100 at the end of the semester.
e) If there is a 5 percent inflation, then Tom need pay Pat only $95 at the end of the semester.

22.10
Correct: d)
Difficulty: 3
Page(s): 567
Scramble range: All
Topic: Workers/employers and inflation

22.10
If all prices and wages increased by 10 percent during the same time period, then
a) poor people would be hurt more than rich people.
b) workers would be hurt more than employers.
c) lenders would be hurt more than borrowers.
d) no group would be hurt as a result of the inflation.
e) the value of money would rise.

22.11
Correct: a)
Difficulty: 3
Page(s): 567
Scramble range: All
Topic: Workers/employers and inflation

22.11
Inflation does not redistribute income from employers to workers if
a) wages rise slower than inflation.
b) inflation affects the unemployed only.
c) prices of necessities remain the same.
d) worker productivity increases.
e) wages rise faster than inflation.

22.12
Correct: a)
Difficulty: 2
Page(s): 567
Scramble range: All
Topic: Workers and inflation

22.12
If the price level rises faster than your income, and all else remains the same, then your real standard of living will
a) decrease.
b) increase.
c) stay the same.
d) remain the same only if prices continue to rise at the same pace.
e) increase only if inflation is low enough.

22.13
Correct: c)
Difficulty: 4
Page(s): 566
Scramble range: All
Topic: Inflation and expectation

22.13
If inflation persists over the term of a loan contract,
a) then borrowers or lenders must realize an unanticipated decline in purchasing power.
b) then borrowers will realize an unanticipated loss in purchasing power if the inflation was not anticipated when the loan contract was signed.
c) then borrowers will realize an unanticipated gain in purchasing power if the inflation was not anticipated when the loan contract was signed.
d) then lenders will realize an unanticipated decline in income.
e) the interest rate will be too high if the inflation is anticipated.

22.14
Correct: a)
Difficulty: 3
Page(s): 567
Scramble range: All
Topic: Historic inflation/international

22.14
Countries that borrowed funds from the Western countries during the late 1970s and early 1980s and were still under contract to repay those nonindexed loans in the middle to late 1980s
a) repaid with dollars that were worth more than they anticipated at the time the loan contract was signed.
b) repaid with dollars that were worth less than they anticipated at the time the loan contract was signed.
c) received more revenue than they expected due to export prices that were higher because of the inflation.
d) received the same revenue that they expected from sale of exports.
e) gained from the unanticipated inflation.

22.15
Correct: c)
Difficulty: 3
Page(s): 567
Scramble range: a)–d)
Topic: Inflation and opportunity

22.15
Suppose you have $100 in a chequing account for one year that pays zero percent interest. There are no fees charged on the account since the minimum balance requirement has been met. Select the best statement.

a) A 20 percent annual inflation imposes a $120 opportunity cost on your account.
b) A 20 percent annual inflation imposes an $80 opportunity cost on your account.
c) A 20 percent annual inflation imposes a $20 opportunity cost on your account.
d) A 20 percent annual inflation does not impose an opportunity cost on your account.
e) None of the above.

22.16
Correct: d)
Difficulty: 3
Page(s): 567
Scramble range: All
Topic: Anticipated inflation

22.16
Anticipated inflation is an economic problem because

a) it reduces the volume and frequency of transactions undertaken by economic decision makers.
b) the reduced opportunity cost of holding money increases the frequency of transactions by economic decision makers.
c) it reduces the opportunity cost of holding money.
d) it increases the opportunity cost of holding money.
e) it redistributes money from lenders to borrowers.

22.17
Correct: e)
Difficulty: 4
Page(s): 567
Scramble range: All
Topic: Inflation/frequency of transactions

22.17
Which of the following statements is true concerning the opportunity cost of holding money during periods of inflation?

a) If the inflation is anticipated, it can be built into interest rates and therefore has no impact.
b) The faster the inflation rate the larger the amount of money people will hold.
c) The faster the inflation rate the lower the opportunity cost of holding money.
d) Inflation does not affect the opportunity cost of holding money if the inflation rate is less than 8 percent.
e) The faster the inflation rate, the smaller the amount of money that people will hold.

22.18
Correct: b)
Difficulty: 2
Page(s): 568
Scramble range: All
Topic: Hyperinflation

22.18
The text defines hyperinflation as occurring when the inflation rate is higher than

a) 50 percent per year.
b) 50 percent per month.
c) 500 percent per year.
d) 25 percent per month.
e) 5 percent per month.

22.19
Correct: c)
Difficulty: 3
Page(s): 569
Scramble range: All
Topic: Unanticipated inflation

22.19
Which of the following is most likely to lose due to an unanticipated inflation?
a) A person paying back a fixed-interest-rate mortgage loan.
b) A union worker operating under an indexed wage contract.
c) The mortgage company receiving payments on a fixed-interest-rate mortgage loan.
d) The taxpayer whose taxes are indexed.
e) The mortgage company receiving payments on an indexed interest rate mortgage loan.

22.20
Correct: c)
Difficulty: 2
Page(s): 570
Scramble range: All
Topic: Labour force

22.20
The labour force
a) includes all people who can work.
b) does not include people who are looking for work.
c) is the total number of people over 16 years old who are employed and unemployed.
d) is divided into four distinct categories in order to determine the number of people who are unemployed.
e) is the total number of people over 16 years old.

22.21
Correct: a)
Difficulty: 3
Page(s): 568
Scramble range: All
Topic: Calculate unemployment rate

22.21
If there are 15 million people in the total labour force and 2 million people are unemployed, then the unemployment rate is
a) 13.3 percent.
b) 10 percent.
c) 9 percent.
d) 15 percent.
e) 20 percent.

22.22
Correct: e)
Difficulty: 3
Page(s): 568
Scramble range: All
Topic: Calculate unemployment rate

22.22
If there are 25 million people in Canada and 2 million people are unemployed, then the unemployment rate is
a) 13.3 percent.
b) 10 percent.
c) 5 percent.
d) 8 percent.
e) unknown based on the information given.

22.23
Correct: c)
Difficulty: 3
Page(s): 573
Scramble range: All
Topic: Discouraged workers

22.23
If a person wishes to have a job but gives up the search because she cannot find one,
a) then she is considered to be unemployed by the Labour Force Survey.
b) then she is considered to be employed by the Labour Force Survey.
c) then she does not count in the unemployment figures determined by the Labour Force Survey.
d) then she is considered to be lazy by the Labour Force Survey.
e) then she is considered to have unrealistic wage expectations by the Labour Force Survey.

22.24
Correct: b)
Difficulty: 3
Page(s): 573
Scramble range: All
Topic: Discouraged workers

22.24
Because of discouraged workers
a) the official unemployment statistics tend to overstate the true underlying unemployment rate.
b) the official unemployment statistics tend to understate the true underlying unemployment rate.
c) during recessions the true underlying unemployment rate tends to be smaller than the official rate would indicate.
d) the official employment rate is more than if these people were to continue to look.
e) if the unemployment data were corrected for wage and job expectations, then the measured unemployment rate would be lower.

22.25
Correct: d)
Difficulty: 3
Page(s): 573
Scramble range: All
Topic: Official unemployment statistics

22.25
Which of the following people would be considered officially unemployed?
a) One who is currently working but expects to be laid off by the end of the month before next month's survey can be completed.
b) One who is 15 years of age and has been looking for an after-school job every day for the past month.
c) One who has been looking for a job but is taking a month-long break from the job-seeking effort due to her lack of skills.
d) One who is waiting to start a new job within 30 days.
e) One who has quit looking because they believe that there is no work available for them.

22.26
Correct: c)
Difficulty: 3
Page(s): 573
Scramble range: All
Topic: Official unemployment statistics

22.26
Which of the following people would be considered unemployed?
a) A part-time worker who repeatedly expresses a desire to become a full-time worker.
b) A person who has been seeking a job for the last six months, but recently gave up looking because he was discouraged by his job prospects.
c) A person who has been offered a job at $4.50 per hour but who refuses to take the job at such a low rate.
d) A person who expects to be laid off by the end of the month before next month's survey can be completed.
e) A person who has been laid off for 30 weeks and is waiting to be called back to a job.

22.27
Correct: b)
Difficulty: 3
Page(s): 574
Scramble range: All
Topic: Frictional unemployment

22.27
According to the textbook, frictional unemployment arises in part because
a) there are not enough jobs available.
b) of technological change.
c) people become discouraged when they cannot find a job.
d) people will not quit from their present job until they can find suitable employment in a new job.
e) of unrealistic wage expectations.

22.28
Correct: d)
Difficulty: 2
Page(s): 572
Scramble range: All
Topic: Definition of unemployment rate

22.28
The unemployment rate is defined as the number of
a) unemployed people divided by the number of employed people.
b) employed people divided by the number of people who are over 16 years old in the country.
c) unemployed people divided by the number of people in the population who are over 16 years old.
d) unemployed people, divided by the number of people employed plus the number of people unemployed.
e) unemployed people, divided by the number of people over the age of 16 years old who are employed.

22.29
Correct: b)
Difficulty: 2
Page(s): 574
Scramble range: All
Topic: Full employment

22.29
Full employment does not mean that there is zero unemployment because
a) some people will always be unemployed so that they can collect unemployment cheques, drink beer, and watch soap operas on television.
b) some frictional unemployment is beneficial.
c) business fluctuations are inevitable.
d) of discouraged workers.
e) of unrealistic wage expectations.

22.30
Correct: b)
Difficulty: 2
Page(s): 574
Scramble range: All
Topic: Full employment

22.30
In a dynamic economy under ideal conditions, the unemployment rate
a) should be within plus or minus 0.005 percent of zero.
b) would be positive due to frictional unemployment.
c) would tend to move upward as the price level rises.
d) would tend to move downward as the price level falls.
e) would tend to be 6 percent.

22.31
Correct: c)
Difficulty: 2
Page(s): 574
Scramble range: All
Topic: Full employment

22.31
Full employment corresponds to
a) a zero rate of unemployment.
b) a 4 percent unemployment rate regardless of changing labour market conditions.
c) the natural rate of unemployment.
d) 6 percent, the rate that all economists agree it should be.
e) frictional unemployment plus discouraged workers minus those with unrealistic wage expectations.

22.32
Correct: e)
Difficulty: 3
Page(s): 574
Scramble range: All
Topic: Unemployment

22.32
According to estimates made by Arthur Okun, for every
a) 1 percentage point rise in the unemployment rate, GDP will fall by 5 percent.
b) 1 percentage point rise in GDP, the unemployment rate will fall by 2.5 percent.
c) 1 percentage point fall in the unemployment rate, GDP will fall by 2.5 percent.
d) 2.5 percentage point rise in the unemployment rate, GDP will fall by 1 percent.
e) 1 percentage rise in the unemployment rate, GDP will fall by 2.5 percent.

22.33
Correct: b)
Difficulty: 3
Page(s): 574–575
Scramble range: All
Topic: Costs of unemployment

22.33
Which of the following sets of statements most accurately reflects the costs associated with unemployment?
a) All costs associated with unemployment can be expressed in terms of opportunity costs. Therefore, the exact, undisputable, measurement of the costs can be obtained.
b) The career development of an unemployed worker is slowed due to a depreciation of human capital.
c) The higher the unemployment rate, the lower the crime rate. Therefore, if the unemployment rate is at an all-time high, then the crime cost of unemployment should be low.
d) The most important cost of unemployment must be the loss of output since economists measure unemployment costs this way.
e) The most important cost of unemployment must be the lost income of the unemployed.

22.34
Correct: c)
Difficulty: 2
Page(s): 575–578
Scramble range: All
Topic: GDP

22.34
Gross Domestic Product is defined as
a) the final value of all goods produced in the economy in a given time period.
b) the market value of all goods and services produced in the economy during a given time period.
c) the total market value of all the final goods and services produced in the economy during a given time period.
d) the average value of output produced in the economy in a given time period.
e) the total market value of all the intermediate goods and services produced in the economy for a given time period.

22.35
Correct: b)
Difficulty: 4
Page(s): 575–576
Scramble range: a)–d)
Topic: Intermediate goods

22.35
Which of the following would be counted in GDP for this year?
a) The new printer purchased by a publishing company.
b) The personal computer purchased by the student who wishes to write his term papers.
c) The purchase of a new automobile by the dealer from the manufacturer.
d) The banking services bought by a car producer.
e) All of the above.

22.36
Correct: c)
Difficulty: 2
Page(s): 576
Scramble range: All
Topic: Real versus nominal GDP

22.36
In comparison to nominal GDP, real GDP refers to nominal GDP
a) minus the value of intermediate goods.
b) corrected for the depreciation of capital.
c) corrected for price level changes.
d) minus the value of goods exported to foreign countries.
e) minus the inflation rate.

22.37
Correct: b)
Difficulty: 2
Page(s): 576
Scramble range: All
Topic: Nominal GDP

22.37
Nominal GDP
a) is calculated by valuing output at prices that prevailed during the time period in question, and therefore is also called real GDP.
b) is calculated by valuing output at the prices that prevailed during the time period in question, and therefore is also called current dollar GDP.
c) is calculated by valuing output at the prices that prevailed during some base year, and therefore is also called real GDP.
d) is not related to real GDP through price differences prevailing in different time periods but through quantity differences.
e) is calculated by using a price index, and therefore is also called constant dollar GDP.

22.38
Correct: e)
Difficulty: 4
Page(s): 576
Scramble range: All
Topic: Real versus nominal GDP

22.38
Suppose that, in current dollar terms, GDP increased by approximately 7 percent between one period and the next, but real GDP fell by 2 percent. Which of the following explanations is most likely?
a) Prices fell by 9 percent.
b) Prices fell by 2 percent.
c) Output rose by 2 percent.
d) Prices increased by 7 percent.
e) Prices increased by 9 percent.

22.39
Correct: b)
Difficulty: 3
Page(s): 575–576
Scramble range: All
Topic: Intermediate goods

22.39
Which of the following statements concerning GDP is false?
a) GDP can be calculated using current prices or base year prices.
b) Intermediate goods and final goods are both included when GDP is calculated.
c) Only goods and services produced during the given time period are included.
d) GDP measures only current production.
e) Nominal GDP corrected for the rate of inflation is real GDP.

22.40
Correct: b)
Difficulty: 3
Page(s): 577
Scramble range: a)–d)
Topic: Trend GDP

22.40
Trend GDP will rise if
a) all else constant, the average level of prices rises.
b) all else constant, the stock of capital equipment increases.
c) all else constant, current dollar GDP rises.
d) population growth is curtailed.
e) all of the above.

22.41
Correct: a)
Difficulty: 3
Page(s): 576
Scramble range: All
Topic: Real versus nominal GDP

22.41
Radio WKYS reported that GDP for 1989 had risen to its highest level yet. Radio WWIT reported that GDP for 1989 was less than it had been for 1988. Which of the following statements best explains the difference in the reports?
a) WWIT was referring to real GDP and WKYS was referring to nominal GDP.
b) WWIT got its information from the AP wire service and WKYS got its information from the CP wire service.
c) WWIT was referring to nominal GDP and WKYS was referring to real GDP.
d) WWIT was referring to current dollar GDP and WKYS was referring to nominal GDP.
e) WWIT was referring to current dollar GDP and WKYS was referring to constant dollar GDP.

22.42
Correct: c)
Difficulty: 2
Page(s): 576
Scramble range: All
Topic: Constant dollar GDP

22.42
When economists refer to constant dollar GDP, they mean that
a) current dollar GDP is constant.
b) the price level is constant.
c) a price index has been used to adjust nominal GDP for price level changes.
d) nominal GDP has been adjusted for population changes.
e) the trend rate of GDP growth is flat.

22.43
Correct: d)
Difficulty: 2
Page(s): 576
Scramble range: All
Topic: Real versus nominal GDP

22.43
In recent history, real GDP has risen less rapidly than nominal GDP. This is because the
a) general price level has fallen.
b) stock of capital has increased.
c) goal of zero population growth has been reached.
d) general price level has risen.
e) level of population has risen.

22.44
Correct: e)
Difficulty: 4
Page(s): 576
Scramble range: All
Topic: Real versus nominal GDP

22.44
If nominal GDP increased by 11 percent during a year while real GDP increased by only 5 percent, then the
a) price level must have decreased by 6 percent.
b) price level must have increased by 16 percent.
c) price level remained steady but real output fell by 6 percent.
d) unemployment rate must have fallen during the year.
e) price level must have increased by 6 percent.

22.45
Correct: e)
Difficulty: 3
Page(s): 576
Scramble range: All
Topic: Real versus nominal GDP

22.45
According to your textbook, nominal GDP increased more than sevenfold between 1967 and 1989. Which one of the following statements is true?
a) Real GDP has increased each year, but nominal GDP has increased by even more.
b) Nominal GDP fell in 1982.
c) During the 1982 recession, real GDP did not fall, but its growth rate slowed.
d) Real GDP and nominal GDP have increased by the same rate.
e) Nominal GDP has increased in every year, but real GDP fell in 1982.

22.46
Correct: d)
Difficulty: 3
Page(s): 575–576
Scramble range: All
Topic: Intermediate goods

22.46
The value of intermediate goods is not counted in GDP
a) to keep from including goods that reduce society's welfare.
b) because of the tremendous difficulty of keeping track of all the intermediate goods produced in an economy as large as that of Canada.
c) because they are only sold in factor markets.
d) so as to avoid counting their value twice and thereby overstating the value of GDP.
e) because they are not consumed in the current year.

22.47
Correct: b)
Difficulty: 2
Page(s): 575–576
Scramble range: All
Topic: Intermediate goods

22.47
Intermediate goods can be defined as goods that are
a) sold to their ultimate user.
b) used in the production of other goods and services.
c) included directly in the measure of GDP.
d) always the same as capital goods.
e) purchased this year but consumed in future years.

22.48
Correct: a)
Difficulty: 2
Page(s): 576
Scramble range: All
Topic: Final goods

22.48
Final goods can be defined as goods that
a) are sold to their ultimate user.
b) are used in the production of other goods and services.
c) are included directly in the measure of GDP.
d) cannot be returned to the retailer.
e) are purchased this year but consumed next year.

22.49
Correct: e)
Difficulty: 2
Page(s): 576
Scramble range: All
Topic: Real values

22.49
A value that has been adjusted for changes in the price level is called
a) an inferior value.
b) a current dollar value.
c) a nominal value.
d) a net value.
e) a real value.

22.50
Correct: d)
Difficulty: 3
Page(s): 573
Scramble range: All
Topic: Discouraged workers

22.50
The existence of discouraged workers in the economy will mean that the official measures of unemployment
a) tend to overstate the unemployment problem.
b) are worthless in tracking economic activity.
c) are unaffected as a worker becomes discouraged.
d) tend to understate the unemployment problem.
e) ignore the effect of unrealistic wage expectations.

22.51
Correct: b)
Difficulty: 2
Page(s): 579
Scramble range: All
Topic: Recession

22.51
According to the text, a recession is defined as
a) two consecutive quarters during which real GDP does not increase.
b) two consecutive quarters during which real GDP declines.
c) a period in which 8 percent of the labour force is unemployed.
d) two consecutive years of declining real GDP.
e) two consecutive quarters in which nominal GDP declines.

22.52
Correct: d)
Difficulty: 2
Page(s): 579–582
Scramble range: All
Topic: Business cycles

22.52
The phases of the business cycle, in order, are
a) contraction, expansion, trough, peak.
b) contraction, peak, expansion, trough.
c) contraction, trough, peak, expansion.
d) contraction, trough, expansion, peak.
e) contraction, peak, trough, expansion.

22.53
Correct: d)
Difficulty: 2
Page(s): 563
Scramble range: All
Topic: Inflation

22.53
Inflation is defined as
a) a one-time increase in the average price level.
b) any increase in prices.
c) when an important price such as the price of crude oil increases.
d) a sustained upward trend in the average price level.
e) a sustained downward trend in the average price level.

22.54
Correct: a)
Difficulty: 3
Page(s): 572
Scramble range: All
Topic: Indexing

22.54
In economics, the term "indexing" refers to adjusting
a) the nominal value of something in order for it to maintain its real value.
b) the rate of interest for anticipated inflation.
c) nominal values for output changes.
d) prices in contracts for changes in federal government tax rates.
e) real values for changes in nominal values.

22.55
Correct: a)
Difficulty: 3
Page(s): 581
Scramble range: All
Topic: Costs of inflation

22.55
During inflationary times, economic decision makers have purchased commodities such as real estate and gold. This behaviour
a) imposes opportunity costs on society.
b) benefits society.
c) neither imposes costs nor brings benefits to anyone as it is clearly a waste of society's resources.
d) increases economic efficiency.
e) hurts the decision maker in question.

22.56
Correct: d)
Difficulty: 3
Page(s): 582
Scramble range: All
Topic: Wages and inflation

22.56
All else the same, the purchasing power of nominal wages is decreased when
a) average wages rise faster than inflation.
b) the price level exceeds the total level of wages.
c) the price level is less than the total level of wages.
d) average wages rise slower than inflation.
e) the price level is falling.

22.57
Correct: a)
Difficulty: 3
Page(s): 582
Scramble range: All
Topic: Wages and inflation

22.57
All else the same, the purchasing power of nominal wages is increased when
a) average wages rise faster than inflation.
b) the price level exceeds the total level of wages.
c) the price level is less than the total level of wages.
d) average wages rise slower than inflation.
e) the price level is rising.

22.58
Correct: b)
Difficulty: 3
Page(s): 572
Scramble range: All
Topic: Historic unemploymnt rate

22.58
Since 1926, the largest Canadian unemployment rate
a) was 13 percent of the labour force during the 1982 recession.
b) was between 15 and 20 percent of the labour force in the early 1930s.
c) was during the OPEC recession of the mid-1970s.
d) was during the banking panic of 1929.
e) was during the stock market crash of 1987.

22.59
Correct: c)
Difficulty: 2
Page(s): 572
Scramble range: All
Topic: Historic unemployment rate

22.59
Average unemployment rate in Canada from 1926 to 1989 was
a) 10.6 percent.
b) 20.6 percent.
c) 6.6 percent.
d) 5.6 percent.
e) 4.6 percent.

22.60
Correct: c)
Difficulty: 3
Page(s): 574
Scramble range: All
Topic: Full employment

22.60
A zero percent unemployment rate
a) is one of the economic goals of the Canadian government.
b) would alleviate scarcity.
c) is not consistent with the notion of full employment.
d) was last achieved during World War II when everyone was willing to work at the going wage rate in order to end the war.
e) is the only efficient unemployment rate.

22.61
Correct: e)
Difficulty: 2
Page(s): 574
Scramble range: All
Topic: Full employment

22.61
Full employment
a) is not consistent with the natural rate of unemployment.
b) equals frictional unemployment plus discouraged workers.
c) means than there is zero unemployment in the economy.
d) means than there is zero unemployment in the economy when frictional unemployment is eliminated.
e) is thought by some economists to be consistent with an unemployment rate between 5 and 6 percent of the total labour force.

22.62
Correct: c)
Difficulty: 2
Page(s): 573
Scramble range: All
Topic: Discouraged workers

22.62
Discouraged workers are defined as those
a) who periodically leave one job to look for another.
b) whose productivity is low, because they are working in dead-end jobs which hurts their morale.
c) who have given up looking for a job and are not counted as unemployed because they are out of the labour force.
d) who lack training for the skilled positions that they hold so their morale is low.
e) who have been forced to take a part-time job.

22.63
Correct: d)
Difficulty: 2
Page(s): 567
Scramble range: All
Topic: Deflation

22.63
Deflation occurs when
a) the price of some major item in your market basket falls substantially.
b) the inflation rate falls.
c) the average level of prices remains stable.
d) the average level of prices falls.
e) there are two or more consecutive quarters in which real GDP declines.

22.64
Correct: c)
Difficulty: 3
Page(s): 567
Scramble range: All
Topic: Historic record/deflation

22.64
Deflation
a) has never occurred in the Canadian economy. It is a phenomenon that only occurred in the ancient economies of Greece and Rome.
b) refers to when the average level of prices remains stable for at least two consecutive periods.
c) occurred in Canada following World War II and during the Great Depression.
d) regularly occurs after major wars.
e) has occurred every year since the end of World War II.

22.65
Correct: c)
Difficulty: 4
Page(s): 568
Scramble range: All
Topic: Calculating inflation/deflation rates

22.65
Refer to Table 22.1. Between which two years was the inflation rate the largest?
a) 1 and 2.
b) 2 and 3.
c) 3 and 4.
d) 4 and 5.
e) 5 and 6.

Table 22.1

Year	Price level
1	100
2	90
3	85
4	90
5	95
6	100

22.66
Correct: a)
Difficulty: 4
Page(s): 568
Scramble range: All
Topic: Calculating inflation/deflation rates

22.66
Refer to Table 22.1. Between which two years was the deflation rate the largest?
a) 1 and 2.
b) 2 and 3.
c) 3 and 4.
d) 4 and 5.
e) 5 and 6.

22.67
Correct: e)
Difficulty: 4
Page(s): 568
Scramble range: All
Topic: Calculating inflation/deflation rates

22.67
Refer to Table 22.1. Between which two years were prices the most stable?
a) 1 and 2.
b) 2 and 3.
c) 3 and 4.
d) 4 and 5.
e) 5 and 6.

22.68
Correct: d)
Difficulty: 3
Page(s): 575–576
Scramble range: All
Topic: Intermediate goods

22.68
An intermediate good is a good
a) produced in a previous year. GDP includes intermediate goods only if they are sold during the current year.
b) produced in a previous year. GDP does not include intermediate goods even if they are sold during the current year.
c) purchased for use in producing another good. GDP does include sales of intermediate goods.
d) purchased for use in producing another good. GDP does not include sales of intermediate goods.
e) purchased for use in producing another good. GDP does not include sales of intermediate goods unless the next good is sold during the current year.

22.69
Correct: e)
Difficulty: 2
Page(s): 576
Scramble range: All
Topic: Nominal GDP

22.69
Nominal GDP is
a) a concept used to distinguish between price level changes and changes in the rate at which output is produced in the economy.
b) currently being measured in 1981 dollars.
c) measured in constant dollars.
d) an unerring tool used to measure how the economic welfare of a society changes.
e) measured in current dollars.

22.70
Correct: d)
Difficulty: 3
Page(s): 577
Scramble range: All
Topic: Trend GDP

22.70
In Canada, trend real GDP
a) has been relatively constant since World War II.
b) and actual real GDP differ only during wartime.
c) rises in part because of growth in the money supply.
d) rises in part because of advances in technology over time.
e) rises in part because of rises in the inflation rate.

22.71
Correct: e)
Difficulty: 3
Page(s): 579–582
Scramble range: All
Topic: Business cycles

22.71
Over time, deviations of actual real GDP from trend real GDP
a) are due to price level changes.
b) are due to changes in the inflation rate.
c) occur during times of war only.
d) are measured by subtracting the value of real GDP from nominal GDP.
e) reveal information about the timing of historical business cycles.

22.72
Correct: c)
Difficulty: 3
Page(s): 574
Scramble range: None
Topic: Unemployment

22.72
A rise in real GDP
a) is generally associated with a decline in the employment rate.
b) is generally associated with an increase in the unemployment rate.
c) is generally associated with a decline in the unemployment rate.
d) is not related to the unemployment rate.
e) both a) and b).

22.73
Correct: a)
Difficulty: 3
Page(s): 582
Scramble range: All
Topic: Costs/benefits of rising GDP

22.73
If the economy experiences a rise in real GDP, then
a) more consumption goods and services become available and environmental damage can occur.
b) the benefits of the increased number of consumption goods and services outweigh the costs of environmental pollution associated with increased industrial output rates.
c) the benefits of the increased number of consumption goods and services are less than the costs of environmental pollution associated with increased industrial output rates.
d) only the increased benefits are felt. Environmental damage is not a problem due to recent federal regulation.
e) the unemployment rate cannot rise over this time period.

22.74
Correct: d)
Difficulty: 3
Page(s): 580–581
Scramble range: All
Topic: Stock price/business cycles

22.74
When the inflation-adjusted average stock market prices decline
a) real GDP tends to decline after a time lag.
b) recessions are likely to follow.
c) then the future profitability of firms is known.
d) then real GDP may rise or fall after a time lag.
e) expansions are likely to follow.

22.75
Correct: b)
Difficulty: 2
Page(s): 576–577
Scramble range: a)–c)
Topic: Real GDP

22.75
There is a strong systematic relation between real GDP changes and
a) average real stock market prices.
b) the unemployment rate.
c) inflation.
d) all of the above.
e) none of the above.

22.76
Correct: b)
Difficulty: 3
Page(s): 581–582
Scramble range: All
Topic: Inflation/business cycles

22.76
The inflation rate and differences in the average rate of inflation
a) are closely linked to fluctuations in the business cycle.
b) at times seem to be closely linked to the business cycle.
c) are linked to the business cycle during recessions but not during expansions.
d) are linked to the business cycle during expansions but not during recessions.
e) are negatively linked to the business cycle.

22.77
Correct: e)
Difficulty: 3
Page(s): 582–583
Scramble range: All
Topic: Deficits

22.77
The government budget balance is
a) the total expenditure of the federal government minus the revenue received by taxation and other sources.
b) called a deficit when total revenues exceed total expenditures.
c) not related to the business cycle.
d) the same as the current account balance.
e) called a deficit when total expenditures exceed total revenues collected.

22.78
Correct: b)
Difficulty: 2
Page(s): 582–583
Scramble range: All
Topic: Historical deficits

22.78
Since 1975
a) the government's budget deficit averaged about 3 percent of GDP per year.
b) the government's budget deficit averaged about 5 percent of GDP per year.
c) the government's budget balance changed from a surplus to a deficit as economic growth slowed.
d) the government's budget balance changed from a deficit to a surplus as the expansion gained strength.
e) the government's budget balance is not related to the business cycle.

22.79
Correct: d)
Difficulty: 2
Page(s): 582–583
Scramble range: All
Topic: Government budgets/business cycles

22.79
The balance of the government's budget is
a) called a deficit during recessions.
b) called a surplus during contractions.
c) called a balanced budget when the total debt of the government is paid off.
d) to some degree related to the business cycle.
e) always a deficit in Canada.

22.80
Correct: d)
Difficulty: 3
Page(s): 583
Scramble range: All
Topic: Defining current account balance

22.80
The current account balance is the difference between the
a) total revenues received by federal, local, and provincial governments and what they spend.
b) total revenues received by the federal government only and what it spends.
c) value of the goods and services that the government sells to other countries and the value of what it buys from the rest of the world.
d) value of the goods and services that one country sells to other countries and the value of what it buys from the rest of the world.
e) value of the goods and services that one country buys from other countries and the value of what it sells to the rest of the world.

22.81
Correct: b)
Difficulty: 3
Page(s): 563
Scramble range: All
Topic: Inflation

22.81
Inflation has negative effects on an economy because it
a) raises the purchasing value of money.
b) redistributes the purchasing power of income in an arbitrary way.
c) reduces everyone's standard of living.
d) prevents relative price decreases from occurring.
e) reduces the purchasing power of wages.

22.82 (SG 22.1)
Correct: b)
Difficulty: 2
Page(s): 567
Scramble range: All
Topic: Price stability

22.82
Price stability occurs when
a) all prices in the economy are constant.
b) the rate of inflation is zero.
c) the rate of inflation is constant.
d) the base period remains unchanged.
e) the price level increases at a steady rate.

22.83 (SG 22.2)
Correct: d)
Difficulty: 2
Page(s): 567
Scramble range: All
Topic: Price index

22.83
A price index
a) is a technique used to link payments made under contract to the price level.
b) measures the rate of inflation in a base year.
c) measures the value of GDP in current dollars.
d) measures the average level of prices in one period as a percentage of their level in an earlier period.
e) measures the rate of change of prices.

22.84 (SG 22.3)
Correct: c)
Difficulty: 4
Page(s): 567
Scramble range: All
Topic: Price index

22.84
If a price index was 128 at the end of 1987 and 136 at the end of 1988, what was the rate of inflation for 1988?
a) 4.2 percent.
b) 5.9 percent.
c) 6.25 percent.
d) 8 percent.
e) 9.4 percent.

22.85 (SG 22.4)
Correct: a)
Difficulty: 4
Page(s): 567
Scramble range: All
Topic: Anticipated inflation

22.85
If the rate of inflation is lower than anticipated,
a) lenders will gain at the expense of borrowers and workers will gain at the expense of employers.
b) borrowers will gain at the expense of lenders and workers will gain at the expense of employers.
c) lenders will gain at the expense of borrowers and employers will gain at the expense of workers.
d) borrowers will gain at the expense of lenders and employers will gain at the expense of workers.
e) lenders will gain at the expense of borrowers and whether employers or workers gain or lose is uncertain.

22.86 (SG 22.5)
Correct: d)
Difficulty: 3
Page(s): 567
Scramble range: All
Topic: Cost of anticipated inflation

22.86
A fully anticipated increase in the rate of inflation
a) is not costly since contracts can be adjusted.
b) benefits both workers and employers.
c) is costly because it reduces the opportunity cost of holding money.
d) is costly because it encourages an increase in the frequency of transactions that people undertake.
e) is costly because it redistributes from lender to borrower.

22.87 (SG 22.6)
Correct: a)
Difficulty: 3
Page(s): 572
Scramble range: All
Topic: Indexing

22.87
Which of the following is an example of an indexed loan contract?
a) If the rate of inflation increases by 5 percent, the interest rate on an outstanding loan increases by 5 percent.
b) If the rate of inflation increases by 5 percent, the interest rate on a new loan increases by 5 percent.
c) If the rate of inflation increases by 5 percent, the interest rate on a new loan decreases by 5 percent.
d) If the rate of inflation increases by 5 percent, the wage rate will increase by 5 percent.
e) If the rate of inflation increases by 5 percent, the interest rate will be 5 percent.

22.88 (SG 22.7)
Correct: a)
Difficulty: 2
Page(s): 572
Scramble range: All
Topic: Labour force

22.88
Suppose that in a country with a population of 20 million, there are 9 million employed and 1 million unemployed. What is the labour force?
a) 10 million.
b) 20 million.
c) 9 million.
d) 8 million.
e) 1 million.

22.89 (SG 22.8)
Correct: e)
Difficulty: 4
Page(s): 572
Scramble range: All
Topic: Unemployment

22.89
Suppose that in a country with a population of 20 million, there are 9 million employed and 1 million unemployed. What is the unemployment rate?
a) 11 percent.
b) 1 percent.
c) 8 percent.
d) 5 percent.
e) 10 percent.

22.90 (SG 22.9)
Correct: e)
Difficulty: 2
Page(s): 573
Scramble range: All
Topic: Historic unemployment rate

22.90
In which of the following years was the unemployment rate in Canada near 20 percent?
a) 1982.
b) 1976.
c) 1959.
d) 1926.
e) 1933.

22.91 (SG 22.10)
Correct: d)
Difficulty: 3
Page(s): 572
Scramble range: All
Topic: Counting the unemployed

22.91
Which of the following would be counted as unemployed in Canada?
a) Doris works only 5 hours a week but is looking for a full-time job.
b) Kanhaya has stopped looking for work since he was unable to find a suitable job during a two-month search.
c) Sharon is a college student with no job.
d) Maurice has been laid off from his job for 20 weeks but expects to be called back soon.
e) Bogdan has been laid off from his job for 30 weeks but expects to be called back soon.

22.92 (SG 22.11)
Correct: a)
Difficulty: 3
Page(s): 574
Scramble range: All
Topic: Frictional unemployment

22.92
Which of the following would be considered frictionally unemployed?
a) A steelworker loses her job because of technological change.
b) A steelworker is laid off but expects to be called back soon.
c) A steelworker retires.
d) A steelworker decides to leave the labour force and become a full-time ballet student.
e) A steelworker becomes discouraged and stops looking for a job.

22.93 (SG 22.12)
Correct: e)
Difficulty: 2
Page(s): 574
Scramble range: All
Topic: Full employment

22.93
If the economy is at full employment, then the
a) entire population is employed.
b) entire labour force is employed.
c) only unemployment is frictional unemployment plus discouraged workers.
d) unemployment rate is less than 3 percent.
e) only unemployment is frictional unemployment.

22.94 (SG 22.13)
Correct: d)
Difficulty: 2
Page(s): 575–578
Scramble range: All
Topic: Gross domestic product

22.94
Gross domestic product is defined as the value of all
a) goods produced in an economy in a year.
b) goods and services produced in an economy in a year.
c) final goods produced in an economy in a year.
d) final goods and services produced in an economy in a year.
e) final goods and services produced in an economy in a year, controlling for the level of inflation.

22.95 (SG 22.14)
Correct: a)
Difficulty: 2
Page(s): 576–577
Scramble range: None
Topic: Real GDP

22.95
If you want to investigate the claim that more goods and services were produced in the economy during 1989 than 1988, you should look at
a) real GDP.
b) nominal GDP.
c) intermediate GDP.
d) current dollar GDP.
e) either b) or d).

22.96 (SG 22.15)
Correct: e)
Difficulty: 3
Page(s): 576
Scramble range: All
Topic: Nominal GDP

22.96
Nominal GDP will increase
a) only if the average level of prices rises.
b) only if the quantity of goods and services produced increases.
c) only if the unemployment rate rises.
d) if the average level of prices rises and the quantity of goods and services produced increases.
e) if either the average level of prices rises or the quantity of goods and services produced increases.

22.97 (SG 22.16)
Correct: a)
Difficulty: 3
Page(s): 577
Scramble range: All
Topic: Trend GDP

22.97
Which of the following is *not* a reason for rising trend real GDP?
a) Rising stock market prices.
b) Better educated workers.
c) Growing stock of capital equipment.
d) Growing population.
e) Advances in technology.

22.98 (SG 22.17)
Correct: b)
Difficulty: 2
Page(s): 579–582
Scramble range: All
Topic: Business cycles

22.98
An expansion in the business cycle is
a) when there is a slowdown in the pace of economic activity.
b) when there is a speedup in the pace of economic activity.
c) the lower turning point of a business cycle.
d) the upper turning point of a business cycle.
e) the periodic but irregular up and down movement in economic activity.

22.99 (SG 22.18)
Correct: b)
Difficulty: 2
Page(s): 577
Scramble range: All
Topic: Trend GDP

22.99
Which of the following has consistently fluctuated closely with the deviation from trend in real GDP?
a) Inflation rate.
b) Unemployment rate.
c) Government deficit.
d) Real stock prices.
e) International deficit.

22.100 (SG 22.19)
Correct: d)
Difficulty: 3
Page(s): 583
Scramble range: All
Topic: Current account deficit

22.100
Which of the following will increase the Canadian current account deficit?
a) Japan buys wheat from farmers in Canada.
b) Japan buys wheat from farmers in Australia.
c) Japan buys Canada Savings Bonds.
d) Canada buys Toyotas from Japan.
e) Canada sells coal to Japan.

22.101 (SG 22.20)
Correct: e)
Difficulty: 2
Page(s): 583
Scramble range: All
Topic: Current account surplus

22.101
Most of the time since 1950, the current account
a) has had a large deficit.
b) surplus has been consistently large.
c) deficit has mostly been with the United States.
d) surplus has mostly been with Japan.
e) has had a small surplus.

22.102
Correct: c)
Difficulty: 2
Page(s): 563
Scramble range: All
Topic: Inflation/price stability

22.102
Price stability is said to occur when
a) all prices in the economy change at the same rate.
b) the rate of inflation is stable.
c) there is no inflation in the economy.
d) the base period changes.
e) the price level decreases at a stable rate.

22.103
Correct: e)
Difficulty: 3
Page(s): 564
Scramble range: All
Topic: Inflation

22.103
One of the opportunity costs of an anticipated inflation is
a) the lost human dignity due to the unemployment created by the inflation.
b) the redistribution from borrower to lender.
c) the indexation that occurs.
d) the fact that the government deficit gets larger.
e) the increase in the volume and frequency of transactions as individuals hold less money.

22.104
Correct: a)
Difficulty: 4
Page(s): 568
Scramble range: All
Topic: Calculating inflation

22.104
If a price index was 140 at the end of 1987 and 150 at the end of 1988, what was the rate of inflation for 1988?
a) 7.14 percent.
b) 5.9 percent.
c) 6.25 percent.
d) 8 percent.
e) 6.67 percent.

22.105
Correct: d)
Difficulty: 4
Page(s): 567–568
Scramble range: All
Topic: Inflation/winners and losers

22.105
If the rate of inflation is more than anticipated,
a) lenders will gain at the expense of borrowers and workers will gain at the expense of employers.
b) borrowers will gain at the expense of lenders and workers will gain at the expense of employers.
c) lenders will gain at the expense of borrowers and employers will gain at the expense of workers.
d) borrowers will gain at the expense of lenders and employers will gain at the expense of workers.
e) borrowers will gain at the expense of lenders and the gains and losses between workers and employers will be uncertain.

22.106
Correct: a)
Difficulty: 2
Page(s): 572
Scramble range: All
Topic: Unemployment

22.106
The costs of unemployment include all of the following except
a) that workers get discouraged and exit the labour force.
b) lost output and income.
c) depreciation of human capital.
d) that crime increases.
e) that human dignity suffers.

22.107
Correct: e)
Difficulty: 2
Page(s): 572
Scramble range: All
Topic: Labour force

22.107
Suppose that in a country with a population of 500 million, there are 300 million employed and 20 million unemployed. What is the size of the labour force?
a) 500 million.
b) 300 million.
c) 20 million.
d) 280 million.
e) 320 million.

22.108
Correct: c)
Difficulty: 3
Page(s): 572
Scramble range: All
Topic: Unemployment

22.108
Suppose that in a country with a population of 500 million, there are 300 million employed and 20 million unemployed. What is the unemployment rate?
a) 6.67 percent.
b) 4 percent.
c) 6.25 percent.
d) 5 percent.
e) 7.14 percent.

22.109
Correct: a)
Difficulty: 3
Page(s): 572
Scramble range: All
Topic: Counting the unemployed

22.109
Which of the following would be counted as unemployed in Canada?
a) Veena is not working but she is looking for a full-time job.
b) Kathy has stopped looking for work since she was unable to find a suitable job during a one-month search.
c) Sharon is a college student with a job.
d) Christos has been laid off from his job but expects to be called back soon.
e) Benoit has been in a government-sponsored retraining program since his firm closed down 2 months ago.

22.110
Correct: c)
Difficulty: 2
Page(s): 574
Scramble range: a)–d)
Topic: Full employment

22.110
If the economy is operating at full employment, then
a) everyone who wants a job has one.
b) the entire labour force is unemployed.
c) the unemployment rate is approximately 6 percent.
d) the unemployment rate is zero.
e) none of the above.

22.111
Correct: b)
Difficulty: 2
Page(s): 575–578
Scramble range: All
Topic: Real GDP

22.111
Real GDP will increase only if the
a) average level of prices rises.
b) quantity of goods and services produced increases.
c) unemployment rate rises.
d) employment rate rises.
e) employment rate falls.

22.112
Correct: e)
Difficulty: 3
Page(s): 563
Scramble range: All
Topic: Inflation

22.112
At the end of 1989 the price index was 105. At the end of 1990 the price index was 110. During 1990 the inflation rate was
a) 10 percent.
b) 5 percent.
c) 4.55 percent.
d) 4.34 percent.
e) 4.76 percent.

22.113
Correct: e)
Difficulty: 5
Page(s): 567
Scramble range: All
Topic: Inflation and expectation

22.113
Lucy operates the Cone-Heads Ice Cream Parlour. She expects that inflation next year will be 5 percent. The students who work at Cone-Heads expect inflation to be only 2 percent. The most likely contract would involve a wage increase of
a) an amount we cannot tell without more information.
b) 7 percent.
c) 5 percent.
d) 3 percent.
e) 2 percent.

Chapter 23 Measuring Output and the Price Level

23.1
Correct: c)
Difficulty: 2
Page(s): 589
Scramble range: All
Topic: Circular flow

23.1
In the market for goods and services
a) suppliers are households since they own the factors of production.
b) buyers are business firms since they buy the factors of production.
c) buyers are households.
d) sellers are governments who earn needed revenues from taxation of households and business firms.
e) buyers are firms.

23.2
Correct: a)
Difficulty: 2
Page(s): 589
Scramble range: All
Topic: Circular flow

23.2
The simple circular flow diagram indicates that
a) households sell factors of production to business firms.
b) firms buy factors of production from the government.
c) households sell factors of production to the government.
d) firms buy goods and services from households.
e) firms sell factors of production to households.

23.3
Correct: d)
Difficulty: 2
Page(s): 589
Scramble range: All
Topic: Circular flow

23.3
In the simple circular flow model
a) households are sellers of the services of the factors of production in final product markets.
b) households are buyers of goods and services in the factor markets.
c) business firms are sellers of the factors of production in factor markets.
d) business firms are sellers of goods and services in final product markets.
e) business firms are buyers of goods and services in final product markets.

23.4
Correct: d)
Difficulty: 2
Page(s): 589
Scramble range: All
Topic: Circular flow

23.4
The circular flow model is used to
a) show how nominal GDP is distinct from real GDP.
b) explain how the prices of the factors of production are determined.
c) show the effects of inflation in a simple economy.
d) show the real flows and money flows between different sectors of the economy.
e) show the stocks of various sectors of the economy.

23.5
Correct: c)
Difficulty: 2
Page(s): 589–591
Scramble range: All
Topic: GDP calculation

23.5
If the economy of Econoworld produces only two goods, kayaks and birdseed, and in one year 20 kayaks are produced and sold for $1,000 each and 10 bags of birdseed are produced and sold for $30 each, the value of nominal GDP for this year is

a) $20,000.
b) $300.
c) $20,300.
d) $23,000.
e) dependent on the price index used.

23.6
Correct: b)
Difficulty: 3
Page(s): 589–591
Scramble range: All
Topic: GDP measurement

23.6
GDP is measured as the sum of the total expenditures of consumers, investors,

a) exporters, and purchases by all levels of government.
b) net exporters, and purchases by all levels of government.
c) net importers, and purchases by all levels of government.
d) importers, and purchases by all levels of government.
e) exporters, importers, and purchases by all levels of government.

23.7
Correct: d)
Difficulty: 2
Page(s): 595–596
Scramble range: All
Topic: Expenditure approach to GDP

23.7
The expenditure approach measures GDP by adding together

a) wages, salaries and supplementary labour income, corporate profits, interest and miscellaneous investment income, farmers' income, and income of non-farm unincorporated businesses.
b) wages, salaries and supplementary labour income, corporate profits, interest and miscellaneous investment income, farmers' income, subsidies paid by the government, indirect taxes paid, and income of non-farm unincorporated businesses.
c) compensation of employees, rental income, corporate profits, net interest, proprietors' income, indirect taxes paid, and capital consumption expenditures and by subtracting subsidies paid by the government.
d) the total expenditures of consumers, investors, net exporters, and purchases by governments at all levels.
e) the value added of each firm in the economy.

23.8
Correct: c)
Difficulty: 2
Page(s): 596–597
Scramble range: All
Topic: Output approach to GDP

23.8
The output approach to measuring GDP adds together

a) wages, salaries and supplementary labour income, corporate profits, interest and miscellaneous investment income, farmers' income, subsidies paid by the government, indirect taxes paid, and income of non-farm unincorporated businesses.
b) wages, salaries and supplementary labour income, corporate profits, interest and miscellaneous investment income, farmers' income, indirect taxes paid, and capital consumption expenditures and by subtracting subsidies paid by the government.
c) the value added of each firm in the economy.
d) the value added of each firm in the economy, indirect business taxes, and the capital consumption allowance and subtracts subsidies paid by the government.
e) the total expenditures of consumers, investors, net exporters, and purchases by all levels of government.

23.9
Correct: b)
Difficulty: 2
Page(s): 596
Scramble range: All
Topic: Factor income approach to GDP

23.9
The factor incomes approach to measuring GDP is derived by adding together
a) wages, salaries and supplementary labour income, corporate profits, interest and miscellaneous investment income, farmers' income, subsidies paid by the government, indirect taxes paid, and income of non-farm unincorporated businesses.
b) wages, salaries and supplementary labour income, corporate profits, interest and miscellaneous investment income, farmers' income, and income of non-farm unincorporated businesses, plus indirect taxes less subsidies, plus depreciation.
c) the value added of each firm in the economy.
d) the value added of each firm in the economy, indirect business taxes and the capital consumption allowance and by subtracting subsidies paid by the government.
e) the total expenditures of consumers, investors, net exporters, and purchases of all levels of government.

23.10
Correct: e)
Difficulty: 4
Page(s): 595–596
Scramble range: All
Topic: Calculating GDP/factor income approach

23.10
How much would the production of a kayak add to GDP if the shell costs $250, the paint costs $20, the finisher costs $35, the manufacturer sold it to the dealer for $500, and the dealer sold it to his customer for $800?
a) $1,605.
b) $1,300.
c) $500.
d) $305.
e) $800.

23.11
Correct: e)
Difficulty: 4
Page(s): 597–598
Scramble range: All
Topic: GDP accounting

23.11
Which of the following would *not* be included in GDP for 1989?
a) A car produced in 1989 and held in inventory until 1990.
b) A car produced in 1989 and sold in 1990.
c) The value of all corn produced in 1989.
d) A house built in January of 1989 and sold in November of 1989.
e) A car produced in 1988 and sold in 1989.

23.12
Correct: d)
Difficulty: 3
Page(s): 597–598
Scramble range: All
Topic: Financial transactions and GDP

23.12
Stock and bond sales are not included in GDP because they
a) do not occur in the year in which the production represented by them takes place.
b) represent corporate production.
c) represent indebtedness.
d) do not represent goods and services produced.
e) are monetary and therefore not real.

23.13
Correct: b)
Difficulty: 3
Page(s): 597–598
Scramble range: All
Topic: GDP

23.13
In calculating GDP, all of the following are excluded *except*
a) the value of intermediate goods.
b) the value of all homes built in the year in question.
c) the value of used goods.
d) purely financial transactions.
e) subsidies from the government.

23.14
Correct: c)
Difficulty: 3
Page(s): 597–598
Scramble range: All
Topic: GDP

23.14
Out of the following list, choose the item that would be included in a current measure of GDP.
a) The purchase of a previously owned house that was manufactured in the year in question.
b) A social security cheque for $500.
c) The purchase of 10 litres of gasoline for your car.
d) A $2,000 cheque from your aunt Grace.
e) Income from the sale of your Canadian Snowfun stocks.

23.15
Correct: c)
Difficulty: 2
Page(s): 597–598
Scramble range: All
Topic: GDP

23.15
Out of the following list, choose the item that would be included in a current measure of GDP.
a) Your labour in fixing a leaky pipe under your sink.
b) The services of a househusband.
c) A professional gardener who regularly cuts your yard.
d) The illegal sale of a bag of marijuana.
e) The value of safety on the streets of your city.

23.16
Correct: e)
Difficulty: 2
Page(s): 597–598
Scramble range: All
Topic: Measuring GDP/applications

23.16
Suppose that you fall in love with and subsequently marry your regularly employed housekeeper. What effect would this action have on GDP?
a) It would stay the same.
b) It would fall.
c) It would rise.
d) It would fall but then increase after the honeymoon was over.
e) It depends on whether he continues to work in the house free of charge or whether you still pay him.

23.17
Correct: a)
Difficulty: 2
Page(s): 601
Scramble range: All
Topic: Nonmarket transactions in GDP measures

23.17
Since nonmarket exchanges are excluded from measures of GDP, the GDP measure tends to
a) underestimate the total production of an economy.
b) overestimate the total production of an economy.
c) be of little significance in determining the total production of an economy.
d) be of little usefulness to anyone but market economists.
e) place too much value on these transactions.

23.18
Correct: c)
Difficulty: 2
Page(s): 601
Scramble range: All
Topic: Pollution and GDP accounts

23.18
Given that pollution is a by-product of some production processes,
a) GDP accountants adjust downward the GDP accounts for these items.
b) GDP accountants adjust upward the GDP accounts for these items.
c) the GDP accounts tend to overstate economic welfare.
d) the GDP accounts tend to understate economic welfare.
e) the GDP accounts are just about correct.

23.19
Correct: d)
Difficulty: 3
Page(s): 589
Scramble range: All
Topic: Circular flow

23.19
In the circular flow model of an economy with no government sector and no international trade, households

a) receive income from buyers of final products.
b) receive income from the sale of resources in the final product market.
c) pay business firms for the use of their resources.
d) receive income from producers for the use of the factors of production.
e) pay income to producers for the use of their savings.

23.20
Correct: e)
Difficulty: 2
Page(s): 597
Scramble range: All
Topic: NDP from GDP

23.20
Net domestic product can be derived by which of the following?

a) GDP minus taxes.
b) GDP minus retained corporate earnings.
c) GDP minus subsidies.
d) GDP minus transfer payments.
e) GDP minus depreciation.

23.21
Correct: b)
Difficulty: 2
Page(s): 597
Scramble range: All
Topic: NDP from GDP

23.21
Net domestic product plus which of the following yields gross domestic product?

a) Transfer payments plus business transfers.
b) Depreciation.
c) Indirect business taxes and personal taxes.
d) Retained earnings.
e) Subsidies.

23.22
Correct: b)
Difficulty: 3
Page(s): 595
Scramble range: All
Topic: Financial assets/GDP accounts

23.22
Which of the following would *not* be counted as part of this year's GDP?

a) The lumber you purchase when building bookshelves for your room.
b) The government bond you buy for your newborn niece.
c) The purchase of a new personal computer that was produced during the year by your provincial government.
d) The purchase of wheat, which was produced during the year by a Saskatchewan farmer.
e) The purchase of a house, which was produced in the current year.

23.23
Correct: c)
Difficulty: 4
Page(s): 596
Scramble range: All
Topic: Domestic income

23.23
From the information given in Table 23.1, determine which of the following figures represents gross domestic product.

a) $1,280.
b) $1,290.
c) $1,360.
d) $1,120.
e) $1,100.

Table 23.1

Wages, salaries, and supplementary labour income	$800
Farmers' income	80
Government purchases of goods and services	240
Capital consumption allowance	240
Gross private domestic investment	400
Personal income taxes	140
Personal and business taxes net of transfer payments	120
Net exports	80
Consumption expenditures	640
Interest and miscellaneous investment income	100

23.24
Correct: d)
Difficulty: 4
Page(s): 596
Scramble range: All
Topic: Domestic income

23.24
From the information given in Table 23.1, determine which of the following figures represents net domestic product.
a) $1,280.
b) $1,290.
c) $1,360.
d) $1,120.
e) $1,100.

23.25
Correct: e)
Difficulty: 4
Page(s): 596
Scramble range: All
Topic: Capital stock

23.25
From the information given in Table 23.1, determine which of the following figures represents the value of the capital stock.
a) $160.
b) $240.
c) $400.
d) $640.
e) There is not enough information to complete this problem.

23.26
Correct: d)
Difficulty: 5
Page(s): 596–597
Scramble range: All
Topic: Savings/domestic income accounting

23.26
From the information given in Table 23.1, determine which of the following figures represents the total amount of savings.
a) $800.
b) $140.
c) $230.
d) $460.
e) There is not enough information to complete this problem.

23.27
Correct: c)
Difficulty: 3
Page(s): 597
Scramble range: All
Topic: Net domestic product

23.27
Capital consumption is subtracted from gross domestic product in order to determine
a) consumption expenditures plus investment expenditures plus government purchases plus net exports.
b) disposable income.
c) net domestic product.
d) domestic income.
e) net investment.

23.28
Correct: c)
Difficulty: 3
Page(s): 597
Scramble range: All
Topic: Net domestic product

23.28
Net domestic product is a better variable to use than gross domestic product if the goal is to measure the economy's production rate since net domestic product

a) makes allowances for indirect taxes.
b) takes the depreciation of capital into account.
c) tells policy makers how much machinery should be replaced.
d) sums the expenditures made by all sectors of the economy.
e) measures gross investment.

23.29
Correct: b)
Difficulty: 2
Page(s): 595
Scramble range: All
Topic: Relative size/ aggregate expenditure

23.29
Historically, the largest component of GDP from the expenditure approach is

a) gross private domestic investment.
b) personal consumption.
c) exports.
d) government purchases.
e) imports.

23.30
Correct: a)
Difficulty: 2
Page(s): 596
Scramble range: All
Topic: Relative size/factor incomes

23.30
Historically, the largest component of GDP from the factor incomes approach is

a) wages, salaries and supplementary labour income.
b) interest and miscellaneous investment income.
c) corporate profits.
d) farmers' income.
e) income of non-farm unincorporated businesses.

23.31
Correct: c)
Difficulty: 3
Page(s): 596
Scramble range: All
Topic: Net domestic income — factor costs

23.31
By summing the values of wages, salaries and supplementary labour income, corporate profits, interest and miscellaneous investment income, farmers' income, and income of non-farm unincorporated businesses, accountants arrive at a value called

a) gross domestic product.
b) gross domestic income.
c) net domestic income at factor cost.
d) net domestic product.
e) total output of the economy.

23.32
Correct: d)
Difficulty: 3
Page(s): 597
Scramble range: All
Topic: Tax/subsidy wedge/domestic income accounting

23.32
In the Canadian economy, the difference between valuing goods at their market prices and at their factor costs is

a) depreciation.
b) exports.
c) personal taxes.
d) indirect taxes and subsidies.
e) capital consumption.

23.33
Correct: d)
Difficulty: 3
Page(s): 597
Scramble range: All
Topic: Net domestic product

23.33
Net domestic product at market prices equals
a) consumption plus government plus net exports plus investment expenditures.
b) consumption plus government plus exports plus personal taxes.
c) indirect business taxes plus personal income plus net exports.
d) all factor incomes plus indirect taxes minus subsidies.
e) all factor incomes minus depreciation.

23.34
Correct: e)
Difficulty: 2
Page(s): 589
Scramble range: All
Topic: Circular flow

23.34
The purchasers in the goods and services market are
a) consumers and government only.
b) consumers and investors only.
c) consumers and net exporters only.
d) consumers, investors, and government.
e) consumers, investors, government, and net exporters.

23.35
Correct: e)
Difficulty: 3
Page(s): 589
Scramble range: All
Topic: Circular flow

23.35
Financial markets consist of __________ as net borrowers and __________ as net lenders.
a) households; firms and government
b) households and firms; government
c) households and government; firms
d) firms; households and government
e) firms and government; households

23.36
Correct: b)
Difficulty: 4
Page(s): 597–598
Scramble range: All
Topic: GDP

23.36
An art collector recently sold a piece of pottery for $300. He had purchased it for $200 only two years earlier. How will the most recent sale affect GDP?
a) GDP will increase by $100.
b) GDP will not change.
c) GDP will increase by $300.
d) GDP will increase by $200.
e) GDP 2 years ago must be adjusted downwards by $200, and current GDP will rise by $300.

23.37
Correct: d)
Difficulty: 2
Page(s): 596–597
Scramble range: All
Topic: Savings/domestic income accounting

23.37
Saving
a) is considered an injection into the circular flow of income.
b) plus consumption equals national income in the Canadian national income accounts.
c) plus transfer payments equals consumption in the Canadian national accounts.
d) is considered a leakage from the circular flow of income.
e) is always equal to investment.

23.38
Correct: c)
Difficulty: 2
Page(s): 594
Scramble range: All
Topic: Leakages

23.38
Which of the following sets of variables represent leakages from the circular flow?
a) Saving, taxes, and transfers.
b) Consumption, saving, and transfers.
c) Saving, taxes, and imports.
d) Imports, taxes, and transfers.
e) Exports, government expenditures, and investment.

23.39
Correct: b)
Difficulty: 2
Page(s): 594
Scramble range: All
Topic: Injections

23.39
Which of the following sets of variables represent injections into the circular flow?
a) Consumption, government purchases, and exports.
b) Investment, government purchases, and exports.
c) Consumption, investment, and imports.
d) Transfers, consumption, and imports.
e) Savings, taxes, and imports.

23.40
Correct: b)
Difficulty: 3
Page(s): 596–597
Scramble range: All
Topic: Factor income method/GDP measurement

23.40
Suppose there is a 10 percent sales tax on consumption goods and suppose you buy a new bicycle with a $200 price tag. By using the factor incomes approach to measuring GDP, how much does this sale add to GDP?
a) $200.
b) $220.
c) $20.
d) $210.
e) $180.

23.41
Correct: a)
Difficulty: 3
Page(s): 590
Scramble range: a)–d)
Topic: Investment

23.41
Of the following items, which one would be considered an investment in the national income accounts?
a) The purchase of a new van by a potter who packs it up with his wares and travels to art shows on weekends.
b) The purchase of 100 shares of Canadian stock on the Toronto stock exchange.
c) The purchase of a 100-year-old house that was just put on the protected historic sites list in the year in question.
d) The purchase of a Canadian government bond.
e) All of the above.

23.42
Correct: d)
Difficulty: 2
Page(s): 596–597
Scramble range: All
Topic: Expenditure approach/domestic income accounts

23.42
Which of the following would be included in the calculation of GDP by the expenditure approach?
a) The purchase of 20 shares of a new issue of IBM stock.
b) The purchase of an original eighteenth-century work of art.
c) The value of your brother's services when he mows the lawn for the family.
d) The cost of adding a new kitchen to your house.
e) The income you pay to your gardener.

23.43
Correct: a)
Difficulty: 4
Page(s): 597–598
Scramble range: All
Topic: GDP/domestic income accounts

23.43
Refer to Table 23.2. Gross domestic product is equal to
a) $2,400.
b) $1,920.
c) $2,150.
d) $1,940.
e) $2,350.

Table 23.2

Corporate profits	$ 200
Interest and miscellaneous investment income	150
Indirect business taxes	230
Depreciation	250
Wages, salaries and supplementary labour income	1350
Farmers' income	150
Income of nonfarm unincorporated businesses	70
Personal consumption	1400
Government purchases	500
Government transfer payments	50
Net exports	40

23.44
Correct: a)
Difficulty: 4
Page(s): 597
Scramble range: All
Topic: NDP/domestic income accounting

23.44
Refer to Table 23.2. Net domestic product is equal to
a) $2,150.
b) $1,920.
c) $2,400.
d) $1,940.
e) $2,350.

23.45
Correct: a)
Difficulty: 4
Page(s): 590
Scramble range: All
Topic: Gross investment/domestic income accounting

23.45
Refer to Table 23.2. Gross private domestic investment is equal to
a) $460.
b) $260.
c) $400.
d) $560.
e) $250.

23.46
Correct: b)
Difficulty: 4
Page(s): 590
Scramble range: All
Topic: Net investment

23.46
Refer to Table 23.2. Net private domestic investment is equal to
a) $250.
b) $210.
c) $510.
d) $560.
e) $150.

23.47
Correct: e)
Difficulty: 2
Page(s): 596
Scramble range: All
Topic: Factor incomes/domestic income accounting

23.47
Which approach to measuring GDP is being used when Statistics Canada sums wages, salaries and supplementary labour income, corporate profits, interest and miscellaneous investment income, farmers' income, and income of nonfarm unincorporated businesses?
a) Opportunity cost approach.
b) Expenditure approach.
c) Value-added approach.
d) Factor cost approach.
e) Factor incomes approach.

23.48
Correct: a)
Difficulty: 4
Page(s): 596
Scramble range: All
Topic: Domestic income

23.48
Refer to Table 23.3. Gross domestic product equals
a) $3,050.
b) $3,150.
c) $3,400.
d) $5,600.
e) $5,050.

Table 23.3

Government purchases	$ 500
Wages, salaries and supplementary labour income	2000
Capital consumption	400
Gross investment	400
Personal consumption	2200
Net exports	–50
Indirect business taxes	150

23.49
Correct: e)
Difficulty: 4
Page(s): 596
Scramble range: All
Topic: Domestic income

23.49
Refer to Table 23.3. Net domestic product equals
a) $3,050.
b) $3,150.
c) $3,400.
d) $4,650.
e) $2,650.

23.50
Correct: b)
Difficulty: 4
Page(s): 596
Scramble range: All
Topic: Capital stock

23.50
Suppose the economy's capital stock grows over the year. Therefore, it must be true that
a) net private domestic investment was greater than gross private domestic investment.
b) net private domestic investment was positive.
c) depreciation was greater than net private domestic investment.
d) depreciation was greater than gross private domestic investment.
e) depreciation is less than zero.

23.51
Correct: a)
Difficulty: 3
Page(s): 597
Scramble range: All
Topic: Subsidies/ domestic income accounting

23.51
From a national income accounting viewpoint, the immediate effect of a new government subsidy paid to a Saskatchewan wheat farmer is
a) an increase in national income.
b) a decrease in national income.
c) to leave national income the same.
d) to increase disposable income but leave national income unchanged.
e) a decrease in factor income.

23.52
Correct: e)
Difficulty: 3
Page(s): 601–602
Scramble range: All
Topic: CPI

23.52
When the CPI is based on 1967 prices, a consumer price index of 322 in 1985 means that
a) prices of consumer goods have gone up by a factor of 32.2.
b) an item that cost $100 in 1967 now costs $322.
c) prices of consumer goods have less than doubled.
d) the market basket of consumer goods that cost $322 in 1967 could be purchased for $100 in 1985.
e) the market basket of consumer goods that cost $100 in 1967 could be purchased for $322 in 1985.

23.53
Correct: b)
Difficulty: 3
Page(s): 601–602
Scramble range: All
Topic: Calculating CPI

23.53
If a market basket of goods cost $200 in the base year and $450 in a later year, the price index in the later year would be correctly expressed as
a) 450.
b) 225.
c) 300.
d) 250.
e) 44.44.

23.54
Correct: d)
Difficulty: 3
Page(s): 602–608
Scramble range: All
Topic: Prices/real income

23.54
A fall in the standard of living occurs when
a) nominal income falls.
b) the purchasing power of money falls.
c) the CPI rises.
d) average prices do not fall by enough to offset the fall in nominal income.
e) average prices rise by less than the rise in nominal income.

23.55
Correct: d)
Difficulty: 3
Page(s): 602–608
Scramble range: All
Topic: Real versus nominal GDP

23.55
Economists make the distinction between real and nominal GDP to
a) see if the government sector is taking a larger share of the total real product produced.
b) measure the change in nominal interest rates.
c) see if economic welfare has changed.
d) see if real production has changed.
e) account for depreciation.

23.56
Correct: b)
Difficulty: 3
Page(s): 605, 608
Scramble range: All
Topic: Computing real GDP

23.56
If nominal GDP in 1982 was $3,166 billion with a price index of 100, what would be the real GDP in 1985 if the 1985 nominal GDP was $3,992 billion and the GDP deflator for 1985 was 111?
a) $3,573 billion.
b) $3,596 billion.
c) $4,391 billion.
d) $3,552 billion.
e) $4,431 billion.

23.57
Correct: b)
Difficulty: 2
Page(s): 605, 608
Scramble range: All
Topic: Computing CPI

23.57
Refer to Table 23.4. The price index in 1985, using 1975 as the base year, is
a) 1,340.
b) 158.
c) 100.
d) 152.
e) 63.

Table 23.4 Price and output data for three goods produced by a simple economy in selected years

	Price		Quantity	
	1975	1985	1975	1985
Pop	0.75	1.10	100	120
Crackers	1.25	2.10	300	280
Cucumbers	2.00	3.00	200	190

23.58
Correct: a)
Difficulty: 5
Page(s): 608
Scramble range: All
Topic: Interpreting CPI changes

23.58
Refer to Table 23.4. Given that the base year is 1975, which of the following statements is true?
a) From 1975 to 1985, the cost of the market basket has risen by 58 percent.
b) It costs 158 times more in 1985 than it does in 1975 to buy the same market basket.
c) All prices have risen by the same amount.
d) The relative price of pop in terms of cucumbers has risen.
e) The relative price of pop in terms of crackers has risen.

23.59
Correct: b)
Difficulty: 2
Page(s): 605, 608
Scramble range: All
Topic: Computing CPI

23.59
Refer to Table 23.4. The price index in 1985, using 1975 as the base year, is
a) 1,340.
b) 158.
c) 100.
d) 152.
e) 63.

23.60
Correct: d)
Difficulty: 4
Page(s): 605, 608
Scramble range: All
Topic: Computing CPI

23.60
Refer to Table 23.4. The price index in 1975, using 1985 as the base year, is
a) 100.
b) 157.
c) 129.
d) 63.
e) 152.

23.61
Correct: a)
Difficulty: 2
Page(s): 605, 608
Scramble range: All
Topic: Computing CPI

23.61
Refer to Table 23.4. The price index in 1985, using 1985 as the base year, is
a) 100.
b) 157.
c) 129.
d) 63.
e) 153.

23.62
Correct: e)
Difficulty: 3
Page(s): 608
Scramble range: a)–d)
Topic: CPI/inflation

23.62
If the CPI in 1982 was 100 and the CPI in 1983 was 115, then the rate of inflation was

a) 1.5 percent.
b) 100 percent.
c) 15.1515 percent.
d) 115 percent.
e) none of the above.

23.63
Correct: e)
Difficulty: 2
Page(s): 602–604
Scramble range: All
Topic: GDP deflator

23.63
The GDP deflator is used to adjust nominal GDP for changes in

a) national income.
b) the unemployment rate.
c) the cost of the typical urban worker's market basket.
d) depreciation.
e) the general price level.

23.64
Correct: c)
Difficulty: 2
Page(s): 605, 608
Scramble range: All
Topic: Index to compute real GDP

23.64
Suppose that between year 1 and year 2 the nominal GDP of an economy increased from $1 billion to $3 billion and that the appropriate index of prices increased from 100 in year 1 to 200 in year 2. GNP for year 2 in terms of year 1 prices would be

a) $6 billion.
b) $3 billion.
c) $1.5 billion.
d) $2 billion.
e) $4 billion.

23.65
Correct: e)
Difficulty: 3
Page(s): 605, 608
Scramble range: All
Topic: Computing real variation — index

23.65
Suppose that nominal per capita GDP was $18,000 in 1985. The 1982 GDP deflator is 100 and the 1985 GDP deflator is 110. Based on this information, the approximate real per capita GDP in 1985 is

a) $16,634.
b) $19,800.
c) $16,800.
d) $18,480.
e) $16,363.

23.66
Correct: e)
Difficulty: 2
Page(s): 601–602
Scramble range: All
Topic: CPI

23.66
The CPI is

a) a comparison of the cost of the typical basket of goods consumed in period 1 with the cost of the basket of goods typically consumed in period 2.
b) a comparison of the cost of a typical basket of goods during a base period with the cost of the same basket during a given period.
c) a measure of the increase in the prices of the goods included in GDP.
d) the ratio of the average price of a typical market basket of goods compared to the cost of producing those goods during the base year.
e) a comparison of the cost of a typical basket of goods during a given period with the cost of the same basket during a base period.

23.67
Correct: a)
Page(s): 597
Scramble range: All
Topic: Interpreting domestic income accounts

23.67
Suppose that GDP in Econoworld increased at an annual rate of 10 percent between 1970 and 1985. It is likely that disposable income
a) and domestic income rose during this time period.
b) and domestic income fell during this time period.
c) rose and domestic income fell during this time period.
d) fell and domestic income rose during this time period.
e) stayed the same while domestic income rose during this time period.

23.68
Correct: b)
Difficulty: 3
Page(s): 597–598
Scramble range: All
Topic: GDP

23.68
A hypothetical economy produced four items during the year: plates, TVs, bicycles, and computers. Forty plates were produced and sold for $10 each. Five TVs were produced and sold for $300 each. Fifty bicycles were produced and sold for $100 each. Three computers were produced and sold for $750 each. With this information, one could determine
a) the best product mix for this economy.
b) gross domestic product for this economy.
c) net domestic product for this economy.
d) whether resources had been fully employed in this economy.
e) real income for this economy.

23.69
Correct: b)
Difficulty: 2
Page(s): 596
Scramble range: All
Topic: Domestic income

23.69
Which of the following items would be included in GDP?
a) Payments made to unemployed workers during the year as part of their unemployment compensation.
b) The cost of the tools used by a thief to break into your car.
c) The cost of the pollution caused during the processing of steel during the year.
d) The purchase of stocks on the Tokyo exchange.
e) The purchase of stocks on the Toronto exchange.

23.70
Correct: d)
Difficulty: 3
Page(s): 596
Scramble range: All
Topic: Domestic income

23.70
Widgico, Inc., produces plastic parts. At the beginning of the year they held $24 million in inventory. At the end of the year they held $20 million in inventory. All else the same, one can conclude that
a) net investment increased by $4 million.
b) net investment decreased by $4 million.
c) gross investment increased by $4 million.
d) gross investment decreased by $4 million.
e) depreciation equals $4 million.

23.71
Correct: e)
Difficulty: 4
Page(s): 605, 608
Scramble range: All
Topic: Real GDP

23.71
Suppose that nominal GDP increased from $450 billion to $545 billion during the past year. The GDP deflator for the current year is 481.5, an increase of 35.4 over the previous year. Given this information, one can conclude that
a) nominal GDP increased by less than 10 percent from last year to this year.
b) prices increased faster this year than they did the year before.
c) real GDP was $450 billion last year.
d) real GDP is $505 billion this year.
e) real GDP is $113 billion this year.

23.72
Correct: c)
Difficulty: 2
Page(s): 596
Scramble range: All
Topic: Transfer payments

23.72
Which of the following would be considered a transfer payment by national income accountants?
a) Payment for a meal in a fast-food restaurant.
b) A monthly car payment for a car purchased three years ago.
c) A social security payment.
d) A payment for a transfer on a city bus.
e) An interest-free loan from a parent to a child.

23.73
Correct: c)
Difficulty: 2
Page(s): 596
Scramble range: All
Topic: Net exports

23.73
Net exports equals
a) exports divided by imports.
b) exports plus imports.
c) exports minus imports.
d) imports minus exports.
e) foreign borrowing by residents of Canada minus domestic borrowing by nonresidents of Canada.

23.74
Correct: d)
Difficulty: 2
Page(s): 596
Scramble range: All
Topic: Domestic income

23.74
In the national income accounts, government purchases refer to those purchases made by
a) federal and provincial governments only.
b) the federal government only. Provincial and local government purchases are included in provincial GDP calculations.
c) provincial and local governments only.
d) federal, provincial, and local governments.
e) the federal government and local governments only. Provincial government purchases are included in provincial GDP calculations.

23.75
Correct: e)
Difficulty: 3
Page(s): 596
Scramble range: All
Topic: Domestic income

23.75
Gross private domestic investment is made up of
a) all purchases of newly produced capital goods minus changes in business inventories.
b) all purchases of newly produced capital goods plus changes in business inventories plus residential construction plus depreciation.
c) all purchases of newly produced capital goods plus fixed investment minus inventory investment.
d) all purchases of newly produced capital goods plus purchases of capital goods produced in previous years to replace any depreciated capital goods.
e) all purchases of newly produced capital goods plus changes in business inventories plus residential construction.

23.76
Correct: c)
Difficulty: 4
Page(s): 596
Scramble range: All
Topic: Domestic income

23.76
In 1949, the capital consumption allowance was $22 billion, GDP was $260.4 billion, and domestic income at factor cost was $215.2 billion. In 1949, net domestic product was
a) $445.2 billion.
b) smaller than domestic income.
c) $238.4 billion.
d) $215.2 billion.
e) $193.2 billion.

23.77
Correct: e)
Difficulty: 4
Page(s): 596
Scramble range: All
Topic: Domestic income

23.77
In 1949, the capital consumption allowance was $22 billion, GDP was $260.4 billion, and domestic income at factor cost was $215.2 billion. In 1949, indirect taxes less subsidies were
a) $21.3 billion.
b) $22 billion.
c) less than the capital consumption allowance.
d) not determinable from the information given.
e) $23.2 billion.

23.78
Correct: d)
Difficulty: 2
Page(s): 596
Scramble range: All
Topic: Domestic income

23.78
To derive net domestic product from gross domestic product, one must
a) subtract gross private domestic investment from GDP.
b) subtract the statistical discrepancy from GDP.
c) add the statistical discrepancy to GDP.
d) subtract the capital consumption allowance from GDP.
e) add the capital consumption allowance to GDP.

23.79
Correct: c)
Difficulty: 4
Page(s): 601–602
Scramble range: All
Topic: CPI

23.79
The market basket of Econoland consists of 10*A*, 20*B*, and 30*C*. Current prices are $1 per unit of *A*, $2 per unit of *B*, and $3 per unit of *C*. Base year prices are $1 for each unit of *A*,*B*, and *C*. What is the CPI in the current year?
a) 43.
b) 100.
c) 233.
d) 430.
e) 140.

23.80
Correct: e)
Difficulty: 4
Page(s): 603–604
Scramble range: All
Topic: Real GDP

23.80
The market basket of Econoland consists of 10*A*, 20*B*, and 30*C*. Current prices are $1 per unit of *A*, $2 per unit of *B*, and $3 per unit of *C*. Base year prices are $1 for each unit of *A*,*B*, and *C*. What is real GDP for the current year?
a) Approximately $60.
b) Approximately $140.
c) Approximately $110.
d) Approximately $233.
e) Real GDP cannot be determined from the information given.

23.81 (SG 23.1)
Correct: b)
Difficulty: 2
Page(s): 589
Scramble range: All
Topic: Circular flow

23.81
Which of the following is an example of a real flow from households to firms?
a) Goods and services.
b) Factors of production.
c) Payments for goods and services.
d) Payments for factors of production.
e) Loans.

23.82 (SG 23.2)
Correct: c)
Difficulty: 3
Page(s): 596
Scramble range: All
Topic: Investment expenditures

23.82
Which of the following is *not* an example of investment in the expenditure approach to measuring GDP?
a) General Motors buys a new auto stamping machine.
b) General Motors adds 500 new cars to inventories.
c) General Motors buys Canadian government bonds.
d) General Motors builds another assembly plant.
e) General Motors replaces some worn-out stamping machines.

23.83 (SG 23.3)
Correct: c)
Difficulty: 3
Page(s): 596
Scramble range: All
Topic: Domestic income

23.83
Which of the following is true for the aggregate economy?
a) Income equals expenditure, but these are not generally equal to GDP.
b) Income equals GDP, but expenditure is generally less than these.
c) Income equals expenditure equals GDP.
d) Income equals expenditure equals GDP only if there is no government or foreign country.
e) Income equals expenditure equals GDP only if there is no depreciation.

23.84 (SG 23.4)
Correct: a)
Difficulty: 2
Page(s): 596
Scramble range: All
Topic: Domestic income

23.84
Which of the following is *not* true?
a) $Y = C + I + G + IM - EX$.
b) $I + G + EX = S + T + IM$.
c) $Y = C + S + T$.
d) $Y + IM = C + I + G + EX$.
e) $Y = C + I + G + NX$.

23.85 (SG 23.5)
Correct: d)
Difficulty: 2
Page(s): 596–597
Scramble range: All
Topic: Saving

23.85
Saving can be measured as income minus
a) taxes.
b) taxes minus consumption expenditure.
c) transfer payments.
d) net taxes minus consumption.
e) net taxes plus subsidies.

23.86 (SG 23.6)
Correct: b)
Difficulty: 3
Page(s): 596
Scramble range: All
Topic: Capital stock

23.86
Which of the following is *not* a part of the capital stock?
a) The house owned by the Smith family.
b) The Smith family holdings of stock in the Smith Pickle Company.
c) The pickle factory building owned by the Smith family.
d) The pickle packing machine in the pickle factory building owned by the Smith family.
e) The pickle inventories in the pickle factory building owned by the Smith family.

23.87 (SG 23.7)
Correct: a)
Difficulty: 3
Page(s): 596
Scramble range: All
Topic: Net interest

23.87
Interest plus miscellaneous investment income is a component of which approach to measuring GDP?
a) Factor incomes approach.
b) Expenditure approach.
c) Injections approach.
d) Output approach.
e) Opportunity cost approach.

23.88 (SG 23.8)
Correct: a)
Difficulty: 2
Page(s): 596
Scramble range: All
Topic: Factor incomes approach

23.88
Which of the following is *not* a component of the factor incomes approach to GDP?
a) Net exports.
b) Wages, salaries and supplementary labour income.
c) Corporate profits.
d) Farmers' income.
e) Income of nonfarm unincorporated businesses.

23.89 (SG 23.9)
Correct: b)
Difficulty: 3
Page(s): 596
Scramble range: All
Topic: Factor cost

23.89
To obtain the factor cost of a good from its market price, one must
a) add indirect taxes and subtract subsidies.
b) subtract indirect taxes and add subsidies.
c) subtract both indirect taxes and subsidies.
d) add both indirect taxes and subsidies.
e) subtract depreciation.

23.90 (SG 23.10)
Correct: c)
Difficulty: 1
Page(s): 594
Scramble range: All
Topic: Leakages

23.90
Which of the following is an example of a leakage from the circular flow of income?
a) Exports.
b) Investment.
c) Saving.
d) Subsidies.
e) Government purchases.

23.91 (SG 23.11)
Correct: b)
Difficulty: 2
Page(s): 598–599
Scramble range: All
Topic: Value added

23.91
The value of a firm's output minus the value of inputs purchased is
a) net exports.
b) value added.
c) net profit.
d) indirect production.
e) capital consumption allowance.

23.92 (SG 23.12)
Correct: d)
Difficulty: 2
Page(s): 599
Scramble range: All
Topic: Underestimating value output

23.92
The existence of which of the following is *not* a reason for the fact that GDP gives an incorrect estimate of the value of total output in the economy?
a) Crime.
b) Nonmarket activities.
c) The underground economy.
d) Capital consumption allowance.
e) Externalities such as pollution.

23.93 (SG 23.13)
Correct: a)
Difficulty: 2
Page(s): 597
Scramble range: All
Topic: Net investment

23.93
From the data in Table 23.1, compute net investment.
a) $160.
b) $240.
c) $400.
d) –$160.
e) $500.

23.94 (SG 23.14)
Correct: e)
Difficulty: 4
Page(s): 597–598
Scramble range: None
Topic: GDP

23.94
From the data in Table 23.1, what additional data would you need to compute net domestic income at factor cost?
a) Income of non-farm unincorporated businesses.
b) The statistical discrepancy.
c) Corporate profits.
d) Depreciation.
e) Both a) and c).

23.95 (SG 23.15)
Correct: a)
Difficulty: 3
Page(s): 593
Scramble range: All
Topic: Disposable income

23.95
From the data in Table 23.1, compute disposable income.
a) $1,100.
b) $260.
c) $640.
d) $500.
e) $520.

23.96 (SG 23.16)
Correct: a)
Difficulty: 5
Page(s): 602–608
Scramble range: All
Topic: Nominal GDP

23.96
From the data in Table 23.5, compute nominal GDP in the current year.
a) $209.
b) $197.
c) $208.
d) $226.
e) It cannot be calculated.

Table 23.5

	Price		Quantity	
	Base year	Current year	Base year	Current year
Rubber ducks	1.00	1.25	100	100
Beach towels	9.00	6.00	12	14

23.97 (SG 23.17)
Correct: e)
Difficulty: 4
Page(s): 601–602
Scramble range: All
Topic: CPI

23.97
Table 23.5 gives price and quantity data for an economy with only two consumption goods: rubber ducks and beach towels. Compute the Consumer Price Index for the current year.
a) 100.
b) 112.
c) 105.6.
d) 100.5.
e) 94.7.

23.98 (SG 23.18)
Correct: c)
Difficulty: 4
Page(s): 605, 608
Scramble range: All
Topic: Relative prices

23.98
Refer to the data in Table 23.5. Between the base year and the current year, the relative price of rubber ducks
a) remained unchanged.
b) fell.
c) rose.
d) cannot be determined with the amount of information given.
e) depends on what happens to the CPI.

23.99 (SG 23.19)
Correct: a)
Difficulty: 3
Page(s): 602–608
Scramble range: All
Topic: Nominal GDP

23.99
If 1982 is the base year for the GDP deflator, we know that nominal GDP
a) equals real GDP in 1982.
b) is greater than real GDP in 1982.
c) is less than real GDP in 1982.
d) in 1983 will be greater than real GDP in 1983.
e) in 1983 will be greater than nominal GDP in 1982.

23.100 (SG 23.20)
Correct: e)
Difficulty: 4
Page(s): 602–608
Scramble range: All
Topic: GDP deflator

23.100
Consider the data in Table 23.6. What is the GDP deflator in 1988?
a) 160.
b) 250.
c) 200.
d) 88.89.
e) 125.

Table 23.6

Year	Nominal GDP	Real GDP	GDP deflator (1981=100)
1981	125	125	100
1988	250	200	?
1989	275	?	122.22

23.101 (SG 23.21)
Correct: a)
Difficulty: 4
Page(s): 603–604
Scramble range: All
Topic: Real GDP

23.101
Consider the data in Table 23.6. What is real GDP in 1989?
a) 225.
b) 275.
c) 220.
d) 336.11.
e) 110.

23.102 (SG 23.22)
Correct: d)
Difficulty: 3
Page(s): 605, 608
Scramble range: All
Topic: Relative price changes and inflation

23.102
Which of the following is *not* possible?
a) The relative prices of some goods rise during a period of high inflation.
b) The relative prices of some goods fall during a period of high inflation.
c) The relative prices of some goods rise during a period in which the rate of inflation is negative (i.e., the price level is falling).
d) The relative prices of all goods rise.
e) The relative price of some goods stay constant while the average price level is rising.

23.103
Correct: e)
Difficulty: 3
Page(s): 598–599
Scramble range: None
Topic: Value added

23.103
In the output approach to measuring GDP, GDP is
a) the value of all goods produced in the economy.
b) the value of all intermediate goods produced in the economy.
c) the value of all final goods produced in the economy.
d) the sum of all the value added of each firm in the economy.
e) both c) and d).

23.104
Correct: e)
Difficulty: 3
Page(s): 605, 608
Scramble range: All
Topic: CPI versus GDP

23.104
Which of the following statements is true?
a) The CPI and the GDP deflator must have the same value in any given year.
b) The CPI must be greater than the GDP deflator in any given year.
c) The CPI must be less than the GDP deflator in any given year.
d) The CPI measures the price of production, while the GDP deflator measures the price of consumption.
e) The CPI measures the price of consumption, while the GDP deflator measures the price of production.

23.105
Correct: c)
Difficulty: 3
Page(s): 596
Scramble range: All
Topic: Domestic income

23.105
Which of the following is true for the aggregate economy?
a) Value of all wages equals expenditure, but these are not generally equal to GDP.
b) Income equals GDP, but expenditure is generally greater than these.
c) Income equals expenditure.
d) Income equals expenditure equals GDP only for a private, closed economy.
e) Income equals production only if depreciation equals zero.

23.106
Correct: e)
Difficulty: 2
Page(s): 596
Scramble range: All
Topic: Domestic income

23.106
Which of the following is true?
a) $Y = C + I + G + EM - IX$.
b) $I + G + EX = S + I + IM$.
c) $Y = C + S + I$.
d) $Y + IM = C + I + G$.
e) $Y = C + T + S$.

23.107
Correct: d)
Difficulty: 2
Page(s): 589
Scramble range: All
Topic: Consumption

23.107
Consumption can be measured as income
a) minus taxes.
b) minus taxes minus saving.
c) minus transfer payments.
d) minus net taxes minus saving.
e) plus transfer payments minus saving.

23.108
Correct: a)
Difficulty: 2
Page(s): 596
Scramble range: All
Topic: Factor incomes approach

23.108
Wages, salaries, and supplementary labour income is a component of which approach to measuring GDP?
a) Factor incomes approach.
b) Expenditure approach.
c) Injections approach.
d) Output approach.
e) Value added approach.

23.109
Correct: c)
Difficulty: 2
Page(s): 596
Scramble range: All
Topic: Factor incomes approach

23.109
Which of the following is a component of the factor incomes approach to GDP?
a) Government purchases.
b) Transfer payments.
c) Corporate profits.
d) Net exports.
e) Value added.

23.110
Correct: a)
Difficulty: 1
Page(s): 594
Scramble range: All
Topic: Injections

23.110
Which of the following is an example of an injection into the circular flow of expenditures and income?
a) Exports.
b) Imports.
c) Saving.
d) Taxes.
e) Depreciation.

23.111
Correct: c)
Difficulty: 2
Page(s): 598–599
Scramble range: All
Topic: Value added

23.111
The value of a firm's output minus the value of inputs purchased is
a) the method by which factor cost is derived.
b) the net economic profit of producing that unit of output.
c) value added in production by the firm.
d) indirect production.
e) depreciation.

23.112
Correct: c)
Difficulty: 3
Page(s): 599
Scramble range: All
Topic: Underestimating value output

23.112
The existence of which of the following is a reason for the fact that GDP gives an underestimate of the value of total output in the economy?
a) Pollution.
b) Market activities.
c) Underground economy.
d) Capital consumption allowance.
e) Environmental problems.

23.113
Correct: d)
Difficulty: 4
Page(s): 597–598
Scramble range: a)–d)
Topic: GDP

23.113
Consider the economy represented in Table 23.7. GDP in this economy is
a) $800,000.
b) $850,000.
c) $1,350,000.
d) $1,050,000.
e) none of the above.

Table 23.7

Item	Millions of dollars
Wages paid to labour	800,000
Consumption expenditure	650,000
Taxes paid on wages	200,000
Government payments to support the unemployed, sick and aged	50,000
Firms' profits	200,000
Investment	250,000
Taxes paid on profits	50,000
Government purchases of goods and services	200,000
Export earnings	250,000
Saving	200,000
Import payments	300,000

23.114
Correct: d)
Difficulty: 4
Page(s): 598–599
Scramble range: All
Topic: Value added

23.114
Consider the economy represented in Table 23.7. The total value added is
a) $800,000.
b) $850,000.
c) $1,350,000.
d) $1,050,000.
e) not calculable with the given information.

Chapter 24 Aggregate Demand and Aggregate Supply

24.1
Correct: b)
Difficulty: 1
Page(s): 615
Scramble range: All
Topic: Aggregate quantity demanded

24.1
The sum of the quantities of consumption goods and services demanded by households, of investment goods demanded by firms, of goods and services demanded by governments, and of net exports demanded by foreigners is called the
a) aggregate expenditure function.
b) aggregate quantity demanded.
c) total expenditure function.
d) aggregate quantity supplied.
e) demand function.

24.2
Correct: d)
Difficulty: 2
Page(s): 615
Scramble range: All
Topic: Aggregate demand

24.2
The aggregate demand for goods and services is composed of the purchases of
a) households and net exporters.
b) businesses, bondholders, and net exporters.
c) businesses and governments.
d) consumers, investors, governments, and net exporters.
e) consumers, investors, and governments.

24.3
Correct: c)
Difficulty: 2
Page(s): 615
Scramble range: All
Topic: Aggregate quantity demanded

24.3
The aggregate quantity of goods and services demanded does *not* depend on decisions made by
a) foreigners.
b) households.
c) suppliers.
d) governments.
e) firms.

24.4
Correct: d)
Difficulty: 3
Page(s): 615
Scramble range: All
Topic: *AD* curve

24.4
The aggregate demand curve depicts the relationship between
a) real aggregate expenditures and real GDP.
b) real income and real GDP.
c) real prices and real GDP.
d) the average price level and the aggregate quantity demanded.
e) the average price level and real GDP.

24.5
Correct: b)
Difficulty: 3
Page(s): 615
Scramble range: All
Topic: *AD* curve

24.5
A particular aggregate demand curve assumes a constant
a) price level.
b) money supply.
c) capital stock.
d) wage rate.
e) level of price expectations.

24.6
Correct: e)
Difficulty: 2
Page(s): 615–616
Scramble range: All
Topic: *AD* curve

24.6
Which of the following variables is *not* held constant along a given aggregate demand curve?
a) The money supply.
b) Real income.
c) Tax rates.
d) Expectations about inflation.
e) The price level.

24.7
Correct: b)
Difficulty: 2
Page(s): 616
Scramble range: All
Topic: Shifts of the *AD* curve

24.7
Which of the following variables can change without affecting a shift in the aggregate demand curve?
a) Interest rates.
b) Price level.
c) Tax rates.
d) Expectations about inflation.
e) Money supply.

24.8
Correct: c)
Difficulty: 3
Page(s): 616
Scramble range: All
Topic: Negative slope of the *AD* curve

24.8
The aggregate demand curve has a negative slope because
a) people find substitutes when the price of a good that they typically buy increases.
b) of the same reason that individual demand curves have a negative slope.
c) of the real balance effect.
d) firms will increase the quantity supplied as the price level rises.
e) as the price level rises, people shift from consuming foreign goods to consuming domestic goods.

24.9
Correct: d)
Difficulty: 3
Page(s): 616
Scramble range: All
Topic: Negative slope of the *AD* curve

24.9
Which of the following factors help explain why the aggregate demand curve has a negative slope?
a) As the price level falls, domestic consumers have an incentive to purchase more of the cheaper goods and services.
b) As the price level falls, the Bank of Canada will have to increase the supply of money which will lead to an increase in the amount purchased.
c) As the price level falls, the government will have to reduce taxes which will lead to an increase in the amount purchased.
d) As the price level falls, the wealth of people holding a fixed quantity of money increases, causing them to expand their purchases.
e) As the price level falls, people shift to consuming more goods in the future and less in the present.

24.10
Correct: b)
Difficulty: 3
Page(s): 617
Scramble range: All
Topic: Intertemporal substitution

24.10
When economists say that the aggregate demand curve has a negative slope due to the international substitution effect, they mean that when the price level
a) rises people plan to hold a larger amount of real goods and services and a larger quantity of money and other financial assets.
b) rises people plan to buy a smaller amount of real goods and services and hold a larger quantity of money and other financial assets.
c) falls in the home country people tend to substitute purchases of foreign-made products for domestically produced products.
d) rises in the home country people tend to substitute purchases of foreign-made products for domestically produced products.
e) falls people plan to buy a smaller amount of real goods and services and hold a larger quantity of money and other financial assets.

24.11
Correct: d)
Difficulty: 3
Page(s): 617
Scramble range: All
Topic: International substitution

24.11
When economists say that the aggregate demand curve has a negative slope due to the international substitution effect, they mean that when the price level
a) rises people plan to buy a larger amount of real goods and services and hold a larger quantity of money and other financial assets.
b) rises people plan to buy a smaller amount of real goods and services and hold a larger quantity of money and other financial assets.
c) falls in the home country people tend to substitute purchases of foreign-made products for domestically produced products.
d) rises in the home country people tend to substitute purchases of foreign-made products for domestically produced products.
e) falls people plan to buy a smaller amount of real goods and services and hold a larger quantity of money and other financial assets.

24.12
Correct: e)
Difficulty: 3
Page(s): 616
Scramble range: All
Topic: Real balance effect

24.12
When economists discuss the real balance effect in relation to the negative slope of the aggregate demand curve, they are referring to the effect of
a) a price level increase on the amount of foreign-made products that people plan to buy.
b) a real GDP increase on the quantity of real balances that people plan to hold.
c) a price level change on the consumption of current versus future goods.
d) a change in the price of a major factor of production, such as oil, on the quantity of real GDP that people plan to buy.
e) a price level change on the quantity of real money that people wish to hold.

24.13
Correct: a)
Difficulty: 1
Page(s): 617
Scramble range: All
Topic: Quantity of money

24.13
Which of the following items would *not* be included in a list containing what your text refers to as the quantity of money that people plan to hold?
a) Bonds.
b) Currency.
c) Cash in your pocket.
d) Chequing deposits at banks.
e) Chequing deposits at trust companies.

24.14
Correct: c)
Difficulty: 2
Page(s): 616
Scramble range: All
Topic: Real money

24.14
Real money is measured as
a) the actual amount of currency that people are holding.
b) the actual amount of currency and various types of deposits that people are holding at financial institutions.
c) the quantity of money adjusted for price level changes.
d) GDP adjusted for price level changes.
e) disposable income adjusted for price level changes.

24.15
Correct: b)
Difficulty: 2
Page(s): 616
Scramble range: All
Topic: Real balance effect

24.15
The real balance effect is the proposition that the higher the quantity of
a) money, the larger is the quantity of real GDP demanded.
b) real money, the larger is the quantity of real GDP demanded.
c) real money, the smaller is the quantity of real GDP demanded.
d) money, the smaller is the quantity of real GDP demanded.
e) real GDP, the higher is the quantity of real money demanded.

24.16
Correct: d)
Difficulty: 2
Page(s): 616
Scramble range: All
Topic: Real money

24.16
If you are holding $1,000 in money balances and the price level rises by 10 percent, then your real money balance is
a) worth more.
b) unchanged.
c) worth $990.
d) worth 10 percent less than before.
e) worth $1,100.

24.17
Correct: e)
Difficulty: 2
Page(s): 617
Scramble range: All
Topic: Intertemporal substitution

24.17
One reason for the negative slope of the aggregate demand curve can be described as follows: A higher price level leads to a decrease in the supply of loans and an increase in the demand for loans resulting in higher interest rates and a smaller quantity of real GDP demanded. This is a description of the
a) international substitution effect.
b) real balance effect.
c) the loan effect.
d) real substitution effect.
e) the intertemporal substitution effect.

24.18
Correct: b)
Difficulty: 2
Page(s): 616
Scramble range: All
Topic: Real balance effect

24.18
One reason for the negative slope of the aggregate demand curve can be described as follows: A higher price level decreases the real value of money so people hold a larger quantity of money and buy a smaller quantity of goods and services. This is a description of the
a) international substitution effect.
b) real balance effect.
c) the loan effect.
d) real substitution effect.
e) the intertemporal substitution effect.

24.19
Correct: c)
Difficulty: 2
Page(s): 618
Scramble range: All
Topic: Aggregate demand

24.19
Which one of the following factors will not lead to a change in aggregate demand?
a) An increase in interest rates.
b) An increase in the expected inflation rate.
c) An increase in the price level.
d) An increase in expected future profits.
e) An increase in the money supply.

24.20
Correct: a)
Difficulty: 3
Page(s): 620
Scramble range: All
Topic: Movement versus shift in *AD* curve

24.20
If a change in interest rates is induced by a change in the price level, then this would be shown as
a) a movement along the aggregate demand curve.
b) a shift of the aggregate demand curve due to the intertemporal substitution effect.
c) a movement along the aggregate demand curve due to the international substitution effect.
d) a movement along the aggregate supply curve.
e) a shift of the aggregate demand curve due to the real balance effect.

24.21
Correct: d)
Difficulty: 2
Page(s): 618
Scramble range: All
Topic: Aggregate demand

24.21
If an increase in interest rates, other things being equal, leads to a decrease in the quantity of new capital equipment that firms plan to buy, this would lead directly to
a) a decrease in aggregate quantity supplied.
b) a decrease in aggregate supply.
c) a decrease in aggregate demand.
d) a decrease in aggregate quantity demanded.
e) an increase in aggregate quantity demanded.

24.22
Correct: a)
Difficulty: 3
Page(s): 619
Scramble range: All
Topic: Expected inflation/*AD* curve

24.22
If there is an increase in the expected inflation rate, other things being equal, then people will
a) hold a smaller quantity of money and other financial assets.
b) hold a larger quantity of money and other financial assets.
c) buy a smaller amount of goods and services today.
d) not change their current spending patterns.
e) buy more foreign goods.

24.23
Correct: a)
Difficulty: 2
Page(s): 619
Scramble range: All
Topic: Money supply change/*AD* curve

24.23
All else constant, an increase in the quantity of money means that
a) the aggregate demand curve will shift to the right.
b) the aggregate demand curve will shift to the left.
c) the aggregate supply curve will shift to the left.
d) the aggregate supply curve will shift to the right.
e) there will be a movement down an aggregate demand curve.

24.24
Correct: e)
Difficulty: 3
Page(s): 619
Scramble range: All
Topic: Expected future profits

24.24
The aggregate demand curve will shift if
a) there is an increase or decrease in the price level.
b) there is a change in wage rates.
c) the quantity of money stays constant, but the quantity of real money balances falls.
d) foreign exchange rate remains constant.
e) business firms perceive a change in expected future profits.

24.25
Correct: e)
Difficulty: 4
Page(s): 619
Scramble range: a)–d)
Topic: Quantity of money

24.25
All else constant, if the Bank of Canada slows down the rate at which new money is being injected into the economy, then interest rates will tend to
a) fall and the aggregate demand curve will shift right.
b) rise and the aggregate demand curve will shift right.
c) rise and the aggregate demand curve will stay constant.
d) rise and the price level will rise.
e) none of the above.

24.26
Correct: b)
Difficulty: 3
Page(s): 620
Scramble range: All
Topic: Transfer payments/*AD* curve

24.26
All else constant, which of the following will lead to an increase in aggregate demand?
a) An increase in taxes.
b) An increase in transfer payments.
c) A decrease in the rate of government spending.
d) A decrease in the price level.
e) A decrease in the money supply.

24.27
Correct: b)
Difficulty: 2
Page(s): 620
Scramble range: All
Topic: Foreign income/*AD* curve

24.27
All else constant, an increase in the income of foreign countries relative to the income level in Canada, will lead to
a) an increase in aggregate supply.
b) an increase in aggregate demand.
c) a decrease in aggregate demand.
d) no change in aggregate demand.
e) a decrease in aggregate supply.

24.28
Correct: c)
Difficulty: 2
Page(s): 622
Scramble range: All
Topic: Long-run capacity

24.28
If a firm is operating at its long-run capacity output, then
a) its marginal cost is minimized.
b) its fixed costs are minimized.
c) its per unit costs are minimized.
d) only 10 percent of the labour hired by the firm is underemployed.
e) it will always try to expand capacity.

24.29
Correct: b)
Difficulty: 3
Page(s): 622
Scramble range: All
Topic: Long-run capacity

24.29
According to the text, when the economy is operating at long-run capacity
a) the unemployment rate is zero.
b) the only unemployment present is frictional unemployment.
c) the price level tends to rise slower than production costs for the typical firm.
d) the price level tends to rise faster than production costs for the typical firm.
e) the price level is constant.

24.30
Correct: d)
Difficulty: 3
Page(s): 622
Scramble range: All
Topic: Long-run aggregate supply

24.30
The long-run aggregate supply
a) depends on the price level.
b) corresponds to full employment, which implies that the economy is experiencing no unemployment.
c) depends on the quantity of money in circulation.
d) does not vary with the price level.
e) never changes.

24.31
Correct: a)
Difficulty: 3
Page(s): 622
Scramble range: All
Topic: Long-run aggregate supply

24.31
A vertical long-run aggregate supply curve indicates that
a) an increase in the price level will not expand an economy's output capacity in the long run.
b) output rates greater than the long-run capacity output rate cannot be reached.
c) an increase in the price level will permit the economy to achieve a higher level of output.
d) an increase in the price level will promote technological change and hence economic growth.
e) the long-run aggregate supply curve never changes.

24.32
Correct: a)
Difficulty: 3
Page(s): 622
Scramble range: All
Topic: Long-run aggregate supply

24.32
According to the text, the long-run aggregate supply curve is vertical because
a) an increase in the price level does not change the economy's resources base and accompanying production possibilities constraint.
b) actual output can never exceed, even temporarily, the output rate implied by the economy's long-run aggregate supply curve.
c) a vertical long-run aggregate supply curve indicates the maximum output rate that an economy can ever reach.
d) a vertical long-run supply curve indicates that an increase in aggregate demand will lead to a larger real GDP but not a larger nominal GDP.
e) capacity has been reached.

24.33
Correct: d)
Difficulty: 2
Page(s): 623
Scramble range: All
Topic: Short-run aggregate supply curve

24.33
The short-run aggregate supply curve indicates
a) the relationship between the price level and the aggregate quantity of goods and services purchased by consumers, investors, governments, and net exporters.
b) the relationship between the price level and the natural rate of unemployment.
c) the relationship between the purchasing power of wages and the quantity of labour supplied by households.
d) the various quantities of goods and services producers will supply at different price levels.
e) the various quantities of goods and services producers will supply at different income levels.

24.34
Correct: a)
Difficulty: 1
Page(s): 623
Scramble range: All
Topic: Long-run aggregate supply curve/slope

24.34
The long-run aggregate supply curve is
a) vertical.
b) negatively sloped.
c) positively sloped but extremely steep.
d) almost flat.
e) first positively sloped, then vertical.

24.35
Correct: b)
Difficulty: 2
Page(s): 623
Scramble range: All
Topic: Measuring long-run aggregate supply

24.35
The two approaches to measuring long-run aggregate supply
a) always yield the same real GDP estimate but each emphasizes a different aspect of aggregate supply.
b) are the trend approach and the production function approach.
c) are the real production approach and the full employment approach.
d) have helped policy makers to reconcile their differences.
e) are the expenditure and the factor incomes approaches.

24.36
Correct: c)
Difficulty: 3
Page(s): 623
Scramble range: All
Topic: Measuring long-run aggregate supply

24.36
The trend approach to estimating long-run aggregate supply
a) results in the same real GDP measure regardless of the time period chosen for estimating the trend.
b) results in the same nominal GDP measure regardless of the time period chosen for estimating the trend.
c) results in different estimates arising from different time periods over which the trend is assessed.
d) results in an estimate of real GDP that fluctuates around the path of actual real GDP.
e) results in an estimate of real GDP that depends on the stock of capital and the full employment of the labour force.

24.37
Correct: d)
Difficulty: 3
Page(s): 623
Scramble range: All
Topic: Measuring long-run aggregate supply

24.37
The production function approach to measuring long-run aggregate supply
a) is more reliable than the trend approach since it requires knowing only the natural rate of unemployment.
b) was well-received by economists as it finally put an end to the controversy surrounding the use of the trend approach to measuring it.
c) depends upon knowledge of the quantity of money in circulation.
d) depends, in part, on estimating the size of the economy's capital stock.
e) yields estimates of real GDP that are always different in different time periods.

24.38
Correct: e)
Difficulty: 2
Page(s): 623
Scramble range: All
Topic: Short-run aggregate supply curve

24.38
The short-run aggregate supply curve depicts the relationship between the aggregate quantity of goods and services supplied and
a) the price of a major output produced in the economy such as that of General Motors.
b) real GDP.
c) the price level as measured by the CPI.
d) the relative price of real GDP.
e) the price level as measured by the GDP deflator.

24.39
Correct: a)
Difficulty: 2
Page(s): 623
Scramble range: All
Topic: Short-run aggregate supply curve

24.39
To derive the short-run aggregate supply curve, economists hold constant which of the following variables?
a) The price of inputs.
b) The price level.
c) The quantity of money.
d) Tax rates.
e) Expected future profits.

24.40
Correct: d)
Difficulty: 2
Page(s): 623
Scramble range: All
Topic: Short-run aggregate supply curve

24.40
Which of the following variables is *not* held constant in deriving the short-run aggregate supply curve?
a) The level of wages.
b) Raw material prices.
c) Climate.
d) Price level.
e) Technology.

24.41
Correct: c)
Difficulty: 3
Page(s): 624
Scramble range: All
Topic: Slope/short-run supply curve

24.41
Suppose that the typical firm is producing at its full capacity output. If the price of a firm's output rises and its input prices stay the same, then
a) the firm will be unable to expand its output further as it cannot produce beyond its full capacity output rate.
b) the firm does not have the incentive to increase its output any further as its fixed costs will rise and eliminate any profit opportunities.
c) the firm will expand its output if its per unit costs increase by less than the increase in the price of its output.
d) the firm's output rate will fall.
e) the firm's output rate will rise since its capacity will have risen.

24.42
Correct: a)
Difficulty: 4
Page(s): 624
Scramble range: All
Topic: Firm response—fall in price

24.42
According to the text, if output prices fall, with input prices held constant, then
a) firms will reduce their output and reduce their use of labour.
b) firms will reduce their output and hold constant the amount of labour time that they use.
c) firms will reduce their output and increase the amount of labour time that they use since wage rates are still the same.
d) there will be no change in the aggregate production rate or labour hired.
e) there will be no change in the aggregate production rate, but labour hired will fall.

24.43
Correct: d)
Difficulty: 1
Page(s): 624
Scramble range: All
Topic: Slope of the *SAS* curve

24.43
According to the text, the short-run aggregate supply curve
a) has a positive, very steep slope.
b) is flat.
c) is vertical.
d) has a positive slope for output levels around the economy's full capacity output level and eventually becomes vertical.
e) has a positive, very flat slope.

24.44
Correct: d)
Difficulty: 2
Page(s): 626
Scramble range: All
Topic: Shifts of the *LAS* curve

24.44
All else the same, the long-run aggregate supply curve increases if
a) the labour force decreases.
b) wages fall.
c) the capital stock decreases.
d) technology advances.
e) price falls.

24.45
Correct: b)
Difficulty: 3
Page(s): 626
Scramble range: All
Topic: Shifts of the *LAS* curve

24.45
All else the same, the long-run aggregate supply curve decreases if
a) raw material prices increase.
b) climatic conditions deteriorate.
c) the composition of GDP changes slowly.
d) incentives remain the same.
e) wages fall.

24.46
Correct: c)
Difficulty: 3
Page(s): 626
Scramble range: All
Topic: Shifts of the *SAS* curve

24.46
All else the same, the short-run aggregate supply curve increases if
a) wages increase.
b) climatic conditions decrease.
c) the labour force increases.
d) raw material prices increase.
e) the capital stock falls.

24.47
Correct: e)
Difficulty: 3
Page(s): 626
Scramble range: All
Topic: Shifts of the *SAS* curve

24.47
All else the same, the short-run aggregate supply curve decreases if
a) raw material prices decrease.
b) the composition of GDP changes slowly.
c) wages fall.
d) climatic conditions improve.
e) the composition of GDP changes quickly.

24.48
Correct: a)
Difficulty: 3
Page(s): 626
Scramble range: All
Topic: Shifts of *SAS* and *LAS*

24.48
Which one, if any, of the following events will shift the short-run aggregate supply curve but not the long-run aggregate supply curve?
a) A change in raw material prices.
b) Changes in the capital stock.
c) Technological changes.
d) A change in labour supply.
e) There are no events that will satisfy this question.

24.49
Correct: c)
Difficulty: 3
Page(s): 626
Scramble range: All
Topic: Shifts of *SAS* and *LAS*

24.49
If new environmental and safety regulations are enacted, then
a) the aggregate demand curve will decrease.
b) the short-run aggregate supply curve will decrease but the long-run aggregate supply curve will not.
c) both the short-run and long-run aggregate supply curves will decrease.
d) both the short-run and long-run aggregate supply curves will increase.
e) the long-run aggregate supply curve will decrease, but not the short-run aggregate supply curve.

24.50
Correct: b)
Difficulty: 3
Page(s): 626
Scramble range: All
Topic: Shifts of *SAS* and *LAS*

24.50
Suppose that there is an increase in the capital stock. As a result,
a) the *SAS* and the *LAS* curves will both shift to the left. The horizontal distance between the two *SAS* curves and the two LAS curves is the same.
b) the *SAS* and the *LAS* curves will both shift to the right. The horizontal distance between the two *SAS* curves and the two *LAS* curves is the same.
c) the *SAS* curve remains in the same position but the *LAS* curve shifts to the right.
d) the *SAS* curve remains in the same position but the *LAS* curve shifts to the left.
e) the *SAS* will shift right, but the *LAS* stays in the same position.

24.51
Correct: e)
Difficulty: 2
Page(s): 627
Scramble range: All
Topic: *AD/AS* model

24.51
In the aggregate demand/aggregate supply model of the economy, the quantity produced and purchased in the final goods and services market represents
a) nominal GDP.
b) the real quantity of money.
c) the real interest rate.
d) real consumption.
e) real GDP.

24.52
Correct: a)
Difficulty: 3
Page(s): 627
Scramble range: All
Topic: *AD/AS* model

24.52
In the aggregate demand/aggregate supply model of the economy in which the intersection between *AD* and *SAS* is to the right of *LAS*, we will likely experience
a) an increase in the price level.
b) falling resource prices.
c) falling raw material prices.
d) increasing taxes.
e) a shift to the right in the *LAS*.

24.53
Correct: c)
Difficulty: 3
Page(s): 627
Scramble range: All
Topic: Equilibrium in the *AD/AS* model

24.53
Within the aggregate demand/aggregate supply model, if there is excess supply present at the current price level
a) the natural rate of unemployment will rise.
b) government expenditures will rise.
c) the price level will decline.
d) the actual unemployment rate will be less than its natural rate.
e) output will fall.

24.54
Correct: e)
Difficulty: 3
Page(s): 631
Scramble range: All
Topic: Short–run aggregate supply

24.54
In the short-run, an increase in the price level will result in
a) an increase in the purchasing power of money.
b) an increase in wages.
c) an increase in resource prices and a reduction in profit margins, which in turn will lead to a decline in output.
d) an increase in the natural rate of unemployment.
e) an improvement in profit margins since major components of producers' costs are fixed in the short run.

24.55
Correct: d)
Difficulty: 4
Page(s): 629
Scramble range: All
Topic: Long-run adjustment

24.55
Once producers, workers, consumers, and other decision makers fully adjust to an unexpected increase in the price level,
a) the natural rate of unemployment will decrease.
b) the profit margins of producers' will increase beyond their normal levels.
c) producers will expand output beyond the economy's potential capacity.
d) the factors that contributed to a temporary expansion in output are no longer present.
e) the rate of unemployment will always fall.

24.56
Correct: d)
Difficulty: 3
Page(s): 628
Scramble range: All
Topic: Natural rate/full employment

24.56
When the actual rate of unemployment is equal to the natural rate of unemployment, then the
a) anticipated level of inflation must be zero.
b) long-run aggregate supply curve is upward sloping.
c) short-run aggregate supply curve is vertical.
d) economy is operating at its long-run capacity output level.
e) wages will rise.

24.57
Correct: b)
Difficulty: 3
Page(s): 628
Scramble range: All
Topic: Long–run capacity/natural rate

24.57
When an economy is operating at its long-run capacity output rate
a) the actual rate of inflation will be greater than the anticipated rate of inflation.
b) the actual rate of unemployment will equal the natural rate of unemployment.
c) unemployment will fall to an unusually low rate that is not likely to last into the future.
d) the aggregate quantity demanded will exceed the aggregate quantity supplied.
e) inflation must be positive.

24.58
Correct: a)
Difficulty: 3
Page(s): 626
Scramble range: All
Topic: Short–run fluctuation/natural rate

24.58
An unexpected increase in the price level, which results in a temporary reduction in the purchasing power of wages, can
a) result in an actual unemployment rate that is temporarily less than the natural rate of unemployment.
b) result in an actual rate of unemployment that is temporarily greater than the natural rate of unemployment.
c) increase the natural rate of unemployment.
d) decrease the natural rate of unemployment.
e) decrease both the actual and natural rate of unemployment.

24.59
Correct: c)
Difficulty: 4
Page(s): 622
Scramble range: All
Topic: Long-run capacity

24.59
An output rate in the goods and services market can last into the future
a) when aggregate demand and short-run aggregate supply intersect.
b) only when the purchasing power of wages is falling.
c) only when aggregate demand and short-run aggregate supply intersect the long-run aggregate supply curve at the same price level.
d) only when the money supply is increasing and taxes are reduced.
e) only when long-run aggregate supply is increasing as fast as aggregate demand.

24.60
Correct: b)
Difficulty: 2
Page(s): 628
Scramble range: All
Topic: Equilibrium GDP

24.60
Refer to Figure 24.1. Equilibrium real GDP in Econoworld is
a) $360 billion.
b) $400 billion.
c) $440 billion.
d) $480 billion.
e) $520 billion.

Figure 24.1 Aggregate demand (*AD*), short-run aggregate supply (*SAS*), and long-run aggregate supply (*LAS*) curves for Econoworld

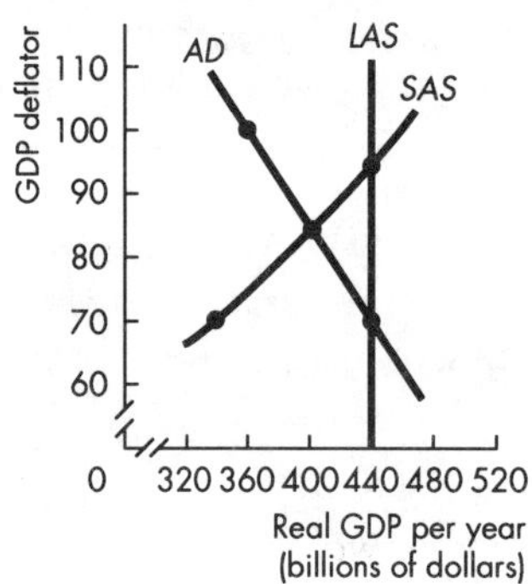

24.61
Correct: e)
Difficulty: 2
Page(s): 628
Scramble range: All
Topic: Equilibrium price level

24.61
Refer to Figure 24.1. When the economy of Econoworld is in equilibrium, the price level is
a) 100.
b) 90.
c) 75.
d) 70.
e) 85.

24.62
Correct: a)
Difficulty: 4
Page(s): 628–629
Scramble range: All
Topic: Disequilibrium real GDP

24.62
Refer to Figure 24.1. If the price level of Econoworld is currently equal to 100, then there is
a) a surplus of real GDP equal to $80 billion.
b) a shortage of real GDP equal to $80 billion.
c) no shortage or surplus.
d) a surplus of real GDP equal to $40 billion.
e) a shortage of real GDP equal to $40 billion.

24.63
Correct: e)
Difficulty: 4
Page(s): 628–629
Scramble range: All
Topic: Disequilibrium real GDP

24.63
Refer to Figure 24.1. If the price level of Econoworld is currently equal to 70, then there is
a) a surplus of real GDP equal to $100 billion.
b) a shortage of real GDP equal to $60 billion.
c) no shortage or surplus.
d) a surplus of real GDP equal to $60 billion.
e) a shortage of real GDP equal to $100 billion.

24.64
Correct: c)
Difficulty: 4
Page(s): 628–629
Scramble range: All
Topic: Above full-employment equilibrium

24.64
Refer to Figure 24.1. In Econoworld there is a difference between the __________ real GDP and capacity output of $__________ billion per year.
a) above full-employment equilibrium; 40
b) above full-employment equilibrium; 20
c) unemployment equilibrium; 40
d) unemployment equilibrium; 20
e) full-employment equilibrium; 0

24.65
Correct: a)
Difficulty: 3
Page(s): 629
Scramble range: All
Topic: Long-run adjustment

24.65
Refer to Figure 24.1. As Econoworld automatically adjusts to long-run equilibrium,
a) *SAS* increases.
b) *AD* increases.
c) *SAS* decreases.
d) *AD* decreases.
e) *LAS* decreases.

24.66
Correct: e)
Difficulty: 4
Page(s): 629
Scramble range: None
Topic: Long-run equilibrium

24.66
Refer to Figure 24.1. If Econoworld automatically adjusts to a long-run equilibrium,
a) the price level will be 70.
b) real GDP will be $440 billion.
c) actual unemployment will exceed the natural rate of unemployment.
d) capacity output will be greater than actual GDP.
e) both a) and b).

24.67
Correct: b)
Difficulty: 4
Page(s): 628–630
Scramble range: All
Topic: Short-run versus long-run equilibrium

24.67
Refer to Figure 24.1. Consider statements 1 and 2 to choose the correct letter. (1) The economy of Econoworld is experiencing an above full-employment equilibrium. (2) The *SAS* will automatically increase as the economy adjusts to long-run equilibrium.
a) 1 is true; 2 is false.
b) 2 is true; 1 is false.
c) 1 and 2 are false.
d) 1 and 2 are true.
e) 1 is true; 2 is true if unemployment is below the natural rate.

24.68
Correct: a)
Difficulty: 4
Page(s): 628–630
Scramble range: All
Topic: Natural rate/long-run adjustment

24.68
Refer to Figure 24.1. Consider statements 1 and 2 to choose the correct letter. (1) Actual unemployment exceeds the natural rate of unemployment. (2) Aggregate supply will automatically decrease as the economy adjusts to long-run equilibrium.
a) 1 is true; 2 is false.
b) 2 is true; 1 is false.
c) 1 and 2 are false.
d) 1 and 2 are true.
e) 1 is true; 2 is true if wages fall.

24.69
Correct: a)
Difficulty: 4
Page(s): 628–630
Scramble range: All
Topic: Natural versus actual unemployment

24.69
Refer to Figure 24.1. Consider statements 1 and 2 to choose the correct letter. (1) The economy of Econworld is experiencing an unemployment equilibrium. (2) Actual unemployment equals the natural rate of unemployment.

a) 1 is true; 2 is false.
b) 2 is true; 1 is false.
c) 1 and 2 are false.
d) 1 and 2 are true.
e) 1 is true; 2 is true if the natural rate of unemployment is too high.

24.70
Correct: d)
Difficulty: 2
Page(s): 628–629
Scramble range: All
Topic: Equilibrium GDP

24.70
Refer to Figure 24.2. Equilibrium real GDP in Mythlo is $__________ billion.

a) 500
b) 650
c) 550
d) 600
e) 475

Figure 24.2 Aggregate demand (*AD*), short-run aggregate supply (*SAS*), and long-run aggregate supply (*LAS*) curves for Mythlo

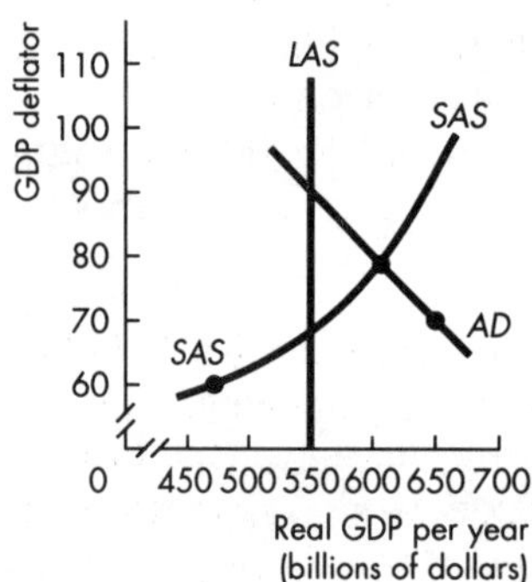

24.71
Correct: e)
Difficulty: 2
Page(s): 628
Scramble range: All
Topic: Equilibrium price level

24.71
Refer to Figure 24.2. When the economy of Mythlo is in equilibrium, the price level is

a) 65.
b) 95.
c) 70.
d) 75.
e) 80.

24.72
Correct: a)
Difficulty: 3
Page(s): 628–629
Scramble range: All
Topic: Equilibrium real GDP/capacity output

24.72
Refer to Figure 24.2. In Mythlo there is a difference between the __________ equilibrium real GDP and capacity output of $__________ billion per year.

a) above full employment; 50
b) above full employment; 25
c) unemployment; 50
d) unemployment; 25
e) full employment; 0

24.73
Correct: c)
Difficulty: 3
Page(s): 629
Scramble range: All
Topic: Long-run adjustment

24.73
Refer to Figure 24.2. As the economy of Mythlo automatically adjusts to long-run equilibrium,
a) *SAS* increases.
b) *AD* increases.
c) *SAS* decreases.
d) *AD* decreases.
e) *LAS* increases.

24.74
Correct: b)
Difficulty: 2
Page(s): 628–630
Scramble range: All
Topic: Actual versus natural unemployment

24.74
Refer to Figure 24.2. Currently in Mythlo
a) there is an unemployment equilibrium.
b) actual unemployment is less than the natural rate of unemployment.
c) capacity output is greater than equilibrium GDP.
d) actual unemployment is equal to the natural rate of unemployment.
e) there is a recessionary gap.

24.75
Correct: c)
Difficulty: 3
Page(s): 625–626
Scramble range: All
Topic: Aggregate quantity supplied/price level

24.75
Refer to Figure 24.2. If the price level is 60 in Mythlo, then
a) the economy is in long-run equilibrium.
b) the aggregate quantity purchased is $650 billion in real GDP.
c) the aggregate quantity supplied is $475 billion of real GDP.
d) widespread surpluses are present.
e) the aggregate quantity supplied is $600 billion of real GDP.

24.76
Correct: b)
Difficulty: 3
Page(s): 627
Scramble range: All
Topic: Aggregate quantity demanded

24.76
Refer to Figure 24.2. If the price level is 70 in Mythlo, then
a) the economy is in long-run equilibrium.
b) the aggregate quantity demanded is $650 billion in real GDP.
c) the aggregate quantity supplied is $550 billion of real GDP.
d) widespread surpluses are present.
e) the aggregate quantity supplied is $650 billion of real GDP.

24.77
Correct: a)
Difficulty: 4
Page(s): 629
Scramble range: All
Topic: Long-run adjustment

24.77
Refer to Figure 24.2. If the economy of Mythlo automatically adjusts to a long-run equilibrium, then
a) the price level will be approximately 90.
b) real GDP will be $600 billion.
c) actual unemployment will exceed the natural rate of unemployment.
d) capacity output will be greater than actual GDP.
e) *SAS* will increase.

24.78
Correct: a)
Difficulty: 4
Page(s): 628
Scramble range: All
Topic: Full-employment equilibrium

24.78
Refer to Figure 24.2. Consider statements 1 and 2 to choose the correct answer. (1) The economy of Mythlo is experiencing an above full-employment equilibrium. (2) The *SAS* will automatically increase as the economy adjusts to long-run equilibrium.
a) 1 is true; 2 is false.
b) 2 is true; 1 is false.
c) 1 and 2 are false.
d) 1 and 2 are true.
e) 1 is true; 2 is true only if *LAS* increases too.

24.79
Correct: c)
Difficulty: 4
Page(s): 628–630
Scramble range: All
Topic: Natural versus actual unemployment

24.79
Refer to Figure 24.2. Consider statements 1 and 2 to choose the correct answer. (1) Actual unemployment exceeds the natural rate of unemployment. (2) The *SAS* automatically increases as the economy adjusts to long-run equilibrium.
a) 1 is true; 2 is false.
b) 2 is true; 1 is false.
c) 1 and 2 are false.
d) 1 and 2 are true.
e) 1 is false; 2 is true if *LAS* increases too.

24.80 (SG 24.1)
Correct: a)
Difficulty: 2
Page(s): 615
Scramble range: All
Topic: Aggregate demand curve

24.80
The aggregate demand curve (*AD*) illustrates that, as the price level falls, the quantity of
a) real GDP demanded increases.
b) real GDP demanded decreases.
c) nominal GDP demanded increases.
d) nominal GDP demanded decreases.
e) real balances fall.

24.81 (SG 24.2)
Correct: c)
Difficulty: 2
Page(s): 616
Scramble range: a)–d)
Topic: Negative slope of the *AD* curve

24.81
Which of the following is *not* a reason for the downward slope of the aggregate demand curve?
a) The intertemporal substitution effect.
b) The international substitution effect.
c) The expected inflation effect.
d) The real balance effect.
e) None of the above is a reason for the downward slope of the *AD* curve.

24.82 (SG 24.3)
Correct: d)
Difficulty: 3
Page(s): 616
Scramble range: All
Topic: Real money and *AD* curve

24.82
As the price level rises, the quantity of real money
a) increases and thus the aggregate quantity of goods and services demanded increases.
b) increases and thus the aggregate quantity of goods and services demanded decreases.
c) decreases and thus the aggregate quantity of goods and services demanded increases.
d) decreases and thus the aggregate quantity of goods and services demanded decreases.
e) decreases and this has no effect on the aggregate quantity of goods and services demanded.

24.83 (SG 24.4)
Correct: e)
Difficulty: 4
Page(s): 617
Scramble range: All
Topic: Quantity of money

24.83
As the quantity of real money increases, interest rates
a) become lower, which has no impact on the quantity of real GDP demanded.
b) become lower, which leads to a decrease in the quantity of real GDP demanded.
c) become higher, which leads to an increase in the quantity of real GDP demanded.
d) become higher, which leads to a decrease in the quantity of real GDP demanded.
e) become lower, which leads to an increase in the quantity of real GDP demanded.

24.84 (SG 24.5)
Correct: b)
Difficulty: 2
Page(s): 620
Scramble range: All
Topic: *AD* shifts

24.84
Which of the following will cause the aggregate demand curve to shift to the right?
a) An increase in interest rates (at a given price level).
b) An increase in expected inflation.
c) An increase in taxes.
d) A decrease in the price level.
e) An increase in the price level.

24.85 (SG 24.6)
Correct: e)
Difficulty: 3
Page(s): 634
Scramble range: All
Topic: Say's Law

24.85
Say's Law argues that
a) wages do not adjust to determine employment.
b) interest rates do not adjust to ensure equality between saving and investment.
c) there is a distinct difference between the short run and the long run in macroeconomics.
d) the *AS* curve is perfectly flat.
e) supply creates its own demand.

24.86 (SG 24.7)
Correct: d)
Difficulty: 3
Page(s): 622
Scramble range: All
Topic: Full employment and *LAS*

24.86
Long-run aggregate supply is the level of real GDP at which
a) each firm is producing its capacity output.
b) there is full employment.
c) the economy is producing its physical limit.
d) each firm is producing its capacity output and there is full employment.
e) prices are sure to rise.

24.87 (SG 24.8)
Correct: e)
Difficulty: 2
Page(s): 623
Scramble range: All
Topic: Short-run aggregate supply

24.87
Short-run aggregate supply is the relationship between the price level and the quantity of real GDP supplied, holding constant the
a) wage rate.
b) quantities of factors of production.
c) level of government spending.
d) price level.
e) prices of factors of production.

24.88 (SG 24.9)
Correct: b)
Difficulty: 2
Page(s): 626
Scramble range: All
Topic: *SAS* curve

24.88
The short-run aggregate supply curve (*SAS*) is positively sloped but becomes vertical at the level of real GDP at which
a) each firm is producing its capacity output.
b) each firm is producing output at its physical limit.
c) there is full employment.
d) it intersects the aggregate demand curve.
e) hyperinflation starts.

24.89 (SG 24.10)
Correct: e)
Difficulty: 3
Page(s): 626
Scramble range: All
Topic: Shifts of the *AS* curves

24.89
A technological improvement will shift
a) both the short-run aggregate supply and the aggregate demand curves to the right, with the long-run aggregate supply curve unchanged.
b) both the short-run aggregate supply and long-run aggregate supply curves to the left.
c) the short-run aggregate supply curve to the right but leave the long-run aggregate supply curve unchanged.
d) the long-run aggregate supply curve to the right but leave the short-run aggregate supply curve unchanged.
e) both the short-run aggregate supply and long-run aggregate supply curves to the right.

24.90 (SG 24.11)
Correct: c)
Difficulty: 3
Page(s): 626
Scramble range: All
Topic: *SAS* curve

24.90
A decrease in wages will shift
a) both the short-run aggregate supply and long-run aggregate supply curves right.
b) both the short-run aggregate supply and long-run aggregate supply curves left.
c) the short-run aggregate supply curve right, but leave the long-run aggregate supply curve unchanged.
d) the long-run aggregate supply curve right, but leave the short-run aggregate supply curve unchanged.
e) the short-run aggregate supply curve left, but leave the long-run aggregate supply curve unchanged.

24.91 (SG 24.12)
Correct: d)
Difficulty: 4
Page(s): 627
Scramble range: All
Topic: Macroeconomic equilibrium

24.91
Macroeconomic equilibrium occurs when the
a) economy is at full employment.
b) economy is producing at its physical limit.
c) aggregate demand curve intersects the short-run aggregate supply curve along its vertical portion.
d) quantity of real GDP demanded equals the quantity of real GDP supplied.
e) aggregate demand curve intersects the long-run aggregate supply curve.

24.92 (SG 24.13)
Correct: a)
Difficulty: 2
Page(s): 628
Scramble range: All
Topic: Unemployment equilibrium

24.92
Which of the graphs in Figure 24.3 illustrates an unemployment equilibrium?
a) (a).
b) (b).
c) (c).
d) (d).
e) Both (c) and (d).

Figure 24.3

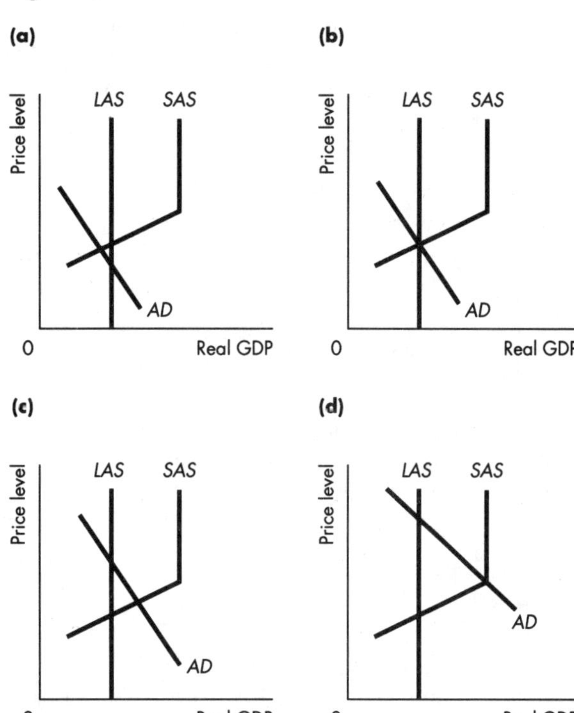

24.93 (SG 24.14)
Correct: e)
Difficulty: 2
Page(s): 629
Scramble range: All
Topic: Full-employment equilibrium

24.93
Which of the graphs in Figure 24.3 illustrates an above full-employment equilibrium?
a) (a).
b) (b).
c) (c).
d) (d).
e) Both (c) and (d).

24.94 (SG 24.15)
Correct: c)
Difficulty: 3
Page(s): 629
Scramble range: All
Topic: Above full-employment equilibrium

24.94
If real GDP is greater than long-run aggregate supply, then the economy is
a) not in macroeconomic equilibrium.
b) in a full-employment equilibrium.
c) in an above full-employment equilibrium.
d) in an unemployment equilibrium.
e) in long-run equilibrium.

24.95 (SG 24.16)
Correct: a)
Difficulty: 4
Page(s): 630
Scramble range: All
Topic: Increasing *AD*

24.95
If input prices remain constant and firms are producing at levels less than their physical limits, an increase in aggregate demand will cause
a) an increase in the price level and an increase in real GDP.
b) an increase in the price level and a decrease in real GDP.
c) a decrease in the price level and an increase in real GDP.
d) a decrease in the price level and a decrease in real GDP.
e) an increase in the price level, but no change in real GDP.

24.96 (SG 24.17)
Correct: c)
Difficulty: 4
Page(s): 630
Scramble range: All
Topic: Shifts of the *SAS*

24.96
We observe an increase in the price level and a decrease in real GDP. Which of the following is a possible explanation?
a) The expectation of future profits has increased.
b) Aggregate wealth has decreased.
c) The price of raw materials has increased.
d) The stock of capital has increased.
e) The money supply has increased.

24.97 (SG 24.18)
Correct: e)
Difficulty: 4
Page(s): 630
Scramble range: All
Topic: *AD* shifts

24.97
We observe an increase in the price level and an increase in real GDP. Which of the following is a possible explanation?
a) The money supply has fallen.
b) Aggregate wealth has decreased.
c) The price of raw materials has increased.
d) The stock of capital has increased.
e) The expectation of future profits has increased.

24.98 (SG 24.19)
Correct: d)
Difficulty: 4
Page(s): 630–631
Scramble range: All
Topic: Long-run adjustment

24.98
The economy cannot stay at a level of real GDP above long-run aggregate supply because input prices will
a) fall, thus shifting the long-run aggregate supply curve right.
b) fall, thus shifting the short-run aggregate supply curve right.
c) rise, thus shifting the long-run aggregate supply curve left.
d) rise, thus shifting the short-run aggregate supply curve left.
e) rise, thus shifting the short-run aggregate supply curve right.

24.99 (SG 24.20)
Correct: b)
Difficulty: 4
Page(s): 633, 636
Scramble range: All
Topic: Business cycles and the*AD/AS* model

24.99
The fact that the short-run aggregate supply and aggregate demand curves do not shift at a fixed, steady pace explains why we observe
a) persistent inflation.
b) business cycles.
c) trend growth in real GDP.
d) large government budget deficits.
e) persistent unemployment.

24.100
Correct: e)
Difficulty: 3
Page(s): 635
Scramble range: All
Topic: Keynesian macroeconomics

24.100
The key difference between classical macroeconomics and Keynesian macroeconomics is his argument
a) that supply creates its own demand.
b) that the demand for labour and the supply of labour interact to decide the level of wages.
c) that there is a flat long-run aggregate supply curve.
d) that there is a vertical long-run aggregate supply curve.
e) of the principle of effective demand.

24.101
Correct: b)
Difficulty: 2
Page(s): 616
Scramble range: All
Topic: Negative slope of the *AD* curve

24.101
Which one of the following is a reason for the negative slope of the aggregate demand curve?
a) The real wage effect.
b) The international substitution effect.
c) The expected inflation effect.
d) The nominal balance effect.
e) The income effect.

24.102
Correct: a)
Difficulty: 3
Page(s): 616
Scramble range: All
Topic: Real money and the *AD* curve

24.102
As the price level falls, the quantity of real money
a) increases and thus the aggregate quantity of goods and services demanded increases.
b) increases and thus the aggregate quantity of goods and services demanded decreases.
c) decreases and thus the aggregate quantity of goods and services demanded increases.
d) decreases and thus the aggregate quantity of goods and services demanded decreases.
e) decreases and thus the aggregate quantity of goods and services supplied rises.

24.103
Correct: e)
Difficulty: 4
Page(s): 617
Scramble range: a)–d)
Topic: Quantity of money

24.103
As the quantity of real money decreases, interest rates
a) become lower, which leads to an increase in the quantity of real GDP demanded.
b) become lower, which leads to a decrease in the quantity of real GDP demanded.
c) become higher, which leads to an increase in the quantity of real GDP supplied.
d) become higher, which leads to a decrease in the quantity of real GDP supplied.
e) none of the above.

24.104
Correct: c)
Difficulty: 3
Page(s): 620
Scramble range: All
Topic: *AD* shifts

24.104
Which of the following will cause the aggregate demand curve to shift to the left?
a) A decrease in interest rates (at a given price level).
b) An increase in expected inflation.
c) An increase in taxes.
d) An increase in the price level.
e) An increase in the wage rate.

24.105
Correct: e)
Difficulty: 3
Page(s): 634–635
Scramble range: All
Topic: Modern macroeconomics

24.105
Modern macroeconomics (the neoclassical synthesis)
a) ignores the difference between the short run and the long run.
b) believes supply creates its own demand.
c) assumes a vertical aggregate supply curve.
d) assumes a flat aggregate supply curve.
e) is a mixture of the classical model and Keynes' model.

24.106
Correct: e)
Difficulty: 3
Page(s): 636
Scramble range: All
Topic: Free Trade Agreement

24.106
The likely long-run macroeconomic effects of the Canada–United States Free Trade Agreement are
a) a lower inflation rate.
b) a lower growth rate of real GDP.
c) higher growth rates of both prices and real GDP.
d) almost nothing.
e) a higher rate of real GDP and a lower inflation rate.

24.107
Correct: c)
Difficulty: 4
Page(s): 626
Scramble range: All
Topic: Shifts of the *AS* curves

24.107
An increase in oil prices to a country that is a net importer of oil will shift
a) both the short-run aggregate supply and long-run aggregate supply curves to the right.
b) both the short-run aggregate supply and long-run aggregate supply curves to the left.
c) the short-run aggregate supply curve to the left, but leave the long-run aggregate supply curve unchanged.
d) the long-run aggregate supply curve to the right, but leave the short-run aggregate supply curve unchanged.
e) the short-run aggregate supply curve left, but shift the long-run aggregate supply curve right.

24.108
Correct: c)
Difficulty: 3
Page(s): 623
Scramble range: All
Topic: *SAS* curve

24.108
An increase in wages will shift
a) both the short-run aggregate supply and long-run aggregate supply curves right.
b) both the short-run aggregate supply and long-run aggregate supply curves left.
c) the short-run aggregate supply curve left, but leave the long-run aggregate supply curve unchanged.
d) the long-run aggregate supply curve right, but leave the short-run aggregate supply curve unchanged.
e) the short-run aggregate supply curve left, but shift the long-run aggregate supply curve right.

24.109
Correct: d)
Difficulty: 4
Page(s): 628
Scramble range: All
Topic: Unemployment equilibrium

24.109
If real GDP is less than long-run aggregate supply, then more than likely the economy is
a) not in macroeconomic equilibrium.
b) in a full-employment equilibrium.
c) in an above full-employment equilibrium.
d) in an unemployment equilibrium.
e) in long-run equilibrium.

24.110
Correct: d)
Difficulty: 5
Page(s): 626
Scramble range: All
Topic: Shifts in the *SAS*

24.110
Consider Figure 24.3. In which of the graphs would we predict that in the near future prices will rise and real GDP will fall, all else being equal?
a) (a).
b) (d).
c) (b).
d) (c) and (d).
e) (c).

24.111
Correct: e)
Difficulty: 5
Page(s): 626
Scramble range: All
Topic: Shifts in the *SAS*

24.111
Consider Figure 24.3. In which graphs would we predict that price and output would fall?
a) (a).
b) (b).
c) (c).
d) (d).
e) None of the graphs.

24.112
Correct: d)
Difficulty: 5
Page(s): 637
Scramble range: All
Topic: GST

24.112
The likely macroeconomic effects of the goods and services tax (GST) are

a) a fall in aggregate demand, a fall in aggregate supply, and therefore a rise in the inflation rate.
b) a rise in aggregate demand, a fall in aggregate supply, and therefore a rise in the inflation rate.
c) a rise in aggregate demand, a rise in aggregate supply, and therefore an uncertain effect on inflation.
d) a fall in aggregate demand, a rise in aggregate supply, and therefore a fall in the inflation rate.
e) a fall in aggregate demand, a rise in aggregate supply, and therefore a rise in the inflation rate.

Chapter 25 Expenditure Decisions

25.1
Correct: c)
Difficulty: 2
Page(s): 651
Scramble range: All
Topic: Volatile components of *AE*

25.1
The components of aggregate expenditures that fluctuate the most are
a) consumption expenditures and net exports.
b) net exports and government purchases.
c) net exports and investment expenditures.
d) investment expenditures and consumption expenditures.
e) consumption expenditures and government purchases.

25.2
Correct: b)
Difficulty: 2
Page(s): 651
Scramble range: All
Topic: Consumption/investment fluctuations

25.2
Over time, fluctuations in consumption expenditures
a) have a much larger range than those in investment.
b) move in sympathy with fluctuations in investment.
c) move opposite to fluctuations in investment.
d) always follow fluctuations in investment.
e) move inversely to fluctuations in investment.

25.3
Correct: c)
Difficulty: 1
Page(s): 651
Scramble range: All
Topic: Components of *AE*

25.3
The components of aggregate expenditures are consumption expenditures, investment expenditures,
a) government expenditures, and exports.
b) government expenditures, and imports.
c) government purchases, and net exports.
d) and net exports. Only private sector expenditures are included.
e) government purchases, savings, and net exports.

25.4 (SG 25.1)
Correct: a)
Difficulty: 2
Page(s): 651
Scramble range: All
Topic: Relative size of expenditure components

25.4
The largest component of aggregate expenditures is
a) consumption expenditures.
b) government purchases, especially since the 1960s.
c) exports.
d) investment expenditures.
e) savings.

25.5
Correct: b)
Difficulty: 2
Page(s): 654
Scramble range: All
Topic: Disposable income

25.5
Disposable income is
a) used only for consumption purposes.
b) used only for consumption and saving purposes.
c) equal to national income plus transfer payments.
d) not a very important determinant of the level of total consumption expenditures in the economy.
e) equal to national income minus transfer payments.

25.6
Correct: c)
Difficulty: 2
Page(s). 654
Scramble range: All
Topic: Change in expected household income

25.6
If household income is expected to rise, other things being equal, then
a) consumption expenditures will fall.
b) consumption expenditures will remain the same until the expected rise in income actually occurs.
c) consumption expenditures will rise.
d) the government will raise taxes.
e) savings will fall.

25.7
Correct: e)
Difficulty: 1
Page(s): 654
Scramble range: All
Topic: Consumption

25.7
Which of the following items is not a determinant of household consumption?
a) Degree of patience of the household.
b) Expected future income.
c) Interest rates.
d) Stage in life of the household.
e) Depreciation of capital.

25.8
Correct: b)
Difficulty: 2
Page(s): 654
Scramble range: All
Topic: Consumption function

25.8
The consumption function depicts the relationship between the
a) level of saving and the level of disposable income.
b) level of consumption and the level of disposable income.
c) level of consumption and the level of saving.
d) level of consumption and the level of real GDP.
e) change in consumption and the change in real GDP.

25.9
Correct: d)
Difficulty: 3
Page(s): 655
Scramble range: All
Topic: Dissaving

25.9
Dissaving occurs when a household
a) spends less than it receives in disposable income.
b) spends more than it saves.
c) saves more than it spends.
d) consumes more than it receives in disposable income.
e) borrows.

25.10
Correct: c)
Difficulty: 2
Page(s): 655
Scramble range: All
Topic: Household choice/disposable income

25.10
A household can
a) only consume or pay taxes out of disposable income.
b) only consume, save, or pay taxes out of disposable income.
c) only consume or save out of disposable income.
d) consume out of disposable income.
e) save out of disposable income and consume out of income.

25.11
Correct: c)
Difficulty: 2
Page(s): 656
Scramble range: All
Topic: Average propensity to consume

25.11
The average propensity to consume is measured as
a) total consumption divided by total saving.
b) total consumption divided by the change in disposable income.
c) total consumption divided by total disposable income.
d) total consumption plus saving divided by total disposable income.
e) the change in consumption divided by the change in disposable income.

25.12
Correct: b)
Difficulty: 2
Page(s): 656
Scramble range: All
Topic: *APS/APC*

25.12
The average propensity to consume
a) ranges in value between 0 and 1.
b) can be any positive value.
c) added to the average propensity to save must equal zero.
d) subtracted from disposable income must equal one.
e) is less than the marginal propensity to consume.

25.13
Correct: c)
Difficulty: 2
Page(s): 656
Scramble range: All
Topic: Average propensity to save

25.13
The average propensity to save is the ratio of
a) total saving to total consumption.
b) total saving to total GDP.
c) total saving to total disposable income.
d) total saving to total consumption.
e) the change in saving to the change in disposable income.

25.14
Correct: a)
Difficulty: 3
Page(s): 656
Scramble range: All
Topic: Average propensity to consume

25.14
As disposable income increases, the average propensity to consume
a) falls.
b) rises.
c) remains the same.
d) falls until it reaches a minimum at 1 and then begins to rise again.
e) rises until it reaches a maximum of 1 and then begins to fall again.

25.15
Correct: b)
Difficulty: 3
Page(s): 656
Scramble range: All
Topic: Average propensity to save

25.15
As disposable income increases, the average propensity to save
a) falls.
b) rises.
c) remains the same.
d) falls until it reaches a minimum at 1 and then begins to rise again.
e) rises until it reaches a maximum of 1 and then begins to fall again.

25.16
Correct: d)
Difficulty: 2
Page(s): 657
Scramble range: All
Topic: Marginal propensity to consume

25.16
The marginal propensity to consume refers to the
a) fraction of the first dollar of disposable income saved.
b) fraction of the first dollar of disposable income consumed.
c) fraction of the last dollar received that is saved.
d) fraction of the last dollar received that is consumed.
e) total amount of consumption over the total amount of disposable income.

25.17
Correct: e)
Difficulty: 2
Page(s): 657
Scramble range: All
Topic: Marginal propensity to consume

25.17
The marginal propensity to consume is calculated as
a) total consumption divided by the change in disposable income.
b) the change in total consumption divided by disposable income.
c) total consumption divided by total disposable income.
d) the change in total consumption divided by saving.
e) the change in total consumption divided by the change in total disposable income.

25.18
Correct: d)
Difficulty: 2
Page(s): 657
Scramble range: All
Topic: Marginal propensity to save

25.18
The marginal propensity to save is calculated as
a) total saving divided by total disposable income.
b) total saving divided by the change in total disposable income.
c) the change in total saving divided by the change in total consumption.
d) the change in total saving divided by the change in total disposable income.
e) the change in total saving divided by total disposable income.

25.19
Correct: a)
Difficulty: 3
Page(s): 657
Scramble range: All
Topic: Marginal propensity to consume/save

25.19
The marginal propensity to save plus the
a) marginal propensity to consume equals 1.
b) marginal propensity to consume equals 0.
c) average propensity to consume equals 1.
d) average propensity to consume equals 0.
e) marginal propensity to tax equals 1.

25.20
Correct: e)
Difficulty: 2
Page(s): 657
Scramble range: All
Topic: Marginal propensity to consume

25.20
The marginal propensity to consume
a) can take on a negative value only if dissaving is present.
b) must take on a value that is greater than 1.
c) must take on a value that is between 1/2 and 1.
d) must take on a value that is greater than 1 but less than 2.
e) must take on a value that is between 0 and 1.

25.21
Correct: e)
Difficulty: 2
Page(s): 657
Scramble range: All
Topic: Marginal propensity to save

25.21
The marginal propensity to save
a) can take on a negative value only if dissaving is present.
b) must take on a value that is between 0 and 1/2.
c) must take on a value that is greater than 1.
d) must take on a value that is greater than 1 but less than 2.
e) must take on a value that is between 0 and 1.

25.22
Correct: c)
Difficulty: 3
Page(s): 656
Scramble range: All
Topic: Average propensity to consume

25.22
Total consumption divided by disposable income
a) always equals 1.
b) equals saving divided by disposable income.
c) falls as disposable income increases.
d) rises as disposable income increases.
e) plus the marginal propensity to save equals 1.

25.23
Correct: d)
Difficulty: 3
Page(s): 656
Scramble range: All
Topic: *APS/APC*

25.23
If the average propensity to save equals 0, it is true that the
a) average propensity to consume is also 0.
b) marginal propensity to save is also 0.
c) saving function is horizontal.
d) average propensity to consume is 1.
e) marginal propensity to save equals 1.

25.24
Correct: c)
Difficulty: 3
Page(s): 656
Scramble range: All
Topic: Average propensity to consume

25.24
If an economy is operating below the point where consumption expenditures are equal to disposable income, it is true that
a) the average propensity to save is greater than 1.
b) the marginal propensity to consume is greater than 1.
c) the average propensity to consume is greater than 1.
d) induced consumption must be 0.
e) the marginal propensity to save must be negative.

25.25
Correct: d)
Difficulty: 3
Page(s): 655–656
Scramble range: All
Topic: Consumption/disposable income

25.25
The text assumptions concerning consumption and saving include all of the following *except* the
a) marginal propensity to save and the marginal propensity to consume are both positive and less than 1.
b) average propensity to consume falls as disposable income rises.
c) average propensity to save rises as disposable income rises.
d) marginal propensity to consume is negative below the level of disposable income that equals consumption.
e) marginal propensity to save plus the marginal propensity to consume equals one.

25.26
Correct: b)
Difficulty: 3
Page(s): 655
Scramble range: All
Topic: Slope of consumption function

25.26
If a household's disposable income increases from $10,000 to $15,000 and subsequently its consumption expenditures increase from $8,000 to $11,000, then
a) the household is dissaving.
b) the slope of the consumption function is 0.6.
c) the slope of the consumption function is 0.4.
d) the average propensity to consume over this range is negative.
e) the average propensity to save over this range is negative.

25.27
Correct: b)
Difficulty: 3
Page(s): 657–658
Scramble range: All
Topic: Marginal–average relationship

25.27
When the marginal variable is above the average variable, then the
a) average must be falling.
b) average must be rising.
c) average may be rising or falling.
d) average must be constant.
e) marginal must be rising.

25.28
Correct: d)
Difficulty: 3
Page(s): 657–658
Scramble range: All
Topic: Marginal–average relationship

25.28
If the average variable is rising, then the
a) marginal must be rising.
b) marginal must be falling.
c) marginal must be above or equal to the average.
d) marginal must be above the average.
e) average must be above the marginal.

25.29
Correct: a)
Difficulty: 2
Page(s): 654
Scramble range: All
Topic: Consumption schedule

25.29
The consumption schedule can be described as the relationship between
a) consumption decisions of households and the level of disposable income.
b) consumption decisions of households and investment decisions by firms.
c) consumption and saving decisions of households.
d) saving decisions of households and the level of disposable income.
e) consumption decisions of households and the level of real GDP.

25.30
Correct: e)
Difficulty: 4
Page(s): 657
Scramble range: None
Topic: Marginal propensity to consume

25.30
The marginal propensity to consume reveals
a) how much of a given level of disposable income will be consumed.
b) how much of a change in disposable income is likely to be saved.
c) how much consumption will occur at the equilibrium income.
d) how much of a change in disposable income is likely to be consumed.
e) both b) and d).

25.31
Correct: b)
Difficulty: 3
Page(s): 657
Scramble range: All
Topic: Marginal propensity to consume

25.31
If consumption expenditures for a household increase from $500 to $800 when disposable income increases from $400 to $800, the marginal propensity to consume is
a) equal to 1.
b) equal to 0.75.
c) equal to the average propensity to consume.
d) negative.
e) equal to 1.33.

25.32
Correct: d)
Difficulty: 3
Page(s): 657
Scramble range: None
Topic: Marginal propensity to consume

25.32
If the marginal propensity to consume is equal to 0.8, every $10 increase in disposable income is likely to
a) result in an $0.80 increase in consumption expenditures.
b) result in a $10 increase in consumption expenditures.
c) result in a $0.20 increase in saving.
d) result in an $8.00 increase in consumption expenditures.
e) both a) and c).

25.33
Correct: c)
Difficulty: 2
Page(s): 657
Scramble range: All
Topic: Marginal propensity to consume

25.33
If the marginal propensity to consume is equal to 0.9 for an economy, what change in consumption would you expect if disposable income increases by $200 million?
a) $20 million.
b) $200 million.
c) $180 million.
d) $1800 million.
e) $18 million.

25.34
Correct: e)
Difficulty: 4
Page(s): 656
Scramble range: All
Topic: Average propensity to consume

25.34
If consumption is $8,000 when disposable income is $10,000, the marginal propensity to consume
a) is 0.50.
b) is 0.75.
c) is 0.80.
d) is 1.25.
e) cannot be determined from the information given.

25.35
Correct: c)
Difficulty: 3
Page(s): 656
Scramble range: All
Topic: Average propensity to consume

25.35
If consumption is $8,000 when disposable income is $10,000, the average propensity to consume
a) is 0.50.
b) is 0.75.
c) is 0.80.
d) is 1.25.
e) cannot be determined from the information given.

25.36
Correct: a)
Difficulty: 2
Page(s): 656
Scramble range: All
Topic: Average propensity to consume

25.36
The average propensity to consume shows
a) the proportion of a specified level of income that will be spent on consumption.
b) the proportion of any increase in income that will be spent.
c) the relationship between saving and disposable income.
d) that increases in income generally lead to decreases in spending because saving increases.
e) the proportion of any increase in income that will be saved.

25.37
Correct: b)
Difficulty: 3
Page(s): 655
Scramble range: All
Topic: Dissaving

25.37
An average propensity to consume of greater than 1
a) is not possible.
b) indicates that households are dissaving.
c) means the marginal propensity to consume will also be greater than 1.
d) indicates that households desire to increase their saving.
e) indicates that households are saving.

25.38
Correct: c)
Difficulty: 3
Page(s): 654
Scramble range: All
Topic: Consumption function

25.38
Refer to Figure 25.1. Consumption and disposable income are equal at
a) any point along the consumption function.
b) a saving level equal to $40 billion and income equal to $540 billion.
c) an income level of $500 billion.
d) an income level of $600 billion.
e) none of the income levels.

Figure 25.1

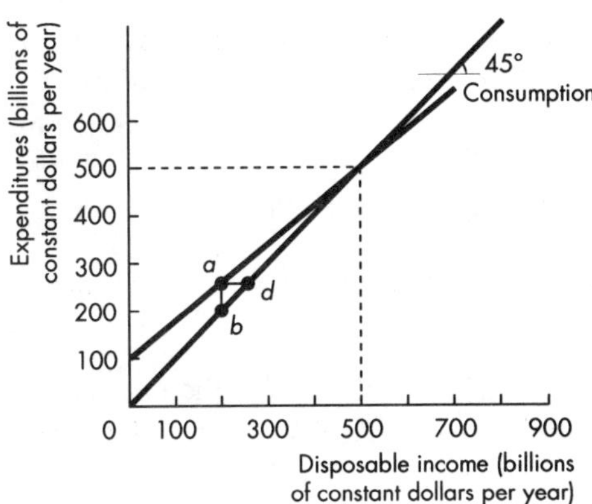

25.39
Correct: b)
Difficulty: 2
Page(s): 654
Scramble range: All
Topic: Consumption function

25.39
Refer to Figure 25.1. At an income level of $500 billion, saving is equal to

a) disposable income.
b) zero.
c) $20 billion.
d) consumption.
e) $40 billion.

25.40
Correct: c)
Difficulty: 2
Page(s): 654
Scramble range: All
Topic: Consumption function

25.40
Refer to Figure 25.1. Consumption spending is equal to disposable income

a) at all points along the consumption function.
b) only when saving is negative.
c) all along the 45° line.
d) when spending is equal to saving.
e) only when saving is positive.

25.41
Correct: d)
Difficulty: 4
Page(s): 654
Scramble range: All
Topic: Consumption function

25.41
Refer to Figure 25.1. When disposable income equals $200 billion

a) saving is equal to line segment *ad*.
b) households are consuming something less that $200 billion.
c) businesses are spending more than households because the consumption function lies above the 45° line.
d) households are dissaving in an amount equal to line segment *ab*.
e) households are saving in an amount equal to line segment *ab*.

25.42
Correct: e)
Difficulty: 4
Page(s): 654
Scramble range: All
Topic: Consumption function

25.42
Refer to Figure 25.1. When disposable income is equal to $200 billion, saving is equal to

a) zero.
b) $200 billion.
c) $150 billion.
d) $50 billion.
e) a dissaving of $75 billion.

25.43
Correct: c)
Difficulty: 3
Page(s): 654
Scramble range: All
Topic: Consumption function

25.43
When the consumption function lies below the 45° line, households
a) spend all of any increase in income.
b) consume more than their disposable income.
c) will be saving some portion of their disposable income.
d) save all of any increase in income.
e) are dissaving.

25.44
Correct: a)
Difficulty: 3
Page(s): 654
Scramble range: All
Topic: Saving

25.44
Refer to Table 25.1. If *YD* is $400, then saving is
a) –$50.
b) $50.
c) zero.
d) $100.
e) –$125.

Table 25.1 The relationship between consumption expenditures (*C*), and disposable income (*YD*) for a hypothetical economy

YD ($)	*C* ($)
100	225
200	300
300	375
400	450
500	525
600	600

25.45
Correct: c)
Difficulty: 3
Page(s): 657
Scramble range: All
Topic: Marginal propensity to consume

25.45
Refer to Table 25.1. The marginal propensity to consume is
a) increasing as *YD* rises.
b) equal to 1.0 when *YD* equals $600.
c) constant at 0.75.
d) constant at 0.25.
e) constant at 1.33.

25.46
Correct: d)
Difficulty: 3
Page(s): 657
Scramble range: All
Topic: Marginal propensity to save

25.46
Refer to Table 25.1. The marginal propensity to save is
a) decreasing as *YD* rises.
b) equal to zero when *YD* equals $600.
c) constant at 0.75.
d) constant at 0.25.
e) constant at 4.

25.47
Correct: b)
Difficulty: 4
Page(s): 654
Scramble range: All
Topic: Consumption

25.47
Refer to Table 25.1. Based on the information in the table, if *YD* were zero, then
a) consumption would be zero.
b) consumption would be $150.
c) saving would be zero.
d) consumption would be –$150.
e) consumption would $100.

25.48
Correct: b)
Difficulty: 5
Page(s): 654
Scramble range: All
Topic: Saving

25.48
Refer to Table 25.1. Based on the information in the table, saving would be $125 if *YD* were
a) $1,000.
b) $1,100.
c) $1,200.
d) $1,300.
e) not enough information is given to calculate the answer.

25.49
Correct: e)
Difficulty: 5
Page(s): 656
Scramble range: All
Topic: Average propensity to consume

25.49
Refer to Table 25.1. If *YD* were $900, the average propensity to consume would be closest to
a) 0.25.
b) 0.75.
c) 0.83.
d) 0.11.
e) 0.92.

25.50
Correct: a)
Difficulty: 2
Page(s): 659
Scramble range: All
Topic: Canadian consumption function

25.50
The time-series consumption function for the Canadian economy covering the period from 1969 to 1988 indicates an average propensity to consume out of disposable income equal to
a) 0.9.
b) 0.6.
c) 0.8.
d) 0.75.
e) 0.54.

25.51
Correct: e)
Difficulty: 3
Page(s): 659
Scramble range: All
Topic: Canadian consumption function

25.51
The marginal propensity to consume for Canada over the time period 1969 to 1988 indicates that consumption rises
a) $0.90 for every dollar rise in real GDP.
b) $0.80 for every dollar rise in real GDP.
c) $0.75 for every dollar rise in real GDP.
d) $0.60 for every dollar rise in real GDP.
e) $0.54 for every dollar rise in real GDP.

25.52
Correct: a)
Difficulty: 3
Page(s): 660
Scramble range: All
Topic: Transfer payments

25.52
In the aggregate consumption function model, transfer payments are treated as if they
a) were the opposite of taxes.
b) did not exist.
c) were consumption.
d) were always the same.
e) were taxes.

25.53
Correct: a)
Difficulty: 2
Page(s): 660
Scramble range: All
Topic: Net taxes and GDP

25.53
All else constant, net taxes
a) increase as GDP rises.
b) remain constant as GDP rises.
c) decrease as GDP rises.
d) decrease as GDP stays the same.
e) increase as GDP falls.

25.54
Correct: c)
Difficulty: 3
Page(s): 660
Scramble range: All
Topic: Net taxes and GDP

25.54
All else constant, which of the following variables does *not* increase as GDP increases?
a) Personal taxes.
b) Corporate taxes.
c) Welfare benefits.
d) Social security taxes.
e) Sales taxes.

25.55
Correct: d)
Difficulty: 3
Page(s): 660
Scramble range: All
Topic: Net taxes and GDP

25.55
All else constant, which of the following variables increases as GDP increases?
a) Government purchases.
b) Transfer payments.
c) Unemployment benefits.
d) Personal income tax payments.
e) Welfare benefits.

25.56
Correct: e)
Difficulty: 3
Page(s): 660
Scramble range: All
Topic: Net tax/aggregate consumption function

25.56
All else constant, which of the following events will cause the aggregate consumption function to shift upward when consumption expenditures are measured out of GDP?
a) An increase in personal taxes.
b) An increase in GDP.
c) A decrease in impatience.
d) A decrease in GDP.
e) An increase in transfer payments.

25.57
Correct: a)
Difficulty: 3
Page(s): 660
Scramble range: All
Topic: Net tax/aggregate consumption function

25.57
All else constant, which of the following events will cause the aggregate consumption function to shift downward when consumption expenditures are measured out of GDP?
a) An increase in personal taxes.
b) An increase in GDP.
c) A decrease in GDP.
d) An increase in transfer payments.
e) A decrease in interest rates.

25.58
Correct: c)
Difficulty: 3
Page(s): 659
Scramble range: All
Topic: *MPC* out of GDP

25.58
If the net tax rate is 50 percent and the marginal propensity to consume (*MPC*) out of disposable income is 0.8, what is the marginal propensity to consume out of GDP?
a) 0.1.
b) 0.2.
c) 0.4.
d) 0.8.
e) 0.5.

25.59
Correct: b)
Difficulty: 2
Page(s): 665
Scramble range: All
Topic: Investment

25.59
Investment is
a) a relatively stable component of GDP.
b) the purchase of new plant, equipment, buildings, and additions to inventories by business firms.
c) a constant fraction of consumption over time in Canada.
d) is generally larger in value than consumption.
e) is generally more stable than consumption.

25.60
Correct: c)
Difficulty: 2
Page(s): 665
Scramble range: All
Topic: Investment

25.60
Which of the following variables is a determinant of investment?
a) Disposable income.
b) Degree of patience.
c) Expected future profit.
d) Expected future income.
e) Foreign income.

25.61
Correct: d)
Difficulty: 2
Page(s): 665
Scramble range: All
Topic: Investment

25.61
Which of the following variables is a determinant of investment?
a) Expected future income.
b) Expected disposable income.
c) Consumption.
d) Interest rates.
e) Appreciation.

25.62
Correct: a)
Difficulty: 2
Page(s): 665
Scramble range: All
Topic: Interest rates/investment

25.62
All else constant, as interest rates fall
a) investment increases.
b) consumption decreases.
c) government purchases increase.
d) investment decreases.
e) net exports rise.

25.63
Correct: b)
Difficulty: 1
Page(s): 665
Scramble range: All
Topic: Real interest rates

25.63
Refer to Figure 25.2. Suppose the economy's planned investment demand is represented initially by the curve labelled Ib. If the real interest rate is 4 percent, then total planned investment is
a) $300 billion.
b) $400 billion.
c) $600 billion.
d) $200 billion.
e) $500 billion.

Figure 25.2 The relationship between the real interest rate and real investments in a hypothetical economy

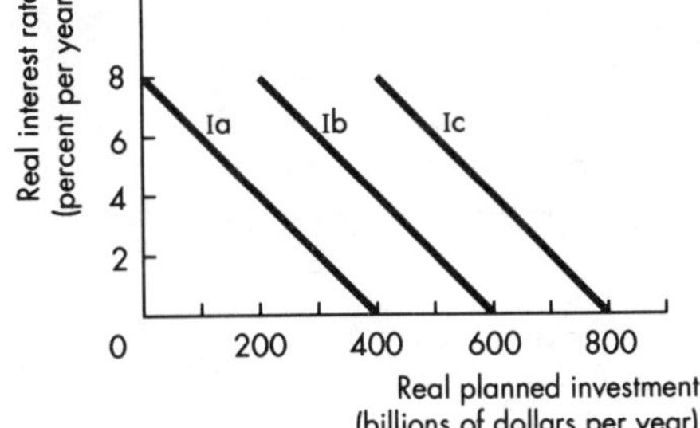

25.64
Correct: b)
Difficulty: 4
Page(s): 666
Scramble range: All
Topic: Investment/ expected inflation

25.64
Refer to Figure 25.2. Suppose the economy's planned investment demand is represented initially by the curve labelled Ib. An increase in expected inflation might be best illustrated by

a) the curve labelled Ia.
b) the curve labelled Ib.
c) none of the curves as the real interest rate is the only relevant shift variable.
d) the curve labelled Ic.
e) either the curve labelled Ia or the curve labelled Ic; it depends on the economy in question.

25.65
Correct: d)
Difficulty: 3
Page(s): 667
Scramble range: All
Topic: Investment/profit expected

25.65
Refer to Figure 25.2. Suppose the economy's planned investment demand is represented initially by the curve labelled Ib. Hold constant the real interest rate at 4 percent to determine the new level of investment if firms believe that sales are expected to fall off. In this case, planned investment will

a) be greater than $400 billion.
b) be greater than $500 billion.
c) be $400 billion.
d) be less than $400 billion.
e) change, but we cannot tell in which direction without more information.

25.66
Correct: d)
Difficulty: 3
Page(s): 667
Scramble range: All
Topic: Expected/ investment demand

25.66
Refer to Figure 25.2. Suppose the economy's planned investment demand is represented initially by the curve labelled Ib. Expectations of booming business conditions could shift the investment demand to

a) the curve labelled Ia.
b) the curve labelled Ib.
c) none of the curves as the real interest rate is the only relevant shift variable.
d) the curve labelled Ic.
e) either the curve labelled Ia or the curve labelled Ic; it depends on the economy in question.

25.67
Correct: a)
Difficulty: 3
Page(s): 665
Scramble range: All
Topic: Investment determinants

25.67
All else the same, investment by business firms will be higher

a) the higher the expected sales of the firm and the lower the rate of interest.
b) the lower the expected sales of the firm and the higher the rate of interest.
c) the higher the expected sales of the firm and the rate of interest.
d) the lower the expected sales of the firm and the rate of interest.
e) the lower the depreciation rate on capital.

25.68
Correct: c)
Difficulty: 3
Page(s): 665
Scramble range: All
Topic: Interest rates/investment

25.68
Which of the following would be the most likely cause of an increase in investment in plant and equipment?

a) A decline in the rate of technological advance.
b) A decrease in GDP.
c) A decrease in the real rate of interest.
d) A decline in the level of profits.
e) A decline in the depreciation rate.

25.69
Correct: c)
Difficulty: 3
Page(s): 669
Scramble range: All
Topic: Accelerator principle

25.69
According to the accelerator principle, net investment will increase whenever
a) sales are increasing.
b) sales are held constant.
c) sales are increasing quickly.
d) there is replacement of worn out capital along with the new investment in the economy.
e) sales are decreasing.

25.70
Correct: a)
Difficulty: 3
Page(s): 669
Scramble range: All
Topic: Accelerator principle

25.70
The accelerator principle differs from other theories of investment in that
a) investment is seen as related to how quickly or slowly GDP changes.
b) investment is seen as related to the level of GDP.
c) GDP is related to the level of investment.
d) investment is related to changes in the interest rate.
e) investment is related to changes in the rate of depreciation.

25.71
Correct: b)
Difficulty: 2
Page(s): 665
Scramble range: All
Topic: Investment determinants

25.71
Which of the following items are not components of planned investment expenditures?
a) Technological change and innovation.
b) The average size and age composition of typical households.
c) Expectations about the business climate.
d) Real interest rates.
e) Expectations about inflation.

25.72
Correct: a)
Difficulty: 2
Page(s): 654
Scramble range: All
Topic: Saving

25.72
Refer to Table 25.2. When *S* is zero, what is the level of *YD*?
a) $325.
b) $400.
c) $475.
d) $550.
e) $625.

Table 25.2

Disposable income *YD* ($)	Consumption *C* ($)
325	325
400	375
475	425
550	475
625	525

25.73
Correct: e)
Difficulty: 4
Page(s): 657
Scramble range: All
Topic: Marginal propensity to consume

25.73
Refer to Table 25.2. What is the value of the marginal propensity to consume?
a) 0.75.
b) 0.25.
c) 1.33.
d) 0.34.
e) 0.67.

25.74
Correct: d)
Difficulty: 4
Page(s): 657
Scramble range: All
Topic: Marginal propensity to save

25.74
Refer to Table 25.2. What is the value of the marginal propensity to save?
a) 0.27.
b) 0.25.
c) 0.67.
d) 0.33.
e) 1.33.

25.75
Correct: a)
Difficulty: 4
Page(s): 654
Scramble range: All
Topic: Consumption

25.75
Refer to Table 25.2. The average propensity to consume at disposable income equal to $425
a) is more than the marginal propensity to consume.
b) is equal to 0.67.
c) cannot be determined without more information.
d) is approximately 0.98.
e) is approximately 0.75.

25.76
Correct: e)
Difficulty: 5
Page(s): 654
Scramble range: All
Topic: Saving

25.76
Refer to Table 25.2. If the average propensity to consume is 0.82 at disposable income equal to $700, consumption is
a) $525.
b) $744.
c) $416.
d) $500.
e) $575.

25.77
Correct: b)
Difficulty: 4
Page(s): 654
Scramble range: All
Topic: Saving

25.77
Refer to Table 25.2. Saving will be equal to $75 at disposable income equal to
a) $475.
b) $550.
c) $525.
d) $575.
e) $625.

25.78
Correct: e)
Difficulty: 4
Page(s): 654
Scramble range: All
Topic: Saving
562

25.78
Refer to Table 25.2. If the average propensity to consume is 0.82 at disposable income equal to $700, saving must be
a) $50.
b) $100.
c) $150.
d) $175.
e) $125.

25.79
Correct: d)
Difficulty: 1
Page(s): 674
Scramble range: All
Topic: Imports

25.79
Imports are
a) goods that are produced in Canada and sold to the rest of the world.
b) taxes on goods produced in foreign countries.
c) goods that are produced in foreign countries that count toward Canadian GDP.
d) goods that are produced in foreign countries and sold in Canada.
e) goods that are produced in foreign countries and sold in foreign countries.

25.80
Correct: e)
Difficulty: 3
Page(s): 671, 674
Scramble range: All
Topic: Exports

25.80
The level of exports in Canada depends directly on the
a) level of GDP in Canada.
b) level of investment in Canada.
c) level of production in Canada.
d) level of consumption in Canada.
e) degree of international specialization.

25.81
Correct: b)
Difficulty: 2
Page(s): 671, 674
Scramble range: All
Topic: Exports

25.81
Which of the following factors does *not* influence the level of Canadian exports?
a) The level of GDP in the rest of the world.
b) The level of GDP in Canada.
c) The foreign exchange rate.
d) The prices of Canadian-made goods relative to the prices of similar goods made in foreign countries.
e) The degree of international specialization.

25.82
Correct: d)
Difficulty: 3
Page(s): 674
Scramble range: All
Topic: Export demand

25.82
All else constant, the higher the level of income in foreign countries,
a) the lower the demand for Canadian exports.
b) the lower the demand for imports in Canada.
c) the higher the demand for imports in Canada.
d) the higher the demand for Canadian exports.
e) the lower the demand for Canadian net exports.

25.83
Correct: a)
Difficulty: 3
Page(s): 674
Scramble range: All
Topic: Export demand

25.83
When the value of the Canadian dollar falls relative to the value of foreign currencies, all else constant,
a) the demand for Canadian exports will rise.
b) the demand for Canadian exports will fall.
c) the demand for Canadian exports will be unaffected.
d) the Bank of Canada is obligated by law to buy dollars.
e) the Bank of Canada is obligated by law to sell dollars.

25.84
Correct: c)
Difficulty: 2
Page(s): 674
Scramble range: All
Topic: Net export function

25.84
The net export function shows the relationship between
a) net exports and foreign real income.
b) exports and imports.
c) net exports and Canadian real GDP.
d) imports and Canadian real GDP.
e) exports and Canadian real GDP.

25.85
Correct: a)
Difficulty: 2
Page(s): 674
Scramble range: All
Topic: Net export function

25.85
Refer to Figure 25.3. At what level of GDP do exports exceed imports?
a) Y_0.
b) Y_1.
c) Y_2.
d) Y_3.
e) None of them, since net exports are always negative.

Figure 25.3 The relationship between net exports and real GDP of a hypothetical economy

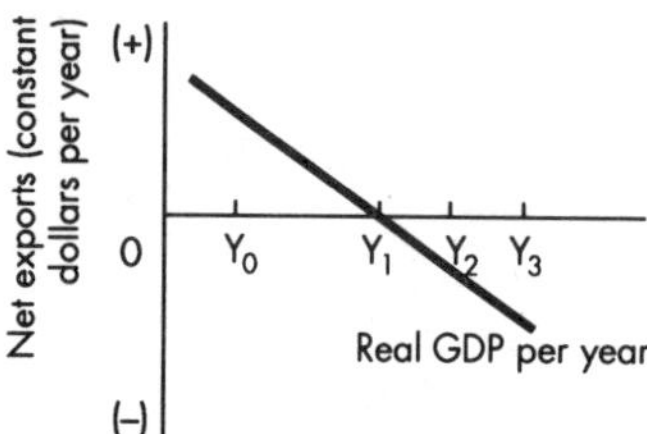

25.86
Correct: c)
Difficulty: 3
Page(s): 674
Scramble range: All
Topic: Net export function

25.86
Refer to Figure 25.3. At what level of GDP do imports begin to exceed exports?
a) Y_0.
b) Y_1.
c) Y_2.
d) Y_3.
e) None of them, since net exports are always positive.

25.87
Correct: b)
Difficulty: 2
Page(s): 674
Scramble range: a)–d)
Topic: Net export function

25.87
Refer to Figure 25.3. At what level of GDP are imports equal to exports?
a) Y_0.
b) Y_1.
c) Y_2.
d) Y_3.
e) None of the above.

25.88
Correct: a)
Difficulty: 4
Page(s): 671, 674
Scramble range: All
Topic: Net exports

25.88
Refer to Figure 25.3. Suppose that initially the level of Canadian income is equal to Y_1. All else constant, if the value of the Canadian dollar falls relative to foreign currencies, then
a) net exports will become positive.
b) net exports will become negative.
c) net exports will become zero.
d) imports will become zero.
e) exports will become zero.

25.89
Correct: e)
Difficulty: 4
Page(s): 674
Scramble range: All
Topic: Net export function

25.89
All else constant, if the real GDP of foreign nations with which a country trades should rise, then
a) its net export function will shift downward.
b) its net export function will swivel counterclockwise.
c) this can be shown on the country's net export function as a movement from right to left along the curve.
d) this can be shown on the country's net export function as a movement from left to right along the curve.
e) its net export function will shift upward.

25.90
Correct: d)
Difficulty: 3
Page(s): 674
Scramble range: All
Topic: Net export/ movement along

25.90
All else constant, if the real GDP of a country rises, this can be shown on its net export function as a
a) shift downward.
b) shift upward.
c) movement from right to left along the curve.
d) movement from left to right along the curve.
e) swivel counterclockwise in the curve.

25.91
Correct: a)
Difficulty: 3
Page(s): 674
Scramble range: All
Topic: Net export/ movement along

25.91
All else constant, if the value of the dollar rises against the value of foreign currencies, this can be shown on its net export function as a
a) shift downward.
b) shift upward.
c) movement from right to left along the curve.
d) movement from left to right along the curve.
e) swivel clockwise in the curve.

25.92
Correct: e)
Difficulty: 4
Page(s): 674–675
Scramble range: All
Topic: Slope/net export function

25.92
The slope of the net export function is equal to the
a) change in exports divided by a change in real GDP.
b) marginal propensity to import.
c) change in imports divided by a change in real GDP.
d) marginal propensity to export.
e) change in net exports divided by a change in real GDP.

25.93 (SG 25.21)
Correct: e)
Difficulty: 3
Page(s): 654
Scramble range: All
Topic: Consumption function

25.93
Important contributions to the theory of the consumption function were made by all of the following *except*
a) John Maynard Keynes.
b) Irving Fisher.
c) Franco Modgliani.
d) Milton Friedman.
e) Arthur Okun.

25.94 (SG 25.2)
Correct: d)
Difficulty: 3
Page(s): 654
Scramble range: All
Topic: Determinants of saving

25.94
Which of the following would cause a household to increase the amount it saves?
a) A decrease in current disposable income.
b) An increase in expected future income.
c) A decrease in patience.
d) An increase in interest rates.
e) A decrease in interest rates.

25.95 (SG 25.3)
Correct: e)
Difficulty: 2
Page(s): 654
Scramble range: All
Topic: Consumption function

25.95
The consumption function shows the relationship between consumption expenditure and
a) the interest rate.
b) the price level.
c) real GDP.
d) saving.
e) disposable income.

25.96 (SG 25.4)
Correct: d)
Difficulty: 4
Page(s): 656
Scramble range: All
Topic: Average propensity to consume

25.96
Consider a household with annual disposable income of $20,000. If the household makes consumption expenditures of $17,000, then its
a) marginal propensity to consume is 0.7.
b) marginal propensity to consume is 0.85.
c) average propensity to consume is 0.7.
d) average propensity to consume is 0.85.
e) marginal propensity to save is 0.15.

25.97 (SG 25.5)
Correct: b)
Difficulty: 1
Page(s): 657
Scramble range: All
Topic: Marginal propensity to save

25.97
The fraction of the last dollar of disposable income saved is called the
a) marginal propensity to consume.
b) marginal propensity to save.
c) average propensity to save.
d) marginal tax rate.
e) average propensity to consume.

25.98 (SG 25.6)
Correct: c)
Difficulty: 4
Page(s): 657
Scramble range: All
Topic: Average and marginal propensities

25.98
Which of the following statements is true regarding the relationship among the average propensity to consume (*APC*), the average propensity to save (*APS*), the marginal propensity to consume (*MPC*), and the marginal propensity to save (*MPS*)?
a) If the *MPC* increases, then the *MPS* must also increase.
b) $MPC + APC = 1$.
c) $MPC + MPS = APC + APS$.
d) $MPC + MPS$ is greater than $APC + APS$.
e) $APS > MPS$.

25.99 (SG 25.7)
Correct: e)
Difficulty: 5
Page(s): 657
Scramble range: None
Topic: Marginal propensity to consume

25.99
If the marginal propensity to consume (*MPC*) is less than the average propensity to consume (*APC*), then, as disposable income increases, the
a) *APC* falls.
b) *APS* rises.
c) *MPC* falls.
d) *MPC* rises.
e) both a) and b) occur.

25.100 (SG 25.8)
Correct: c)
Difficulty: 2
Page(s): 654
Scramble range: All
Topic: Consumption function

25.100
The slope of the consumption function is equal to the
a) *APC*.
b) *APS*.
c) *MPC*.
d) *MPS*.
e) $APC - MPC$.

25.101 (SG 25.9)
Correct: b)
Difficulty: 3
Page(s): 655
Scramble range: All
Topic: Consumption function shifts

25.101
Which of the following would shift the consumption function upward?
a) An increase in current disposable income.
b) An increase in future expected income.
c) An increase in interest rates.
d) A change of stage in life from a young household with children at home to an older household with any children gone and on their own.
e) A decrease in future expected income.

25.102 (SG 25.10)
Correct: d)
Difficulty: 2
Page(s): 654
Scramble range: All
Topic: Aggregate consumption function

25.102
The aggregate consumption function shows the relationship between aggregate real consumption expenditure and
a) the interest rate.
b) the price level.
c) disposable income.
d) real GDP.
e) expected future income.

25.103 (SG 25.11)
Correct: e)
Difficulty: 4
Page(s): 659
Scramble range: All
Topic: *MPC* out of real GDP

25.103
If net taxes are one-fourth (1/4) of real GDP and the marginal propensity to consume out of disposable income is 0.8, then the marginal propensity to consume out of real GDP is
a) 0.2.
b) 0.4.
c) 0.25.
d) 0.8.
e) 0.6.

25.104 (SG 25.12)
Correct: b)
Difficulty: 3
Page(s): 665
Scramble range: All
Topic: Investment determinants

25.104
Which of the following would lead to an increase in the amount of investment?
a) An increase in interest rates.
b) An increase in the expected inflation rate.
c) A decrease in expected future profit.
d) A smaller rate of depreciation.
e) A decrease in the expected inflation rate.

25.105 (SG 25.13)
Correct: a)
Difficulty: 3
Page(s): 665
Scramble range: All
Topic: Real interest rates

25.105
If the interest rate is 12 percent and the expected inflation rate is 8 percent, then the real interest rate is
a) 4 percent.
b) 8 percent.
c) 12 percent.
d) 20 percent.
e) 4.8 percent.

25.106 (SG 25.14)
Correct: d)
Difficulty: 2
Page(s): 667
Scramble range: All
Topic: Investment demand curve

25.106
The investment demand curve shows the relationship between the level of planned investment and
a) disposable income.
b) real GDP.
c) expected future profit.
d) the real interest rate.
e) the expected inflation rate.

25.107 (SG 25.15)
Correct: a)
Difficulty: 3
Page(s): 669
Scramble range: All
Topic: Accelerator principle

25.107
The accelerator principle implies that if real GDP begins to increase quite rapidly, then the
a) investment demand curve will shift to the right.
b) investment demand curve will shift to the left.
c) consumption function will shift to the right.
d) consumption function will shift to the left.
e) net export function will shift downwards.

25.108 (SG 25.16)
Correct: b)
Difficulty: 2
Page(s): 669
Scramble range: All
Topic: Invest demand volatility

25.108
Which of the following is the most important factor explaining the fluctuations in investment demand?
a) Fluctuations in the real interest rate.
b) Fluctuations in expected future profits.
c) Fluctuations in depreciation.
d) Fluctuations in expected inflation.
e) Fluctuations in the interest rate.

25.109 (SG 25.17)
Correct: c)
Difficulty: 3
Page(s): 674
Scramble range: All
Topic: Export demand

25.109
Which of the following would increase the demand for Canada's exports?
a) A decrease in the degree of international specialization.
b) An increase in Canadian real GDP.
c) An increase in the level of GDP in the rest of the world.
d) An increase in the foreign exchange value of the dollar.
e) A decrease in the level of real GDP in the rest of the world.

25.110 (SG 25.18)
Correct: d)
Difficulty: 3
Page(s): 674
Scramble range: All
Topic: Imports

25.110
Which of the following would increase Canadian imports from the rest of the world?
a) A decrease in the degree of international specialization.
b) A decrease in Canadian real GDP.
c) An increase in the level of GDP in the rest of the world.
d) An increase in the foreign exchange value of the dollar.
e) A decrease in the foreign exchange value of the dollar.

25.111 (SG 25.19)
Correct: b)
Difficulty: 2
Page(s): 674
Scramble range: All
Topic: Net export function

25.111
The net export function for Canada shows the relationship between net exports and
a) the level of GDP in the rest of the world.
b) the level of Canadian real GDP.
c) the foreign exchange rate.
d) disposable income.
e) the interest rate.

25.112 (SG 25.20)
Correct: c)
Difficulty: 3
Page(s): 674
Scramble range: All
Topic: Net export function

25.112
Which of the following will shift the net export function upward?
a) An increase in the foreign exchange value of the dollar.
b) An increase in the level of Canadian real GDP.
c) An increase in the level of GDP in the rest of the world.
d) An increase in interest rates.
e) A decrease in the level of GDP in the rest of the world.

25.113
Correct: b)
Difficulty: 2
Page(s): 669
Scramble range: All
Topic: Investment volatility

25.113
Which is the most volatile component of aggregate expenditure?
a) Consumption expenditure.
b) Investment.
c) Government purchases of goods and services.
d) Exports.
e) Imports.

25.114
Correct: e)
Difficulty: 3
Page(s): 654
Scramble range: All
Topic: Determinants of consumption

25.114
Which of the following would cause a household to increase the amount it consumes per time period?
a) A decrease in current disposable income.
b) A decrease in expected future income.
c) A decrease in saving.
d) An increase in interest rates.
e) An increase in expected future income.

25.115
Correct: c)
Difficulty: 2
Page(s): 654
Scramble range: All
Topic: Saving function

25.115
The saving function shows the relationship between saving and
a) the interest rate.
b) the price level.
c) disposable income.
d) consumption.
e) real GDP.

25.116
Correct: e)
Difficulty: 4
Page(s): 656
Scramble range: None
Topic: Average propensity to save

25.116
Consider a household with annual disposable income of $40,000. If the household makes consumption expenditures of $34,000, then its
a) marginal propensity to consume is 0.7.
b) marginal propensity to consume is 0.85.
c) average propensity to consume is 0.85.
d) average propensity to save is 0.15.
e) both c) and d).

25.117
Correct: e)
Difficulty: 2
Page(s): 654
Scramble range: All
Topic: Consumption function

25.117
Milton Friedman, as well as Franco Modigliani and Richard Brumberg, argued that consumption is determined primarily by
a) the rate of interest.
b) the expected rate of inflation.
c) disposable income.
d) business profits.
e) wealth.

25.118
Correct: a)
Difficulty: 4
Page(s): 657
Scramble range: a)–d)
Topic: Marginal propensity to consume

25.118
If the marginal propensity to consume (*MPS*) is less than the average propensity to consume (*APS*), then, as disposable income increases, the
a) *APC* rises.
b) *APC* falls.
c) *MPC* falls.
d) *MPC* rises.
e) none of the above.

25.119
Correct: e)
Difficulty: 4
Page(s): 654
Scramble range: None
Topic: Saving function

25.119
The slope of the saving function is equal to the
a) *APC.*
b) *APS.*
c) $1 - MPC$.
d) *MPS.*
e) both c) and d).

25.120
Correct: e)
Difficulty: 5
Page(s): 654
Scramble range: All
Topic: Consumption function shifts

25.120
You have just found out that your income this year (1991) and in 1992 will be $100,000 higher than you previously thought, but that in 1993 through 1998 it will $100,000 lower than you previously thought. As a result, your consumption in 1991 and 1992 will ________ while your consumption in 1993–1998 will ________.

a) rise; rise
b) rise; fall
c) stay the same; fall
d) fall; rise
e) fall; fall

25.121
Correct: a)
Difficulty: 3
Page(s): 665
Scramble range: All
Topic: Investment

25.121
Which of the following statements about investment is true?

a) Net investment is the most sensitive type of investment with respect to the real interest rate.
b) Gross investment is the most sensitive type of investment with respect to the real interest rate.
c) Replacement of depreciated capital stock is the most sensitive type of investment with respect to the real interest rate.
d) Replacement of depreciated capital stock is the most sensitive type of investment with respect to real GDP.
e) Gross investment is the most sensitive type of investment with respect to real GDP.

25.122
Correct: a)
Difficulty: 3
Page(s): 665
Scramble range: All
Topic: Investment determinants

25.122
Which of the following would lead to a decrease in the amount of investment?

a) An increase in interest rates.
b) A decrease in the expected inflation rate.
c) An increase in expected future profit.
d) A larger rate of depreciation.
e) A decrease in interest rates.

25.123
Correct: d)
Difficulty: 4
Page(s): 657
Scramble range: All
Topic: *MPC*

25.123
Consider Fact 25.1. Batman's marginal propensity to consume is

a) 0.7.
b) 0.3.
c) 0.6.
d) equal to his *MPS.*
e) 0.4.

Fact 25.1
You are given the following information about Batman:

Disposable income (dollars per year)	Consumption expenditure (dollars per year)
0	10,000
10,000	15,000
20,000	20,000
30,000	25,000
40,000	30,000

25.124
Correct: a)
Difficulty: 5
Page(s): 656
Scramble range: All
Topic: *APS*

25.124
Consider Fact 25.1. At an income level of $10,000, Batman's *APS* is

a) –0.5.
b) 1.5.
c) –1.5.
d) 0.5.
e) –0.67.

Chapter 26 Expenditure and Income

26.1
Correct: b)
Difficulty: 2
Page: 685
Scramble range: All
Topic: Aggregate expenditure

26.1
The aggregate expenditure schedule shows the total amount
a) spent on an economy's real GDP at each level of real GDP.
b) all sectors plan to spend on real GDP given their total income, at each level of real GDP.
c) all sectors would like to spend on real GDP in the absence of any income constraint, at each level of real GDP.
d) spent on an economy's real GDP at each level of national income.
e) all sectors plan to spend on consumption given their total income, at each level of real GDP.

26.2
Correct: c)
Difficulty: 1
Page: 687
Scramble range: All
Topic: Induced consumption

26.2
A change in consumption in response to a change in income is called
a) unplanned consumption.
b) autonomous consumption.
c) induced consumption.
d) equilibrium consumption.
e) planned consumption.

26.3
Correct: b)
Difficulty: 2
Page: 687
Scramble range: All
Topic: Induced consumption

26.3
Suppose real GDP increases by $1 billion and, as a result, consumption increases by $500 million. The change in consumption is considered to be
a) unplanned.
b) induced.
c) autonomous.
d) too little.
e) planned.

26.4
Correct: c)
Difficulty: 2
Page: 687
Scramble range: All
Topic: Autonomous consumption expenditure

26.4
All else constant, autonomous consumption
a) increases as the level of disposable income decreases.
b) increases as the level of disposable income increases.
c) does not change as the level of disposable income changes.
d) is usually assumed to be zero.
e) decreases as the level of disposable income decreases.

26.5
Correct: a)
Difficulty: 2
Page: 687
Scramble range: All
Topic: Autonomous consumption/function

26.5
Increases in autonomous consumption result in
a) an upward shift of the consumption function.
b) a downward shift of the consumption function.
c) a movement from right to left along the consumption function.
d) a movement from left to right along the consumption function.
e) a swivel counterclockwise in the consumption function.

26.6
Correct: b)
Difficulty: 2
Page: 687
Scramble range: a)–d)
Topic: Induced aggregate expenditure

26.6
Which one of the following variables does the textbook assume to have an induced component?
a) Investment.
b) Consumption.
c) Exports.
d) Government purchases.
e) All of the above.

26.7
Correct: d)
Difficulty: 2
Page: 687
Scramble range: All
Topic: Imports/real GDP

26.7
As real GDP increases
a) autonomous consumption tends to increase.
b) planned investment expenditures tend to increase.
c) exports tend to increase.
d) imports tend to increase.
e) imports tend to decrease.

26.8
Correct: e)
Difficulty: 2
Page: 687
Scramble range: All
Topic: Induced consumption

26.8
As real GDP increases
a) induced consumption tends to decrease.
b) planned investment expenditures tend to increase.
c) exports tend to increase.
d) imports tend to decrease.
e) induced consumption tends to increase.

26.9
Correct: c)
Difficulty: 1
Page: 687
Scramble range: All
Topic: Marginal propensity to import

26.9
If the level of real GDP is increasing, the amount by which imports will increase is calculated using
a) the change in total consumption divided by the change in real GDP.
b) the size of the shift in the aggregate expenditure schedule.
c) the marginal propensity to import.
d) total imports divided by the increase in real GDP.
e) the marginal propensity to spend.

26.10
Correct: d)
Difficulty: 1
Page: 685
Scramble range: All
Topic: Aggregate expenditure schedule

26.10
The schedule that relates the level of total planned expenditure to the level of real GDP is the
a) dissaving function.
b) consumption function.
c) equilibrium GDP function.
d) aggregate expenditure schedule.
e) aggregate demand function.

26.11
Correct: c)
Difficulty: 3
Page: 688
Scramble range: All
Topic: Unplanned inventories

26.11
If the planned level of aggregate expenditures exceeds the level of real GDP, then inventories will
a) build up, causing real GDP to rise.
b) build up, causing real GDP to fall.
c) be depleted, causing real GDP to rise.
d) be depleted, causing real GDP to fall.
e) stay constant, and so will real GDP.

26.12
Correct: e)
Difficulty: 2
Page: 689
Scramble range: All
Topic: Net exports/real GDP

26.12
Economists generally assume that as real GDP increases
a) exports will increase.
b) imports will decrease.
c) net exports will be constant.
d) net exports will increase.
e) net exports will decrease.

26.13
Correct: c)
Difficulty: 3
Page: 688–690
Scramble range: All
Topic: Unplanned inventories

26.13
If real GDP is $2 billion and planned aggregate expenditure is $2.25 billion, then inventories will
a) pile up and output will increase.
b) pile up and output will decrease.
c) be depleted and output will increase.
d) be depleted and output will decrease.
e) stay constant and so will output.

26.14
Correct: a)
Difficulty: 3
Page: 689–690
Scramble range: All
Topic: Actual versus planned investment

26.14
Refer to Figure 26.1. When real GDP is equal to Y_a, then
a) actual investment is less than planned investment.
b) actual investment is greater than planned investment.
c) planned investment is equal to actual investment.
d) the economy is in equilibrium.
e) real GDP will fall.

Figure 26.1

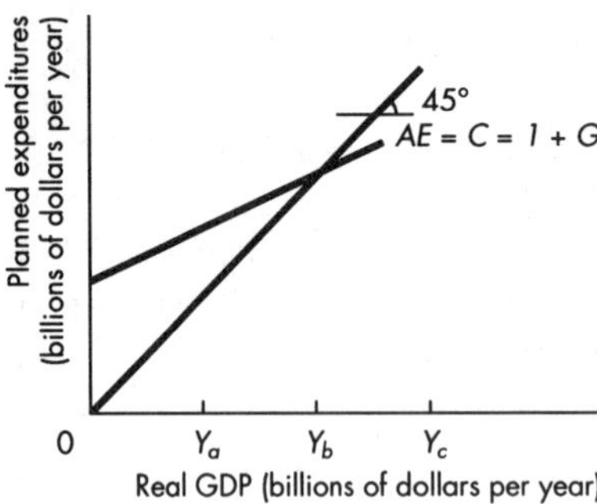

26.15
Correct: c)
Difficulty: 3
Page: 689–690
Scramble range: All
Topic: Actual versus planned investment

26.15
Refer to Figure 26.1. When real GDP is equal to Y_b, then
a) actual investment is less than planned investment.
b) actual investment is greater than planned investment.
c) planned investment is equal to actual investment.
d) real GDP will increase.
e) real GDP will decrease.

26.16
Correct: b)
Difficulty: 3
Page: 689–690
Scramble range: All
Topic: Actual versus planned investment

26.16
Refer to Figure 26.1. When real GDP is equal to Y_c, then
a) actual investment is less than planned investment.
b) actual investment is greater than planned investment.
c) planned investment is equal to actual investment.
d) the economy is in equilibrium.
e) real GDP will rise.

26.17
Correct: c)
Difficulty: 3
Page: 688–690
Scramble range: All
Topic: Equilibrium real GDP

26.17
Refer to Figure 26.1. Equilibrium real GDP
a) cannot be determined from the information given.
b) is equal to Y_a.
c) is equal to Y_b.
d) is equal to Y_c.
e) is Y_b or higher.

26.18
Correct: a)
Difficulty: 4
Page: 690
Scramble range: All
Topic: Equilibrium adjustment

26.18
Refer to Figure 26.1. When real GDP is equal to Y_a, then aggregate expenditure
a) exceeds real GDP and real GDP will rise.
b) is less than real GDP and real GDP will fall.
c) exceeds real GDP and real GDP will fall.
d) is equal to real GDP and real GDP will neither rise nor fall.
e) is less than real GDP and real GDP will rise.

26.19
Correct: e)
Difficulty: 3
Page: 688
Scramble range: All
Topic: Equilibrium GDP

26.19
Refer to Figure 26.1. When real GDP is equal to Y_b, then aggregate expenditure is
a) less than real GDP and real GDP will fall.
b) less than real GDP and real GDP will rise.
c) greater than real GDP and real GDP will rise.
d) greater than real GDP and real GDP will fall.
e) equal to real GDP and real GDP will neither rise nor fall.

26.20
Correct: a)
Difficulty: 4
Page: 688
Scramble range: All
Topic: Equilibrium GDP

26.20
Refer to Figure 26.1. When real GDP is equal to Y_c, then aggregate expenditure is
a) less than real GDP and real GDP will fall.
b) less than real GDP and real GDP will rise.
c) greater than real GDP and real GDP will fall.
d) equal to real GDP and real GDP will neither rise nor fall.
e) greater than real GDP and real GDP will rise.

26.21
Correct: d)
Difficulty: 3
Page: 688
Scramble range: All
Topic: Equilibrium analysis

26.21
In the real world
a) economies are usually in equilibrium.
b) changes in expenditures and leakages cancel each other out very quickly so that changes in real GDP are not very significant.
c) the concept of equilibrium real GDP is not very useful.
d) GDP changes continuously.
e) GDP changes seldom, but these changes are large when they do occur.

26.22
Correct: c)
Difficulty: 2
Page: 693
Scramble range: All
Topic: Marginal propensity to import

26.22
If real GDP is increasing, the amount by which imports will increase can be calculated by using
a) the magnitude of the shift in the aggregate expenditure function.
b) total imports divided by the change in real GDP.
c) the marginal propensity to import.
d) total imports divided by real GDP.
e) the slope of the aggregate expenditure function.

26.23
Correct: e)
Difficulty: 3
Page: 691–695
Scramble range: All
Topic: Factors changing real GDP

26.23
A decrease in real GDP could result from an increase in all of the following *except*
a) saving.
b) imports.
c) real interest rates.
d) tax rates.
e) government spending.

26.24
Correct: a)
Difficulty: 3
Page: 693
Scramble range: All
Topic: Marginal propensity to spend/shift in *AE*

26.24
If there is a downward shift in the aggregate expenditure (*AE*) function the new *AE* function will be
a) flatter than the old one if the marginal propensity to spend has decreased.
b) steeper than the old one if the marginal propensity to spend has increased.
c) parallel to the old function and will be above it.
d) parallel to the old function and will be below it.
e) flatter than the old one if the marginal propensity to spend has increased.

26.25
Correct: e)
Difficulty: 4
Page: 693–694
Scramble range: a)–d)
Topic: Tax rates/*AE* function

26.25
All else constant, a decrease in the marginal tax rate will result in
a) a movement down the aggregate expenditure function.
b) an upward parallel shift of the aggregate expenditure function.
c) a downward shift of the aggregate expenditure function.
d) a decrease in the consumption function.
e) none of the above.

26.26
Correct: d)
Difficulty: 3
Page: 695
Scramble range: All
Topic: Multiplier

26.26
All else constant, an autonomous decrease in the aggregate expenditure function will generally result in
a) an increase in equilibrium national income.
b) no additional change in expenditure.
c) an induced increase in expenditure.
d) an induced decrease in expenditure.
e) a decrease in the marginal propensity to spend.

26.27
Correct: b)
Difficulty: 3
Page: 689
Scramble range: All
Topic: Changes in exports/real GDP

26.27
All else constant, which one of the following would increase equilibrium real GDP?
a) An increase in the savings function.
b) An increase in exports.
c) A decrease in investment.
d) An increase in taxes.
e) A decrease in exports.

26.28
Correct: d)
Difficulty: 3
Page: 688–690
Scramble range: All
Topic: Equilibrium condition

26.28
If total exports exceed total imports, then real GDP
a) must be rising.
b) must be falling.
c) cannot be in equilibrium, although it may be rising or falling.
d) may or may not be in equilibrium.
e) must be in equilibrium.

26.29
Correct: e)
Difficulty: 4
Page: 688–690
Scramble range: All
Topic: Equilibrium real GDP

26.29
If real GDP is not at its equilibrium value
a) government intervention is necessary to make sure that real GDP changes in the correct direction.
b) real GDP will change until it reaches an equilibrium level at the capacity output level of the economy.
c) there must be excessive inflation in the economy.
d) there must be excessive unemployment in the economy.
e) there will always be a tendency for real GDP to change until planned expenditures equal real GDP.

26.30
Correct: d)
Difficulty: 2
Page: 688
Scramble range: All
Topic: Marginal propensity to spend

26.30
The fraction of the last dollar spent on real GDP is the
a) marginal propensity to consume.
b) marginal propensity to import.
c) slope of the saving function.
d) marginal propensity to spend.
e) multiplier.

26.31
Correct: b)
Difficulty: 2
Page: 688
Scramble range: All
Topic: Marginal propensity to spend

26.31
The marginal propensity to spend can also be thought of as the
a) slope of the consumption function.
b) slope of the aggregate expenditure function.
c) slope of the net export function.
d) slope of the import function.
e) multiplier.

26.32
Correct: b)
Difficulty: 2
Page: 688
Scramble range: All
Topic: Calculating marginal propensity to spend

26.32
The marginal propensity to spend is calculated as
a) total aggregate expenditures divided by real GDP.
b) the change in total aggregate expenditures divided by the change in real GDP.
c) the change in total consumption divided by the change in real GDP.
d) the change in total consumption plus government purchases divided by the change in national income.
e) the change in income divided by the change in autonomous expenditure.

26.33
Correct: b)
Difficulty: 2
Page: 687
Scramble range: All
Topic: Slope of the *AE* function

26.33
The slope of the aggregate expenditure function
a) is negative, due to the leakage called imports.
b) is positive, since the positive marginal leakages outweigh the negative marginal leakages from the expenditure flow.
c) is sometimes negative and sometimes positive depending on the relative weight of the marginal leakages and injections into the expenditure flow.
d) for Canada is 1.
e) for Canada is 1.25.

26.34
Correct: b)
Difficulty: 3
Page: 688
Scramble range: All
Topic: Marginal propensity to spend

26.34
If the marginal propensity to consume out of real GDP is 0.75, and the marginal propensity to import is 0.10, then the marginal propensity to spend out of real GDP is
a) 0.50.
b) 0.65.
c) 0.15.
d) 0.45.
e) 0.85.

26.35
Correct: e)
Difficulty: 4
Page: 688
Scramble range: All
Topic: Marginal propensity to spend

26.35
Suppose that real GDP increases by $100 billion and as a result net imports decline by $9 billion and all other expenditures rise by $80 billion. The marginal propensity to spend out of real GDP is
a) 0.80.
b) 0.79.
c) 0.89.
d) 0.67.
e) 0.71.

26.36
Correct: d)
Difficulty: 4
Page: 687
Scramble range: All
Topic: Slope of the *AE* function

26.36
The aggregate expenditure curve will become steeper if
a) people become thriftier on the margin.
b) people show an increased taste for foreign-made products.
c) firms expect an increase in future profits.
d) marginal tax rates are lowered.
e) marginal tax rates are raised.

26.37
Correct: b)
Difficulty: 4
Page: 692
Scramble range: All
Topic: Paradox of thrift

26.37
All else constant, if people become thriftier on the margin, then
a) real GDP will tend to rise in the short run.
b) real GDP will tend to fall in the short run.
c) there will be an offsetting shift of purchasing to domestically produced goods.
d) real GDP will be unaffected in the long run or the short run.
e) there will be an offsetting shift of purchasing to foreign-produced goods.

26.38
Correct: b)
Difficulty: 3
Page: 689
Scramble range: All
Topic: Investment expenditures

26.38
Refer to Figure 26.2. The value of investment expenditures is
a) $50 billion.
b) $25 billion.
c) $75 billion.
d) $100 billion.
e) calculable only with information on the level of real GDP.

Figure 26.2 The economy depicted does not engage in international trade and has no government. Planned aggregate expenditures (AE) are equal to the sum of consumption expenditures (C) and investment expenditures (I). Assume a constant price level in answering each question.

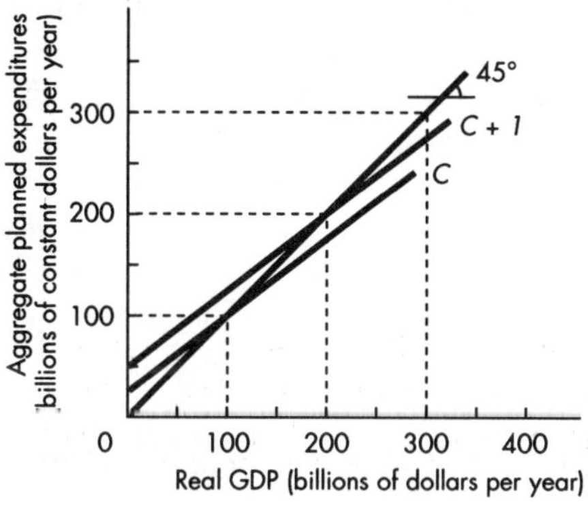

26.39
Correct: e)
Difficulty: 4
Page: 688
Scramble range: All
Topic: Aggregate expenditure

26.39
Refer to Figure 26.2. When real GDP is equal to $400 billion, aggregate expenditure is equal to
a) $50 billion.
b) $25 billion.
c) $300 billion.
d) $325 billion.
e) $350 billion.

26.40
Correct: c)
Difficulty: 3
Page: 687
Scramble range: a)–d)
Topic: Autonomous expenditures

26.40
Refer to Figure 26.2. Autonomous expenditures are equal to
a) $100 billion.
b) $25 billion.
c) $50 billion.
d) $125 billion.
e) none of the above.

26.41
Correct: d)
Difficulty: 3
Page: 687
Scramble range: All
Topic: Autonomous expenditures

26.41
Refer to Figure 26.2. The equilibrium level of real GDP for this economy is
a) $100 billion.
b) $300 billion.
c) $250 billion.
d) $200 billion.
e) $400 billion.

26.42
Correct: d)
Difficulty: 4
Page: 688–690
Scramble range: All
Topic: Equilibration process

26.42
Refer to Figure 26.2. When real GDP is equal to $300 billion, real GDP is
a) less than planned expenditures by $25 billion, so firms will cut back on their production rate.
b) greater than planned expenditures by $25 billion, so firms will increase their production rate.
c) the same as planned expenditures, so there is no reason for firms to change their production plans.
d) greater than planned expenditures by $25 billion, so firms will cut back on their production rate.
e) greater than planned expenditures by $50 billion, so firms will increase their production rate.

26.43
Correct: a)
Difficulty: 4
Page: 688–690
Scramble range: All
Topic: Equilibration process

26.43
Refer to Figure 26.2. When real GDP is equal to $100 billion
a) real GDP is less than planned expenditures, so firms will increase their production rate.
b) planned expenditures are greater than real GDP, so firms will decrease their production rate.
c) real GDP is greater than planned expenditures, so firms will decrease their production rate.
d) planned expenditures are equal to real GDP, so the economy is in equilibrium.
e) planned expenditures are less than real GDP, so firms will increase their production rate.

26.44
Correct: a)
Difficulty: 4
Page: 688
Scramble range: All
Topic: Marginal propensity to spend

26.44
Refer to Figure 26.2. The marginal propensity to spend in this economy is
a) 0.75.
b) 0.25.
c) 0.50.
d) 0.67.
e) not calculable.

26.45
Correct: b)
Difficulty: 4
Page: 695
Scramble range: All
Topic: Multiplier

26.45
Refer to Figure 26.2. The value of the multiplier for this economy is
a) 2.
b) 4.
c) 2.5.
d) 1.
e) 3.

26.46
Correct: d)
Difficulty: 5
Page: 695
Scramble range: All
Topic: Multiplier

26.46
Refer to Figure 26.2. If investment increases by $25 billion, then real GDP will increase by
a) $25 billion.
b) $125 billion.
c) $50 billion.
d) $100 billion.
e) $75 billion.

26.47
Correct: c)
Difficulty: 4
Page: 688–689
Scramble range: All
Topic: Marginal propensities

26.47
If an economy has no government and does not engage in international trade, then the marginal propensity to
a) spend will be 1.
b) consume will be 1 minus the marginal propensity to import.
c) consume will be the same as the marginal propensity to spend.
d) consume will be the same as the marginal propensity to import.
e) consume will be less than the marginal propensity to spend.

26.48
Correct: b)
Difficulty: 3
Page: 695
Scramble range: All
Topic: Multiplier

26.48
As the aggregate expenditure curve becomes steeper, the value of the multiplier becomes
a) closer to the value of the marginal propensity to spend.
b) larger.
c) smaller.
d) negative.
e) closer to a value of 1.

26.49
Correct: c)
Difficulty: 4
Page: 691
Scramble range: All
Topic: Shifts of the *AE* function

26.49
Consider the aggregate expenditure model. Suppose that an economy is in equilibrium initially. If interest rates increase, then
a) the government will automatically increase its expenditures, which will lead to an increase in real GDP.
b) the aggregate expenditure function will shift upward and real GDP will rise.
c) the aggregate expenditure function will shift downward and real GDP will fall.
d) consumption expenditures will rise and investment expenditures will fall, thereby leaving real GDP unchanged.
e) investment expenditures will fall, but this will induce a rise in consumption expenditures so that the overall fall in income is less than the initial fall in investment.

26.50
Correct: d)
Difficulty: 3
Page: 691
Scramble range: All
Topic: Shifts of the *AE* function

26.50
Which one of the following events is likely to lead to an increase in aggregate expenditures?
a) An increase in interest rates.
b) An increase in imports.
c) An increase in taxes.
d) An increase in the rate of defence spending.
e) A decrease in expected future profits for business.

26.51
Correct: b)
Difficulty: 4
Page: 704
Scramble range: All
Topic: Temporary versus permanent change in income

26.51
The multiplier effect of increased consumption expenditures at the beginning of an economic recovery is likely to be
a) larger as people tend to perceive the increase in income as temporary.
b) larger as people tend to perceive the increase in income as permanent.
c) smaller because people will wait to see if the increased income is temporary or permanent.
d) zero for at least 6 months because people want to see if the increased income is temporary or permanent.
e) smaller because people will tend to perceive the increased income as temporary.

26.52
Correct: a)
Difficulty: 4
Page: 704
Scramble range: All
Topic: Temporary versus permanent change in income

26.52
When the economy goes into a recession, a dollar decrease in disposable income
a) leads to a smaller decrease in consumption than later in the recession.
b) leads to a larger decrease in consumption than later in the recession.
c) will not affect peoples' consumption decisions.
d) can actually increase consumption expenditures as people decide whether the economic downturn is going to be short-lived.
e) has the same effect on consumption as later in the recession.

26.53
Correct: a)
Difficulty: 1
Page: 692–693
Scramble range: All
Topic: Thrift and saving functions

26.53
All else constant, if households become concerned about their future income prospects and increase their saving rate, which of the following will shift?
a) Saving function.
b) Export function.
c) Money supply function.
d) Investment function.
e) Tax function.

26.54
Correct: e)
Difficulty: 2
Page: 692–693
Scramble range: All
Topic: Thrift and consumption functions

26.54
All else constant, if households become concerned about their future income prospects and increase their saving rate, which of the following will shift?
a) Investment line.
b) Tax function.
c) Aggregate supply curve.
d) Export function.
e) Consumption function.

26.55
Correct: c)
Difficulty: 3
Page: 708
Scramble range: All
Topic: Multiplier/*SAS* curve considered

26.55
The value of the autonomous expenditure multiplier as calculated in the textbook, or 1/(1 – *MPS*), explains the relationship between an autonomous shift in aggregate demand and the resulting change in real GDP
a) no matter what happens to the price level.
b) only if the price level is rising.
c) if the short-run aggregate supply curve is flat.
d) if the short-run aggregate supply curve has a positive slope.
e) if the short-run aggregate supply curve has a vertical slope.

26.56
Correct: b)
Difficulty: 3
Page: 695
Scramble range: All
Topic: Multiplier

26.56
The idea behind the multiplier principle is that
a) one sector's spending is another sector's income.
b) one person's spending becomes income to another person.
c) private sector spending becomes public sector revenue.
d) public sector spending is the only variable that can multiply into greater income.
e) as consumption rises, this lowers saving and therefore investment.

26.57
Correct: b)
Difficulty: 2
Page: 695
Scramble range: All
Topic: Multiplier

26.57
The autonomous expenditure multiplier can be defined as
a) real GDP divided by aggregate demand.
b) the change in real GDP divided by the initial change in expenditure that brought it about.
c) the change in real GDP resulting from a change in expenditure, multiplied by the number of time periods since the initial change took place.
d) a change in aggregate demand multiplied by the equilibrium level of real GDP.
e) the induced change in consumption divided by the initial change in autonomous expenditures.

26.58
Correct: d)
Difficulty: 2
Page: 695
Scramble range: All
Topic: Multiplier

26.58
The formula for the autonomous expenditure multiplier is
a) 1/(1 + *MPS*).
b) 1/(1 - *MPI*).
c) 1/(1 + *MPI*).
d) 1/(1 – *MPS*).
e) 1/(1 – *MPC*).

26.59
Correct: e)
Difficulty: 2
Page: 702–704
Scramble range: All
Topic: Canadian multiplier

26.59
Studies concerning the value of the multiplier in Canada estimate its value as closest to
a) 5.25.
b) 4.25.
c) 3.25.
d) 2.25.
e) 1.25.

26.60
Correct: e)
Difficulty: 2
Page: 695
Scramble range: All
Topic: Possible multiplier value

26.60
The autonomous expenditure multiplier could take on any value
a) between 0 and 1.
b) between –1 and 1.
c) between 1 and 2.
d) greater than 1.
e) greater than 0.

26.61
Correct: b)
Difficulty: 3
Page: 703–704
Scramble range: All
Topic: Multiple values and business cycles

26.61
In the real world, the value of the multiplier
a) is constant over time with a value of 1.25.
b) tends to be higher at the beginning of a recovery than at other times.
c) tends to be smaller at the beginning of a recovery than at other times.
d) is not related to the business cycle.
e) moves countercyclically to the business cycle.

26.62
Correct: c)
Difficulty: 3
Page: 699
Scramble range: All
Topic: Multipliers

26.62
The relationship between the tax multiplier and the transfer payments multiplier is that
a) they have the same value.
b) they add up to one.
c) they add up to zero.
d) the tax multiplier is twice the value of the transfer payments multiplier.
e) the transfer payments multiplier is twice the value of the tax multiplier.

26.63
Correct: a)
Difficulty: 2
Page: 699
Scramble range: All
Topic: Fiscal policy

26.63
Fiscal policy refers to changes in
a) government taxing and spending policy.
b) policy by the Bank of Canada.
c) budgeting policy by aggregate households.
d) real GDP due to changes in tax rates.
e) import duties levied by the government.

26.64
Correct: d)
Difficulty: 2
Page: 700
Scramble range: All
Topic: Autonomous taxes

26.64
Autonomous taxes are taxes that
a) increase government revenues as real GDP decreases.
b) increase government revenues as real GDP increases.
c) are dependent on the level of business activity in the public sector.
d) are levied independently of the level of income.
e) are levied independently of the price level.

26.65
Correct: a)
Difficulty: 2
Page: 700
Scramble range: All
Topic: Induced taxes

26.65
Induced taxes
a) depend on the level of income.
b) do not depend on the level of income earned.
c) do not affect the level of real GDP.
d) are not important in multiplier analysis.
e) depend on the price level.

26.66
Correct: e)
Difficulty: 2
Page: 700
Scramble range: All
Topic: Tax multiplier

26.66
The tax multiplier is defined as
a) $(1 - MPS)/MPS$.
b) $1/(1 - MPS)$.
c) $MPS/(MPS - 1)$.
d) $MPS/(1 - MPS)$.
e) $-MPS/(1 - MPS)$.

26.67
Correct: a)
Difficulty: 2
Page: 701
Scramble range: All
Topic: Relative sizes of multipliers

26.67
Which of the following statements is true? The tax multiplier
a) is smaller than the autonomous expenditure multiplier.
b) is larger than the autonomous expenditure multiplier.
c) has the same value as the autonomous expenditure multiplier except during recessions.
d) is larger than the autonomous expenditure multiplier during recoveries.
e) always equals the autonomous expenditure multiplier.

26.68
Correct: c)
Difficulty: 3
Page: 695
Scramble range: All
Topic: Multiplier

26.68
Suppose the *MPS* is equal to 0.6. The autonomous expenditure multiplier is
a) 1.5.
b) 2.
c) 2.5.
d) 5.2.
e) 1.33.

26.69
Correct: a)
Difficulty: 3
Page: 700
Scramble range: All
Topic: Tax multiplier

26.69
Suppose the *MPS* is equal to 0.6. The tax multiplier is
a) –1.5.
b) 2.
c) –2.5.
d) 5.2.
e) 1.5.

26.70
Correct: d)
Difficulty: 3
Page: 705
Scramble range: All
Topic: Price level/ consumption function

26.70
When the price level rises, the consumption function shifts
a) upward because households have higher money income.
b) upward because the nominal value of household balances rises.
c) downward because households have higher real income.
d) downward because of the real balance effect.
e) downward because goods are relatively more expensive.

26.71
Correct: e)
Difficulty: 3
Page: 705
Scramble range: All
Topic: Price level/ consumption function

26.71
When the price level falls, the consumption function shifts
a) downward due to the intertemporal substitution effect.
b) downward due to the internal substitution effect.
c) downward due to the international substitution effect.
d) upward due to the international substitution effect.
e) upward due to the real balance effect.

26.72
Correct: e)
Difficulty: 4
Page: 706–707
Scramble range: All
Topic: *AD*/*AE* relationship

26.72
A shift in the aggregate expenditure function as a result of an increase in the price level will result in
a) a leftward shift in the aggregate demand curve.
b) no change in the aggregate demand curve.
c) a rightward shift in the aggregate demand curve.
d) a move from left to right along the aggregate demand curve.
e) a move from right to left along the aggregate demand curve.

26.73
Correct: b)
Difficulty: 3
Page: 709
Scramble range: All
Topic: Multiplier values/price level change

26.73
When the short-run aggregate supply curve has a positive slope, the multiplier effect on real GDP
a) is zero.
b) is smaller than the simple text formula would suggest.
c) is the same as the simple text formula would suggest.
d) is larger than the simple text formula would suggest.
e) is negative.

26.74
Correct: e)
Difficulty: 4
Page: 709
Scramble range: All
Topic: Price level change/*AE* function

26.74
Suppose that an autonomous increase in aggregate expenditure causes the *AE* function to shift upward. If the price level rises as a result, the
a) *AE* function must return to its original position.
b) *AD* function will shift to the left.
c) *AE* function will increase even further.
d) *AD* function may shift part of the way down again due to the multiplier effects.
e) *AD* curve will rise initially, and then there will a movement up the new *AD* curve as a result of the price level rise.

26.75
Correct: c)
Difficulty: 3
Page: 709
Scramble range: All
Topic: Price level change/*AD* function

26.75
A rightward shift in the aggregate demand curve could be caused by all of the following *except*
a) a decrease in imports.
b) a decrease in tax rates.
c) an increase in the price level.
d) an increase in exports.
e) a decrease in interest rates.

26.76
Correct: d)
Difficulty: 4
Page: 705
Scramble range: All
Topic: *AE* model versus *AD/AS* model

26.76
By using the aggregate expenditure function, we can determine
a) the equilibrium level of real GDP and the price level.
b) the price level, but not the equilibrium level of real GDP.
c) equilibrium level of consumption and the equilibrium price level.
d) the equilibrium level of real GDP if the price level is constant.
e) the equilibrium level of real GDP, but not the level of consumption.

26.77
Correct: a)
Difficulty: 3
Page: 688
Scramble range: All
Topic: Marginal propensity to spend

26.77
Refer to Table 26.1. What is the marginal propensity to spend for this economy?
a) 0.8.
b) 0.6.
c) 0.75.
d) 1.
e) 1.3.

Table 26.1 The relationship between aggregate expenditures and GDP in the hypothetical economy of Econoworld. Each variable is expressed in constant dollars.

Real GDP per year	Aggregate expenditures per year
0	100
200	260
400	420
600	580
800	740

26.78
Correct: d)
Difficulty: 2
Page: 688–690
Scramble range: a)–d)
Topic: Equilibrium real GDP

26.78
Refer to Table 26.1. The equilibrium level of real GDP is
a) 525.
b) 550.
c) 450.
d) 500.
e) none of the above.

26.79
Correct: a)
Difficulty: 2
Page: 687
Scramble range: All
Topic: Autonomous expenditures

26.79
Refer to Table 26.1. The level of autonomous expenditures for this economy is
a) 100.
b) 125.
c) 50.
d) 500.
e) 0.

26.80
Correct: c)
Difficulty: 3
Page: 687
Scramble range: All
Topic: Slope of the *AE* function

26.80
Refer to Table 26.1. The slope of the aggregate expenditure function is
a) 3/4.
b) 4/9.
c) 4/5.
d) 1/5.
e) 4/3.

26.81
Correct: a)
Difficulty: 4
Page: 695
Scramble range: All
Topic: Multiplier

26.81
Refer to Table 26.1. The autonomous expenditure multiplier for this economy
a) is 5.
b) is 2.5.
c) is 4.
d) is 1.8.
e) cannot be determined without more information.

26.82
Correct: c)
Difficulty: 4
Page: 700
Scramble range: All
Topic: Tax multiplier

26.82
Refer to Table 26.1. The tax multiplier for this economy
a) cannot be determined without more information.
b) is –5.
c) is –4.
d) is –2.5.
e) is –1.8.

26.83
Correct: b)
Difficulty: 4
Page: 689–690
Scramble range: All
Topic: Changes in equilibrium real GDP

26.83
Refer to Table 26.1. Find the new level of equilibrium real GDP if investment increases by 25.
a) 525.
b) 625.
c) 725.
d) 600.
e) 675.

26.84
Correct: a)
Difficulty: 4
Page: 689–690
Scramble range: All
Topic: Planned versus actual real GDP

26.84
Refer to Table 26.1. If investment rises by 25, find the level of planned expenditures when real GDP equals 500.
a) 525.
b) 625.
c) 600.
d) 725.
e) 500.

26.85
Correct: a)
Difficulty: 2
Page: 687
Scramble range: All
Topic: Autonomous versus induced expenditure

26.85
Refer to Table 26.1. Suppose the marginal propensity to spend falls to 0.5. Find the new level of autonomous expenditures.
a) 100.
b) 150.
c) 200.
d) 250.
e) This cannot be determined without more information.

26.86
Correct: e)
Difficulty: 4
Page: 688
Scramble range: All
Topic: Marginal propensity to spend

26.86
Refer to Table 26.1. Suppose that people become thriftier on the margin and wish to save an additional $0.30 on every $1 received. What is the new marginal propensity to spend?
a) 0.6.
b) 0.56.
c) 0.4.
d) 0.75.
e) 0.5.

26.87 (SG 26.1)
Correct: b)
Difficulty: 2
Page: 688
Scramble range: All
Topic: Aggregate expenditure curve

26.87
The aggregate expenditure curve shows the relationship between aggregate planned expenditure and
a) disposable income.
b) real GDP.
c) the interest rate.
d) consumption expenditure.
e) the price level.

26.88 (SG 26.2)
Correct: c)
Difficulty: 2
Page: 687
Scramble range: All
Topic: Autonomous expenditures

26.88
Autonomous expenditure is not influenced by
a) the interest rate.
b) the foreign exchange rate.
c) real GDP.
d) any other variable.
e) the price level.

26.89 (SG 26.3)
Correct: e)
Difficulty: 2
Page: 687
Scramble range: All
Topic: Induced expenditures

26.89
The fact that imports increase as real GDP increases implies that imports are a part of
a) marginal expenditure.
b) autonomous expenditure.
c) consumption expenditure.
d) equilibrium expenditure.
e) induced expenditure.

26.90 (SG 26.4)
Correct: a)
Difficulty: 2
Page: 687
Scramble range: All
Topic: Slope of the *AE* function

26.90
The slope of the aggregate expenditure curve is equal to
a) the marginal propensity to spend (on domestic goods and services).
b) the marginal propensity to consume.
c) the marginal propensity to import.
d) one minus the marginal propensity to import.
e) the autonomous expenditure multiplier.

26.91 (SG 26.5)
Correct: d)
Difficulty: 2
Page: 688
Scramble range: a)–d)
Topic: Marginal propensity to spend

26.91
The marginal propensity to spend is equal to
a) one minus the marginal propensity to save.
b) one minus the marginal propensity to import.
c) the marginal propensity to consume out of disposable income minus the marginal propensity to import.
d) the marginal propensity to consume out of real GDP minus the marginal propensity to import.
e) none of the above.

26.92 (SG 26.6)
Correct: d)
Difficulty: 3
Page: 688–690
Scramble range: All
Topic: Unplanned inventories

26.92
If unplanned inventories rise, aggregate planned expenditure is
a) greater than real GDP and firms will increase output.
b) greater than real GDP and firms will decrease output.
c) less than real GDP and firms will increase output.
d) less than real GDP and firms will decrease output.
e) less than real GDP and firms will decrease investment.

26.93 (SG 26.7)
Correct: e)
Difficulty: 3
Page: 689–690
Scramble range: None
Topic: Real GDP and planned expenditure

26.93
If real GDP is less than aggregate planned expenditure, then
a) aggregate planned expenditure will increase.
b) real GDP will increase.
c) the price level must fall to restore equilibrium.
d) imports must be too large.
e) both a) and b).

26.94 (SG 26.8)
Correct: a)
Difficulty: 2
Page: 687
Scramble range: All
Topic: Autonomous expenditures

26.94
An increase in autonomous expenditure will shift the *AE* curve
a) up but leave its slope unchanged.
b) up and make it steeper.
c) down but leave its slope unchanged.
d) down and make it steeper.
e) up and make it flatter.

26.95 (SG 26.9)
Correct: d)
Difficulty: 3
Page: 688
Scramble range: All
Topic: Marginal propensity to spend

26.95
Which of the following will lead to an increase in the marginal propensity to spend?
a) An increase in the marginal propensity to import.
b) An increase in the marginal tax rate.
c) A decrease in the marginal propensity to consume.
d) A decrease in the marginal propensity to save.
e) An increase in the marginal propensity to save.

26.96 (SG 26.10)
Correct: c)
Difficulty: 4
Page: 693
Scramble range: All
Topic: Marginal tax rate

26.96
A decrease in the marginal tax rate will
a) make the *AE* curve flatter and increase the multiplier.
b) make the *AE* curve flatter and decrease the multiplier.
c) make the *AE* curve steeper and increase the multiplier.
d) make the *AE* curve steeper and decrease the multiplier.
e) shift the *AE* curve upwards and leave the multiplier unchanged.

26.97 (SG 26.11)
Correct: a)
Difficulty: 2
Page: 692
Scramble range: All
Topic: Paradox of thrift

26.97
When all households in the economy decide to increase saving in order to accumulate wealth, it turns out that real GDP decreases. This is known as the
a) paradox of thrift.
b) expenditure paradox.
c) negative multiplier effect.
d) autonomous saving effect.
e) savings multiplier effect.

26.98 (SG 26.12)
Correct: d)
Difficulty: 3
Page: 687
Scramble range: All
Topic: Autonomous expenditure multiplier

26.98
If the marginal propensity to spend is 0.75, then the (autonomous expenditure) multiplier is
a) 0.57.
b) 1.5.
c) 2.
d) 4.
e) 1.33.

26.99 (SG 26.13)
Correct: e)
Difficulty: 4
Page: 695
Scramble range: All
Topic: Multiplier

26.99
The government wants to increase real GDP by $12 billion. If the multiplier is 3, by how much should the government increase its spending on goods and services?
a) $3 billion.
b) $3.6 billion.
c) $12 billion.
d) $36 billion.
e) $4 billion.

26.100 (SG 26.14)
Correct: a)
Difficulty: 3
Page: 704
Scramble range: All
Topic: Historical marginal propensity to spend

26.100
In recent years in Canada, the marginal propensity to spend has been
a) falling due to a gradual increase in the marginal propensity to import.
b) falling due to a gradual decrease in the marginal propensity to import.
c) rising due to a gradual increase in the marginal propensity to import.
d) rising due to a gradual decrease in the marginal propensity to import.
e) fluctuating around a constant level of 1.25.

26.101 (SG 26.15)
Correct: c)
Difficulty: 4
Page: 703–704
Scramble range: All
Topic: Recession and multiplier

26.101
When an economy goes into recession, the multiplier tends to be
a) large since the income changes are viewed to be temporary.
b) large since the income changes are viewed to be permanent.
c) small since the income changes are viewed to be temporary.
d) small since the income changes are viewed to be permanent.
e) constant since the income changes are viewed to be temporary.

26.102 (SG 26.16)
Correct: d)
Difficulty: 3
Page: 707
Scramble range: All
Topic: Price level *AE* and *AD* model

26.102
An increase in the price level will
a) shift the *AE* curve up and increase equilibrium expenditure.
b) shift the *AE* curve up and decrease equilibrium expenditure.
c) shift the *AE* curve down and increase equilibrium expenditure.
d) shift the *AE* curve down and decrease equilibrium expenditure.
e) have no impact on the *AE* curve.

26.103 (SG 26.17)
Correct: a)
Difficulty: 3
Page: 707
Scramble range: All
Topic: Price level *AE* and *AD* model

26.103
A fall in the price level will
a) cause autonomous expenditure to increase and thus produce a movement along the aggregate demand curve.
b) cause autonomous expenditure to increase and thus produce a rightward shift in the aggregate demand curve.
c) cause autonomous expenditure to increase and thus produce a leftward shift in the aggregate demand curve.
d) have no effect on autonomous expenditure.
e) cause aggregate expenditure to rise, but this will have no effect on the aggregate demand curve.

26.104 (SG 26.18)
Correct: a)
Difficulty: 4
Page: 691–693
Scramble range: All
Topic: Investment/ expected future profit

26.104
Suppose that, due to an increase in expected future profit, investment increases by $10 billion. If the multiplier is 2, the aggregate demand curve will
a) shift to the right by the horizontal distance of $20 billion.
b) shift to the right by a horizontal distance greater than $20 billion.
c) shift to the right by a horizontal distance less than $20 billion.
d) not be affected.
e) shift upwards by a vertical distance equal to $20 billion.

26.105 (SG 26.19)
Correct: e)
Difficulty: 4
Page: 695
Scramble range: All
Topic: Multiplier

26.105
Suppose the multiplier is 2 and that the aggregate supply curve is positively sloped. Suppose further that, due to an increase in expected future profit, investment increases by $10 billion. Equilibrium real GDP will
a) increase by $20 billion.
b) increase by more than $20 billion.
c) decrease by less than $20 billion.
d) be unaffected.
e) increase by less than $20 billion.

26.106 (SG 26.20)
Correct: d)
Difficulty: 4
Page: 695
Scramble range: All
Topic: Multiplier

26.106
Suppose that, due to an increase in expected future profit, investment increases by $10 billion. Which of the following would reduce the effect of this increase in autonomous expenditure on equilibrium real GDP?
a) An increase in the marginal propensity to consume.
b) A decrease in the marginal propensity to import.
c) A decrease in the marginal tax rate.
d) A steeper aggregate supply curve.
e) A flatter aggregate supply curve.

26.107
Correct: a)
Difficulty: 2
Page: 689
Scramble range: a)–d)
Topic: Autonomous investment

26.107
Autonomous investment is influenced by
a) the interest rate.
b) an increase in real GDP.
c) the level of real GDP.
d) a decrease in real GDP.
e) all of the above.

26.108
Correct: d)
Difficulty: 5
Page: 695
Scramble range: All
Topic: Multipliers

26.108
If the economy has a marginal propensity to spend of 0.3, and the government raises both taxes *and* transfer payments by $50 million, then the change in equilibrium income equals _________ times $50 million.
a) 1.43
b) 3.33
c) 0.43
d) 0
e) 1

26.109
Correct: e)
Difficulty: 4
Page: 695
Scramble range: All
Topic: Multipliers

26.109
If the economy has a marginal propensity to spend of 0.3, and the government raises both taxes *and* government purchases by $50 million, then the change in equilibrium income will equal _________ times $50 million.
a) 1.43
b) 3.33
c) 0.43
d) 0
e) 1

26.110
Correct: b)
Difficulty: 2
Page: 687
Scramble range: All
Topic: Marginal propensity to import

26.110
The marginal propensity to import is equal to
a) one minus the marginal propensity to save.
b) a leakage from the expenditure flow.
c) the marginal propensity to consume out of disposable income minus the marginal propensity to save.
d) the marginal propensity to consume out of real GDP minus the marginal propensity to save.
e) one minus the marginal propensity to consume.

26.111
Correct: a)
Difficulty: 4
Page: 688–690
Scramble range: All
Topic: Unplanned inventories

26.111
If unplanned inventories fall, aggregate planned expenditure is
a) greater than real GDP and firms will increase output.
b) greater than real GDP and firms will decrease output.
c) less than real GDP and firms will increase output.
d) less than real GDP and firms will decrease output.
e) greater than real GDP and firms will increase investment.

26.112
Correct: c)
Difficulty: 3
Page: 700
Scramble range: All
Topic: Transfer payment multiplier

26.112
Consider Table 26.1. In this economy, the transfer payments multiplier is
a) 5.
b) 1.25.
c) 4.
d) –4.
e) 1.

26.113
Correct: e)
Difficulty: 3
Page: 701
Scramble range: All
Topic: Balanced budget multiplier

26.113
Consider Table 26.1. The balanced budget multiplier in this economy is
a) 5.
b) 1.25.
c) 4.
d) –4.
e) 1.

26.114
Correct: e)
Difficulty: 5
Page: 701
Scramble range: All
Topic: Automatic stabilizers

26.114
All of the following are automatic stabilizers *except*
a) induced taxes.
b) induced transfers.
c) imports.
d) savings.
e) investment.

26.115
Correct: e)
Difficulty: 4
Page: 689–690
Scramble range: All
Topic: Changes in expenditure and GDP

26.115
Suppose that business confidence rises dramatically after a brilliant speech by the prime minister. As a result,
a) autonomous consumption expenditure rises, leading to a rise in real GDP.
b) saving will fall, leading to a rise in real GDP.
c) saving will rise, leading to a fall in real GDP.
d) net export expenditures will rise, leading to a rise in real GDP.
e) investment expenditures will rise, leading to a rise in real GDP.

26.116
Correct: c)
Difficulty: 4
Page: 691
Scramble range: All
Topic: Autonomous expenditure multiplier

26.116
If the marginal propensity to consume is 0.5, and the marginal tax rate is 0.5, then the (autonomous expenditure) multiplier is
a) 0.57.
b) 1.5.
c) 1.33.
d) 4.
e) 0.75.

26.117
Correct: c)
Difficulty: 4
Page: 701
Scramble range: All
Topic: Automatic stabilizers

26.117
An automatic stabilizer works by
a) decreasing fluctuations in aggregate expenditure and therefore increasing fluctuations in real GDP
b) increasing fluctuations in aggregate expenditure and therefore decreasing fluctuations in real GDP.
c) decreasing fluctuations in aggregate expenditure and therefore decreasing fluctuations in real GDP.
d) increasing fluctuations in aggregate expenditure and therefore increasing fluctuations in real GDP.
e) making the aggregate supply curve steeper and therefore decreasing fluctuations in real GDP.

26.118
Correct: d)
Difficulty: 5
Page: 695
Scramble range: All
Topic: Changes in the *MPS*

26.118
Suppose we were to change the theory of investment such that investment now depends on the *level* of real GDP (not the change in the level of real GDP). The result is that
a) this has no effect on any of our previous analysis.
b) this shifts aggregate expenditure upwards in a parallel manner.
c) this shifts aggregate expenditure downwards in a parallel manner.
d) this swivels aggregate expenditure upwards in a counterclockwise manner.
e) this swivels aggregate expenditure downwards in a clockwise manner.

26.119
Correct: b)
Difficulty: 5
Page: 689–690
Scramble range: All
Topic: Changes in expenditure and GDP

26.119
Consider a simple economy, where the marginal propensity to consume out of disposable income is 0.75, and the marginal propensity to import is 0.25. Suppose that investment rises by $200. As a result, equilibrium income will rise, with the components of the rise consisting of a rise in investment of $__________ and a rise in consumption of $__________.
a) 200; 400
b) 200; 200
c) 100; 300
d) 200; 300
e) 0; 400

26.120
Correct: b)
Difficulty: 5
Page: 689
Scramble range: All
Topic: Equilbrium GDP

26.120

You are given the following information about a model economy. The autonomous part of consumption is $100 million. The marginal propensity to consume out of disposable income is 0.8. Investment is $460 million; government purchases of goods and services are $400 million; taxes are a constant $400 million and do not vary as income varies. Both imports and exports are zero. The equilibrium level of GDP is $__________ million and the equilibrium level of consumption is $__________ million.

a) 1,360; 1,088
b) 3,200; 2,340
c) 6,800; 5,440
d) 4,800; 3,840
e) 1,700; 1,360

Chapter 27 Money, Banking, and Finance

27.1
Correct: d)
Difficulty: 2
Page(s): 719
Scramble range: All
Topic: Money

27.1
Money is
a) in every sense equivalent to barter.
b) in every sense equivalent to the exchange of goods for goods.
c) the same as gold.
d) a medium of exchange.
e) currency plus coins.

27.2
Correct: c)
Difficulty: 2
Page(s): 719
Scramble range: All
Topic: Double coincidence of wants

27.2
If you can find someone to swap what you have for what you want, then
a) money is necessary for the exchange to work.
b) specialization is impossible in the society in which you live.
c) there exists a double coincidence of wants.
d) there exists a double system of money.
e) there exists a monetary exchange system.

27.3
Correct: c)
Difficulty: 2
Page(s): 719
Scramble range: All
Topic: Inefficiency of barter

27.3
Without money to act as a medium of exchange
a) the standard of living in the economy would increase.
b) barter exchange would allow for a much simpler yet increased standard by which people would live.
c) the increased transactions costs associated with trading would prohibit some trades from taking place.
d) independence in production would lead to a proliferation of new products being produced.
e) all exchanges that take place under a monetary system would still take place.

27.4
Correct: d)
Difficulty: 2
Page(s): 719
Scramble range: All
Topic: Functions of money

27.4
Which of the following is not a function of money?
a) Medium of exchange.
b) Standard of deferred payment.
c) Store of value.
d) An alternative commodity that necessarily has intrinsic value.
e) Unit of account.

27.5
Correct: d)
Difficulty: 2
Page(s): 720
Scramble range: All
Topic: Money as a store of values

27.5
Money's function as a store of value can best be described as
a) an agreed measure for quoting prices.
b) a guarantee of a double coincidence of wants.
c) an efficient means of writing contracts over a long time period.
d) a commodity that can be held and exchanged for some other commodity later in time.
e) a generally acceptable exchange system.

27.6
Correct: b)
Difficulty: 3
Page(s): 719
Scramble range: All
Topic: Money

27.6
The higher and more unpredictable the changes in a monetary unit, the
a) more likely it will be used as a store of value.
b) less likely it will be used as a store of value.
c) more confidence will people have in holding it for the future.
d) less likely that contracts will be written to counterbalance the uncertainty of its value in the future.
e) more likely it will be used as a standard of deferred payment.

27.7
Correct: c)
Difficulty: 3
Page(s): 720
Scramble range: All
Topic: Inflation/money as a store of value

27.7
The higher and more unpredictable the changes in the monetary unit, the
a) lower the opportunity cost of using it as a medium of exchange.
b) lower the opportunity cost of using it as a store of value.
c) higher the opportunity cost of using it as a store of value.
d) less likely that barter exchange will replace it.
e) lower the opportunity cost of using it as a standard of deferred payment.

27.8
Correct: a)
Difficulty: 2
Page(s): 721
Scramble range: All
Topic: Forms of money

27.8
Money can take the form of any one of the following *except*
a) credit cards.
b) chequable deposits.
c) private debt.
d) fiat.
e) commodity.

27.9
Correct: d)
Difficulty: 2
Page(s): 722
Scramble range: All
Topic: Fiat money

27.9
Fiat money is
a) widely sought after for its commodity value.
b) the same as bonds.
c) the same as gold.
d) backed by faith in the issuer.
e) backed by an amount of gold that is less than the value of the fiat money.

27.10
Correct: c)
Difficulty: 2
Page(s): 721
Scramble range: All
Topic: Gresham's law

27.10
The tendency for bad money to drive out good money is known as
a) the Ming law.
b) the fiduciary principle.
c) Gresham's law.
d) an outdated principle.
e) the quantity theory of money.

27.11
Correct: b)
Difficulty: 2
Page(s): 721
Scramble range: All
Topic: Convertible paper money

27.11
A paper claim to a commodity that circulates as a medium of exchange is known as
a) a government bond.
b) convertible paper money.
c) a widely accepted poor risk.
d) fiat money.
e) deposit money.

27.12
Correct: e)
Difficulty: 2
Page(s): 723
Scramble range: All
Topic: Definitions of money

27.12
The official definitions of money can include all of the following *except*
a) currency held outside banks.
b) privately held demand deposits.
c) personal savings accounts.
d) deposits at trust and mortgage and loan companies.
e) cheques.

27.13
Correct: d)
Difficulty: 2
Page(s): 722
Scramble range: All
Topic: Fiat money

27.13
The currency circulated in Canada today is
a) backed up by eurodollars.
b) backed up by silver certificates.
c) fractionally backed by gold.
d) backed up by faith in the Canadian government.
e) fractionally backed by cash held in bank vaults.

27.14
Correct: b)
Difficulty: 2
Page(s): 723
Scramble range: All
Topic: Private debt money

27.14
A loan that the borrower promises to repay in currency on demand is called
a) partially backed money.
b) private debt money.
c) public debt money.
d) fiat money.
e) commodity money.

27.15
Correct: e)
Difficulty: 3
Page(s): 723
Scramble range: None
Topic: M1

27.15
Which of the following items is not included in the M1 definition of the money supply?
a) Currency held outside banks.
b) Nonpersonal notice deposits held at chartered banks.
c) Privately held demand deposits held at chartered banks.
d) Privately held demand deposits held at trust companies.
e) Neither b) nor d).

27.16
Correct: c)
Difficulty: 3
Page(s): 723
Scramble range: All
Topic: M2

27.16
Which of the following items is not included in the M2 definition of the money supply?
a) Currency held outside banks.
b) Privately held demand deposits at chartered banks.
c) Privately held demand deposits at trust companies.
d) Nonpersonal notice deposits at chartered banks.
e) Personal savings deposits at chartered banks.

27.17
Correct: c)
Difficulty: 3
Page(s): 723
Scramble range: All
Topic: M3

27.17
Which of the following is not considered part of M3?
a) Currency held outside banks.
b) Privately held demand deposits at chartered banks.
c) Privately held demand deposits at trust companies.
d) Nonpersonal fixed term deposits of Canadian residents.
e) Nonpersonal notice deposits held at chartered banks.

27.18
Correct: c)
Difficulty: 2
Page(s): 723
Scramble range: All
Topic: M1

27.18
The largest component of M1 is
a) currency held outside banks.
b) savings deposits.
c) demand deposits at chartered banks.
d) fixed term deposits.
e) demand deposits at trust companies.

27.19
Correct: a)
Difficulty: 2
Page(s): 728
Scramble range: All
Topic: Credit cards

27.19
Using a credit card can best be likened to
a) taking out a loan.
b) a barter exchange.
c) using any other form of money since you immediately get to take the goods home.
d) writing a cheque on your demand deposit account.
e) withdrawing money from a savings account.

27.20
Correct: a)
Difficulty: 2
Page(s): 730
Scramble range: All
Topic: Financial intermediaries

27.20
Which of the following institutions would not be considered a financial intermediary?
a) The Bank of Canada.
b) A credit union.
c) A caisse populaire.
d) A trust company.
e) The Bank of Montreal.

27.21
Correct: b)
Difficulty: 2
Page(s): 730
Scramble range: All
Topic: Financial intermediaries

27.21
The best term to describe a firm that takes deposits from households and firms and makes loans to other households and firms is a
a) usurer.
b) financial intermediary.
c) credit company.
d) stockbroker.
e) credit union.

27.22
Correct: b)
Difficulty: 2
Page(s): 730
Scramble range: All
Topic: Liabilities

27.22
Your demand deposit account is
a) a liability to you.
b) a liability to the bank.
c) subject to a six-month delay if your bank so chooses to deny your request to withdraw funds.
d) an asset to the bank.
e) part of the bank's reserves.

27.23
Correct: c)
Difficulty: 2
Page(s): 730
Scramble range: All
Topic: Commercial banks

27.23
The major purpose of a chartered bank is to
a) make mortgage loans.
b) sell shares and use the proceeds to buy a portfolio of stocks.
c) receive deposits and make loans.
d) serve the needs of their labour union owners.
e) process cheques.

27.24
Correct: e)
Difficulty: 1
Page(s): 730
Scramble range: All
Topic: Financial intermediaries

27.24
Which of the following is *not* a financial intermediary?
a) A trust company.
b) A foreign chartered bank.
c) A credit union.
d) A caisse populaire.
e) A car insurance company.

27.25
Correct: e)
Difficulty: 3
Page(s): 727
Scramble range: All
Topic: Liquidity

27.25
The most liquid measure of the Canadian money supply is
a) credit card balances.
b) M1.
c) M2.
d) M3.
e) currency outside banks.

27.26
Correct: c)
Difficulty: 2
Page(s): 732
Scramble range: All
Topic: Banking profit

27.26
The overriding reason that banks are in business is the
a) desire to take deposits and lend money.
b) need for deposit institutions in our highly specialized economy.
c) profit motive.
d) regulation of the Bank of Canada.
e) need for the lower risk of the banks' pooled loans.

27.27
Correct: e)
Difficulty: 3
Page(s): 727
Scramble range: All
Topic: Economic definition of M2

27.27
An economically relevant definition of M2 would include all of the following *but*
a) currency outside banks.
b) privately held demand deposits at chartered banks.
c) privately held demand deposits at trust companies and credit unions.
d) chequable notice deposits.
e) personal term deposits at chartered banks.

27.28
Correct: b)
Difficulty: 2
Page(s): 732
Scramble range: All
Topic: Banking profit

27.28
Which of the following assets of a chartered bank would be considered a major source of profit for the bank?
a) Demand deposit accounts.
b) Outstanding loans.
c) Cash in the bank vault.
d) Savings deposits.
e) Deposits held at the Bank of Canada.

27.29
Correct: a)
Difficulty: 2
Page(s): 727
Scramble range: All
Topic: Liquidity

27.29
Liquidity is referred to
a) as the ease with which an asset can be converted into a medium of exchange.
b) the degree of certainty of the price of an asset.
c) as the same thing as a demand deposit.
d) as the net flow of gold into the Bank of Canada.
e) as the same thing as currency.

27.30
Correct: b)
Difficulty: 2
Page(s): 731
Scramble range: All
Topic: Reserves

27.30
The reserves of a bank include
a) the cash in its vault plus the value of its demand depositors' accounts.
b) the cash in its vault plus any deposits held on account with the Bank of Canada.
c) the cash in its vault plus any gold held for the bank at the Bank of Canada.
d) all of its common stock holdings, the cash in its vault, and all deposits held on account with the Bank of Canada.
e) the cash in its vault plus any deposits held on account with the Bank of Canada plus the value of any government bonds that it holds.

27.31
Correct: a)
Difficulty: 3
Page(s): 723, 726
Scramble range: All
Topic: Money market

27.31
In redefining the definitions of money, our goal is to
a) create economically relevant calculations of the medium of exchange.
b) capture the true liquidity of money.
c) account for accounting errors in the official definitions.
d) eliminate the accounts denominated in foreign currency.
e) capture the profit motive of banks.

27.32
Correct: b)
Difficulty: 2
Page(s): 732
Scramble range: All
Topic: Financial intermediaries

27.32
Which of the following are not services of financial intermediaries?
a) Minimizing the cost of obtaining funds.
b) Providing a place for reserve account deposits.
c) Pooling risk.
d) Creating liquidity.
e) Minimizing the cost of monitoring borrowers.

27.33
Correct: b)
Difficulty: 2
Page(s): 732
Scramble range: All
Topic: Pooling risk

27.33
Pooling risk
a) refers to a default contract made by a bank to other banks.
b) refers to spreading the risk of loan default among all the depositors within the financial intermediary.
c) is now illegal under the Nuisance Act of 1987.
d) is when one person lends to an entire group or pool of borrowers.
e) refers to the lower cost of obtaining funds from a financial intermediary.

27.34
Correct: e)
Difficulty: 3
Page(s): 733
Scramble range: None
Topic: Financial innovation

27.34
Financial innovation
a) has been largely stifled in the 1980s due to recent legislation.
b) refers to the development of new financial products.
c) refers to inventive ways in which financial intermediaries avoid the costs the government imposes on borrowers and lenders.
d) has fallen since financial intermediaries were deregulated.
e) both b) and c).

27.35
Correct: b)
Difficulty: 4
Page(s): 727
Scramble range: All
Topic: Liquidity

27.35
When a person makes a deposit with a trust company that can be withdrawn on immediately and the trust company makes a mortgage loan for 30 years,
a) the trust company is lending short and borrowing long.
b) the trust company is lending long and borrowing short.
c) the individual is lending long and borrowing short.
d) the trust company is likely to go bankrupt since it takes on too much risk in this scenario.
e) the individual is creating liquidity.

27.36
Correct: e)
Difficulty: 3
Page(s): 723
Scramble range: All
Topic: Definition of the money supply

27.36
If Wolfgang transfers $1,000 out of his savings account and places it in his chequing account,
a) M1 and M2 fall.
b) M1 falls and M2 rises.
c) M1 falls and M3 rises.
d) M1 falls and M2 remains the same.
e) M1 rises and M2 remains the same.

27.37
Correct: b)
Difficulty: 2
Page(s): 733
Scramble range: All
Topic: Reserve ratio

27.37
The reserve ratio of a depository institution refers to
a) the ratio of excess reserves to total deposits.
b) the fraction of a bank's total reserve deposits that are held in its vault or on deposit with the Bank of Canada.
c) the fraction of a bank's total reserve deposits that are held in its vault in cash only.
d) the fraction of a bank's total reserve deposits that are held in an account with the Bank of Canada only.
e) the ratio of reserves to the deposits that a bank regards as necessary to conduct its business.

27.38
Correct: c)
Difficulty: 3
Page(s): 733
Scramble range: All
Topic: Reserve ratio

27.38
If a customer of a bank makes a withdrawal from his demand deposit account,
a) M3 falls.
b) the bank's reserve ratio increases.
c) the bank's reserve ratio decreases.
d) the bank's reserve ratio remains the same.
e) M1 falls.

27.39
Correct: c)
Difficulty: 2
Page(s): 733
Scramble range: All
Topic: Desired reserve ratio

27.39
The desired reserve ratio is the ratio of reserves to
a) deposits that banks must hold because of Bank of Canada regulations.
b) deposits that banks must hold because of a parliamentary regulation.
c) deposits that banks regard as prudent as well as necessary to conduct their business.
d) total savings deposits.
e) total deposits.

27.40
Correct: a)
Difficulty: 2
Page(s): 732
Scramble range: All
Topic: Functions of financial intermediaries

27.40
The main economic functions of financial intermediaries include all but which one of the following?
a) Maximize the cost of monitoring borrowers.
b) Minimize the cost of getting funds to lend.
c) Pooling risk of lenders.
d) Creating liquidity.
e) Minimize the cost of monitoring borrowers.

27.41
Correct: d)
Difficulty: 2
Page(s): 733
Scramble range: All
Topic: Excess reserves

27.41
Excess reserves are defined as
a) desired reserves minus actual reserves.
b) required reserves minus actual reserves.
c) liquidity funds minus actual reserves.
d) actual reserves minus desired reserves.
e) required reserves minus desired reserves.

27.42
Correct: d)
Difficulty: 4
Page(s): 733–734
Scramble range: All
Topic: Money creation

27.42
Suppose that you deposit $2,000 in your bank. The bank wishes to hold 20 percent of all deposits on reserve. How much new money can it create as a direct result of your deposit?
a) $200.
b) $400.
c) $8,000.
d) $1,600.
e) $10,000.

27.43
Correct: b)
Difficulty: 2
Page(s): 733–734
Scramble range: All
Topic: Bank lending/profit motive

27.43
The reason a bank manager will authorize a new loan based on the excess reserves created when new deposits come in is to
a) create new money in the economy.
b) make a profit.
c) deplete required reserves.
d) deplete desired reserves.
e) help borrowers.

27.44
Correct: b)
Difficulty: 4
Page(s): 735
Scramble range: All
Topic: Banking withdrawals

27.44
Suppose that you withdraw $1,000 from your bank. All else constant, since the bank has a desired reserve ratio of 20 percent, this transaction will directly reduce
a) the money supply by $1,000.
b) deposits by $1,000.
c) the money supply by $5,000.
d) deposits by $5,000.
e) deposits by $800.

27.45
Correct: d)
Difficulty: 2
Page(s): 734–735
Scramble range: All
Topic: Money multiplier

27.45
The simple money multiplier can be calculated as
a) change in reserves divided by change in deposits.
b) total reserves divided by deposits.
c) deposits divided by the change in reserves.
d) change in deposits divided by change in reserves.
e) change in real GDP divided by change in money.

27.46
Correct: c)
Difficulty: 3
Page(s): 734–735
Scramble range: All
Topic: Money multiplier

27.46
The formula for finding the simple money multiplier is
a) 1/(1 – actual reserves).
b) 1/(1 – desired reserves).
c) 1/desired reserve ratio.
d) 1/(1 – desired reserve ratio).
e) 1/actual reserve ratio.

27.47
Correct: b)
Difficulty: 3
Page(s): 735
Scramble range: All
Topic: Negative excess reserves

27.47
Whenever desired reserves exceed actual reserves, the bank
a) can lend out additional funds.
b) will call in loans.
c) will go out of business.
d) is in a profit-making position.
e) has excess reserves.

27.48
Correct: a)
Difficulty: 3
Page(s): 735
Scramble range: All
Topic: Positive excess reserves

27.48
Whenever actual reserves exceed desired reserves, the bank
a) can lend out additional funds.
b) will go out of business.
c) needs to call in loans.
d) will borrow funds from another bank.
e) is in a profit-making position.

27.49
Correct: c)
Difficulty: 4
Page(s): 733–735
Scramble range: All
Topic: Money creation

27.49
Suppose that a customer comes in to the New Money Bank of Speedy Creek and makes a deposit of $500. The New Money Bank and all other banks in the banking system have a desired reserve ratio of 0.20. All else the same, how much new money can be created after this new deposit has worked its way through the banking system?
a) $1,600.
b) $400.
c) $2,000.
d) $1,500.
e) $2,500.

27.50
Correct: a)
Difficulty: 4
Page(s): 734–735
Scramble range: All
Topic: Money multiplier

27.50
The higher the desired reserve ratio of banks in the banking system,
a) the lower the money multiplier.
b) the higher the money multiplier.
c) the larger the amount of total deposits that can be created from a new deposit.
d) the larger the amount of total money that can be created from a withdrawal.
e) the smaller the amount of total deposits that are reduced by a withdrawal.

27.51
Correct: d)
Difficulty: 4
Page(s): 734–735
Scramble range: All
Topic: Money multiplier

27.51
If people decide to hold in currency part of any payments received, then the money multiplier
a) will be larger.
b) will be unaffected.
c) will be increased by a factor of 2.
d) will be smaller.
e) is no longer relevant.

27.52
Correct: a)
Difficulty: 4
Page(s): 734–735
Scramble range: a)–d)
Topic: Money multiplier

27.52
Which of the following items will reduce the value of the money multiplier?
a) People tend to increase their demand for currency.
b) The desired reserve ratio of banks decreases.
c) People tend to reduce their vacation travel.
d) People spend a smaller fraction of their income on food.
e) All of the above.

27.53
Correct: e)
Difficulty: 3
Page(s): 736–737
Scramble range: All
Topic: Money in the *AD*/*AS* model

27.53
An increase in the quantity of money leads to
a) an increase in the short-run aggregate supply curve.
b) no effects in the long run.
c) a decrease in real GDP.
d) a decrease in the price level.
e) an increase in the aggregate demand curve.

27.54
Correct: d)
Difficulty: 3
Page(s): 734–735
Scramble range: All
Topic: Money multiplier

27.54
A desired reserve ratio of 0.15 suggests a simple money multiplier of
a) 6.
b) 5.
c) 4.33.
d) 6.67.
e) 15.00.

27.55
Correct: e)
Difficulty: 3
Page(s): 734–735
Scramble range: All
Topic: Money multiplier

27.55
A desired reserve ratio of 0.20 suggests a simple money multiplier of
a) 6.
b) 20.
c) 4.
d) 6.67.
e) 5.

27.56
Correct: d)
Difficulty: 4
Page(s): 734–735
Scramble range: All
Topic: Simple/actual money multplier

27.56
If the desired reserve ratio is 0.25 and the banking public has a positive demand for currency, then the money multiplier will be
a) 6.
b) 4.
c) greater than 4.
d) less than 4.
e) greater than 6.

27.57
Correct: c)
Difficulty: 4
Page(s): 733–735
Scramble range: All
Topic: Money creation

27.57
If you deposit $2,500 in a demand deposit account at your local bank, the immediate effect is
a) a decrease in the money supply of $2,500.
b) an increase in the money supply of $2,500.
c) no change in the money supply, but in the future the money supply may expand because the bank now has excess reserves.
d) a reduction in excess reserves equal to the amount that you took out of circulation.
e) an increase in the money supply of $2,500, but in the future the money supply may expand because the bank now has excess reserves.

27.58
Correct: e)
Difficulty: 4
Page(s): 733
Scramble range: All
Topic: Bank reserves

27.58
If people decide to transfer their currency into demand deposit accounts then, all else the same, their decisions will
a) cause the money supply to decline.
b) cause lower inflation.
c) cause higher real interest rates.
d) cause the money supply to increase immediately.
e) increase the actual reserves of banks.

27.59
Correct: d)
Difficulty: 4
Page(s): 737–738
Scramble range: All
Topic: Quantity theory of money

27.59
The purchasing power of a fixed amount of money
a) is unrelated to the amount of money in circulation.
b) increases as the level of prices increases.
c) tends to increase as the quantity of money in circulation increases.
d) tends to decrease as the money supply expands relative to the amount of goods in circulation.
e) is positively related to the quantity of money in circulation.

27.60
Correct: c)
Difficulty: 2
Page(s): 736
Scramble range: All
Topic: CFDIC

27.60
The Canadian Federal Deposit Insurance Corporation
a) insures the end of bank failures.
b) insures that the reserves of member banks never fall below the legal requirement.
c) insures deposits of individuals against bank failure.
d) was bankrupt as of 1989.
e) insures banks against bad loans.

27.61
Correct: a)
Difficulty: 3
Page(s): 730
Scramble range: All
Topic: Assets and liabilities

27.61
Your chequing account is
a) an asset to you and a liability to your bank.
b) a liability to you and an asset to your bank.
c) an asset to both you and your bank.
d) a liability to both you and your bank.
e) an asset to you and a reserve to your bank.

27.62
Correct: c)
Difficulty: 4
Page(s): 738
Scramble range: All
Topic: Money supply changes

27.62
An increase in the money supply
a) is thought to increase real GDP in the long run.
b) is thought to decrease real GDP in the long run.
c) may create an increase in the price level if the production rate of goods and services in the economy remains the same.
d) may create an increase in the short-run aggregate supply curve.
e) may create a decrease in the short-run aggregate demand curve.

27.63
Correct: c)
Difficulty: 4
Page(s): 736–738
Scramble range: a)–d)
Topic: *AD/AS* and increase in money supply

27.63
Refer to Figure 27.1. Which of the graphs best depicts the short-run and long-run effects of an increase in the money supply?
a) (a).
b) (b).
c) (c).
d) (d).
e) None of the above.

Figure 27.1

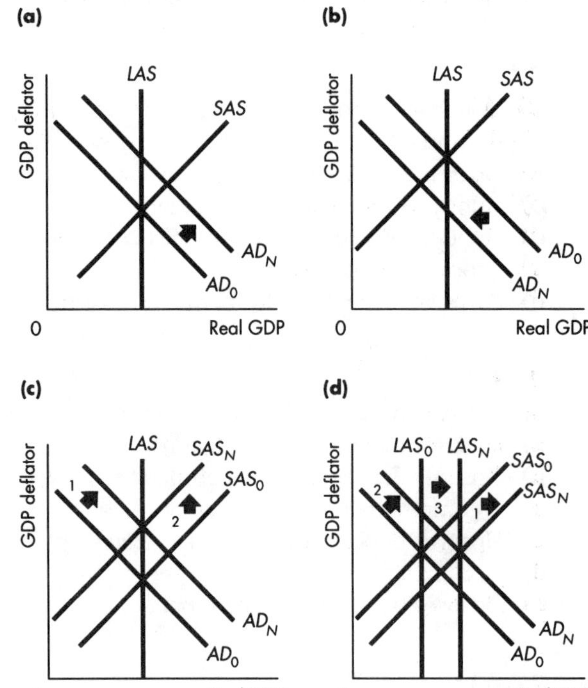

27.64
Correct: a)
Difficulty: 3
Page(s): 736–738
Scramble range: a)–d)
Topic: *AD/AS* and increase in money supply

27.64
Refer to Figure 27.1. Which of the graphs best depicts the short-run effect of an increase in the money supply?
a) (a).
b) (b).
c) (c).
d) (d).
e) None of the above.

27.65
Correct: b)
Difficulty: 3
Page(s): 736–738
Scramble range: a)–d)
Topic: *AD/AS* and increase in money supply

27.65
Refer to Figure 27.1. Which of the graphs best depicts the short-run effect of an decrease in the money supply?
a) (a).
b) (b).
c) (c).
d) (d).
e) None of the above.

27.66
Correct: d)
Difficulty: 3
Page(s): 737–738
Scramble range: All
Topic: Quantity theory of money

27.66
The quantity theory of money is the proposition that
a) an increase in the money supply will decrease the price level by an offsetting amount rendering money policy useless.
b) an increase in the money supply by n percent will lead to an increase in the price level by $(n + 1)$ percent.
c) an increase in the quantity of money will lead to an equal percentage increase in real GDP.
d) an increase in the quantity of money will lead to an equal percentage increase in the price level.
e) the quantity of money times the velocity of circulation equals the price level times the level of real GDP.

27.67
Correct: d)
Difficulty: 2
Page(s): 737–738
Scramble range: All
Topic: Quantity theory of money

27.67
The basis of the quantity theory of money is the
a) aggregate demand model.
b) aggregate supply model.
c) aggregate demand and aggregate supply model.
d) equation of exchange.
e) money multiplier.

27.68
Correct: e)
Difficulty: 3
Page(s): 737–738
Scramble range: All
Topic: Quantity theory of money

27.68
According to the quantity theory of money, a tripling of the money supply would lead to a
a) doubling of the price level.
b) more than tripling of the price level.
c) tripling of real GDP in the long run.
d) tripling of real GDP in the short run.
e) tripling of the price level.

27.69
Correct: e)
Difficulty: 3
Page(s): 737–738
Scramble range: a)–d)
Topic: Quantity theory of money

27.69
The quantity theory of money leads to predictions about how
a) changes in the price level affect nominal GDP.
b) changes in the price level affect real GDP.
c) changes in velocity affect nominal GDP.
d) changes in velocity affect real GDP.
e) none of the above.

27.70
Correct: e)
Difficulty: 3
Page(s): 737–738
Scramble range: All
Topic: Quantity theory of money

27.70
An increase in the money supply leads to a proportional increase in the price level. This statement is a prediction of the
a) equation of exchange.
b) Keynesian model of price level determination.
c) money multiplier theory of banking.
d) short-run theory of inflation.
e) quantity theory of money.

27.71
Correct: a)
Difficulty: 2
Page(s): 738
Scramble range: All
Topic: Velocity

27.71
In the quantity theory of money, velocity is assumed to be
a) constant.
b) rising during recessions.
c) falling during recessions.
d) unrelated to the equation of exchange.
e) a positive function of the money supply.

27.72
Correct: b)
Difficulty: 2
Page(s): 738
Scramble range: All
Topic: Velocity

27.72
The velocity of money is the
a) rate of change in the GDP deflator.
b) turnover rate of the money supply per time period.
c) measurement of the changes in the purchasing power of a unit of the money over a given time period.
d) inverse of the price level.
e) dollar value of all expenditures on goods and services.

27.73
Correct: e)
Difficulty: 3
Page(s): 739
Scramble range: a)–d)
Topic: Empirical evidence

27.73
The Canadian historical evidence on the quantity theory of money reveals
a) on average the growth rate of money exceeds the inflation rate.
b) changes in the growth rate of money are correlated with changes in the inflation rate.
c) during and immediately after World War II, the growth rate of money and the inflation rate are relatively unrelated.
d) since 1950, the inflation rate is relatively less volatile than the growth rate of money.
e) all of the above.

27.74 (SG 27.2)
Correct: e)
Difficulty: 3
Page(s): 720
Scramble range: All
Topic: Standard of deferred payment function

27.74
When a contract specifies that a certain number of dollars is to be paid in the future for services rendered, money is functioning as a
a) medium of exchange.
b) measure of liquidity.
c) unit of account.
d) store of value.
e) standard of deferred payment.

27.75 (SG 27.3)
Correct: a)
Difficulty: 2
Page(s): 719–720
Scramble range: All
Topic: Unit of account function

27.75
If the prices of goods and services were stated in terms of kilograms of salt, then salt is a
a) unit of account.
b) standard of deferred payment.
c) store of value.
d) quasi-money.
e) medium of exchange.

27.76 (SG 27.4)
Correct: c)
Difficulty: 3
Page(s): 721
Scramble range: All
Topic: Commodity money

27.76
Which of the following is a disadvantage of a commodity money?
a) It is valued for its own sake.
b) Its value as money is much greater than its value as a commodity.
c) The commodity could be used in other ways if it was not used as a medium of exchange.
d) It has little intrinsic value.
e) It is too bulky to carry around.

27.77 (SG 27.5)
Correct: d)
Difficulty: 2
Page(s): 721
Scramble range: All
Topic: Debasement of currency

27.77
The fact that debased commodity money will drive money which has not been debased out of circulation is an example of
a) liquidity.
b) the effects of near money.
c) convertibility.
d) Gresham's law.
e) the quantity theory of money.

27.78 (SG 27.6)
Correct: a)
Difficulty: 2
Page(s): 722
Scramble range: All
Topic: Fiat money

27.78
Canadian currency today is an example of
a) fiat money.
b) commodity money.
c) convertible paper money.
d) private debt money.
e) fractionally backed gold-convertible money.

27.79 (SG 27.7)
Correct: d)
Difficulty: 2
Page(s): 723
Scramble range: All
Topic: Private debt money

27.79
A chequable deposit in a financial institution is an example of
a) commodity money.
b) fiat money.
c) convertible paper money.
d) private debt money.
e) public debt money.

27.80 (SG 27.8)
Correct: d)
Difficulty: 3
Page(s): 723
Scramble range: All
Topic: M2+

27.80
Which of the following is a component of M2+ but not of M2?
a) Nonpersonal fixed-term deposits of Canadian residents.
b) Personal demand deposits at chartered banks.
c) Personal savings deposits at chartered banks.
d) Personal savings deposits at trust companies.
e) Canada Savings Bonds.

27.81 (SG 27.9)
Correct: e)
Difficulty: 2
Page(s): 727
Scramble range: All
Topic: "Almost" money

27.81
Which of the following is a quasi-money or "almost" money?
a) Credit cards.
b) Demand deposits
c) Term deposits.
d) Other chequable deposits.
e) Savings deposits.

27.82 (SG 27.10)
Correct: a)
Difficulty: 2
Page(s): 723
Scramble range: All
Topic: Chequable deposits as money

27.82
Which of the following is money?
a) A chequable deposit.
b) A blank cheque.
c) A credit card.
d) A large time deposit.
e) A Canada Savings Bond.

27.83 (SG 27.11)
Correct: e)
Difficulty: 4
Page(s): 723–728
Scramble range: All
Topic: Canadian banking

27.83
Which of the following statements about the Canadian banking system versus the American system is true?
a) The Canadian banking system is larger.
b) Banks fail more frequently in Canada.
c) Banks are insured in Canada, but not in the United States.
d) The Canadian banking system is more stable since Canada has more banks, allowing diversification.
e) The Canadian banking system is more stable since Canada has fewer, but larger, and hence more diversified banks.

27.84 (SG 27.12)
Correct: d)
Difficulty: 2
Page(s): 730
Scramble range: All
Topic: Liabilities

27.84
Which of the following is a liability of a chartered bank?
a) Vault cash.
b) Loans.
c) Securities.
d) Demand deposits.
e) Its deposits at the Bank of Canada.

27.85 (SG 27.13)
Correct: a)
Difficulty: 2
Page(s): 727
Scramble range: All
Topic: Liquidity

27.85
Which of the following is most liquid?
a) Demand deposits.
b) Real estate.
c) A government bond.
d) Savings deposits.
e) A cheque.

27.86 (SG 27.14)
Correct: a)
Difficulty: 4
Page(s): 737–738
Scramble range: All
Topic: Evidence of the quantity

27.86
Which of the following is false, given the empirical evidence on the quantity theory of money?
a) The only cause of inflation is higher growth rates of money.
b) Internationally, inflation and high growth rates of money are positively correlated among high inflation countries.
c) Internationally, inflation and high growth rates of money are positively correlated among low inflation countries.
d) A major cause of inflation is higher growth rates of money.
e) As the growth rate of money rose through the 1960s, inflation rose too.

27.87 (SG 27.15)
Correct: c)
Difficulty: 3
Page(s): 733–735
Scramble range: All
Topic: Money creation

27.87
A bank can create money by
a) selling some of its securities.
b) increasing its reserves.
c) lending its excess reserves.
d) printing more cheques.
e) converting reserves into securities.

27.88 (SG 27.16)
Correct: b)
Difficulty: 3
Page(s): 734–735
Scramble range: All
Topic: Money multiplier

27.88
If all banks hold 100 percent reserves, the simple money multiplier is
a) 0.
b) 1.
c) 10.
d) 100.
e) infinite.

27.89 (SG 27.17)
Correct: a)
Difficulty: 4
Page(s): 737–738
Scramble range: None
Topic: Quantity theory of money

27.89
Which of the following will raise the price level?
a) The discovery of a hoard of 1930s currency in someone's barn.
b) The decision by several banks to call in 20 percent of their loans.
c) A massive fire in the vaults of the Bank of Montreal that destroys several million dollars in uninsured reserves.
d) Both a) and b).
e) Both b) and c).

27.90 (SG 27.18)
Correct: e)
Difficulty: 4
Page(s): 734–735
Scramble range: All
Topic: Size of the real world money multplier

27.90
Suppose there is an increase in the tendency for loans to return to banks in the form of reserves; i.e., there is a decrease in the currency drain. Select the best statement.
a) The simple money multiplier will decrease.
b) The simple money multiplier will increase.
c) The real world money multiplier will decrease.
d) The real world money multiplier will stay constant.
e) The real world money multiplier will increase.

27.91 (SG 27.19)
Correct: a)
Difficulty: 4
Page(s): 737–738
Scramble range: All
Topic: Quantity theory of money

27.91
A decrease in the quantity of money will cause
a) both the price level and real GDP to decline in the short run, but, in the long run, only the price level will fall as real GDP returns to its initial level.
b) both the price level and real GDP to increase in the short run, but, in the long run, only the price level will rise as real GDP returns to its initial level.
c) the price level to fall in the short run, but in the long run the price level will return to its initial level.
d) the price level to fall and real GDP to rise in both the short run and the long run.
e) the price level to fall and real GDP to fall in both the short run and the long run.

27.92 (SG 27.20)
Correct: a)
Difficulty: 3
Page(s): 737–738
Scramble range: All
Topic: Quantity theory of money

27.92
According to the quantity theory of money, an increase in the quantity of money will lead to an increase in the price level
a) but have no effect on real GDP or the velocity of circulation.
b) as well as increasing both real GDP and the velocity of circulation.
c) as well as increasing real GDP but decreasing the velocity of circulation.
d) as well as decreasing real GDP but increasing the velocity of circulation.
e) but have no effect on real GDP while decreasing velocity.

27.93 (SG 27.21)
Correct: c)
Difficulty: 3
Page(s): 738
Scramble range: All
Topic: Velocity

27.93
If the price level is 2, real GDP is $100 billion, and the quantity of money is $40 billion, then the velocity of circulation is
a) 2.5.
b) 4.
c) 5.
d) 10.
e) 50.

27.94
Correct: e)
Difficulty: 4
Page(s): 738
Scramble range: All
Topic: Equation of exchange

27.94
Given the equation of exchange is true by definition, then
a) the quantity theory of money must be true.
b) if the money supply rises, then the price level must rise.
c) if the money supply rises, real GDP must rise.
d) if velocity is a positive function of the money supply, the quantity theory of money is true.
e) certain additional assumptions are needed for the quantity theory of money to be true.

27.95
Correct: d)
Difficulty: 3
Page(s): 721
Scramble range: All
Topic: Commodity money

27.95
Which of the following is an advantage of a commodity money?
a) It cannot be used for anything else but money.
b) Its value as money is much less than its value as a commodity.
c) The commodity could be used in other ways if it was not used as a medium of exchange.
d) It has intrinsic value.
e) It is too bulky to carry.

27.96
Correct: a)
Difficulty: 2
Page(s): 722
Scramble range: None
Topic: Fiat money

27.96
Which of the following is considered fiat money?
a) Canadian currency.
b) Gold.
c) Convertible paper money.
d) University residence scrip.
e) Both a) and d).

27.97
Correct: a)
Difficulty: 2
Page(s): 723
Scramble range: All
Topic: Private debt money

27.97
An example of private debt money would be
a) chequable deposits in a financial institution.
b) Canadian currency.
c) convertible paper money.
d) commodity money.
e) a bank loan.

27.98
Correct: c)
Difficulty: 2
Page(s): 723
Scramble range: All
Topic: Chequable deposits as money

27.98
Which of the following is not money?
a) A chequable deposit.
b) Canadian currency.
c) A credit card.
d) Eurodollars.
e) A term deposit.

27.99
Correct: d)
Difficulty: 3
Page(s): 738
Scramble range: a)–d)
Topic: Changes in money supply

27.99
If Jean Dupont deposits $5,000 in the St-Jean Caisse Populaire, the long-run end result is
a) a fall in real GDP.
b) a rise in real GDP.
c) a fall in the price level.
d) a rise in the price level.
e) none of the above.

27.100
Correct: b)
Difficulty: 3
Page(s): 730
Scramble range: None
Topic: Assets

27.100
Which of the following is an asset to a commercial bank?
a) Currency in circulation.
b) Securities.
c) Government of Canada balances with the Bank of Canada.
d) Demand deposits.
e) Both b) and c).

27.101
Correct: b)
Difficulty: 2
Page(s): 727
Scramble range: All
Topic: Liquidity

27.101
Which of the following is least liquid?
a) Demand deposits.
b) Real estate.
c) A government bond.
d) Savings deposits.
e) A cheque.

27.102
Correct: b)
Difficulty: 4
Page(s): 731
Scramble range: All
Topic: Banking reserves

27.102
A bank can slow down the creation of money by
a) selling some of its investment securities.
b) increasing its reserves.
c) lending its excess reserves.
d) printing more cheques.
e) shifting some of its reserves from cash to deposits held at the Bank of Canada.

27.103
Correct: e)
Difficulty: 4
Page(s): 734–735
Scramble range: All
Topic: Money multiplier

27.103
If all banks hold 50 percent reserves, the simple money multiplier is
a) 0.
b) 1.
c) 10.
d) 5.
e) 2.

27.104
Correct: d)
Difficulty: 5
Page(s): 738
Scramble range: a)–d)
Topic: Money growth

27.104
Consider Figure 27.1. Which of the graphs shows the case of an economy where the money supply is growing at a rate just fast enough to meet the growing real GDP level?
a) (a).
b) (b).
c) (c).
d) (d).
e) None of the above.

27.105
Correct: e)
Difficulty: 4
Page(s): 719
Scramble range: All
Topic: Money

27.105
Anything can be money as long as it
a) has low transaction costs.
b) is not too bulky.
c) has intrinsic worth.
d) meets the double coincidence of wants.
e) is acceptable as a medium of exchange.

Chapter 28 The Bank of Canada, Money, and Interest Rates

28.1
Correct: d)
Difficulty: 1
Page(s): 747
Scramble range: All
Topic: Central banks

28.1
A central bank is best described as
a) one that is located in the geographical centre of a country.
b) one that is convenient to all of its depositors.
c) a bank of one country which can only be used by foreign banks desiring to convert their currency to the domestic nation's currency.
d) a public authority charged with regulating and controlling a country's monetary and financial institutions and markets.
e) a bank operated by the United Nations to facilitate international transactions.

28.2
Correct: c)
Difficulty: 2
Page(s): 747
Scramble range: All
Topic: Velocity

28.2
Velocity fluctuates because of
a) the actions of the Bank of Canada.
b) changes in interest rates.
c) changes in the demand for money.
d) fiscal policy.
e) changes in the price level.

28.3
Correct: b)
Difficulty: 2
Page(s): 747
Scramble range: All
Topic: Monetary policy

28.3
The attempt to control inflation and moderate the business cycle by changing the quantity of money in circulation and adjusting interest rates is called
a) public policy.
b) monetary policy.
c) fiscal policy.
d) bank policy.
e) foreign exchange policy.

28.4
Correct: e)
Difficulty: 2
Page(s): 747
Scramble range: All
Topic: Bank of Canada Act

28.4
The Bank of Canada was created by the Bank of Canada Act of
a) 1917 as a result of Canadian involvement in World War I.
b) 1867 as part of Confederation.
c) 1907 as a result of a major banking panic.
d) 1913 following a severe banking panic several years earlier.
e) 1935 during the Great Depression.

28.5
Correct: e)
Difficulty: 2
Page(s): 747
Scramble range: a)–d)
Topic: Bank of Canada

28.5
The Bank of Canada
a) was the first central bank ever set up.
b) has a structure that is modelled after the Bank of Sweden.
c) evolved from the Bank of Montreal, the original central bank.
d) originally was run by the minister of finance.
e) none of the above.

28.6
Correct: e)
Difficulty: 2
Page(s): 747–748
Scramble range: All
Topic: Bank of Canada

28.6
According to the textbook, the three key elements in the structure of the Bank of Canada are the
a) governor, the minister of finance, and the Bank of Montreal.
b) Federal Reserve System, the board of directors, and the governor.
c) minister of finance, the governor, and the board of directors.
d) senior staff, the governor, and the minister of finance.
e) governor, the board of directors, and the senior staff.

28.7
Correct: d)
Difficulty: 2
Page(s): 748
Scramble range: All
Topic: Board of directors

28.7
The board of directors consists of
a) eleven members appointed by parliament.
b) the governor, the deputy governor, and the minister of finance.
c) the governor, the senior deputy governor, and the deputy minister of finance.
d) the governor, the deputy governor, the minister of finance, and eleven members of the public.
e) the governor, the deputy governor, the minister of finance, and the presidents of all the major banks.

28.8
Correct: e)
Difficulty: 3
Page(s): 747–748
Scramble range: a)–d)
Topic: Bank of Canada

28.8
The senior staff of the Bank of Canada
a) are key players in the formulation of the bank's monetary policy.
b) are economists and central bankers with considerable experience.
c) monitor the Canadian and world economies on a day-by-day basis.
d) prepare forecasts of the Canadian and world economies.
e) all of the above.

28.9
Correct: d)
Difficulty: 2
Page(s): 747–748
Scramble range: All
Topic: Bank of Canada

28.9
The Bank of Canada
a) is totally controlled by the minister of finance.
b) is totally independent of the federal government.
c) has always been subservient to the federal government.
d) was originally independent of the federal government, but after 1967 became subservient.
e) was originally subservient to the federal government, but after 1967 became independent.

28.10
Correct: b)
Difficulty: 2
Page(s): 747–748
Scramble range: All
Topic: Bank of Canada

28.10
The Bank of Canada is subservient to the federal government
a) and therefore must just meekly follow its orders.
b) but still has considerable power to make independent policy decisions.
c) and therefore must print money to cover any federal deficit.
d) and therefore is less democratic than an independent central bank.
e) and therefore can only comment on the correct monetary policy.

28.11
Correct: b)
Difficulty: 3
Page(s): 747
Scramble range: All
Topic: Monetary policy

28.11
The policy tools used by the Bank of Canada include
a) reserve requirements, the prime rate, and the bank rate.
b) reserve requirements, the bank rate, and open market operations.
c) the bank rate, open market operations, and the prime rate.
d) reserve requirements, the prime rate, and open market operations.
e) reserve requirements, the exchange rate, and open market operations.

28.12
Correct: b)
Difficulty: 3
Page(s): 751
Scramble range: All
Topic: Open market operations

28.12
The sale of government bonds by the Bank of Canada will cause
a) a decrease in interest rates.
b) a decrease in the reserves of banks.
c) an increase in the supply of money.
d) an increase in the commercial banks' loans to the public.
e) an increase in the reserves of banks.

28.13
Correct: d)
Difficulty: 3
Page(s): 751
Scramble range: All
Topic: Open market operations

28.13
The purchase of government bonds by the Bank of Canada will cause
a) an increase in interest rates.
b) a decrease in bank reserves.
c) a decrease in bank loans.
d) an increase in aggregate demand.
e) a decrease in the supply of money.

28.14
Correct: b)
Difficulty: 3
Page(s): 751
Scramble range: All
Topic: Open market operations

28.14
The purchase of government bonds by the Bank of Canada will
a) decrease bank reserves.
b) increase bank loans.
c) decrease the prices of bonds.
d) be a good tool against inflation.
e) tighten credit conditions.

28.15
Correct: c)
Difficulty: 3
Page(s): 751
Scramble range: All
Topic: Open market operations

28.15
If the Bank of Canada sells $1 million worth of government securities, the money supply will
a) decrease by $1 million.
b) expand by $1 million.
c) decrease by more than $1 million.
d) expand by more than $1 million.
e) expand by less than $1 million.

28.16
Correct: a)
Difficulty: 3
Page(s): 750
Scramble range: All
Topic: Reserve requirements

28.16
An increase in the reserve requirement would most likely lead to
a) a shortage of reserves for banks.
b) an increased rate of investment in the economy.
c) lower interest rates.
d) easier credit for consumers.
e) an increase in the purchase of government bonds.

28.17
Correct: e)
Difficulty: 2
Page(s): 750–751
Scramble range: All
Topic: Discount rate policy

28.17
Loans from the Bank of Canada to chartered banks are
a) made at a rate of interest called the prime rate.
b) short term in nature.
c) made to nonbanking corporations with assets above $1 billion.
d) long term in nature.
e) infrequent in nature.

28.18
Correct: d)
Difficulty: 3
Page(s): 747
Scramble range: All
Topic: Monetary policy

28.18
Which one of the following would be considered a contractionary monetary policy?
a) A decrease in the reserve requirement.
b) An increase in personal income taxes.
c) The Bank of Canada encourages banks to make loans.
d) The Bank of Canada sells government bonds.
e) The Bank of Canada buys government bonds.

28.19
Correct: b)
Difficulty: 3
Page(s): 747
Scramble range: All
Topic: Monetary policy

28.19
An expansionary monetary policy could include
a) increasing the reserve requirement.
b) open market operations to reduce the rate of interest.
c) the Bank of Canada applying moral suasion to chartered banks to reduce bank loans.
d) the sale of government securities by the Bank of Canada.
e) an increase in the bank rate.

28.20
Correct: a)
Difficulty: 3
Page(s): 747
Scramble range: All
Topic: Monetary policy

28.20
To stimulate aggregate demand, the Bank of Canada could
a) buy securities.
b) sell securities.
c) raise the bank rate.
d) raise the reserve requirement.
e) tighten credit conditions.

28.21
Correct: a)
Difficulty: 3
Page(s): 747
Scramble range: All
Topic: Monetary policy

28.21
To discourage economic investment, the Bank of Canada could
a) sell securities.
b) lower the reserve requirement.
c) buy securities.
d) lower the interest rate.
e) lower the exchange rate.

28.22
Correct: c)
Difficulty: 3
Page(s): 747
Scramble range: All
Topic: Monetary policy

28.22
To lower interest rates, the Bank of Canada could
a) increase the treasury bill rate.
b) raise the reserve requirement.
c) buy government securities.
d) decrease bank reserves.
e) raise the bank rate.

28.23
Correct: a)
Difficulty: 3
Page(s): 747
Scramble range: All
Topic: Monetary policy

28.23
To reduce aggregate demand, the Bank of Canada could
a) contract the money supply and raise interest rates.
b) expand the money supply and lower interest rates.
c) contract the money supply and lower interest rates.
d) expand the money supply and raise interest rates.
e) contract the federal deficit and raise interest rates.

28.24
Correct: c)
Difficulty: 3
Page(s): 747–748
Scramble range: All
Topic: Bank of Canada

28.24
Which one of the following is not a function of the Bank of Canada?
a) To hold deposits of chartered banks and to transfer these to the accounts of other banks.
b) To act as a lender of last resort to chartered banks.
c) To make profits.
d) To regulate the supply of money.
e) To choose the exchange rate regime.

28.25
Correct: a)
Difficulty: 2
Page(s): 750–751
Scramble range: All
Topic: Discount rate

28.25
The bank rate refers to
a) the rate of interest that the Bank of Canada charges on loans to chartered banks.
b) when chartered banks fail.
c) the rate of growth of the money supply.
d) the rate of interest on government securities.
e) the rate of interest banks charge their best customers.

28.26
Correct: d)
Difficulty: 3
Page(s): 747–748
Scramble range: All
Topic: Bank of Canada

28.26
The Bank of Canada does not
a) set reserve requirements.
b) make loans to chartered banks.
c) engage in open market operations.
d) make loans to nonbanks.
e) set the exchange rate regime.

28.27
Correct: b)
Difficulty: 4
Page(s): 750
Scramble range: All
Topic: Reserve requirements

28.27
If the reserve requirements are raised when banks are holding no more than they desire to hold in reserves, then
a) the money supply may increase.
b) the money supply may decrease.
c) bank loans will increase.
d) bank deposits will decrease but there will be no change in the money supply.
e) bank reserves will fall and there will be a decrease in the money supply.

28.28
Correct: c)
Difficulty: 2
Page(s): 751
Scramble range: All
Topic: Open market operations

28.28
Open market operations
a) refer to the Bank of Canada's sales and purchases of corporate stock.
b) can change bank deposits but cannot alter the money supply.
c) refer to the purchase or sale of government securities to the public by the Bank of Canada.
d) refer to loans made by the Bank of Canada to chartered banks.
e) refer to changes in reserve requirements by the Bank of Canada.

28.29
Correct: d)
Difficulty: 4
Page(s): 751
Scramble range: All
Topic: Open market operations

28.29
If the Bank of Canada buys government bonds, all of the following will happen *except*
a) bank reserves will increase.
b) the money supply will increase.
c) there will be a multiple expansion of banking deposits.
d) the bank rate will be forced up.
e) credit conditions will loosen.

28.30
Correct: a)
Difficulty: 4
Page(s): 751
Scramble range: All
Topic: Bank of Canada balance sheet

28.30
When the Bank of Canada makes a $20 million loan to a chartered bank
a) the Bank of Canada has offsetting $20 million changes in liabilities.
b) the bank has an offsetting $20 million decrease in assets.
c) the bank has offsetting $20 million changes in liabilities.
d) the assets and liabilities of the Bank of Canada do not change.
e) the Bank of Canada has offsetting $20 million decreases in assets.

28.31
Correct: b)
Difficulty: 3
Page(s): 751
Scramble range: All
Topic: Bank of Canada notes

28.31
Bank of Canada notes show up on chartered bank balance sheets as
a) assets of the Bank of Canada and liabilities of chartered banks.
b) liabilities of the Bank of Canada and assets of chartered banks.
c) liabilities of the Bank of Canada and chartered banks.
d) assets of the Bank of Canada and chartered banks.
e) assets of the Bank of Canada and liabilities of the federal treasury.

28.32
Correct: c)
Difficulty: 2
Page(s): 751
Scramble range: All
Topic: Bank of Canada notes

28.32
Which of the following items is *not* considered a liability of the Bank of Canada?
a) Bank of Canada notes in circulation.
b) Chartered bank deposits.
c) Government of Canada securities.
d) Foreign central bank deposits.
e) Government of Canada deposits.

28.33
Correct: c)
Difficulty: 4
Page(s): 751
Scramble range: All
Topic: Open market operations

28.33
A decrease in chartered bank reserves could be caused by
a) a decision by households to hold less currency.
b) an increase in the reserve requirement.
c) the sale of government bonds by the Bank of Canada.
d) a decrease in the bank rate.
e) the purchase of government bonds by the Bank of Canada.

28.34
Correct: e)
Difficulty: 2
Page(s): 749–750
Scramble range: All
Topic: Exchange rate regimes

28.34
The three possible exchange rate regimes are
a) fixed, flexible, and open.
b) subservient, fixed, and managed.
c) open, fixed, and managed.
d) open, flexible, and managed.
e) fixed, flexible, and managed.

28.35
Correct: e)
Difficulty: 2
Page(s): 749–750
Scramble range: All
Topic: Exchange rate regimes

28.35
A fixed exchange rate regime is one in which the
a) supply of the Canadian dollar remains fixed.
b) demand for the Canadian dollar remains fixed.
c) value of the exchange rate is defined by market forces.
d) value of the exchange rate is influenced by the central bank.
e) central bank defines and maintains a fixed exchange rate value.

28.36
Correct: b)
Difficulty: 2
Page(s): 751
Scramble range: All
Topic: Bank of Canada balance sheet

28.36
The majority of the Bank of Canada's assets are
a) gold and foreign exchange.
b) Government of Canada securities.
c) Bank of Canada notes.
d) commercial stocks.
e) elements of the monetary base.

28.37
Correct: d)
Difficulty: 2
Page(s): 752
Scramble range: All
Topic: Monetary base

28.37
The monetary base consists of
a) Government of Canada securities and Bank of Canada notes.
b) commercial stocks and foreign exchange.
c) gold.
d) Bank of Canada notes, banks' deposits at the Bank of Canada, and coinage in circulation.
e) Bank of Canada notes, banks' deposits at the Bank of Canada, coinage in circulation, and government deposits at the Bank of Canada.

28.38
Correct: b)
Difficulty: 2
Page(s): 752
Scramble range: All
Topic: Convertible notes

28.38
Convertible notes are
a) issued by chartered banks in Canada.
b) bank notes that entitle the owner to convert the note on demand into a precious metal such as gold.
c) issued by the Bank of Canada.
d) issued by the federal government.
e) bank notes that obtain their value by government fiat.

28.39
Correct: a)
Difficulty: 2
Page(s): 753
Scramble range: All
Topic: Money multiplier

28.39
The Canadian money multiplier is calculated as
a) quantity of money/monetary base.
b) quantity of convertible notes/monetary base.
c) monetary base/currency holdings of households.
d) currency holdings of households/monetary base.
e) monetary base/quantity of money.

28.40
Correct: c)
Difficulty: 2
Page(s): 758
Scramble range: All
Topic: Motives for money holding

28.40
Reasons for holding money include the
a) income and speculative motives.
b) precautionary and conversion motives.
c) precautionary and speculative motives.
d) interest rate and transactions motives.
e) speculative and interest rate motives.

28.41
Correct: a)
Difficulty: 2
Page(s): 758
Scramble range: All
Topic: Transactions motive

28.41
The main motive for holding money is the
a) transactions motive.
b) precautionary motive.
c) speculative motive.
d) interest income motive.
e) income motive.

28.42
Correct: e)
Difficulty: 3
Page(s): 758
Scramble range: All
Topic: Transactions motive

28.42
If the reason you hold money is to pay your apartment rent, economists would attribute this to your
a) speculative motive for holding money.
b) income motive for holding money.
c) cautionary motive for holding money.
d) precautionary motive for holding money.
e) transaction motive for holding money.

28.43
Correct: c)
Difficulty: 2
Page(s): 758
Scramble range: All
Topic: Transactions motive

28.43
For which one of the following reasons do people hold money for planned expenditures?
a) M2 motive for holding money.
b) M1 motive for holding money.
c) Transactions motive for holding money.
d) Speculative motive for holding money.
e) Precautionary motive for holding money.

28.44
Correct: c)
Difficulty: 3
Page(s): 758
Scramble range: All
Topic: Transactions motive

28.44
The amount of money that people hold for transactions
a) is constant on a day-to-day basis.
b) is unrelated to the interest rate.
c) varies considerably during any week or month but in the aggregate the amount is stable.
d) is unrelated to the level of income they earn.
e) is unrelated to the price level.

28.45
Correct: d)
Difficulty: 2
Page(s): 758
Scramble range: All
Topic: Precautionary motive

28.45
Money that is held because of possible unforeseen events is so held because of the
a) speculative motive for holding money.
b) transactions motive for holding money.
c) cautionary motive for holding money.
d) precautionary motive for holding money.
e) surprise motive for holding money.

28.46
Correct: a)
Difficulty: 3
Page(s): 758
Scramble range: All
Topic: Precautionary motive

28.46
If you hold extra money balances because you think one of your professors might require you to buy a different book in midterm, then your economics professor would say that your motive forholding this extra money can be attributed to your
a) precautionary demand for money.
b) M1 demand for money.
c) speculative demand for money.
d) transaction demand for money.
e) cautionary demand for money.

28.47
Correct: e)
Difficulty: 4
Page(s): 758
Scramble range: All
Topic: Transactions motive

28.47
Which of the following ideas concerning the transactions motive for holding money is false?
a) It varies directly with the price level.
b) It varies directly with the level of real GDP.
c) If people make more purchases with credit cards, then the transactions demand for money will fall.
d) The longer the time interval between pay cheques received, the greater is the amount of money that people will want to hold for transactions purposes.
e) The shorter the time interval between pay cheques received, the greater is the amount of money that people will want to hold for transactions purposes.

28.48
Correct: c)
Difficulty: 3
Page(s): 759
Scramble range: All
Topic: Speculative motive

28.48
Suppose you are considering purchasing a bond. If you think that bond prices will be lower next week, then the reason you're holding extra money today can be attributed to the
a) transactions motive.
b) nonconvertible motive.
c) speculative motive.
d) precautionary motive.
e) cautionary motive.

28.49
Correct: b)
Difficulty: 3
Page(s): 759
Scramble range: All
Topic: Opportunity cost of holding money

28.49
The cost of holding money balances increases when the
a) purchasing power of money rises.
b) interest rate increases.
c) price of goods and services falls.
d) income of consumers increases.
e) income of consumers decreases.

28.50
Correct: b)
Difficulty: 3
Page(s): 759
Scramble range: All
Topic: Nominal money

28.50
The nominal quantity of money is
a) measured in constant dollars.
b) measured in current dollars.
c) inversely related to the price level.
d) inversely related to the level of real GDP.
e) positively related to the rate of interest.

28.51
Correct: b)
Difficulty: 3
Page(s): 759
Scramble range: All
Topic: Price level/ nominal money demand

28.51
If the price level doubles, all else the same, the quantity of
a) real money demanded will double.
b) nominal money demanded will double.
c) real money supplied will double.
d) nominal money supplied will double.
e) nominal money demanded will remain constant.

28.52
Correct: c)
Difficulty: 2
Page(s): 759
Scramble range: All
Topic: Real money

28.52
Real money is equal to
a) nominal income divided by velocity.
b) nominal income divided by the price level.
c) nominal money divided by the price level.
d) price level divided by nominal money.
e) nominal money divided by nominal income.

28.53
Correct: a)
Difficulty: 2
Page(s): 759
Scramble range: All
Topic: Nominal money

28.53
Nominal money is equal to real
a) money times the price level.
b) GDP times the price level.
c) GDP times the GDP deflator.
d) money divided by the price level.
e) GDP times real money.

28.54
Correct: a)
Difficulty: 3
Page(s): 759
Scramble range: All
Topic: Real money demand

28.54
All else the same, an increase in real GDP will
a) increase the demand for real money balances.
b) decrease the demand for real money balances.
c) not affect the demand for real money balances.
d) increase the demand for real money balances up to a point and then the demand will automatically fall.
e) decrease the demand for real money balances up to a point and then the demand will automatically rise.

28.55
Correct: a)
Difficulty: 3
Page(s): 759
Scramble range: All
Topic: Real income/ money demand

28.55
Refer to Figure 28.1. All else the same, which graph best illustrates an increase in real income?
a) (a).
b) (b).
c) (c).
d) (d).
e) (a) and (c).

28.56
Correct: b)
Difficulty: 3
Page(s): 759
Scramble range: All
Topic: Real income/ money demand

28.56
Refer to Figure 28.1. All else the same, which graph best illustrates a decrease in real income?
a) (a).
b) (b).
c) (c).
d) (d).
e) (a) and (c).

28.57
Correct: c)
Difficulty: 3
Page(s): 751
Scramble range: a)–d)
Topic: Open market operations

28.57
Refer to Figure 28.1. All else the same, which graph best illustrates the effect of an unanticipated Bank of Canada purchase of government securities?
a) (a).
b) (b).
c) (c).
d) (d).
e) None of the above.

Figure 28.1

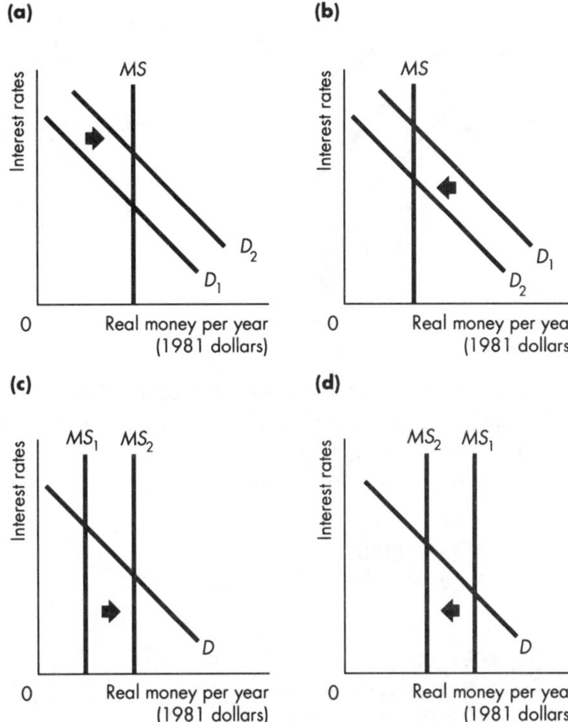

28.58
Correct: d)
Difficulty: 3
Page(s): 751
Scramble range: a)–d)
Topic: Open market operations

28.58
Refer to Figure 28.1. All else the same, which graph best illustrates the effect of an unanticipated Bank of Canada sale of government securities?

a) (a).
b) (b).
c) (c).
d) (d).
e) None of the above.

28.59
Correct: b)
Difficulty: 4
Page(s): 759
Scramble range: a)–d)
Topic: Financial innovations/demand for money

28.59
Refer to Figure 28.1. All else the same, which graph best illustrates the effect of such financial innovations as the automatic teller machine?

a) (a).
b) (b).
c) (c).
d) (d).
e) None of the above.

28.60
Correct: e)
Difficulty: 4
Page(s): 759
Scramble range: a)–d)
Topic: Real money demand

28.60
Refer to Figure 28.2. Which of the following best describes the response of this household to an increase in their annual real income?

a) Movement from *a* to *f*.
b) Movement from *a* to *c*.
c) Movement from *e* to *a*.
d) Movement from *b* to *a*.
e) None of the above.

Figure 28.2 The demand for real money balances by an individual household

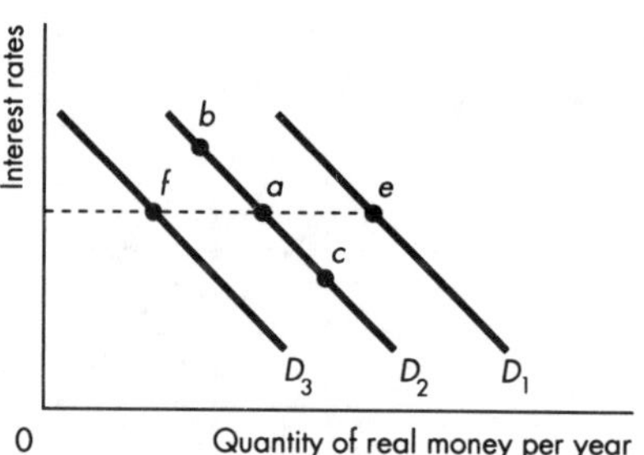

28.61
Correct: e)
Difficulty: 3
Page(s): 759
Scramble range: All
Topic: Real money demand

28.61
Refer to Figure 28.2. Which of the following best describes the response of this household to a decrease in their annual real income?

a) A movement from *a* to *c*.
b) A movement from *a* to *b*.
c) A movement from *a* to *e*.
d) A movement from *e* to *c*.
e) A movement from *e* to *a*.

28.62
Correct: a)
Difficulty: 4
Page(s): 759
Scramble range: All
Topic: Real money demand

28.62
Refer to Figure 28.2. Which of the following best describes the response of this household to a fall in the market price of bonds?

a) A movement from *a* to *b*.
b) A movement from *a* to *c*.
c) A movement from *a* to *f*.
d) A movement from *a* to *e*.
e) A movement from *e* to *a*.

28.63
Correct: c)
Difficulty: 4
Page(s): 759
Scramble range: All
Topic: Real money demand

28.63
Refer to Figure 28.2. Suppose this household acquires a credit card and that they begin to use it. All else the same, which of the following best describes this change?

a) A movement from *a* to *b*.
b) A movement from *a* to *c*.
c) A movement from *e* to *a*.
d) A movement from *a* to *e*.
e) A movement from *b* to *a*.

28.64
Correct: b)
Difficulty: 4
Page(s): 759
Scramble range: All
Topic: Real money demand

28.64
Refer to Figure 28.2. Which of the following best describes the response of this household to a rise in the market price of bonds?

a) A movement from *a* to *b*.
b) A movement from *a* to *c*.
c) A movement from *a* to *f*.
d) A movement from *a* to *e*.
e) A movement from *c* to *a*.

28.65
Correct: d)
Difficulty: 5
Page(s): 759
Scramble range: All
Topic: Real money demand

28.65
Refer to Figure 28.2. Which of the following best describes the response of this household to a simultaneous rise in the interest rate and real income?
a) A movement from *a* to *b*.
b) A movement from *a* to *c*.
c) A movement from *a* to *f*.
d) A movement from *c* to *e*.
e) A movement from *b* to *a*.

28.66
Correct: e)
Difficulty: 4
Page(s): 759
Scramble range: None
Topic: Real money demand

28.66
Refer to Figure 28.2. Which of the following best describes the response of this household to a fall in the interest rate?
a) A movement from *b* to *a*.
b) A movement from *a* to *c*.
c) A movement from *a* to *f*.
d) A movement from *a* to *e*.
e) Both a) and b).

28.67
Correct: e)
Difficulty: 5
Page(s): 760
Scramble range: None
Topic: Velocity

28.67
Velocity of circulation is equal to
a) the real money supply divided by real GDP.
b) nominal GDP divided by the nominal money supply.
c) the interest rate times real GNP.
d) real GNP divided by the real money supply.
e) Both b) and d).

28.68
Correct: b)
Difficulty: 2
Page(s): 760
Scramble range: All
Topic: Velocity

28.68
The velocity of circulation measures
a) how many times income is received by a household each year.
b) on average how many times a unit of money gets used in a given time period.
c) the ratio of real money to real GDP.
d) the ratio of the quantity of bonds to the real money supply.
e) the number of transactions in an economy in a given time period.

28.69
Correct: b)
Difficulty: 3
Page(s): 760
Scramble range: All
Topic: Velocity

28.69
All else the same, the higher the opportunity cost of holding money, the
a) smaller is the interest rate.
b) higher is the velocity of circulation.
c) lower is the velocity of circulation.
d) higher is the money supply.
e) higher is the money demand.

28.70
Correct: e)
Difficulty: 2
Page(s): 765
Scramble range: All
Topic: Perpetuities

28.70
A perpetuity is a
a) bond that promises to pay a fixed amount each year for a fixed period of time.
b) coupon that promises to pay a fixed amount each year forever.
c) nonconvertible note that pays a fixed amount each year for 20 years.
d) nonconvertible note that pays a fixed amount each year for only 3 years.
e) bond that promises to pay a fixed amount each year forever.

28.71
Correct: a)
Difficulty: 4
Page(s): 765
Scramble range: All
Topic: Bond prices/ interest rate

28.71
If you expect interest rates to fall in the near future, you would likely want to
a) buy bonds at current prices.
b) buy bonds after the interest rate falls.
c) sell bonds now.
d) put your money in a savings account and wait until later to buy bonds.
e) buy bonds at future prices.

28.72
Correct: d)
Difficulty: 3
Page(s): 760
Scramble range: All
Topic: Opportunity costs/money demand

28.72
The opportunity cost of holding money relative to other assets such as bonds is
a) the price level.
b) consumption given up.
c) liquidity given up.
d) the rate of interest.
e) the transactions saved.

28.73
Correct: c)
Difficulty: 3
Page(s): 765
Scramble range: All
Topic: Bond prices/ interest rate

28.73
Bond prices are
a) not affected by interest rate changes.
b) positively related to interest rate changes.
c) inversely related to interest rate changes.
d) not affected by changes in speculative balances.
e) negatively related to stock price changes.

28.74
Correct: b)
Difficulty: 3
Page(s): 765
Scramble range: All
Topic: Interest rates/ bond price

28.74
If the interest rate increases, the
a) value of an asset earning a fixed coupon rises.
b) value of an asset earning a fixed amount of income falls.
c) market price of a bond will rise.
d) the sale of bonds will decrease, all else the same.
e) the demand for bonds will fall, all else the same.

28.75
Correct: a)
Difficulty: 3
Page(s): 765
Scramble range: All
Topic: Bond prices/ interest rate

28.75
If a large number of people attempt to sell bonds, then
a) the interest rate will rise.
b) the interest rate will fall.
c) the price of bonds will rise.
d) the price level will rise.
e) money demand will fall.

28.76
Correct: e)
Difficulty: 3
Page(s): 763–765
Scramble range: All
Topic: M1

28.76
Refer to Table 28.1. The money supply as measured by M1 is equal to
a) $4,000.
b) $1,800.
c) $4,500.
d) $5,800.
e) $4,800.

Table 28.1 A hypothetical economy's banking system. Assume that all banks wish to hold zero excess reserves. The reserve ratio is 25 percent.

Actual reserves in banking system	$1,000
Total demand deposits	4,000
Currency in circulation	800

28.77
Correct: a)
Difficulty: 4
Page(s): 754
Scramble range: All
Topic: Excess reserves

28.77
Refer to Table 28.1. The reason that banks cannot create more demand deposits is that
a) excess reserves are equal to zero.
b) they would need to decrease reserves to do so.
c) excess reserves are greater than required reserves.
d) required reserves are greater than excess reserves.
e) they hold too many excess reserves.

27.78
Correct: e)
Difficulty: 5
Page(s): 752
Scramble range: All
Topic: Money creation

28.78
Refer to Table 28.1. If people decide to deposit $200 of their currency into the banking system, how much new money can be created?
a) $400.
b) $200.
c) $1,000.
d) $800.
e) $600.

28.79
Correct: d)
Difficulty: 5
Page(s): 752
Scramble range: All
Topic: Money creation

28.79
Refer to Table 28.1. If people decide to deposit $200 of their currency into the banking system, the value of M1 after the banking system has eliminated all new excess reserves is
a) $6,000.
b) $5,600.
c) $5,800.
d) $5,400.
e) $4,800.

28.80
Correct: d)
Difficulty: 4
Page(s): 753–756
Scramble range: All
Topic: Money multiplier

28.80
Refer to Table 28.1. If the public increases its desire for the currency, then the simple money multiplier will
a) understate the actual multiplier effect of any change in reserves.
b) offset the expansion of the money supply.
c) have an effect on the supply of currency.
d) overstate the actual multiplier effect of any change in reserves.
e) offset the contraction of the money supply.

28.81 (SG 28.1)
Correct: e)
Difficulty: 3
Page(s): 749
Scramble range: All
Topic: International constraints

28.81
The international nature of the Canadian economy
a) means the Bank of Canada has an expanded range of actions to choose from.
b) means the Bank of Canada must ignore exchange rate determination.
c) is due to the many restrictions on capital mobility set by the federal government.
d) means the Bank of Canada has no independence.
e) means the Bank of Canada cannot ignore interest rate pressures from the United States.

28.82 (SG 28.2)
Correct: c)
Difficulty: 2
Page(s): 749–750
Scramble range: All
Topic: Exchange rate regimes

28.82
A flexible exchange rate regime is one in which the
a) supply of Canadian dollars remains flexible.
b) demand for Canadian dollars remains flexible.
c) value of the exchange rate is determined by market forces.
d) value of the exchange rate is influenced by the central bank.
e) central bank defines and maintains a flexible exchange rate value.

28.83 (SG 28.3)
Correct: d)
Difficulty: 2
Page(s): 749–750
Scramble range: All
Topic: Exchange rate regimes

28.83
A managed exchange rate regime is one in which the
a) supply of the Canadian dollar is managed.
b) demand for the Canadian dollar is managed.
c) value of the exchange rate is determined by market forces.
d) value of the exchange rate is influenced by the central bank.
e) central bank defines and maintains a fixed exchange rate value.

28.84 (SG 28.4)
Correct: c)
Difficulty: 2
Page(s): 747
Scramble range: None
Topic: Monetary policy

28.84
Which of the following is *not* one of the main policy tools of the Bank of Canada?
a) Reserve requirements.
b) Exchange rate.
c) Currency ratio.
d) Open market operations.
e) Neither b) nor c).

28.85 (SG 28.5)
Correct: d)
Difficulty: 2
Page(s): 750–751
Scramble range: All
Topic: Bank rate

28.85
The bank rate is the interest rate
a) banks charge their very best loan customers.
b) banks pay on term deposits.
c) the Bank of Canada pays on reserves held by banks.
d) the Bank of Canada charges when it lends reserves to banks.
e) received for holding Government of Canada Treasury Bills.

28.86 (SG 28.6)
Correct: e)
Difficulty: 2
Page(s): 751
Scramble range: All
Topic: Open market operations

28.86
Which of the Bank of Canada's policy tools is the most important?
a) Choosing exchange rate regimes.
b) Setting reserve requirements.
c) Changes in the bank rate.
d) Paying for the government's deficit.
e) Open market operations.

28.87 (SG 28.7)
Correct: b)
Difficulty: 3
Page(s): 752
Scramble range: All
Topic: Monetary base

28.87
Which of the following would *not* affect the size of the monetary base?
a) A bank exchanges government securities for a deposit at the Bank of Canada.
b) A bank exchanges vault cash for a deposit at the Bank of Canada.
c) The Bank of Canada buys government securities from a bank.
d) The Bank of Canada buys government securities from someone other than a bank.
e) The Bank of Canada sells government securities to a bank.

28.88
Correct: b)
Difficulty: 4
Page(s): 751
Scramble range: All
Topic: Open market operations

28.88
An open market sale of government securities by the Bank of Canada will
a) increase bank reserves and thus increase the monetary base.
b) decrease bank reserves and thus decrease the monetary base.
c) increase bank reserves and thus decrease the monetary base.
d) decrease bank reserves and thus increase the monetary base.
e) decrease bank reserves but increase the money supply if banks have excess reserves.

28.89 (SG 28.9)
Correct: c)
Difficulty: 4
Page(s): 753–756
Scramble range: All
Topic: Money multiplier

28.89
If banks want to hold 10 percent of deposits as reserves and households and firms want to hold 20 percent of deposits as currency, the money multiplier is
a) 2.8
b) 3.
c) 4.
d) 10.
e) 2.

28.90 (SG 28.10)
Correct: b)
Difficulty: 4
Page(s): 753–756
Scramble range: a)–d)
Topic: Money multiplier

28.90
The money multiplier will increase if either the fraction of deposits that households and firms want to hold as currency
a) increases or the desired reserve ratio increases.
b) decreases or the desired reserve ratio decreases.
c) decreases or the desired reserve ratio increases.
d) increases or the desired reserve ratio decreases.
e) none of the above.

28.91 (SG 28.11)
Correct: e)
Difficulty: 3
Page(s): 758
Scramble range: None
Topic: Demand for money motives

28.91
Which of the following is *not* a principal motive for holding money by households and firms?
a) Reserve motive.
b) Interest rate motive.
c) Speculative motive.
d) Precautionary motive.
e) Neither a) nor b).

28.92 (SG 28.12)
Correct: d)
Difficulty: 3
Page(s): 759
Scramble range: All
Topic: Real money demand

28.92
The quantity of real money demanded will increase if either real income increases or the
a) price level increases.
b) price level decreases.
c) interest rate increases.
d) interest rate decreases.
e) price of bonds falls.

28.93 (SG 28.13)
Correct: c)
Difficulty: 1
Page(s): 759
Scramble range: All
Topic: Real versus nominal money

28.93
Real money is equal to nominal money
a) divided by real GDP.
b) minus real GDP.
c) divided by the price level.
d) minus the price level.
e) divided by velocity.

28.94 (SG 28.14)
Correct: a)
Difficulty: 3
Page(s): 759
Scramble range: All
Topic: Money demand

28.94
The higher are interest rates, the
a) lower is the quantity of money demanded and the higher is the velocity of circulation.
b) lower is the quantity of money demanded and the lower is the velocity of circulation.
c) higher is the quantity of money demanded and the higher is the velocity of circulation.
d) higher is the quantity of money demanded and the lower is the velocity of circulation.
e) higher is the quantity of money demanded but the money supply remains unaffected.

28.95 (SG 28.15)
Correct: c)
Difficulty: 3
Page(s): 759
Scramble range: All
Topic: Demand curve for money

28.95
Which of the following will cause the demand curve for money to shift to the left?
a) An increase in real GDP.
b) A decrease in interest rates.
c) The expanded use of credit cards.
d) An increase in the quantity of money supplied.
e) An increase in the price level.

28.96 (SG 28.16)
Correct: a)
Difficulty: 4
Page(s): 758
Scramble range: All
Topic: Household/firm and holdings of money

28.96
If households and firms find that their holdings of real money are less than desired, they will
a) sell financial assets, which will cause interest rates to rise.
b) sell financial assets, which will cause interest rates to fall.
c) buy financial assets, which will cause interest rates to rise.
d) buy financial assets, which will cause interest rates to fall.
e) buy goods, which will cause the price level to rise.

28.97 (SG 28.17)
Correct: e)
Difficulty: 4
Page(s): 751
Scramble range: a)–d)
Topic: Open market operations

28.97
If the Bank of Canada buys government securities in the open market, the supply curve of real money will shift to the
a) left and the interest rate will rise.
b) left and the interest rate will fall.
c) right and the interest rate will rise.
d) right and the interest rate will remain constant as money demand will shift right as well.
e) none of the above.

28.98 (SG 28.18)
Correct: c)
Difficulty: 3
Page(s): 759
Scramble range: All
Topic: Demand curve for real money

28.98
If real GDP increases, the demand curve for real money will shift to the
a) left and the interest rate will rise.
b) left and the interest rate will fall.
c) right and the interest rate will rise.
d) right and the interest rate will fall.
e) right and the interest rate will remain constant.

28.99 (SG 28.19)
Correct: d)
Difficulty: 4
Page(s): 760
Scramble range: All
Topic: Velocity

28.99
The costs of a high velocity include
a) a low interest rate and too much investment.
b) a high interest rate and too little investment.
c) a high interest income.
d) too many transactions.
e) a low interest income.

28.100
Correct: d)
Difficulty: 5
Page(s): 753
Scramble range: All
Topic: Money multiplier

28.100
Consider Table 28.1. The money multiplier for this economy is
a) 4.
b) 4.8.
c) 5.
d) 2.67.
e) 1.8.

28.101 (SG 28.20)
Correct: c)
Difficulty: 3
Page(s): 766–767
Scramble range: None
Topic: Money market equilibrium

28.101
Money market equilibrium occurs
a) when interest rates are constant.
b) when the level of real GDP is constant.
c) when money supply equals money demand.
d) only under a fixed exchange rate.
e) both a) and b).

28.102
Correct: c)
Difficulty: 2
Page(s): 750–751
Scramble range: All
Topic: Bank rate

28.102
The interest rate the Bank of Canada charges when it lends is called the
a) open market rate.
b) prime rate.
c) bank rate.
d) federal funds rate.
e) exchange rate.

28.103
Correct: c)
Difficulty: 4
Page(s): 752
Scramble range: All
Topic: Monetary base

28.103
Which of the following would affect the size of the monetary base?
a) A chartered bank buys government securities from a customer.
b) A bank exchanges vault cash for a deposit at the Bank of Canada.
c) An individual buys government securities from the Bank of Canada.
d) The federal government pays out interest to a bondholder.
e) The federal government sells securities to a bank and then spends the money on national defence.

28.104
Correct: e)
Difficulty: 3
Page(s): 758–759
Scramble range: a)–d)
Topic: Demand for money

28.104
The demand for money in Canada (as a percentage of real GDP) reveals
a) an inverse relationship between M1 and the rate of interest.
b) an inverse relationship between M2 and the rate of interest.
c) a fall in the demand for M1 over the 1980s.
d) a rise in the demand for M2 over the 1980s.
e) all of the above.

28.105
Correct: c)
Difficulty: 3
Page(s): 759
Scramble range: All
Topic: Real money demand

28.105
The quantity of real money demanded will decrease if either real income decreases or

a) the price level increases.
b) the price level decreases.
c) the interest rate increases.
d) the interest rate decreases.
e) credit cards are banned.

28.106
Correct: d)
Difficulty: 3
Page(s): 759
Scramble range: a)–d)
Topic: Fighting inflation

28.106
To fight inflation, the Bank of Canada should

a) lower the bank rate.
b) carry out an open market purchase.
c) raise the growth rate of M2.
d) lower the growth rate of M1.
e) all of the above.

28.107
Correct: d)
Difficulty: 4
Page(s): 759
Scramble range: All
Topic: Money demand

28.107
The lower are interest rates, the

a) lower is the quantity of money demanded and the higher is the velocity of circulation.
b) lower is the quantity of money demanded and the lower is the velocity of circulation.
c) higher is the quantity of money demanded and the higher is the velocity of circulation.
d) higher is the quantity of money demanded and the lower is the velocity of circulation.
e) the lower is the quantity of money demanded but the money supply remains unaffected.

28.108
Correct: a)
Difficulty: 3
Page(s): 759
Scramble range: All
Topic: Demand curve for money

28.108
Which of the following will cause the demand curve for money to shift to the right?

a) An increase in real GDP.
b) The expanded use of credit cards.
c) A decrease in the price level.
d) An increase in the quantity of money supplied.
e) The expanded use of automatic teller machines.

28.109
Correct: a)
Difficulty: 4
Page(s): 748–749
Scramble range: All
Topic: Banking system

28.109
Consider Fact 28.1. The amount of loans in the banking system is

a) \$285 million.
b) \$260 million.
c) \$315 million.
d) \$245 million.
e) \$250 million.

Fact 28.1
You are given the following information about a hypothetical economy. The banks have deposits of \$300 million. Their reserves are \$15 million, two-thirds of which are in deposits with the central bank. The monetary base is \$40 million. There are no coins. The chartered banks have only reserves and loans as assets, and deposits as liabilities.

28.110
Correct: d)
Difficulty: 4
Page(s): 752
Scramble range: All
Topic: Money supply

28.110
Consider Fact 28.1. The money supply in this economy is
a) $315 million.
b) $300 million.
c) $40 million.
d) $325 million.
e) $250 million.

28.111
Correct: c)
Difficulty: 5
Page(s): 751
Scramble range: All
Topic: Open market operations

28.111
Consider Fact 28.1. Suppose the central bank carries out an open market purchase of $1 million in securities from an individual. The change in this economy's money supply is
a) –$8.125 million.
b) +$7.5 million.
c) +$8.125 million.
d) +12 million.
e) –$7.5 million.

Chapter 29 International Finance and the Exchange Rate

29.1
Correct: b)
Difficulty: 2
Page(s): 775
Scramble range: All
Topic: Foreign exchange market

29.1
In the foreign exchange market the currency of one country is exchanged for the
a) goods of another country.
b) currency of another country.
c) bonds issued by the government of another country.
d) shares of stock in firms of another country.
e) U.S. dollar.

29.2
Correct: c)
Difficulty: 2
Page(s): 775
Scramble range: All
Topic: Foreign exchange rate

29.2
The foreign exchange rate is the rate at which
a) one country's goods trade for those of another country.
b) the currency of one country trades for the goods of another country.
c) one country's currency trades for another country's currency.
d) one country's currency trades for special drawing rights issued by the International Monetary Fund.
e) the currency of one country trades for the U.S. dollar.

29.3
Correct: a)
Difficulty: 3
Page(s): 775
Scramble range: All
Topic: Currency trading

29.3
If dollars were cheaper in Tokyo than in London, a trader would
a) buy dollars in Tokyo and sell them in London.
b) sell dollars in Tokyo and buy them in London.
c) sell dollars in both Tokyo and London.
d) buy dollars in both Tokyo and London.
e) buy dollars in Tokyo and lend them in London.

29.4
Correct: c)
Difficulty: 3
Page(s): 775
Scramble range: All
Topic: Currency trading

29.4
If dollars were more expensive in Zurich than in Toronto,
a) the demand for dollars would increase in Zurich and decrease in Toronto.
b) the supply of dollars would increase in Zurich and decrease in Toronto.
c) the supply of dollars would increase in Zurich and the demand for dollars would increase in Toronto.
d) the demand for dollars would increase in Zurich and the supply of dollars would increase in Toronto.
e) the supply of dollars would increase in Zurich and stay the same in Toronto.

29.5
Correct: b)
Difficulty: 3
Page(s): 775
Scramble range: All
Topic: Currency trading

29.5
Profitable currency trading in different markets at the same time
a) tends to make currency exchange rates unstable.
b) tends to make currency exchange rates unified in the different markets.
c) tends to make currency exchange rates diverge in the different markets.
d) is the difficulty that led to the breakdown of the Bretton Woods exchange rate system.
e) violates the idea of arbitrage.

29.6
Correct: b)
Difficulty: 2
Page(s): 776
Scramble range: All
Topic: Fixed exchange rates

29.6
A fixed exchange rate system is one in which
a) traders accept only a guaranteed price for their goods, regardless of the supply and demand for the currency.
b) the exchange rate is pegged by the central bank of the country.
c) the currency must exchange for a specified amount of gold.
d) no shortages or surpluses of the currency can exist.
e) the exchange rate is pegged by the International Monetary Fund.

29.7
Correct: b)
Difficulty: 2
Page(s): 776
Scramble range: All
Topic: Fixed exchange rates

29.7
A fixed exchange rate system is one in which
a) traders accept only a guaranteed price for their goods, regardless of the supply and demand for the currency.
b) the government defines its currency to be worth a certain amount of another currency, and then takes action to maintain that rate.
c) the currency must exchange for a specified amount of silver.
d) no shortages or surpluses of the currency can exist.
e) a preset contract guarantees the exchange rate for 3 months in the future.

29.8
Correct: d)
Difficulty: 2
Page(s): 776
Scramble range: All
Topic: Flexible exchange rates

29.8
A flexible exchange rate system is one in which
a) traders accept only a guaranteed price for their goods, regardless of the supply and demand for the currency.
b) the government defines its currency to be worth a certain amount of another currency, and then takes action to maintain that rate.
c) the currency must exchange for a specified amount of silver.
d) shortages of the foreign exchange result in a depreciation of the home currency.
e) a preset contract has a variable exchange rate for three months in the future.

29.9
Correct: c)
Difficulty: 2
Page(s): 776
Scramble range: All
Topic: Flexible exchange rates

29.9
A flexible exchange rate system is one in which
a) traders accept only a guaranteed price for their goods, regardless of the supply and demand for the currency.
b) the government defines its currency to be worth a certain amount of another currency, and then takes action to maintain that rate.
c) the currency exchanges for another at a rate determined in the foreign exchange market itself, not by the central banks.
d) shortages of the foreign exchange result in a appreciation of the home currency.
e) the exchange rate is pegged by the International Monetary Fund.

29.10
Correct: c)
Difficulty: 2
Page(s): 776
Scramble range: All
Topic: Flexible exchange rates

29.10
A flexible exchange rate system is one in which
a) traders accept only a guaranteed price for their goods, regardless of the supply and demand for the currency.
b) the government defines its currency to be worth a certain amount of another currency, and then takes action to maintain that rate.
c) the central banks do not intervene to influence the exchange rate.
d) shortages of the foreign exchange result in an appreciation of the home currency.
e) the central bank intervenes to slow down sharp movements in the exchange rate.

29.11
Correct: b)
Difficulty: 2
Page(s): 776
Scramble range: All
Topic: Managed exchange rates

29.11
A managed exchange rate regime is one in which the government
a) allows managers of trading firms to establish the exchange rate for individual transactions.
b) itself intervenes in the exchange market to influence the exchange rate, but does not maintain a fixed rate.
c) permits private banks to manage their exchange rates, but takes no direct action itself.
d) manages to fix the exchange rate at the most advantageous level.
e) pegs the exchange rate at a predetermined level.

29.12
Correct: d)
Difficulty: 2
Page(s): 776
Scramble range: All
Topic: Monitoring exchange rate

29.12
Exchange rate activities and balance of payments position of countries are monitored by the
a) World Bank.
b) Federal Reserve System of the United States.
c) Bank of Canada.
d) International Monetary Fund.
e) European Monetary System.

29.13
Correct: e)
Difficulty: 2
Page(s): 776
Scramble range: All
Topic: International Monetary Fund

29.13
The International Monetary Fund was established during the closing months of
a) the presidency of Richard Nixon.
b) Ronald Reagan's first term as U.S. President.
c) the Vietnam War.
d) World War I.
e) World War II.

29.14
Correct: a)
Difficulty: 2
Page(s): 776
Scramble range: All
Topic: Bretton Woods System

29.14
The International Monetary Fund was created when the Bretton Woods Exchange Rate System was instituted. This system was
a) a fixed rate system.
b) a flexible rate system.
c) a gold standard.
d) an international taxation system.
e) a managed rate system.

29.15
Correct: c)
Difficulty: 2
Page(s): 776
Scramble range: All
Topic: Bretton Woods System

29.15
The anchor for the Bretton Woods System was the
a) fixed value of the U.S. dollar against silver.
b) fixed rated of exchange of the U.S. dollar and special drawing rights.
c) fixed value of the U.S. dollar against gold.
d) laws of supply and demand applied to currencies.
e) fixed value of all currencies versus the U.S. dollar.

29.16
Correct:a)
Difficulty: 2
Page(s): 776
Scramble range: All
Topic: Bretton Woods System

29.16
The Bretton Woods System established
a) the price of an ounce of gold to be US$35.
b) the price of an ounce of silver to be US$5.
c) the price of a British pound sterling to be US$0.50.
d) that the exchange rate of the dollar could vary with the supply of and the demand for the currency.
e) that the Canadian dollar could float freely.

29.17
Correct:a)
Difficulty: 3
Page(s): 776
Scramble range: All
Topic: Bretton Woods System

29.17
The Bretton Woods System established
a) the price of the U.S. dollar in terms of gold, and then fixed the exchange rate of other currencies to the dollar.
b) the price of an ounce of silver to be US$5, and then tied other currencies at the same rate to gold.
c) the price of a British pound sterling to be one ounce of gold, then allowed the price of the U.S. dollar to vary against the British pound sterling.
d) that the exchange rate of the U.S. dollar could vary with the supply of and the demand for the currency.
e) the price of the U.S. dollar in terms of gold, and then allowed all other exchange rates to float against the U.S. dollar.

29.18
Correct: a)
Difficulty: 2
Page(s): 776
Scramble range: All
Topic: Post-1970 exchange rate system

29.18
Since 1970, the exchange rate system has been a
a) combination of a flexible rate system and a managed rate system.
b) combination of a fixed rate system and a flexible rate system.
c) combination of a gold standard and a flexible rate system.
d) fixed exchange rate system.
e) flexible exchange rate system.

29.19
Correct: c)
Difficulty: 2
Page(s): 776
Scramble range: All
Topic: Currency depreciation

29.19
Currency depreciation is a reduction in the
a) precious metal content in coins, such as the replacement of silver with copper in quarters.
b) goods and services that a currency can purchase within its own country, usually the result of a period of inflation.
c) amount of foreign exchange that can be obtained in trade for each unit of domestic currency.
d) amount of domestic currency that must be exchanged for a unit of foreign exchange.
e) amount of domestic goods foreign currency can purchase.

29.20
Correct: e)
Difficulty: 2
Page(s): 776
Scramble range: All
Topic: Currency depreciation

29.20
Currency appreciation is an increase in the
a) precious metal content in coins, such as an increase in the silver content in quarters.
b) goods and services that a currency can purchase within its own country, usually the result of a period of declining inflation.
c) amount of domestic goods foreign currency can purchase.
d) amount of domestic currency that must be exchanged for a unit of foreign exchange.
e) amount of foreign exchange that can be obtained in trade for each unit of domestic currency.

29.21
Correct:a)
Difficulty: 2
Page(s): 776
Scramble range: All
Topic: Dollar index

29.21
A trade-weighted index of the dollar such as the Canadian dollar index against the G-10 countries depends on the
a) exchange rates for the G-10 currencies and the relative magnitudes of trade conducted with those countries.
b) value as well as the volume of Canadian exports and imports.
c) volume of Canadian exports and imports, but not the value.
d) relative amounts of gold, silver, and currencies traded at different points in time.
e) average price of Canadian goods.

29.22
Correct:a)
Difficulty: 2
Page(s): 776
Scramble range: All
Topic: Exchange rates

29.22
Since 1985, the Canadian dollar has
a) lost value against the Japanese yen.
b) gained value against the Japanese yen.
c) remained constant against the Japanese yen.
d) not been able to vary against the Japanese yen since the exchanged rate has been fixed against the yen.
e) first risen drastically in value against the Japanese yen, but then more recently it has fallen slightly in value.

29.23
Correct: b)
Difficulty: 2
Page(s): 777
Scramble range: All
Topic: Exchange rate determination

29.23
In a flexible exchange rate system, the value of the dollar is determined by the
a) Canadian government.
b) demand for the dollar and the supply of the dollar.
c) influx of foreign workers into Canada.
d) level of tariffs and quotas levied on foreign goods.
e) influence of the Bank of Canada.

29.24
Correct: c)
Difficulty: 2
Page(s): 777
Scramble range: All
Topic: Exchange rate determination

29.24
The equilibrium exchange rate adjusts in order to equate the flow
a) demand for the dollar to the stock demand for the dollar.
b) demand for the dollar to the stock supply of the dollar.
c) demand for the dollar to the flow supply of the dollar.
d) supply of the dollar to the stock supply of the dollar.
e) supply of the dollar to the portfolio demand.

29.25
Correct: b)
Difficulty: 3
Page(s): 779
Scramble range: All
Topic: Flow theory of the exchange rate

29.25
One weakness in the flow theory of exchange rate is that it
a) does not take into account the demand and the supply of the currency.
b) does not consider the net flows associated with international borrowing.
c) places too much emphasis on the interventions of the Bank of Canada.
d) places too much emphasis on the role of the International Monetary Fund.
e) does not allow for a managed exchange rate.

29.26
Correct: b)
Difficulty: 3
Page(s): 779
Scramble range: All
Topic: Portfolio balance theory of the exchange rate

29.26
The decision to change the international assets held by investors results in
a) a change in the exchange rate.
b) a flow which is the consequence of a decision concerning stocks.
c) an overvalued exchange rate.
d) an undervalued exchange rate.
e) a change in the flow of the assets but no change in the stocks of the assets.

29.27
Correct: d)
Difficulty: 3
Page(s): 779
Scramble range: All
Topic: Monetary theory of the exchange rate

29.27
The monetary theory of the exchange rate suggests that the exchange rate adjusts to equate the
a) money supply of one country to that of the other.
b) money demand of one country to that of the other.
c) flow of a currency demanded to the flow of the currency supplied.
d) stock of a currency demanded to the stock of the currency supplied.
e) portfolio balance between countries.

29.28
Correct:a)
Difficulty: 3
Page(s): 779
Scramble range: All
Topic: Portfolio balance theory of the exchange rate

29.28
The portfolio balance theory of exchange rates suggests that exchange rate adjusts to
a) make the stock of financial assets (in dollars) equal to the stock of dollars supplied.
b) make the flow of financial assets (in dollars) equal to the stock of dollars supplied.
c) make the stock of financial assets (in the foreign exchange) equal to the stock of dollars supplied.
d) minimize the risk involved in investing in a basket of foreign currencies.
e) make the flow of financial assets (in dollars) equal to the change in the stock of dollars demanded.

29.29
Correct: b)
Difficulty: 3
Page(s): 780
Scramble range: None
Topic: Demand for dollar assets

29.29
The lower the value of the dollar on international exchanges, the
a) greater will be the amount of the dollar supplied by traders.
b) greater will be the amount of the dollar demanded by traders.
c) less will be the amount of the dollar supplied by traders.
d) less will be the amount of the dollar demanded by traders.
e) both b) and c).

29.30
Correct: d)
Difficulty: 3
Page(s): 780
Scramble range: None
Topic: Demand for dollar assets

29.30
The greater the value of the dollar on international exchanges, the
a) greater will be the amount of the dollar supplied by traders.
b) greater will be the amount of the dollar demanded by traders.
c) less will be the amount of the dollar supplied by traders.
d) less will be the amount of the dollar demanded by traders.
e) both a) and d).

29.31
Correct: b)
Difficulty: 2
Page(s): 780
Scramble range: All
Topic: Change in demand for the dollar

29.31
The demand for the dollar will increase due to
a) a decrease in the price of the dollar.
b) a decrease in the prices of Canadian goods and services.
c) a decrease in Canadian interest rates.
d) an increase in foreign interest rates.
e) a decrease in the expected future value of the dollar.

29.32
Correct: e)
Difficulty: 3
Page(s): 782
Scramble range: a)–d)
Topic: Change in supply of the dollar

29.32
The supply of the dollar under a flexible exchange rate will increase due to
a) an increase in the price of the dollar.
b) a decrease in the prices of Canadian goods and services.
c) an increase in Canadian interest rates
d) an increase in foreign interest rates.
e) none of the above.

29.33
Correct:a)
Difficulty: 3
Page(s): 782
Scramble range: All
Topic: Maintaining fixed exchange rates

29.33
Under fixed exchange rates, when there is a change in the demand for dollar assets, the Bank of Canada must
a) change the supply of dollar assets.
b) change the price level in Canada.
c) change the demand for dollar assets.
d) defer to the International Monetary Fund for supporting action.
e) let market forces determine the new equilibrium.

29.34
Correct: c)
Difficulty: 3
Page(s): 782
Scramble range: All
Topic: Maintaining fixed exchange rates

29.34
Under fixed exchange rates, when there is an increase in the demand for dollar assets, the Bank of Canada must
a) decrease the supply of dollar assets.
b) change the price level in Canada.
c) increase the supply of dollar assets.
d) defer to the International Monetary Fund for supporting action.
e) let market forces determine the new equilibrium.

29.35
Correct: d)
Difficulty: 3
Page(s): 782
Scramble range: All
Topic: Flexible rate systems

29.35
Under a flexible rate regime, when there is an increase in the demand for dollar assets, the Bank of Canada
a) must decrease the supply of dollar assets.
b) must change the price level in Canada.
c) must increase the supply of dollar assets.
d) need not take any action.
e) must lower the demand for dollar assets.

29.36
Correct: c)
Difficulty: 3
Page(s): 782
Scramble range: All
Topic: Flexible rate systems

29.36
Under a flexible rate regime, when there is an increase in the demand for dollar assets,
a) the Bank of Canada must decrease the supply of dollar assets.
b) the Bank of Canada must change the price level in Canada.
c) there is no change in the official holdings of foreign exchange.
d) there is a rise in the official holdings of foreign exchange.
e) there is a fall in the official holdings of foreign exchange.

29.37
Correct: b)
Difficulty: 2
Page(s): 785
Scramble range: All
Topic: Currency arbitrage

29.37
Currency arbitrage is the act of
a) buying high in one market and selling lower in another.
b) buying low in one market and selling higher in another market.
c) speculating in the foreign exchange to earn profit.
d) trading currency to avoid exchange rate risk as an international trader.
e) trying to outwit the central bank.

29.38
Correct: b)
Difficulty: 2
Page(s): 785–786
Scramble range: All
Topic: Currency arbitrage

29.38
Profitable currency arbitrage
a) pushes prices apart in the different markets.
b) pushes prices closer together in the different markets.
c) results in an increase in the Canadian trade deficit.
d) results in a decrease in the Canadian current account deficit.
e) occurs due to a mismanaged exchange rate.

29.39
Correct: b)
Difficulty: 3
Page(s): 786
Scramble range: All
Topic: Purchasing power parity

29.39
Purchasing power parity is the principle that the exchange rate adjusts to equate the
a) standard of living in the trading countries.
b) value of the money stock in one country with the value of the money stock in the other country.
c) currency values relative to gold.
d) cost of living in the two countries.
e) interest rate in one country with that of the other country.

29.40
Correct:a)
Difficulty: 4
Page(s): 786
Scramble range: All
Topic: Purchasing power parity

29.40
Purchasing power parity states that the
a) value of money, when converted to common prices, is the same in both countries.
b) exchange rate adjusts to equate the money stock in one country with the money stock in the other country.
c) exchange rate adjusts to equate the currency values relative to silver.
d) exchange rate adjusts to equate the benefits of living in the two countries.
e) exchange rate will adjust to a value of 1.00.

29.41
Correct: c)
Difficulty: 3
Page(s): 786
Scramble range: All
Topic: The real exchange rate

29.41
The real exchange rate is the
a) present value of the purchasing power of the currency.
b) exchange rate of the currencies, adjusted for the interest rate differences between the two countries.
c) ratio of the price index in one country to that of another, after converting the second country's prices into the first using the nominal exchange rate.
d) ratio of the producer price index in one country to the producer price index of another, after converting the second country's interest rates into equivalent units of the other.
e) nominal exchange rate adjusted for the impact of inflation.

29.42 (SG 29.1)
Correct: d)
Difficulty: 3
Page(s): 775
Scramble range: All
Topic: Foreign exchange market

29.42
Suppose the exchange rate between the Canadian dollar and the British pound is 2 pounds per dollar. If a radio sells for 38 pounds in Britain, what is the dollar price of the radio?
a) \$19.
b) \$26.
c) \$38.
d) \$76.
e) \$57.

29.43 (SG 29.2)
Correct: c)
Difficulty: 2
Page(s): 775
Scramble range: All
Topic: Foreign exchange market

29.43
The market in which the currency of one country is exchanged for the currency of another is called the
a) money market.
b) capital market.
c) foreign exchange market.
d) forward exchange market.
e) international trading market.

29.44 (SG 29.3)
Correct: d)
Difficulty: 3
Page(s): 776
Scramble range: All
Topic: Flexible exchange rates

29.44
Under a flexible exchange rate regime, if the foreign exchange value of a country's currency starts to rise, that country's central bank will
a) increase the supply of assets denominated in its own currency.
b) decrease the supply of assets denominated in its own currency.
c) decrease the demand for assets denominated in its own currency.
d) do nothing.
e) do nothing unless there is a government budget deficit, in which case it will increase the supply of assets denominated in its own currency.

29.45 (SG 29.4)
Correct: d)
Difficulty: 3
Page(s): 775
Scramble range: All
Topic: Foreign exchange market

29.45
Suppose that the dollar-yen foreign exchange rate changes from 140 yen per dollar to 130 yen per dollar. Then the yen has
a) depreciated against the dollar and the dollar has appreciated against the yen.
b) depreciated against the dollar and the dollar has depreciated against the yen.
c) appreciated against the dollar and the dollar has appreciated against the yen.
d) appreciated against the dollar and the dollar has depreciated against the yen.
e) neither appreciated or depreciated, but the dollar has depreciated against the yen.

29.46 (SG 29.5)
Correct: c)
Difficulty: 3
Page(s): 780
Scramble range: All
Topic: Demand for dollar assets

29.46
Which of the following will shift the demand curve for dollar assets to the right?
a) An increase in the demand for foreign goods by Canadian citizens.
b) A decrease in the demand for Canadian goods by foreigners.
c) The dollar is expected to appreciate.
d) The government has a budget deficit.
e) The government has a budget surplus.

29.47 (SG 29.6)
Correct: e)
Difficulty: 4
Page(s). 781–782
Scramble range: a)–c)
Topic: Supply of the dollar

29.47
Which of the following will shift the supply curve of dollar assets to the right under flexible exchange rates?
a) An increase in the demand for foreign goods by Canadian citizens.
b) A decrease in the demand for Canadian goods by foreigners.
c) The dollar is expected to appreciate.
d) The government has a budget surplus.
e) None of the above.

29.48 (SG 29.7)
Correct: c)
Difficulty: 3
Page(s): 781–782
Scramble range: All
Topic: Supply of the dollar

29.48
Under a managed exchange rate regime, the supply curve of dollar assets is
a) vertical.
b) horizontal.
c) positively sloped.
d) negatively sloped.
e) positively sloped if there is a government budget surplus.

29.49 (SG 29.8)
Correct: b)
Difficulty: 4
Page(s): 776
Scramble range: All
Topic: Flexible exchange rates

29.49
Under a managed exchange rate regime, a Canadian government budget deficit will cause the foreign exchange price of the dollar to
a) fall and the quantity of dollar assets held to fall.
b) fall and the quantity of dollar assets held to rise.
c) rise and the quantity of dollar assets held to fall.
d) rise and the quantity of dollar assets held to rise.
e) stay constant, but the quantity of dollar assets held will rise.

29.50 (SG 29.9)
Correct:a)
Difficulty: 4
Page(s): 776
Scramble range: All
Topic: Flexible exchange rates

29.50
Under a flexible exchange rate regime, an increase in interest rates in Canada relative to those in Japan would cause
a) the dollar to appreciate against the yen.
b) the dollar to depreciate against the yen.
c) an increase in the supply of dollar assets.
d) a decrease in the supply of dollar assets.
e) interest rates to fall in Japan.

29.51 (SG 29.10)
Correct: c)
Difficulty: 4
Page(s): 786
Scramble range: None
Topic: Purchasing power parity

29.51
Suppose the exchange rate between the Canadian dollar and the Japanese yen is initially 120 yen per dollar. According to purchasing power parity, if the prices of
a) nontraded goods rise by 10 percent in Canada and remain unchanged in Japan, the exchange rate will become about 108 yen per dollar.
b) nontraded goods rise by 10 percent in Canada and remain unchanged in Japan, the exchange rate will become about 132 yen per dollar.
c) traded goods rise by 10 percent in Canada and remain unchanged in Japan, the exchange rate will become about 108 yen per dollar.
d) traded goods rise by 10 percent in Canada and remain unchanged in Japan, the exchange rate will become about 132 yen per dollar.
e) both a) and c).

29.52 (SG 29.11)
Correct: c)
Difficulty: 4
Page(s): 786
Scramble range: All
Topic: Real exchange rate

29.52
Suppose the exchange rate between the dollar and the yen is 120 yen per dollar. If the price level in Canada is 150 and the price level in Japan is 100, what is the *real* exchange rate between the dollar and the yen?
a) 80 yen per dollar.
b) 120 yen per dollar.
c) 180 yen per dollar.
d) 240 yen per dollar.
e) 150 yen per dollar.

29.53 (SG 29.12)
Correct: d)
Difficulty: 4
Page(s): 787
Scramble range: All
Topic: Interest rate parity

29.53
If the interest rate in Canada is greater than the interest rate in Japan, interest rate parity implies that
a) the inflation rate is higher in Japan.
b) Japanese financial assets are poor investments.
c) the yen is expected to depreciate against the dollar.
d) the yen is expected to appreciate against the dollar.
e) Canadian financial assets are poor investments.

29.54 (SG 29.13)
Correct:a)
Difficulty: 4
Page(s): 776
Scramble range: All
Topic: Currency depreciation

29.54
Which of the following would cause the dollar to depreciate against the yen?
a) An increase in the Canadian money supply.
b) An increase in interest rates in Canada.
c) A decrease in interest rates in Japan.
d) An increase in imports from Canada purchased by Japan.
e) A government budget surplus.

29.55
Correct: b)
Difficulty: 3
Page(s): 776
Scramble range: All
Topic: Exchange rates

29.55
Suppose the exchange rate between the dollar and the German mark is 3 marks per dollar. If a clock sells for 39 marks in Germany, what is the dollar price of the clock?
a) \$3.
b) \$13.
c) \$42.
d) \$117.
e) \$36.

29.56
Correct: c)
Difficulty: 2
Page(s): 776
Scramble range: All
Topic: Exchange rates

29.56
What is exchanged in a "foreign exchange market"?
a) Bonds and stocks from different countries.
b) Exports and imports from different countries.
c) Currencies from different countries.
d) Intangible services from different countries.
e) Tradable goods from different countries.

29.57
Correct: b)
Difficulty: 2
Page(s): 776
Scramble range: All
Topic: Fixed/flexible exchange rates

29.57
Under which of the following exchange rate regimes would a country's central bank do nothing if the foreign exchange value of a currency began to rise?
a) Fixed exchange rates.
b) Flexible exchange rates.
c) The managed float system.
d) Gold-denominated fixed exchange rates.
e) The Bretton Woods system.

29.58
Correct: d)
Difficulty: 3
Page(s): 776
Scramble range: All
Topic: Exchange rates

29.58
Which of the following will shift the supply curve of dollar assets to the left?
a) A decrease in the demand for foreign goods by Canadian citizens.
b) An increase in the demand for Canadian goods by foreigners.
c) An expectation that the dollar will depreciate.
d) A government budget surplus.
e) A government budget deficit.

29.59
Correct: b)
Difficulty: 2
Page(s): 776
Scramble range: None
Topic: Fixed/flexible exchange rates

29.59
Under which exchange rate regime would the supply curve of dollar assets be vertical?
a) Fixed exchange rates.
b) Flexible exchange rates.
c) The managed float system.
d) Gold-denominated fixed exchange rates.
e) Both b) and c).

29.60
Correct: e)
Difficulty: 4
Page(s): 776
Scramble range: a)–d)
Topic: Fixed/flexible exchange rates

29.60
Under a fixed exchange rate regime, an increase in interest rates in Japan relative to those in Canada would cause
a) an increase in the supply of dollar assets.
b) a decrease in the supply of dollar assets.
c) an appreciation of the dollar against the yen.
d) a depreciation of the dollar against the yen.
e) none of the above.

29.61
Correct: c)
Difficulty: 4
Page(s): 776
Scramble range: All
Topic: Exchange rates

29.61
Which of the following would cause the dollar to appreciate against the yen?
a) An increase in the Canadian money supply.
b) A decrease in interest rates in Canada.
c) A decrease in interest rates in Japan.
d) A decrease in imports from Canada purchased by Japan.
e) A government budget deficit.

29.62
Correct: e)
Difficulty: 2
Page(s): 776
Scramble range: a)–d)
Topic: Canada's exchange rate

29.62
Since the inception of the International Monetary Fund, Canada has
a) maintained only a fixed exchange rate system.
b) maintained only a managed exchange rate system.
c) maintained only a flexible exchange rate system.
d) been on a gold standard.
e) none of the above.

29.63 (SG 29.14)
Correct: e)
Difficulty: 4
Page(s): 777–778
Scramble range: All
Topic: Calculating the dollar index

29.63
Consider the information given in Table 29.1. The value of the trade-weighted dollar index in year 2 is
a) 100.00.
b) 98.00.
c) 125.40.
d) 88.12.
e) 102.04.

Table 29.1

Currency	Trade weights	Exchange rates (units of foreign currency per C$) Year 1	Year 2	Contents of the basket	Value of the basket (C$) Year 1	Year 2
U.S.$	0.4	0.85	1.00	US$34.0	40.00	?
Japanese Yen	0.3	100	125	3,000 Yen	30.00	?
German Marks	0.3	4	3	120 marks	30.00	?
	1.0				100.00	?

29.64
Correct: d)
Difficulty: 4
Page(s): 776
Scramble range: All
Topic: Dollar index

29.64
Suppose we are examining a trade-weighted Canadian dollar index, between 1991 and 1992. Suppose over this period the U.S. dollar appreciates 10 percent against the Canadian dollar and the Japanese yen depreciates 10 percent. As a result, we would predict that the value of the index would
a) rise.
b) fall.
c) stay the same.
d) rise if Canada trades more with the Japanese than with the Americans.
e) fall if Canada trades more with the Japanese than with the Americans.

29.65
Correct: d)
Difficulty: 3
Page(s): 780
Scramble range: All
Topic: Demand for the dollar

29.65
The volume of dollar-financed trade is crucial to the demand for the dollar because
a) the dollar value of any given volume of transactions is proportional to the price level.
b) investors will switch out of Canadian dollar assets if the volume is low.
c) investors will switch out of foreign currency assets if the volume is low.
d) by holding an inventory of dollars people can avoid transactions costs.
e) people expect the dollar to appreciate if there is a high volume.

29.66
Correct: d)
Difficulty: 4
Page(s): 780
Scramble range: a)–d)
Topic: Demand for the dollar

29.66
The demand for Canadian dollar assets is similar to the demand for
a) imports.
b) capital goods.
c) consumption goods.
d) money.
e) all of the above.

29.67
Correct: e)
Difficulty: 4
Page(s): 781
Scramble range: All
Topic: Supply of the dollar

29.67
If the federal government has a budget deficit, then the
a) demand for the Canadian dollar rises if the deficit is financed by selling bonds to the Bank of Canada.
b) demand for the Canadian dollar rises if the deficit is financed by selling bonds to the public.
c) supply of the Canadian dollar rises if the deficit is financed by selling bonds to the Bank of Canada.
d) supply of the Canadian dollar rises if the deficit is financed by selling bonds to the public.
e) supply of the Canadian dollar rises regardless of how the deficit is financed, unless it is financed by selling bonds denominated in foreign currency.

29.68
Correct: e)
Difficulty: 3
Page(s): 781
Scramble range: All
Topic: Supply of the dollar

29.68
Under a flexible exchange rate system, the supply curve for the Canadian dollar is
a) always flat.
b) always upward sloping.
c) flat if there is no government intervention.
d) upward sloping if there is some government intervention.
e) always vertical.

29.69
Correct: e)
Difficulty: 3
Page(s): 784
Scramble range: All
Topic: Exchange rate volatility

29.69
The exchange rate is volatile because
a) the Bank of Canada's management of the dollar is very slow to react.
b) the Bank of Canada's management of the dollar is very quick to react.
c) foreign exchange markets have high transactions costs.
d) the supply and demand for the dollar are very independent of each other.
e) the supply and demand for the dollar are very interdependent.

29.70
Correct: d)
Difficulty: 3
Page(s): 786
Scramble range: All
Topic: Real exchange rate

29.70
The real exchange rate changes
a) due to the law of one price.
b) because the purchasing power parity theory is wrong.
c) because of changes in interest rates in different countries.
d) because of the existence of nontraded goods.
e) because of arbitrage.

29.71
Correct: e)
Difficulty: 2
Page(s): 787
Scramble range: None
Topic: Nontraded goods

29.71
An example of a nontraded good is
a) a doughnut.
b) flour.
c) an automobile.
d) a hamburger.
e) both a) and d).

29.72
Correct: e)
Difficulty: 2
Page(s): 785–786
Scramble range: None
Topic: Arbitrage

29.72
Arbitrage operates to bring about equality in the market for
a) goods and services.
b) traded goods.
c) nontraded goods.
d) assets.
e) both b) and d).

29.73
Correct: e)
Difficulty: 4
Page(s): 787
Scramble range: a)–d)
Topic: Interest rate parity

29.73
If the interest rate is 14.5 percent in Canada and 10 percent in the United States, then
a) interest rate parity is violated.
b) purchasing power parity is violated.
c) some assets must be nontradable.
d) interest rates must rise in the United States and fall in Canada.
e) none of the above.

29.74
Correct: d)
Difficulty: 5
Page(s): 787
Scramble range: All
Topic: Interest rate parity

29.74
Refer to Fact 29.1. How much would you gain or lose if you borrowed 1 million choos and invested the proceeds of the loan in Ecoland bonds, covering your transaction in the forward market?
a) Lose 1,580,000 turkies.
b) Gain 1,580,000 turkies.
c) Zero.
d) Gain 6,667 turkies.
e) Lose 6,667 turkies.

Fact 29.1
The interest rate on bank loans in Pioneerland is 11 percent a year. The interest rate on bonds in Ecoland is 4 percent a year. The currency of Pioneerland is the choo and the currency of Ecoland is the turky. In the foreign exchange market, turkies can be bought for choos at a rate of 8 choos per turky. In the forward market, turkies can be bought for delivery in one year at a rate of 9 choos per turky.

29.75
Correct: d)
Difficulty: 5
Page(s): 792
Scramble range: All
Topic: Inflation rates

29.75
All the goods and services that are bought and sold in Pioneerland are also bought and sold in Ecoland and there are no nontraded goods. There are no tariffs or other impediments to trade between the two economies. Prices are rising in Pioneerland at 7 percent per year. Given the information presented in Fact 29.1 about interest rates and foreign exchange rates, what is the inflation rate in Ecoland?
a) +7 percent.
b) +12.5 percent.
c) –12.5 percent.
d) –5.5 percent.
e) +5.5 percent.

29.76 (SG 29.16)
Correct:a)
Difficulty: 5
Page(s): 792
Scramble range: All
Topic: Relative inflation rates

29.76
Under a fixed exchange rate, with no nontraded goods, no impediments to trade, and no risk differences between Canada and the United States, then the inflation rate in Canada will equal the inflation rate in the United States

a) and the interest rate in Canada will equal the interest rate in the United States.
b) minus the percentage appreciation of the Canadian dollar and the expected interest rate in Canada will equal the interest rate in the United States minus the percentage appreciation of the Canadian dollar.
c) and the interest rate in Canada will equal the interest rate in the United States minus the percentage appreciation of the Canadian dollar.
d) minus the percentage appreciation of the Canadian dollar and the interest rate in Canada will equal the interest rate in the United States.
e) minus the percentage appreciation of the Canadian dollar and the interest rate in Canada will equal the interest rate in the United States plus the percentage appreciation of the Canadian dollar.

29.77 (SG 29.17)
Correct: b)
Difficulty: 5
Page(s): 792
Scramble range: All
Topic: Relative inflation rates

29.77
Under a flexible exchange rate, with no nontraded goods, no impediments to trade, and no risk differences between Canada and the United States, then the inflation rate in Canada will equal the inflation rate in the United States

a) and the interest rate in Canada will equal the interest rate in the United States.
b) minus the percentage appreciation of the Canadian dollar and the expected interest rate in Canada will equal the interest rate in the United States minus the percentage appreciation of the Canadian dollar.
c) and the interest rate in Canada will equal the interest rate in the United States minus the percentage appreciation of the Canadian dollar.
d) minus the percentage appreciation of the Canadian dollar and the interest rate in Canada will equal the interest rate in the United States.
e) minus the percentage appreciation of the Canadian dollar and the interest rate in Canada will equal the interest rate in the United States plus the percentage appreciation of the Canadian dollar.

29.78
Correct: e)
Difficulty: 3
Page(s): 792
Scramble range: All
Topic: Monetary independence

29.78
Under a fixed exchange rate, the Bank of Canada

a) has complete monetary independence.
b) has no ability to alter the value of the exchange rate.
c) has complete monetary dependence.
d) must keep the Canadian interest rate equal to the U.S. rate.
e) has strongly reduced monetary independence.

29.79
Correct: d)
Difficulty: 3
Page(s): 792
Scramble range: All
Topic: Monetary independence

29.79
Insulation of an economy from external shocks can be best achieved by

a) balancing the federal budget.
b) interest rate parity.
c) having a managed exchange rate.
d) having a flexible exchange rate.
e) having a fixed exchange rate.

29.80
Correct: c)
Difficulty: 3
Page(s): 787–788
Scramble range: All
Topic: Interest rate parity

29.80
Interest rate parity comes about due to
a) monetary independence.
b) monetary dependence.
c) arbitrage.
d) the Bank of Canada maintaining a fixed exchange rate.
e) a flexible exchange rate.

29.81
Correct: c)
Difficulty: 3
Page(s): 786
Scramble range: All
Topic: Purchasing power parity

29.81
Purchasing power parity comes about due to
a) monetary independence.
b) monetary dependence.
c) arbitrage.
d) the Bank of Canada maintaining a fixed exchange rate.
e) a flexible exchange rate.

29.82
Correct: d)
Difficulty: 2
Page(s): 775–794
Scramble range: All
Topic: International interdependence

29.82
"When America sneezes, the rest of the world catches a cold" because of
a) fixed exchanges rates.
b) flexible exchange rates.
c) purchasing power parity.
d) international interdependence of economies.
e) interest rate parity.

29.83 (SG 29.19)
Correct: e)
Difficulty: 4
Page(s): 793
Scramble range: All
Topic: Insulation

29.83
A flexible exchange rate will
a) completely insulate an economy from external forces.
b) create monetary dependence.
c) stop the impact of arbitrage.
d) lead to purchasing power parity.
e) partially insulate an economy from external forces.

29.84 (SG 29.20)
Correct: c)
Difficulty: 3
Page(s): 794
Scramble range: All
Topic: Lowering interest rates

29.84
To bring down interest rates, the Bank of Canada should
a) adopt a flexible exchange rate.
b) adopt a fixed exchange rate.
c) slow the growth rate of the money supply.
d) raise the growth rate of the money supply.
e) create a depreciation of the exchange rate.

29.85 (SG 29.18)
Correct: d)
Difficulty: 4
Page(s): 792
Scramble range: All
Topic: Fixed exchange rates

29.85
Suppose Canada has a 5 percent inflation rate and the United States has a 9 percent inflation rate. The Bank of Canada decides to keep the exchange rate fixed at its current level. The two countries have no risk differences, there are no nontraded goods, and there are no impediments to trade. You would predict that
a) purchasing power parity would be violated.
b) interest rate parity would be violated.
c) interest rates in Canada will be 4 percent lower than in the United States.
d) the Canadian inflation rate will rise to the U.S. rate.
e) the U.S. inflation rate will fall to the Canadian rate.

Chapter 30 Aggregate Demand Management

30.1
Correct: b)
Difficulty: 2
Page(s): 806
Scramble range: All
Topic: Real GDP/money demand relation

30.1
If the level of real GDP increases,
a) the demand for real money curve decreases.
b) the demand for real money curve increases.
c) the supply of real money increases.
d) the supply of real money decreases.
e) both the demand and supply of real money increases.

30.2
Correct: d)
Difficulty: 2
Page(s): 807
Scramble range: All
Topic: Money supply curve

30.2
The position of the supply curve of real money is determined by
a) the interest rate.
b) the demand for real money.
c) the investment curve.
d) policy actions of the Bank of Canada.
e) the level of real GDP.

30.3
Correct: c)
Difficulty: 2
Page(s): 807
Scramble range: All
Topic: Money supply curve

30.3
All of the following are factors that determine the position of the supply curve of real money *except*
a) policy actions of the Bank of Canada.
b) the price level.
c) the interest rate.
d) bank lending policy.
e) open market operations.

30.4
Correct: b)
Difficulty: 2
Page(s): 807
Scramble range: All
Topic: Investment demand

30.4
If the interest rate increases, then the
a) investment demand curve shifts left.
b) amount of investment decreases.
c) money supply decreases.
d) demand for real money curve shifts to the right.
e) demand for real money curve shifts to the left.

30.5
Correct: c)
Difficulty: 2
Page(s): 807
Scramble range: All
Topic: Investment demand

30.5
If investors expect greater profits, then the
a) money supply curve shifts to the left.
b) money supply curve shifts to the right.
c) investment demand curve shifts to the right.
d) investment demand curve shifts to the left.
e) amount of investment increases.

30.6
Correct: a)
Difficulty: 4
Page(s): 807
Scramble range: All
Topic: Demand curve for real money

30.6
Refer to Figure 30.1. All else the same, if real GDP is equal to $300 billion, then the

a) demand curve for real money will be to the left of the one shown in the figure.
b) demand curve for real money will be to the right of the one shown in the figure.
c) amount of real money demanded will be less than $300 billion and can be shown as a movement along the demand for real money curve.
d) amount of real money demanded will be greater than $300 billion and can be shown as a movement along the demand for real money curve.
e) interest rate will rise.

Figure 30.1 The position of the demand for money corresponds to real GDP of $400 billion

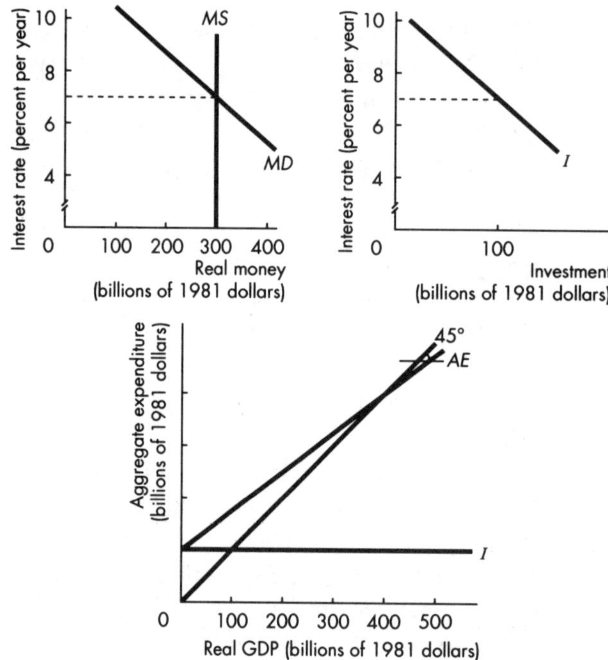

30.7
Correct: c)
Difficulty: 4
Page(s): 807
Scramble range: None
Topic: Interest rate/ position of *AE* curve

30.7
Refer to Figure 30.1. All else the same, if the interest rate is less than 7 percent, then

a) investment will be less than $100 billion.
b) the aggregate expenditure curve will shift downward.
c) the aggregate expenditure curve will shift upward.
d) the equilibrium level of real GDP will decrease.
e) both b) and d).

30.8
Correct: d)
Difficulty: 4
Page(s): 807
Scramble range: None
Topic: Equilibrium real GDP

30.8
Refer to Figure 30.1. All else the same, if the interest rate is greater than 7 percent, then

a) investment will be greater than $100 billion.
b) the aggregate expenditure curve will shift upward.
c) inventories will fall below planned levels.
d) equilibrium real GDP will fall.
e) both b) and d).

30.9
Correct: e)
Difficulty: 3
Page(s): 807
Scramble range: All
Topic: Equilibrium investment

30.9
Refer to Figure 30.1. When this economy is in equilibrium
a) investment is equal to $110 billion dollars.
b) autonomous consumption will increase.
c) real GDP is equal to $300 billion.
d) the interest rate is 5 percent.
e) investment is equal to $100 billion.

30.10
Correct: e)
Difficulty: 3
Page(s): 807
Scramble range: None
Topic: Stock equilibrium/money market

30.10
Refer to Figure 30.1. When this hypothetical economy is in equilibrium, there is a
a) flow equilibrium in the market for goods and services.
b) stock equilibrium in the factor input market which includes investment.
c) flow equilibrium in the money market.
d) stock equilibrium in the money market.
e) both a) and d).

30.11
Correct: c)
Difficulty: 3
Page(s): 806–808
Scramble range: None
Topic: Flow equilibrium/final goods/service

30.11
Refer to Figure 30.1. When this hypothetical economy is in equilibrium, there is a
a) stock equilibrium in the factor market which includes investment.
b) flow equilibrium in the money market.
c) flow equilibrium in the market for final goods and services.
d) stock equilibrium in the labour market.
e) both a) and b).

30.12
Correct: d)
Difficulty: 4
Page(s): 808
Scramble range: All
Topic: Bank of Canada policy/investment demand

30.12
Refer to Figure 30.1. Starting from the stock and flow equilibrium pictured, if the Bank of Canada sells government securities in the open market, then
a) the investment demand curve will shift to the right.
b) real GDP will rise.
c) there will be an increase in investment expenditures.
d) there will be a decrease in investment expenditures.
e) the interest rate will fall.

30.13
Correct: b)
Difficulty: 4
Page(s): 810
Scramble range: None
Topic: Bank of Canada policy/money supply

30.13
Refer to Figure 30.1. Starting from the stock and flow equilibrium pictured, if the Bank of Canada buys government securities in the open market, then the
a) money supply curve will shift to the left.
b) money supply curve will shift to the right.
c) money demand curve will shift to the left.
d) slope of the aggregate expenditure curve will become steeper.
e) both b) and d).

30.14
Correct: b)
Difficulty: 4
Page(s): 811
Scramble range: All
Topic: Real money balance and real GDP

30.14
Refer to Figure 30.1. Starting from the stock and flow equilibrium pictured, if the demand for real money balances increases,
a) investment expenditures will rise above $100 billion.
b) real GDP will fall below $400 billion.
c) real GDP will rise above $400 billion.
d) the interest rate will be 7 percent.
e) nothing will happen since the money supply stays constant.

30.15
Correct: d)
Difficulty: 4
Page(s): 811
Scramble range: All
Topic: Investment and real GDP

30.15
Refer to Figure 30.1. Starting from the stock and flow equilibrium pictured, if investors' profit expectations become more optimistic, then
a) the money demand curve will shift to the left.
b) the aggregate expenditure curve will shift downward.
c) real GDP will rise and the money supply curve will increase.
d) real GDP will rise.
e) real GDP will fall.

30.16
Correct: e)
Difficulty: 3
Page(s): 812
Scramble range: All
Topic: Actual versus equilibrium real GDP

30.16
Actual real GDP
a) is always equivalent to equilibrium real GDP.
b) is always equivalent to equilibrium real GDP if it is above capacity output.
c) can be above or below equilibrium real GDP but inventories will be at planned levels.
d) is equal to equilibrium real GDP when planned expenditures are equal to the change in inventories.
e) is equal to equilibrium real GDP when there are no unplanned expenditures.

30.17
Correct: b)
Difficulty: 3
Page(s): 811
Scramble range: All
Topic: Equilibrium adjustment process

30.17
With an unplanned increase in inventories, firms will
a) increase their production rate and real GDP will increase to the equilibrium level.
b) decrease their production rate and real GDP will decrease to the equilibrium level.
c) leave the production rate unchanged as the economy's automatic adjustment process kicks in to bring real GDP up to the equilibrium level.
d) leave their production rate unchanged as the economy's automatic adjustment process kicks in to bring real GDP down to the equilibrium level.
e) lower investment to compensate.

30.18
Correct: d)
Difficulty: 4
Page(s): 811
Scramble range: All
Topic: Equilibrium adjustment process

30.18
Which one of the following sequences of events would be part of the total sequence of events stemming from a Bank of Canada decision to lower aggregate demand?
a) The money supply decreases, the interest rate falls, investment decreases, and aggregate planned expenditure decreases.
b) Unplanned inventories accumulate, real GDP begins to fall, and the demand for money curve increases.
c) The money supply decreases, the interest rate falls, investment increases, and aggregate planned expenditure increases.
d) The money supply decreases, the interest rate rises, investment decreases, and aggregate planned expenditure decreases.
e) The money supply increases, the interest rate rises, investment decreases, and aggregate planned expenditure decreases.

30.19
Correct: c)
Difficulty: 3
Page(s): 812–813
Scramble range: All
Topic: Monetary policy

30.19
The effectiveness of monetary policy depends on the
a) size of the Bank of Canada.
b) backing of Bank of Canada policy by parliament when the prime minister is opposed to that policy.
c) sensitivity of investment demand to the interest rate.
d) sensitivity of the supply of money to the interest rate.
e) sensitivity of consumption demand to the exchange rate.

30.20
Correct: a)
Difficulty: 4
Page(s): 812–813
Scramble range: None
Topic: Monetary policy

30.20
Given a change in monetary policy, the
a) steeper the money demand curve, the larger the effect of that policy change.
b) flatter the money demand curve, the larger the effect of that policy change.
c) steeper the investment demand curve, the larger the effect of that policy change.
d) relative slopes of the investment demand and money demand curves will not alter the effects of that policy change.
e) both b) and c).

30.21
Correct: e)
Difficulty: 3
Page(s): 812–813
Scramble range: All
Topic: Monetary policy

30.21
All else the same, which one of the investment demand curves depicted in Figure 30.2 reflects the greater sensitivity of investment demand to changes in Bank of Canada policy?
a) I_a.
b) MD_b.
c) I_c.
d) MD_d.
e) I_b.

Figure 30.2

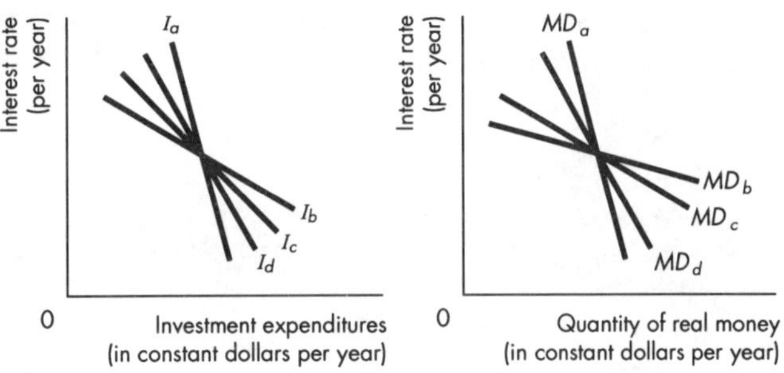

30.22
Correct: a)
Difficulty: 3
Page(s): 812–813
Scramble range: a)–d)
Topic: Monetary policy

30.22
All else the same, which one of the money demand curves depicted in Figure 30.2 would bring about the greatest response of investors to changes in Bank of Canada policy?
a) MD_a.
b) MD_b.
c) MD_c.
d) MD_d.
e) None of the above.

30.23
Correct: b)
Difficulty: 3
Page(s): 812–813
Scramble range: All
Topic: Monetary policy

30.23
Which combination of demand curves shown in Figure 30.2 supports the argument that monetary policy is not effective in altering the position of the aggregate demand curve?

a) I_a and MD_a.
b) I_a and MD_b.
c) I_b and MD_b.
d) I_b and MD_a.
e) I_c and MD_c.

30.24
Correct: b)
Difficulty: 3
Page(s): 819, 822
Scramble range: a)–d)
Topic: Keynesianism

30.24
Which combination of demand curves shown in Figure 30.2 best supports the extreme Keynesian viewpoint concerning the effectiveness of monetary policy?

a) I_a and MD_a.
b) I_a and MD_b.
c) I_b and MD_b.
d) I_b and MD_a.
e) All of the above.

30.25
Correct: e)
Difficulty: 3
Page(s): 819, 822
Scramble range: a)–d)
Topic: Monetarist/ potential monetary policy

30.25
Which combination of demand curves shown in Figure 30.2 best supports the extreme monetarist viewpoint concerning the effectiveness of monetary policy?

a) I_a and MD_a.
b) I_a and MD_b.
c) I_b and MD_b.
d) I_c and MD_c.
e) None of the above.

30.26
Correct: a)
Difficulty: 3
Page(s): 822
Scramble range: All
Topic: Sensitivity of investment

30.26
Which of the curves shown in Figure 30.2 best depicts a situation where an investment can easily be postponed or brought forward in time at a low opportunity cost?

a) I_b.
b) I_a.
c) I_c.
d) MD_a.
e) I_d.

30.27
Correct: b)
Difficulty: 3
Page(s): 822
Scramble range: All
Topic: Sensitivity of money demand

30.27
Which of the curves shown in Figure 30.2 best depicts a situation where there are the greatest number of substitutes available for money?

a) MD_a.
b) MD_b.
c) MD_c.
d) MD_d.
e) I_b.

30.28
Correct: a)
Difficulty: 2
Page(s): 813, 816
Scramble range: All
Topic: Time lags

30.28
All else the same, the longer the time period under consideration, the
a) greater will be the response of investors to changes in Bank of Canada policy.
b) smaller will be the response of investors to changes in Bank of Canada policy.
c) smaller the amount of money that will be created in response to an open market sale of securities by the Bank of Canada.
d) smaller the amount of money that will be created in response to an open market purchase of securities by the Bank of Canada.
e) smaller will be the induced rise in expenditure.

30.29
Correct: a)
Difficulty: 3
Page(s): 813, 816
Scramble range: All
Topic: Time lags

30.29
All else the same, if interest rates rise, which one of the following investment projects might be the last to be cut?
a) The continued financing of a new electric power generating station that is already under way.
b) The purchase of a house by a growing family.
c) The purchase of a new computer system to replace the old one at the university.
d) The purchase of a new saw by a carpenter.
e) The purchase of a new automobile by a car rental agency.

30.30
Correct: c)
Difficulty: 2
Page(s): 815
Scramble range: All
Topic: Wealth effect

30.30
Suppose the Bank of Canada buys $100 million worth of government securities from General Motors and GM uses the proceeds to buy stock in other firms. Further suppose that the stock prices of those other firms increase inducing individuals to convert those stocks into consumer durables. This is known as the
a) multiplier effect.
b) real balance effect.
c) wealth effect.
d) conversion effect.
e) induced expenditure effect.

30.31
Correct: d)
Difficulty: 2
Page(s): 815
Scramble range: All
Topic: Real balance effect

30.31
All else the same, if a change in the quantity of real money in the economy induces people to hold less money and increase their holdings of capital goods, this can be described as the
a) wealth effect.
b) exchange rate effect.
c) substitution effect.
d) real balance effect.
e) capital effect.

30.32
Correct: b)
Difficulty: 2
Page(s): 815
Scramble range: All
Topic: Exchange rate effect

30.32
If an increase in the money supply leads to an increase in net exports, this can be described as the
a) wealth effect.
b) exchange rate effect.
c) substitution effect.
d) international effect.
e) export effect.

30.33
Correct: d)
Difficulty: 2
Page(s): 822
Scramble range: All
Topic: Liquidity trap

30.33
A situation in which the demand curve for real money is horizontal at a given rate depicts the phenomenon referred to as the
a) real balance effect.
b) wealth effect.
c) crowding-out effect.
d) liquidity trap.
e) money trap.

30.34
Correct: a)
Difficulty: 2
Page(s): 822
Scramble range: All
Topic: Liquidity trap

30.34
A situation in which people are willing to hold any amount of money at a given interest rate is referred to as the
a) liquidity trap.
b) monetarist effect.
c) crowding-out effect.
d) substitution effect.
e) interest rate effect.

30.35
Correct: e)
Difficulty: 2
Page(s): 816–817
Scramble range: All
Topic: Crowding out

30.35
The tendency for an increase in government expenditure to increase interest rates and lead to a decline in investment is referred to as the
a) real balance reduction effect.
b) interest rate effect.
c) liquidity trap effect.
d) wealth reduction effect.
e) crowding-out effect.

30.36
Correct: d)
Difficulty: 2
Page(s): 822
Scramble range: All
Topic: Monetarism

30.36
An economist who holds the view that the market economy is inherently stable, might be called a
a) Samuelsonian.
b) Keynesian.
c) Adamsian.
d) monetarist.
e) stablist.

30.37
Correct: a)
Difficulty: 2
Page(s): 822
Scramble range: All
Topic: Keynesianism

30.37
An economist who holds the view that the market economy is inherently unstable might be most closely aligned with the views of
a) the Keynesians.
b) the monetarists.
c) Adam Smith.
d) the classical economists.
e) John Hicks.

30.38
Correct: c)
Difficulty: 2
Page(s): 818
Scramble range: All
Topic: Monetary policy

30.38
A change in the money supply affects aggregate demand by changing all of the following *except*
a) real money balances.
b) wealth.
c) taxes.
d) the foreign exchange rate.
e) the interest rate.

30.39
Correct: a)
Difficulty: 3
Page(s): 818
Scramble range: All
Topic: Fiscal policy/money market

30.39
All else the same, an increase in the rate of government expenditures induces
a) an increase in the demand for real money balances.
b) a decrease in the demand for real money balances.
c) no change in the demand for real money balances.
d) a decrease in the money supply.
e) an increase in the money supply.

30.40
Correct: d)
Difficulty: 3
Page(s): 816–817
Scramble range: All
Topic: Complete crowding out

30.40
Complete crowding out occurs if
a) a 10 percent increase in government expenditures reduces investment by 1 percent.
b) the aggregate demand curve does increase by the full multiplier effect predicted by the government expenditure multiplier.
c) the aggregate demand curve does not increase by the full multiplier effect predicted by the government expenditure multiplier.
d) any increase in government expenditures is offset by an equal reduction in investment expenditures.
e) any increase in government expenditures is offset by an equal rise in taxes.

30.41
Correct: d)
Difficulty: 2
Page(s): 818
Scramble range: All
Topic: Money supply change/bonds/interest rate

30.41
If the supply of money increases, bond prices are most likely to
a) fall as the interest rate rises.
b) rise as the interest rate rises.
c) fall as the interest rate falls.
d) rise as the interest rate falls.
e) stay constant.

30.42
Correct: b)
Difficulty: 4
Page(s): 815–816
Scramble range: All
Topic: Transmission mechanism

30.42
A decrease in the money supply is most likely to
a) increase interest rates, investment, and aggregate demand.
b) increase interest rates, decrease investment, and decrease aggregate demand.
c) decrease interest rates, increase investment, and increase aggregate demand.
d) decrease interest rates, investment, and aggregate demand.
e) increase interest rates, decrease investment, and increase aggregate demand.

30.43
Correct: d)
Difficulty: 3
Page(s): 818
Scramble range: All
Topic: Monetary policy

30.43
The impact of monetary policy on aggregate demand will be greater the
a) flatter the demand for real money curve and the investment demand curve.
b) steeper the demand for real money curve and the investment demand curve.
c) flatter the demand for real money curve and the steeper the investment demand curve.
d) steeper the demand for real money curve and the flatter the investment demand curve.
e) steeper the demand for real money curve and the flatter the aggregate expenditure curve.

30.44
Correct: c)
Difficulty: 3
Page(s): 822
Scramble range: All
Topic: Keynesianism

30.44
Monetary policy is relatively ineffective according to Keynesians because the
- **a)** demand for money and investment demand curves are relatively flat.
- **b)** demand for money curve is relatively steep and the investment demand curve is relatively flat.
- **c)** demand for money curve is relatively flat and the investment demand curve is relatively steep.
- **d)** aggregate expenditure curve is relatively steep.
- **e)** demand for money and the investment demand curves are relatively steep.

30.45
Correct: c)
Difficulty: 4
Page(s): 818
Scramble range: All
Topic: Fiscal and monetary policy

30.45
If the government pursues a fiscal policy designed to increase aggregate demand, which of the following Bank of Canada policies will frustrate that effort?
- **a)** An increase in open market sales of government securities by the department of finance.
- **b)** A decrease in open market sales of government securities by the Bank of Canada.
- **c)** An increase in open market sales of government securities by the Bank of Canada.
- **d)** An increase in open market purchases of government securities by the Bank of Canada.
- **e)** Lowering the bank rate.

30.46
Correct: b)
Difficulty: 4
Page(s): 818
Scramble range: All
Topic: Fiscal and monetary policy

30.46
Which of the following pairs of policies are consistent with respect to their effect on the position of the aggregate demand curve?
- **a)** An increase in the money supply and tax rates.
- **b)** An increase in transfer payments and the money supply.
- **c)** A decrease in the money supply and tax rates.
- **d)** An increase in Bank of Canada sales of government securities and any transfer payments.
- **e)** An increase in the money supply and a decrease in government purchases.

30.47
Correct: e)
Difficulty: 3
Page(s): 822
Scramble range: All
Topic: Monetary view of money supply change

30.47
The monetarist position might be expressed best by which of the following? Changes in the money supply cause
- **a)** small changes in interest rates that cause large changes in expenditures.
- **b)** small changes in interest rates that cause small changes in expenditures.
- **c)** large changes in interest rates that cause small changes in expenditures.
- **d)** small changes in interest rates that cause large changes in government expenditures.
- **e)** large changes in interest rates that cause large changes in expenditures.

30.48
Correct: c)
Difficulty: 3
Page(s): 822
Scramble range: All
Topic: Keynesianism

30.48
The Keynesian position might be expressed best by which of the following? Fiscal policy is effective because it predicts that a given fiscal stimulus will
- **a)** be offset by a large decrease in investment.
- **b)** produce a large decrease in interest rates.
- **c)** have a relatively slight effect on investment.
- **d)** produce a large increase in interest rates.
- **e)** have a relatively large effect on investment.

30.49
Correct: b)
Difficulty: 3
Page(s): 822
Scramble range: All
Topic: Monetary view of fiscal policy

30.49
Monetarists predict that expansionary fiscal policy will result in crowding out for all of the following reasons *except*
a) the demand for real money function will shift upwards.
b) the investment curve is relatively steep (inelastic).
c) interest rates will rise.
d) the transactions demand for money will increase.
e) income levels will rise as a result of the fiscal policy.

30.50
Correct: a)
Difficulty: 3
Page(s): 819
Scramble range: All
Topic: *SAS* and effects of fiscal policy

30.50
If the short-run aggregate supply curve was vertical, expansionary fiscal policy would cause all of the following *except*
a) an increase in investment.
b) an increase in the demand for real money.
c) an increase in interest rates.
d) an increase in the price level.
e) a decrease in investment.

30.51
Correct: d)
Difficulty: 2
Page(s): 807
Scramble range: All
Topic: Aggregate demand curve

30.51
Each price level is associated with an equilibrium level of real GDP. This relationship is shown by the
a) aggregate expenditure curve.
b) investment demand curve.
c) demand for real money function.
d) aggregate demand curve.
e) money supply curve.

30.52
Correct: e)
Difficulty: 3
Page(s): 818
Scramble range: All
Topic: Movement versus shift/change in interest rates

30.52
A change in interest rates will affect aggregate demand through which one of the following changes?
a) A shift of the investment demand curve and a movement along the aggregate expenditure curve.
b) A shift of the demand for real money curve and the investment demand curve.
c) A shift of the investment demand curve and the aggregate expenditure function.
d) Movements along both the investment demand and the aggregate expenditure curves.
e) A movement along the investment demand curve and a shift of the aggregate expenditure curve.

30.53
Correct: c)
Difficulty: 3
Page(s): 818
Scramble range: None
Topic: Fiscal policy

30.53
An increase in aggregate demand brought about by fiscal policy changes can be offset by all of the following *except* the
a) crowding-out effect.
b) exchange rate effect.
c) expenditure effect.
d) time lag effect.
e) neither b) nor c).

30.54
Correct: e)
Difficulty: 5
Page(s): 818
Scramble range: All
Topic: Exchange rate and monetary policy

30.54
If monetary expansion occurs, all else the same, then which of the following sequence of events could moderate the effect of this monetary policy's effect on aggregate demand?

a) Interest rates decrease, Canadian dollar depreciates, prices of exports fall, and prices of imports rise.
b) Interest rates increase, Canadian dollar appreciates, prices of exports rise, and prices of imports fall.
c) Interest rates decrease, Canadian dollar appreciates, prices of exports rise, and prices of imports fall.
d) Interest rates increase, Canadian dollar depreciates, prices of exports fall, and prices of imports rise.
e) Interest rates decrease, investment demand rises, aggregate expenditure rises, real GDP rises, and demand for real money rises.

30.55
Correct: b)
Difficulty: 5
Page(s): 818
Scramble range: All
Topic: Exchange rate and monetary policy

30.55
If monetary contraction occurs, all else the same, then which of the following sequence of events could enhance the effect of this monetary policy's effect on aggregate demand?

a) Interest rates decrease, Canadian dollar depreciates,prices of exports fall, and prices of imports rise.
b) Interest rates increase, Canadian dollar appreciates, prices of exports rise, and prices of imports fall.
c) Interest rates decrease, Canadian dollar appreciates, prices of exports rise, and prices of imports fall.
d) Interest rates increase, Canadian dollar depreciates, prices of exports fall, and prices of imports rise.
e) Interest rates increase, investment decreases, aggregate expenditure decreases, real GDP decreases, and demand for real money decreases.

30.56
Correct: c)
Difficulty: 3
Page(s): 813–815
Scramble range: All
Topic: Time lags

30.56
Which of the following policy actions is associated with the shortest time lag between the implementation of the policy and when the effect of the policy is felt?

a) An increase in tax rates.
b) An increase in the purchase of government securities by the Bank of Canada.
c) An increase in government expenditures.
d) A decrease in tax rates.
e) A decrease in the purchase of government securities by the Bank of Canada.

30.57
Correct: a)
Difficulty: 3
Page(s): 813–815
Scramble range: All
Topic: Time lags

30.57
Which of the following policy actions would take the shortest period of time to implement?

a) An increase in the purchase of government securities by the Bank of Canada.
b) A decrease in government expenditures.
c) An increase in government expenditures.
d) A decrease in tax rates.
e) An increase in tax rates.

30.58
Correct: c)
Difficulty: 3
Page(s): 818
Scramble range: All
Topic: Real money demand

30.58
The quantity of real money demanded falls as the interest rate rises because
a) the Department of Finance borrows more at higher interest rates.
b) the price of bonds rises as the interest rate rises.
c) the opportunity cost of holding money as an asset rises as the interest rate rises.
d) as interest rates rise, bankers fear they will go back down again so they do not lend.
e) people put off investment decisions for which the timing is less important.

30.59
Correct: d)
Difficulty: 2
Page(s): 817
Scramble range: All
Topic: Stock and flow

30.59
Money (M1) and income (real GDP) are
a) two ways of looking at the same thing.
b) both flow variables.
c) both stock variables.
d) distinctly different in that money is a stock and income is a flow.
e) distinctly different in that money is a flow and income is a stock.

30.60
Correct: c)
Difficulty: 3
Page(s): 822
Scramble range: All
Topic: Sensitivity of interest rate/money policy

30.60
If an economist is using a Keynesian model to study the economy,
a) monetary policy is usually ignored.
b) monetary policy is ignored since it is considered to be ineffective.
c) the sensitivity of interest rates to changes in the money supply must be considered.
d) only fiscal policy will be considered.
e) only monetary policy will be considered.

30.61
Correct: a)
Difficulty: 4
Page(s): 822
Scramble range: All
Topic: Interest rate sensitivity/*AE* shifts

30.61
The more sensitive investment is to changes in interest rates, the
a) more the *AE* schedule will shift from a given change in the money supply.
b) less the *AE* schedule will shift from a given change in the money supply.
c) larger will be the marginal propensity to spend.
d) smaller will be the marginal propensity to spend.
e) steeper will be the slope of the *AE* function.

30.62
Correct: d)
Difficulty: 4
Page(s): 814
Scramble range: All
Topic: Transmission mechanism

30.62
The proper order of the intermediate steps in the chain of events from a change in Bank of Canada policy to a change in GDP is
a) $C + I + G + NX$, then money supply and interest rates, then investment.
b) $C + I + G + NX$, then investment, then money supply, then interest rates.
c) money supply and interest rates, then $C + I + G + NX$, then investment.
d) money supply and interest rates, then investment, then $C + I + G + NX$.
e) interest rates and money demand, then investment, then $C + I + G + NX$.

30.63
Correct: d)
Difficulty: 3
Page(s): 822
Scramble range: All
Topic: Conflict between monetary/fiscal policy

30.63
The Bank of Canada and the federal government are pursuing different goals with respect to the position of aggregate demand if, as the government cuts taxes to promote economic growth, the Bank of Canada
a) buys government securities.
b) lowers the reserve requirement.
c) lowers the bank rate.
d) sells government securities.
e) does nothing.

30.64
Correct: e)
Difficulty: 4
Page(s): 818
Scramble range: All
Topic: Fiscal/monetary policy combination

30.64
If the level of government spending rises and the money supply decreases due to a change in Bank of Canada policy, then we know for certain that
a) the interest rate will fall.
b) the demand for real money will shift left.
c) real GDP will rise.
d) real GDP will fall.
e) the interest rate will rise.

30.65
Correct: a)
Difficulty: 3
Page(s): 814
Scramble range: All
Topic: Fiscal/monetary policy time lag

30.65
A major advantage of an expansionary monetary policy over fiscal policy is that monetary policy
a) can be implemented more quickly.
b) affects all sectors of the economy the same way.
c) once implemented has a more direct and predictable impact on spending.
d) is implemented by people who are better able to predict the proper timing of implementation given business cycle changes.
e) is definitely much more powerful.

30.66
Correct: d)
Difficulty: 3
Page(s): 817–818
Scramble range: All
Topic: Partial crowding out

30.66
Partial crowding out is said to occur if a 1 percent increase in government induces an increase in interest rates and a
a) 1 percent increase in investment.
b) 1 percent decrease in investment.
c) less than 1 percent increase in investment.
d) less than 1 percent decrease in investment.
e) more than 1 percent decrease in investment.

30.67
Correct: a)
Difficulty: 3
Page(s): 812–813
Scramble range: All
Topic: Monetary policy

30.67
If the Bank of Canada lowers the reserve ratio, then
a) the money supply will increase and private sector spending will be stimulated.
b) the money supply will increase and private sector spending will be crowded out.
c) the national debt must increase.
d) it is contracting the money supply.
e) this will crowd out fiscal policy.

30.68
Correct: d)
Difficulty: 2
Page(s): 817–818
Scramble range: All
Topic: Crowding out

30.68
The crowding-out effect is the
a) increase in consumption expenditures caused by lower taxes.
b) increase in the interest rate caused by contractionary monetary policy.
c) extent to which government contractionary policy is counteracted by lower private spending resulting from higher interest rates.
d) extent to which government expansionary policy is counteracted by lower private spending resulting from higher interest rates.
e) increase in interest rates caused by contractionary fiscal policy.

30.69
Correct: b)
Difficulty: 4
Page(s): 817–818
Scramble range: All
Topic: Crowding out

30.69
Which one of the following events might moderate or eliminate the crowding-out effect?
a) A decrease in real money balances.
b) An in-flow of foreign savings which increases the supply of loanable funds in the home country.
c) An increase in tax rates.
d) An increase in transfer payments.
e) A decrease in transfer payments.

30.70
Correct: c)
Difficulty: 3
Page(s): 817
Scramble range: All
Topic: Opportunity costs/crowding out

30.70
Which of the following might be considered an opportunity cost of a government borrowing to pay its bills?
a) A stronger national defence.
b) The tradeoff between social problems and economic problems.
c) Reduced private investment caused by higher interest rates.
d) Higher real GDP and employment caused by expansionary policy.
e) Higher future capital stock.

30.71
Correct: e)
Difficulty: 4
Page(s): 814
Scramble range: All
Topic: Money supply/stock prices

30.71
All else constant, if there is an increase in the money supply,
a) stock prices will rise forcing down interest rates and forcing down bond prices.
b) interest rates will increase, bond prices will fall and stock prices will rise.
c) interest rates will fall, bond prices will fall, and stock prices will rise.
d) interest rates will fall and stock prices will fall as people substitute stocks for the now lower-yielding bonds.
e) interest rates will fall and stock prices will rise as people substitute stocks for the now lower-yielding bonds.

30.72
Correct: b)
Difficulty: 3
Page(s): 816
Scramble range: All
Topic: Monetary theory/stock price

30.72
Changing profit expectations and supply shocks are examples of why the __________ is not a good predictor of changes in __________
a) exchange rate theory; interest rates.
b) monetary theory of stock markets; stock prices.
c) Sprinkler theory; investment levels.
d) crowding-out theory; stock prices.
e) Keynesian theory; money supply.

30.73
Correct: c)
Difficulty: 3
Page(s): 822
Scramble range: All
Topic: Liquidity trap

30.73
Once an economy is in the liquidity trap, an increase in the money supply will
a) decrease interest rates and raise investment.
b) increase interest rates and decrease investment.
c) not change interest rates, thereby preventing growth in spending and employment.
d) cause an increase in the price of bonds.
e) be completely crowded out by a rise in interest rates.

30.74
Correct: c)
Difficulty: 2
Page(s): 822
Scramble range: All
Topic: Liquidity trap

30.74
The liquidity trap would be best illustrated by which line in Figure 30.3?
a) *A.*
b) *B.*
c) *C.*
d) *D.*
e) *E.*

Figure 30.3

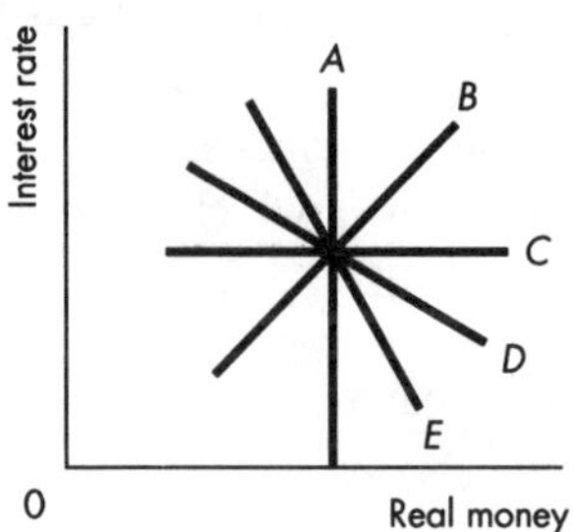

30.75
Correct: e)
Difficulty: 2
Page(s): 822
Scramble range: All
Topic: Keynesianism

30.75
Which of the curves depicted in Figure 30.3 would best represent the compromise position between the Keynesians and the monetarists concerning the demand for real money curve?
a) *B* or *C*.
b) *A*.
c) *B*.
d) *C*.
e) *D* or *E*.

30.76
Correct: b)
Difficulty: 2
Page(s): 827–828
Scramble range: All
Topic: *IS* curve

30.76
The curve that shows the combinations of real GDP and the interest rate at which aggregate planned expenditure equals real GDP is called the
a) investment demand curve.
b) *IS* curve.
c) *LM* curve.
d) *AE* curve.
e) *AD* curve.

30.77
Correct: a)
Difficulty: 3
Page(s): 827–828
Scramble range: None
Topic: *IS* curve

30.77
Points on the *IS* curve represent cases where
a) planned injections into the circular flow of expenditure and income are equal to the planned leakages from the circular flow.
b) actual injections into the circular flow of expenditure and income are equal to the actual leakages from the circular flow.
c) actual injections into the circular flow of expenditure and income are equal to the planned leakages from the circular flow.
d) planned injections into the circular flow of expenditure and income are equal to the actual leakages from the circular flow.
e) both a) and b).

30.78
Correct: b)
Difficulty: 2
Page(s): 827–828
Scramble range: All
Topic: *IS* curve

30.78
The developer of the *IS–LM* framework was
a) John Maynard Keynes.
b) John Hicks.
c) Milton Friedman.
d) John Tower.
e) Michael Parkin.

30.79
Correct: c)
Difficulty: 3
Page(s): 827–828
Scramble range: All
Topic: *IS* curve

30.79
In a private closed economy, points along the *IS* curve represent where
a) planned money supply equals planned investment.
b) transactions demand equals aggregate demand.
c) planned saving equals planned investment.
d) planned taxes equal planned government expenditures.
e) planned money demand equals money supply.

30.80
Correct: c)
Difficulty: 3
Page(s): 827–828
Scramble range: All
Topic: *IS* curve

30.80
Which of the following statements concerning the *IS* curve is true?
a) A point on the *IS* curve reveals the level of investment (cause) and the corresponding level of real GDP (effect).
b) A point on the *IS* curve reveals the level of investment (effect) and the corresponding level of real GDP (cause).
c) The *IS* curve is not a cause and effect relationship.
d) The *IS* curve shows the relationship between real GDP and the price level.
e) The *IS* curve is a form of a demand curve.

30.81
Correct: a)
Difficulty: 3
Page(s): 827–828
Scramble range: All
Topic: *IS* curve

30.81
Which of the following statements would most accurately reflect the way a point on the *IS* curve should be interpreted?
a) If the interest rate is n percent, then real GDP is x dollars.
b) If the interest rate is n percent, then real investment is x dollars.
c) If the interest rate is n percent, then real saving is x dollars.
d) A rise in the interest rate to n percent will cause real GDP to change to x dollars.
e) If the interest rate is n percent, then real money demand is x dollars.

30.82
Correct: e)
Difficulty: 3
Page(s): 829–830
Scramble range: All
Topic: *LM* curve

30.82
The curve that shows the combinations of real GDP and the interest rate at which the quantity of real money demanded is constant and equals the quantity of real money supplied is called the
a) *IS* curve.
b) liquidity preference curve.
c) marginal efficiency of investment curve.
d) *AD* curve.
e) *LM* curve.

30.83 (SG 30.1)
Correct: a)
Difficulty: 3
Page(s): 814
Scramble range: All
Topic: Transmission mechanism

30.83
Which of the following correctly describes the initial steps of the interest rate transmission mechanism? An increase in the money supply will cause investment to
a) increase and thus aggregate planned expenditure to increase.
b) increase and thus aggregate planned expenditure to decrease.
c) decrease and thus aggregate actual expenditure to increase.
d) decrease and thus aggregate planned expenditure to decrease.
e) increase and thus aggregate actual expenditure to increase.

30.84 (SG 30.2)
Correct: c)
Difficulty: 3
Page(s): 808
Scramble range: All
Topic: Stock/flow equilibrium

30.84
Consider Figure 30.4. Why is the situation depicted there not a stock and flow equilibrium?

a) The level of aggregate planned spending is inconsistent with the interest rate.
b) The money market and the goods market are not individually in equilibrium.
c) The expenditure equilibrium occurs at a different level of real GDP than the level of real GDP assumed when drawing the demand curve for real money.
d) The level of investment in part (c) is inconsistent with the level of investment in part (b).
e) Aggregate expenditure is greater than aggregate supply.

Figure 30.4

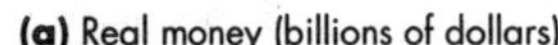

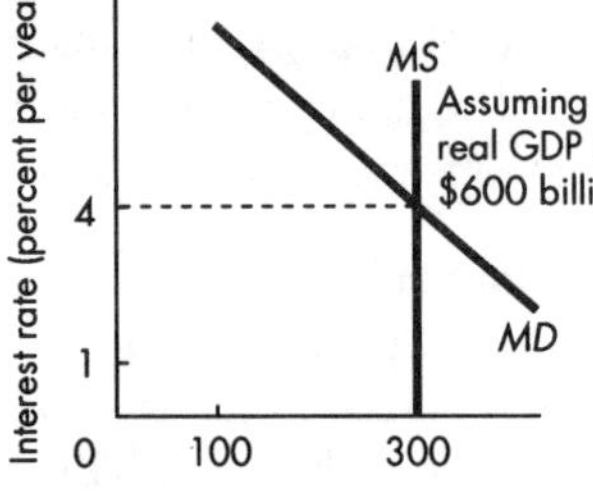

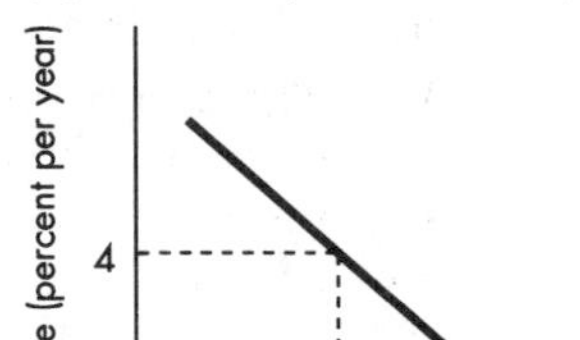

(c) Real GDP (billions of dollars)

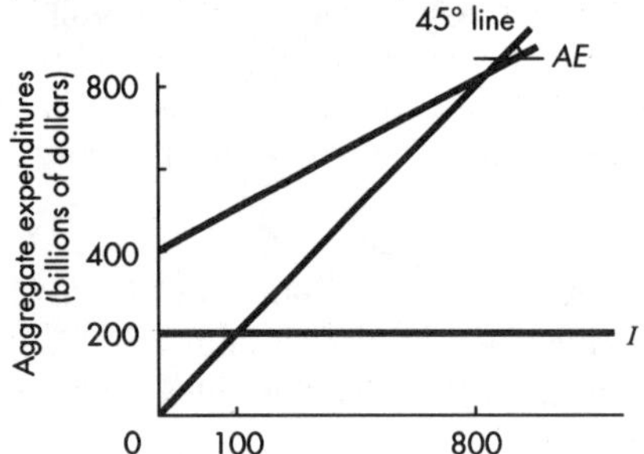

30.85
Correct: a)
Difficulty: 3
Page(s): 808
Scramble range: a)–d)
Topic: Stock/flow equilibrium

30.85
Suppose Figure 30.1 depicts the actual current position of an economy. In stock and flow equilibrium, real GDP will be

a) less than $800 billion and the interest rate will be higher than 6 percent.
b) less than $800 billion and the interest rate will be lower than 6 percent.
c) more than $800 billion and the interest rate will be higher than 6 percent.
d) more than $800 billion and the interest rate will be lower than 6 percent.
e) none of the above.

30.86 (SG 30.4)
Correct: d)
Difficulty: 3
Page(s): 812–813
Scramble range: All
Topic: Monetary policy

30.86
An increase in the money supply will generally lead to an increase in real GDP which will shift the demand curve for real money to the

a) left causing the interest rate to fall.
b) left causing the interest rate to rise.
c) right causing the interest rate to fall.
d) right causing the interest rate to rise.
e) right causing the money supply to rise.

30.87 (SG 30.5)
Correct: b)
Difficulty: 3
Page(s): 814
Scramble range: All
Topic: Monetary effect

30.87
Monetary policy will have the *smallest* effect on aggregate demand when the sensitivity of the demand curve for real money to the interest rate is
a) large and the sensitivity of the investment demand curve to the interest rate is large.
b) large and the sensitivity of the investment demand curve to the interest rate is small.
c) small and the sensitivity of the consumption function to the interest rate is large.
d) small and the sensitivity of the investment demand curve to the interest rate is small.
e) small and the sensitivity of the consumption function to the interest rate is small.

30.88 (SG 30.6)
Correct: c)
Difficulty: 3
Page(s): 806
Scramble range: None
Topic: Interest rate transmission

30.88
The demand curve for real money will be more sensitive to the interest rate the
a) more people care about the timing of investment.
b) less people care about the timing of investment.
c) more substitutable other financial assets are for money.
d) less substitutable other financial assets are for money.
e) both a) and c).

30.89 (SG 30.7)
Correct: e)
Difficulty: 3
Page(s): 812–813
Scramble range: All
Topic: Monetary policy

30.89
Which of the following is true? Monetary policy affects the interest rate
a) immediately and fiscal policy affects the interest rate immediately.
b) immediately and fiscal policy does not affect the interest rate at all.
c) after a time lag and fiscal policy affects the interest rate immediately.
d) after a time lag and fiscal policy affects the interest rate after a time lag.
e) immediately and fiscal policy affects the interest rate after a time lag.

30.90 (SG 30.8)
Correct: e)
Difficulty: 2
Page(s): 814
Scramble range: All
Topic: Interest rate effect

30.90
Which of the following is the main transmission mechanism by which a change in the money supply affects aggregate demand?
a) The real balance effect.
b) The exchange rate effect.
c) The wealth effect.
d) The crowding-out effect.
e) The interest rate effect.

30.91 (SG 30.9)
Correct: b)
Difficulty: 4
Page(s): 815
Scramble range: All
Topic: Wealth effect

30.91
Which of the following is an example of the transmission of monetary policy through the wealth effect?
a) The Bank of Canada increases the money supply through the purchase of stocks in the open market. Thus stock prices rise, which stimulates aggregate planned expenditure.
b) The Bank of Canada increases the money supply by purchasing government securities in the open market. The individual who sold the securities uses the proceeds to buy stocks. Thus stock prices rise, which stimulates aggregate planned expenditure.
c) An increase in the money supply causes a decrease in the value of the dollar relative to foreign currencies which increases aggregate planned expenditure.
d) An increase in the money supply leads to an increase in the price level, a reduction in real money, and thus a reduction in aggregate planned expenditure.
e) An increase in the money supply causes a fall in wealth, which lowers consumption and therefore lowers aggregate expenditure.

30.92 (SG 30.10)
Correct: a)
Difficulty: 3
Page(s): 819
Scramble range: All
Topic: Tax effects

30.92
A tax cut will
a) increase aggregate planned expenditure by causing disposable income to increase.
b) increase aggregate planned expenditure by causing the interest rate to fall.
c) decrease aggregate planned expenditure by causing disposable income to fall.
d) decrease aggregate planned expenditure by causing the interest rate to rise.
e) increase aggregate planned expenditure by causing investment to rise.

30.93 (SG 30.11)
Correct: e)
Difficulty: 5
Page(s): 816–817
Scramble range: All
Topic: Crowding out

30.93
There will be no crowding out if
a) the demand for real money is totally unresponsive to changes in the interest rate.
b) the supply of real money is totally unresponsive to changes in the interest rate.
c) investment is very responsive to changes in the interest rate.
d) investment is totally unresponsive to changes in real GDP.
e) the demand for real money is totally unresponsive to changes in real GDP.

30.94 (SG 30.12)
Correct: b)
Difficulty: 4
Page(s): 818
Scramble range: All
Topic: Monetary versus fiscal policy

30.94
Aggregate demand can be increased by increasing the money supply (expansionary monetary policy) or by increasing government purchases of goods and services (expansionary fiscal policy). Which of the following is a correct comparison?
a) The interest rate will rise under the monetary policy and fall under the fiscal policy, while consumption will increase under both.
b) The interest rate will fall under the monetary policy and rise under the fiscal policy, while consumption will increase under both.
c) Consumption will rise under the monetary policy and fall under the fiscal policy, while the interest rate will increase under both.
d) Consumption will rise under the monetary policy and fall under the fiscal policy, while the interest rate will decrease under both.
e) Consumption will fall under the monetary policy and fall under the fiscal policy, while the interest rate will increase under both.

30.95 (SG 30.13)
Correct: d)
Difficulty: 4
Page(s): 819
Scramble range: All
Topic: Tax effects

30.95
A tax cut will cause
a) a decrease in the interest rate, which will lead to a decrease in the foreign exchange value of the dollar.
b) a decrease in the interest rate, which will lead to an increase in the foreign exchange value of the dollar.
c) an increase in the interest rate, which will lead to a decrease in the foreign exchange value of the dollar.
d) an increase in the interest rate, which will lead to an increase in the foreign exchange value of the dollar.
e) no change in the interest rate.

30.96 (SG 30.14)
Correct: a)
Difficulty: 3
Page(s): 822
Scramble range: All
Topic: Keynesianism

30.96
Which of the following sets of beliefs is characteristic of a Keynesian?
a) The economy is inherently unstable and fiscal policy is more important than monetary policy.
b) The economy is inherently unstable and monetary policy is more important than fiscal policy.
c) The economy is inherently stable and fiscal policy is more important than monetary policy.
d) The economy is inherently stable and monetary policy is more important than fiscal policy.
e) The economy is inherently stable, and crowding out is strong.

30.97 (SG 30.15)
Correct: c)
Difficulty: 2
Page(s): 822
Scramble range: All
Topic: Monetarism

30.97
The founder of modern monetarism is
a) Adam Smith.
b) John Maynard Keynes.
c) Milton Friedman.
d) James Tobin.
e) John Hicks.

30.98 (SG 30.16)
Correct: b)
Difficulty: 3
Page(s): 822
Scramble range: All
Topic: Monetarism

30.98
Which of the following would characterize the extreme monetarist position?
a) A horizontal investment demand curve and a horizontal demand curve for real money.
b) A horizontal investment demand curve and a vertical demand curve for real money.
c) A vertical investment demand curve and a horizontal demand curve for real money.
d) A vertical investment demand curve and a vertical demand curve for real money.
e) A vertical investment demand curve and a horizontal supply curve of real money.

30.99 (SG 30.17)
Correct: d)
Difficulty: 4
Page(s): 822
Scramble range: All
Topic: Liquidity trap

30.99
If an economy is in a liquidity trap, then
a) a change in the interest rate will have no effect on investment.
b) a change in investment will have no effect on aggregate planned expenditure.
c) open market operations will not shift the supply curve of real money.
d) an increase in the supply of real money will have no effect on the interest rate.
e) fiscal policy is totally crowded out.

30.100 (SG 30.18)
Correct: c)
Difficulty: 2
Page(s): 818
Scramble range: All
Topic: Monetary versus fiscal policy

30.100
Statistical evidence from a variety of historical and national experiences suggests that
a) fiscal policy affects aggregate demand and monetary policy does not.
b) monetary policy affects aggregate demand and fiscal policy does not.
c) both fiscal policy and monetary policy affect aggregate demand.
d) neither fiscal policy nor monetary policy affect aggregate demand.
e) fiscal policy affected aggregate demand only during the Great Depression of the 1930s.

30.101
Correct: d)
Difficulty: 3
Page(s): 808
Scramble range: All
Topic: Stock/flow equilibrium

30.101
Which of the following is *not* true of an economy in stock and flow equilibrium?
a) The level of aggregate planned spending is consistent with the interest rate.
b) The money market is in equilibrium.
c) The goods market is in equilibrium.
d) Real interest rates are increasing.
e) Unplanned inventory accumulation equals zero.

30.102
Correct: e)
Difficulty: 4
Page(s): 814
Scramble range: a)–d)
Topic: Monetary effects

30.102
Monetary policy will have the *greatest* effect on aggregate demand when the sensitivity of the demand curve for real money to the interest rate is
a) large and the sensitivity of the investment demand curve to the interest rate is large.
b) large and the sensitivity of the investment demand curve to the interest rate is small.
c) small and the sensitivity of the consumption function to the interest rate is large.
d) small and the sensitivity of the investment demand curve to the interest rate is small.
e) none of the above.

30.103
Correct: c)
Difficulty: 3
Page(s): 814
Scramble range: None
Topic: Monetary effects

30.103
Which of the following would make the demand curve for real money more sensitive to the interest rate?
a) High degree of concern about the timing of investment.
b) Low degree of concern about the timing of investment.
c) High degree of substitutability between money and other financial assets.
d) Low degree of substitutability between money and other financial assets.
e) Both b) and c).

30.104
Correct: a)
Difficulty: 3
Page(s): 814
Scramble range: All
Topic: Monetary effects

30.104
Which of the following effects is the strongest in transforming changes in the money supply into changes in aggregate demand?
a) Effect of changes in interest rates.
b) Effect of changes in the value of real balances.
c) Effect of changes in imports and exports induced by monetary changes.
d) Effect of changes in aggregate wealth.
e) Effect of changes in crowding out.

30.105
Correct: b)
Difficulty: 2
Page(s): 814
Scramble range: All
Topic: Monetary effects

30.105
The Bank of Canada purchases government securities on the open market and the individuals who sold the securities buy stocks, pushing stock prices up and expanding aggregate planned expenditure. What monetary transmission effect was involved?
a) Real balance effect.
b) Wealth effect.
c) Exchange rate effect.
d) Interest rate effect.
e) Crowding-out effect.

30.106
Correct: c)
Difficulty: 3
Page(s): 819
Scramble range: All
Topic: Tax effects

30.106
A tax increase will
a) increase aggregate planned expenditure by causing disposable income to increase.
b) increase aggregate planned expenditure by causing the interest rate to fall.
c) decrease aggregate planned expenditure by causing disposable income to fall.
d) decrease aggregate planned expenditure by causing the interest rate to rise.
e) decrease aggregate planned expenditure by causing investment to rise.

30.107
Correct: d)
Difficulty: 4
Page(s): 817–818
Scramble range: None
Topic: Crowding out

30.107
There will be severe crowding out if
a) the demand for real money is highly responsive to changes in the interest rate.
b) the supply of real money is highly unresponsive to changes in the interest rate.
c) investment is highly responsive to changes in real GDP.
d) investment is highly responsive to changes in the interest rate.
e) both a) and d).

30.108
Correct: a)
Difficulty: 2
Page(s): 822
Scramble range: All
Topic: Monetarist/Keynesian

30.108
Which of the following groups of economists would be most likely to believe that the economy is inherently unstable and that fiscal policy is more important than monetary policy?
a) Keynesians.
b) Monetarists.
c) Classical economists.
d) Rational expectations economists.
e) Hicksian economists.

30.109
Correct: b)
Difficulty: 2
Page(s): 822
Scramble range: All
Topic: Monetarist/Keynesian

30.109
Which of the following labels is best applied to economist Milton Friedman?
a) Author of *The Wealth of Nations.*
b) Founder of modern monetarism.
c) Founder of the field of macroeconomics.
d) Discoverer of rational expectations.
e) A leading Keynesian.

30.110
Correct: e)
Difficulty: 2
Page(s): 822
Scramble range: All
Topic: Monetarist/Keynesian

30.110
According to statistical evidence from a variety of historical and national experiences, which of the following affects aggregate demand?
a) Fiscal policy only.
b) Monetary policy only.
c) Exchange rate policy and monetary policy.
d) Exchange rate policy only.
e) Both fiscal policy and monetary policy.

30.111 (SG 30.19)
Correct: e)
Difficulty: 4
Page(s): 818
Scramble range: All
Topic: Effectiveness of monetary policy

30.111
Consider an economy where the demand for real money is very sensitive to changes in the interest rate, and where the investment demand curve is also very sensitive to the interest rate. The problem with monetary policy in this economy is that
a) there will be a high level of crowding out.
b) monetary policy will create changes in the exchange rate that offset the monetary policy.
c) a change in the interest rate creates only a small change in investment demand.
d) a change in the money supply creates a large change in the interest rate.
e) a change in the money supply creates only a small change in the interest rate.

30.112 (SG 30.20)
Correct: e)
Difficulty: 4
Page(s): 818
Scramble range: All
Topic: Effectiveness of fiscal policy

30.112
Consider an economy where the demand for real money is very sensitive to changes in the interest rate, and where the investment demand curve is also very sensitive to the rate of interest. In this economy,
a) fiscal policy is ineffective due to a high level of crowding out.
b) fiscal policy will create changes in the exchange rate that augment the fiscal policy.
c) a change in interest rates creates only a small change in investment demand.
d) a change in government purchases creates a large change in interest rates.
e) a change in government purchases creates a small change in interest rates and a small amount of crowding out.

30.113
Correct: d)
Difficulty: 2
Page(s): 813–815
Scramble range: All
Topic: Time lags

30.113
The time lags associated with monetary policy actions include all of the following but
a) an autonomous expenditure lag.
b) an induced expenditure lag.
c) a price adjustment lag.
d) an investment lag.
e) a policy formation lag.

30.114
Correct: d)
Difficulty: 5
Page(s): 815–816
Scramble range: a)–d)
Topic: composition of *AD*

30.114
At the end of a change in government policy, interest rates are higher, consumption is higher, and investment is lower. The change in government policy was
a) an expansionary monetary policy.
b) a contractionary monetary policy.
c) a contractionary fiscal policy.
d) an expansionary fiscal policy.
e) none of the above.

30.115
Correct: a)
Difficulty: 4
Page(s): 832–833
Scramble range: All
Topic: *IS*/*LM* curves

30.115
An increase in taxes will shift the
a) *IS* curve left and the *AD* curve left.
b) *IS* curve right and the *AD* curve left.
c) *IS* curve left and the *AD* curve right.
d) *LM* curve left and the *AD* curve left.
e) *LM* curve right and the *AD* curve left.

30.116
Correct: d)
Difficulty: 4
Page(s): 832–833
Scramble range: All
Topic: *IS*/*LM* curves

30.116
A decrease in the money supply will shift the
a) *IS* curve left and the *AD* curve left.
b) *IS* curve right and the *AD* curve left.
c) *IS* curve left and the *AD* curve right.
d) *LM* curve left and the *AD* curve left.
e) *LM* curve right and the *AD* curve left.

Chapter 31 Unemployment and Aggregate Supply

31.1
Correct: a)
Difficulty: 2
Page(s): 839
Scramble range: All
Topic: Monetarist view of unemployment

31.1
Monetarists tend to view wages as
a) flexible and unemployment as natural.
b) sticky and unemployment as natural.
c) sticky and unemployment as unnatural.
d) flexible and unemployment as unnatural.
e) fixed and unemployment as unnatural.

31.2
Correct: c)
Difficulty: 2
Page(s): 839
Scramble range: All
Topic: Keynesian view of unemployment

31.2
Keynesians tend to take the view that wages are
a) flexible and unemployment is unnatural.
b) sticky and unemployment is natural.
c) sticky and some unemployment arises from insufficient wage flexibility.
d) flexible and all unemployment arises from insufficient wage recontracting.
e) fixed and unemployment is unnatural.

31.3
Correct: a)
Difficulty: 3
Page(s): 839
Scramble range: All
Topic: Production function

31.3
A production function shows
a) how the maximum output varies as the employment of inputs varies.
b) the maximum amount of money that can be created as the reserve requirement is met and banks are fully loaned up.
c) the maximum amount of labour that will be used when the wage rate is at the market equilibrium wage rate.
d) the maximum amount of labour that will be used at all of the possible wage rates.
e) the amount of output that can be produced from a fixed amount of inputs.

31.4
Correct: c)
Difficulty: 2
Page(s): 839
Scramble range: All
Topic: Production function

31.4
How maximum output varies as the employment of inputs varies is the definition of the
a) short-run aggregate supply curve.
b) short-run aggregate expenditure curve.
c) production function.
d) marginal production function.
e) labour demand curve.

31.5
Correct: c)
Difficulty: 2
Page(s): 839
Scramble range: All
Topic: Short-run aggregate production function

31.5
The short-run aggregate production function shows
a) how much of each input will be employed in the macroeconomy.
b) the maximum amount of labour that will be employed as the price level changes.
c) how maximum real GDP varies as the employment of labour varies, holding the capital stock and state of technology constant.
d) how minimum real GDP varies as the employment of labour varies, holding the capital stock and state of technology constant.
e) how much real GDP will be produced for each amount of capital used.

31.6
Correct: e)
Difficulty: 2
Page(s): 839
Scramble range: All
Topic: Short-run aggregate production function

31.6
The function that shows how maximum real GDP varies as the employment of labour varies, holding the capital stock and state of technology constant, is called the
a) short-run labour production function.
b) labour supply curve.
c) long-run aggregate supply curve.
d) short-run aggregate supply curve.
e) short-run aggregate production function.

31.7
Correct: b)
Difficulty: 2
Page(s): 839
Scramble range: All
Topic: Short-run production function

31.7
The curve depicted in Figure 31.1 is called the
a) marginal product of labour.
b) short-run aggregate production function.
c) long-run aggregate production function.
d) short-run aggregate supply curve.
e) labour supply curve.

Figure 31.1

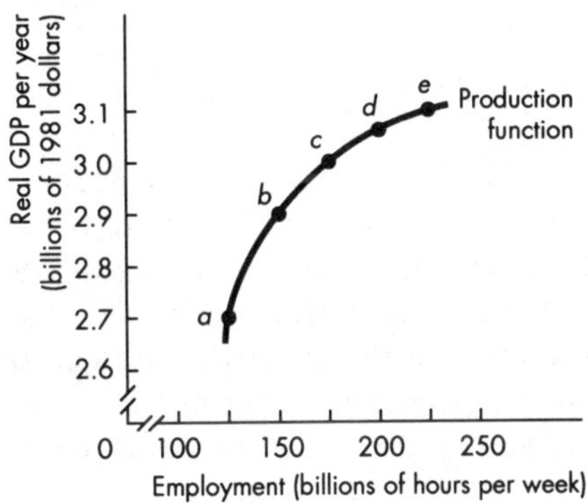

31.8
Correct: e)
Difficulty: 3
Page(s): 839
Scramble range: All
Topic: Short-run aggregate production function

31.8
According to the curve shown in Figure 31.1, as the employment of labour increases,
a) real GDP declines.
b) real wages rise.
c) the marginal product of labour increases.
d) the marginal product of labour is constant.
e) aggregate output increases.

31.9
Correct: a)
Difficulty: 3
Page(s): 839
Scramble range: All
Topic: Marginal product of labour

31.9
According to Figure 31.1, as the employment of labour increases,
a) the marginal product of labour diminishes.
b) the marginal product of labour increases.
c) the marginal product of labour is constant.
d) the corresponding short-run aggregate supply curve is flat.
e) real GDP declines.

31.10
Correct: b)
Difficulty: 2
Page(s): 839
Scramble range: All
Topic: Short-run aggregate production function

31.10
Refer to Figure 31.1. The maximum output that can be produced when 150 billion hours of labour are employed is
a) \$2.6 billion in real GDP.
b) \$2.9 billion in real GDP.
c) \$3 billion in real GDP.
d) \$2.8 billion in real GDP.
e) \$2.7 billion in real GDP.

31.11
Correct: e)
Difficulty: 4
Page(s): 839
Scramble range: All
Topic: Short-run aggregate production function

31.11
Refer to Figure 31.1. As the number of labour hours employed increases from 125 to 150 billion hours per year,
a) the marginal product of labour is 0.004.
b) the marginal product of labour is –0.008.
c) real GDP increases from \$125 billion to \$150 billion.
d) real GDP is \$125 billion.
e) real GDP increases from \$2.7 billion to \$2.9 billion.

31.12
Correct: e)
Difficulty: 4
Page(s): 839
Scramble range: a)–d)
Topic: Marginal product of labour

31.12
Refer to Figure 31.1. As the number of labour hours employed increases from 125 to 150 billion hours per year,
a) the marginal product of labour is \$8 per hour.
b) the marginal product of labour is 0.004.
c) real GDP increases from \$100 billion to \$150 billion.
d) real GDP is \$150 billion.
e) none of the above.

31.13
Correct: b)
Difficulty: 3
Page(s): 840
Scramble range: All
Topic: Diminished marginal product of labour

31.13
Refer to Figure 31.1. The marginal product of labour
a) increases as the economy moves from point *a* to *b* to *c*.
b) increases as the economy moves from point *c* to *b* to *a*.
c) decreases as the economy moves from point *b* to *a*.
d) remains constant as the economy moves from point *d* to *e*.
e) eventually becomes negative.

31.14
Correct: c)
Difficulty: 4
Page(s): 839
Scramble range: All
Topic: Marginal product of labour

31.14
Refer to Figure 31.1. As the economy moves from point *b* to *c*, the marginal product of labour is equal to
a) 0.008.
b) –0.008.
c) 0.004.
d) –0.004.
e) 4.

31.15
Correct: b)
Difficulty: 2
Page(s): 840
Scramble range: All
Topic: Diminishing marginal produc

31.15
Given that the use of all other factor inputs are held constant, a diminishing marginal product of labour might best be described as when the total number of labour hours worked in the economy
a) increases and total output increases.
b) increases and total output increases at a decreasing rate.
c) increases and total output decreases.
d) decreases and total output increases.
e) increases and total output increases at an increasing rate.

31.16
Correct: d)
Difficulty: 2
Page(s): 841
Scramble range: All
Topic: Short-run production function

31.16
The phenomenon known as the diminishing marginal product of labour is directly shown by the
a) long-run production function.
b) short-run aggregate supply curve.
c) long-run aggregate supply curve.
d) short-run production function.
e) labour supply curve.

31.17
Correct: c)
Difficulty: 2
Page(s): 840–841
Scramble range: All
Topic: Economic growth

31.17
Economic growth
a) is the expansion of the use of labour.
b) occurs when output increases.
c) is the expansion of the economy's productive capacity.
d) is always constant.
e) occurs when the capital stock rises.

31.18
Correct: b)
Difficulty: 3
Page(s): 840–841
Scramble range: All
Topic: Economic growth

31.18
Which of the following would not contribute to economic growth directly?
a) The building of new capital equipment.
b) The increase in the use of labour time in the economy.
c) The development of new technologies in production.
d) An increase in the size of the labour force.
e) The replacement of older capital stock with newer capital stock.

31.19
Correct: d)
Difficulty: 2
Page(s): 841
Scramble range: All
Topic: Short-run production function

31.19
Refer to Figure 31.2. Which of the following best expresses the name of the curve labelled *O* in this figure?
a) Long-run production function.
b) Long-run aggregate supply curve.
c) Short-run aggregate supply curve.
d) Short-run aggregate production function.
e) Intermediate aggregate production function.

Figure 31.2

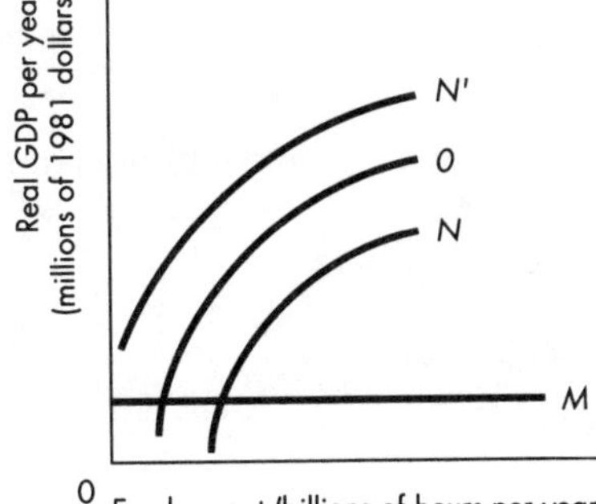

31.20
Correct: c)
Difficulty: 3
Page(s): 840
Scramble range: a)–d)
Topic: Deterioration of capital/production function

31.20
Refer to Figure 31.2. Suppose the original curve is the one labelled *O*. All else the same, if the capital stock should deteriorate, then the new relevant curve would be best represented by the curve labelled
a) *N*.
b) *O*.
c) *N'*.
d) *M*.
e) none of the above.

31.21
Correct: a)
Difficulty: 2
Page(s): 840–841
Scramble range: a)–d)
Topic: Technology change/production function

31.21
Refer to Figure 31.2. Suppose the original curve is labelled *O*. All else the same, if there is a new technology introduced in production, then the new relevant curve would be best represented by the curve labelled
a) *N*.
b) *O*.
c) *N'*.
d) *M*.
e) none of the above.

31.22
Correct: c)
Difficulty: 2
Page(s): 841
Scramble range: All
Topic: Short-run production function

31.22
The normal or average direction of change for the Canadian economy's short-run production function is to
a) remain constant.
b) shift downward.
c) shift upward.
d) become flatter.
e) become longer.

31.23
Correct: b)
Difficulty: 2
Page(s): 841
Scramble range: All
Topic: Short-run aggregate production function

31.23
All else the same, if net investment is negative, then the economy's short-run production function will
a) remain the same.
b) shift downward.
c) shift upward.
d) become steeper.
e) swivel around the original point.

31.24
Correct: d)
Difficulty: 2
Page(s): 841
Scramble range: All
Topic: Invention

31.24
The discovery of a new production technique is referred to as
a) economic investment.
b) an innovation.
c) capital accumulation.
d) an invention.
e) economic growth.

31.25
Correct: a)
Difficulty: 2
Page(s): 841
Scramble range: All
Topic: Innovation

31.25
The act of putting a new technique into operation is called
a) innovation.
b) economic investment.
c) inventing.
d) capital accumulation.
e) economic growth.

31.26
Correct: e)
Difficulty: 3
Page(s): 841
Scramble range: All
Topic: Short-run production function/shift

31.26
All else the same, which of the following events might shift the economy's production function downward?
a) An increase in unemployment.
b) A rise in wages.
c) Capital accumulation.
d) Innovation.
e) Widespread droughts.

31.27
Correct: d)
Difficulty: 2
Page(s): 841
Scramble range: All
Topic: Short-run production function/shift

31.27
All else the same, which of the following events might shift the economy's production function upward?
a) Widespread droughts.
b) Civil war.
c) An oil embargo that raises oil prices in the country.
d) Capital accumulation.
e) A fall in wages.

31.28
Correct: c)
Difficulty: 3
Page(s): 841
Scramble range: None
Topic: Movement versus shift/short-run production function

31.28
All else the same, an increase in employment causes
a) the economy's short-run production function to shift upward.
b) the economy's short-run production function to shift downward.
c) a movement from left to right along the economy's short-run production function.
d) a movement from right to left along the economy's short-run production function.
e) both a) and c).

31.29
Correct: d)
Difficulty: 3
Page(s): 841
Scramble range: All
Topic: Movement versus shift/short-run production function

31.29
Refer to Figure 31.3. All else the same, an increase in the economy's capital stock would best be illustrated by a movement from
a) *a* to *d*.
b) *a* to *b*.
c) *c* to *a*.
d) *a* to *e*.
e) *d* to *b*.

Figure 31.3

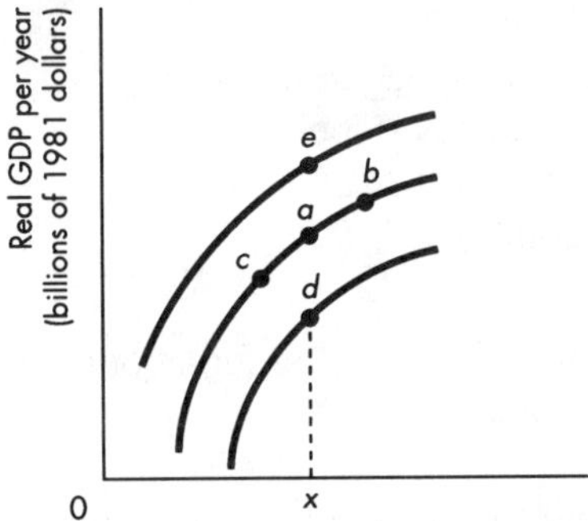

31.30
Correct: a)
Difficulty: 3
Page(s): 841
Scramble range: All
Topic: Movement versus shift/short-run production function

31.30
Refer to Figure 31.3. Suppose this figure represents the Canadian economy in 1970. An oil embargo would best be illustrated by a movement from
a) *e* to *a*.
b) *a* to *b*.
c) *a* to *c*.
d) *a* to *e*.
e) *b* to *a*.

31.31
Correct: b)
Difficulty: 3
Page(s): 841
Scramble range: All
Topic: Movement versus shift/short-run production function

31.31
Refer to Figure 31.3. An increase in employment would best be illustrated by a movement from
a) *d* to *a*.
b) *a* to *b*.
c) *a* to *c*.
d) *a* to *e*.
e) *b* to *a*.

31.32
Correct: d)
Difficulty: 1
Page(s): 842–843
Scramble range: All
Topic: Demand for labour

31.32
A schedule or curve that shows the quantity of labour demanded at each level of the real wage rate represents
a) a short-run production function.
b) a long-run production function.
c) a short-run aggregate supply curve.
d) demand for labour.
e) supply of labour.

31.33
Correct: e)
Difficulty: 2
Page(s): 842–843
Scramble range: All
Topic: Money wage rate

31.33
The wage rate expressed in current dollars is the same as the
a) constant dollar wage rate.
b) fixed wage rate.
c) real wage rate.
d) real income.
e) money wage rate.

31.34
Correct: c)
Difficulty: 2
Page(s): 842
Scramble range: All
Topic: Real wage rate

31.34
If the money wage rate is $10 per hour and the GDP deflator is 200, then the
a) real wage rate is $2.50 per hour.
b) real wage rate is $20 per hour.
c) real wage rate is $5 per hour.
d) nominal wage rate is $5 per hour.
e) nominal wage rate is $20 per hour.

31.35
Correct: c)
Difficulty: 2
Page(s): 842
Scramble range: All
Topic: Demand for labour

31.35
According to the text, the demand for labour curve is
a) positively sloped.
b) flat.
c) negatively sloped.
d) vertical.
e) upward sloping at low real wages and backward-bending at high real wages.

31.36
Correct: d)
Difficulty: 2
Page(s): 842
Scramble range: All
Topic: Real wages

31.36
The quantity of labour demanded by an individual firm depends on the
a) price level.
b) money wage rate.
c) nominal wage rate.
d) real wage rate.
e) quantity of labour supplied.

31.37
Correct: a)
Difficulty: 3
Page(s): 844
Scramble range: All
Topic: Shift versus movement/demand for labour

31.37
Which one of the following factors will not shift the demand for labour curve?
a) A change in the real wage rate.
b) Capital accumulation.
c) Development of new technologies in production.
d) A discovery of a new source of an essential input which lowers its price.
e) A rise in human capital.

31.38
Correct: c)
Difficulty: 3
Page(s): 842
Scramble range: All
Topic: Real wage rate

31.38
For an individual firm, the real wage rate is the money wage rate divided by the
a) GDP deflator.
b) producer price index.
c) price of the firm's output.
d) number of units of output produced by its labour force per time period.
e) CPI.

31.39
Correct: c)
Difficulty: 3
Page(s): 842
Scramble range: All
Topic: Demand for labour

31.39
Refer to Table 31.1. Suppose that the firm's output sells for $1 and that they can sell all that they want to at that price. If the wage rate per hour is $5, how many units of labour should the profit-maximizing firm hire per day?
a) 1.
b) 2.
c) 3.
d) 4.
e) 5.

Table 31.1 Data for an individual firm

Marginal product of labour per day	Labour units
7	1
6	2
5	3
4	4
3	5

31.40
Correct: b)
Difficulty: 3
Page(s): 842
Scramble range: All
Topic: Demand for labour

31.40
Refer to Table 31.1. Suppose that the firm's output sells for $0.75 and that they can sell all that they want to at that price. If the wage rate per hour is $4.50, how many units of labour should the firm hire?
a) 1.
b) 2.
c) 3.
d) 4.
e) 5.

31.41
Correct: e)
Difficulty: 2
Page(s): 842
Scramble range: All
Topic: Real wage rate

31.41
For the economy as a whole, the real wage rate is the money wage rate divided by the
a) price of a representative firm's output, such as IBM.
b) price of land.
c) average wage rate for the last 50 years.
d) real GDP.
e) price level.

31.42
Correct: b)
Difficulty: 2
Page(s): 842
Scramble range: All
Topic: Demand for labour

31.42
In general, over time, the demand for labour curve in Canada
a) remains in the same position.
b) shifts to the right.
c) shifts to the left.
d) becomes steeper.
e) becomes flatter.

31.43
Correct: d)
Difficulty: 1
Page(s): 845
Scramble range: All
Topic: Quantity of labour supplied

31.43
The number of hours of labour services that households supply to firms is called the
a) demand for labour.
b) short-run aggregate supply curve.
c) long-run aggregate supply curve.
d) quantity of labour supplied.
e) short-run aggregate production function.

31.44
Correct: d)
Difficulty: 2
Page(s): 842
Scramble range: All
Topic: Money wage rate

31.44
The wage rate expressed in current dollars is called the
a) real wage rate.
b) constant dollar wage rate.
c) true wage rate.
d) money wage rate.
e) flexible wage rate.

31.45
Correct: c)
Difficulty: 1
Page(s): 845
Scramble range: All
Topic: Supply of labour

31.45
A schedule or curve showing how the quantity of labour supplied varies as the real wage varies is called the
a) money wage supply.
b) short-run aggregate supply.
c) supply of labour.
d) demand for labour.
e) short-run aggregate production function.

31.46
Correct: d)
Difficulty: 3
Page(s): 845
Scramble range: All
Topic: Labour supply

31.46
In the aggregate, when the money wage rate increases, the
a) supply of labour increases.
b) quantity supplied of labour increases.
c) quantity supplied of labour decreases.
d) quantity supplied of labour may increase, decrease, or remain the same since the quantity of labour supplied depends on the real wage.
e) real wage rate increases.

31.47
Correct: b)
Difficulty: 2
Page(s): 845
Scramble range: All
Topic: Labour supply

31.47
The opportunity cost of an hour of not working is
a) the money wage given up.
b) the real wage given up
c) leisure.
d) household production.
e) the income effect.

31.48
Correct: a)
Difficulty: 2
Page(s): 847
Scramble range: All
Topic: Reservation wage

31.48
The lowest wage at which a person will supply any labour is called the
a) reservation wage.
b) real wage.
c) substitution wage.
d) income wage.
e) minimum wage.

31.49
Correct: b)
Difficulty: 3
Page(s): 846
Scramble range: All
Topic: Income versus substitution effect

31.49
If the income effect of an increase in the real wage is stronger than the substitution effect for an individual, then given the choice, he will want to
a) work the same amount of hours.
b) work fewer hours.
c) work more hours.
d) quit his job.
e) take on an extra job or work overtime hours.

31.50
Correct: a)
Difficulty: 3
Page(s): 846
Scramble range: All
Topic: Income versus substitution effect

31.50
If the substitution effect of an increase in the real wage is stronger than the income effect for an individual, then given the choice she will want to
a) work more hours.
b) work fewer hours.
c) work the same amount of hours.
d) quit her job.
e) work harder, but put in the same amount of hours.

31.51
Correct: e)
Difficulty: 3
Page(s): 846
Scramble range: All
Topic: Aggregate labour supply curve

31.51
In the aggregate, the higher the real wage rate, the
a) fewer labour hours that will be supplied.
b) number of labour hours that will be supplied tends to remain constant.
c) number of labour hours that will be supplied could be greater or fewer depending on the income effect versus the substitution effect.
d) greater the number of labour hours that will be demanded.
e) greater the number of labour hours that will be supplied.

31.52
Correct: d)
Difficulty: 2
Page(s): 847
Scramble range: All
Topic: Labour force participation rate

31.52
The proportion of the working-age population that is employed or unemployed is called the
a) labour force.
b) employment force.
c) work force.
d) labour force participation rate.
e) population ratio.

31.53
Correct: d)
Difficulty: 3
Page(s): 847
Scramble range: All
Topic: Reservation wage

31.53
Those people who have a reservation wage below or equal to the actual real wage
a) will not work.
b) will only work if the wage rate increases.
c) are indifferent as to whether or not they work.
d) will work if hired.
e) do not consider working worth the opportunity cost.

31.54
Correct: b)
Difficulty: 3
Page(s): 847
Scramble range: All
Topic: Intertemporal substitution of labour

31.54
All else the same, if the wage rate is higher today than it is expected to be later, then
a) people will be willing to work less today in hopes of securing a better job later.
b) people will be willing to work more today than in the future.
c) it will not alter their work decision since they must eat today and tomorrow.
d) firms will hire fewer workers in the future.
e) firms will hire more workers today since there will fewer in the future.

31.55
Correct: b)
Difficulty: 2
Page(s): 846
Scramble range: All
Topic: Labour supply

31.55
Which one of the following reasons might lead to a negatively sloped supply of labour curve?
a) Intertemporal substitution.
b) Income effect.
c) Substitution effect.
d) Increased participation rate.
e) Sticky wages.

31.56
Correct: d)
Difficulty: 3
Page(s): 847
Scramble range: All
Topic: Flexible wage theory

31.56
According to the flexible wage theory the short-run
a) aggregate supply curve is positively sloped, however, the long-run aggregate supply curve is vertical.
b) and long-run aggregate supply curves are positively sloped.
c) production function is vertical.
d) aggregate supply curve is vertical.
e) labour supply curve is vertical.

31.57
Correct: e)
Difficulty: 1
Page(s): 847–848
Scramble range: All
Topic: Labour market equilibrium

31.57
Refer to Figure 31.4. When the real wage rate is $5.00 per hour, the number of labour hours worked in the economy (in billions of hours) is
a) 150.
b) 100.
c) 125.
d) 75.
e) 112.

Figure 31.4

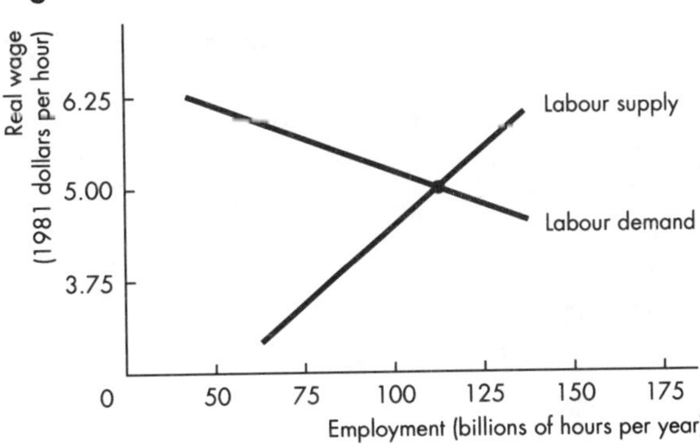

31.58
Correct: e)
Difficulty: 3
Page(s): 853–860
Scramble range: All
Topic: Unemployment

31.58
Refer to Figure 31.4. When the real wage rate is $6.25 per hour, there is a(n) __________ of labour equal to __________ billion labour hours per year.
a) unemployment; 125
b) shortage; 125
c) unemployment; 75
d) shortage; 75
e) unemployment; 100

31.59
Correct: e)
Difficulty: 4
Page(s): 842
Scramble range: All
Topic: Real wages

31.59
Refer to Figure 31.4. When the real wage rate is $5.00 per hour, the GDP deflator is 100. If the GDP deflator falls to 80, under the flexible wage theory the real wage is equal to approximately
a) $6.67.
b) $6.00.
c) $4.
d) $6.25.
e) $5.00.

31.60
Correct: b)
Difficulty: 5
Page(s): 848–850
Scramble range: All
Topic: Flexible money wage/labour market equilibrium

31.60
Refer to Figure 31.4. When the real wage rate is $6.25, the GDP deflator is 80. Money wages must __________ to __________ to bring the labour market back into equilibrium.
a) rise; $7
b) fall; $4
c) rise; $7.25
d) fall; $4.25
e) fall; $6.25

31.61
Correct: a)
Difficulty: 3
Page(s): 842
Scramble range: All
Topic: Real wages

31.61
Refer to Figure 31.4. When the real wage is $5.00, the GDP deflator is 100. Suppose the GDP deflator rises to 120. Find the new real wage rate.
a) $4.17.
b) $4.25.
c) $4.00.
d) $6.25.
e) $4.50.

31.62
Correct: c)
Difficulty: 4
Page(s): 848–850
Scramble range: All
Topic: Flexible money wage/labour market equilibrium

31.62
Refer to Figure 31.4. When the real wage is $4.50, the GDP deflator is 120. Money wages must __________ to $ __________ per hour to bring the labour market back into equilibrium.
a) rise; 6.25
b) fall; 6.00
c) rise; 6.00
d) fall; 6.25
e) rise; 5.40

31.63
Correct: d)
Difficulty: 3
Page(s): 843
Scramble range: All
Topic: Demand for labour/short-run production function

31.63
A shift up of the production function brings about
a) an increase in the supply of labour.
b) a decrease in the supply of labour.
c) a decrease in the demand for labour.
d) an increase in the demand for labour.
e) an increase in both the demand and supply of labour.

31.64
Correct: c)
Difficulty: 3
Page(s): 843
Scramble range: All
Topic: Demand for labour/short-run production function

31.64
Capital formation will __________ the short-run production function and __________ the demand for labour curve.
a) increase; leave constant
b) decrease; leave constant
c) increase; increase
d) decrease; increase
e) leave constant; leave constant

31.65
Correct: a)
Difficulty: 3
Page(s): 848–850
Scramble range: All
Topic: Flexible wage theory

31.65
According to the flexible wage theory, a change in the price level generates
a) a proportional change in the money wage rate.
b) no changes in the money wage rate even in the long run.
c) a less than proportional change in the money wage rate.
d) a change in the real wage only and no change in the money wage rate.
e) a greater than proportional change in the money wage rate.

31.66
Correct: b)
Difficulty: 2
Page(s): 848–850
Scramble range: All
Topic: Flexible wage theory

31.66
Which of one the following viewpoints suggests that the short-run and long-run aggregate supply curves are vertical?
a) Sticky wage proponents.
b) Flexible wage proponents.
c) Keynesian viewpoint.
d) Substitutionists.
e) Insider–outsider proponents.

31.67
Correct: c)
Difficulty: 3
Page(s): 850–851
Scramble range: All
Topic: Sticky wages

31.67
According to the sticky wage theory
a) the labour market can never reach an equilibrium.
b) the short-run aggregate supply curve is vertical.
c) money wage rates are fixed by wage contracts and do not adjust quickly.
d) an increase in the price level brings about a proportionate change in the money wage.
e) an increase in the price level brings about a more than proportionate change in the money wage rate.

31.68
Correct: a)
Difficulty: 3
Page(s): 848–851
Scramble range: All
Topic: Flexible/sticky wages

31.68
Sticky wage proponents reject the flexible wage theory because
a) of long-term fixed money wage contracts.
b) they reject the argument that a bonus is a wage since they are offered only to higher salaried employees.
c) they tend to have an inherent dislike of free market solutions to market problems.
d) it is outdated.
e) they argue workers never care about real wages.

31.69
Correct: b)
Difficulty: 4
Page(s): 850–851
Scramble range: a)–d)
Topic: Sticky wages

31.69
Suppose the GDP deflator moves in the same direction as the price of the output of a firm entering into a new labour contract. All else the same, if workers expect the GDP deflator to be 100 in the coming year and agree on a money wage of $10 per hour, then a
a) rise in the deflator will cause them to rejoice since their real wage has not gone down.
b) rise in the deflator will raise the profits of their employers.
c) rise in the deflator will lower the profits of their employers.
d) fall in the deflator will raise the profits of their employers.
e) none of the above.

31.70
Correct: c)
Difficulty: 5
Page(s): 850–851
Scramble range: All
Topic: Sticky wages

31.70
According to the sticky wage theory, if the labour market starts out in equilibrium and the price level falls, unemployment
a) will be short-lived since money wages will quickly adjust downward to eliminate the surplus of labour.
b) will be short-lived, since real wages will quickly adjust downward to eliminate the surplus of labour.
c) will persist until labour contracts can be renegotiated with a lower money wage.
d) will persist until labour contracts can be renegotiated with a higher money wage.
e) will be short-lived, since real wages will quickly adjust upward to eliminate the shortage of labour.

31.71
Correct: e)
Difficulty: 5
Page(s): 848–850
Scramble range: All
Topic: Flexible wage theory

31.71
According to the flexible wage theory, if the labour market starts out in equilibrium and the price level falls, unemployment
a) will be short-lived since money wages will quickly adjust upward to eliminate the surplus of labour.
b) will be short-lived, since real wages will quickly adjust upward to eliminate the surplus of labour.
c) will persist until labour contracts can be renegotiated with a higher money wage.
d) will persist until labour contracts can be renegotiated with a lower money wage.
e) will be short-lived, since real wages will quickly adjust downward to eliminate the surplus of labour.

31.72
Correct: b)
Difficulty: 3
Page(s): 850–851
Scramble range: All
Topic: Sticky wages

31.72
Which of the following reasons for unemployment would a sticky wage proponent emphasize?
a) Households have incomplete information about available jobs.
b) Wage contracts prevent the wage adjustments that would be needed to keep the quantity of labour demanded equal to the quantity supplied.
c) Firms have imperfect information about people looking for work.
d) To vary employment, it pays firms to vary the number of workers employed rather than the number of hours per worker.
e) Fluctuations in the pace of technological change create fluctuations in unemployment.

31.73
Correct: b)
Difficulty: 3
Page(s): 850–851
Scramble range: All
Topic: Sticky wages

31.73
According to the sticky wage theory, when the level of unemployment is below the natural rate, then wages
a) are "too high."
b) are "too low."
c) are "just right."
d) will adjust quickly to bring the unemployment level up to full employment.
e) will adjust slowly to bring the unemployment level down to full employment.

31.74
Correct: c)
Difficulty: 3
Page(s): 850–851
Scramble range: a)–d)
Topic: Sticky wages

31.74
According to the sticky wage theory, wages are "too high" when the
a) unemployment rate is about the same as the natural rate.
b) unemployment rate is below the natural rate.
c) unemployment rate is above the natural rate.
d) employment level is below full employment.
e) none of the above.

31.75
Correct: a)
Difficulty: 3
Page(s): 848–850
Scramble range: All
Topic: Flexible wage theory

31.75
If the unemployment rate is above the natural rate, a proponent of the flexible wage theory would suggest that
a) money wages would fall to eliminate the excess unemployment.
b) money wages would rise to eliminate the excess unemployment.
c) money wages would remain "too high."
d) money wages would remain "too low."
e) real wages would rise to eliminate the excess unemployment.

31.76
Correct: b)
Difficulty: 2
Page(s): 856
Scramble range: All
Topic: Real GDP and unemployment

31.76
In the short run, as real GDP increases,
a) employment decreases.
b) unemployment decreases.
c) employment remains the same.
d) unemployment eventually will go to zero percent.
e) unemployment will eventually go to six percent.

31.77
Correct: a)
Difficulty: 2
Page(s): 842
Scramble range: All
Topic: Real wages

31.77
The real wage rate
a) is the purchasing power of one's wage rate.
b) is of no consequence to employees when making working decisions.
c) is of no consequence to employers when making hiring decisions.
d) is always constant.
e) equals the general price level divided by the money wage rate.

31.78
Correct: c)
Difficulty: 2
Page(s): 848
Scramble range: All
Topic: Flexible wage theory

31.78
Flexible wage theory holds
a) the supply of labour is determined by the money wage rate as opposed to the real wage rate.
b) that government involvement in stabilizing the business cycle is needed.
c) if unemployment occurred it would cause wages and prices to fall.
d) the leakage of saving from the circular flow would not always be matched by an equal amount of investment.
e) that wages adjust only if there is a change in the price level.

31.79
Correct: a)
Difficulty: 3
Page(s): 851
Scramble range: All
Topic: Efficiency wage hypothesis

31.79
The hypothesis that firms can get greater effort from their workers by paying them a higher wage but that the higher wage results in unemployment and thus elicits greater effort from workers is called
a) the efficiency wage hypothesis.
b) the "insider–outsider" theory.
c) the natural rate theory.
d) the sticky wage extension theory.
e) Okun's law.

31.80
Correct: d)
Difficulty: 3
Page(s): 851
Scramble range: All
Topic: Hysteresis

31.80
Consider the idea that a large shock to the economy can create a high unemployment rate that then persists until another large shock knocks the economy back to a low unemployment rate. This idea reflects
a) the efficiency wage hypothesis.
b) the unnatural rate extension theory.
c) the "insider–outsider" theory.
d) the "hysteresis" theory.
e) Okun's law.

31.81
Correct: c)
Difficulty: 2
Page(s): 842
Scramble range: All
Topic: Equilibrium real wage

31.81
Refer to Table 31.2. At which real wage is this labour market in equilibrium?
a) $8.
b) $7.
c) $6.
d) $5.
e) $4.

Table 31.2

Real wage (1981 dollars per hour)	Quantity of labour demanded (billions of hours)	Quantity of labour supplied (billions of hours)
8	100	200
7	125	175
6	150	150
5	175	125
4	200	100

31.82
Correct: a)
Difficulty: 3
Page(s): 853–860
Scramble range: All
Topic: Unemployment

31.82
Refer to Table 31.2. Above which real wage would unemployment occur?
a) $6.
b) $7.
c) $8.
d) $4.
e) $5.

31.83 (SG 31.1)
Correct: c)
Difficulty: 2
Page(s): 839
Scramble range: All
Topic: Marginal product of labour

31.83
The marginal product of labour curve is
a) positively sloped and shifts when there is a change in the capital stock.
b) positively sloped and shifts when there is a change in the quantity of labour employed.
c) negatively sloped and shifts when there is a change in the capital stock.
d) negatively sloped and shifts when there is a change in the quantity of labour employed.
e) negatively sloped and shifts when there is a change in the wage rate.

31.84 (SG 31.2)
Correct: e)
Difficulty: 3
Page(s): 841
Scramble range: All
Topic: Short-run aggregate production function

31.84
Which of the following would shift the short-run aggregate production function upward?
a) A decrease in the stock of capital.
b) A fall in the wage rate.
c) An increase in labour employed.
d) An increase in the price level.
e) A technological advance.

31.85 (SG 31.3)
Correct: e)
Difficulty: 3
Page(s): 842
Scramble range: All
Topic: Real wages

31.85
The demand for labour shows that, holding other things constant, as the
a) price level increases, the quantity of labour demanded decreases.
b) real wage rate increases, the quantity of labour demanded increases.
c) money wage rate increases, the quantity of labour demanded decreases.
d) money wage rate increases, the quantity of labour demanded increases.
e) real wage rate increases, the quantity of labour demanded decreases.

31.86 (SG 31.4)
Correct: b)
Difficulty: 2
Page(s): 842–843
Scramble range: All
Topic: Demand for labour

31.86
Why is the demand for labour curve negatively sloped?
a) At lower wage rates, workers don't work as hard and so firms must hire more of them.
b) The tendency for the marginal product of labour to decline as the labour input increases, holding other things constant.
c) As technology advances, less labour is required to produce a given output.
d) As the price of output rises, firms will want to hire less labour.
e) As the marginal product of labour increases, fewer workers are needed.

31.87 (SG 31.5)
Correct: c)
Difficulty: 2
Page(s): 842
Scramble range: All
Topic: Real wage rate

31.87
If the money wage rate is $12 per hour and the GDP deflator is 150, the real wage rate is
a) $18 per hour.
b) $12 per hour.
c) $8 per hour.
d) $6 per hour.
e) $15 per hour.

31.88 (SG 31.6)
Correct: d)
Difficulty: 2
Page(s): 839
Scramble range: All
Topic: Marginal product of labour

31.88
A profit-maximizing firm will hire additional units of labour up to the point at which
a) workers are no longer willing to work.
b) the marginal product of labour is zero.
c) the marginal product of labour is a maximum.
d) the marginal product of labour is equal to the real wage.
e) the marginal product of labour is equal to the money wage.

31.89 (SG 31.7)
Correct: c)
Difficulty: 3
Page(s): 845
Scramble range: All
Topic: Income effect

31.89
Which of the following is *not* a reason for a positively sloped labour supply curve?
a) Intertemporal substitution of labour.
b) Individuals choose to enter the labour force only if the real wage is at least as high as their reservation wage.
c) The income effect of a change in the real wage.
d) The substitution effect of a change in the real wage.
e) Individuals choose to exit the labour force only if the real wage is lower than their reservation wage.

31.90 (SG 31.8)
Correct: d)
Difficulty: 3
Page(s): 848
Scramble range: All
Topic: Flexible wage theory

31.90
According to the flexible wage theory of the labour market, an increase in the price level will cause the
a) real wage rate to fall and therefore increase employment.
b) real wage rate to fall and therefore decrease employment.
c) money wage rate to rise by the same proportion and therefore increase employment.
d) money wage rate to rise by the same proportion and therefore leave employment unchanged.
e) money wage rate to rise by the same proportion and therefore increase unemployment.

31.91 (SG 31.9)
Correct: a)
Difficulty: 3
Page(s): 847–848
Scramble range: All
Topic: Labour market equilibrium

31.91
The aggregate supply curve is vertical at full-employment real GDP if
a) the real wage rate adjusts continually so as to leave the labour market always in equilibrium.
b) the money wage rate is fixed but the real wage rate changes due to changes in the price level.
c) employment is determined by the quantity of labour demanded.
d) employment is determined by the quantity of labour supplied.
e) employment is determined by both demand and supply of labour.

31.92 (SG 31.10)
Correct: b)
Difficulty: 4
Page(s): 847–848
Scramble range: All
Topic: Labour market equilibrium

31.92
The demand for labour and the supply of labour are both increasing over time but the demand for labour increases at a faster rate. Over time, therefore, we expect to see the
a) real wage rate rising and thus employment falling.
b) real wage rate rising and employment rising.
c) real wage rate falling and thus employment rising.
d) real wage rate falling and employment falling.
e) aggregate supply curve shifting left.

31.93 (SG 31.11)
Correct: a)
Difficulty: 4
Page(s): 848
Scramble range: All
Topic: Flexible wage theory

31.93
According to the flexible wage theory of the labour market, an increase in real GDP implies that
a) long-run aggregate supply has increased.
b) aggregate demand has increased.
c) the economy has moved up its short-run aggregate supply curve.
d) the price level has increased.
e) real wages have fallen.

31.94 (SG 31.12)
Correct: d)
Difficulty: 3
Page(s): 850–851
Scramble range: All
Topic: Sticky wages

31.94
According to the sticky wage theory of the labour market, a wage contract will set the money wage rate at a level
a) equal to the real wage rate.
b) equal to the maximum marginal product of labour.
c) so that the money wage rate is equal to the marginal product of labour.
d) so that, if the actual price level turns out to be what is expected, the labour market will be in equilibrium.
e) so that the real wage is always equal to the marginal product of labour no matter what price level comes about.

31.95 (SG 31.13)
Correct: a)
Difficulty: 4
Page(s): 850–851
Scramble range: All
Topic: Sticky wages

31.95
According to the sticky wage theory, employment is determined by the
a) quantity of labour demanded at the actual real wage rate.
b) quantity of labour supplied at the actual real wage rate.
c) intersection of the demand for labour and supply of labour curves.
d) intersection of the aggregate demand and aggregate supply curves.
e) price level.

31.96 (SG 31.14)
Correct: c)
Difficulty: 4
Page(s): 850–851
Scramble range: All
Topic: Sticky wages

31.96
According to the sticky wage theory, if the actual price level turns out to be less than the expected price level, the real wage rate will be

a) less than the equilibrium real wage rate and employment will fall.
b) less than the equilibrium real wage rate and employment will rise.
c) higher than the equilibrium real wage and employment will fall.
d) higher than the equilibrium real wage rate and employment will rise.
e) equal to the equilibrium real wage rate and employment will stay constant.

31.97 (SG 31.15)
Correct: a)
Difficulty: 3
Page(s): 848–850
Scramble range: All
Topic: Flexible wage theory

31.97
According to the flexible wage theory, if the price level increases, then real GDP supplied will

a) remain unchanged but, according to the sticky wage theory, real GDP supplied will increase.
b) increase and, according to the sticky wage theory, real GDP supplied will increase also.
c) increase but, according to the sticky wage theory, real GDP supplied will remain unchanged.
d) decrease but, according to the sticky wage theory, real GDP supplied will increase.
e) decrease and, according to the sticky wage theory, real GDP supplied will decrease also.

31.98 (SG 31.16)
Correct: d)
Difficulty: 3
Page(s): 848–850
Scramble range: a)–d)
Topic: Flexible wage theory

31.98
Which of the following is *not* a reason for unemployment according to the flexible wage theory?

a) When firms vary employment, they will tend to vary the number of workers rather than the number of hours per worker.
b) Firms have imperfect information about people looking for work.
c) Households have imperfect information about available jobs.
d) The effects of wage contracts in labour markets.
e) None of the above are reasons for unemployment according to the theory.

31.99 (SG 31.17)
Correct: b)
Difficulty: 3
Page(s): 854
Scramble range: All
Topic: Indivisible labour

31.99
The fact that labour is an economically indivisible factor of production implies that

a) firms will tend to adjust the quantity of labour demanded by changing hours per worker rather than changing the number of workers.
b) firms will tend to adjust the quantity of labour demanded by changing the number of workers rather than changing hours per worker.
c) firms cannot hire fractions of workers.
d) workers will tend to work for a single firm.
e) firms have a difficult time telling the quality of workers.

31.100 (SG 31.18)
Correct: e)
Difficulty: 2
Page(s): 853–860
Scramble range: All
Topic: Unemployment

31.100
Which of the following would generally increase unemployment?
a) An increase in the number of people entering retirement.
b) An increase in the number of people withdrawing from the labour force.
c) An increase in the number of people recalled from layoffs.
d) An increase in the number of people leaving jobs to go to school.
e) An increase in the number of people leaving school to find jobs.

31.101 (SG 31.19)
Correct: e)
Difficulty: 3
Page(s): 850–851
Scramble range: All
Topic: Sticky wages

31.101
Figure 31.5 depicts the labour market. The price level, as measured by the GDP deflator, is 150. According to the sticky wage theory, if the price level is expected to remain constant, what money wage rate will be set by a wage contract?
a) $8.
b) $12.
c) $15.
d) $24.
e) $18.

Figure 31.5

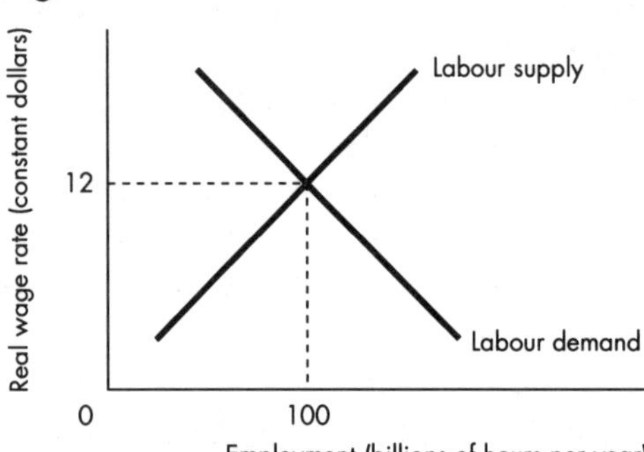

31.102 (SG 31.20)
Correct: b)
Difficulty: 4
Page(s): 842
Scramble range: All
Topic: Real wage rate

31.102
Refer to Figure 31.5 and assume that when the money wage was set, the GDP deflator was expected to remain constant at 150. If the GDP deflator actually turns out to be 200, the real wage rate will be
a) $9 and employment will be less than 100 billion hours per year.
b) $9 and employment will be more than 100 billion hours per year.
c) $24 and employment will be less than 100 billion hours per year.
d) $24 and employment will be more than 100 billion hours per year.
e) $6 and employment will be more than 100 billion hours per year.

31.103 (SG 31.21)
Correct: e)
Difficulty: 4
Page(s): 848
Scramble range: a)–d)
Topic: Flexible real wages

31.103
If real wages are very flexible, then
a) all unemployment is natural unemployment.
b) aggregate demand has no role to play in determining output.
c) fluctuations in real GDP are associated with shifts in aggregate supply only.
d) monetary and fiscal policy can be used only to affect prices and inflation.
e) all of the above.

31.104
Correct: b)
Difficulty: 2
Page(s): 842–843
Scramble range: All
Topic: Labour demand

31.104
The demand for labour curve shows that, holding other things constant, the quantity of labour demanded decreases when the
a) real wage rate decreases.
b) real wage rate increases.
c) money wage rate decreases.
d) money wage rate increases.
e) price level rises.

31.105
Correct: d)
Difficulty: 3
Page(s): 842
Scramble range: All
Topic: Money versus real wage

31.105
If the real wage rate is $5 per hour and the money wage rate is $10 per hour, it must be true that the GDP deflator is
a) 0.
b) 50.
c) 100.
d) 200.
e) 20.

31.106
Correct: c)
Difficulty: 2
Page(s): 842
Scramble range: All
Topic: Labour demand

31.106
A profit-maximizing firm will find that the marginal product of labour equals the
a) marginal product of capital.
b) marginal product of natural resources.
c) real wage of the last worker hired.
d) average money wage of the work force.
e) money wage of the last worker hired.

31.107
Correct: a)
Difficulty: 3
Page(s): 848–851
Scramble range: None
Topic: Flexible/sticky wages

31.107
If the real wage rate adjusts continually so as to leave the labour market always in equilibrium, then
a) the aggregate supply curve will be vertical at full-employment real GDP.
b) the aggregate demand curve will be vertical at full-employment real GDP.
c) the labour demand curve will be vertical at full employment.
d) the labour supply curve will be vertical at full employment.
e) both a) and d).

31.108
Correct: d)
Difficulty: 3
Page(s): 842–845
Scramble range: All
Topic: Demand/supply for labour

31.108
The demand for labour and the supply of labour are both increasing over time but the supply of labour increases at a faster rate. Over time, therefore, we expect to see the real wage
a) rising and employment falling.
b) rising and employment rising.
c) falling and employment falling.
d) falling and employment rising.
e) constant and employment rising.

31.109
Correct: a)
Difficulty: 3
Page(s): 848–851
Scramble range: All
Topic: Flexible/sticky wages

31.109
According to the sticky wage theory of the labour market, under what condition would the labour market be in equilibrium?
a) Actual price level equal to the expected price level.
b) Money wage rate equal to the marginal product of labour.
c) Money wage rate equal to maximum marginal product of labour.
d) Real wage rate equal to GDP deflator.
e) Money wage rate equal to real wage rate.

31.110
Correct: d)
Difficulty: 3
Page(s): 848–851
Scramble range: All
Topic: Flexible/sticky wages

31.110
According to the sticky wage theory, what determines the level of employment?
a) Aggregate demand for the entire economy's output.
b) Real wage and marginal product of labour.
c) Real wage and supply price of labour.
d) The intersection of the demand and supply for labour in money wages.
e) The level of natural unemployment.

31.111
Correct: a)
Difficulty: 3
Page(s): 848–851
Scramble range: All
Topic: Flexible/sticky wages

31.111
Which of the following is a possible reason for unemployment under the flexible wage theory?
a) Firms' imperfect information about people looking for work.
b) Failure of labour markets to reach equilibrium.
c) The effects of labour contracts.
d) Failure of wages to move to clear excess labour supply or demand.
e) Multiple equilibriums of search unemployment.

31.112
Correct: e)
Difficulty: 3
Page(s): 848–851
Scramble range: All
Topic: Flexible/sticky wages

31.112
Why do firms tend to adjust the quantity of labour demanded by changing the number of workers rather than changing hours per worker?
a) Legislation prohibits work weeks under 40 hours.
b) The demand for labour depends on the money wage, not the real wage.
c) Workers prefer to be unemployed rather than work a few less hours.
d) Firms pay reduced unemployment compensation taxes if they lay workers off frequently.
e) Labour is an economically indivisible factor of production.

31.113
Correct: e)
Difficulty: 3
Page(s): 853–860
Scramble range: All
Topic: Unemployment

31.113
Okun's law states that
a) the natural unemployment rate is constant and slow moving.
b) the business cycle is caused by fluctuations in the pace of technological change.
c) the business cycle is caused by sectoral shifts.
d) the natural rate of unemployment fluctuates with the business cycle.
e) fluctuations in aggregate demand produce fluctuations in real GDP that lead to fluctuations in unemployment.

31.114
Correct: a)
Difficulty: 4
Page(s): 853–860
Scramble range: All
Topic: Unemployment

31.114
New theories of unemployment include all of the following *but*
a) Okun's law.
b) real business cycle theory.
c) sectoral shift theory.
d) insider–outsider theory.
e) multiple equilibrium search theory.

31.115
Correct: e)
Difficulty: 4
Page(s): 851
Scramble range: a)–d)
Topic: Sticky real wages

31.115
If wages are not sufficiently flexible, then
a) some unemployment results from sticky wages.
b) the short-run aggregate supply curve slopes upwards.
c) a fall in aggregate demand can create some unemployment.
d) there is a role for monetary and fiscal policy.
e) all of the above.

Chapter 32 Expectations and Inflation

32.1
Correct: c)
Difficulty: 3
Page(s): 866
Scramble range: All
Topic: Real wages and inflation

32.1
Suppose that wage contracts between workers and employers are based on an expected inflation of 5 percent. An 8 percent increase in money wages is agreed upon. If inflation runs at 11 percent, then
a) real wages rise by 3 percent.
b) real wages fall by 5 percent.
c) real wages fall by 3 percent.
d) money wages fall by 3 percent.
e) real wages rise by 2 percent.

32.2
Correct: c)
Difficulty: 3
Page(s): 867
Scramble range: All
Topic: Macroeconomic equilibrium

32.2
For the economy to be in macroeconomic equilibrium several conditions must be true. Which one of the following conditions is *not* a macroeconomic equilibrium condition?
a) Aggregate planned expenditures equal real GDP.
b) Real GDP demanded equals real GDP supplied.
c) The money wage rate equals the real wage rate.
d) Quantity of labour demanded equals the quantity of labour supplied.
e) Real money demanded equals real money supplied.

32.3
Correct: d)
Difficulty: 2
Page(s): 867
Scramble range: All
Topic: Macroeconomic equilibrium

32.3
One macroeconomic equilibrium condition requires that
a) aggregate planned expenditures equals quantity of labour supplied.
b) aggregate planned expenditures equals quantity of labour demanded.
c) the aggregate demand curve intersects either one of the aggregate supply curves at the same price level.
d) the aggregate quantity demanded equals the aggregate quantity supplied.
e) real money supply equals nominal money supply.

32.4
Correct: a)
Difficulty: 2
Page(s): 867
Scramble range: All
Topic: Macroeconomic equilibrium

32.4
One macroeconomic equilibrium condition requires that
a) real money demanded equals real money supplied.
b) aggregate quantity demanded equals the price level.
c) real GDP is at least greater than the level planned by business firms.
d) real wages equals money wages.
e) the price level is equal to 100.

32.5
Correct: b)
Difficulty: 3
Page(s): 867
Scramble range: All
Topic: Macroeconomic equilibrium

32.5
Refer to Figure 32.1. If the price level is 100, then
a) the expected price level is 90.
b) the expected price level is 100.
c) the money wage rate can be greater than or less than the real wage rate.
d) the money market is not necessarily in equilibrium.
e) the economy is in short-run equilibrium but not in long-run equilibrium.

Figure 32.1

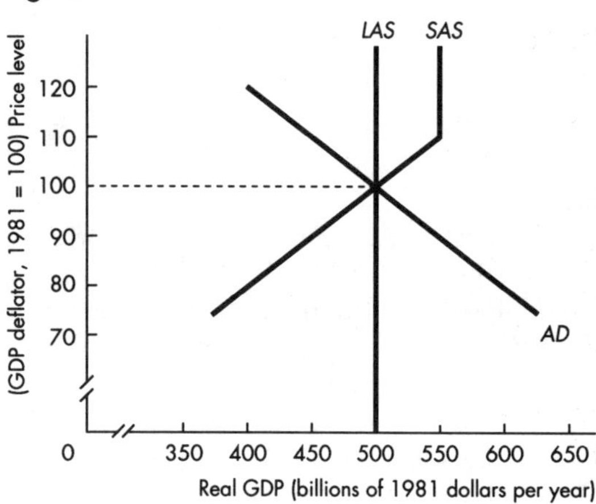

32.6
Correct: c)
Difficulty: 2
Page(s): 867
Scramble range: a)–d)
Topic: Macroeconomic equilibrium

32.6
Refer to Figure 32.1. Real GDP is equal to ________ when this economy is in macroeconomic equilibrium.
a) \$5 billion divided by the GDP deflator
b) \$5 trillion minus the GDP deflator
c) \$500 billion
d) 100
e) none of the above

32.7
Correct: e)
Difficulty: 3
Page(s): 867
Scramble range: All
Topic: Macroeconomic equilibrium

32.7
Refer to Figure 32.1. When real GDP is equal to \$500 billion, unemployment is equal to
a) zero.
b) the full employment level of real GDP.
c) structural unemployment only.
d) a rate greater than the natural rate of unemployment.
e) the natural rate of unemployment.

32.8
Correct: a)
Difficulty: 3
Page(s): 867
Scramble range: All
Topic: Macroeconomic equilibrium

32.8
Refer to Figure 32.1. When real GDP is equal to \$500 billion, inflationary expectations suggest a price level
a) of 100 for all decision makers in the economy.
b) greater than 100 for workers.
c) greater than 100 for bondholders.
d) greater than 100 for employers.
e) less than 100 for all decision makers in the economy.

32.9
Correct: b)
Difficulty: 3
Page(s): 867
Scramble range: All
Topic: Macroeconomic equilibrium

32.9
Refer to Figure 32.1. When real GDP is equal to $500 billion and the money interest rate is equal to 5 percent, then
a) real wages are equal to $5 per hour.
b) the real interest rate is 5 percent.
c) money wages are equal to real wages plus 5 percent.
d) the money market may or may not be in equilibrium.
e) the labour market may or may not be in equilibrium.

32.10
Correct: e)
Difficulty: 4
Page(s): 868
Scramble range: All
Topic: Inflationary expectations

32.10
Refer to Figure 32.2. Suppose the macroeconomy is in equilibrium when the price level is 100 and real GDP is $500 billion. If the *SAS* shifts from SAS_0 to SAS_N, then people expect
a) a 10 percent inflation.
b) the price level to rise to 110.
c) a real wage decline of 10 percent.
d) a real GDP decline of $50 billion.
e) a 15 percent inflation.

Figure 32.2

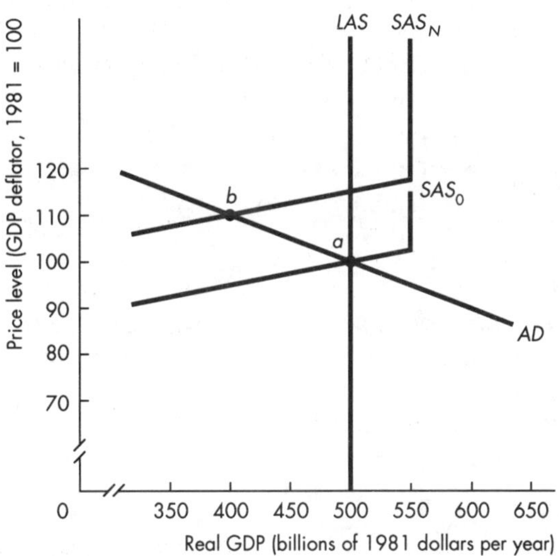

32.11
Correct: b)
Difficulty: 3
Page(s): 868–869
Scramble range: All
Topic: Actual versus expected inflation

32.11
Refer to Figure 32.2. If *SAS* shifts from SAS_0 to SAS_N, then the actual inflation rate
a) is greater than the expected inflation rate.
b) is less than the expected inflation rate.
c) is the same as the expected inflation rate.
d) cannot be determined without more information.
e) depends on what happens to wage settlements.

32.12
Correct: d)
Difficulty: 4
Page(s): 868–869
Scramble range: All
Topic: Expected inflation rate

32.12
Refer to Figure 32.2. The vertical distance between SAS_0 and SAS_N represents the
a) actual inflation rate.
b) expected increase in real GDP.
c) actual reduction in real GDP.
d) expected inflation rate.
e) expected decrease in real wages.

32.13
Correct: a)
Difficulty: 3
Page(s): 868
Scramble range: All
Topic: Inflationary expectations

32.13
Refer to Figure 32.2. If the *SAS* is stable at SAS_0, then the expected inflation rate is
a) zero.
b) 10 percent.
c) 15 percent.
d) 5 percent.
e) –10 percent.

32.14
Correct: e)
Difficulty: 4
Page(s): 869
Scramble range: None
Topic: Recession

32.14
Refer to Figure 32.2. If *SAS* shifts from SAS_0 to SAS_N, then
a) inflation is expected to be 10 percent.
b) inflation is 10 percent.
c) a recession will occur.
d) unemployment will fall.
e) both b) and c).

32.15
Correct: d)
Difficulty: 4
Page(s): 870
Scramble range: All
Topic: Inflationary expectations

32.15
Refer to Figure 32.2. Consider the market for labour as *SAS* shifts from SAS_0 to SAS_0. This shift could have been caused by an agreement by workers and employers to a
a) 10 percent decrease in the money wage.
b) 10 percent increase in the money wage.
c) 15 percent decrease in the money wage.
d) 15 percent increase in the money wage.
e) 10 percent increase in the real wage.

32.16
Correct: a)
Difficulty: 4
Page(s): 870
Scramble range: All
Topic: Money wages

32.16
Refer to Figure 32.2. Suppose the *SAS* shifts from SAS_0 to SAS_N due to inflationary expectations in the labour market. This means that the
a) money wage rises.
b) real wage rises by 5 percent.
c) real wage rises by 10 percent.
d) real wage rises by 15 percent.
e) real wage falls.

32.17
Correct: d)
Difficulty: 5
Page(s): 869
Scramble range: All
Topic: Real wages and inflation

32.17
Refer to Figure 32.2. Suppose the *SAS* shifts from SAS_0 to SAS_N due entirely to inflationary expectations in the labour market. The money wage was $10 per hour before the shift. After the shift, the real wage is
a) now equal to the money wage.
b) 15 percent lower.
c) $11.50 per hour.
d) $10.45 per hour.
e) $9.00 per hour.

32.18
Correct: a)
Difficulty: 4
Page(s): 870
Scramble range: All
Topic: Deflationary expectations/ unemployment

32.18
Suppose that an economy is in macroeconomic equilibrium initially. All else constant, if the price level is expected to fall by 15 percent and the GDP deflator falls from 100 to 80, then
a) the unemployment rate will increase.
b) the unemployment rate will decrease.
c) real wages will fall by 20 percent.
d) real wages will fall by 15 percent.
e) money wages will rise.

32.19
Correct: c)
Difficulty: 4
Page(s): 870
Scramble range: All
Topic: Inflationary expectations

32.19
Suppose that an economy is in macroeconomic equilibrium initially. All else the same, if the price level is expected to rise by 15 percent and the GDP deflator rises from 110 to 120, then
a) the unemployment rate will decrease.
b) the inflationary expectations were off by approximately –6 percent.
c) the inflationary expectations were off by approximately 6 percent.
d) inflationary expectations were correct.
e) real wages will fall.

32.20
Correct: e)
Difficulty: 3
Page(s): 870
Scramble range: All
Topic: Expected price level/real GDP

32.20
Assuming that wages and prices are not fully flexible and all else remains the same, the higher the expected price level, the
a) lower is the actual price level and the higher is real GDP.
b) higher is the actual price level and the higher is real GDP.
c) lower is the actual price level and the lower is real GDP.
d) higher is the actual price level and real GDP remains the same.
e) higher is the actual price level and the lower is real GDP.

32.21
Correct: a)
Difficulty: 3
Page(s): 870
Scramble range: All
Topic: Expected price level/unemployment

32.21
Assuming that wages and prices are not fully flexible and all else the same, the higher the expected price level, the
a) higher is the actual price level and the higher is the unemployment rate.
b) lower is the actual price level and the higher is the unemployment rate.
c) lower is the actual price level and the lower is the unemployment rate.
d) higher is the actual price level and the lower is the unemployment rate.
e) higher is the actual price level and the unemployment rate remains the same.

32.22
Correct: a)
Difficulty: 3
Page(s): 870
Scramble range: All
Topic: Expected price level/real GDP

32.22
Assuming that wages and prices are not fully flexible and all else the same, the lower the expected price level, the
a) lower is the actual price level and the higher is real GDP.
b) higher is the actual price level and the lower is real GDP.
c) lower is the actual price level and the lower is real GDP.
d) higher is the actual price level and the higher is real GDP.
e) lower is the actual price level, and real GDP remains the same.

32.23
Correct: a)
Difficulty: 3
Page(s): 870
Scramble range: All
Topic: Expected price level/unemployment

32.23
Assuming that wages and prices are not fully flexible and all else the same, the higher the expected price level, the
a) higher is the actual price level and the higher is the unemployment rate.
b) lower is the actual price level and the higher is the unemployment rate.
c) lower is the actual price level and the lower is the unemployment rate.
d) higher is the actual price level and the lower is the unemployment rate.
e) lower is the actual price level and the unemployment rate remains the same.

32.24
Correct: e)
Difficulty: 4
Page(s): 870
Scramble range: All
Topic: Labour market/incorrect inflation forecast

32.24
All else the same, when workers and employers base future wage payments on an inflation forecast that turns out to be too high, then in an economic sense any workers employed the same number of hours both before and after the new contract period are
a) neither helped nor hurt but employers are hurt.
b) helped and employers are helped.
c) hurt and employers are hurt.
d) hurt but employers are helped.
e) helped but employers are hurt.

32.25
Correct: d)
Difficulty: 4
Page(s): 870
Scramble range: All
Topic: Labour market/incorrect inflation forecast

32.25
All else the same, when workers and employers base future wage payments on an inflation forecast that turns out to be too low, then in an economic sense any workers employed the same number of hours both before and after the new contract period are
a) helped but employers are hurt.
b) helped and employers are helped.
c) hurt and employers are hurt.
d) hurt but employers are helped.
e) hurt but employers are left just as well off.

32.26
Correct: a)
Difficulty: 4
Page(s): 870
Scramble range: All
Topic: Costs — incorrect inflation forecast

32.26
All else the same, when workers and employers base future wage payments on an inflation forecast that turns out to be too high,
a) both workers and employers are hurt due to higher unemployment and production costs.
b) both workers and employers are helped due to lower unemployment and production costs.
c) workers are hurt due to higher unemployment but employers are helped due to lower production costs.
d) workers are helped due to lower unemployment but employers are hurt due to higher production costs.
e) workers are hurt due to higher unemployment but employers are just as well off as if the forecast had been correct.

32.27
Correct: a)
Difficulty: 3
Page(s): 870
Scramble range: All
Topic: Money market/incorrect inflation forecast

32.27
All else the same, if lenders and borrowers base their lending contract on an inflation forecast that turns out to be too high then, in an economic sense, borrowers
a) are hurt but lenders are helped.
b) are helped but lenders are hurt.
c) and lenders are hurt.
d) and lenders are helped.
e) are helped and lenders are just as well off.

32.28
Correct: b)
Difficulty: 3
Page(s): 870
Scramble range: All
Topic: Money market/incorrect inflation forecast

32.28
All else the same, if lenders and borrowers base their lending contract on an inflation forecast that turns out to be too low then, in an economic sense, borrowers

a) are hurt but lenders are helped.
b) are helped but lenders are hurt.
c) and lenders are hurt.
d) and lenders are helped.
e) are left just as well off while lenders are helped.

32.29
Correct: c)
Difficulty: 3
Page(s): 870
Scramble range: All
Topic: Correct inflation forecast/money market

32.29
All else the same, if lenders and borrowers base their loan contract on an inflation forecast that turns out to be just right, then

a) borrowers gain at the expense of lenders.
b) lenders gain at the expense of lenders.
c) there are no losses and no gains due to the inflation.
d) both gain due to the inflation.
e) both lose due to the inflation.

32.30
Correct: d)
Difficulty: 3
Page(s): 870
Scramble range: All
Topic: Correct inflation forecast/labour market

32.30
All else the same, if workers and employers base their wage contract on an inflation forecast that turns out to be just right, then

a) workers gain at the expense of the employer.
b) employers gain at the expense of the workers.
c) both lose due to the inflation.
d) there are no gains and no losses due to the inflation.
e) both gain due to the inflation.

32.31
Correct: b)
Difficulty: 3
Page(s): 870
Scramble range: All
Topic: Incorrect inflation forecast/money market

32.31
All else the same, if lenders and borrowers base their lending contract on an inflation forecast that turns out to be too low then, in an economic sense, borrowers will be

a) unhappy because they did not borrow more, and lenders will be unhappy because they did not lend more.
b) unhappy because they did not borrow more, and lenders will be unhappy because they lent out as much as they did.
c) happy because they did not borrow more, and lenders will be happy because they did not lend out more.
d) unhappy because they borrowed so much, and lenders will be unhappy because they did not lend out more.
e) unhappy because they did not borrow less, and lenders will be neither happy nor unhappy.

32.32
Correct: c)
Difficulty: 3
Page(s): 870
Scramble range: a)–d)
Topic: Incorrect inflation forecast/money market

32.32
If inflation forecasts turn out to be too high, which one of the following statements most accurately describes the regrets of borrowers and lenders with respect to the volume of contracts made during the period?

a) Both groups wish that the volume of loans had been higher.
b) Borrowers wish they had borrowed more and lenders wish they had lent less.
c) Borrowers wish they had borrowed less and lenders wish they had lent more.
d) Both groups wish that the volume of loans had been lower.
e) None of the above.

32.33
Correct: c)
Difficulty: 2
Page(s): 870
Scramble range: All
Topic: Rational expectations

32.33
A forecast based on the available information, such that the expected forecast error is zero is called
a) an adaptive expectation.
b) a future expectation.
c) a rational expectation.
d) an always correct expectation.
e) a perfect forecast.

32.34
Correct: e)
Difficulty: 3
Page(s): 870
Scramble range: None
Topic: Rational expectations

32.34
Which one of the following features is true of rational expectations theory?
a) Forecasts of the inflation rate will never be wrong if all of the available information is used.
b) The range of forecast error is zero.
c) All available information will be used.
d) A rational expectation is correct on the average.
e) Both c) and d).

32.35
Correct: c)
Difficulty: 3
Page(s): 870
Scramble range: All
Topic: Rational expectations

32.35
Rational expectations theory
a) assumes that market decision makers form their expectations solely on past information.
b) assumes that market decision makers form their expectations solely on past and present information.
c) assumes that market decision makers form their expectations based on past, present, and projected future information.
d) argues that fiscal and monetary policy will be effective in the short run but not in the long run.
e) argues that forecasts always will be correct.

32.36
Correct: a)
Difficulty: 3
Page(s): 870
Scramble range: All
Topic: Rational expectations

32.36
According to the rational expectations theory, if people form their expectations rationally, then
a) monetary and fiscal policy may be nullified.
b) their actions will be based on gut feelings and not actual experience.
c) the intentions of the Bank of Canada with respect to expansionary policy will be reinforced by people's decision-making activities.
d) fiscal and monetary policy will have an even larger effect than intended.
e) unemployment will always equal the natural rate.

32.37
Correct: d)
Difficulty: 2
Page(s): 870
Scramble range: All
Topic: Rational expectations

32.37
Which one of the following variables is emphasized in rational expectations theory?
a) Money.
b) Inventory accumulation.
c) Total spending.
d) Expectations.
e) Prices.

32.38
Correct: e)
Difficulty: 3
Page(s): 870
Scramble range: All
Topic: Rational expectations

32.38
Rational expectations theory suggests that
a) short-run expansionary fiscal policy may be effective.
b) long-run expansionary monetary policy may be effective.
c) only short-run fiscal policy may be effective.
d) only short-run monetary policy may be effective.
e) short-run and long-run monetary and fiscal policy may not be effective.

32.39
Correct: b)
Difficulty: 4
Page(s): 870
Scramble range: All
Topic: Rational expectations

32.39
Rational expectations theory suggests that
a) self-interested people will gather a rationally determined amount of information on the past consequences of government policy and behave in a way that enforces those policies.
b) self-interested people will gather a rationally determined amount of information on the past consequences of government policy and behave in a way that nullifies those policies.
c) expectations about higher prices will cause the actual price level to decrease in the future.
d) expectations about lower prices will cause the actual price level to increase in the future.
e) each individual in the economy makes complicated calculations in forming their rational expectations.

32.40
Correct: a)
Difficulty: 4
Page(s): 871
Scramble range: All
Topic: Adjustment to changed expectation

32.40
Rational expectations theory suggests that
a) people adjust very quickly to expected changes in monetary policy.
b) the short-run aggregate supply curve is flat.
c) the long-run aggregate supply curve is positively sloped.
d) people adjust very slowly to expected changes in fiscal policy since the implementation lag is longer for fiscal policy than monetary policy.
e) changes in monetary policy have strong effects.

32.41
Correct: c)
Difficulty: 4
Page(s): 870
Scramble range: All
Topic: Rational expectations

32.41
According to rational expectations theory
a) wages and prices are sticky.
b) the cost of getting more information is always too high.
c) expectations about future events cause the events to happen.
d) expectations are based on past experience only.
e) expectations are always correct.

32.42
Correct: b)
Difficulty: 3
Page(s): 871
Scramble range: All
Topic: Expectations/ unemployment

32.42
If contractionary fiscal policy is not expected, all else constant, then
a) the aggregate demand curve will decrease but there will be no unemployment.
b) the aggregate demand curve will decrease and unemployment will increase.
c) the money supply will expand.
d) rational expectations theory must be wrong.
e) prices will rise more than expectations.

32.43
Correct: e)
Difficulty: 2
Page(s): 871
Scramble range: All
Topic: Time lag/rational expectations

32.43
Which one of the following schools of thought studied so far might be more inclined to argue that time lags associated with fiscal and monetary policy are shortest?
a) Keynesian.
b) Monetarist.
c) Real business cycle theory.
d) Classical.
e) Rational expectations.

32.44
Correct: d)
Difficulty: 5
Page(s): 871
Scramble range: All
Topic: Rational expectations

32.44
If you are a bondholder and you formulate your expectations rationally, then an expectation of a rise in interest rates in the future would lead you to
a) buy more bonds today.
b) buy fewer bonds today.
c) sell bonds in the future when interest rates rise.
d) sell bonds immediately.
e) do nothing.

32.45
Correct: a)
Difficulty: 3
Page(s): 871
Scramble range: All
Topic: Rational expectations

32.45
If people form their expectations rationally then, if they expect higher inflation rates in the future, they will
a) ask for higher money wages immediately.
b) wait to see what happens before changing their consumption and saving habits.
c) ask for lower money wages immediately.
d) increase their investment expenditures.
e) lower their money wage demands to avoid unemployment.

32.46
Correct: e)
Difficulty: 3
Page(s): 871
Scramble range: All
Topic: Rational expectations

32.46
A rational expectations equilibrium
a) can only occur above capacity output.
b) can only occur below capacity output.
c) can occur above or below capacity output.
d) occurs only when the economy is producing its capacity output rate.
e) can occur above, below, or at capacity output.

32.47
Correct: b)
Difficulty: 3
Page(s): 871
Scramble range: All
Topic: Rational expectations

32.47
A rational expectations equilibrium will occur _________ capacity output if inflation is less than anticipated.
a) above
b) below
c) above or below
d) exactly at
e) at or below

32.48
Correct: a)
Difficulty: 3
Page(s): 871
Scramble range: All
Topic: Rational expectations

32.48
A rational expectations equilibrium will occur _________ capacity output if inflation is greater than anticipated.
a) above
b) below
c) above or below
d) exactly at
e) at or above

32.49
Correct: c)
Difficulty: 3
Page(s): 871
Scramble range: All
Topic: Rational expectations

32.49
According to rational expectations theory, an increase in the money supply, all else the same, will cause
a) a decrease in anticipated inflation.
b) any increase in aggregate demand to be partially offset by a decrease in aggregate supply.
c) workers to ask for higher wages right away.
d) any decrease in aggregate demand to be completely offset by an increase in aggregate supply.
e) real wages to fall.

32.50
Correct: b)
Difficulty: 3
Page(s): 877–879
Scramble range: None
Topic: Explanation of historic inflation

32.50
In 1969 and 1970 in Canada, inflation was greater than anticipated and real GDP grew faster than anticipated rising above capacity output. This situation might best be explained by
a) aggregate demand increasing by less than it was expected to increase.
b) aggregate demand increasing by more than it was expected to increase.
c) aggregate supply increasing by more than it was expected to increase.
d) a reduction in the money supply.
e) either c) or d).

32.51
Correct: e)
Difficulty: 3
Page(s): 878
Scramble range: All
Topic: Anticipating Bank of Canada policy

32.51
All else the same, if the Bank of Canada increases the money supply at a rate of 10 percent per year and people come to expect this constant policy, then
a) the price level will remain the same.
b) real GDP will grow.
c) real GDP will fall.
d) the price level will fall.
e) real GDP will remain the same.

32.52
Correct: c)
Difficulty: 4
Page(s): 878
Scramble range: All
Topic: Actual versus anticipated Bank of Canada policy

32.52
All else the same, if the Bank of Canada increases the money supply at a rate of 10 percent per year and people come to expect this constant policy, then a reduction in the rate of money supply growth will cause
a) aggregate demand to be greater than expected.
b) long-run aggregate supply to be greater than expected.
c) aggregate demand to be less than expected.
d) long-run aggregate supply to be less than expected.
e) prices to fall.

32.53
Correct: a)
Difficulty: 4
Page(s): 878
Scramble range: All
Topic: Unanticipated Bank of Canada policy/inflation

32.53
All else the same, if the Bank of Canada increases the money supply at a rate of 10 percent per year and people come to expect this constant policy, then a reduction in the rate of money supply growth will cause
a) actual inflation to be less than anticipated inflation.
b) actual inflation to be greater than anticipated inflation.
c) aggregate demand to be greater than expected.
d) an increase in the employment rate.
e) a decrease in the unemployment rate.

32.54
Correct: c)
Difficulty: 1
Page(s): 879
Scramble range: All
Topic: Inflation

32.54
Inflation is defined as an increase in
a) the prices of specific products.
b) wages of all workers.
c) the general level of prices.
d) money GDP.
e) real versus money wages.

32.55
Correct: d)
Difficulty: 4
Page(s): 876–878
Scramble range: All
Topic: Un/anticipated inflation

32.55
Anticipated inflation
a) results in lower prices over time as people make adjustments.
b) is more of a problem than unanticipated inflation.
c) tends to result in an increased level of saving.
d) does not create as much inefficiency in the economy as does unanticipated inflation.
e) increase wages by less than unanticipated inflation.

32.56
Correct: c)
Difficulty: 3
Page(s): 877–878
Scramble range: None
Topic: Unanticipated inflation/ income redistribution

32.56
Unanticipated inflation tends to redistribute income toward
a) fixed income groups.
b) lenders who loan at fixed interest rates.
c) borrowers who borrow at fixed interest rates.
d) savers.
e) both b) and d).

32.57
Correct: b)
Difficulty: 2
Page(s): 881
Scramble range: All
Topic: Real interest rates

32.57
The expected real rate of interest is equal to
a) the expected inflation rate minus the nominal interest rate.
b) nominal interest rate minus the expected inflation rate.
c) the total interest expense over the life of the loan.
d) nominal interest rate divided by the expected inflation rate.
e) expected nominal interest rate minus the inflation rate.

32.58
Correct: a)
Difficulty: 3
Page(s): 881
Scramble range: All
Topic: Inflation results

32.58
Inflation results in
a) a decrease in the real income of some people.
b) lower interest rates over time.
c) lenders benefiting if they lent at fixed interest rates.
d) benefits to those who hold money.
e) lenders losing if they lent at floating interest rates.

32.59
Correct: a)
Difficulty: 3
Page(s): 881
Scramble range: All
Topic: Anticipated inflation/interest rate

32.59
When inflation is anticipated
a) there is a positive relationship between the inflation rate and interest rates.
b) there is an inverse relationship between the inflation rate and interest rates.
c) there is no clear-cut relationship between the inflation rate and interest rates.
d) no one loses.
e) everyone still loses.

32.60
Correct: e)
Difficulty: 3
Page(s): 881
Scramble range: All
Topic: Winners–losers/ unanticipated inflation

32.60
Which one of the following individuals or groups of individuals stand to lose from unanticipated inflation?
a) Workers who receive regular cost-of-living wage increases.
b) Someone with a mortgage.
c) Debtors.
d) Businesses that stock up on inventories today.
e) A mortgage lender.

32.61
Correct: d)
Difficulty: 4
Page(s): 881
Scramble range: All
Topic: Inflation and incentives

32.61
If inflation could be anticipated, which one of the following activities would be beneficial to the decision makers?
a) Workers should wait to renew labour contracts.
b) Doing nothing.
c) Consumers should increase their rate of saving today so they will be able to afford to buy durable goods in the future.
d) Business should increase their rate of production now.
e) Workers should take wage cuts to avoid unemployment.

32.62
Correct: e)
Difficulty: 4
Page(s): 888
Scramble range: All
Topic: Income redistribution/ unanticipated inflation

32.62
Unanticipated inflation tends to redistribute income away from
a) employers.
b) workers with automatic cost-of-living agreements.
c) borrowers with fixed interest loans.
d) lenders with variable interest rate agreements.
e) those who hold money as currency or in chequing accounts.

32.63
Correct: c)
Difficulty: 2
Page(s): 887
Scramble range: All
Topic: Opportunity cost of holding money

32.63
The opportunity cost of holding money is
a) the expected inflation rate only.
b) the real interest rate only.
c) the expected inflation rate plus the real interest rate.
d) bond prices.
e) the transactions costs from switching money into bonds and vice versa.

32.64
Correct: d)
Difficulty: 2
Page(s): 887
Scramble range: All
Topic: Opportunity cost of holding money

32.64
The opportunity cost of holding money is the
a) real interest rate only.
b) expected inflation rate only.
c) price of government securities only.
d) nominal interest rate only.
e) actual inflation rate.

32.65
Correct: a)
Difficulty: 2
Page(s): 887
Scramble range: All
Topic: Opportunity cost of holding money

32.65
Which one of the following events would decrease the opportunity cost of holding money?
a) A fall in real interest rates.
b) A rise in the expected inflation rate.
c) A fall in bond prices.
d) A rise in nominal interest rates.
e) A rise in real interest rates.

32.66
Correct: b)
Difficulty: 3
Page(s): 880
Scramble range: All
Topic: Nominal interest rate

32.66
Which one of the following "prices" is used to bring the quantity of real money demanded in line with the quantity of real money supplied?
a) The real interest rate.
b) The nominal interest rate.
c) Expected inflation rate.
d) The inverse of the price of government securities.
e) Bond prices.

32.67
Correct: d)
Difficulty: 3
Page(s): 880
Scramble range: All
Topic: Anticipated inflation

32.67
In general, an anticipated inflation tends to
a) lower both average living standards and the overall level of output.
b) cause money income to rise faster than money prices.
c) cause a redistribution of income from borrowers to lenders.
d) have little effect on the level of real output.
e) have a large effect on the level of real output.

32.68
Correct: e)
Difficulty: 3
Page(s): 881
Scramble range: All
Topic: Expectational theories of inflation

32.68
Which of the following is not a true statement concerning expectational theories of inflation?
a) They explain the persistence of inflation, but not its cause.
b) Unanticipated changes in aggregate demand produce unanticipated changes in the price level.
c) The supply curve can shift upward purely as a result of decision makers' expectations.
d) They are an example of demand/supply theories of inflation.
e) The best policy for eliminating expectational inflation is to increase aggregate demand.

32.69
Correct: d)
Difficulty: 3
Page(s): 879
Scramble range: All
Topic: Money supply growth/inflation

32.69
It is said that inflation is a "monetary phenomenon." This means that
a) the price level cannot rise without an increase in the money supply.
b) only an increase in the money supply can start an inflation.
c) repeated supply shocks cannot drive up prices if there is no increase in the money supply.
d) a continuous rise in prices is possible only with continuing increases in the money supply.
e) fiscal policy is irrelevant to the inflation rate.

32.70
Correct: c)
Difficulty: 4
Page(s): 880
Scramble range: All
Topic: Aggregate supply adjustment

32.70
If the unemployment rate is above the natural rate of unemployment, all of the following are likely to occur *except*
a) there will be downward pressure on money wages.
b) real GDP will rise.
c) the short-run supply curve will shift to the left.
d) there will be downward pressure on prices.
e) there will be downward pressure on real wages.

32.71
Correct: d)
Difficulty: 3
Page(s): 881
Scramble range: All
Topic: Money and inflation

32.71
A prolonged period with very high rates of inflation is likely to be a period in which
a) unions have a relatively low degree of power in the bargaining session with management.
b) there has been a harvest failure.
c) fiscal policy is contractionary.
d) there have been large increases in the money supply.
e) the inflation has been anticipated.

32.72
Correct: b)
Difficulty: 3
Page(s): 881
Scramble range: All
Topic: Money and inflation

32.72
Long-run trends in the rate of inflation are generally associated with
a) supply shocks such as those experienced in the 1970s in Canada as a result of OPEC actions.
b) trends in the growth rate of the money supply.
c) expansionary fiscal policy.
d) contractionary fiscal policy.
e) trends in the growth rate of real wages.

32.73
Correct: e)
Difficulty: 3
Page(s): 888
Scramble range: All
Topic: Money/inflation in Canadian history

32.73
In part, the disinflation of the early 1980s reflected
a) structural shifts from high-priced services to low-cost manufacturing.
b) restrictive fiscal policy.
c) fewer union negotiations.
d) an effort by the Bank of Canada to keep the economy growing quickly.
e) an effort by the Bank of Canada to slow the growth rate of money.

32.74
Correct: b)
Difficulty: 4
Page(s): 889
Scramble range: All
Topic: Policy problems/inflation

32.74
A major reason that it is so difficult to rid the economy of a persistent inflation is that inflationary expectations
a) make it impossible to stop the *AD* curve from shifting to the right.
b) keep shifting the short-run aggregate supply curve upward.
c) make it impossible to reduce aggregate expenditure.
d) keep shifting the short-run production function upward.
e) keep shifting the unemployment rate upward.

32.75
Correct: d)
Difficulty: 2
Page(s): 884
Scramble range: All
Topic: Phillips curve

32.75
A.W. Phillips discovered the Phillips curve relationship by studying which one of the following pairs of variables?
a) Money supply and real GDP.
b) Price level and real GDP.
c) Inflation rate and real GDP.
d) The rate of change of wages and the unemployment rate.
e) The price level and the unemployment rate.

32.76
Correct: a)
Difficulty: 3
Page(s): 884
Scramble range: All
Topic: Phillips curve

32.76
The central proposition of the theory of the Phillips curve is, other things remaining constant, the higher the
a) unemployment rate, the lower the inflation rate.
b) price level, the lower the inflation rate.
c) price level, the lower the unemployment rate.
d) money supply, the lower the unemployment rate.
e) growth rate of the money supply, the higher the inflation rate.

32.77
Correct: c)
Difficulty: 2
Page(s): 884
Scramble range: All
Topic: Phillips curve

32.77
The Phillips curve illustrates the relationship between the rate of
a) inflation and the rate of growth.
b) unemployment and the rate of growth.
c) inflation and the rate of unemployment.
d) growth and potential GDP.
e) inflation and the growth of money wages.

32.78
Correct: b)
Difficulty: 3
Page(s): 884
Scramble range: All
Topic: Phillips curve

32.78
To draw a Phillips curve, which one of the following is held constant?
a) The price level.
b) The natural rate of unemployment.
c) The rate of employment.
d) The rate of inflation.
e) The level of real GDP.

32.79
Correct: d)
Difficulty: 2
Page(s): 884
Scramble range: All
Topic: Phillips curve

32.79
If the unemployment rate rises and the inflation rate falls, while the natural rate of unemployment and inflationary expectations remain constant, then we would be studying the variables measured by the
a) short-run aggregate supply curve.
b) long-run aggregate supply curve.
c) Friedman curve.
d) Phillips curve.
e) Phelps–Friedman curve.

32.80
Correct: c)
Difficulty: 3
Page(s): 885
Scramble range: All
Topic: Phelps–Friedman theory

32.80
For a given expected inflation rate, the higher the unemployment rate, the lower is the actual inflation rate. This relationship is the short-run Phillips curve. When the expected inflation rate changes, the Phillips curve shifts. This extension is known as the
a) Phillips–Phelps theory of the Phillips curve.
b) Samuelson–Phelps theory of the Phillips curve.
c) Phelps–Friedman theory of the Phillips curve.
d) Samuelson–Friedman theory of the Phillips curve.
e) Samuelson–Phillips theory of the Phillips curve.

32.81 (SG 32.1)
Correct: e)
Difficulty: 3
Page(s): 867
Scramble range: All
Topic: Macroeconomic equilibrium

32.81
Which of the following is *not necessarily* true in macroeconomic equilibrium?
a) The price level is such that the quantity of real GDP demanded equals the quantity of real GDP supplied.
b) The interest rate is such that the quantity of real money demanded equals the quantity of real money supplied.
c) The real wage rate is such that the quantity of labour demanded equals the quantity of labour supplied.
d) Real GDP is the level at which the aggregate planned expenditure curve intersects the 45° line.
e) The real wage rate is such that the quantity of labour demanded equals the quantity of labour supplied at full-employment.

32.82 (SG 32.2)
Correct: a)
Difficulty: 4
Page(s): 867
Scramble range: All
Topic: Macroeconomic equilibrium

32.82
Figure 32.3 illustrates an economy initially in equilibrium at the intersection of AD_0 and SAS_0. What would cause the short-run aggregate supply curve to shift from SAS_0 to SAS_1?
a) An expected increase in the money supply.
b) An increase in the price level.
c) An increase in the marginal product of labour.
d) An increase in the aggregate demand.
e) A decrease in wages.

Figure 32.3

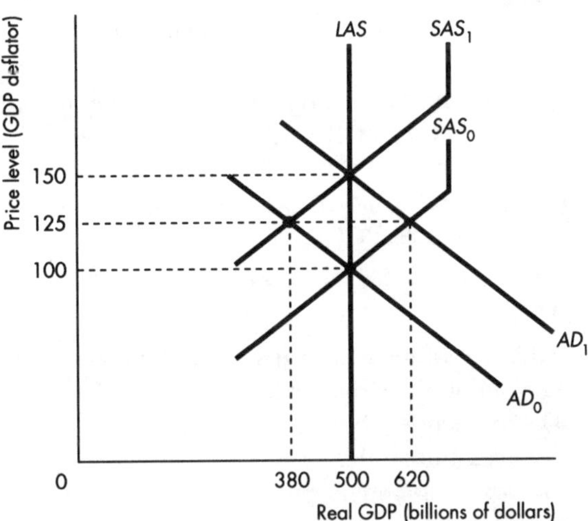

32.83 (SG 32.3)
Correct: b)
Difficulty: 4
Page(s): 867
Scramble range: All
Topic: Macroeconomic equilibrium

32.83
Figure 32.3 illustrates an economy initially in equilibrium at the intersection of AD_0 and SAS_0. If the *AD* curve is *correctly* expected to shift from AD_0 to AD_1, the new macroeconomic equilibrium will be real GDP =
a) $380 billion and price level = 125.
b) $500 billion and price level = 150.
c) $500 billion and price level = 100.
d) $620 billion and price level = 125.
e) $500 billion and price level = 125.

32.84 (SG 32.4)
Correct: e)
Difficulty: 4
Page(s): 867
Scramble range: All
Topic: Macroeconomic equilibrium

32.84
Figure 32.3 illustrates an economy initially in equilibrium at the intersection of AD_0 and SAS_0. If the *AD* curve is expected to shift from AD_0 to AD_1 but it actually remains at AD_0, the new macroeconomic equilibrium will be real GDP =
a) $380 billion and price level = 100.
b) $500 billion and price level = 150.
c) $500 billion and price level = 100.
d) $620 billion and price level = 125.
e) $380 billion and price level = 125.

32.85 (SG 32.5)
Correct: d)
Difficulty: 4
Page(s): 867
Scramble range: All
Topic: Macroeconomic equilibrium

32.85
Figure 32.3 illustrates an economy initially in equilibrium at the intersection of AD_0 and SAS_0. If the *AD* curve is expected to remain at AD_0 but, in fact, it shifts to AD_1, the new macroeconomic equilibrium will be real GDP =
a) $380 billion and price level = 125.
b) $500 billion and price level = 150.
c) $500 billion and price level = 100.
d) $620 billion and price level = 125.
e) $500 billion and price level = 125.

32.86 (SG 32.6)
Correct: e)
Difficulty: 4
Page(s): 867
Scramble range: All
Topic: Macroeconomic equilibrium

32.86
If the price level is expected to fall but aggregate demand remains unchanged, then the price level will
a) stay the same and real GDP will stay the same.
b) fall and real GDP will decrease.
c) rise and real GDP will increase.
d) rise and real GDP will decrease.
e) fall and real GDP will increase.

32.87 (SG 32.7)
Correct: d)
Difficulty: 3
Page(s): 869
Scramble range: All
Topic: Inflationary expectations

32.87
If the rate of inflation turns out to be lower than expected, borrowers
a) and lenders both lose.
b) and lenders both gain.
c) gain but lenders lose.
d) lose but lenders gain.
e) lose but lenders are just as well off.

32.88 (SG 32.8)
Correct: b)
Difficulty: 3
Page(s): 869
Scramble range: All
Topic: Inflationary expectations

32.88
If the rate of inflation turns out to be lower than expected, then
a) expectations could not be rational expectations.
b) real GDP will be less than full-employment (capacity) real GDP.
c) the real interest rate will be lower than expected.
d) the real wage rate will be lower than expected.
e) the money wage rate will be higher than expected.

32.89 (SG 32.9)
Correct: c)
Difficulty: 3
Page(s): 870
Scramble range: All
Topic: Rational expectations

32.89
Which of the following is *not* true of a rational expectation forecast?
a) It uses all available information.
b) It makes the range of forecast errors as small as possible.
c) It is correct.
d) The forecast errors are zero on average.
e) Sometimes economic agents purchase their forecasts from specialists.

32.90 (SG 32.10)
Correct: d)
Difficulty: 4
Page(s): 870
Scramble range: All
Topic: Rational expectations

32.90
Figure 32.4 illustrates an economy initially in macroeconomic equilibrium at point *a*. If the money supply is expected to increase by 50 percent, what is the rational expectation of the price level?
a) 100.
b) 120.
c) 130.
d) 150.
e) We cannot tell without more information on wage negotiations.

Figure 32.4

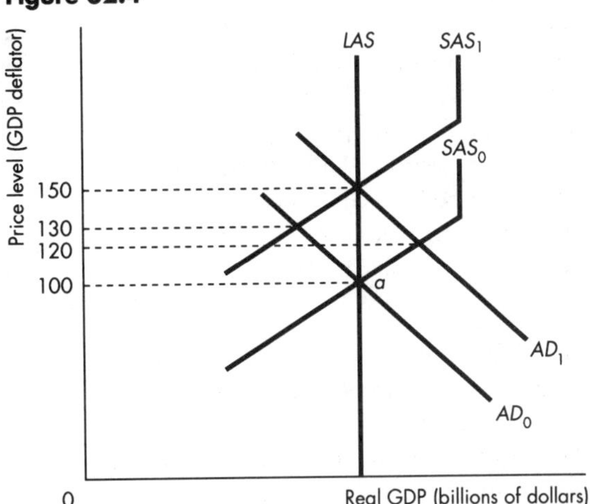

32.91 (SG 32.11)
Correct: b)
Difficulty: 3
Page(s): 873
Scramble range: All
Topic: Rational expectations

32.91
A rational expectations equilibrium is the price level and real GDP given by the intersection of the

a) actual aggregate demand curve and the actual long-run aggregate supply curve.
b) actual aggregate demand curve and the actual short-run aggregate supply curve.
c) expected aggregate demand curve and the expected short-run aggregate supply curve.
d) expected aggregate demand curve and the expected long-run aggregate supply curve.
e) expected aggregate demand curve and the actual short-run aggregate supply curve.

32.92 (SG 32.12)
Correct: c)
Difficulty: 4
Page(s): 875
Scramble range: All
Topic: Rational expectations

32.92
According to the rational expectations hypothesis, a correctly anticipated increase in the money supply in an economy with a given long-run aggregate supply will result in

a) an increase in the price level and an increase in real GDP.
b) an increase in the price level and a decrease in real GDP.
c) a proportional increase in the price level and no change in real GDP.
d) no change in the price level and an increase in real GDP.
e) no change in the price level and no change in real GDP.

32.93 (SG 32.13)
Correct: a)
Difficulty: 4
Page(s): 875
Scramble range: All
Topic: Rational expectations

32.93
Suppose the money supply is expected to remain unchanged but it actually increases. According to the rational expectations hypothesis, the price level will

a) rise and real GDP will increase.
b) rise and real GDP will decrease.
c) fall and real GDP will increase.
d) fall and real GDP will decrease.
e) rise and real GDP will stay the same.

32.94 (SG 32.14)
Correct: b)
Difficulty: 4
Page(s): 876–888
Scramble range: All
Topic: Inflation

32.94
Suppose OPEC unexpectedly increases the price of oil. This is a negative aggregate supply shock. As a result, the price level will
a) rise and real GDP will increase.
b) rise and real GDP will decrease.
c) fall and real GDP will increase.
d) fall and real GDP will decrease.
e) rise and real GDP will stay the same.

32.95 (SG 32.15)
Correct: b)
Difficulty: 2
Page(s): 876–888
Scramble range: All
Topic: Inflation

32.95
The current year's price level is 180 and the rate of inflation over the past year has been 20 percent. What was last year's price level?
a) 144.
b) 150.
c) 160.
d) 216.
e) 100.

32.96 (SG 32.16)
Correct: e)
Difficulty: 3
Page(s): 879
Scramble range: All
Topic: Quantity theory of money

32.96
Which of the following would cause the aggregate demand curve to keep shifting upward year after year?
a) A tax cut.
b) An increase in government purchases of goods and services.
c) Inflation.
d) Excess wages demands.
e) A positive rate of growth in the quantity of money.

32.97 (SG 32.17)
Correct: c)
Difficulty: 4
Page(s): 876–877
Scramble range: All
Topic: Inflation and *AD*

32.97
Suppose aggregate demand increases by less than anticipated. This will result in an unanticipated
a) rise in inflation and real GDP falls below capacity.
b) rise in inflation and real GDP rises above capacity.
c) fall in inflation and real GDP falls below capacity.
d) fall in inflation and real GDP rises above capacity.
e) fall in inflation and real GDP stays at capacity.

32.98 (SG 32.18)
Correct: a)
Difficulty: 3
Page(s): 870–880
Scramble range: All
Topic: Unanticipated inflation

32.98
If the actual price level is higher than the expected price level, then real GDP
a) must be above capacity.
b) must be below capacity.
c) must be equal to capacity.
d) can be above, below, or equal to capacity depending on the position of the aggregate demand curve.
e) can be above or equal to capacity depending on the position of the aggregate demand curve.

32.99 (SG 32.19)
Correct: d)
Difficulty: 4
Page(s): 881
Scramble range: All
Topic: Interest rates

32.99
A correctly anticipated increase in the rate of growth of the money supply will cause nominal interest rates to
a) fall and real interest rates to fall.
b) fall and leave real interest rates unchanged.
c) rise and real interest rates to rise.
d) rise and leave real interest rates unchanged.
e) rise and real interest rates to fall.

32.100 (SG 32.20)
Correct: e)
Difficulty: 4
Page(s): 881
Scramble range: All
Topic: Interest rate and inflation

32.100
Suppose that initially the nominal rate of interest is 8 percent and the expected rate of inflation is 5 percent. If the expected rate of inflation increases to 8 percent, what will the new nominal rate of interest be?
a) 8 percent.
b) 3 percent.
c) 13 percent.
d) 16 percent.
e) 11 percent.

32.101 (SG 32.21)
Correct: e)
Difficulty: 2
Page(s): 887
Scramble range: All
Topic: Opportunity cost of holding money

32.101
The opportunity cost of holding money is the
a) real rate of interest.
b) nominal rate of interest minus the expected rate of inflation.
c) inflation rate.
d) expected inflation rate.
e) nominal rate of interest.

32.102
Correct: a)
Difficulty: 3
Page(s): 867
Scramble range: All
Topic: Macroeconomic equilibrium

32.102
Which of the following must be true in macroeconomic equilibrium?
a) The interest rate is such that the quantity of real money demanded equals the quantity of real money supplied.
b) The economy is at full employment.
c) Frictional unemployment is zero.
d) The price level is such that the aggregate demand and aggregate supply curves meet at a point that lies on the 45° line.
e) The price level is 100.

32.103
Correct: d)
Difficulty: 4
Page(s): 868
Scramble range: All
Topic: Expectations

32.103
If the price level is expected to rise but aggregate demand remains unchanged, then the price level will
a) fall and real GDP will increase.
b) fall and real GDP will decrease.
c) rise and real GDP will increase.
d) rise and real GDP will decrease.
e) stay the same as will real GDP.

32.104
Correct: c)
Difficulty: 3
Page(s): 870
Scramble range: All
Topic: Expectations

32.104
If there is an unanticipated increase in the inflation rate, borrowers
a) and lenders both lose.
b) and lenders both gain.
c) gain but lenders lose.
d) lose but lenders gain.
e) gain but lenders are just as well off.

32.105
Correct: b)
Difficulty: 4
Page(s): 870
Scramble range: All
Topic: Expectations

32.105
If the rate of inflation turns out to be higher than expected,
a) this is proof that expectations were not rational.
b) real GDP will be more than full-employment (capacity) real GDP.
c) workers with fixed nominal contracts will be made better off.
d) the real wage rate will be higher than expected.
e) the nominal wage rate will turn out to be too high.

32.106
Correct: d)
Difficulty: 3
Page(s): 870
Scramble range: All
Topic: Expectations

32.106
A rational expectations forecast is characterized by
a) absence of error.
b) perfect foresight of world events.
c) absence of after-the-fact surprises.
d) forecast errors that are zero on average.
e) complex calculations by all individuals with these expectations.

32.107
Correct: e)
Difficulty: 5
Page(s): 870
Scramble range: All
Topic: Expectations

32.107
According to the rational expectations hypothesis, a correctly anticipated increase in the money supply with increasing long-run aggregate supply conditions will result in
a) an increase in the price level and no change in real GDP.
b) no change in the price level and no change in real GDP.
c) no change in the price level and an increase in real GDP.
d) an increase in the price level and an increase in real GDP.
e) an uncertain change in prices and an increase in real GDP.

32.108
Correct: e)
Difficulty: 4
Page(s): 870
Scramble range: All
Topic: Expectations

32.108
If the money supply were expected to remain unchanged but actually increased in a totally unanticipated manner, the rational expectations hypothesis would predict
a) an increase in the price level and no change in real GDP.
b) no change in the price level and no change in real GDP.
c) no change in the price level and an increase in real GDP.
d) an increase in the price level and a decrease in real GDP.
e) an increase in the price level and an increase in real GDP.

32.109
Correct: e)
Difficulty: 2
Page(s): 875
Scramble range: All
Topic: Inflation

32.109
The price level in an economy goes from 200 to 230 in a year. What is the rate of inflation?
a) 10 percent.
b) 13 percent.
c) 60 percent.
d) 30 percent.
e) 15 percent.

32.110
Correct: d)
Difficulty: 3
Page(s): 881
Scramble range: All
Topic: Interest rates

32.110
An economy has 9 percent nominal interest rates when the inflation rate is 4 percent. If inflation now becomes 10 percent, what will the nominal interest rate be?
a) 10 percent.
b) 13 percent.
c) 14 percent.
d) 15 percent.
e) 19 percent.

32.111
Correct: c)
Difficulty: 4
Page(s): 881
Scramble range: None
Topic: Lowering unemployment

32.111
Suppose the government attempts to use fiscal policy to permanently lower the unemployment rate. The result will be
a) a lower unemployment rate in the short run if the fiscal policy is expected.
b) a lower unemployment rate in the long run.
c) no change in the unemployment rate in the long run.
d) a higher unemployment rate in the long run.
e) both a) and c).

32.112
Correct: e)
Difficulty: 4
Page(s): 875
Scramble range: All
Topic: Expected changes

32.112
What are the effects of an expected rise in income taxes?
a) Both prices and real GDP rise.
b) Prices rise but real GDP falls.
c) Both prices and real GDP fall.
d) Prices rise, while real GDP stays the same.
e) Prices fall, while real GDP stays the same.

32.113
Correct: c)
Difficulty: 4
Page(s): 875
Scramble range: All
Topic: Unexpected changes

32.113
What are the effects of an unexpected rise in income taxes?
a) Both prices and real GDP rise.
b) Prices fall but real GDP rises.
c) Both prices and real GDP fall.
d) Prices rise while real GDP stays the same.
e) Prices fall while real GDP stays the same.

32.114
Correct: a)
Difficulty: 4
Page(s): 875
Scramble range: All
Topic: Unexpected changes

32.114
If we observe the growth rate of money considerably lower than the inflation rate, this implies that
a) the growth rate of money fell unexpectedly.
b) the growth rate of money rose unexpectedly.
c) the growth rate of money must rise.
d) the rational expectations model is clearly false.
e) expectations will now adjust upwards.

32.115
Correct: c)
Difficulty: 4
Page(s): 875
Scramble range: All
Topic: Rational expectations

32.115
In 1990, the expected aggregate demand for 1991 is as shown in Table 32.1. In 1990, the level of capacity real GDP expected for 1991 is $3.8 billion. The 1990 rational expectation of the 1991 price level is
a) 120.
b) 121.
c) 122.
d) 123.
e) 124.

Table 32.1

Price level (GDP deflator)	Expected real GDP demanded (billions of 1981 dollars)
120	4.0
121	3.9
122	3.8
123	3.7
124	3.6

Chapter 33 Recessions and Depressions

33.1
Correct: d)
Difficulty: 2
Page(s): 892
Scramble range: All
Topic: Prosperity of the 1920s

33.1
The 1920s in Canada might be characterized as
a) a period of stagnation.
b) a period of particularly deep recession.
c) a time when we always produced above full employment.
d) years of unprecedented prosperity for Canadians.
e) a period of strong hyperinflation.

33.2
Correct: c)
Difficulty: 2
Page(s): 892
Scramble range: All
Topic: Great Depression

33.2
The period following the prosperous 1920s is known as
a) the Volcker depression period.
b) the Kennedy contraction.
c) the Great Depression.
d) the Hoover heydays.
e) the Great Meltdown.

33.3
Correct: a)
Difficulty: 2
Page(s): 892
Scramble range: All
Topic: Great Depression

33.3
The Great Depression lasted from
a) 1929 to 1933.
b) 1982 to 1983.
c) 1974 to 1975.
d) 1907 to 1908.
e) 1920 to 1929.

33.4
Correct: e)
Difficulty: 2
Page(s): 892
Scramble range: All
Topic: Unemployment/ Great Depression

33.4
During the Great Depression, the unemployment rate went as high as
a) 10 percent.
b) 25 percent.
c) 30 percent.
d) 9 percent.
e) 20 percent.

33.5
Correct: e)
Difficulty: 2
Page(s): 892
Scramble range: All
Topic: Prices/Great Depression

33.5
During the Great Depression, the price level
a) rose by 25 percent.
b) remained constant.
c) rose by only 1 percent.
d) fell by 30 percent.
e) fell by 22 percent.

33.6
Correct: e)
Difficulty: 2
Page(s): 892
Scramble range: All
Topic: Stock market crash

33.6
In the stock market crash of 1929, the values of stocks fell by as much as
a) 5 percent.
b) 15 percent.
c) 50 percent.
d) 25 percent.
e) 30 percent.

33.7
Correct: c)
Difficulty: 2
Page(s): 892
Scramble range: All
Topic: Real GDP/Great Depression

33.7
By the height of the Great Depression, real GDP had fallen by
a) 20 percent.
b) 25 percent.
c) 30 percent.
d) 35 percent.
e) 50 percent.

33.8
Correct: b)
Difficulty: 3
Page(s): 892
Scramble range: All
Topic: Stock market crashes/recession

33.8
Stock market crashes
a) are always followed by recessions.
b) are sometimes followed by recessions.
c) are never followed by recessions.
d) used to be followed by recessions but due to safeguards built in to the macroeconomy it is unlikely that a recession will ever follow one again.
e) are followed by recessions if the Bank of Canada cuts interest rates in response to the crash.

33.9
Correct: d)
Difficulty: 2
Page(s): 892
Scramble range: All
Topic: 1987 stock market crash

33.9
The period following the stock market crash of 1987
a) is likened to Chernobyl.
b) is often likened to Three Mile Island.
c) is associated with declining real GDP.
d) was incorrectly predicted by many to be a recessionary period.
e) was as severe a recession as the 1929–1933 recession.

33.10
Correct: d)
Difficulty: 2
Page(s): 893
Scramble range: All
Topic: 1982 recession

33.10
The most severe recession since the Great Depression occurred in
a) 1929–1933.
b) 1939–1945.
c) 1974–1975.
d) 1982.
e) 1987.

33.11
Correct: c)
Difficulty: 2
Page(s): 893
Scramble range: All
Topic: 1982 recession

33.11
The most severe recession since the Great Depression occurred in
a) 1980.
b) 1974–1975.
c) 1982.
d) 1929–1933.
e) 1987.

33.12
Correct: e)
Difficulty: 3
Page(s): 893
Scramble range: None
Topic: 1982 recession

33.12
One of the causes of the 1982 recession was
a) falling real prices.
b) rising imported oil prices.
c) a decline in the nominal money supply.
d) an increase in the nominal money supply.
e) both b) and d).

33.13
Correct: d)
Difficulty: 3
Page(s): 893
Scramble range: None
Topic: 1982 recession

33.13
The 1982 recession can be thought of as a
a) fiscal-policy-induced recession.
b) demand-side recession.
c) supply-side recession.
d) monetary-policy-induced recession.
e) both a) and d).

33.14
Correct: b)
Difficulty: 3
Page(s): 893
Scramble range: All
Topic: 1982 recession

33.14
Prior to the 1982 recession in Canada, real GDP was
a) 25 percent less than capacity real GDP.
b) close to its trend value.
c) quite a bit above its trend value.
d) stagnating.
e) falling dramatically.

33.15
Correct: e)
Difficulty: 3
Page(s): 893
Scramble range: All
Topic: Condition prior to the 1982 recession

33.15
Prior to the 1982 recession, the Canadian economy was experiencing an unemployment rate of
a) between 3 and 6 percent a year and a growth rate of real GDP of almost 4 percent.
b) between 5 and 6 percent a year and an inflation rate between 3 and 6 percent a year.
c) zero percent.
d) 12 percent with an inflation rate of 2 percent.
e) between 7 and 8 percent.

33.16
Correct: c)
Difficulty: 3
Page(s): 893
Scramble range: a)–d)
Topic: 1982 recession

33.16
Which one of the graphs in Figure 33.1 best depicts the beginning of the 1981 U.S. recession?
a) (a).
b) (b).
c) (c).
d) (d).
e) None of the above.

(b)

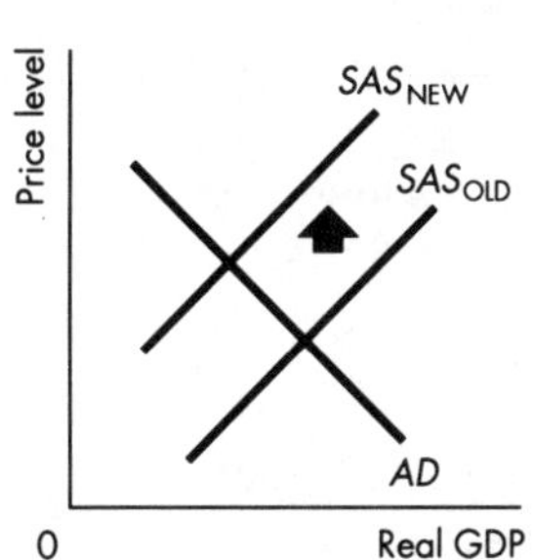

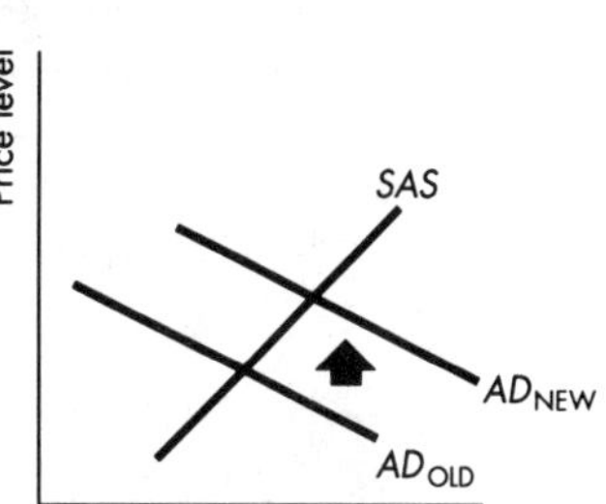

(c)

(d)

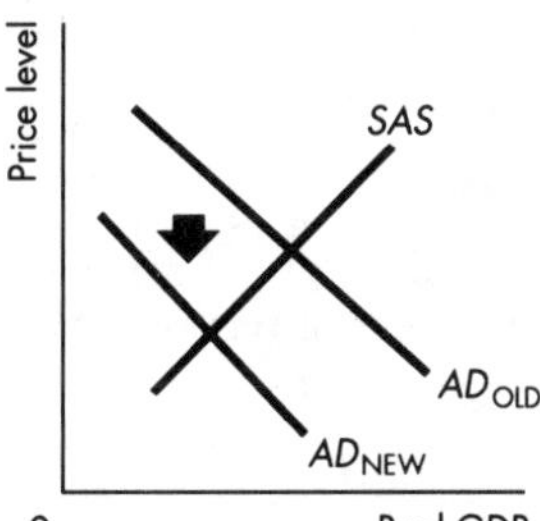

Price level
SAS_{OLD}
SAS_{NEW}
AD
0
Real GDP

33.17
Correct: c)
Difficulty: 3
Page(s): 901–904
Scramble range: a)–d)
Topic: Great Depression

33.17
Which one of the graphs in Figure 33.1 best depicts the beginning of the Great Depression?
a) (a).
b) (b).
c) (c).
d) (d).
e) None of the above.

33.18
Correct: c)
Difficulty: 3
Page(s): 894
Scramble range: a)–d)
Topic: 1982 recession

33.18
Which one of the graphs in Figure 33.1 best depicts the beginning of the 1982 recession?
a) (a).
b) (b).
c) (c).
d) (d).
e) None of the above.

33.19
Correct: d)
Difficulty: 3
Page(s): 897
Scramble range: None
Topic: 1982 recession

33.19
In the 1982 recession real GDP fell by 3 percent
a) as did consumption.
b) but investment fell by about 26 percent.
c) but government purchases rose by 20 percent.
d) both a) and b).
e) both a) and c).

33.20
Correct: b)
Difficulty: 3
Page(s): 894
Scramble range: All
Topic: Reallocation of resources/1982

33.20
The 1982 recession period is different from the Great Depression in that
a) prices continued to fall.
b) there was an unusually large reallocation of resources taking place.
c) real GDP was falling.
d) it was characterized by rising real GDP.
e) government purchases fell dramatically during the recession.

33.21
Correct: d)
Difficulty: 3
Page(s): 893
Scramble range: All
Topic: Unequal distribution of unemployment

33.21
The 1981 recession in the United States created
a) an equal amount of unemployment throughout the country.
b) a greater amount of unemployment in the Sun Belt than in other areas of the country.
c) more unemployment in Florida than in other states.
d) more unemployment in the Rust Belt than in the Sun Belt.
e) an economic boom in Canada.

33.22
Correct: d)
Difficulty: 3
Page(s): 893
Scramble range: All
Topic: Reallocation of resources/1981

33.22
The unusually large reallocation of resources during the 1981 U.S. recession is attributed to
a) fiscal policy.
b) monetary policy.
c) Ronald Reagan.
d) continued increases in the price of energy and expanded applications for microprocessors.
e) continued decreases in the price of energy and expanded applications for microprocessors.

33.23
Correct: e)
Difficulty: 3
Page(s): 894
Scramble range: All
Topic: Inflation expected/pre–1982

33.23
Prior to the 1982 recession, inflation
a) was running at an annual rate of 5 percent.
b) was expected to run at close to an annual rate of 8 percent.
c) rates slowed.
d) was above the natural rate of inflation.
e) was expected to run at an annual rate above 10 percent.

33.24
Correct: c)
Difficulty: 3
Page(s): 895
Scramble range: All
Topic: Restrictive monetary policy/1982

33.24
The 1982 recession began because of
a) restrictive fiscal policy.
b) inflationary expectations.
c) restrictive monetary policy.
d) provincial policies.
e) excessive wage demands.

33.25
Correct: d)
Difficulty: 3
Page(s): 895
Scramble range: All
Topic: Decrease in real money supply

33.25
The real money supply decreases when
a) aggregate demand decreases.
b) short-run aggregate supply increases.
c) long-run aggregate supply increases.
d) the GDP deflator increases by an amount larger than the increase in the nominal money supply.
e) the GDP deflator increases by an amount smaller than the increase in the nominal money supply.

33.26
Correct: a)
Difficulty: 4
Page(s): 896
Scramble range: All
Topic: Real money market/recession

33.26
A possible explanation for why interest rates tend to rise at the beginning of a recession might be that
a) the decrease in the real money demand is less than the decrease in the real money supply.
b) the increase in the real money demand is less than the decrease in the real money supply.
c) the increase in the real money supply is greater than the increase in the real money demand.
d) only the real money supply decreases.
e) the decrease in the real money demand is more than the decrease in the real money supply.

33.27
Correct: b)
Difficulty: 2
Page(s): 895
Scramble range: All
Topic: Real money supply

33.27
The real money supply is the
a) relationship between the amount of funds that banks want to lend and the real interest rate.
b) nominal money supply divided by the price level.
c) nominal money supply minus the price level.
d) amount of real money that people wish to keep in their demand deposit accounts.
e) amount of currency in circulation divided by the price level.

33.28
Correct: a)
Difficulty: 3
Page(s): 896
Scramble range: All
Topic: Real aggregate expenditures/recession

33.28
When a recession begins
a) real aggregate expenditures fall.
b) real aggregate expenditures may rise if the recession is a supply-induced recession.
c) real GDP growth slows.
d) the nominal money supply increases.
e) interest rates must fall.

33.29
Correct: c)
Difficulty: 3
Page(s): 897
Scramble range: All
Topic: Investment expenditures/recession

33.29
The main component of real aggregate expenditure that falls at the onset of a recession is
a) government purchases.
b) government transfer payments.
c) investment expenditures.
d) exports.
e) consumption.

33.30
Correct: b)
Difficulty: 3
Page(s): 896–897
Scramble range: All
Topic: Investment/interest rates

33.30
Investment expenditures tend to fall during recessions because of
a) increased demand.
b) higher interest rates at the beginning of the recession.
c) increased expected future profits.
d) government policy.
e) higher taxes.

33.31
Correct: b)
Difficulty: 3
Page(s): 898
Scramble range: All
Topic: Short-run production function

33.31
During a recession, the
a) short-run aggregate supply curve always decreases.
b) short-run production function tends to rise less rapidly.
c) employment rate tends to remain steady but the unemployment rate falls.
d) price level tends to increase rapidly.
e) short-run production function tends to rise.

33.32
Correct: c)
Difficulty: 3
Page(s): 898
Scramble range: All
Topic: Short-run production function

33.32
A downward shift of the short-run production function is associated with
a) a decrease in the supply of labour.
b) an increase in the demand for labour.
c) a reduction in the marginal productivity of labour.
d) an increase in the marginal productivity of labour.
e) an increase in the supply of labour.

33.33
Correct: c)
Difficulty: 3
Page(s): 898
Scramble range: All
Topic: Oil prices

33.33
An increase in the price of a major input such as oil will cause the
a) short-run aggregate supply curve to shift to the right.
b) short-run production function to shift upward.
c) short-run production function to shift downward.
d) aggregate demand curve to shift to the left.
e) labour demand curve to shift upwards.

33.34
Correct: c)
Difficulty: 4
Page(s): 898
Scramble range: All
Topic: Sector demand/labour shift

33.34
When the price of a major input such as oil increases and is expected to remain relatively high, then
a) unemployment tends to remain constant since people who lose their job in the oil business simply shift over to the natural gas industry.
b) employment in industries producing energy-efficient products tends to decline.
c) the unemployment rate tends to increase as fewer people can find jobs for which their skills are suited.
d) the automobile industry is likely to remain unaffected.
e) unemployment falls since people get new jobs in the oil and gas industry.

33.35
Correct: b)
Difficulty: 3
Page(s): 901
Scramble range: All
Topic: Keynesianism

33.35
Modern Keynesians believe that
a) wages are flexible during recessions.
b) wages tend to be sticky during recessions.
c) wages tend to be sticky during recessions but the quantity demanded of labour always equals the quantity supplied of labour.
d) the monetarists are correct concerning their assumptions of a negatively sloped money stock curve.
e) wages are flexible at the start of a recession, but become sticky as the recession grows in severity.

33.36
Correct: b)
Difficulty: 3
Page(s): 901
Scramble range: All
Topic: Labour supply curve controversy

33.36
The slope of the labour supply curve is
a) known to be between 0.75 and 0.85 during recessions.
b) is the source of controversy in modern macroeconomics.
c) thought to be flat during recessions but steep during recoveries.
d) thought to be steep during recessions but flat during recoveries.
e) believed to be irrelevant during a recession.

33.37
Correct: c)
Difficulty: 4
Page(s): 901
Scramble range: All
Topic: Labour supply curve controversy

33.37
The source of controversy in macroeconomics over the labour market can be attributed to different schools of thought concerning the

a) steepness of the demand for labour curve.
b) position of the demand for labour curve at the outset of a recession.
c) responsiveness of the quantity supplied of labour to the wage rate.
d) potency of monetary policy.
e) size of shifts in the short-run production function.

33.38
Correct: a)
Difficulty: 3
Page(s): 898
Scramble range: All
Topic: Sticky wages

33.38
Which of the following reasons might explain why the quantity demanded and the quantity supplied of labour does not come into equilibrium quickly?

a) Workers are reluctant to take a lower wage when wages are not falling anywhere else.
b) Wages are sticky both upward and downward.
c) The aggregate demand for labour has fallen.
d) The aggregate supply of labour has fallen.
e) Workers have too low a level of skills.

33.39
Correct: d)
Difficulty: 4
Page(s): 898
Scramble range: All
Topic: Sticky wages

33.39
Labour markets may not always adjust to a new equilibrium quickly because

a) the supply of labour is horizontal at the going wage rate.
b) the supply of labour is sensitive to changes in the wage rate.
c) workers are reluctant to take a lower wage when they are still working at the higher wage.
d) of long term labour contracts.
e) of the differentials in skill levels between different types of workers.

33.40
Correct: a)
Difficulty: 3
Page(s): 898
Scramble range: All
Topic: Sticky wages

33.40
Sticky wages may be explained by assuming that

a) wage contracts signed by workers in many industries call for a fixed nominal wage to be maintained for a certain period of time.
b) nonunion workers do not sign wage contracts.
c) firms prefer to pay higher nominal wages during a recession.
d) firms sign wage contracts that only allow an adjustment of wages downward.
e) firms prefer to hire skilled workers, and will not raise the wages of unskilled workers.

33.41
Correct: a)
Difficulty: 3
Page(s): 897–898
Scramble range: All
Topic: Population increases/labour markets

33.41
Increases in the population tend to

a) increase employment.
b) decrease the labour supply curve.
c) decrease the demand for labour.
d) leave the labour supply curve the same.
e) increase the demand for labour.

33.42
Correct: e)
Difficulty: 2
Page(s): 898
Scramble range: All
Topic: Sticky wages

33.42
Which one of the following groups would adhere to the sticky wage theory of labour markets?
a) Rational expectation theorists.
b) Monetarists.
c) Neomonetarists.
d) Real business cycle theorists.
e) Keynesians.

33.43
Correct: e)
Difficulty: 3
Page(s): 899–900
Scramble range: All
Topic: Flexible wage theory

33.43
Flexible wage theorists assume that the
a) demand for labour is unaffected by changes in the price of oil.
b) supply of labour is unaffected by changes in the population.
c) supply of labour curve is fairly steep.
d) supply of labour curve is fairly flat.
e) combination of the real wage rate and the level of employment observed in the labour market is a point on the supply of labour curve.

33.44
Correct: d)
Difficulty: 3
Page(s): 899
Scramble range: All
Topic: Flexible wage theory

33.44
The statement that all unemployment arises from job market turnover would be most clearly associated with the views of
a) flexible rule advocates.
b) Keynesians.
c) sticky wage theorists.
d) flexible wage theorists.
e) Neokeynesians.

33.45
Correct: b)
Difficulty: 3
Page(s): 899
Scramble range: All
Topic: Flexible wage theory

33.45
Flexible wage theorists suggest that the amount of
a) unemployment is determined by the demand for labour curve.
b) employment is determined by the intersection of the supply and demand for labour curve.
c) employment is determined by the demand for labour only.
d) employment is determined by the supply of labour only.
e) unemployment is determined by the supply of labour only.

33.46
Correct: a)
Difficulty: 3
Page(s): 898
Scramble range: All
Topic: Sticky wages

33.46
Sticky wage theorists suggest that the amount of
a) employment is determined by the demand for labour.
b) unemployment is determined by the intersection of the demand for labour and the supply of labour.
c) employment is determined by the demand and supply of labour.
d) employment is determined by the supply of labour.
e) unemployment is determined by the labour supply.

33.47
Correct: a)
Difficulty: 3
Page(s): 899
Scramble range: All
Topic: Aggregate supply/flexible wage theory

33.47
Flexible wage theory suggests a
a) vertical aggregate supply curve.
b) horizontal aggregate supply curve.
c) positively sloped aggregate supply curve.
d) flat aggregate demand curve.
e) vertical aggregate demand curve.

33.48
Correct: d)
Difficulty: 3
Page(s): 899
Scramble range: All
Topic: Aggregate supply/sticky wages

33.48
Sticky wage theory suggests a
a) flat aggregate demand curve.
b) flat labour demand curve.
c) vertical aggregate supply curve.
d) relatively flat aggregate supply curve.
e) a vertical aggregate demand curve.

33.49
Correct: c)
Difficulty: 3
Page(s): 899
Scramble range: All
Topic: Aggregate demand policy/sticky wages

33.49
If the sticky wage theory is the correct one, then in the face of a recession a proper stabilization policy would be
a) a decrease in the money supply.
b) an increase in tax rates.
c) a decrease in tax rates.
d) a decrease in runaway government spending.
e) an increase in investment.

33.50
Correct: c)
Difficulty: 3
Page(s): 899
Scramble range: All
Topic: Flexible wages/stabilization policy

33.50
If the flexible wage theory is the correct one, then in the face of an inflation problem in the economy a proper stabilization policy would be
a) an increase in government spending.
b) a cut in tax rates.
c) a decrease in the real money supply.
d) an increase in the real money supply.
e) to do nothing.

33.51
Correct: a)
Difficulty: 3
Page(s): 900
Scramble range: All
Topic: 1982 recession

33.51
One reason that employment fell in the 1982 recession was that
a) the marginal product of labour declined.
b) workers went on strike.
c) workers caused production slowdowns.
d) the government raised taxes.
e) the marginal product of labour increased.

33.52
Correct: e)
Difficulty: 3
Page(s): 900
Scramble range: All
Topic: Flexible wages/stabilization policy

33.52
If the flexible wage theory is the correct one, then in the face of a recession a proper stabilization policy would be
a) a cut in tax rates.
b) an increase in government spending.
c) a decrease in the real money supply.
d) an increase in the real money supply.
e) to do nothing.

33.53
Correct: e)
Difficulty: 3
Page(s): 900
Scramble range: All
Topic: Flexible versus sticky wages

33.53
In comparing the flexible wage theory to the sticky wage theory,
a) we can conclude that the flexible wage theory is better.
b) we can conclude that the fixed wage theory is better.
c) neither can be used to explain the events of the 1982 recession.
d) the major area of disagreement centres around the demand for labour.
e) no conclusion can be made as to which theory is better.

33.54
Correct: c)
Difficulty: 3
Page(s): 896
Scramble range: All
Topic: Comparing *S* versus *D*-side recessions

33.54
The mechanism that transmits the effects of a macroeconomic shock to interest rates and aggregate expenditure is
a) stronger when it is a supply side shock.
b) stronger when it is a demand side shock.
c) the same whether the shock emanates from the supply or demand side of the economy.
d) not very strong at all, in fact, some would say that it is ineffective.
e) a rise in real wages, which triggers off more borrowing.

33.55
Correct: b)
Difficulty: 3
Page(s): 901
Scramble range: All
Topic: Recovery in the 1980s

33.55
A supply-side reason for the period of long sustained recovery following the 1982 recession might be a
a) reduction in the technological innovations.
b) steady accumulation of capital and technological change.
c) declining population.
d) stable labour force.
e) rising money supply.

33.56
Correct: b)
Difficulty: 3
Page(s): 901
Scramble range: All
Topic: Keynesianism

33.56
The Great Depression provided support for the Keynesian view that
a) government action was necessary to ensure that interest rates remained at the equilibrium level.
b) prolonged periods of unemployment were possible.
c) falling interest rates would stimulate spending by consumers.
d) the marginal propensity to consume is zero.
e) the labour market is always in equilibrium.

33.57
Correct: a)
Difficulty: 2
Page(s): 901
Scramble range: All
Topic: Pessimism and investment

33.57
Increased pessimism of business decision makers about the future is likely to
a) decrease the level of planned investment, which will cause employment and income to decline.
b) increase the level of planned investment, which will cause employment and income to rise.
c) increase the level of planned investment, which will cause employment and income to fall.
d) decrease the level of planned investment, which will cause employment and income to rise.
e) increase the level of planned investment, which will cause aggregate supply to rise.

33.58
Correct: a)
Difficulty: 3
Page(s): 902
Scramble range: All
Topic: Factors/Great Depression

33.58
Which one of the following most directly contributed to the severity of the Great Depression in the 1930s?
a) Large increases in taxes designed to balance the budget in the early 1930s.
b) Large increases in the money supply during the early 1930s.
c) A reduction in tariffs protecting many industries.
d) A substantial tax rate reduction.
e) Wage cuts taken by unemployed workers.

33.59
Correct: a)
Difficulty: 4
Page(s): 903
Scramble range: All
Topic: Interest rate transmission/restrictive monetary policy

33.59
Which of the following statements accurately summarizes the interest rate transmission of restrictive monetary policy to the goods and services market?
a) An unanticipated decline in the money supply causes higher real interest rates, leading to a decrease in both investment and aggregate demand.
b) An unanticipated decline in the money supply causes lower real interest rates, leading to business pessimism and a decline in aggregate demand.
c) An unanticipated decline in the money supply reduces the inflation rate, leading to a decrease in nominal GDP and a decline in aggregate demand.
d) An unanticipated decline in the money supply leads to higher taxes, thereby decreasing disposable income and aggregate demand.
e) An unanticipated decline in the money supply leads to lower consumption spending, and therefore lower aggregate demand.

33.60
Correct: c)
Difficulty: 4
Page(s): 903–904
Scramble range: All
Topic: Monetary policy/Great Depression

33.60
Which one of the following factors contributed to the decline in real output during the Great Depression?
a) Deflation, which changed the terms of long-term contracts and discouraged long-term exchange.
b) Inflation, which reduced the value of the dollar and reduced the purchasing power of the savings of old people.
c) A stable monetary policy in the United States, which caused business firms to lose confidence in the U.S. central bank's ability to fine-tune the economy.
d) The establishment of the Canada Deposit Insurance Corporation.
e) Increases in the monetary base carried out by the Bank of Canada.

33.61
Correct: b)
Difficulty: 3
Page(s): 904
Scramble range: All
Topic: Monetary view/Great Depression

33.61
According to monetarists, the Great Depression provides evidence that monetary policy is
a) effective against inflation but not useful against declining real output.
b) a source of economic instability if used in a perverse manner.
c) incapable of reversing a major downturn, unless the recession stems from inflation.
d) incapable of reversing an economic downturn when the money supply is increasing at a constant rate.
e) capable of reversing a recession, but not effective against inflation.

33.62
Correct: c)
Difficulty: 3
Page(s): 905
Scramble range: All
Topic: Deposit insurance/bank panics

33.62
The banking panic that came in the United States at the beginning of the Great Depression is
a) likely to occur in Canada since nothing has been done to correct for the problem.
b) not likely to occur in Canada due to tax policy changes made by the federal government.
c) not likely to occur in Canada due to the existence of bank deposit insurance programs that have been started since that time.
d) not likely to occur in Canada due to increased government spending as a percentage of GDP.
e) likely to occur in Canada if there is another stock market crash.

33.63
Correct: e)
Difficulty: 3
Page(s): 905
Scramble range: All
Topic: Likelihood of another Great Depression

33.63
The fear of another Great Depression is less today. Which one of the following does not represent a change in the economy's features that contributes to a lessening of that fear?
a) The level of government spending as a percentage of GDP is higher.
b) The existence of automatic stabilizers in the economy, such as transfer payments and income taxes.
c) The existence of multi-income families.
d) The Bank of Canada's ability to act as a lender of last resort.
e) The presence of more investment in the stock market.

33.64
Correct: e)
Difficulty: 3
Page(s): 901
Scramble range: All
Topic: Keynesianism

33.64
Modern Keynesians believe that wages
a) tend to rise slowly when output is above capacity output.
b) change slowly at all times.
c) are very flexible.
d) change rapidly at all times.
e) tend to rise rapidly when output is above capacity and fall slowly when output is below capacity.

33.65
Correct: b)
Difficulty: 3
Page(s): 894
Scramble range: All
Topic: Inflation expectations/*SAS* shifts

33.65
The reason it is so hard to get rid of an ongoing inflation is that inflationary expectations
a) make it impossible to stop the rightward shift of the aggregate demand curve.
b) keep shifting the short-run aggregate supply curve upward.
c) make it impossible to reduce aggregate expenditure.
d) keep shifting the short-run aggregate supply curve downward.
e) keep creating rises in the money supply.

33.66
Correct: b)
Difficulty: 4
Page(s): 901
Scramble range: None
Topic: Bank of Canada policy/inflation expectations

33.66
It is difficult for the Bank of Canada to remove an entrenched inflation in the economy without producing stagflation because inflationary expectations cause the aggregate
a) demand curve to shift to the right.
b) supply curve to shift to the left continuously (upward).
c) supply curve to shift to the right continuously (downward).
d) demand curve to shift to the left.
e) both a) and b).

33.67
Correct: a)
Difficulty: 4
Page(s): 901
Scramble range: All
Topic: Inflation expectations

33.67
Which one of the following statements concerning inflation is false?
a) The cost-push theory of inflation says that the root cause of inflation is a rise in costs resulting from a situation of excess demand relative to capacity.
b) Expectational inflation may prolong the effect of an inflation that got started on the demand side of the economy.
c) Inflationary expectations can be reduced if the Bank of Canada is able to surprise decision makers with an unexpected policy change.
d) If the economy is already at full employment, an increase in the rate of government spending is likely to put upward pressure on prices.
e) A rise in inflationary expectations cannot increase inflation in the long-run without accompanying increases in aggregate demand.

33.68
Correct: a)
Difficulty: 3
Page(s): 898–900
Scramble range: All
Topic: Flexible wage theory/unemployment

33.68
Flexible wage theory advocates might argue that the official unemployment rate is an estimate and may overstate unemployment by
a) including people who are voluntarily unemployed, because they could have a job if they would take a lower wage.
b) counting part-time workers as unemployed.
c) ignoring discouraged workers.
d) including workers in the underground economy.
e) ignoring sticky wages.

33.69
Correct: d)
Difficulty: 5
Page(s): 898
Scramble range: All
Topic: Oil prices

33.69
An oil price shock that reduces oil prices shifts the __________ curve rightward, causing real GDP to __________ and the price level to __________.
a) aggregate demand; fall; rise
b) aggregate supply; rise; rise
c) aggregate supply; fall; rise
d) aggregate supply; rise; fall
e) aggregate demand; rise; rise

33.70
Correct: d)
Difficulty: 3
Page(s): 903
Scramble range: All
Topic: Money supply/Great Depression

33.70
Which of the following statements is true concerning the events of 1930 to 1933?
a) Economists generally agree as to why the Great Depression ended so quickly.
b) Economists generally disagree as to all of the reasons that the recession became a Great Depression.
c) Economists generally agree as to why the recession was so short-lived.
d) Economists agree over some of the reasons the recession became a depression but disagreement remains concerning the importance of the role played by changes in the money supply.
e) Economists generally agree that the role of investment in the Great Depression was insignificant.

33.71
Correct: e)
Difficulty: 3
Page(s): 901
Scramble range: All
Topic: Pessimism in the Great Depression

33.71
Which of the following events do economists agree turned the recession of 1930 into a depression?
a) An increase in the nominal money supply.
b) An increase in tax collection activity.
c) Increases in government transfer payments.
d) Decreases in saving by households.
e) Increased pessimism and uncertainty contributing to further decreases in autonomous expenditures.

33.72
Correct: a)
Difficulty: 3
Page(s): 901
Scramble range: a)–d)
Topic: Real money supply

33.72
There is still disagreement over what caused a recession to turn into a Great Depression in the early 1930s. On which one of the following events do economists agree?
a) There was a massive contraction of the real money supply.
b) There was a massive tax increase in 1930.
c) There was a massive increase in government purchases in 1929.
d) The budget deficits of the 1920s were a contributing factor.
e) All of the above.

33.73
Correct: e)
Difficulty: 2
Page(s): 903
Scramble range: All
Topic: Friedman/real money supply

33.73
Which of the following is widely known for advocating that the fall in the real money supply was the major reason that the recession turned into a Great Depression in the early 1930s?
a) John Maynard Keynes and Paul Samuelson.
b) Peter Temin.
c) Michael Parkin.
d) Paul Volcker and Alan Greenspan.
e) Milton Friedman and Anna K. Schwartz.

33.74
Correct: c)
Difficulty: 4
Page(s): 903
Scramble range: All
Topic: Temin/ deepening recession

33.74
In writing on what exacerbated the recession of the early 1930s so that it turned into a depression, Peter Temin assigns
a) primary importance to the falling real money supply and secondary importance to the failure of the federal government to pay federal deposit insurance claims.
b) secondary importance to the falling real money supply and primary importance to the failure of the federal government to pay federal deposit insurance claims.
c) primary importance to the fall in autonomous expenditure and secondary importance to the role of the money supply.
d) primary importance to the fall in autonomous expenditures and secondary importance to the multi-income family structure.
e) primary importance to the fall in world trade and secondary importance to the fall in government purchases.

33.75
Correct: b)
Difficulty: 4
Page(s): 903
Scramble range: All
Topic: Government purchases/stability factor

33.75
Which one of the following statements helps to explain why government purchases in our modern economy help to stabilize the economy and lessen the possibility of another depression?
a) Government purchases as a percentage of aggregate demand are smaller today than during the Great Depression.
b) Government purchases as a percentage of *AD* are larger today, and since they are a stable component *AD* fluctuates less.
c) Government purchases as a percentage of *AD* are smaller today, and since they are a stable component *AD* fluctuates less.
d) Government purchases as a percentage of *AD* are larger today, and since they fluctuate almost as much as investment they are a source of stability in the economy.
e) Government purchases as a percentage of *AD* are smaller today, and since they are an unstable component *AD* fluctutates less.

33.76 (SG 33.1)
Correct: e)
Difficulty: 3
Page(s): 901–903
Scramble range: All
Topic: Great Depression

33.76
During the Great Depression, which was caused by an aggregate
a) supply shock, the rate of inflation increased.
b) supply shock, the rate of inflation decreased.
c) demand shock, the rate of inflation increased.
d) demand shock, the rate of inflation decreased.
e) demand shock, the rate of inflation became negative.

33.77 (SG 33.2)
Correct: d)
Difficulty: 3
Page(s): 893
Scramble range: All
Topic: 1982 recession

33.77
During the 1982 recession, which was caused by an aggregate
a) supply shock, the rate of inflation increased.
b) supply shock, the rate of inflation decreased.
c) demand shock, the rate of inflation increased.
d) demand shock, the rate of inflation decreased.
e) demand shock, the rate of inflation became negative.

33.78 (SG 34.15)
Correct: b)
Difficulty: 2
Page(s): 892
Scramble range: All
Topic: Stagflation

33.78
Stagflation means that real GDP stops growing or even declines *and* the
a) rate of inflation declines.
b) rate of inflation increases.
c) rate of inflation remains stable.
d) economy experiences deflation.
e) rate of inflation becomes negative.

33.79 (SG 33.4)
Correct: a)
Difficulty: 4
Page(s): 893–895
Scramble range: All
Topic: Recession

33.79
Which of the following describes the typical behaviour of interest rates during a recession?
a) In the early stages of recession interest rates increase but then fall as the recession gets underway.
b) In the early stages of recession interest rates decrease but then rise as the recession gets underway.
c) In the early stages of recession interest rates increase and remain high throughout the recession.
d) In the early stages of recession interest rates decrease and remain low throughout the recession.
e) In the early stages of recession interest rates are unchanged but then fall as the recession gets underway.

33.80 (SG 33.5)
Correct: d)
Difficulty: 3
Page(s): 902
Scramble range: All
Topic: Great Depression

33.80
Comparing the performances of the Canadian and U.S. economies in the Great Depression shows that
a) the stock market crashed in the United States but not in Canada.
b) the stock market crashed in Canada but not in the United States.
c) the banking system had a series of failures in Canada but not in the United States.
d) the banking system has a series of failures in the United States but not in Canada.
e) government purchases fell in Canada but not in the United States.

33.81 (SG 33.6)
Correct: b)
Difficulty: 3
Page(s): 898
Scramble range: a)–d)
Topic: Labour supply curve controversy

33.81
Modern Keynesians believe that the supply of labour curve is
a) not very sensitive to changes in the real wage rate, and that wages themselves are flexible.
b) not very sensitive to changes in the real wage rate, and that wages themselves are sticky.
c) very sensitive to changes in the real wage rate, and that wages themselves are flexible.
d) very sensitive to changes in the real wage rate, and that wages themselves are sticky.
e) none of the above.

33.82 (SG 33.7)
Correct: d)
Difficulty: 4
Page(s): 898–900
Scramble range: All
Topic: Labour supply and flexible wages

33.82
According to modern monetarists and real business cycle theorists, the increase in the unemployment rate during the 1982 recession was an increase in the
a) deviation of the rate of unemployment from the natural rate of unemployment resulting from a real wage rate that is too high to clear the labour market.
b) deviation of the rate of unemployment from the natural rate of unemployment resulting from an increase in job market turnover.
c) natural rate of unemployment resulting from a real wage that is too high to clear the labour market.
d) natural rate of unemployment resulting from an increase in job market turnover.
e) rate of new entries into the labour market.

33.83 (SG 33.9)
Correct: e)
Difficulty: 3
Page(s): 893
Scramble range: All
Topic: 1982 recession

33.83
During the 1982 recession, the real wage rate
a) fell and employment fell.
b) fell and employment rose.
c) stayed constant and employment fell.
d) rose and employment rose.
e) rose and employment fell.

33.84 (SG 33.10)
Correct: d)
Difficulty: 3
Page(s): 902
Scramble range: All
Topic: Great Depression

33.84
During the Great Depression (1930–1933), the money wage rate
a) rose and the real wage rate remained about the same.
b) rose and the real wage rate rose.
c) fell and the real wage rate remained about the same.
d) fell and the real wage rate rose.
e) fell and the real wage rate fell.

33.85 (SG 33.11)
Correct: d)
Difficulty: 3
Page(s): 902
Scramble range: All
Topic: Great Depression

33.85
During the Great Depression, the money supply
a) increased and the real interest rate was low.
b) increased and the real interest rate was high.
c) decreased and the real interest rate was low.
d) decreased and the real interest rate was high.
e) decreased and the real interest rate was normal.

33.86 (SG 33.12)
Correct: b)
Difficulty: 3
Page(s): 902
Scramble range: All
Topic: Great Depression

33.86
During the Great Depression, aggregate demand was expected to
a) fall, but it didn't fall as rapidly as expected.
b) fall, but it fell faster than expected.
c) rise, but it actually fell.
d) rise, which it did due to an increase in the money supply.
e) rise, but it rose less than expected.

33.87 (SG 33.13)
Correct: c)
Difficulty: 3
Page(s): 902
Scramble range: None
Topic: Great Depression

33.87
The major cause of the Great Depression was
a) a dramatic increase in the prices of raw materials during 1929.
b) a fall in the money supply during 1929.
c) a fall in investment and consumer spending due to uncertainty about the future.
d) the stock market crash of 1929.
e) both b) and c).

33.88 (SG 33.14)
Correct: d)
Difficulty: 3
Page(s): 905
Scramble range: All
Topic: Likelihood of another Great Depression

33.88
Which of the following is a reason that a recession as deep as the Great Depression is quite unlikely in Canada today?
a) The Federal Depositors Banking Corporation.
b) The value of the dollar is defined in terms of gold.
c) The federal government is prepared to lend money to companies.
d) Multi-income families.
e) Lower tax rates.

33.89 (SG 33.15)
Correct: c)
Difficulty: 2
Page(s): 905
Scramble range: All
Topic: CDIC

33.89
The Canada Deposit Insurance Corporation (CDIC)
a) keeps reserve requirements high so that banks can meet large withdrawals.
b) loans reserves to banks.
c) insures deposits thereby reducing the incentive for depositors to make large withdrawals.
d) insures banks against large withdrawals.
e) insures banks against bad loans.

33.90 (SG 33.16)
Correct: a)
Difficulty: 3
Page(s): 902–903
Scramble range: a)–d)
Topic: Great Depression

33.90
Multi-income families reduce the probability of another Great Depression by
a) reducing the probability of everyone in the family being simultaneously unemployed.
b) investing more in the economy.
c) paying more taxes.
d) increasing fluctuations in consumption.
e) none of the above.

33.91 (SG 33.17)
Correct: e)
Difficulty: 3
Page(s): 902–903
Scramble range: a)–d)
Topic: Great Depression

33.91
During the Great Depression, real GDP fell and
a) consumption fell as well.
b) investment fell dramatically.
c) exports fell.
d) imports fell.
e) all of the above.

33.92
Correct: a)
Difficulty: 2
Page(s): 892
Scramble range: All
Topic: Stagflation

33.92
"Stagflation" refers to stagnation in the growth of GDP together with
a) an increased rate of inflation.
b) a stable rate of inflation.
c) a decreased rate of inflation.
d) deflation.
e) a fall in real wages.

33.93 (SG 33.3)
Correct: d)
Difficulty: 3
Page(s): 893–895
Scramble range: All
Topic: Recession

33.93
During a recession
a) what happens to interest rates is irrelevant to the economy.
b) imports usually rise.
c) the decrease in income raises exports.
d) imports usually fall.
e) government transfer payments usually fall.

33.94
Correct: d)
Difficulty: 4
Page(s): 898
Scramble range: All
Topic: Real business cycles

33.94
According to the real business cycle theorists, why has unemployment increased in recent decades?
a) Too-high real wages that kept unemployment from reaching the natural rate of unemployment.
b) Increased job market turnover that kept unemployment from reaching the natural rate of unemployment.
c) Too-high real wages that increased the natural rate of unemployment.
d) Increased job market turnover that increased the natural rate of unemployment.
e) Increased use of contracts that prevented wages from being flexible.

33.95
Correct: e)
Difficulty: 3
Page(s): 902
Scramble range: a)–d)
Topic: Great Depression

33.95
During the Great Depression (1930–1933), what was the behaviour of real and money wages?
a) The money wage rate fell, and the increasing price level made real wages even lower.
b) The money wage rate fell, but the falling price level left real wages virtually unchanged.
c) The money wage rate was sticky, but the increasing price level made real wages fall.
d) The money wage rate rose, but the increasing price level left real wages virtually unchanged.
e) None of the above.

33.96 (SG 33.18)
Correct: a)
Difficulty: 3
Page(s): 902
Scramble range: All
Topic: Great Depression

33.96
How did monetary policy affect interest rates during the Great Depression (1930–1933)?
a) High real interest rates resulted from a decrease in the money supply.
b) Low real interest rates resulted from a decrease in the money supply.
c) High real interest rates resulted from an increase in the money supply.
d) Low real interest rates resulted from an increase in the money supply.
e) High real interest rates resulted from the negative inflation.

33.97
Correct: e)
Difficulty: 4
Page(s): 902
Scramble range: All
Topic: Great Depression

33.97
How do economic historians view the importance of the stock market crash of 1929 in causing the Great Depression?
a) The stock market crash directly caused the Great Depression.
b) The stock market crash was totally independent of the Great Depression.
c) The stock market crash caused the fall in investment and consumer spending that caused the Great Depression.
d) The stock market crash only reflected the fall in the money supply in 1929 that caused the Great Depression.
e) The stock market crash only reflected the fall in investment and consumer spending that caused the Great Depression.

33.98
Correct: a)
Difficulty: 3
Page(s): 902
Scramble range: All
Topic: Great Depression

33.98
Which of the following measures was adopted after the Great Depression in an effort to prevent future depressions?
a) Federal deposit insurance.
b) Mandatory 100 percent reserve requirements.
c) Full backing of Canadian currency by gold.
d) Government ownership of all banks.
e) Rigid wages.

33.99
Correct: d)
Difficulty: 3
Page(s): 905
Scramble range: All
Topic: CDIC

33.99
Why are bank runs relatively unlikely today?
a) Banks no longer loan out deposited funds.
b) The Bank of Canada provides deposit insurance.
c) The Department of Finance provides reserves to banks facing unusual levels of withdrawals.
d) The Canada Deposit Insurance Corporation insures deposits and reduces the incentive for depositors to make large withdrawals.
e) Banks are much more careful.

33.100 (SG 33.19)
Correct: e)
Difficulty: 4
Page(s): 893–905
Scramble range: All
Topic: Recession

33.100
Consider Figure 33.1. Which graph(s) represents an economy that is recovering from a recession without any government involvement?
a) (a).
b) (b).
c) (b) and (d).
d) (c).
e) (d).

33.101 (SG 33.20)
Correct: b)
Difficulty: 4
Page(s): 893–905
Scramble range: All
Topic: Recession

33.101
Consider Figure 33.1. Which graph(s) represents an economy where the government is helping it recover from a recession?
a) (a).
b) (b).
c) (b) and (d).
d) (c).
e) (d).

Chapter 34 Stabilizing the Economy

34.1
Correct: a)
Difficulty: 2
Page(s): 917
Scramble range: All
Topic: Natural rate target for policy

34.1
Macroeconomic policy targets might include
a) unemployment at its natural rate.
b) unemployment of zero.
c) an unpredictable inflation rate.
d) a rising unemployment rate.
e) a high and variable real GDP growth rate.

34.2
Correct: d)
Difficulty: 2
Page(s): 918
Scramble range: All
Topic: Misery Index

34.2
The Misery Index is defined as the
a) inflation rate minus the unemployment rate.
b) unemployment rate minus the popularity index.
c) inflation rate minus the popularity index.
d) inflation rate plus the unemployment rate.
e) inflation rate plus nine times the unemployment rate.

34.3
Correct: a)
Difficulty: 2
Page(s): 918
Scramble range: All
Topic: Misery Index

34.3
The inflation rate plus the unemployment rate is an index of macroeconomic performance known as
a) the Misery Index.
b) the Unpopularity Index.
c) Okun's law.
d) the Stabilization Policy Index.
e) the Popularity Index.

34.4
Correct: e)
Difficulty: 2
Page(s): 919
Scramble range: All
Topic: Stabilization Policy Index

34.4
The inflation rate plus three times unemployment rate is an index of macroeconomic performance known as
a) the Misery Index.
b) the Unpopularity Index.
c) Okun's law.
d) the Popularity Index.
e) the Stabilization Policy Index.

34.5
Correct: b)
Difficulty: 2
Page(s): 919
Scramble range: All
Topic: Unpopularity Index

34.5
The inflation rate minus three times real GDP growth rate is an index of macroeconomic performance known as
a) the Misery Index.
b) the Unpopularity Index.
c) Okun's law.
d) the Stabilization Policy Index.
e) Fair's Index.

34.6
Correct: c)
Difficulty: 2
Page(s): 919
Scramble range: All
Topic: Okun's law

34.6
The relationship that states that, other things being equal, for each decrease of 3 percentage points in real GDP relative to trend, the unemployment rate increases by 1 percentage point, is known as
a) the Misery Index.
b) the Unpopularity Index.
c) Okun's law.
d) the Stabilization Policy Index.
e) the Fair Index.

34.7
Correct: d)
Difficulty: 2
Page(s): 919
Scramble range: All
Topic: Okun's law

34.7
Which one of the following formulas best represents Okun's law?
a) Inflation rate plus nine times unemployment rate.
b) Inflation rate plus unemployment rate.
c) Inflation rate minus three times real GDP growth rate.
d) For each 3 percentage points by which real GDP decreases relative to trends, the unemployment rate increases by 1 percentage point, all else constant.
e) Inflation rate plus three times unemployment rate.

34.8
Correct: b)
Difficulty: 2
Page(s): 918
Scramble range: All
Topic: Misery Index

34.8
Which one of the following formulas best represents the Misery Index?
a) Inflation rate plus nine times unemployment rate.
b) Inflation rate plus unemployment rate.
c) Inflation rate minus three times real GDP growth rate.
d) For each 3 percentage points by which real GDP decreases relative to trends, the unemployment rate increases by 1 percentage point, all else constant.
e) Inflation rate plus three times unemployment rate.

34.9
Correct: a)
Difficulty: 2
Page(s): 919
Scramble range: All
Topic: Unpopularity Index

34.9
Which one of the following formulas best represents the macroeconomic performance index known as the Unpopularity Index?
a) Inflation rate plus nine times unemployment rate.
b) Inflation rate plus unemployment rate.
c) Inflation rate minus three times real GDP growth rate.
d) For each 3 percentage points by which real GDP decreases relative to trends, the unemployment rate increases by 1 percentage point, all else constant.
e) Inflation rate plus three times unemployment rate.

34.10
Correct: e)
Difficulty: 2
Page(s): 919
Scramble range: All
Topic: Stabilization Policy Index

34.10
Which one of the following formulas best represents the macroeconomic performance index known as the Stabilization Policy Index?
a) Inflation rate plus nine times unemployment rate.
b) Inflation rate plus unemployment rate.
c) Inflation rate minus three times real GDP growth rate.
d) For each 3 percentage points by which real GDP decreases relative to trends, the unemployment rate increases by 1 percentage point, all else constant.
e) Inflation rate plus three times unemployment rate.

34.11
Correct: c)
Difficulty: 3
Page(s): 919–920
Scramble range: All
Topic: Macroeconomic performance indexes

34.11
Macroeconomic performance indexes are stated in terms of
a) nominal targets only.
b) real targets only.
c) nominal and real targets in combination.
d) the unemployment rate only.
e) the inflation rate and unemployment rate only.

34.12
Correct: b)
Difficulty: 3
Page(s): 919
Scramble range: None
Topic: Misery Index

34.12
The macroeconomic performance index that contains the least basis in fact is
a) the Stabilization Policy Index.
b) the Misery Index.
c) Unpopularity Index.
d) Okun's law.
e) both b) and d).

34.13
Correct: e)
Difficulty: 2
Page(s): 921
Scramble range: All
Topic: Policy makers

34.13
The key players in macroeconomic policy formulation are the
a) U.S. Treasury and the Federal Reserve System.
b) Bank of Canada and the provincial treasuries.
c) provinces and the federal government.
d) federal government and the U.S. Treasury.
e) Bank of Canada and the federal government.

34.14
Correct: e)
Difficulty: 2
Page(s): 921
Scramble range: All
Topic: Federal government budget

34.14
The federal government's taxing and spending plan is called its
a) debt.
b) macroeconomic plan.
c) deficit.
d) surplus.
e) budget.

34.15
Correct: e)
Difficulty: 3
Page(s): 922
Scramble range: None
Topic: Stabilization policy

34.15
Macroeconomic stabilization policy is carried out
a) primarily by the Bank of Canada, unconstrained by the federal government.
b) primarily by the federal government, unconstrained by the public's actions.
c) by the Bank of Canada, constrained by the decisions of the federal government.
d) by the federal government, constrained by the actions of the public.
e) both c) and d).

34.16
Correct: b)
Difficulty: 2
Page(s): 922
Scramble range: All
Topic: Fixed rules

34.16
A policy that specifies an action to be pursued independently of the state of the economy is called a
a) feedback rule.
b) fixed rule.
c) crowding out rule.
d) standardizing rule.
e) stabilization rule.

34.17
Correct: c)
Difficulty: 2
Page(s): 922
Scramble range: All
Topic: Feedback rules

34.17
A policy that specifies that action be taken in response to current economic conditions is known as a
a) springboard rule.
b) fixed rule.
c) feedback rule.
d) Ricardian rule.
e) stabilization rule.

34.18
Correct: b)
Difficulty: 2
Page(s): 922
Scramble range: All
Topic: Fixed rules

34.18
A policy whereby the money supply is allowed to grow at a rate that would hold the average inflation rate equal to zero is known as a
a) feedback rule.
b) fixed rule.
c) monetary rule.
d) standardizing rule.
e) stabilization rule.

34.19
Correct: a)
Difficulty: 4
Page(s): 823
Scramble range: All
Topic: Bank of Canada action — feedback

34.19
If the economy goes into a recession, under a feedback rule policy, which one of the following would be a proper action for the Bank of Canada to take?
a) Increase purchases of government bonds.
b) Reduce tax rates.
c) Increase rate of government spending.
d) Hold sales and purchases of bonds at the same rate.
e) Decrease purchases of government bonds.

34.20
Correct: d)
Difficulty: 4
Page(s): 823
Scramble range: All
Topic: Bank of Canada action — fixed

34.20
Under a fixed rule policy, the proper action for the Bank of Canada to take when the economy goes into a recession is to
a) increase purchases of government bonds.
b) reduce tax rates.
c) increase rate of government spending.
d) hold sales and purchases of bonds at the same rate.
e) decrease purchases of government bonds.

34.21
Correct: b)
Difficulty: 2
Page(s): 926
Scramble range: All
Topic: Stabilization policy

34.21
Policies undertaken by governing authorities for the purpose of maintaining full employment and a stable price level would be the domain of which of the following?
a) Monetary policy.
b) Stabilization policy.
c) Fiscal policy.
d) Expansionary policy.
e) Contractionary policy.

34.22
Correct: d)
Difficulty: 2
Page(s): 927
Scramble range: All
Topic: Expansionary monetary policy

34.22
Action taken by the Bank of Canada to increase the monetary base or its rate of growth is the best definition for which one of the following?
a) Monetary policy.
b) Stabilization policy.
c) Fiscal policy.
d) Expansionary monetary policy.
e) Contractionary monetary policy.

34.23
Correct: c)
Difficulty: 3
Page(s): 927
Scramble range: All
Topic: Expansionary monetary policy

34.23
If the economy is producing a real GDP less than potential GDP, then __________ monetary policy could be used to __________ aggregate demand and __________ real GDP.
a) contractionary; decrease; decrease
b) contractionary; increase; decrease
c) expansionary; increase; increase
d) expansionary; decrease; decrease
e) expansionary; increase; decrease

34.24
Correct: b)
Difficulty: 3
Page(s): 927
Scramble range: All
Topic: Contractionary monetary policy

34.24
Which one of the following is true of contractionary monetary policy?
a) The monetary base expands.
b) Aggregate demand decreases.
c) The tax rate increases.
d) Real interest rates fall.
e) Aggregate demand rises.

34.25
Correct: e)
Difficulty: 3
Page(s): 925
Scramble range: All
Topic: Contractionary monetary policy

34.25
If the economy is producing a real GDP that is greater than capacity output, __________ monetary policy could be used to __________ aggregate demand and __________ the general price level.
a) contractionary; decrease; increase
b) contractionary; increase; decrease
c) expansionary; increase; increase
d) expansionary; decrease; decrease
e) contractionary; decrease; decrease

34.26
Correct: d)
Difficulty: 2
Page(s): 925
Scramble range: All
Topic: Monetarism

34.26
Which of the following groups is associated with the policy recommendation that the money stock should grow only at the rate of growth in real GDP?
a) Keynesians.
b) Liberals.
c) New Democrats.
d) Monetarists.
e) Conservatives.

34.27
Correct: c)
Difficulty: 4
Page(s): 923
Scramble range: All
Topic: Fixed rules

34.27
An inflationary expansion of the economy increases the demand for money. If the Bank of Canada follows a fixed interest rate rule, then what is the likely consequence of its policy response?
a) The economy will go immediately into recession.
b) The inflation rate will fall.
c) The inflation rate will rise.
d) Unemployment will rise and the inflation rate will fall.
e) The economy will enter a period of stagflation.

34.28
Correct: c)
Difficulty: 2
Page(s): 922–926
Scramble range: All
Topic: Fiscal policy

34.28
The use of government spending and taxation for the purpose of stabilizing the economy is called
a) budget policy.
b) monetary policy.
c) fiscal policy.
d) trade policy.
e) stabilization policy.

34.29
Correct: c)
Difficulty: 3
Page(s): 921
Scramble range: All
Topic: Budget deficit

34.29
A budget deficit exists when
a) net tax revenue exceeds government spending.
b) government spending equals government revenues.
c) government spending exceeds government revenues.
d) the public debt decreases.
e) transfer payments are higher than government purchases.

34.30
Correct: a)
Difficulty: 3
Page(s): 926
Scramble range: All
Topic: Fiscal policy

34.30
A deliberate increase in the budget deficit __________ aggregate __________
a) increases; demand.
b) increases; supply.
c) decreases; demand.
d) decreases; supply.
e) has no impact on; demand.

34.31
Correct: c)
Difficulty: 4
Page(s): 926
Scramble range: All
Topic: Fiscal policy

34.31
A deliberate increase in the budget surplus or a decrease in a budget deficit __________ aggregate demand and __________ real GDP.
a) increases; decreases
b) increases; increases
c) decreases; decreases
d) decreases; increases
e) increases; leaves unchanged

34.32
Correct: a)
Difficulty: 3
Page(s): 926
Scramble range: All
Topic: Fiscal policy

34.32
Which of the following fiscal policies might be most appropriate under a feedback rule if the economy is operating below its capacity output rate?
a) An increase in government spending.
b) An increase in taxes.
c) An increase in the money supply.
d) A decrease in the money supply.
e) To do nothing.

34.33
Correct: d)
Difficulty: 4
Page(s): 922
Scramble range: All
Topic: Supply shocks

34.33
Given an adverse supply shock, which one of the following is not an important consideration in choosing a policy response?
a) Whether no policy action is better than a feedback response.
b) The speed with which automatic forces in the economy begin to work.
c) The expected extra costs and extra benefits associated with each possible policy response.
d) How quickly prices will begin to rise again after such a shocking fall.
e) How quickly prices will begin to fall again after such a shocking fall.

34.34
Correct: d)
Difficulty: 4
Page(s): 922
Scramble range: All
Topic: Feedback rules

34.34
Advocates of feedback rules believe that
a) the federal government should maintain a cyclically balanced budget at all times.
b) the economy's automatic adjustment mechanism has no effect.
c) stable money growth and a balanced budget are the most effective means of achieving macroeconomic stability.
d) it is necessary, desirable, and practical to revise policies periodically to stabilize the economy.
e) an unchanging policy rule should be adopted.

34.35
Correct: b)
Difficulty: 4
Page(s): 923
Scramble range: All
Topic: Fixed rules

34.35
Advocates of fixed rules believe that
a) it is necessary and desirable to revise policies periodically to stabilize the economy.
b) stable money growth and a cyclically adjusted balanced budget are the most effective means of maintaining macroeconomic stability.
c) the economy has no inherent adjustment mechanism.
d) the federal government should increase tax rates when the economy's growth rate exceeds the long-term growth rate.
e) following a countercyclical policy rule is the best policy.

34.36
Correct: c)
Difficulty: 4
Page(s): 922
Scramble range: All
Topic: Expectations and policy rules

34.36
Advocates of fixed rules are likely to argue that the slow response of wages and prices during past recessions occurs because
a) the economy's automatic adjustment mechanism works too slowly.
b) the government has been too slow to take policy action.
c) workers and business managers have come to expect expansionary policies and therefore have little reason to reduce wages and prices during a recession.
d) individuals do not seek enough information about the state of the economy.
e) of the presence of wage contracts.

34.37
Correct: d)
Difficulty: 4
Page(s): 923
Scramble range: All
Topic: Fixed versus feedback rules

34.37
Which one of the following arguments might *not* be used by a fixed rules advocate against the use of feedback rules?
a) A large amount of information is required to formulate policy.
b) It takes time for policy makers to recognize that a problem exists.
c) It takes time for the effects of a policy to be felt.
d) Despite information limitations, policy makers can know enough to give the economy a shove in the right direction.
e) Feedback rules can make aggregate demand more variable.

34.38
Correct: e)
Difficulty: 4
Page(s): 922
Scramble range: All
Topic: Feedback rules

34.38
The link between deficit financing and inflation concerns
a) the price at which the government can sell bond issues.
b) the amount of debt reaching maturity.
c) whether higher deficits are accompanied by expansionary fiscal policy.
d) whether the public is willing to purchase additional debt.
e) whether higher deficits are accompanied by expansionary monetary policy.

34.39
Correct: c)
Difficulty: 2
Page(s): 927
Scramble range: All
Topic: Negative supply shocks

34.39
The result of a negative supply shock is
a) inflation and growth.
b) deflation and recession.
c) inflation and recession.
d) deflation and growth.
e) inflation and stagnant growth.

34.40
Correct: c)
Difficulty: 2
Page(s): 926
Scramble range: All
Topic: Stagflation

34.40
Stagflation is said to occur when the economy experiences both
a) inflation and growth.
b) deflation and recession.
c) inflation and recession.
d) deflation and growth.
e) low inflation and low growth.

34.41
Correct: e)
Difficulty: 5
Page(s): 928–929
Scramble range: All
Topic: Feedback rules

34.41
Suppose the Bank of Canada is following a feedback rule whereby every time real GDP is below capacity the money supply is increased. Suppose that real GDP equals capacity when an unexpected decrease in supply occurs; then the resulting
a) contraction will slow down inflation.
b) contraction will reduce unemployment.
c) expansion will increase unemployment.
d) expansion will slow down inflation.
e) expansion will decrease unemployment.

34.42
Correct: a)
Difficulty: 5
Page(s): 928–929
Scramble range: None
Topic: Feedback rules

34.42
Suppose the government is using a feedback rule whereby every time inflation is above the expected rate, contractionary policy is implemented. Suppose that real GDP equals capacity when an unexpected decrease in supply occurs; then the resulting
a) contraction will slow down inflation.
b) contraction will reduce unemployment.
c) expansion will decrease unemployment.
d) expansion will slow down inflation.
e) both a) and b).

34.43
Correct: e)
Difficulty: 5
Page(s): 928–929
Scramble range: All
Topic: Feedback rules

34.43
Suppose the government is using a feedback rule whereby every time unemployment is below the natural rate, expansionary policy is used. Suppose that real GDP equals capacity when an unexpected decrease in supply occurs; then the resulting

a) contraction will slow down inflation.
b) contraction will reduce unemployment.
c) expansion will increase unemployment.
d) expansion will slow down inflation.
e) expansion will decrease unemployment.

34.44
Correct: a)
Difficulty: 5
Page(s): 928–929
Scramble range: All
Topic: Feedback rules

34.44
Suppose the government is using a feedback rule whereby every time real GDP is above capacity output, contractionary policy is used. Suppose that real GDP equals capacity when an unexpected decrease in supply occurs; then the resulting

a) contraction will slow down inflation.
b) contraction will reduce unemployment.
c) expansion will decrease unemployment.
d) expansion will slow down inflation.
e) expansion will increase unemployment.

34.45
Correct: a)
Difficulty: 5
Page(s): 928–929
Scramble range: All
Topic: Feedback rules

34.45
Suppose the government is using a feedback rule whereby every time real GDP is above capacity output, contractionary policy is used. Currently aggregate quantity demanded equals aggregate quantity supplied at the expected price level. All else constant, if an unexpected increase in aggregate demand occurs, then as a result of the policy action taken the resulting

a) contraction will slow down inflation.
b) contraction will reduce unemployment.
c) expansion will decrease unemployment.
d) expansion will slow down inflation.
e) contraction will have no impact on inflation.

34.46
Correct: e)
Difficulty: 5
Page(s): 928–929
Scramble range: All
Topic: Feedback rules

34.46
Suppose the government is using a feedback rule whereby every time real GDP is below capacity output, expansionary policy is used. Currently aggregate quantity demanded equals aggregate quantity supplied at the expected price level. All else constant, if an unexpected decrease in aggregate demand occurs, then as a result of the policy action taken the resulting

a) contraction will slow down inflation.
b) contraction will reduce unemployment.
c) expansion will increase unemployment.
d) expansion will slow down inflation.
e) expansion will decrease unemployment.

34.47
Correct: d)
Difficulty: 4
Page(s): 927, 929
Scramble range: All
Topic: Fixed rules

34.47
If a fixed rule approach to stabilizing the price level is implemented during a time of unacceptably high inflation, it might involve

a) a drastic reduction in government regulation.
b) a significant tax increase to balance the federal budget.
c) an across-the-board reduction in government expenditures to balance the federal budget.
d) major but consistent reductions in money supply growth in order to fight inflation.
e) an expected fall in inflation.

34.48
Correct: a)
Difficulty: 3
Page(s): 927, 929
Scramble range: All
Topic: Fixed rules

34.48
Fixed rule monetary policies are intended to

a) bring long-run inflationary pressures under control.
b) counteract temporary increases in aggregate demand.
c) counteract temporary decreases in real output.
d) offset supply shocks.
e) offset demand shocks.

34.49
Correct: a)
Difficulty: 4
Page(s): 927
Scramble range: All
Topic: Slowdown in capacity growth/fixed rule

34.49
If capacity real GDP falls (or its growth rate slows down), a fixed rule results in

a) lower real output and a higher price level.
b) lower real output and a lower price level.
c) higher real output and a higher price level.
d) higher real output and a lower price level.
e) no overall change in real output or the price level.

34.50
Correct: a)
Difficulty: 4
Page(s): 928
Scramble range: All
Topic: Slowdown in capacity growth/feedback

34.50
If capacity real GDP falls (or its growth rate slows down), a feedback rule that increases the money supply results in

a) a higher price level and higher inflation.
b) a lower price level and deflation.
c) disinflation.
d) a change in the minimum wage.
e) no change in the price level.

34.51
Correct: b)
Difficulty: 4
Page(s): 929
Scramble range: All
Topic: Policy dilemma — inflation/unemployment

34.51
Adverse supply shocks create a policy dilemma because

a) contractionary policy may cause higher inflation and higher unemployment.
b) contractionary policy designed to reduce inflation may lead to even higher unemployment and expansionary policy designed to reduce unemployment may lead to even higher inflation.
c) expansionary policy may cause higher inflation and higher unemployment.
d) contractionary policy designed to reduce unemployment may lead to even higher inflation and expansionary policy designed to reduce inflation may lead to even higher unemployment.
e) expansionary policy will lead to lower inflation at the cost of higher unemployment.

34.52
Correct: b)
Difficulty: 2
Page(s): 917
Scramble range: All
Topic: Stabilization targets

34.52
The targets of stabilization policy include all of the following *except*
a) a low and predictable rate of inflation.
b) balancing the budget.
c) maintaining a steady rate of real GDP growth.
d) keeping unemployment close to the natural rate.
e) maintaining a stable exchange rate.

34.53
Correct: e)
Difficulty: 3
Page(s): 928–929
Scramble range: All
Topic: Evaluate macroeconomic policy

34.53
Which one of the following questions would *not* be relevant to an economic evaluation of a macroeconomic policy?
a) What is the effect of doing nothing?
b) Are there reasons to suspect the policy to be ineffective?
c) Are the costs of the policy higher or lower than the benefits?
d) How will the policy affect unemployment and inflation?
e) Will the policy benefit everyone in the economy equally?

34.54
Correct: e)
Difficulty: 4
Page(s): 928–929
Scramble range: All
Topic: Disagreement on proper policy actions

34.54
"Economists agree that the economy is currently producing above its full capacity output rate; thus economists likely agree that expansionary policy actions are desirable." This statement is essentially
a) false because some economists are likely to favour contractionary policy actions.
b) true because economic principles indicate that expansionary policies are necessary to correct this situation.
c) true because economists generally believe that government policy actions are an effective means to stabilize the economy.
d) false because some economists believe the economy has the ability to quickly correct for short-run problems such as this.
e) false because economic principles would indicate that such a policy would worsen the situation.

34.55
Correct: a)
Difficulty: 4
Page(s): 928–929
Scramble range: All
Topic: Effects of supply shocks

34.55
Given that the economy is in long-run equilibrium when a supply shock occurs, which one of the following is not a short-run effect of an adverse supply shock?
a) An increase in real GDP above capacity output.
b) An increase in the general price level.
c) A decrease in real GDP.
d) An increase in unemployment.
e) A decrease in employment.

34.56
Correct: d)
Difficulty: 4
Page(s): 928–929
Scramble range: All
Topic: Monetary feedback rules

34.56
One who advocates a monetary feedback rule to validate a cost-push inflation would argue that
a) the economy will quickly adjust after a supply shock occurs.
b) the inflationary effects of other policy options are too high.
c) time lags in carrying out other policies rule out these other policy options.
d) the unemployment costs of other policy options are too high.
e) policy action to relieve the problems of a supply shock are ineffective.

34.57
Correct: d)
Difficulty: 3
Page(s): 928–929
Scramble range: All
Topic: Inflation and monetary policy

34.57
Long-term continuing inflation is
a) politically less popular than policies of disinflation.
b) usually the result of adverse supply shocks.
c) generally the result of shifts in the Phillips–Schenck curve.
d) usually caused by rapid and sustained increases in the money supply.
e) usually caused by rapid and sustained increases in the budget deficit.

34.58
Correct: b)
Difficulty: 4
Page(s): 926
Scramble range: All
Topic: Cost-push inflation

34.58
If workers demand wage compensation in advance of an inflation, the economy will
a) realize larger than expected gains in output.
b) likely experience no increase in output.
c) experience an expansion.
d) experience a recovery.
e) experience a recession.

34.59
Correct: b)
Difficulty: 3
Page(s): 928
Scramble range: All
Topic: Politicians/contractionary feedback policy

34.59
Fighting inflation through the use of contractionary policy is
a) generally endorsed by politicians.
b) generally unpopular with politicians.
c) is a zero cost way to reduce inflation.
d) always easily accepted by workers.
e) rarely effective.

34.60
Correct: b)
Difficulty: 4
Page(s): 929
Scramble range: All
Topic: Feedback versus fixed rules

34.60
A fixed rule advocate might argue that policy makers should avoid stabilization policy because
a) it never works.
b) lags make the policy impact unpredictable.
c) no tax increase has ever reduced demand.
d) stabilization policies have not been tried often enough to know their effect.
e) the costs of doing nothing are too high.

34.61
Correct: d)
Difficulty: 4
Page(s): 929
Scramble range: All
Topic: Feedback rules

34.61
Some economists argue that feedback policy rules should be used in a very limited way because
a) fighting among economists has become too personal.
b) forecasting is very reliable.
c) the economy always operates at capacity so there is no reason to engage in stabilization policy.
d) predicting the response of decision makers in the economy to the policy change is very difficult to do well.
e) the costs of doing nothing are too high.

34.62
Correct: c)
Difficulty: 4
Page(s): 929
Scramble range: All
Topic: Fixed rules

34.62
Believers in fixed rules suggest that the
a) Bank of Canada should keep money supply growth adjusted for changes in the business cycle.
b) economy is inherently unstable.
c) federal government should balance the cyclically adjusted budget.
d) federal government should relinquish its money creation powers over to the Bank of Canada.
e) Bank of Canada should adopt a countercyclical monetary policy.

34.63
Correct: c)
Difficulty: 4
Page(s): 929
Scramble range: All
Topic: Feedback rules

34.63
When economists refer to an inflation that is validated in a feedback rule scenario, they are referring to a situation in which
a) the rate of increase in the price level is greater than the rate of increase in the inflation rate.
b) inflations cause interest rates to increase and aggregate demand to increase.
c) the money supply is expanding at the same rate as the inflation.
d) expectational inflation prolongs the effects of inflation caused by excess aggregate demand.
e) the federal government argues that the level of inflation is valid.

34.64
Correct: a)
Difficulty: 3
Page(s): 927
Scramble range: All
Topic: Stagflation

34.64
Which one of the following explanations is least likely to explain the stagflation of the 1970s?
a) An aggregate demand inflation caused by excessive government spending.
b) Higher wage costs decreased aggregate supply.
c) Higher oil prices decreased aggregate supply.
d) A great increase, over the last decade, in the power of firms and unions to determined prices and wages independent of market conditions.
e) Higher price expectations decreased aggregate supply.

34.65
Correct: a)
Difficulty: 3
Page(s): 929
Scramble range: All
Topic: Fixed rules

34.65
Fixed rule advocates tend to believe that
a) the economy has within it forces that will lead to full employment and a relatively stable price level.
b) neither monetary nor fiscal policy has any noticeable effect on aggregate output even in the short run.
c) sharp decreases in the money supply can cause inflation.
d) changing fiscal policy is the best means of achieving macroeconomic stability.
e) changing monetary policy is the best means of achieving macroeconomic stability.

34.66
Correct: b)
Difficulty: 4
Page(s): 928
Scramble range: All
Topic: Short-run aggregate supply shock

34.66
Suppose the economy is operating at full employment and the short-run aggregate supply curve decreases due to a one-time increase in the price of oil. If the money supply is not increased, then

a) prices will rise and stay at the higher level with no further increase in the price level.
b) real GDP will be less than capacity output and the short-run aggregate supply curve will eventually increase again.
c) aggregate demand will shift up and cause further inflation.
d) aggregate demand will shift down and worsen the shock's impact on real GDP.
e) aggregate demand will shift down and eventually offset the shock.

34.67
Correct: c)
Difficulty: 4
Page(s): 929
Scramble range: None
Topic: *S* shock/ distinguishing policy approach

34.67
If the economy is operating at its capacity output rate when hit by a supply shock so that the short-run aggregate supply curve shifts upward, then

a) *AD* will shift to the right if the Bank of Canada is following a fixed rule policy.
b) the *SRAS* will shift down if the Bank of Canada is following a feedback rule policy.
c) the *SRAS* will shift down if the Bank of Canada is following a fixed rule policy.
d) *AD* will shift to the left if the Bank of Canada is following a feedback rule policy.
e) both a) and c).

34.68
Correct: d)
Difficulty: 4
Page(s): 929
Scramble range: All
Topic: Effect of feedback rule/*S* shock

34.68
When the Bank of Canada follows a feedback rule and there is a short-run aggregate supply shock, then one can expect an increase in

a) the money supply, but a decrease in costs and prices.
b) costs, but a decrease in real GDP.
c) real GDP over capacity real GDP.
d) costs, the price level, and the money supply.
e) costs, the price level, and then the money supply decreases.

34.69
Correct: e)
Difficulty: 4
Page(s): 929
Scramble range: All
Topic: Effect of fixed rule/*S* shock

34.69
If the Bank of Canada is following a fixed rule policy when there is a one-time shift up of the short-run aggregate supply curve, then real GDP will

a) not change.
b) increase and then decrease.
c) increase to a new long-run equilibrium level.
d) decrease to a new long-run equilibrium level.
e) decrease and then increase.

34.70
Correct: c)
Difficulty: 4
Page(s): 929
Scramble range: All
Topic: Fixed rules

34.70
If the economy is faced with continued supply shocks, such as annual wage increases for union workers, and the Bank of Canada is following a fixed policy rule, then the economy will be faced with

a) a one-time increase in prices.
b) real GDP above capacity real GDP.
c) rising unemployment until the wage increases stop.
d) an increase in capacity real GDP.
e) falling inflation until the Bank of Canada reverses its policy.

34.71
Correct: c)
Difficulty: 4
Page(s): 927
Scramble range: None
Topic: Stagflation

34.71
If the economy is producing at an output rate above its capacity, it is difficult for the Bank of Canada to bring the output rate back to capacity without producing stagflation because inflationary expectations cause the

a) *AD* curve to shift too far to the right.
b) *AD* curve to shift too far to the left.
c) *SRAS* curve to continue to shift up.
d) *SRAS* curve to continue to shift down.
e) both b) and c).

34.72
Correct: c)
Difficulty: 2
Page(s): 929
Scramble range: a)–d)
Topic: Long-run equilibrium

34.72
Consider Figure 34.1. Suppose the relevant demand curve is AD_0. The long-run equilibrium output level is

a) $1 trillion.
b) $2 trillion.
c) $3 trillion.
d) $4 trillion.
e) none of the above.

Figure 34.1

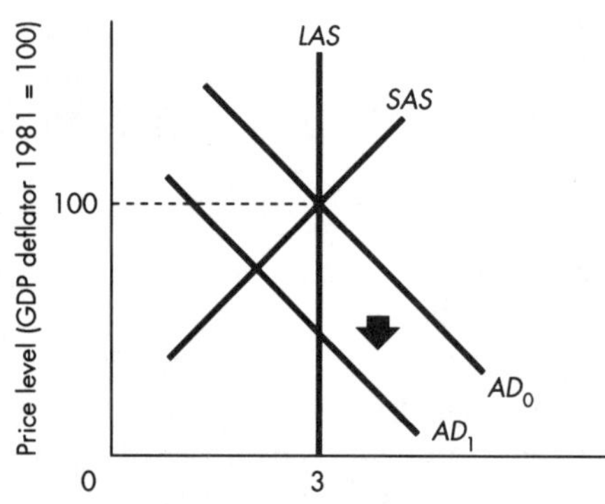

34.73
Correct: c)
Difficulty: 2
Page(s): 929
Scramble range: a)–d)
Topic: Expected price level

34.73
Consider Figure 34.1. Suppose the relevant demand curve is AD_0. The expected price level is

a) 80.
b) 90.
c) 100.
d) 110.
e) none of the above.

34.74
Correct: b)
Difficulty: 4
Page(s): 929
Scramble range: All
Topic: Bank of Canada feedback rule/ unanticipated *AD*

34.74
Consider Figure 34.1. The economy experiences an unanticipated decrease in aggregate demand from AD_0 to AD_1. Given that the Bank of Canada is following a feedback rule, the appropriate policy action to take would be to

a) reduce the money supply.
b) purchase bonds on the open market.
c) raise the reserve requirement.
d) sell bonds on the open market.
e) raise the bank rate.

34.75
Correct: a)
Difficulty: 4
Page(s): 928
Scramble range: All
Topic: Bank of Canada feedback rule/ unanticipated *AD*

34.75
Consider Figure 34.1. The economy experiences an unanticipated decrease in aggregate demand from AD_0 to AD_1. Given that the Bank of Canada is following a feedback rule, what change must be made to show this in the diagram?
a) An increase in the *AD* curve.
b) A decrease in the *AD* curve.
c) A decrease in the *LAS* curve.
d) An increase in the *SAS* curve.
e) A decrease in the *SAS* curve.

34.76
Correct: d)
Difficulty: 3
Page(s): 930
Scramble range: All
Topic: Monetarism

34.76
Monetarists argue that
a) monetary policy never influences the economy.
b) the economy can only attain long-run equilibrium when the money supply is small.
c) money is an asset that is preferable at all times to a bond.
d) changes in the money supply are significant causes of short-run changes in nominal GDP.
e) monetary policy is ineffective, so a fixed rule should be used.

34.77
Correct: d)
Difficulty: 2
Page(s): 930
Scramble range: All
Topic: Monetarism

34.77
Monetarist views would be most closely aligned with the views of which one of the following groups?
a) Keynesians.
b) Feedback rule advocates.
c) Walrasians.
d) Fixed rule advocates.
e) Fisherians.

34.78 (SG 34.18)
Correct: e)
Difficulty: 2
Page(s): 930
Scramble range: All
Topic: Monetarism

34.78
Who argued that the quantity theory of money, in its modern form, is a theory about the demand for money?
a) J.M. Keynes.
b) J.B. Say.
c) M. Parkin.
d) T. Sargent.
e) M. Friedman.

34.79
Correct: d)
Difficulty: 2
Page(s): 925
Scramble range: All
Topic: Neo-Keynesians

34.79
The viewpoint that characterized and tended to dominate macroeconomic policy formulation during the 1950s and 1960s was that of the followers of
a) Milton Friedman.
b) Ludwig von Mises.
c) fixed rule policy.
d) John Maynard Keynes.
e) Michael Parkin.

34.80
Correct: e)
Difficulty: 2
Page(s): 930
Scramble range: All
Topic: Keynes

34.80
Who advocated the viewpoint that there is a weak connection between money and the price level?
a) Milton Friedman.
b) Michael Parkin.
c) Anna Schwartz.
d) Jacques Parizeau.
e) John Maynard Keynes.

34.81 (SG 34.19)
Correct: c)
Difficulty: 2
Page(s): 930
Scramble range: a)–d)
Topic: Monetarism

34.81
Which group advocates the viewpoint that there is a very strong connection between money and the price level?
a) Keynesians.
b) Neo-Keynesians.
c) Monetarists.
d) Feedback rule advocates.
e) None of the above.

34.82 (SG 34.1)
Correct: d)
Difficulty: 3
Page(s): 917
Scramble range: All
Topic: Policy targets

34.82
Which of the following is *not* one of the five main macroeconomic policy targets?
a) Unemployment at its natural rate.
b) Steady growth in real GDP.
c) A balance of trade.
d) A flexible exchange rate.
e) Low and predictable inflation.

34.83 (SG 34.2)
Correct: c)
Difficulty: 3
Page(s): 918
Scramble range: All
Topic: Misery Index

34.83
Looking at Table 34.1, in which year is the Misery Index the highest?
a) Year 1.
b) Year 2.
c) Year 3.
d) Year 4.
e) Year 5.

Table 34.1

Year	Inflation rate (percent per year)	Unemployment rate (percent)
1	6	6
2	8	5
3	10	4
4	6	7
5	3	10

34.84 (SG 34.3)
Correct: c)
Difficulty: 4
Page(s): 919
Scramble range: All
Topic: Unpopularity Index

34.84
Looking at Table 34.1, in which year is the Unpopularity Index the lowest?
a) Year 1.
b) Year 2.
c) Year 3.
d) Year 4.
e) Year 5.

34.85 (SG 34.4)
Correct: b)
Difficulty: 4
Page(s): 919
Scramble range: All
Topic: Stabilization Policy Index

34.85
Looking at Table 34.1, what is the value of the Stabilization Policy Index in year 2?
a) 13.
b) 23.
c) 53.
d) 24.
e) 7.

34.86 (SG 34.5)
Correct: e)
Difficulty: 2
Page(s): 919
Scramble range: None
Topic: Nominal targets

34.86
Which of the following is an example of a nominal target of macroeconomic policy?
a) Unemployment at its natural rate.
b) A stable foreign exchange rate.
c) Steady growth in real GDP.
d) Low and predictable inflation.
e) Both b) and d).

34.87 (SG 34.16)
Correct: e)
Difficulty: 4
Page(s): 929
Scramble range: All
Topic: Fighting inflation

34.87
From 1975 to 1982, the Bank of Canada tried to rid the Canadian economy of high inflation. From examining this period, we can conclude which of the following?
a) Monetarist fixed rules do not work in practice.
b) The Bank of Canada was very lax in lowering the growth rate of M1.
c) The Bank of Canada successfully defeated the inflation by using fixed rules.
d) The Bank of Canada successfully defeated the inflation by using feedback rules.
e) The Bank of Canada failed to defeat the inflation because it failed to control the growth rate of M2.

34.88 (SG 34.17)
Correct: e)
Difficulty: 4
Page(s): 929
Scramble range: All
Topic: Fighting inflation

34.88
From mid-1981 on to the end of the 1980s the Bank of Canada became very serious about defeating Canada's inflation problem. We can conclude from examining this period that
a) there is no link between controlling the money supply and fighting inflation.
b) there is a strong link between controlling M1 and controlling inflation.
c) fiscal policy is better at aggregate demand management than monetary policy.
d) a fixed rule cannot be used to control inflation.
e) there is a strong link between controlling M2 and controlling inflation.

34.89 (SG 34.8)
Correct: c)
Difficulty: 3
Page(s): 922
Scramble range: All
Topic: Fixed rules

34.89
Which of the following is an example of a fixed "policy" rule?
a) Wear your boots if it snows.
b) Leave your boots home if it does not snow.
c) Wear your boots every day.
d) Take your boots off in the house if they are wet.
e) Listen to the weather forecast and then decide whether to wear your boots.

34.90 (SG 34.9)
Correct: b)
Difficulty: 4
Page(s): 928–929
Scramble range: All
Topic: Feedback rules

34.90
Suppose that, starting from equilibrium at capacity real GDP, there is a temporary unexpected decline in aggregate demand. Our feedback rule is: increase the money supply whenever there is a fall in aggregate demand and decrease the money supply whenever there is a rise in aggregate demand. In this case, our rule would result in

a) an increase in real GDP to above capacity and a rise in the price level above its original value.
b) real GDP jumping back to capacity and the price level jumping back to its original value.
c) an increase in real GDP but not back to capacity and no effect on the price level.
d) a slow increase in real GDP back to capacity and a slow rise in the price level.
e) a jump in the price level back to the original level, and no change in real GDP.

34.91 (SG 34.10)
Correct: d)
Difficulty: 3
Page(s): 928–929
Scramble range: All
Topic: Feedback rules

34.91
Which of the following is *not* an argument *against* a feedback rule?

a) Feedback rules require greater knowledge of the economy than we have.
b) Feedback rules introduce unpredictability.
c) Aggregate supply shocks cause most economic fluctuations.
d) Aggregate demand shocks cause most economic fluctuations.
e) Feedback rules generate bigger fluctuations in aggregate demand.

34.92 (SG 34.11)
Correct: b)
Difficulty: 4
Page(s): 928–929
Scramble range: All
Topic: Feedback rules

34.92
Which of the following is the basic reason for the claim that feedback rules generate bigger fluctuations in aggregate demand? Policy makers

a) use the wrong feedback rules to achieve their goals.
b) must take actions today that will not have their effects until well into the future.
c) do not really want to stabilize the economy.
d) try to make their policies unpredictable.
e) do not have enough knowledge of the economy.

34.93 (SG 34.12)
Correct: e)
Difficulty: 3
Page(s): 923
Scramble range: All
Topic: Fixed rules

34.93
A fixed rule for monetary policy

a) requires considerable knowledge of how changes in the money supply affect the economy.
b) would be impossible for the Bank of Canada to achieve.
c) generates bigger fluctuations in aggregate demand.
d) would result in constant real GDP.
e) minimizes the threat of cost-push inflation.

34.94 (SG 34.13)
Correct: a)
Difficulty: 3
Page(s): 919
Scramble range: All
Topic: Real business cycles

34.94
According to real business cycle theories,

a) any decline in real GDP is a decline in capacity.
b) wages are flexible but labour market equilibrium does not necessarily imply full employment.
c) fluctuations in aggregate demand change capacity real GDP.
d) fluctuations in aggregate demand cannot affect the price level.
e) flexible rules are best.

34.95 (SG 34.14)
Correct: d)
Difficulty: 3
Page(s): 919
Scramble range: All
Topic: Real business cycles

34.95
According to real business cycle theories, if the Bank of Canada increases the money supply when real GDP declines, real GDP
a) will increase but only temporarily.
b) will increase permanently.
c) and the price level will both be unaffected.
d) will be unaffected but the price level will rise.
e) will fall due to the inefficiencies introduced into production as a result.

34.96
Correct: e)
Difficulty: 3
Page(s): 918
Scramble range: a)–d)
Topic: Macroeconomic goals

34.96
Which of the following is one of the five main macroeconomic policy targets?
a) A balance of trade deficit.
b) Unemployment above the natural rate.
c) Ever-increasing value of the dollar against foreign currencies.
d) A government budget surplus.
e) None of the above.

34.97
Correct: a)
Difficulty: 2
Page(s): 919
Scramble range: All
Topic: Indexes

34.97
Which of the following is defined to equal the inflation rate plus nine times the unemployment rate?
a) Unpopularity Index.
b) Stabilization Policy Index.
c) Misery Index.
d) Cost of Living Index.
e) Popularity Index.

34.98
Correct: b)
Difficulty: 3
Page(s): 918
Scramble range: All
Topic: Macro goals

34.98
Which of the following is an example of a real (as opposed to nominal) target of macroeconomic policy?
a) Low prime rate of interest.
b) Unemployment at its natural rate.
c) Steady growth of money incomes.
d) Low and predictable inflation.
e) Stable exchange rate.

34.99
Correct: a)
Difficulty: 4
Page(s): 929
Scramble range: All
Topic: Bank of Canada policy

34.99
During the 1980s, the Bank of Canada's monetary policy can be best described as
a) trying to stay on a tightrope.
b) a fixed rule.
c) one of raising the money supply to fight inflation, and lowering it to fight unemployment.
d) concerned solely with fighting inflation.
e) concerned solely with fighting unemployment.

34.100
Correct: d)
Difficulty: 4
Page(s): 929
Scramble range: All
Topic: Policy

34.100
In using fiscal and monetary policy in Canada, policy makers are
a) free to use one or the other.
b) able to use monetary policy most easily.
c) able to use fiscal policy most easily.
d) constrained in the use of either.
e) forced to use a fixed rule.

34.101
Correct: a)
Difficulty: 3
Page(s): 922
Scramble range: All
Topic: Policy rules

34.101
Which of the following is an example of a fixed "policy" rule?
a) Always have a spare tire in your car.
b) Make sure you have a spare tire in your car if a safety inspection is due.
c) Make sure you have a spare tire in your car if you are driving over rough roads.
d) Keep your spare tire inflated to 34 pounds pressure when the weather is hot and 30 pounds pressure when the weather is cold.
e) Buy a spare tire whenever you get a flat tire.

34.102
Correct: d)
Difficulty: 4
Page(s): 922
Scramble range: All
Topic: Policy rules

34.102
Feedback policy rules are most useful when the main source of economic fluctuation is
a) changes in the natural rate of unemployment.
b) changes in the economy's aggregate production function.
c) aggregate supply shocks.
d) aggregate demand shocks.
e) unpredictable changes in the money supply.

34.103
Correct: b)
Difficulty: 4
Page(s): 922
Scramble range: All
Topic: Policy rules

34.103
Which of the following is *not* considered to be an advantage of a fixed rule for monetary policy?
a) It would promote stable expectations.
b) It would permit quick reactions to unexpected aggregate supply shocks.
c) It would minimize the threat of cost-push inflation.
d) It would reduce uncertainty in the financial markets about the course of Bank of Canada policy.
e) It requires less knowledge of the economy than a feedback rule.

34.104
Correct: c)
Difficulty: 3
Page(s): 919
Scramble range: All
Topic: Real business cycles

34.104
According to real business cycle theories, which of the following could cause a decline in real GDP?
a) Insufficient aggregate demand.
b) Absence of labour market equilibrium.
c) A decline in capacity.
d) Increases in inflation.
e) A fall in foreign income levels.

34.105
Correct: d)
Difficulty: 3
Page(s): 919
Scramble range: All
Topic: Real business cycles

34.105
According to real business cycle theories, what would be the result if the Bank of Canada increased the money supply after a decrease in real GDP?
a) A temporary increase in real GDP.
b) A permanent increase in real GDP.
c) Unchanged real GDP with an unchanged price level.
d) Unchanged real GDP and a higher price level.
e) Decreased prices but increased real GDP.

34.106
Correct: b)
Difficulty: 3
Page(s): 917
Scramble range: All
Topic: Economic trouble

34.106
In times of economic trouble, it is typically found that
a) people buckle down and work their way out of the trouble.
b) people turn to the government for help.
c) the economy quickly stabilizes itself.
d) the economy never stabilizes itself.
e) the electorate usually re-elects the current government because it is fearful of change.

34.107
Correct: a)
Difficulty: 3
Page(s): 929
Scramble range: All
Topic: Fixed versus feedback rules

34.107
The most credible method of achieving zero inflation involves a
a) credible and consistent monetary *and* fiscal policy.
b) fixed monetary policy.
c) fixed rule fiscal policy.
d) feedback monetary policy.
e) feedback fiscal policy.

Chapter 35 **The Federal Deficit**

35.1
Correct: a)
Difficulty: 2
Page(s): 943–944
Scramble range: All
Topic: Actual budget figures

35.1
Every year since __________, the federal government has run a deficit and spent __________

a) 1975; up to $30 billion more than it has raised in revenue.
b) 1984; up to $30 billion more than it has raised in revenue.
c) 1900; up to $60 billion more than it has raised in revenue.
d) 1975; up to $30 billion less than it has raised in revenue.
e) 1948; up to $60 billion less than it has raised in revenue.

35.2
Correct: c)
Difficulty: 2
Page(s): 944
Scramble range: All
Topic: Budget balance

35.2
The federal government's budget balance is equal to

a) revenue + transfers – (purchases + interest payments).
b) purchases - (revenue + transfers + interest payments).
c) revenue – (purchases + transfers + interest payments).
d) expenditures – receipts.
e) interest payments + transfers – expenditures.

35.3
Correct: b)
Difficulty: 2
Page(s): 944
Scramble range: All
Topic: Budget surplus

35.3
If receipts exceed expenditures, the federal government's budget balance is __________, and the government has a budget __________

a) negative; deficit.
b) positive; surplus.
c) positive; deficit.
d) negative; surplus.
e) zero; deficit.

35.4
Correct: a)
Difficulty: 2
Page(s): 944
Scramble range: All
Topic: Budget deficit

35.4
If expenditures exceed receipts, the federal government's budget balance is __________, and the government has a budget __________

a) negative; deficit.
b) positive; surplus.
c) positive; deficit.
d) negative; surplus.
e) zero; surplus.

35.5
Correct: b)
Difficulty: 3
Page(s): 944–945
Scramble range: All
Topic: Stocks versus flows

35.5
Government debt is a
a) flow, whereas its budget balance is a stock.
b) stock, whereas its budget balance is a flow.
c) flow, as is its budget balance.
d) stock, as is its budget balance.
e) stock, while its budget balance is a flow if it is a deficit and a stock if it is a surplus.

35.6
Correct: d)
Difficulty: 2
Page(s): 944
Scramble range: All
Topic: Government debt

35.6
Government debt is defined as the total amount of
a) expenditures minus the total amount of receipts per year.
b) receipts minus the total amount of expenditures per year.
c) spending that the government has undertaken since 1867.
d) borrowing that the government has undertaken and the total amount that it owes to households, firms, and foreigners.
e) interest payments made since 1867.

35.7
Correct: e)
Difficulty: 3
Page(s): 945
Scramble range: All
Topic: Historical budget surplus

35.7
The last time that Canada had a budget surplus was
a) 1867.
b) 1960.
c) 1969.
d) 1980.
e) 1974.

35.8
Correct: e)
Difficulty: 3
Page(s): 945
Scramble range: All
Topic: Historical budget deficit

35.8
Which of the following statements concerning the government's budget in the period since 1969 is true?
a) The government's budget balance was at its greatest value in 1984.
b) The government's budget balance was at its smallest value in 1969.
c) The government's budget balance was at its smallest value in 1982.
d) The government's budget deficit was at its greatest value in 1969.
e) The government's budget deficit was at its greatest value in 1984.

35.9
Correct: e)
Difficulty: 3
Page(s): 945
Scramble range: All
Topic: Historical government debt

35.9
Since 1969, the federal government's debt outstanding
a) has risen constantly.
b) has fallen constantly.
c) rose until the late 1970s, and then fell dramatically.
d) fell until the mid-1970s, and then stayed constant.
e) fell until the mid-1970s, and then rose slowly through the 1980s.

35.10
Correct: d)
Difficulty: 3
Page(s): 945
Scramble range: All
Topic: Historical government revenue

35.10
Since 1969, total federal government revenue has
a) increased from 4.5 to 7.5 percent of GDP.
b) decreased from 6 to 3 percent of GDP.
c) remained at an average of 9 percent of GDP.
d) fluctuated between 16 and 20 percent of GNP.
e) remained fairly constant at about 25 percent of GDP.

35.11
Correct: e)
Difficulty: 3
Page(s): 945
Scramble range: a)–d)
Topic: Federal government revenue

35.11
During the 1970s and 1980s in Canada,
a) investment income as a percentage of GDP increased.
b) indirect taxes as a percentage of GDP increased steadily.
c) income taxes as a percentage of GDP decreased.
d) indirect taxes as a percentage of GDP increased.
e) none of the above.

35.12
Correct: b)
Difficulty: 3
Page(s): 946
Scramble range: All
Topic: Interest payments on debt

35.12
The interest payments on the government's debt
a) have been rising steadily throughout this century.
b) have been rising since 1975.
c) have been forgiven continuously by the Bank of Canada.
d) do not have to be paid since the Monetary Control Act of 1980 was passed.
e) have no impact on the size of the debt.

35.13
Correct: c)
Difficulty: 3
Page(s): 947
Scramble range: All
Topic: Budget changes

35.13
All else the same, as the economy enters a recession
a) tax receipts tend to rise and interest payments on the debt tend to rise.
b) tax receipts and transfer payments tend to rise.
c) government expenditures tend to rise and tax receipts tend to fall.
d) government expenditures tend to fall and tax receipts tend to fall.
e) interest payments on the debt tend to rise and tax receipts tend to fall.

35.14
Correct: a)
Difficulty: 3
Page(s): 947
Scramble range: All
Topic: Budget changes

35.14
All else the same, as the economy enters a recovery period
a) tax receipts tend to rise and transfer payments tend to decline.
b) tax receipts and transfer payments tend to decline.
c) tax receipts and transfer payments tend to rise.
d) tax receipts tend to fall and transfer payments tend to stay the same.
e) transfer payments and interest on the debt tend to rise.

35.15
Correct: d)
Difficulty: 3
Page(s): 943
Scramble range: None
Topic: Fiscal policy

35.15
Which one of the following statements is true?
a) In Canada, the government body with the power to tax incomes can also create money.
b) Parliament and the Bank of Canada determine fiscal policy.
c) The Bank of Canada may monetize the debt by selling government securities.
d) Parliament and the prime minister determine fiscal policy.
e) Both c) and d).

35.16
Correct: b)
Difficulty: 2
Page(s): 942
Scramble range: All
Topic: National debt

35.16
The national debt is
a) equal to exports minus imports.
b) the amount owed by the federal government as result of past budget deficits and surpluses.
c) zero at the full employment level of real GDP.
d) the amount owed by the taxpayers to the federal government.
e) equal to expenditures minus revenue.

35.17
Correct: c)
Difficulty: 3
Page(s): 951
Scramble range: All
Topic: Financing the debt

35.17
Government borrowing
a) is negatively related to the amount of revenues collected.
b) is positively related to the amount of funds available to finance private sector spending.
c) can reduce the amount of funds available to the private sector.
d) is represented by open market sales of the Bank of Canada.
e) is represented by open market purchases of the Bank of Canada.

35.18
Correct: c)
Difficulty: 3
Page(s): 951
Scramble range: All
Topic: Deficit financing

35.18
A deficit financed by borrowing
a) reduces the national debt.
b) does not affect the national debt if the funds come from foreign sources.
c) increases the national debt.
d) always increases the money supply.
e) always decreases the money supply.

35.19
Correct: b)
Difficulty: 3
Page(s): 947
Scramble range: All
Topic: Surpluses and the debt

35.19
A budget surplus
a) reduces funds available for private investment.
b) reduces the national debt.
c) is always related to tax cuts.
d) is not related to government spending.
e) makes the economy worse off.

35.20
Correct: d)
Difficulty: 3
Page(s): 947
Scramble range: None
Topic: Deficit and business cycle

35.20
The relationship between the unemployment rate and the deficit is such that
a) a change in the unemployment rate has no impact on the deficit.
b) if the economy enters a recession, the deficit will rise, causing the unemployment rate to rise.
c) if the economy enters a recovery period, the deficit will fall, causing the unemployment rate to fall.
d) they are positively related.
e) both c) and d).

35.21
Correct: d)
Difficulty: 3
Page(s): 949
Scramble range: None
Topic: National debt

35.21
The federal government's recent deficits have been mainly caused by
a) falls in government expenditures.
b) rises in government revenues.
c) falls in government revenues.
d) rises in government expenditures.
e) both c) and d).

35.22
Correct: b)
Difficulty: 3
Page(s): 949
Scramble range: All
Topic: National debt

35.22
During the decade of the 1970s, the deficit caused the debt to
a) double.
b) fall by 50 percent.
c) increase at a moderate rate.
d) increase at the same rate as during the 1980s.
e) stay constant.

35.23
Correct: d)
Difficulty: 3
Page(s): 949
Scramble range: All
Topic: National debt

35.23
Between 1980 and 1985, the debt
a) remained constant.
b) fell substantially.
c) increased at a moderate rate.
d) rose dramatically in value.
e) fluctuated widly in value, but the average stayed constant.

35.24
Correct: e)
Difficulty: 3
Page(s): 949
Scramble range: All
Topic: Federal government's deficit

35.24
Throughout the 1980s, the federal government's budget deficit
a) fell consistently.
b) remained close to 8 percent of GDP.
c) remained constant.
d) finally became a surplus.
e) fluctuated quite a bit, but averaged just over 3 percent of GDP.

35.25
Correct: a)
Difficulty: 3
Page(s): 949
Scramble range: All
Topic: National debt

35.25
Between 1986 and 1989, the debt
a) remained constant.
b) fell substantially.
c) increased at a moderate rate.
d) rose dramatically in value.
e) fluctuated wildly in value, but the average value stayed constant.

35.26
Correct: a)
Difficulty: 3
Page(s): 951
Scramble range: All
Topic: Federal government revenue

35.26
The main categories of federal government revenue are
a) investment income, indirect taxes, and income taxes.
b) investment income, income taxes, and transfers.
c) income taxes, indirect taxes, and transfers.
d) income taxes, indirect taxes, and debt interest.
e) transfers, debt interest, and income taxes.

35.27
Correct: c)
Difficulty: 3
Page(s): 951
Scramble range: All
Topic: Federal government revenue

35.27
The category of federal government revenue that fluctuates the most is
a) investment income.
b) transfers.
c) income taxes.
d) debt interest.
e) indirect taxes.

35.28
Correct: e)
Difficulty: 3
Page(s): 952
Scramble range: All
Topic: Federal government expenditure

35.28
The three main categories of federal government expenditures are
a) investment income, indirect taxes, and income taxes.
b) transfers, government expenditures, and investment income.
c) transfers, investment income, and debt interest.
d) government expenditures, transfers, and farm subsidies.
e) government expenditures, transfers, and debt interest.

35.29
Correct: e)
Difficulty: 3
Page(s): 951
Scramble range: All
Topic: Federal deficit

35.29
The federal deficit rose dramatically in 1975 because
a) the government cut taxes dramatically.
b) the government raised expenditures on defence.
c) interest rates rose dramatically and therefore raised debt interest payments.
d) farm subsides rose dramatically.
e) the government cut energy taxes and increased energy subsidies.

35.30
Correct: a)
Difficulty: 3
Page(s): 952
Scramble range: All
Topic: Change budget balance/recession

35.30
If the government's budget is balanced and then the economy goes into a recession, the budget balance will be
a) negative.
b) positive.
c) the same.
d) hard to determine.
e) positive only if interest rates rise, negative otherwise.

35.31
Correct: b)
Difficulty: 3
Page(s): 952
Scramble range: All
Topic: Change budget balance/expansion

35.31
If the government's budget is balanced and then the economy goes into an expansion, the budget balance will be
a) negative.
b) positive.
c) the same.
d) hard to determine.
e) negative if interest rates rise, and positive otherwise.

35.32
Correct: a)
Difficulty: 3
Page(s): 952
Scramble range: All
Topic: Budget changes

35.32
If the economy goes into an expansion, then the federal government's outlays
a) will automatically fall but receipts will automatically rise.
b) will automatically rise but receipts will automatically fall.
c) and receipts will automatically rise.
d) and receipts will automatically fall.
e) will remain constant but receipts will automatically fall.

35.33
Correct: b)
Difficulty: 3
Page(s): 952
Scramble range: All
Topic: Budget changes

35.33
If the economy goes into a recession, then the federal government's outlays
a) will automatically fall but receipts will automatically rise.
b) will automatically rise but receipts will automatically fall.
c) and receipts will automatically rise.
d) and receipts will automatically fall.
e) will automatically rise but receipts will stay constant.

35.34
Correct: e)
Difficulty: 3
Page(s): 952
Scramble range: None
Topic: Deficits during recession

35.34
If the economy is in an expansion and the federal government is running a deficit, then a recession would automatically
a) decrease the deficit.
b) raise government taxes.
c) raise government expenditures.
d) increase the deficit.
e) both c) and d).

35.35
Correct: c)
Difficulty: 3
Page(s): 952
Scramble range: All
Topic: Deficit during recoveries

35.35
If the economy is in a recession and the federal government is running a deficit, then a recovery would
a) automatically bring the budget into balance.
b) automatically increase the deficit.
c) automatically reduce the deficit.
d) leave the deficit unchanged.
e) increase the deficit only if the rate of interest rose.

35.36
Correct: b)
Difficulty: 3
Page(s): 947
Scramble range: All
Topic: Source of 1980s deficit

35.36
The federal government's budget deficit of the 1980s is due to the
a) decrease in tax revenues relative to a constant spending rate.
b) increase in the government's rate of spending relative to an almost constant rate of tax collection.
c) decrease in tax revenues relative to an increase in the government's spending rate.
d) increase in tax revenues relative to a decrease in the government's spending rate.
e) increase in government spending being higher than the increase in tax revenues.

35.37
Correct: d)
Difficulty: 3
Page(s): 949
Scramble range: All
Topic: Real deficit

35.37
The real deficit or surplus is
a) adjusted for cyclical downturns but not expansions.
b) adjusted for cyclical upturns but not recessions.
c) adjusted for recessions and expansions.
d) the change in the real value of outstanding government debt.
e) the nominal deficit divided by the price level.

35.38
Correct: c)
Difficulty: 3
Page(s): 949
Scramble range: All
Topic: Real deficit

35.38
The government debt outstanding at the end of the current year adjusted for the price level during the year minus the government debt outstanding at the end of the previous year adjusted for the price level in the previous year is known as the
a) government budget deficit/surplus.
b) cyclically adjusted government deficit/surplus.
c) real government deficit/surplus.
d) real debt.
e) nominal debt.

35.39
Correct: d)
Difficulty: 3
Page(s): 949
Scramble range: All
Topic: Real deficit

35.39
The government's real budget deficit is the change in the
a) nominal value of outstanding government debt.
b) nominal value of the deficit.
c) real value of the deficit.
d) real value of outstanding government debt.
e) real value of government expenditures minus the change in the real value of tax revenues.

35.40
Correct: d)
Difficulty: 5
Page(s): 950
Scramble range: All
Topic: Real versus nominal deficit

35.40
If the nominal value of the government's debt increases from year 1 to year 2, then the
a) price level must have risen.
b) amount of goods and services purchased by the government must have risen.
c) real deficit must have increased.
d) nominal budget balance must be negative.
e) real budget balance must be negative.

35.41
Correct: b)
Difficulty: 5
Page(s): 950
Scramble range: None
Topic: Real versus nominal deficit

35.41
If the nominal value of the government's debt increases by 15 percent and the price level increases by 10 percent, then the
a) nominal deficit is negative.
b) real budget balance is negative.
c) real budget balance is positive.
d) real budget balance is either positive or negative.
e) both a) and b).

35.42
Correct: a)
Difficulty: 5
Page(s): 950
Scramble range: All
Topic: Real budget balance

35.42
If the nominal value of the government's debt increases by 10 percent and the price level increases by 10 percent, then the real budget balance is
a) zero.
b) 10 percent.
c) 20 percent.
d) indeterminant.
e) less than zero.

35.43
Correct: d)
Difficulty: 5
Page(s): 950
Scramble range: None
Topic: Real budget surplus

35.43
If the nominal value of the government's debt increases by 10 percent and the price level increases by 11 percent, then
a) the government's total debt will decline.
b) one can say that the government is running a nominal surplus.
c) one can say that the government is running a real deficit.
d) one can say that the government is running a real surplus.
e) both b) and d).

35.44
Correct: e)
Difficulty: 5
Page(s): 950
Scramble range: All
Topic: Deficit versus debt

35.44
If the nominal debt of the government increases by 10 percent and the price level increases by 15 percent, then the
a) real deficit has increased by 5 percent.
b) real deficit has decreased by 5 percent.
c) real deficit may have increased or decreased.
d) nominal deficit must have increased.
e) nominal deficit may have increased or decreased.

35.45
Correct: b)
Difficulty: 5
Page(s): 950
Scramble range: All
Topic: Real budget surplus

35.45
If the nominal debt of the government increases by 10 percent and the price level increases by 15 percent, the
a) current budget balance is positive.
b) current real budget balance is positive.
c) current real budget balance is negative.
d) debt will decrease.
e) debt will stay the same.

35.46
Correct: c)
Difficulty: 3
Page(s): 950
Scramble range: All
Topic: Nominal/real deficit in the 1970s

35.46
The reason that the large nominal deficits of the late 1970s were not real deficits is that the
a) government reduced its rate of spending during that time period.
b) government slowed its increases in the rate of spending at that time.
c) inflation rate was high during those years.
d) inflation rate was low during those years.
e) interest rates were low during those years.

35.47
Correct: c)
Difficulty: 3
Page(s): 950
Scramble range: All
Topic: Real deficit

35.47
Since 1982, the Canadian government has been running a real deficit that has averaged close to
a) 4 percent of GDP.
b) zero, since tax revenues have increased to offset increases in government spending.
c) 3 percent of GDP.
d) 1 percent of GDP.
e) –1 percent of GDP (a real surplus).

35.48
Correct: d)
Difficulty: 3
Page(s): 951
Scramble range: All
Topic: Money financing

35.48
Which one of the following statements is true?
a) When the government runs a deficit, inflation always follows.
b) When the government runs a surplus, deflation always follows.
c) When the government runs a deficit and finances it by selling government bonds to the public, inflation always follows.
d) When the government runs a deficit and finances it by selling government bonds to the Bank of Canada, higher average prices will be the result.
e) When the government runs a surplus, inflation always follows.

35.49
Correct: b)
Difficulty: 2
Page(s): 951
Scramble range: All
Topic: Debt financing

35.49
The financing of the government deficit by selling bonds to any holder other than the Bank of Canada is called
a) money financing.
b) debt financing.
c) inflationary.
d) tax financing.
e) an open market operation.

35.50
Correct: d)
Difficulty: 2
Page(s): 951
Scramble range: All
Topic: Money financing

35.50
The financing of the government deficit by the sale of bonds to the Bank of Canada is called
a) debt financing.
b) tax financing.
c) revenue enhancement.
d) money financing.
e) an open market operation.

35.51
Correct: c)
Difficulty: 3
Page(s): 951
Scramble range: All
Topic: Money financing

35.51
Money financing is said to occur when the
a) federal government finances its debt by selling bonds to the Department of Finance.
b) federal government finances its debt by buying bonds from the Bank of Canada.
c) federal government finances its debt by selling bonds to the Bank of Canada.
d) Bank of Canada sells government bonds to the banking public.
e) federal government finances its debt by selling bonds to the public.

35.52
Correct: b)
Difficulty: 3
Page(s): 951
Scramble range: All
Topic: Debt financing

35.52
Debt financing is said to occur when the federal government finances its debt by
a) selling bonds to the Bank of Canada.
b) selling bonds to the public but not the Bank of Canada.
c) buying bonds from the public.
d) buying bonds from the Bank of Canada directly.
e) selling bonds to the Department of Finance.

35.53
Correct: c)
Difficulty: 3
Page(s): 951
Scramble range: All
Topic: Tax revenue

35.53
Tax revenues are
a) always rising when the tax rate rises.
b) the percentage rate at which a tax is levied.
c) the product of the tax rate and the tax base.
d) the difference between the tax base and the tax rate.
e) the product of the income level and the income tax rate.

35.54
Correct: e)
Difficulty: 3
Page(s): 951
Scramble range: All
Topic: Tax base

35.54
The tax base is
a) the change in tax revenues divided by the change in income earned.
b) the same thing as the tax law.
c) always constant.
d) the level of income.
e) the activity on which a tax is levied.

35.55
Correct: c)
Difficulty: 3
Page(s): 951
Scramble range: None
Topic: Financing the debt

35.55
Which one of the following is not a method used by the federal government to finance its debt?
a) Money financing.
b) Tax financing.
c) Crowding financing.
d) Debt financing.
e) Neither a) nor c).

35.56
Correct: c)
Difficulty: 3
Page(s): 951
Scramble range: All
Topic: Debt financing

35.56
The government can sell bonds
a) at any price it wants to.
b) to the Bank of Canada whenever the prime minister issues an executive order stating that this is the method that must be followed to finance the debt.
c) only if people are convinced that given the price paid the interest payment promised will cover the expected opportunity cost of the purchaser.
d) only if the Bank of Canada will purchase the bonds.
e) only if there is an economic expansion occurring

35.57
Correct: d)
Difficulty: 3
Page(s): 951
Scramble range: All
Topic: Debt financing

35.57
If the going interest rate is 10 percent and the government wishes to engage in debt financing, then the government must offer at least $__________ as return for a $1000 bond.
a) 200
b) 10
c) 1,000
d) 100
e) 110

35.58
Correct: c)
Difficulty: 3
Page(s): 951
Scramble range: All
Topic: Money financing

35.58
If the going interest rate is 10 percent and the government engages in money financing, then the government
a) must offer at least $100 as return for a $1,000 bond.
b) must offer at least $10 as return for a $1,000 bond.
c) does not have to pay any interest if the Bank of Canada does not require that it do so.
d) action does not have any real affect on resource allocation.
e) can pay less than $100 as return on a $100 bond if the Bank of Canada purchases it.

35.59
Correct: a)
Difficulty: 4
Page(s): 951
Scramble range: All
Topic: Mushrooming debt financing

35.59
All else the same, when the government finances the debt through bond sales to the banking public the size of the debt will
a) continually increase.
b) increase at first but will reach a maximum and begin to decline.
c) decrease at first but will reach a minimum and begin to increase.
d) continually decline.
e) remain constant.

35.60
Correct: a)
Difficulty: 3
Page(s): 951
Scramble range: All
Topic: Mushrooming debt financing

35.60
A mushrooming scale of debt and interest payments can occur if the federal government uses
a) debt financing only to pay its bills.
b) money financing only to pay its bills.
c) the foreign exchange market to pay its bills.
d) tax increases to pay its bills.
e) the incorrect mixture of debt and money financing to pay its bills.

35.61
Correct: b)
Difficulty: 2
Page(s): 954
Scramble range: All
Topic: Crowding out

35.61
The tendency for an increase in government purchases of goods and services to bring a decrease in investment is called
a) crowding in.
b) crowding out.
c) debt financing.
d) money financing.
e) countering effects.

35.62
Correct: d)
Difficulty: 2
Page(s): 954
Scramble range: All
Topic: Crowding out

35.62
The crowding-out hypothesis
a) was first present by Wallace and Sargent.
b) has been proven time and again.
c) states that when foreigners buy Canadian government bonds they bid up the price so that Canadians cannot afford them.
d) suggests that when governments borrow in the private market that interest rates will rise and reduce private borrowing.
e) states that money financing will create excess inflation.

35.63
Correct: b)
Difficulty: 3
Page(s): 954
Scramble range: All
Topic: Crowding out

35.63
If crowding out does occur,
a) private investment replaces government investment in the building of roads and factories.
b) the private stock of capital does not accumulate as fast as it otherwise would.
c) the private stock of capital necessarily declines.
d) the government stock of capital necessarily declines.
e) future income levels will be lower than current levels.

35.64
Correct: e)
Difficulty: 3
Page(s): 955
Scramble range: All
Topic: Ricardian equivalence

35.64
The idea that debt financing causes people to save more and consume less today in order to pay for the expected higher taxes tomorrow is the basis for
a) crowding out.
b) the substitution of tax financing for money financing.
c) some unpleasant arithmetic.
d) Wallace neutrality.
e) Ricardian equivalence.

35.65
Correct: a)
Difficulty: 3
Page(s): 954
Scramble range: All
Topic: Crowding out

35.65
Refer to Figure 35.1. If the government engages in debt financing, then the interest rate will be
a) 3.5 percent.
b) 2 percent.
c) 3 percent.
d) 4 percent.
e) greater than 4 percent.

Figure 35.1 The demand curve labelled D_0 represents the private demand for loanable funds in the economy. The demand curve labelled D_1 represents the demand for loanable funds by the private sector plus the government sector of the economy.

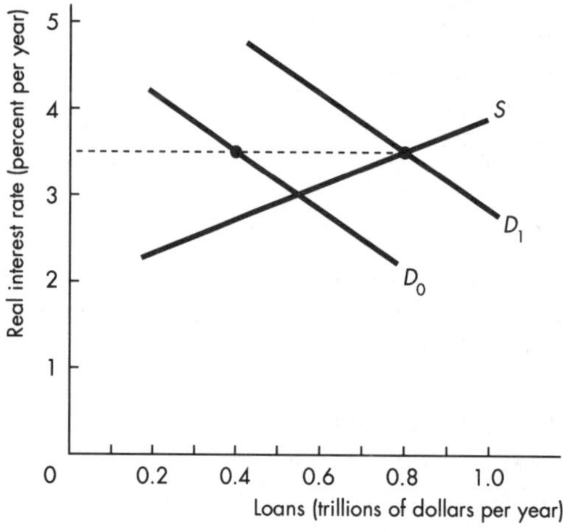

35.66
Correct: a)
Difficulty: 5
Page(s): 954
Scramble range: None
Topic: Crowding out

35.66
Refer to Figure 35.1. If the government engages in debt financing, then the
a) total amount of funds loaned will increase from \$0.55 to \$0.8 trillion.
b) total value of private investment projects in the economy will not be affected.
c) total value of private investment projects in the economy will increase.
d) future capital stock will not be affected by the government borrowing.
e) both a) and b).

35.67
Correct: a)
Difficulty: 2
Page(s): 954
Scramble range: All
Topic: Crowding out

35.67
Refer to Figure 35.1. If the government does not engage in any debt financing, then the real interest rate will be
a) 3 percent.
b) 2 percent.
c) 3.5 percent.
d) 4 percent.
e) greater than 4 percent.

35.68
Correct: e)
Difficulty: 2
Page(s): 954
Scramble range: All
Topic: Crowding out

35.68
Refer to Figure 35.1. If the government does not engage in any debt financing, then the total amount of private financing that will take place per annum will be
a) \$0.4 trillion.
b) \$0.6 trillion.
c) \$0.8 trillion.
d) \$0.7 trillion.
e) \$0.55 trillion.

35.69
Correct: a)
Difficulty: 4
Page(s): 954
Scramble range: All
Topic: Crowding out

35.69
Refer to Figure 35.1. If the government does engage in debt financing, then the total amount of private financing that will take place per annum will be
a) $0.4 trillion.
b) $0.55 trillion.
c) $0.8 trillion.
d) $0.7 trillion.
e) $0.6 trillion.

35.70
Correct: e)
Difficulty: 4
Page(s): 954
Scramble range: All
Topic: Crowding out

35.70
Refer to Figure 35.1. If the government does engage in debt financing, then the amount borrowed by the government is equal to
a) $0.3 trillion.
b) $0.8 trillion.
c) $0.7 trillion.
d) $0.25 trillion.
e) $0.4 trillion.

35.71
Correct: b)
Difficulty: 2
Page(s): 956
Scramble range: All
Topic: Budget deficit

35.71
Which of the following best describes when federal government receipts for a year exceed government outlays?
a) Federal budget deficit.
b) Federal budget surplus.
c) Balanced federal budget.
d) Federal budget debt.
e) Ricardian equivalence.

35.72
Correct: a)
Difficulty: 3
Page(s): 956
Scramble range: All
Topic: Financing the deficit

35.72
Of the ways listed below for financing or eliminating a deficit, which policy is the least expansionary?
a) Tax financing.
b) Debt financing.
c) Money financing.
d) Cyclically financing.
e) Foreign exchange financing.

35.73
Correct: c)
Difficulty: 3
Page(s): 956
Scramble range: All
Topic: Financing the deficit

35.73
Of the ways listed below for financing or eliminating a deficit, which policy is the most expansionary?
a) Tax financing.
b) Debt financing.
c) Money financing.
d) Cyclically financing.
e) Foreign exchange financing.

35.74
Correct: d)
Difficulty: 4
Page(s): 956
Scramble range: a)–d)
Topic: Aggregate demand/money finance

35.74
Money financing results in an aggregate demand curve that
a) lies to the left of the *AD* curve when deficits are financed by taxes.
b) lies to the left of the *AD* curve when deficits are financed by selling government securities to the public.
c) does not shift.
d) lies to the right of the *AD* curve when deficits are financed by selling government securities to the public.
e) none of the above.

35.75
Correct: a)
Difficulty: 4
Page(s): 954
Scramble range: All
Topic: Crowding out

35.75
If debt financing of the deficit results in _________ interest rates and _________ private investment, there is said to be _________

a) higher; less; crowding out.
b) higher; less; money financing.
c) lower; more; crowding in.
d) lower; less; crowding out.
e) higher; less; Ricardian equivalence.

35.76
Correct: b)
Difficulty: 4
Page(s): 950
Scramble range: All
Topic: Real versus actual deficit/losers and winners

35.76
During periods of high inflation and high interest rates, the actual deficit _________ the real deficit, resulting in a gain to _________ at the expense of _________

a) overstates; the government's creditors; the government.
b) overstates; the government; the government's creditors.
c) understates; the government's creditors; the government.
d) understates; the government; the government's creditors.
e) understates; the government; foreign creditors.

35.77
Correct: e)
Difficulty: 2
Page(s): 953
Scramble range: All
Topic: Loanable funds market

35.77
Refer to Table 35.1. The equilibrium interest rate in this private market is

a) 8 percent.
b) 6 percent.
c) 12 percent.
d) 14 percent.
e) 10 percent.

Table 35.1

Quantity demanded* (private)	Quantity supplied*	Real interest rate (percent)
400	1,200	14
600	1,000	12
800	800	10
1,000	600	8
1,200	400	6

*Quantity demanded and supplied of loanable funds in billions of dollars.

35.78
Correct: a)
Difficulty: 2
Page(s): 953
Scramble range: All
Topic: Loanable funds market

35.78
Refer to Table 35.1. The quantity exchange of loanable funds when this market is in equilibrium is

a) $800 billion.
b) $600 billion.
c) $1,000 billion.
d) $1,200 billion.
e) $400 billion.

35.79
Correct: d)
Difficulty: 4
Page(s): 954
Scramble range: All
Topic: Government debt

35.79
Refer to Table 35.1. Suppose the government enters the loanable funds market to borrow $200 billion to finance the deficit. The equilibrium interest rate will be
a) 8 percent.
b) 9 percent.
c) 10 percent.
d) 11 percent.
e) 12 percent.

35.80
Correct: c)
Difficulty: 5
Page(s): 954
Scramble range: All
Topic: Crowding out

35.80
Refer to Table 35.1. Suppose the government enters the loanable funds market to borrow $200 billion to finance the deficit. The amount loaned to private investors will be $__________ billion once this market has reached a new equilibrium.
a) 700
b) 800
c) 900
d) 1,000
e) 1,100

35.81
Correct: b)
Difficulty: 5
Page(s): 955
Scramble range: All
Topic: Ricardian equivalence

35.81
Refer to Table 35.1. Suppose the government enters the loanable funds market to borrow $100 billion to finance the current deficit and at the same time future taxpayers decide to save $100 billion at the going interest rate to pay the future implied taxes of the government policy. The equilibrium interest rate will be
a) 9 percent.
b) 10 percent.
c) 11 percent.
d) 12 percent.
e) 8 percent.

35.82 (SG 35.1)
Correct: e)
Difficulty: 3
Page(s): 944
Scramble range: All
Topic: Government debt

35.82
Suppose the government starts with a debt of $0. Then, in year 1, there is a deficit of $100 billion, in year 2 there is a deficit of $60 billion, in year 3 there is a surplus of $40 billion, and in year 4 there is a deficit of $20 billion. What is government debt at the end of year 4?
a) $20 billion.
b) $140 billion.
c) $180 billion.
d) Somewhat greater than $220 billion, depending on the interest rate.
e) Somewhat greater than $140 billion, depending on the interest rate.

35.83 (SG 35.2)
Correct: d)
Difficulty: 2
Page(s): 944
Scramble range: All
Topic: Budget deficit

35.83
Which of the following would *not* increase the budget deficit?
a) An increase in interest on the government debt.
b) An increase in government purchases of goods and services.
c) An increase in government transfer payments.
d) An increase in indirect business taxes.
e) A decrease in investment income.

35.84
Correct: a)
Difficulty: 5
Page(s): 955
Scramble range: All
Topic: Ricardian equivalence

35.84
Refer to Figure 35.1. If the government is using debt financing to pay for its deficit, and Ricardian equivalence holds, then the rate of interest will be _________ and the amount of loanable funds lent will be _________

a) 3 percent; $0.55 trillion.
b) 3.5 percent; $0.4 trillion.
c) 3.5 percent; $0.8 trillion.
d) 3 percent; $0.4 trillion.
e) 3 percent; $0.95 trillion.

35.85 (SG 35.4)
Correct: b)
Difficulty: 2
Page(s): 952
Scramble range: All
Topic: Budget changes

35.85
During a recession tax revenue

a) declines and government expenditure declines.
b) declines and government expenditure increases.
c) increases and government expenditure declines.
d) increases and government expenditure increases.
e) stays constant and government revenue increases.

35.86 (SG 35.5)
Correct: c)
Difficulty: 3
Page(s): 952
Scramble range: All
Topic: Deficit

35.86
A large deficit is of greater concern if it occurs during a period of

a) recession.
b) increasing inflation.
c) low inflation and sustained economic growth.
d) high unemployment.
e) high government debt.

35.87 (SG 35.6)
Correct: a)
Difficulty: 3
Page(s): 951
Scramble range: All
Topic: Transfer payments/deficit

35.87
What are the main elements of government spending that have increased (relative to GDP) since 1969?

a) Transfer payments and debt interest.
b) Government purchases of goods and services and defence spending.
c) Government purchases of goods and services and debt interest.
d) Government purchases of goods and services and transfer payments.
e) Debt interest alone.

35.88 (SG 35.8)
Correct: a)
Difficulty: 5
Page(s): 949
Scramble range: All
Topic: Real deficit

35.88
According to Table 35.2, what is the real deficit in year 2?

a) $0.
b) $180 billion.
c) $198 billion.
d) $360 billion.
e) $18 billion.

Table 35.2

	Year 1	Year 2
Government debt	$180 billion	$198 billion
Price level	1.0	1.1

35.89 (SG 35.9)
Correct: d)
Difficulty: 4
Page(s): 949
Scramble range: All
Topic: Real deficit

35.89
If, in a given year, government debt increases by 6 percent and the rate of inflation is 10 percent,
a) the real deficit has increased by 4 percent.
b) the real deficit has increased by 6 percent.
c) the real deficit has increased by 10 percent.
d) there is a real surplus.
e) there is a nominal surplus.

35.90 (SG 35.10)
Correct: c)
Difficulty: 2
Page(s): 951
Scramble range: All
Topic: Money financing

35.90
When the deficit is financed by selling bonds to the Bank of Canada, it is called
a) credit financing.
b) debt financing.
c) money financing.
d) reserves financing.
e) bank financing.

35.91 (SG 35.11)
Correct: b)
Difficulty: 3
Page(s): 951
Scramble range: All
Topic: Money financing

35.91
Money financing of a deficit may be preferred by government because
a) the Bank of Canada is willing to pay a higher price for bonds than households and firms.
b) debt financing leaves the government with an ongoing obligation to pay interest.
c) it reduces the prospect of inflation.
d) it disciplines the government to reduce its level of spending.
e) it is easier to sell to the voters.

35.92 (SG 35.12)
Correct: b)
Difficulty: 4
Page(s): 954
Scramble range: All
Topic: Deficit for future generations

35.92
An increase in the deficit will leave future generations with a smaller capital stock if it causes the
a) supply of loans to increase more than the demand for loans.
b) demand for loans to increase more than the supply of loans.
c) demand for loans to increase by the same amount as the supply of loans.
d) supply of loans to increase and the demand for loans to decrease.
e) supply of loans to decrease and the demand for loans to increase.

35.93 (SG 35.13)
Correct: c)
Difficulty: 4
Page(s): 955
Scramble range: All
Topic: Ricardian equivalence

35.93
Ricardian equivalence implies that, for a given level of government spending, as the deficit increases
a) the real rate of interest falls.
b) the real rate of interest rises.
c) saving increases.
d) consumption expenditure increases.
e) investment decreases.

35.94 (SG 35.14)
Correct: e)
Difficulty: 3
Page(s): 956
Scramble range: All
Topic: Reducing the deficit

35.94
Which of the following has *not* been suggested as a method for reducing deficits?
a) De-indexing income tax rates.
b) Privatizing health care.
c) Increasing tax rates.
d) Decreasing tax rates.
e) Using monetary financing.

35.95 (SG 35.15)
Correct: a)
Difficulty: 3
Page(s): 956
Scramble range: None
Topic: Increasing revenue

35.95
A decrease in tax rates
a) can increase tax revenue if the percent increase in the tax base it causes is greater than the percent fall in the tax rate.
b) can increase tax revenue if the percent increase in the tax base it causes is less than the percent fall in the tax rate.
c) cannot increase tax revenue since each activity being taxed will be taxed at a lower rate.
d) cannot increase tax revenue since the tax base will decline as well.
e) both c) and d).

35.96 (SG 35.16)
Correct: e)
Difficulty: 2
Page(s): 957
Scramble range: All
Topic: Laffer curve

35.96
The curve that relates the tax rate and tax revenue is called the
a) tax curve.
b) revenue curve.
c) Ricardian curve.
d) Buchanan curve.
e) Laffer curve.

35.97
Correct: b)
Difficulty: 4
Page(s): 944
Scramble range: All
Topic: Debt versus deficit

35.97
If the government has a $140 billion debt at the beginning of the year and a $160 billion debt at the end of the year, and the price level rises from 100 to 110 over the year, what was the deficit for that year?
a) $0.
b) $20 billion.
c) $40 billion.
d) $300 billion.
e) $4 billion.

35.98
Correct: e)
Difficulty: 5
Page(s): 951
Scramble range: All
Topic: Monetary financing

35.98
Refer to Figure 35.1. Suppose that the government decides to finance its deficit with monetary financing. As a result, the interest rate will be __________ percent and the quantity of loanable funds exchanged will be $__________ trillion.
a) 3.5; 0.4
b) 3.5; 0.8
c) 3; 0.4
d) 3; 0.8
e) 3; 0.55

35.99
Correct: b)
Difficulty: 3
Page(s): 946
Scramble range: All
Topic: Deficit

35.99
Why does the deficit increase in a recession?
a) Tax revenue declines and government expenditure declines.
b) Tax revenue declines and government expenditure increases.
c) Tax revenue increases and government expenditure declines.
d) Tax revenue increases and government expenditure increases.
e) Tax revenue stays constant and government expenditure increases.

35.100
Correct: c)
Difficulty: 3
Page(s): 946
Scramble range: All
Topic: Deficit

35.100
Under which of the following conditions would a deficit be considered normal?
a) A time of low inflation and sustained economic growth.
b) A time of low unemployment.
c) A time of recession.
d) A time of high capacity utilization.
e) A time of expansion.

35.101
Correct: d)
Difficulty: 4
Page(s): 947
Scramble range: All
Topic: Real deficit

35.101
If, in a given year, government debt increases by 5 percent and the rate of inflation is 8 percent, then
a) the real deficit has increased by 3 percent.
b) the real deficit has increased by 5 percent.
c) the real deficit has increased by 8 percent.
d) there is a real surplus.
e) there is a nominal surplus.

35.102
Correct: a)
Difficulty: 2
Page(s): 951
Scramble range: All
Topic: Deficit financing

35.102
A deficit is financed by what is known as "money financing." What method was used?
a) Selling bonds to the Bank of Canada.
b) Raising taxes on money incomes.
c) Borrowing from foreign central banks.
d) Buying bonds from chartered banks.
e) Selling bonds to the public.

35.103
Correct: c)
Difficulty: 4
Page(s): 953
Scramble range: All
Topic: Deficit effects

35.103
An increase in the deficit has caused the demand for loans to increase more than the supply of loans. What will be the effect?
a) Lower interest rates.
b) Higher prices of bonds.
c) A smaller capital stock for future generations.
d) Lower quantity of total loans in the economy.
e) Decreased real GDP.

35.104
Correct: b)
Difficulty: 2
Page(s): 955
Scramble range: All
Topic: Ricardian equivalence

35.104
What name is given to the proposition that real economic variables are unaffected by the choice of deficit financing?
a) Keynes neutrality.
b) Ricardian equivalence.
c) Smith neutrality.
d) Hicks neutrality.
e) Deficit neutrality.

35.105
Correct: a)
Difficulty: 3
Page(s): 957
Scramble range: All
Topic: Laffer curve

35.105
Under what circumstances could a decrease in the tax rate cause an increase in tax revenues?
a) If the percentage increase in the tax base were larger than the percentage decrease in the tax rate.
b) If the percentage increase in the tax base were smaller than the percentage decrease in the tax rate.
c) If the tax base remained constant after the decrease in the tax rate.
d) Under no circumstances; a decrease in the tax rate cannot cause an increase in tax revenues.
e) If the resulting deficit was money financed.

35.106
Correct: d)
Difficulty: 2
Page(s): 957
Scramble range: All
Topic: Laffer curve

35.106
What two variables does the Laffer curve relate?
a) Inflation and unemployment.
b) Real GDP and the price level.
c) Tax revenue and real GDP.
d) Tax rate and tax revenue.
e) Tax rate and the deficit.

35.107
Correct: e)
Difficulty: 4
Page(s): 951
Scramble range: All
Topic: Money financing

35.107
Refer to Table 35.1. Suppose the government has a $100 billion deficit, that it decides to finance by monetary financing. As a result, the real interest rate will be _____ percent, and the quantity of loanable funds exchanged will be $__________ billion.
a) 6; 1,200
b) 9; 900
c) 12; 1,000
d) 11; 900
e) 10; 800

35.108
Correct: e)
Difficulty: 5
Page(s): 955
Scramble range: All
Topic: Ricardian equivalence

35.108
Refer to Table 35.1. Suppose that the government has a $100 billion deficit, which it finances by debt financing. In addition, suppose that Ricardian equivalence holds true. As a result, the real rate of interest will be _____ percent and the quantity of loanable funds exchanged will be $__________.
a) 9; 900
b) 11; 1,100
c) 12; 1,000
d) 8; 700
e) 10; 800

35.109
Correct: e)
Difficulty: 3
Page(s): 952
Scramble range: All
Topic: Unpleasant arithmetic

35.109
Sargent and Wallace's "unpleasant monetarist arithmetic" showed that
a) money financing causes inflation.
b) the quantity theory of money is true.
c) how government expenditure is financed is irrelevant, it is only the size of the expenditure that matters.
d) deficit financing will drive up the interest rate and crowd out private investment.
e) persistent deficits financed by borrowing can still cause inflationary problems.

Chapter 36 Trading with the World

36.1
Correct: e)
Difficulty: 2
Page(s): 969
Scramble range: All
Topic: Canadian trade

36.1
The largest component of Canadian exports and imports is
a) agricultural products.
b) raw materials.
c) manufactured goods.
d) services.
e) motor vehicles.

36.2
Correct: c)
Difficulty: 2
Page(s): 971
Scramble range: All
Topic: Balance of trade

36.2
The balance of trade is the
a) volume of trade minus the value of trade.
b) volume of exports minus the volume of imports.
c) value of exports minus the value of imports.
d) total of Canadian trade minus the total trade of the rest of the world.
e) price of exports minus the price of imports.

36.3
Correct: b)
Difficulty: 3
Page(s): 970
Scramble range: All
Topic: Canadian trade

36.3
Canada is a net
a) exporter of manufactured goods.
b) importer of manufactured goods.
c) importer of agricultural products.
d) importer of oil.
e) exporter of travel services.

36.4
Correct: c)
Difficulty: 2
Page(s): 969–970
Scramble range: All
Topic: Imports of services

36.4
An example of an import of a service is
a) a foreign newspaper.
b) an automobile.
c) a flight on a foreign airline.
d) a book written by a foreign author.
e) a flight to Europe on Air Canada.

36.5
Correct: b)
Difficulty: 2
Page(s): 969–970
Scramble range: All
Topic: Export of services

36.5
An example of an export of a service is a
a) domestic newspaper.
b) visit to Canada by a foreigner.
c) bushel of wheat.
d) De Haviland Dash-8 aircraft.
e) flight on a foreign airline.

36.6
Correct: b)
Difficulty: 2
Page(s): 971
Scramble range: All
Topic: Leading trade partner

36.6
The leading trade partner of Canada, as measured by total trade, is
a) Japan.
b) the United States.
c) Mexico.
d) England.
e) the Soviet Union.

36.7
Correct: e)
Difficulty: 3
Page(s): 971–972
Scramble range: All
Topic: Trade balance

36.7
Since 1978, Canada has maintained
a) a trade balance of zero on average.
b) a trade deficit every single year.
c) first a trade deficit, then a trade surplus.
d) first a trade surplus, then a trade deficit.
e) a trade surplus every single year.

36.8
Correct: a)
Difficulty: 2
Page(s): 969
Scramble range: All
Topic: Canadian trade

36.8
One of the sectors of the Canadian economy that has been hurt recently by imports is the __________ sector.
a) automobile
b) food
c) services
d) sports
e) lumber and newsprint

36.9
Correct: e)
Difficulty: 2
Page(s): 969
Scramble range: All
Topic: National Policy

36.9
Canada's National Policy on tariffs was introduced in
a) 1988.
b) the last years of World War II.
c) 1867.
d) 1933.
e) 1879.

36.10
Correct: e)
Difficulty: 2
Page(s): 971
Scramble range: All
Topic: Magnitude of fuel imports

36.10
Imports of fuel
a) decreased in the 1970s and decreased in the 1980s.
b) increased in the 1970s and decreased in the 1980s.
c) increased in the 1970s and increased in the 1980s.
d) decreased in the 1970s and increased in the 1980s.
e) increased in the mid-1970s and turned into net exports in the 1980s.

36.11
Correct: d)
Difficulty: 4
Page(s): 969–970
Scramble range: All
Topic: Canadian trade

36.11
Canada has a trade __________ with the United States, a trade __________ with the European Community, and a trade __________ with Japan.
a) surplus; surplus; deficit
b) deficit; surplus; deficit
c) deficit; deficit; balance
d) surplus; deficit; balance
e) surplus; balance; deficit

36.12
Correct: e)
Difficulty: 2
Page(s): 969
Scramble range: All
Topic: Canadian trade

36.12
In the late 1980s, Canada has had its largest trade deficit with
a) the United States.
b) Japan.
c) West Germany.
d) England.
e) the European Community.

36.13
Correct: d)
Difficulty: 2
Page(s): 972
Scramble range: All
Topic: Opportunity cost

36.13
Opportunity cost can be measured by the
a) marginal cost of production.
b) average cost of production.
c) total cost of production.
d) slope of the production possibilities frontier.
e) slope of the international demand curve.

36.14
Correct: c)
Difficulty: 4
Page(s): 972–973
Scramble range: All
Topic: Opportunity cost

36.14
Refer to Table 36.1. In the home country the opportunity cost of producing each unit of wheat is
a) zero.
b) 25 units of cloth.
c) 2.5 units of cloth.
d) 0.4 units of cloth.
e) 0.75 units of cloth.

Table 36.1 Production possibilities

	Output		
Country	Wheat		Cloth
Home	100	or	250
Foreign	200	or	150

36.15
Correct: d)
Difficulty: 4
Page(s): 972–973
Scramble range: All
Topic: Opportunity cost

36.15
Refer to Table 36.1. In the foreign country the opportunity cost of producing each unit of wheat is
a) zero.
b) 15 units of cloth.
c) 1.5 units of cloth.
d) 0.75 units of cloth.
e) 2.5 units of cloth.

36.16
Correct: b)
Difficulty: 4
Page(s): 972
Scramble range: All
Topic: Comparative advantage

36.16
Refer to Table 36.1. Which country has the comparative advantage in the production of wheat?
a) The home country.
b) The foreign country.
c) Both countries.
d) Neither country.
e) It could be either country; it depends on the price of wheat.

36.17
Correct: d)
Difficulty: 4
Page(s): 972
Scramble range: All
Topic: Opportunity cost

36.17
Refer to Table 36.1. In the home country the opportunity cost of producing each unit of cloth is
a) zero.
b) 10 units of wheat.
c) 1 unit of wheat.
d) 0.4 units of wheat.
e) 2.5 units of wheat.

36.18
Correct: b)
Difficulty: 4
Page(s): 972
Scramble range: All
Topic: Opportunity cost

36.18
Refer to Table 36.1. In the foreign country the opportunity cost of producing each unit of cloth is
a) zero.
b) 1.33 units of wheat.
c) 13.33 units of wheat.
d) 200 units of wheat.
e) 0.75 units of wheat.

36.19
Correct: a)
Difficulty: 4
Page(s): 973
Scramble range: All
Topic: Comparative advantage

36.19
Refer to Table 36.1. Which country has the comparative advantage in the production of cloth?
a) The home country.
b) The foreign country.
c) Both countries.
d) Neither country.
e) It could be either country; it depends on the price of cloth.

36.20
Correct: b)
Difficulty: 3
Page(s): 973
Scramble range: All
Topic: Comparative advantage

36.20
Refer to Table 36.1. If trade is permitted between the home country and the foreign country at zero transportation costs, which country would export wheat?
a) The home country.
b) The foreign country.
c) Both countries.
d) Neither country.
e) It could be either country; it depends on the price of wheat.

36.21
Correct: a)
Difficulty: 4
Page(s): 973
Scramble range: All
Topic: Comparative advantage

36.21
Refer to Table 36.1. If trade is permitted between the home country and the foreign country at zero transportation costs, which country would export cloth?
a) The home country.
b) The foreign country.
c) Both countries.
d) Neither country.
e) It could be either country; it depends on the price of cloth.

36.22
Correct: c)
Difficulty: 5
Page(s): 973
Scramble range: All
Topic: Relative prices and opportunity costs

36.22
Refer to Table 36.1. What range of relative prices would make both countries better off by trading?
a) Each 1 unit of wheat would sell for between 0.1 and 0.5 units of cloth.
b) Each 1 unit of wheat would sell for between 0.5 and 1.0 units of cloth.
c) Each 1 unit of wheat would sell for between 0.75 and 2.5 units of cloth.
d) Each 1 unit of wheat would sell for between 2.5 and 5.0 units of cloth.
e) Each 1 unit of wheat would sell for between 5.0 and 7.5 units of cloth.

36.23
Correct: a)
Difficulty: 4
Page(s): 974
Scramble range: All
Topic: Relative prices and trade gains

36.23
Refer to Table 36.1. Any trade that will make both countries better off must take place at a relative price of wheat, which is
a) lower than the relative price in the home country.
b) higher than the relative price in the home country.
c) lower than the relative price in the foreign country.
d) equal to the relative price in the foreign country.
e) equal to the relative price in the home country.

36.24
Correct: b)
Difficulty: 4
Page(s): 975
Scramble range: All
Topic: Production changes due to trade

36.24
Refer to Table 36.1. What are the changes in production that would accompany mutually beneficial trade between the two countries?
a) Wheat production would increase in the home country.
b) Wheat production would decrease in the home country.
c) There would be no change in wheat production in the home country.
d) Wheat production would decrease in the foreign country.
e) It would depend on the price of wheat.

36.25
Correct: b)
Difficulty: 4
Page(s): 975
Scramble range: All
Topic: Production changes due to trade

36.25
Refer to Table 36.1. What are the changes in production that would accompany mutually beneficial trade between the two countries?
a) Cloth production would increase in the foreign country.
b) Cloth production would decrease in the foreign country.
c) There would be no change in cloth production in either country.
d) Cloth production would decrease in the home country.
e) It depends on the price of cloth.

36.26
Correct: d)
Difficulty: 3
Page(s): 973
Scramble range: All
Topic: Comparative advantage

36.26
Comparative advantage means that one country can produce
a) more of one product than can another country.
b) one product at lower marginal cost than can the other country.
c) one product at lower long-run average total cost than can another country.
d) one product at lower opportunity cost than can another country.
e) more of one product than of another product.

36.27
Correct: c)
Difficulty: 4
Page(s): 971
Scramble range: All
Topic: Opportunity cost

36.27
Refer to Table 36.2. In the home country the opportunity cost of producing each unit of wheat is
a) zero.
b) 25 units of cloth.
c) 5 units of cloth.
d) 0.5 units of cloth.
e) 0.2 units of cloth.

Table 36.2 Production possibilities

	Output		
Country	Wheat		Cloth
Home	1,000	or	5,000
Foreign	200	or	2,000

36.28
Correct: c)
Difficulty: 4
Page(s): 972
Scramble range: All
Topic: Opportunity cost

36.28
Refer to Table 36.2. In the foreign country the opportunity cost of producing each unit of wheat is
a) zero.
b) 14 units of cloth.
c) 10 units of cloth.
d) 0.4 units of cloth.
e) 0.1 units of cloth.

36.29
Correct: a)
Difficulty: 4
Page(s): 974
Scramble range: All
Topic: Comparative advantage

36.29
Refer to Table 36.2. Which country has the comparative advantage in the production of wheat?
a) The home country.
b) The foreign country.
c) Both countries.
d) Neither country.
e) It could be either country; it depends on the price of wheat.

36.30
Correct: c)
Difficulty: 4
Page(s): 973
Scramble range: All
Topic: Opportunity cost

36.30
Refer to Table 36.2. In the home country the opportunity cost of producing each unit of cloth is
a) zero.
b) 0.1 units of wheat.
c) 0.2 units of wheat.
d) 0.4 units of wheat.
e) 5 units of wheat.

36.31
Correct: c)
Difficulty: 4
Page(s): 969
Scramble range: All
Topic: Opportunity cost

36.31
Refer to Table 36.2. In the foreign country the opportunity cost of producing each unit of cloth is
a) zero.
b) 1.25 units of wheat.
c) 0.1 units of wheat.
d) 500 units of wheat..
e) 10 units of wheat.

36.32
Correct: b)
Difficulty: 4
Page(s): 974
Scramble range: All
Topic: Comparative advantage

36.32
Refer to Table 36.2. Which country has the comparative advantage in the production of cloth?
a) The home country.
b) The foreign country.
c) Both countries.
d) Neither country.
e) It could be either country; it depends on the price of cloth.

36.33
Correct: a)
Difficulty: 4
Page(s): 974
Scramble range: All
Topic: Comparative advantage

36.33
Refer to Table 36.2. If trade is permitted between the home country and the foreign country at zero transportation costs, which country would export wheat?
a) The home country.
b) The foreign country.
c) Both countries.
d) Neither country.
e) It could be either country; it depends on the price of wheat.

36.34
Correct: b)
Difficulty: 4
Page(s): 974
Scramble range: All
Topic: Comparative advantage

36.34
Refer to Table 36.2. If trade is permitted between the home country and the foreign country at zero transportation costs, which country would export cloth?
a) The home country.
b) The foreign country.
c) Both countries.
d) Neither country.
e) It could be either country; it depends on the price of cloth.

36.35
Correct: e)
Difficulty: 5
Page(s): 973
Scramble range: All
Topic: Relative prices and opportunity costs

36.35
Refer to Table 36.2. What range of relative prices would make both countries better off by trading?
a) Each 1 unit of wheat would sell for between 0.1 and 0.5 units of cloth.
b) Each 1 unit of wheat would sell for between 0.4 and 0.5 units of cloth.
c) Each 1 unit of wheat would sell for between 0.5 and 4 units of cloth.
d) Each 1 unit of wheat would sell for between 4 and 5 units of cloth.
e) Each 1 unit of wheat would sell for between 5 and 10 units of cloth.

36.36
Correct: b)
Difficulty: 5
Page(s): 973
Scramble range: All
Topic: Relative prices and trade gains

36.36
Refer to Table 36.2. Any trade that will make both countries better off must take place at a relative price of wheat, which is
a) lower than the relative price in the home country.
b) higher than the relative price in the home country.
c) higher than the relative price in the foreign country.
d) equal to the relative price in the foreign country.
e) equal to the relative price in the home country.

36.37
Correct: a)
Difficulty: 4
Page(s): 975
Scramble range: All
Topic: Production changes due to trade

36.37
Refer to Table 36.2. What are the changes in production that would accompany mutually beneficial trade between the two countries?
a) Wheat production would increase in the home country.
b) Wheat production would decrease in the home country.
c) There would be no change in wheat production in the home country.
d) There would be no change in wheat production in the foreign country.
e) Wheat production would increase in both countries.

36.38
Correct: a)
Difficulty: 4
Page(s): 975
Scramble range: All
Topic: Production changes due to trade

36.38
Refer to Table 36.2. What are the changes in production that would accompany mutually beneficial trade between the two countries?
a) Cloth production would increase in the foreign country.
b) Cloth production would decrease in the foreign country.
c) There would be no change in cloth production in either country.
d) There would be a decrease in cloth production in both countries.
e) There would be an increase in cloth production in both countries.

36.39
Correct: e)
Difficulty: 3
Page(s): 973
Scramble range: All
Topic: Gains from trade

36.39
"Gains from trade" means that
a) both countries have eliminated their economic problem.
b) one country gains what another country loses.
c) both countries gain by expanding their production possibility frontier.
d) both countries see the prices going down for both goods.
e) both countries gain by consuming beyond their production possibility frontier.

36.40
Correct: d)
Difficulty: 3
Page(s): 977
Scramble range: All
Topic: Absolute advantage

36.40
"Absolute advantage" means
a) the same thing as comparative advantage.
b) one country has a lower opportunity cost of producing one product than another.
c) one country requires less money to produce one product than another.
d) one country requires fewer units of the input to produce each unit of output compared to the other country.
e) that producers will specialize in the production of that product.

36.41
Correct: a)
Difficulty: 4
Page(s): 977
Scramble range: All
Topic: Absolute advantage

36.41
Refer to Table 36.3. Which country has the absolute advantage in the production of food?
a) The home country.
b) The foreign country.
c) Neither country.
d) Both countries.
e) It could be either country; it depends on the price of food.

Table 36.3

Country	Units of labour per unit of food output	Units of labour per unit of cloth output
Home	2	6
Foreign	6	8

36.42
Correct: a)
Difficulty: 4
Page(s): 977
Scramble range: All
Topic: Absolute advantage

36.42
Refer to Table 36.3. Which country has the absolute advantage in the production of cloth?
a) The home country.
b) The foreign country.
c) Neither country.
d) Both countries.
e) It could be either country; it depends on the price of cloth.

36.43
Correct: a)
Difficulty: 4
Page(s): 977
Scramble range: All
Topic: Absolute advantage

36.43
Refer to Table 36.3. Which country has the comparative advantage in the production of food?
a) The home country.
b) The foreign country.
c) Neither country.
d) Both countries.
e) It could be either country; it depends on the price of food.

36.44
Correct: b)
Difficulty: 4
Page(s): 977
Scramble range: All
Topic: Absolute advantage

36.44
Refer to Table 36.3. Which country has the comparative advantage in the production of cloth?
a) The home country.
b) The foreign country.
c) Neither country.
d) Both countries.
e) It could be either country; it depends on the price of cloth.

36.45
Correct: a)
Difficulty: 3
Page(s): 974–977
Scramble range: All
Topic: Gains from trade

36.45
Refer to Table 36.3. Does the home country potentially have anything to gain by trading with the foreign country?
a) Yes.
b) No.
c) To answer this, more information is needed concerning the wage rates of the labour in the two countries.
d) To answer this, more information is needed concerning the costs of production in the two countries.
e) To answer this, more information is needed on the size of the labour force in each country.

36.46
Correct: b)
Difficulty: 3
Page(s): 974–977
Scramble range: All
Topic: Gains from trade

36.46
Refer to Table 36.3. In order for the home country to gain from trade, which product must it import from the foreign country?
a) Food.
b) Cloth.
c) Neither product.
d) Either product.
e) Both products.

36.47
Correct: c)
Difficulty: 5
Page(s): 974–977
Scramble range: All
Topic: Trade gains and relative prices

36.47
Refer to Table 36.3. Within what range must the terms of trade lie in order for both countries to gain from trade?
a) 1 unit of cloth must trade for between 0.33 and 1.00 units of food.
b) 1 unit of cloth must trade for between 1.00 and 1.33 units of food.
c) 1 unit of cloth must trade for between 1.33 and 3.00 units of food.
d) 1 unit of cloth must trade for between 3.00 and 6.00 units of food.
e) 1 unit of cloth must trade for between 6.00 and 8.00 units of food.

36.48
Correct: d)
Difficulty: 5
Page(s): 974–977
Scramble range: All
Topic: Trade gains and relative prices

36.48
Refer to Table 36.3. Within what range must the terms of trade lie in order for both countries to gain from trade?
a) 1 unit of food must trade for between 1.33 and 3.00 units of cloth.
b) 1 unit of food must trade for between 0.75 and 1.00 units of cloth.
c) 1 unit of food must trade for between 1.00 and 1.33 units of cloth.
d) 1 unit of food must trade for between 0.33 and 0.75 units of cloth.
e) 1 unit of food must trade for between 2 and 6 units of cloth.

36.49
Correct: b)
Difficulty: 3
Page(s): 977
Scramble range: All
Topic: Comparative advantage

36.49
Whenever opportunity costs diverge
a) one country must have an absolute advantage in the production of both products.
b) each country must have a comparative advantage in some product.
c) one country may have a comparative advantage in both products.
d) one country cannot have an absolute advantage in both products.
e) one country can have a comparative advantage in neither product.

36.50
Correct: e)
Difficulty: 4
Page(s): 978
Scramble range: All
Topic: Trade/diversity of tastes

36.50
Canada exports and imports cars. This is so because
a) Canada has a comparative advantage and a comparative disadvantage in the production of cars.
b) Canada has an absolute advantage and an absolute disadvantage in the production of cars.
c) comparative advantage does not hold for cars, since they have such high economies of scale.
d) Canadian car exports are heavily subsidized by the government.
e) a diversity of taste allows for other countries to demand Canadian cars while Canadian consumers demand foreign cars.

36.51
Correct: d)
Difficulty: 3
Page(s): 978
Scramble range: All
Topic: Trade in similar manufactured goods

36.51
Trade in similar, but not identical, manufactured products is made possible by
a) increasing opportunity costs in Canada.
b) taste similarities between countries.
c) diseconomies of scale in the production of these goods.
d) economies of scale in the production of these goods.
e) tariffs and quotas on imports.

36.52
Correct: c)
Difficulty: 3
Page(s): 978
Scramble range: All
Topic: Adjacent trade-induced job loss

36.52
Groups that are employed in industries that have lost their comparative advantage
a) do not lose from trade, even in the short run.
b) do not lose from trade in the long run or the short run.
c) may lose from trade if the adjustment costs of relocating in a new job are quite high.
d) are typically ignored by the political process.
e) will do well if transportation costs are low enough.

36.53
Correct: c)
Difficulty: 2
Page(s): 979
Scramble range: All
Topic: Protectionism

36.53
The restriction of international trade is called
a) Canadianism.
b) rationalism.
c) protectionism.
d) patriotism.
e) nationalism.

36.54
Correct: b)
Difficulty: 2
Page(s): 980
Scramble range: All
Topic: Tariffs

36.54
A tariff is a
a) tax on an exported good or service.
b) tax on an imported good or service.
c) subsidy on an exported good.
d) subsidy on an imported good.
e) restriction on the quantity of imported goods.

36.55
Correct: a)
Difficulty: 2
Page(s): 980
Scramble range: All
Topic: Nontariff barriers

36.55
A nontariff barrier is
a) a nontax barrier of any sort that limits the importation of goods and services.
b) a nontax barrier of any sort that limits the exportation of goods and services.
c) an amount of money paid in penalty for the privilege of buying an import.
d) a licence fee that must be paid to get an export licence in Canada.
e) a restriction on the quantity of imported goods.

36.56
Correct: d)
Difficulty: 3
Page(s): 980
Scramble range: All
Topic: Nontariff barriers

36.56
Examples of non-tariff barriers include all of the following *except*
a) "Voluntary" quotas on imported Japanese automobiles.
b) An "orderly marketing agreement" that places a quota on T-shirts imported from Hong Kong.
c) The "voluntary restraint agreement" that limits imports of steel into the United States.
d) A $0.50 per pack tax on imported cigarettes.
e) Safety inspections on cars imported into Japan.

36.57
Correct: c)
Difficulty: 3
Page(s): 980
Scramble range: All
Topic: Average tariff rate in Canada

36.57
The average tariff level in Canada in the 1980s is
a) about the same as it has always been.
b) much above what it had been in the past century.
c) positive, but much below what it had been in the past century.
d) zero, as there are no longer any tariffs in Canada.
e) one of the highest in the world.

36.58
Correct: e)
Difficulty: 3
Page(s): 980
Scramble range: All
Topic: Average Canadian tariffs

36.58
During the Great Depression years in the 1930s, the average tariff rate in Canada was about
a) 0.
b) 6 percent.
c) 30 percent.
d) 60 percent.
e) 15 percent.

36.59
Correct: d)
Difficulty: 3
Page(s): 981
Scramble range: All
Topic: High tariff protection

36.59
The sector that has the highest tariff protection in the 1980s is
a) automobiles.
b) steel.
c) semiconductors.
d) textiles and footwear.
e) jewellery.

36.60
Correct: e)
Difficulty: 3
Page(s): 981–983
Scramble range: All
Topic: Tariffs

36.60
Tariffs
a) earn revenue for consumers.
b) earn revenue for the producer.
c) encourage consumers to buy more imports.
d) encourage consumers to produce more for export.
e) earn revenue for the government.

36.61
Correct: d)
Difficulty: 3
Page(s): 981
Scramble range: All
Topic: Tariffs

36.61
Tariffs
a) turn all producers against government officials.
b) turn no consumers against the government.
c) enable government to please consumers.
d) enable government to please special interest groups.
e) enable government to please importers.

36.62
Correct: d)
Difficulty: 2
Page(s): 981
Scramble range: All
Topic: GATT

36.62
The multilateral trade agreement signed following World War II is called the
a) International Trade Organization.
b) League of Nation Traders.
c) North Atlantic Trade Association.
d) General Agreement on Tariffs and Trade.
e) Free Trade Agreement.

36.63
Correct: c)
Difficulty: 3
Page(s): 981
Scramble range: All
Topic: GATT

36.63
One goal of the GATT was to
a) maximize the tariff revenue earned by governments.
b) maximize the profit to producers by imposing quotas on manufactured goods.
c) reduce tariff barriers to trade.
d) encourage bilateral trade agreements between pairs of countries.
e) raise Canada's share of world trade.

36.64
Correct: c)
Difficulty: 3
Page(s): 981
Scramble range: All
Topic: GATT

36.64
One goal of the GATT was to
a) maximize the revenue earned by governments through the imposition of quotas.
b) maximize the profit to producers by imposing tariffs on manufactured goods.
c) provide an organization to administer freer trade relations among nations.
d) encourage bilateral trade agreements between pairs of countries.
e) raise the U.S. share of world trade.

36.65
Correct: e)
Difficulty: 3
Page(s): 981
Scramble range: All
Topic: GATT

36.65
The two "rounds" of GATT negotiations that resulted in substantial tariff reductions were the
a) Eisenhower Round and the Johnson Round.
b) Kennedy Round and the Nixon Round.
c) Kennedy Round and the Uruguay Round.
d) Nixon Round and the Uruguay Round.
e) Kennedy Round and the Tokyo Round.

36.66
Correct: a)
Difficulty: 3
Page(s): 981
Scramble range: All
Topic: Uruguay Round goals

36.66
The GATT Round to be completed in the 1990s has as its goal a reduction in barriers to trade in
a) services and agricultural goods.
b) automobiles and steel.
c) manufactured products and human resources.
d) compact discs and high-definition television.
e) automobiles and textiles.

36.67
Correct: c)
Difficulty: 3
Page(s): 980–981
Scramble range: All
Topic: Canada–U.S. Free Trade Agreement

36.67
The Canada–United States Free Trade Agreement that became effective on January 1, 1989
a) stiffened protection for U.S. breweries against competition from Canadian beer brewers.
b) lowered the subsidies U.S. lumber producers were receiving from the Canadian government.
c) provided for a gradual reduction of tariffs over a ten-year period.
d) eliminated the trade agreement on autos signed in 1965.
e) raised tariffs against third countries.

36.68
Correct: e)
Difficulty: 3
Page(s): 981
Scramble range: All
Topic: Europe 1992

36.68
Within Western Europe,
a) tariffs are to be doubled gradually over a ten-year period.
b) all tariffs are to be eliminated by 1992.
c) quotas are to be stiffened on trade with the United States by the year 1992.
d) quotas are to be stiffened on trade with Japan by the year 1992.
e) tariffs are to be eliminated within the EC by 1992.

36.69
Correct: d)
Difficulty: 3
Page(s): 978–979
Scramble range: All
Topic: Free trade in automobiles

36.69
Refer to Figure 36.1. With free trade between Canada and Japan in automobiles,
a) Canada will export 4 million autos to Japan per year.
b) Japan will export 4 million autos to Canada per year.
c) Canada will export 5 million autos to Japan per year.
d) Japan will export 5 million autos to Canada per year.
e) Japan will export 1 million autos to Canada per year.

Figure 36.1

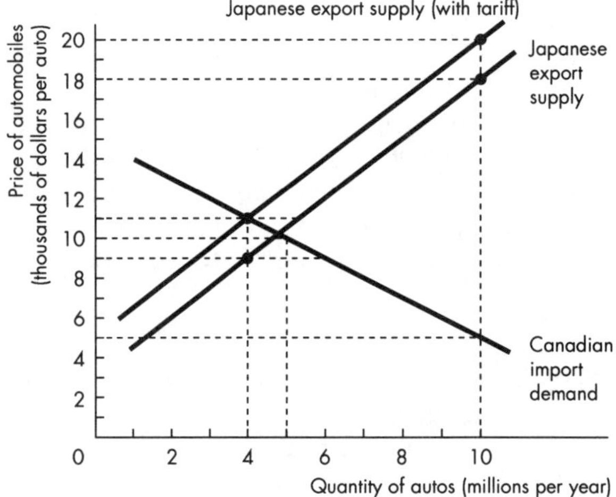

36.70
Correct: c)
Difficulty: 3
Page(s): 981
Scramble range: All
Topic: Import prices/Japanese cars

36.70
Refer to Figure 36.1. With free trade in automobiles, the price of an imported car will be
a) $5,000.
b) $9,000.
c) $10,000.
d) $11,000.
e) $18,000.

36.71
Correct: b)
Difficulty: 4
Page(s): 980–983
Scramble range: All
Topic: Tariffs

36.71
Refer to Figure 36.1. Now suppose that the Canadian government imposes a tariff on imported Japanese cars equal to $2,000 per automobile. The price of imported automobiles to Canadian consumers will increase to
a) $12,000.
b) $11,000.
c) $10,000.
d) $9,000.
e) $20,000.

36.72
Correct: b)
Difficulty: 4
Page(s): 981–986
Scramble range: All
Topic: Tariffs

36.72
Refer to Figure 36.1. Now suppose that the Canadian government imposes a tariff on imported Japanese cars equal to $2,000 per automobile. Imports of Japanese automobiles by Canadian consumers will decrease by
a) zero, as the tariff will have no effect.
b) 1 million automobiles.
c) 2 million automobiles.
d) 3 million automobiles.
e) 5 million automobiles, as the market will disappear.

36.73
Correct: e)
Difficulty: 4
Page(s): 982
Scramble range: All
Topic: Tariffs

36.73
Refer to Figure 36.1. Now suppose that the Canadian government imposes a tariff on imported Japanese cars equal to $2,000 per automobile. The total tariff revenue collected by the Canadian government is equal to
a) zero, as no more automobiles will be imported.
b) $8,000,000.
c) $10,000,000,000.
d) $6,000,000,000.
e) $8,000,000,000.

36.74
Correct: b)
Difficulty: 2
Page(s): 983, 986
Scramble range: All
Topic: Import quotas

36.74
Import quotas
a) are the same as import tariffs.
b) are limits to the number of units that can be imported.
c) were used often in the last century, but are not used in this century by Canada.
d) are limits to the value of the imported goods allowed into Canada.
e) are agreements between countries to limit the volume of imports.

36.75
Correct: d)
Difficulty: 3
Page(s): 983, 986
Scramble range: All
Topic: Voluntary export restraints

36.75
A voluntary export restraint is
a) the same as a quota since imports are restricted.
b) the same as a tariff.
c) not the same as a tariff since a tariff is not mandatory.
d) not the same as a quotas since a VER is imposed by the foreign government on its own exports.
e) not the same as a tariff, but has the same impact on the importing country.

36.76
Correct: e)
Difficulty: 3
Page(s): 986
Scramble range: All
Topic: Multifibre Arrangement

36.76
The Multifibre Arrangement is a comprehensive system of
a) tariffs on imported footwear of all materials.
b) tariffs on imported only on cloth shoes.
c) product regulations on imported textiles composed of many natural and manmade materials.
d) tariffs on imported textiles composed of many natural and manmade materials.
e) quotas on imported textiles composed of many natural and manmade materials.

36.77
Correct: e)
Difficulty: 2
Page(s): 983, 986
Scramble range: All
Topic: Product standards regulations

36.77
Product standards regulations are
a) a tax on imports to pay for inspecting their safety.
b) a restriction on the number of unsafe imports.
c) a voluntary agreement by the exporter to meet the product standards.
d) minimum amounts of imports that will be inspected before they leave the exporting nation.
e) legally defined standards of product design and quality.

36.78
Correct: d)
Difficulty: 4
Page(s): 987
Scramble range: All
Topic: Tariffs

36.78
The key difference between a tariff and a quota is that the
a) consumer gets hurt with quotas, but not with tariffs.
b) consumer gets hurt with tariffs, but not with quotas.
c) government gets the added revenue under a system of quotas, but the industry receives the added revenue under a system of tariffs.
d) government gets the added revenue under a system of tariffs, but the industry receives the added revenue under a system of quotas.
e) quotas are illegal internationally.

36.79
Correct: a)
Difficulty: 3
Page(s): 983
Scramble range: All
Topic: Nontariff barriers

36.79
The three types of nontariff barriers are
a) quotas, VERs, and product standards regulations.
b) countervailing duties, quotas, and VERs.
c) quotas, taxes, and VERs.
d) product standards regulations, quotas, and taxes.
e) countervailing duties, VERs, and taxes.

36.80 (SG 36.1)
Correct: d)
Difficulty: 3
Page(s): 969–971
Scramble range: All
Topic: Canadian trade

36.80
Canada is a net
a) exporter of manufactured goods and net importer of crude petroleum.
b) exporter of manufactured goods and net exporter of agricultural products.
c) importer of manufactured goods and net importer of forestry products.
d) importer of manufactured goods and net exporter of agricultural products.
e) importer of travel and a net exporter of textiles and footwear.

36.81 (SG 36.2)
Correct: b)
Difficulty: 3
Page(s): 969–970
Scramble range: None
Topic: Exports of services

36.81
Which of the following is a Canadian export of a service?
a) A Canadian citizen buys a restaurant meal while travelling in Switzerland.
b) A Swiss citizen buys a restaurant meal while travelling in Canada.
c) A Canadian citizen buys a clock made in Switzerland.
d) A Swiss citizen buys a computer made in Canada.
e) Both a) and b).

36.82 (SG 36.3)
Correct: a)
Difficulty: 2
Page(s): 969
Scramble range: All
Topic: Free Trade Agreement

36.82
Canada recently signed a free trade agreement with
a) the United States.
b) Japan.
c) Mexico.
d) the European Community.
e) Great Britain.

36.83 (SG 36.4)
Correct: a)
Difficulty: 3
Page(s): 972
Scramble range: All
Topic: Comparative advantage

36.83
Suppose there are two countries, *A* and *B*, producing two goods, *X* and *Y*. Country *A* has a comparative advantage in the production of good *X* if less
a) of good *Y* must be given up to produce one unit of *X* than in country *B*.
b) labour is required to produce one unit of *X* than in country *B*.
c) capital is required to produce one unit of *X* than in country *B*.
d) labour and capital is required to produce one unit of *X* than in country *B*.
e) of good *X* must be given up to produce one unit of *Y* than in country *B*.

36.84 (SG 36.5)
Correct: a)
Difficulty: 4
Page(s): 972
Scramble range: All
Topic: Comparative advantage

36.84
Suppose there are two countries, *A* and *B*, producing two goods, *X* and *Y* and that country *A* has a comparative advantage in the production of *X*. If the countries trade, the price of *X* in terms of *Y* will be
a) greater than the opportunity cost of *X* in country *A* and less than the opportunity cost of *X* in country *B*.
b) less than the opportunity cost of *X* in country *A* and greater than the opportunity cost of *X* in country *B*.
c) greater than the opportunity cost of *X* in both countries.
d) less than the opportunity cost of *X* in both countries.
e) dependent on the relative size of each economy.

36.85 (SG 36.6)
Correct: c)
Difficulty: 3
Page(s): 972
Scramble range: None
Topic: Comparative advantage

36.85
International trade according to comparative advantage allows each country to consume
a) more of the goods it exports but less of the goods it imports than without trade.
b) more of the goods it imports but less of the goods it exports than without trade.
c) more of both goods it exports and goods it imports than without trade.
d) less of both goods it exports and goods it imports than without trade.
e) either a) or b); it depends on the price of the goods.

36.86 (SG 36.7)
Correct: d)
Difficulty: 3
Page(s): 972
Scramble range: All
Topic: Opportunity cost

36.86
In country *A*, it requires one unit of capital and one unit of labour to produce a unit of *X* and it requires two units of capital and two units of labour to produce a unit of *Y*. What is the opportunity cost of good *X*?
a) The price of a unit of capital plus the price of a unit of labour.
b) One unit of capital and one unit of labour.
c) Two units of capital and two units of labour.
d) One-half unit of *Y*.
e) Two units of *Y*.

36.87 (SG 36.8)
Correct: c)
Difficulty: 3
Page(s): 977
Scramble range: All
Topic: Absolute advantage

36.87
If country *A* has an absolute advantage in the production of everything,
a) no trade will take place because country *A* will have a comparative advantage in everything.
b) no trade will take place because no country will have a comparative advantage in anything.
c) trade will probably take place and all countries will gain.
d) trade will probably take place but country *A* will not gain.
e) trade will probably take place but country *A* will be the only one to gain.

36.88 (SG 36.9)
Correct: a)
Difficulty: 4
Page(s): 980
Scramble range: All
Topic: Tariffs

36.88
The imposition of a tariff on imported goods will increase the price consumers pay for imported goods and
a) reduce the volume of imports and the volume of exports.
b) reduce the volume of imports and increase the volume of exports.
c) reduce the volume of imports and leave the volume of exports unchanged.
d) will not affect either the volume of imports or the volume of exports.
e) increase the volume of imports but decrease the volume of exports.

36.89 (SG 36.10)
Correct: b)
Difficulty: 3
Page(s): 980
Scramble range: All
Topic: Tariffs

36.89
Who benefits from a tariff on good *X*?
a) Domestic consumers of good *X*.
b) Domestic producers of good *X*.
c) Foreign consumers of good *X*.
d) Foreign producers of good *X*.
e) No one.

36.90 (SG 36.11)
Correct: d)
Difficulty: 2
Page(s): 981
Scramble range: All
Topic: GATT

36.90
Which of the following is responsible for significant reduction in trade restrictions since World War II?
a) The Smoot–Hawley Act.
b) The voluntary exports restraint agreement between the United States and Japan.
c) The United Nations.
d) The General Agreement on Tariffs and Trade.
e) The Free Trade Agreement.

36.91 (SG 36.12)
Correct: c)
Difficulty: 3
Page(s): 981
Scramble range: All
Topic: Tariffs

36.91
A tariff on good *X* which is imported by country *A* will cause the
a) demand curve for *X* in country *A* to shift upward.
b) demand curve for *X* in country *A* to shift downward.
c) supply curve of *X* in country *A* to shift upward.
d) supply curve of *X* in country *A* to shift downward.
e) demand and the supply curve of *X* in country *A* to shift upward.

36.92 (SG 36.13)
Correct: a)
Difficulty: 4
Page(s): 981
Scramble range: All
Topic: Tariffs

36.92
Country *A* and country *B* are currently engaging in free trade. Country *A* imports good *X* from country *B* and exports *Y* to *B*. If country *A* imposes a tariff on *X*, the *X*-producing industry will
a) expand and the *Y*-producing industry will contract in country *A*.
b) expand and the *Y*-producing industry will expand in country *A*.
c) contract and the *Y*-producing industry will contract in country *A*.
d) contract and the *Y*-producing industry will expand in country *A*.
e) expand and the *Y*-producing industry will be unchanged in country *A*.

36.93 (SG 36.14)
Correct: a)
Difficulty: 4
Page(s): 981
Scramble range: All
Topic: Quotas

36.93
Country *A* and country *B* are currently engaging in free trade. Country *A* imports good *X* from country *B* and exports *Y* to *B*. If country *A* imposes a quota on *X*, the *X*-producing industry will
a) expand and the *Y*-producing industry will contract in country *A*.
b) expand and the *Y*-producing industry will expand in country *A*.
c) contract and the *Y*-producing industry will contract in country *A*.
d) contract and the *Y*-producing industry will expand in country *A*.
e) expand and the *Y*-producing industry will be unchanged in country *A*.

36.94 (SG 36.15)
Correct: e)
Difficulty: 4
Page(s): 987
Scramble range: All
Topic: Tariffs

36.94
When a tariff is imposed, the gap between the domestic price and the export price is captured by
a) consumers in the importing country.
b) the person with the right to import the good.
c) the domestic producers of the good.
d) foreign exporters.
e) the government of the importing country.

36.95 (SG 36.16)
Correct: e)
Difficulty: 4
Page(s): 987
Scramble range: All
Topic: Tariffs

36.95
When a quota is imposed, the gap between the domestic price and the export price is captured by
a) consumers in the importing country.
b) the domestic producers of the good.
c) the government of the importing country.
d) foreign exporters.
e) the person with the right to import the good.

36.96 (SG 36.17)
Correct: d)
Difficulty: 4
Page(s): 987
Scramble range: All
Topic: VERs

36.96
When a voluntary export restraint agreement is reached, the gap between the domestic price and the export price is captured by
a) consumers in the importing country.
b) the person with the right to import the good.
c) the government of the importing country.
d) foreign exporters.
e) the domestic producers of the good.

36.97 (SG 36.18)
Correct: b)
Difficulty: 3
Page(s): 987
Scramble range: All
Topic: VERs

36.97
Country *A* imports good *X* from country *B* and exports *Y* to *B*. Which of the following is a reason that country *A* might prefer arranging a voluntary export restraint rather than a quota on *X*?
a) Not to reduce the volume of its own exports of *Y*.
b) To prevent country *B* from retaliating by restricting country *A*'s exports.
c) To keep the domestic price of *X* low.
d) To increase government revenue.
e) This will help domestic consumers more than the quota.

36.98
Correct: e)
Difficulty: 3
Page(s): 969–970
Scramble range: All
Topic: Trade patterns

36.98
The foreign country that has the largest surplus of exports to Canada over imports from Canada is
a) Japan.
b) the United States.
c) Mexico.
d) Britain.
e) the European Community.

36.99
Correct: c)
Difficulty: 4
Page(s): 969
Scramble range: All
Topic: Imports

36.99
Which of the following is a Canadian import of a service?
a) A Canadian citizen buys a watch made in Switzerland.
b) A Swiss citizen buys a restaurant meal while travelling in Canada.
c) A Canadian citizen flies on Swissair from Geneva to Paris.
d) A Swiss citizen buys a computer made in Canada.
e) A Canadian travelling abroad goes to a hockey camp run by a Canadian hockey instructor temporarily working in the United States.

36.100
Correct: d)
Difficulty: 3
Page(s): 973
Scramble range: All
Topic: Comparative advantage

36.100
Country *A* and country *B* both produce goods *X* and *Y*. Country *A* has a comparative advantage in good *X*. This means that
a) Country *B* is unable to produce good *X*.
b) Country *A* can produce good *X* with a smaller amount of real resources than country *B*.
c) Country *A* has placed a comparatively high tariff on imports of good *X* so that its producers have an advantage in domestic markets.
d) less of good *Y* must be given up to produce one unit of *X* in country *A* than in country *B*.
e) less of good *Y* must be given up to produce one unit of *X* in country *B* than in country *A*.

36.101
Correct: e)
Difficulty: 3
Page(s): 973
Scramble range: All
Topic: Comparative advantage

36.101
If countries specialize and trade according to comparative advantage each country can consume
a) less of the goods it imports and exports than without trade.
b) more of the goods it imports and exports than without trade, if the prices of the goods it exports rise more than the prices of the goods it imports.
c) more if the goods it exports but less of the goods it imports than without trade.
d) more of the goods it imports but less of the goods it exports than without trade.
e) more of the goods it imports and exports than without trade.

36.102
Correct: e)
Difficulty: 3
Page(s): 979
Scramble range: All
Topic: Transportation costs

36.102
Canada simultaneously exports and imports crude petroleum because of
a) diversity of taste.
b) economies of scale.
c) tariffs.
d) quotas.
e) transportation costs.

36.103
Correct: d)
Difficulty: 4
Page(s): 973
Scramble range: All
Topic: Comparative advantage

36.103
In country *A*, it requires one unit of capital and one unit of labour to produce a unit of *X*, and it requires three units of capital and three units of labour to produce a unit of *Y*. What is the opportunity cost of good *X*?
a) The price of a unit of capital plus the price of a unit of labour.
b) One unit of capital and one unit of labour.
c) Three units of capital and two units of labour.
d) One-third unit of *Y*.
e) Three units of *Y*.

36.104
Correct: a)
Difficulty: 4
Page(s): 981–983
Scramble range: All
Topic: Tariffs

36.104
Which of the following would result from a tariff on imported goods?
a) Increased price of imported goods and reduced volume of exports.
b) Increased price of imported goods and increased volume of exports.
c) Reduced price of imported goods and increased volume of exports.
d) Reduced price of imported goods and reduced volume of exports.
e) Increased price of imported goods and same volume of exports.

36.105
Correct: d)
Difficulty: 2
Page(s): 981
Scramble range: All
Topic: Tariffs

36.105
What has been the major effect of the General Agreement on Tariffs and Trade since World War II?
a) Punishment of countries that engage in unfair trade practices.
b) Stabilization of the world's major currencies at fixed relationships to each other.
c) Closer connection of the central banks of different countries.
d) Significant reduction in trade restrictions.
e) Replacement of tariffs with nontariff barriers of the same strength.

36.106
Correct: a)
Difficulty: 3
Page(s): 988
Scramble range: All
Topic: Trade restrictions

36.106
Which of the following measures would allow the gap between the domestic price and the export price to be captured by foreign exporters?
a) Voluntary export restraint.
b) Quota.
c) Tariff.
d) Tax on imports.
e) Product standards regulation.

36.107
Correct: a)
Difficulty: 3
Page(s): 988
Scramble range: All
Topic: Trade restrictions

36.107
Which of the following measures would minimize the chance that a country would retaliate in foreign trade by restricting a trading partner's exports?
a) Voluntary export restraint.
b) Quota.
c) Tariff.
d) Tax on imports.
e) Product standards regulation.

36.108 (SG36.19)
Correct: c)
Difficulty: 3
Page(s): 971–972
Scramble range: None
Topic: Balance of trade

36.108
If we import more than we export, then
a) we are going to be unable to buy as many foreign goods as we desire.
b) we will make loans to foreigners to enable them to buy our goods.
c) we will have to finance the difference by borrowing from foreigners.
d) our patterns of trade, including the directions of exports and imports, will be different than if exports equal imports.
e) both c) and d).

36.109 (SG 36.20)
Correct: e)
Difficulty: 3
Page(s): 988–989
Scramble range: All
Topic: Free Trade Agreement

36.109
The implementation of the Canada–United States Free Trade Agreement has revealed that
a) Canada has been severely damaged by the agreement.
b) Canada has been helped enormously by the agreement.
c) free trade does not work.
d) all losers from free trade will be compensated.
e) it is too early to isolate the effects of the agreement and, therefore, it is too early to arrive at any conclusions on its worth.

36.110
Correct: e)
Difficulty: 4
Page(s): 981–983
Scramble range: a)–d)
Topic: Tariffs

36.110
We can conclude from our examination of tariffs that
a) they make a country unambiguously better off.
b) every member of a country gains when one of that country's markets is opened up to free trade.
c) it is better to protect a market from imports with quotas.
d) all of the above.
e) none of the above.

36.111
Correct: c)
Difficulty: 4
Page(s): 973
Scramble range: a)–c)
Topic: Gains from trade

36.111
If a country specializes in the production of goods it has a comparative advantage in and then trades to a new consumption bundle, then this country
a) will be producing only one good in a two-good world.
b) will consume more of the good it imports than of the good it exports.
c) can consume outside its production possiblity frontier.
d) all of the above.
e) none of the above.

Chapter 37 The Balance of Payments and the Dollar

37.1
Correct: c)
Difficulty: 2
Page(s): 995
Scramble range: All
Topic: Balance of payments accounting

37.1
In Canada's balance of payments accounting there are three major sections in the accounts. These are the

a) current account, capital account, and net interest account.
b) capital account, official settlements account, and merchandise trade account.
c) current account, capital account, and official settlements account.
d) official settlements account, current account, and net interest account.
e) capital account, current account, and merchandise trade account.

37.2
Correct: c)
Difficulty: 2
Page(s): 995
Scramble range: All
Topic: Current account

37.2
The largest item in the current account is

a) the value of Canadian exports.
b) the interest payments on foreign loans.
c) net exports.
d) military spending overseas.
e) long-term capital flows.

37.3
Correct: d)
Difficulty: 2
Page(s): 995
Scramble range: All
Topic: The balance of trade

37.3
The balance of trade is the

a) net value of the Canadian balance of payments.
b) difference between the value of the current account and the capital account.
c) difference in value between Canadian trade and foreign trade.
d) difference in value between Canadian exports and Canadian imports in goods and services.
e) net value of cash flows in and out of Canada.

37.4
Correct: d)
Difficulty: 2
Page(s): 995
Scramble range: All
Topic: The balance of trade

37.4
The balance of trade does not include the value of

a) Canadian merchandise purchased by foreigners.
b) foreign goods purchased by Canada.
c) Canadian exports of services.
d) gifts sent abroad.
e) Canadian imports of services.

37.5
Correct: b)
Difficulty: 2
Page(s): 995
Scramble range: All
Topic: The capital account

37.5
The capital account measures the
a) net value of the Canadian balance of payments.
b) difference between the value of the current borrowing from foreigners and foreign borrowing from Canada.
c) difference in value between Canadian trade and foreign trade.
d) difference in value between Canadian exports and Canadian imports in goods and services.
e) net increase or decrease in Canada's holdings of official foreign exchange reserves.

37.6
Correct: d)
Difficulty: 2
Page(s): 995
Scramble range: All
Topic: Official settlements account

37.6
The official settlements account measures the
a) value of Canadian merchandise purchased by foreigners.
b) net value of foreign goods officially purchased by Canada.
c) net value of Canadian official exports of services.
d) change in the country's net holding of foreign currency.
e) net value of cash flows between Canada and the world.

37.7 (SG 37.3)
Correct: b)
Difficulty: 2
Page(s): 996
Scramble range: All
Topic: Trade deficit

37.7
Canada has a trade deficit when the
a) value of Canadian exports of goods and services exceeds the value of Canadian imports of goods and services.
b) value of Canadian exports of goods and services is exceeded by the value of Canadian imports of goods and services.
c) value of Canadian exports of goods exceeds the value of Canadian imports of goods.
d) value of Canadian exports of goods is exceeded by the value of Canadian imports of goods.
e) current account balance is less than zero.

37.8
Correct: a)
Difficulty: 2
Page(s): 995
Scramble range: All
Topic: Trade surplus

37.8
Canada has a trade surplus when the
a) value of Canadian exports of goods and services exceeds the value of Canadian imports of goods and services.
b) value of Canadian exports of goods and services is exceeded by the value of Canadian imports of goods and services.
c) value of Canadian exports of goods exceeds the value of Canadian imports of goods.
d) value of Canadian exports of goods is exceeded by the value of Canadian imports of goods.
e) current account is positive.

37.9
Correct: c)
Difficulty: 3
Page(s): 996
Scramble range: All
Topic: Trade deficit

37.9
The largest component of the Canadian deficit on the current account in the 1980s is the
a) merchandise trade deficit.
b) deficit in trade in services.
c) deficit in interest payments for international borrowing.
d) deficit in Canadian official purchases.
e) deficit in foreign investment in Canada.

37.10
Correct: d)
Difficulty: 3
Page(s): 996
Scramble range: All
Topic: Item not in balance of payments

37.10
A large item that does not show up in the official balance of payments accounts is
a) borrowing from abroad by private citizens in Canada.
b) borrowing from Canada by foreign nationals.
c) borrowing from Canada by foreign governments.
d) money flows from various illegal activities such as the drug trade.
e) net transfers.

37.11
Correct: e)
Difficulty: 3
Page(s): 996
Scramble range: All
Topic: Official reserves

37.11
The change in official Canadian reserves is the
a) balance of payments.
b) trade deficit.
c) net transfers.
d) difference between the merchandise trade deficit and the net borrowing from abroad.
e) difference between the current account deficit and the net borrowing from abroad.

37.12
Correct: d)
Difficulty: 2
Page(s): 997
Scramble range: All
Topic: Net borrower nations

37.12
A net borrower is a country that
a) borrows from foreign creditors.
b) borrows from net foreign creditors.
c) consumes more exports than imports.
d) borrows more from foreigners than it lends to foreigners.
e) has its official settlements account falling in value.

37.13
Correct: c)
Difficulty: 3
Page(s): 998
Scramble range: All
Topic: Creditor nation

37.13
A creditor nation is one
a) which has contributed much money for the advancement of health care in less developed countries.
b) which does not borrow money from foreign nations.
c) which borrows less from foreign nations than it lends to them.
d) which has active monetary policy to ensure adequate loans for housing of the poor.
e) whose official settlements account is rising in value.

37.14 (SG 37.8)
Correct: c)
Difficulty: 3
Page(s): 997
Scramble range: All
Topic: Debtor/creditor versus net borrower/lender

37.14
The distinction between a debtor or creditor nation and a net borrower or net lender nation depends on
a) the distinction between the level of saving in the economy and the saving rate.
b) the distinction between the level of government borrowing and the rate of borrowing.
c) the distinction between the stock of investments and the flow of interest payments on those investments.
d) the distinction between exports and imports.
e) really nothing; they are the same.

37.15
Correct: a)
Difficulty: 2
Page(s): 998
Scramble range: All
Topic: International debt

37.15
International debts are
a) stocks.
b) flows.
c) neither stocks nor flows.
d) both stocks and flows.
e) either stocks or flows depending on the type of debt.

37.16
Correct: b)
Difficulty: 3
Page(s): 998
Scramble range: All
Topic: International debt

37.16
Borrowing or lending is a
a) stock.
b) flow.
c) neither a stock nor a flow.
d) both a stock and a flow.
e) a stock when borrowing and a flow when lending.

37.17
Correct: e)
Difficulty: 3
Page(s): 996
Scramble range: All
Topic: Canadian balance of payments

37.17
Throughout the 1970s Canada had a
a) surplus in the current account and a deficit in the capital account.
b) deficit in the current account and a deficit in the capital account.
c) surplus in the current account and a surplus in the capital account.
d) deficit in the current account and a surplus in the capital account.
e) rough balance in both the capital and the current account until 1974. After that, it had a surplus in the capital account and a deficit in the current account.

37.18
Correct: a)
Difficulty: 3
Page(s): 996
Scramble range: All
Topic: Canadian balance of payments

37.18
Throughout the 1970s Canada was
a) a net borrower from the rest of the world.
b) a net lender to the rest of the world.
c) neither a borrower nor a lender to the rest of the world.
d) borrowing and lending in equal amounts with the rest of the world.
e) a net borrower in the early part of the decade, but then was a strong net lender in the last half of the decade.

37.19
Correct: e)
Difficulty: 3
Page(s): 996
Scramble range: None
Topic: Canadian balance of payments

37.19
Since 1985, Canada has become a
a) net borrower from the rest of the world.
b) net lender to the rest of the world.
c) debtor nation.
d) borrower and lender in equal amounts with the rest of the world.
e) both a) and c).

37.20
Correct: e)
Difficulty: 3
Page(s): 995
Scramble range: All
Topic: Current account

37.20
The closest analogy to a country's current account is an individual's difference between their
a) income and savings.
b) investment outside their business and outside investment in their business.
c) mortgage payments and their rent.
d) spending and saving.
e) expenditure and income.

37.21
Correct: a)
Difficulty: 2
Page(s): 997
Scramble range: All
Topic: Net borrowing and lending

37.21
In the 1980s, the majority of the world's nations were
a) net borrowers.
b) net lenders.
c) refusing to pay their interest payments on their debt.
d) breaking even on net borrowing and net lending.
e) running current balance surpluses.

37.22
Correct: c)
Difficulty: 2
Page(s): 997
Scramble range: All
Topic: Net borrower nations

37.22
In the late 1980s, net lender countries included all of the following countries *except*
a) Japan.
b) Kuwait.
c) Mexico.
d) West Germany.
e) Venezuela.

37.23
Correct: d)
Difficulty: 2
Page(s): 997
Scramble range: All
Topic: Net borrower nations

37.23
In the late 1980s, net borrower countries included all of the following countries *except*
a) Brazil.
b) Argentina.
c) Mexico.
d) Venezuela.
e) Canada.

37.24
Correct: b)
Difficulty: 3
Page(s): 998
Scramble range: a)–c)
Topic: International debt

37.24
Borrowing is not a problem if the money is used to finance
a) extravagant living by individuals or governments.
b) education which increases the productivity of workers.
c) consumption not connected with productivity increases or increased ability to repay such debts.
d) all of the above.
e) none of the above.

37.25
Correct: e)
Difficulty: 3
Page(s): 998
Scramble range: a)–d)
Topic: International debt

37.25
Borrowing is not a problem if
a) the money is used to finance extravagant living by individuals who expect their incomes, and hence their ability to repay the loan with interest, to grow rapidly in the future.
b) the money is used to finance consumption without any chance of an increase in the ability to repay in the future.
c) the money is used to finance consumption not connected with productivity increases.
d) it is by individuals and not nations.
e) none of the above.

37.26
Correct: b)
Difficulty: 2
Page(s): 1000
Scramble range: All
Topic: Net exports

37.26
Net exports enter the balance of payments as
a) a debit.
b) a credit.
c) neither a credit nor a debit.
d) a liability.
e) an asset.

37.27
Correct: b)
Difficulty: 3
Page(s): 1001
Scramble range: All
Topic: Balance of trade

37.27
The balance of trade deficit is equal to the government budget
a) deficit minus the private sector deficit.
b) deficit plus the private sector deficit.
c) surplus minus the private sector deficit.
d) surplus plus the private sector surplus.
e) surplus minus the current account deficit.

37.28
Correct: b)
Difficulty: 3
Page(s): 1001
Scramble range: All
Topic: Public deficit/balance or trade

37.28
In Canada in 1988, the largest important component deficit of the balance of trade was the
a) private sector deficit.
b) public sector deficit.
c) consumption of imports.
d) reduction in private saving.
e) net interest paid.

37.29
Correct: e)
Difficulty: 3
Page(s): 996
Scramble range: All
Topic: Canadian current account

37.29
In 1988, the Canadian current account balance was
a) +$4 billion.
b) –$16 billion.
c) +$10 billion.
d) +$20 billion.
e) –$10 billion.

37.30
Correct: e)
Difficulty: 4
Page(s): 1001
Scramble range: All
Topic: Private sector deficit

37.30
In 1988, Canadian net exports were +$4 billion. Of this $4 billion, the private sector deficit accounted for
a) a deficit of $1.3 billion, with the rest accounted for by the public sector surplus.
b) a surplus of $13 billion, with the rest accounted for by the public sector deficit.
c) a deficit of $10 billion, with the rest accounted for by the public sector surplus of $14.
d) exactly all of this surplus.
e) a surplus of $20 billion, with the rest accounted for by the public sector deficit.

37.31
Correct: a)
Difficulty: 3
Page(s): 1001–02
Scramble range: All
Topic: Trade and public deficit

37.31
The public sector deficit and the trade deficit are not the same since the
a) private sector can be in surplus or deficit.
b) Gramm–Rudman law prohibits this connection.
c) Jackson–Vanek amendment prohibits this connection.
d) government cannot borrow abroad.
e) government can borrow abroad.

37.32
Correct: a)
Difficulty: 3
Page(s): 1001–02
Scramble range: All
Topic: Trade and public deficit

37.32
The public sector deficit and the trade deficit are not the same since
a) private saving does not always equal investment.
b) the government can print money to pay for added expenditures.
c) the Simpson–Mizzoli amendment prohibits this connection.
d) private saving must equal investment.
e) the government can borrow abroad.

37.33
Correct: c)
Difficulty: 4
Page(s): 1002
Scramble range: All
Topic: Private sector surplus

37.33
Other things being equal, anything that lowers interest rates or increases future profit expectations
a) increases investment and increases the private sector surplus.
b) decreases investment and increases the private sector surplus.
c) increases investment and decreases the private sector surplus.
d) decreases investment and decreases the public sector surplus.
e) decreases investment and increases the public sector surplus.

37.34 (SG 37.12)
Correct: d)
Difficulty: 4
Page(s): 1002
Scramble range: All
Topic: Public deficit/private surplus

37.34
The link between the public sector deficit and the private sector surplus can be weak because
a) the interest rate will tend to do the adjusting to a change in public deficits rather than the private sector.
b) real GDP will tend to do the adjusting to a change in public deficits rather than the private sector.
c) the economy may not be operating at close to capacity, and changes in public deficits will not affect the private sector.
d) international capital mobility may cut any strong link between changes in the public sector deficit and changes in interest rates.
e) the government's deficit is partially caused by borrowing abroad.

37.35
Correct: e)
Difficulty: 4
Page(s): 1002
Scramble range: None
Topic: Relation among three deficits

37.35
Which of the following three must add up to zero?
a) The public surplus, the private surplus, and the trade deficit.
b) The public deficit, the private deficit, and the trade surplus.
c) The public deficit, the private deficit, and the trade deficit.
d) The public surplus, the private surplus, and the trade surplus.
e) Both c) and d).

37.36
Correct: e)
Difficulty: 3
Page(s): 998
Scramble range: All
Topic: Creditor nations

37.36
Canada is a debtor nation because
a) there is not net borrowing from abroad.
b) the interest payments from foreigners to Canadian citizens equals the interest payments to citizens abroad for Canadian borrowing.
c) there is not net lending from abroad.
d) the interest payments from foreigners to Canadian citizens exceeds the interest payments to citizens abroad for Canadian borrowing.
e) the interest payments from foreigners to Canadian citizens is exceeded by the interest payments to citizens abroad for Canadian borrowing.

37.37 (SG 37.1)
Correct: a)
Difficulty: 2
Page(s): 995
Scramble range: All
Topic: Balance of payments accounting

37.37
Which of the following is one of the balance of payments accounts?
a) Current account.
b) Nontraded goods account.
c) Official reserves account.
d) Net interest account.
e) Public account.

37.38 (SG 37.2)
Correct: c)
Difficulty: 3
Page(s): 995
Scramble range: All
Topic: Current account

37.38
Suppose Canada initially has all balance of payments accounts in balance (no surplus or deficit). Then Canadian firms increase the amount they import from Japan, financing that increase in imports by borrowing from Japan. There will now be a current account
a) surplus and a capital account surplus.
b) surplus and a capital account deficit.
c) deficit and a capital account surplus.
d) deficit and a capital account deficit.
e) deficit and a capital account balance.

37.39 (SG 37.4)
Correct: b)
Difficulty: 4
Page(s): 997
Scramble range: All
Topic: Debtor/creditor and net borrower/lender nations

37.39
The country Plato came into existence at the beginning of year 1. Given the information in Table 37.1, in year 4 Plato is a
a) net lender and a creditor nation.
b) net lender and a debtor nation.
c) net borrower and a creditor nation.
d) net borrower and a debtor nation.
e) net lender and neither a creditor nor a debtor nation.

Table 37.1

Year	Borrowed from rest of world (billions of dollars)	Loaned to rest of world (billions of dollars)
1	60	20
2	60	40
3	60	60
4	60	80

37.40 (SG 37.9)
Correct: d)
Difficulty: 4
Page(s): 1000
Scramble range: All
Topic: Net exports

37.40
Suppose that in a country, government purchases of goods and services is $400 billion, taxes (net of transfer payments) is $300 billion, saving is $300 billion, and investment is $250 billion. Net exports are in a
a) surplus of $150 billion.
b) surplus of $50 billion.
c) deficit of $150 billion.
d) deficit of $50 billion.
e) deficit of $250 billion.

37.41 (SG 37.10)
Correct: c)
Difficulty: 4
Page(s): 1001
Scramble range: All
Topic: Deficit/surplus

37.41
Suppose that in a country, government purchases of goods and services is $400 billion, taxes (net of transfer payments) is $300 billion, saving is $300 billion, and investment is $250 billion. The country described here has a government budget
a) surplus and a private sector surplus.
b) surplus and a private sector deficit.
c) deficit and a private sector surplus.
d) deficit and a private sector deficit.
e) surplus and a private sector balance.

37.42
Correct: d)
Difficulty: 3
Page(s): 995
Scramble range: All
Topic: Balance of payments

37.42
Which of the following is one of the balance of payments accounts?
a) Capital consumption account.
b) Gross private domestic investment account.
c) Nontraded goods account.
d) Official settlements account.
e) Net exports.

37.43 (SG 37.11)
Correct: b)
Difficulty: 3
Page(s): 995
Scramble range: All
Topic: Balance of payments

37.43
Suppose Canada initially has all balance of payments accounts in balance (no surplus or deficit). Then Canadian firms increase the amount they export to Japan, and the Japanese finance that increase by borrowing from Canada. In Canada there will now be a
a) current account surplus and capital account surplus.
b) current account surplus and capital account deficit.
c) current account deficit and capital account surplus.
d) current account deficit and capital account deficit.
e) current account surplus and capital account balance.

37.44 (SG 37.6)
Correct: a)
Difficulty: 4
Page(s): 997
Scramble range: All
Topic: Debtor–creditor status

37.44
A nation is currently a net lender and a debtor nation. Which of the following statements applies to that nation?
a) It has loaned more capital than it borrowed from abroad this year, but borrowed more than it loaned during its history.
b) It has borrowed more capital from abroad than it loaned this year and also borrowed more than it loaned during its history.
c) It has loaned more capital than it borrowed from abroad this year and has loaned more than it borrowed during its history.
d) Its accounting system must be in error if it shows the nation to be a net lender and a debtor nation at the same time.
e) Its debts must be currently growing.

37.45
Correct: e)
Difficulty: 3
Page(s): 997
Scramble range: All
Topic: Debtor nations

37.45
A debtor nation is a nation that
a) lends more to the rest of the world than it borrows from the rest of the world.
b) borrows more from the rest of the world than it lends to the rest of the world.
c) has invested more in the rest of the world than the rest of the world has invested in it.
d) has a public sector deficit that is larger than its net exports.
e) has negative net receipts of interest on debt.

37.46 (SG 37.7)
Correct: e)
Difficulty: 3
Page(s): 998
Scramble range: All
Topic: International borrowing

37.46
Canada has tended to borrow

a) heavily for consumption throughout its history.
b) heavily for investment throughout its history.
c) about evenly for consumption and investment throughout its history.
d) heavily for consumption up to 1981, and since then has borrowed for investment.
e) heavily for investment up to 1981, for consumption from 1981 to 1988, and since then for investment again.

37.47
Correct: a)
Difficulty: 3
Page(s): 995
Scramble range: All
Topic: Official settlements

37.47
Consider Fact 37.1. What is the value of the official settlements balance of payments?

a) +3 billion choos.
b) –3 billion choos.
c) +87 billion choos.
d) –207 billion choos.
e) +147 billion choos.

Fact 37.1
The citizens of Pioneerland, whose currency is the choo, conduct the following transactions in 1990:

Variable	Billions of choos
Imports of goods and services	250
Exports of goods and services	397
Borrowing from the rest of the world	80
Lending to the rest of the world	20
Increase in official holdings of foreign currency	3

37.48
Correct: b)
Difficulty: 3
Page(s): 995
Scramble range: All
Topic: Capital account

37.48
Consider Fact 37.1. What is the value of the capital account balance of payments?

a) –3 billion choos.
b) +60 billion choos.
c) –60 billion choos.
d) +147 billion choos.
e) +87 billion choos.

37.49
Correct: b)
Difficulty: 5
Page(s): 995
Scramble range: All
Topic: Current account

37.49
Consider Fact 37.1. What is the value of the current account balance of payments

a) +147 billion choos.
b) –57 billion choos.
c) +57 billion choos.
d) +3 billion choos.
e) –60 billion choos.

37.50
Correct: d)
Difficulty: 5
Page(s): 995
Scramble range: All
Topic: Current account

37.50
Consider Fact 37.1. What is the total value of net interest payments plus other transfers?
a) +57 billion choos.
b) –57 billion choos.
c) +147 billion choos.
d) –240 billion choos.
e) Not calculable with the given data.

37.51
Correct: a)
Difficulty: 3
Page(s): 999
Scramble range: All
Topic: Government sector deficit

37.51
Consider Fact 37.2. What is the amount of taxes (net of transfers) that the people of Ecoland pay?
a) 10 billion turkies.
b) 12 billion turkies.
c) 2 billion turkies.
d) 8 billion turkies.
e) 14 billion turkies.

Fact 37.2
You are told the following about Ecoland, a country whose currency is the turky and whose exchange rate is flexible:

Variable	Billions of turkies
Real GDP	50
Consumption expenditure	30
Government purchases of goods and services	12
Investment	11
Exports of goods and services	10
Government budget deficit	2

37.52
Correct: b)
Difficulty: 4
Page(s): 999
Scramble range: All
Topic: Private sector deficit

37.52
Consider Fact 37.2. What is the amount of saving by the people of Ecoland?
a) 8 billion turkies.
b) 10 billion turkies.
c) 20 billion turkies.
d) 6 billion turkies.
e) 12 billion turkies.

37.53
Correct: d)
Difficulty: 4
Page(s): 999
Scramble range: All
Topic: Net exports

37.53
Consider Fact 37.2. What is the amount of the net exports of Ecoland?
a) –2 billion turkies.
b) –1 billion turkies.
c) 3 billion turkies.
d) –3 billion turkies.
e) 1 billion turkies.

37.54
Correct: a)
Difficulty: 4
Page(s): 999
Scramble range: All
Topic: Imports

37.54
Consider Fact 37.2. What is the amount of imports of goods and services by Ecoland?
a) 13 billion turkies.
b) 7 billion turkies.
c) 11 billion turkies.
d) 9 billion turkies.
e) 12 billion turkies.

37.55
Correct: e)
Difficulty: 5
Page(s): 999
Scramble range: All
Topic: Current account

37.55
Consider Fact 37.2. What is the current account balance of payments of Ecoland, given that the value of their net interest payments plus other transfers is +3 billion turkies?
a) –3 billion turkies.
b) –6 billion turkies.
c) +3 billion turkies.
d) +1 billion turkies.
e) Zero.

37.56
Correct: e)
Difficulty: 5
Page(s): 999
Scramble range: All
Topic: Capital account

37.56
Consider Fact 37.2. What is the value of the capital account balance of payments for Ecoland, given that the value of net interest payments plus other transfers is +3 billion turkies? (*Hint*: recall that the exchange rate is flexible.)
a) +3 billion turkies.
b) +6 billion turkies.
c) –3 billion turkies.
d) –1 billion turkies.
e) Zero.

37.57
Correct: c)
Difficulty: 4
Page(s): 999
Scramble range: All
Topic: Private sector deficit

37.57
Consider Fact 37.2. What is the value of the private sector deficit or surplus?
a) Zero.
b) –3 billion turkies.
c) –1 billion turkies.
d) –2 billion turkies.
e) +1 billion turkies.

37.58
Correct: d)
Difficulty: 4
Page(s): 1001
Scramble range: None
Topic: Government sector deficit

37.58
An increase in the government sector deficit will tend to
a) increase the current account deficit in a time of full employment.
b) increase the current account deficit at all times.
c) lead to a private sector deficit when the economy has excess capacity.
d) both a) and c).
e) both b) and c).

37.59 (SG 37.13)
Correct: e)
Difficulty: 3
Page(s): 1002
Scramble range: None
Topic: Relative versus money prices

37.59
In Pioneerland, a car exchanges for 100 bushels of wheat. In Ecoland, a car exchanges for 500 bushels of wheat. (There is no trade between the two countries.) A car costs 4,000 choos in Pioneerland, and 8,000 turkies in Ecoland. What is the price of a bushel of wheat in Pioneerland?
a) 1/100 of a car.
b) 40 choos.
c) 1/500 of a car.
d) 16 turkies.
e) Both a) and b).

37.60
Correct: b)
Difficulty: 3
Page(s): 1002
Scramble range: All
Topic: Exchange rates

37.60
Consider Fact 37.3. Suppose that Canada exports cars to the United States and imports grain from the United States. What is the value of an exported car in Canadian dollars, if the exchange rate is C$1.25 per US$1?
a) C$3,750.
b) C$6,250.
c) C$2,857.
d) C$5,000.
e) C$6,520.

Fact 37.3
World market prices in U.S. dollar

Grain	$5 a bushel
Cars	$5,000 each

World market prices in Canadian dollars

	Canadian-dollar price	
Exchange Rate	Grain (bushel)	Cars (each)
C$1.75 per US$1	$8.75	$8,750
C$1.25 per US$1	?	?
C$0.75 per US$1	?	?

37.61
Correct: c)
Difficulty: 3
Page(s): 1002
Scramble range: All
Topic: Exchange rates

37.61
Consider Fact 37.3. Suppose that Canada exports grain to the United States and import cars from the United States. What is the value of grain in Canadian dollars, if the exchange rate is C$0.75 per US$1?
a) C$5.00.
b) C$6.25.
c) C$3.75.
d) C$6.67.
e) This cannot be calculated without knowing how much grain Canada exports.

37.62
Correct: a)
Difficulty: 4
Page(s): 1002
Scramble range: All
Topic: Exports and the dollar

37.62
Consider Fact 37.3. Suppose Canada exports cars and imports grain. Which exchange rate would exporters prefer?
a) C$1.75 per US$1.
b) C$1.25 per US$1.
c) C$0.75 per US$1.
d) It does not matter; they are indifferent since the U.S. price is the same in all cases.
e) It depends on how many cars they export.

37.63
Correct: c)
Difficulty: 4
Page(s): 1002
Scramble range: All
Topic: Imports and the dollar

37.63
Consider Fact 37.3. Suppose Canada exports cars and imports grain. Which exchange rate would importers prefer?
a) C$1.75 per US$1.
b) C$1.25 per US$1.
c) C$0.75 per US$1.
d) It does not matter to them, since the U.S. price of grain is the same in all cases.
e) It depends on how much grain Canada imports.

37.64
Correct: c)
Difficulty: 5
Page(s): 1003–06
Scramble range: All
Topic: Money and the balance of trade

37.64
Consider Table 37.2. Suppose that the exchange rate is C$1.50 per US$1. In this case, Canada will
a) import 2 million bushels of grain.
b) export 1 million bushels of grain.
c) export 2 million bushels of grain.
d) import 2 million bushels of grain.
e) neither export nor import grain.

Table 37.2 Domestic markets for grain and cars

Price of grain (C$ per bushel)	Supply of grain (millions of bushels)	Demand for grain (millions of bushels)
1	1	9
2	2	8
3	3	7
4	4	6
5	5	5
6	6	4
7	7	3
8	8	2
9	9	1

Price of cars (C$ per car)	Supply of cars (thousands)	Demand for cars (thousands)
1,000	2	14
2,000	3	13
3,000	4	12
4,000	5	11
5,000	6	10
6,000	7	9
7,000	8	8
8,000	9	7

The world price for grain is US$4 per bushel, and for cars is US$4,000 each.

37.65
Correct: d)
Difficulty: 5
Page(s): 1003–06
Scramble range: All
Topic: Money and the balance of trade

37.65
Consider Table 37.2. If the exchange rate is C$1.50 per US$1, Canada will
a) import 1,000 cars.
b) export 1,000 cars.
c) export 2,000 cars.
d) import 2,000 cars.
e) neither export nor import cars.

37.66
Correct: e)
Difficulty: 5
Page(s): 1003–06
Scramble range: All
Topic: Money and the balance of trade

37.66
Consider Table 37.2. If the exchange rate is C$1.50 per US$1, what is the balance of trade (net exports)?
a) A deficit of $1 million.
b) A deficit of $2 million.
c) A surplus of $1 million.
d) A surplus of $2 million.
e) Zero.

37.67
Correct: b)
Difficulty: 5
Page(s): 1003–06
Scramble range: All
Topic: Money and the balance of trade

37.67
Consider Table 37.2. Suppose that the exchange rate is C$1 per US$1. In this case, Canada will
a) export 2 million bushels of grain.
b) import 2 million bushels of grain.
c) export 1 million bushels of grain.
d) import 1 million bushels of grain.
e) neither export nor import grain.

37.68
Correct: a)
Difficulty: 5
Page(s): 1003–06
Scramble range: All
Topic: Money and the balance of trade

37.68
Consider Table 37.2. If the exchange rate is C$1 per US$1, then Canada will
a) import 6,000 cars.
b) import 4,000 cars.
c) import 2,000 cars.
d) neither export nor import cars.
e) export 2,000 cars.

37.69
Correct: d)
Difficulty: 5
Page(s): 1003–06
Scramble range: All
Topic: Money and the balance of trade

37.69
Consider Table 37.2. If the exchange rate is C$1 per US$1, what is the balance of trade (net exports)?
a) A surplus of $2 million.
b) A deficit of $2 million.
c) A deficit of $16 million.
d) A deficit of $32 million.
e) A deficit of $64 million.

37.70 (SG 37.14)
Correct: e)
Difficulty: 3
Page(s): 1006
Scramble range: All
Topic: Equilibrium exchange rate

37.70
The equilibrium exchange rate is determined by the
a) interaction of the demand and supply for Canadian goods and services.
b) demand for the U.S. dollar, since they are our major trading partner.
c) private sector deficit.
d) public sector deficit.
e) demand and supply for Canadian-dollar assets.

37.71 (SG 37.15)
Correct: a)
Difficulty: 3
Page(s): 1003–06
Scramble range: All
Topic: Balance of trade

37.71
The balance of trade is determined by the
a) Canadian-dollar prices of our goods and services, given the exchange rate.
b) demand and supply for Canadian-dollar assets.
c) public sector deficit.
d) private sector deficit.
e) exchange rate.

37.72
Correct: e)
Difficulty: 4
Page(s): 1003–06
Scramble range: a)–d)
Topic: Balance of trade

37.72
If the Bank of Canada wished to lower a balance of trade deficit, they could
a) force the exchange rate to a lower value.
b) reduce the private sector deficit.
c) reduce the public sector deficit.
d) force the exchange rate to a higher level.
e) none of the above.

37.73
Correct: c)
Difficulty: 4
Page(s): 1006
Scramble range: a)–d)
Topic: Exchange rate stability

37.73
If the Bank of Canada wishes to prevent the exchange rate from depreciating in value, the best way is to
a) lower the public sector deficit.
b) lower the private sector surplus.
c) raise interest rates and lower the growth rate of the money supply.
d) lower interest rates and raise the growth rate of the money supply.
e) none of the above.

37.74
Correct: a)
Difficulty: 3
Page(s): 1006
Scramble range: All
Topic: Balance of trade

37.74
The balance of trade is a
a) real variable, determined by intertemporal choices.
b) nominal variable, determined by the demand and supply of assets.
c) real variable, solely determined by the value of the exchange rate.
d) nominal variable, determined by the value of the exchange rate.
e) both a real and a nominal variable, depending on whether it is divided by the price level or not.

37.75
Correct: d)
Difficulty: 3
Page(s): 1006
Scramble range: All
Topic: Exchange rate

37.75
The exchange rate is a
a) real variable, determined by the demand and supply of exports and imports.
b) real variable, determined by intertemporal choices.
c) nominal variable, determined by the public sector deficit.
d) nominal variable, determined by the supply and demand of Canadian-dollar assets.
e) nominal variable, determined by the demand and supply of exports and imports.

Chapter 38 Growth and Development

38.1
Correct: b)
Difficulty: 2
Page(s): 1016
Scramble range: All
Topic: Japan's economic experience

38.1
At the end of the World War II, the income per capita in Japan was
a) 50 percent of that in the United States.
b) less than 20 percent of that in the United States.
c) about the same as in Germany and France.
d) about the same as that in the United States.
e) about 75 percent of that in the United States.

38.2
Correct: c)
Difficulty: 2
Page(s): 1017
Scramble range: All
Topic: Population distribution

38.2
Which of the following is true for the world population of 5 billion?
a) Most of the people live in the wealthier industrialized west than in the poorer countries.
b) About half the world's people live in rich countries and half live in poorer countries.
c) Only about 1 billion live in the richer countries and 4 billion live in poorer countries.
d) Most of the people live in sub-Saharan regions of Africa.
e) Most of the people live in the newly industrialized countries.

38.3
Correct: d)
Difficulty: 3
Page(s): 1017
Scramble range: All
Topic: Measures of development

38.3
Perhaps the most useful of the measures of development used by economists is
a) GDP.
b) the average wage rate.
c) the minimum wage rate.
d) real per capita income.
e) lifespan.

38.4
Correct: c)
Difficulty: 3
Page(s): 1017
Scramble range: All
Topic: Size of development aid

38.4
In the mid-1980s, development aid given officially by the richer nations to the poorer nations was
a) $850,000,000.
b) $8,500,000,000.
c) $85,000,000,000.
d) $850,000,000,000.
e) $8,500,000,000,000.

38.5
Correct: c)
Difficulty: 3
Page(s): 1017
Scramble range: All
Topic: Distribution of development aid payments

38.5
Of the total official development aid given by the rich nations to the poor, the U.S. payments account for approximately
a) 90 percent of the total.
b) half of the total.
c) one-third of the total.
d) 10 percent of the total.
e) none of the total.

38.6
Correct: e)
Difficulty: 2
Page(s): 1017
Scramble range: All
Topic: Donor countries

38.6
Large donations for development aid are made by all of the following countries *except*
a) Japan.
b) Canada.
c) the United States.
d) United Kingdom.
e) Mexico.

38.7
Correct: c)
Difficulty: 2
Page(s): 1017
Scramble range: All
Topic: Area receiving bulk of development aid transfers

38.7
The countries receiving the bulk of the development aid transferred from the rich to the poor include primarily
a) Europe and the Mediterranean islands.
b) North and South America.
c) Asia, Africa, and Central and South America.
d) China and the U.S.S.R.
e) Africa and Eastern Europe.

38.8 (SG 38.3)
Correct: d)
Difficulty: 3
Page(s): 1017
Scramble range: All
Topic: Development strategies

38.8
To promote economic growth, various countries pursue a diversity of policies. These policies include all of the following *except*
a) an open economy, looking to trade opportunities to stimulate exports and growth.
b) protectionism, trying to promote import competing industries and keep the jobs at home.
c) encouragement of rapid growth in resources, including human resources.
d) environmental policies encouraging the saving of funds by adding effluents to the rivers and streams.
e) trying to encourage the developed nations to give more foreign aid.

38.9 (SG 38.4)
Correct: a)
Difficulty: 3
Page(s): 1017
Scramble range: All
Topic: Character of poor countries

38.9
The poorest nations are typically characterized by all of the following *except*
a) high literacy rates.
b) high birth rates.
c) limited availability of capital.
d) low per capita incomes.
e) poor capital accumulation.

38.10
Correct: b)
Difficulty: 3
Page(s): 1017
Scramble range: All
Topic: Difference between rich and poor nations

38.10
The degree of occupational specialization
a) tends to be greater in poor countries than in richer countries.
b) tends to be greater in richer countries than in poor countries.
c) is about the same in richer and poorer countries.
d) is impossible to compare between rich and poor nations since such different technology is available in each situation.
e) is greater in newly industrialized countries, but less in developing countries, compared to the richer countries.

38.11
Correct: e)
Difficulty: 3
Page(s): 1017
Scramble range: All
Topic: Income of poor nations

38.11
In the very poorest countries on earth, the average per capita income is as low as
a) half the income in the United States.
b) one-third the income in the United States.
c) 12 percent of the income in the United States.
d) one-half of 1 percent of the income in the United States.
e) 4 percent of the income in the United States.

38.12
Correct: b)
Difficulty: 3
Page(s): 1017
Scramble range: All
Topic: Income/population distribution

38.12
Taken together, the poorest countries in the world accounting for only 6 percent of world income
a) represent about two-thirds of the world population.
b) represent about one-fourth of the world population.
c) represent about 6 percent of the world population.
d) are, in most cases, located in East Asia.
e) are, in most cases, located in South America.

38.13
Correct: c)
Difficulty: 3
Page(s): 1018
Scramble range: All
Topic: Developing nations

38.13
A "developing country" is one
a) which has income equal to that in the United States.
b) which has half the income of the United States and is growing.
c) with 10 to 30 percent of the United States per capita income.
d) which has yet to institute complete projects in manufacturing and industry.
e) in which large numbers of people are on the verge of starvation.

38.14
Correct: b)
Difficulty: 3
Page(s): 1018
Scramble range: All
Topic: Newly industrialized countries

38.14
A country with a rapidly developing industrial base and a low but rising per capita income is a
a) traditional industrial country.
b) newly industrialized country.
c) goal and not yet a reality, as industrial countries do not remain poor.
d) country following Marxist development strategy.
e) developing nation.

38.15
Correct: d)
Difficulty: 3
Page(s): 1018
Scramble range: All
Topic: Newly industrialized countries

38.15
Countries included in what are called "newly industrialized countries" include all of the following *except*
a) Israel.
b) South Korea.
c) Taiwan.
d) Italy.
e) Trinidad.

38.16
Correct: e)
Difficulty: 3
Page(s): 1018
Scramble range: All
Topic: Industrialized countries

38.16
The wealthiest countries such as the United States, Japan, Germany, the U.K., and Canada are all
a) oil-rich nations.
b) self-sufficient in agricultural production.
c) newly industrialized economies.
d) suffering from high infant mortality rates.
e) industrialized countries.

38.17
Correct: d)
Difficulty: 3
Page(s): 1018
Scramble range: All
Topic: Wealth/specialization of labour

38.17
Compared to the poorer nations, in the wealthiest countries such as the United States, Japan, Germany, the U.K., and Canada, labour tends to be
a) well-rounded and not highly specialized.
b) not burdened by human capital.
c) younger and less well-educated.
d) more skilled and specialized.
e) harder working.

38.18
Correct: c)
Difficulty: 3
Page(s): 1018
Scramble range: All
Topic: Oil-exporting nations

38.18
Per capita income and income inequality is high along with a relatively low state of development in which type of country?
a) Members of the European Community.
b) Countries with limited material resources.
c) A small number of oil exporting nations which earn a significant portion of national income from that one product.
d) The western industrialized democracies.
e) Newly industrialized countries.

38.19
Correct: a)
Difficulty: 3
Page(s): 1018
Scramble range: All
Topic: Population in communist economies

38.19
Approximately what percent of the world's population lives in economies dominated by the communist system?
a) 33 percent.
b) 13 percent.
c) 1 percent.
d) 67 percent.
e) 20 percent.

38.20
Correct: c)
Difficulty: 3
Page(s): 1018
Scramble range: All
Topic: Communist system

38.20
In a communist economy, there is all of the following *except*
a) controls on wages and prices.
b) limited dependence on the market for the allocation of goods and services.
c) extensive private ownership of the means of production, if not the distribution of that product.
d) government production and distribution of most goods.
e) limited private ownership of the means of production, if not the distribution of that product.

38.21
Correct: b)
Difficulty: 3
Page(s): 1018
Scramble range: All
Topic: Communism and capitalism

38.21
As a general observation, communist countries
a) have about the same income as capitalist countries.
b) have anywhere from almost 70 percent of the U.S. per capita income to very much poorer indeed.
c) all have per capita income levels of about half that in the United States.
d) occasionally have per capita income levels which exceed that in the United States.
e) are all very close to the newly industrialized countries in income and industrialization.

38.22
Correct: a)
Difficulty: 3
Page(s): 1018
Scramble range: All
Topic: World/Canadian income distribution

38.22
Compared to the equality of the distribution of world income,
a) the income distribution is more equal in Canada than in the rest of the world.
b) the income distribution is less equal in Canada than in the rest of the world.
c) the equality of the income distribution in Canada is about the same as that in the rest of the world.
d) no comparison of any validity can be made since different countries have different standards of living.
e) Canadian income levels are higher.

38.23
Correct: c)
Difficulty: 3
Page(s): 1018–19
Scramble range: All
Topic: World income distribution

38.23
The richest 20 percent of the people on earth account for
a) 95 percent of world income.
b) 75 percent of world income.
c) 55 percent of world income.
d) 35 percent of world income.
e) 25 percent of world income.

38.24
Correct: d)
Difficulty: 3
Page(s): 1018–19
Scramble range: All
Topic: Percentage of world's poor people

38.24
The world's poorest people, representing the lowest 10 percent of the world's income distribution, account for about what percentage of world's population?
a) 80 percent.
b) 75 percent.
c) 60 percent.
d) 40 percent.
e) 20 percent.

38.25
Correct: a)
Difficulty: 3
Page(s): 1019
Scramble range: All
Topic: Relative growth rates

38.25
When rich countries have faster rates of economic growth than poorer countries, the
a) income gap widens between the rich and the poor nations.
b) income gap stays the same in relative terms.
c) income gap between the rich and the poor nations begins to close.
d) transfers from poor to rich must have increased.
e) world income distribution will improve.

38.26 (SG 38.6)
Correct: e)
Difficulty: 4
Page(s): 1019
Scramble range: All
Topic: Relative/absolute growth

38.26
Suppose rich country *A* enjoys a per capita income of $100,000 per year and poorer country B has a per capita income of only $1,000. Rich country *A* has a per capita income which is $99,000 greater than in poor country *B*. With constant populations, what happens to this income gap if per capita income in poor country grows at a rate of 100 percent, while growth in the rich country is only 2 percent?
a) The income gap between the two must narrow since the poor country grew faster.
b) The income gap stays the same.
c) The income gap widens despite the faster growth in the poor country.
d) The income gap initially narrows, then widens.
e) The income gap initially widens, then narrows.

38.27
Correct: a)
Difficulty: 4
Page(s): 1019–21
Scramble range: All
Topic: Relative/absolute income gap

38.27
Suppose Canadian per capita income is double that of country *B*. Holding population constant, what can be concluded if both countries grow at a rate of 10 percent?
a) The absolute difference in per capita income will increase even though Canadian income will remain double that of country *B*.
b) The gap will remain the same in percentage terms and in absolute dollar amounts.
c) The gap will narrow in dollar amounts and as a percentage of Canadian income.
d) The income gap initially narrows, then widens.
e) Initially, the per capita income gap widens, and then it narrows.

38.28
Correct: e)
Difficulty: 4
Page(s): 1019–21
Scramble range: All
Topic: Relative/absolute growth

38.28
Suppose rich country *A* enjoys a per capita income of $100,000 per year and poorer country *B* has a per capita income of only $1,000. Rich country *A* has a per capita income which is $99,000 greater than in poor country *B*. With constant populations, what happens to this income gap if per capita income in poor country grows at a rate of 100 percent, while growth in the rich country is only 1 percent?
a) The dollar amount of the income gap between the two must narrow since the poor country grew faster.
b) The absolute dollar income gap stays the same even though country *B* grew much faster.
c) The income gap widens despite the faster growth in the poor country.
d) The income gap initially narrows, then widens.
e) The income gap is initially constant, and then it narrows.

38.29
Correct: b)
Difficulty: 3
Page(s): 1019
Scramble range: All
Topic: High per capita income

38.29
The key to preserving high per capita income levels is
a) many hours on the job.
b) keeping high rates of economic growth.
c) encouraging child bearing by the use of tax incentives.
d) the removal of environmental regulations which hamper industrial growth.
e) raising population growth.

38.30
Correct: c)
Difficulty: 3
Page(s): 1021
Scramble range: All
Topic: Change in sources of wealth

38.30
In the absence of warfare, countries cannot increase their economic growth by
a) increasing the rate of saving.
b) promoting reduced population growth.
c) increasing the stock of resources available.
d) using inputs more efficiently.
e) raising education levels.

38.31
Correct: c)
Difficulty: 3
Page(s): 1021
Scramble range: All
Topic: Change in sources of wealth

38.31
Countries can have their economic growth reduced by
a) increasing the rate of saving.
b) promoting reduced population growth.
c) adverse changes in prices of their fixed stock of resources.
d) using inputs more efficiently.
e) avoiding warfare.

38.32
Correct: c)
Difficulty: 3
Page(s): 1021
Scramble range: All
Topic: Growth for oil–exporting countries

38.32
Economic growth increased in the 1970s for oil-exporting nations due to
a) an advance in refining technologies.
b) a rapid decline of oil prices in a market in which demand was quite elastic in the short run.
c) a rapid increase in oil prices in a market in which demand was quite inelastic in the short run.
d) dramatic increases in their rates of saving.
e) dramatic increases in their education levels.

38.33
Correct: d)
Difficulty: 3
Page(s): 1021
Scramble range: All
Topic: Population growth/ per capita incomes

38.33
Population growth creating more workers will decrease the standard of living
a) if total production increases.
b) if there is an even greater increase in per capita productivity.
c) only if total production decreases.
d) unless there is an increase in per capita output.
e) if the new workers are uneducated.

38.34 (SG 38.10)
Correct: b)
Difficulty: 3
Page(s): 1021
Scramble range: All
Topic: Capital accumulation

38.34
As capital is accumulated and capital per unit of labour increases,
a) this leads to less output since workers tend to become less hard working when working with big machines.
b) this increases the productivity of labour and economic growth.
c) the marginal productivity of capital increases.
d) this leads to reduced rate of economic growth as workers lose their jobs to the machines.
e) population growth typically increases as a result.

38.35 (SG 38.11)
Correct: e)
Difficulty: 4
Page(s): 1022
Scramble range: All
Topic: Labour force growth

38.35
As the labour force grows with a constant capital stock,
a) there is less output in total since the capital–labour ratio declines.
b) the marginal productivity of labour is increased as the marginal productivity of capital is decreased.
c) the marginal productivity of labour and capital both increase.
d) the marginal productivity of labour and capital both decrease.
e) the marginal productivity of labour is reduced.

38.36
Correct: c)
Difficulty: 3
Page(s): 1022–23
Scramble range: All
Topic: Capital accumulation

38.36
Countries similar to Canada have
a) relatively low per capita capital and low growth rates.
b) relatively low per capita capital and low productivity rates.
c) high per capita capital and high productivity rates.
d) little capital per worker compared to the developing nations.
e) high per capita capital and low marginal productivity of workers as a result.

38.37
Correct: a)
Difficulty: 3
Page(s): 1022–23
Scramble range: All
Topic: Capital accumulation

38.37
Countries similar to Ethiopia have
a) relatively low per capita capital and low growth rates.
b) relatively low per capita capital and low productivity rates.
c) high per capita capital and high productivity rates.
d) little capital per worker compared to the developing nations.
e) low per capita capital per worker and therefore relatively high marginal productivity of labour.

38.38 (SG 38.12)
Correct: b)
Difficulty: 3
Page(s): 1021
Scramble range: All
Topic: Capital accumulation

38.38
There is a limit to growth induced by capital accumulation in the short run since
a) labour growth rates may become negative.
b) even as capital per capita increases, the rate of increase in total output will eventually begin to diminish.
c) even as capital per capita increases, the rate of increase in total output will eventually begin to increase causing excessive inflation.
d) there is a strong limit to the amount of capital that can be accumulated.
e) low population growth means too few workers for the amount of new capital.

38.39
Correct: b)
Difficulty: 3
Page(s): 1021
Scramble range: All
Topic: Per capita capital/technology level

38.39
Even if per capita capital is the same in two different countries,
a) the output cannot be compared since different currencies are used.
b) output per capita can be different if a superior technology is available in one country but not both.
c) output per worker will be the same.
d) the countries cannot be at the same standard of living.
e) the countries must be at the same standard of living if they have the same size of labour force.

38.40
Correct: b)
Difficulty: 3
Page(s): 1021–22
Scramble range: All
Topic: Attributes of economic growth

38.40
Faster technological advance and capital accumulation are typically accompanied by
a) a widening gap between rich and poor.
b) an increase in economic growth.
c) a decrease in economic growth.
d) a decrease in the degree of specialization of labour.
e) a decrease in the marginal product of labour.

38.41
Correct: b)
Difficulty: 3
Page(s): 1021
Scramble range: All
Topic: Capital accumulation

38.41
Compared with Singapore, the per capita capital accumulation of Ethiopia is
a) equal to that of Singapore.
b) less than that of Singapore.
c) greater than that of Singapore.
d) impossible to compare since the currencies are different.
e) impossible to compare since the two countries have very different population sizes.

38.42
Correct: b)
Difficulty: 3
Page(s): 1021
Scramble range: All
Topic: Per capita income growth

38.42
Compared with Singapore, the growth in per capita income of Ethiopia is
a) equal to that of Singapore.
b) less than that of Singapore.
c) greater than that of Singapore.
d) impossible to compare since the currencies are different.
e) impossible to compare since the two countries have very different population sizes.

38.43
Correct: e)
Difficulty: 3
Page(s): 1022
Scramble range: All
Topic: Income distribution

38.43
The richest 20 percent of consumers in the world consume
a) 20 percent of the world's goods and services.
b) 30 percent of the world's goods and services.
c) 40 percent of the world's goods and services.
d) 50 percent of the world's goods and services.
e) more than half of the world's goods and services.

38.44
Correct: a)
Difficulty: 3
Page(s): 1022
Scramble range: All
Topic: Income distribution

38.44
The poorest 20 percent of consumers in the world consume about
a) 5 percent of the world's goods and services.
b) 10 percent of the world's goods and services.
c) 15 percent of the world's goods and services.
d) 20 percent of the world's goods and services.
e) 25 percent of the world's goods and services.

38.45
Correct: b)
Difficulty: 3
Page(s): 1022
Scramble range: All
Topic: Economic growth

38.45
The slower the rate of capital accumulation or technological advance, the
a) greater will be economic growth.
b) lower will be economic growth.
c) greater is the saving rate.
d) higher is population growth.
e) lower is population growth.

38.46
Correct: e)
Difficulty: 3
Page(s): 1022–24
Scramble range: All
Topic: Causes of slow growth

38.46
Important reasons for weak economic growth include all of the following *except*
a) excessive population growth.
b) international debt.
c) negative rates of productivity growth.
d) low rates of saving.
e) high rates of saving and capital accumulation.

38.47
Correct: d)
Difficulty: 3
Page(s): 1022
Scramble range: All
Topic: Population growth

38.47
One of the constraints on economic growth is population growth. The average rate of population growth in the world over the last 20 years is
a) 1 percent.
b) 10 percent.
c) 5 percent.
e) 15 percent.
d) 2 percent.

38.48
Correct: d)
Difficulty: 3
Page(s): 1024
Scramble range: All
Topic: Population growth

38.48
With a population growth rate of 2 percent, about how many years will it take for the population to double?
a) 2 years.
b) 10 years.
c) 20 years.
d) 37 years.
e) 50 years.

38.49
Correct: b)
Difficulty: 3
Page(s): 1024
Scramble range: All
Topic: Population growth

38.49
With a population growth rate of 10 percent, about how many years will it take for the population to double?
a) 2 years.
b) 7 years.
c) 10 years.
d) 25 years.
e) 17 years.

38.50
Correct: d)
Difficulty: 3
Page(s): 1024
Scramble range: All
Topic: Population growth

38.50
Which of the following generalizations is accurate?
a) Rich countries have relatively high population growth rates, and poor countries have relatively low population growth rates.
b) Rich countries have relatively high population growth rates, and poor countries have relatively high population growth rates.
c) Rich countries have relatively low population growth rates, but poor countries have relatively low population growth rates.
d) Rich countries have relatively low population growth rates, but poor countries have relatively high population growth rates.
e) Rich countries have both low and high population growth rates, while poor countries have relatively low population growth rates.

38.51 (SG 38.14)
Correct: c)
Difficulty: 3
Page(s): 1024
Scramble range: All
Topic: Population growth

38.51
Population growth can reduce economic growth if
a) per capita productivity increases as well.
b) the population increase consists of able-bodied workers.
c) the population increase consists of children or other dependents not yet in the work force.
d) too many workers push up wages.
e) the population increase consists of immigrants.

38.52
Correct: c)
Difficulty: 3
Page(s): 1024
Scramble range: All
Topic: Population growth

38.52
Population growth can reduce economic growth if
a) per capita saving increases even more.
b) the population increase consists of skilled workers emmigrating from abroad.
c) capital must be devoted to the maintenance of dependents rather than adding to the capital stock.
d) too many workers push down the exchange rate.
e) too many workers push up the exchange rate.

38.53
Correct: b)
Difficulty: 3
Page(s): 1024
Scramble range: All
Topic: Population and age composition

38.53
If the birth rate exceeds the death rate, then the population will
a) increase and become older in average age.
b) increase and become younger in average age.
c) decrease and become older in average age.
d) decrease and become younger in average age.
e) increase but stay the same average age.

38.54
Correct: a)
Difficulty: 3
Page(s): 1024
Scramble range: All
Topic: Population growth

38.54
Population growth will occur when
a) the birth rate exceeds the death rate.
b) the death rate exceeds the growth rate.
c) the death rate exceeds the birth rate.
d) the birth rate exceeds the economic growth rate.
e) the birth rate plus net immigration is less than the death rate.

38.55
Correct: a)
Difficulty: 3
Page(s): 1024
Scramble range: All
Topic: Population growth

38.55
Population growth can become a problem if
a) decreases in death rates exceed decreases in birth rates.
b) decreases in birth rates exceed decreases in death rates.
c) increases in death rates exceed increases in birth rates.
d) increases in birth rates do not exceed increases in death rates.
e) decreases in birth rates do not exceed increases in income growth rates.

38.56
Correct: b)
Difficulty: 3
Page(s): 1024
Scramble range: All
Topic: Population growth

38.56
Population growth will increase if infant mortality rates
a) increase while death rates increase.
b) decrease while birth rates increase and death rates decrease.
c) decrease while death rates increase.
d) increase while death rates decrease.
e) increase, regardless of what happens to death rates.

38.57
Correct: b)
Difficulty: 3
Page(s): 1024
Scramble range: All
Topic: Expenditures and growth

38.57
Money spent on schools, roads, and hospitals
a) is money less well spent than that spent on irrigation systems.
b) does not have as large an impact on current GDP per capita as would money spent for industrial projects.
c) does not even indirectly contribute to the production of goods, and therefore reduces growth.
d) would decrease human capital and therefore decrease growth.
e) decreases human welfare.

38.58
Correct: a)
Difficulty: 3
Page(s): 1024–25
Scramble range: All
Topic: Saving/capital accumulation

38.58
A low rate of saving by poor countries results in all of the following *except*
a) a high rate of productivity growth.
b) a low capital accumulation.
c) low rates of economic growth.
d) lower per capita incomes.
e) a lower marginal productivity of labour.

38.59
Correct: a)
Difficulty: 3
Page(s): 1024–25
Scramble range: All
Topic: Expenditure constraints

38.59
Any income in a developing nation that is not spent on consumption or taxes is
a) saved.
b) spent for vacation expenditures.
c) spent by the government.
d) exported.
e) spent to pay off international debt.

38.60
Correct: e)
Difficulty: 3
Page(s): 1024–25
Scramble range: All
Topic: Expenditure constraints

38.60
If taxes are increased and consumption is already at the minimum sustainable level, then
a) economic growth will accelerate.
b) saving will increase.
c) income will rise.
d) saving must remain unchanged.
e) saving will decrease.

38.61
Correct: d)
Difficulty: 3
Page(s): 1024–25
Scramble range: All
Topic: Capital accumulation

38.61
Strong influences on the rate of capital accumulation are caused by all of the following *except*
a) the government budget deficit.
b) borrowing from the rest of the world.
c) net exports.
d) the greenhouse effect.
e) saving.

38.62
Correct: e)
Difficulty: 3
Page(s): 1025–26
Scramble range: All
Topic: Debt and growth

38.62
The burden of international debt affects growth, all other things being equal, since repayment of loans forces countries to
a) save.
b) raise consumption.
c) save more.
d) raise investment.
e) save less.

38.63
Correct: c)
Difficulty: 3
Page(s): 1025–26
Scramble range: All
Topic: Debt and growth

38.63
A poor country that borrows much from the rest of the world may not decrease its rate of economic growth since the
a) world may continue to extend the repayment period.
b) money may be spent on vacation travel abroad and promote much happiness.
c) money may be spent investing in capital equipment which increases, to a large enough extent, the marginal productivity of labour.
d) money may be spent on new park and recreational facilities, bringing much happiness to people.
e) population growth may rise, raising per capita income.

38.64
Correct: e)
Difficulty: 3
Page(s): 1025–26
Scramble range: All
Topic: Debt and growth

38.64
A poor country that borrows much from the rest of the world will decrease its rate of economic growth since the
a) world may continue to extend the repayment period.
b) prices of its exports may rise at a faster rate than the interest rate.
c) money may be spent investing in capital equipment which decreases, to a large extent, the marginal productivity of labour.
d) money may be spent on investments which greatly increase the productivity of labour.
e) money may be invested at a lower rate of return than the interest rate on the loan.

38.65
Correct: c)
Difficulty: 3
Page(s): 1026
Scramble range: All
Topic: Debt difficulties

38.65
The Latin American debt difficulties involve debts first incurred in the
a) 1950s during the cold war period.
b) 1960s during the great society period.
c) 1970s during the period in which prices on many raw materials were increasing at record rates.
d) early 1980s during the rise of the international banking cartel.
e) late 1980s during the era of high population growth.

38.66
Correct: e)
Difficulty: 3
Page(s): 1026
Scramble range: None
Topic: Debt difficulties

38.66
The Latin American debt difficulties became worse in the
a) 1980s as prices for many important raw materials collapsed.
b) 1970s during the period of exchange rate stability.
c) 1970s during the period in which prices on many raw materials were decreasing at record rates.
d) 1980s as real interest rates increased dramatically.
e) both a) and d).

38.67
Correct: d)
Difficulty: 3
Page(s): 1026
Scramble range: All
Topic: Underdevelopment trap

38.67
The vicious cycle of poverty involving low productivity, low income, low saving, and limited ability to obtain education has been called the
a) capitalist system.
b) conspiracy of the proletariat.
c) wealth trap.
d) underdevelopment trap.
e) international debt crisis.

38.68
Correct: c)
Difficulty: 2
Page(s): 1027
Scramble range: All
Topic: Toward increasing growth

38.68
One important help in breaking out of a cycle of poverty is
a) political instability.
b) rapid population growth.
c) effective control of population growth.
d) through increased capital flight.
e) warfare.

38.69
Correct: c)
Difficulty: 3
Page(s): 1027
Scramble range: All
Topic: Toward increasing growth

38.69
One small help in breaking out of a cycle of poverty is
a) political corruption.
b) generous foreign aid programs from the rich nations which help consolidate any political regime.
c) foreign aid programs from the rich which channel funds into productive investments rather than into a political party's slush fund.
d) increased capital flight.
e) warfare.

38.70
Correct: a)
Difficulty: 3
Page(s): 1027–31
Scramble range: All
Topic: Toward increasing growth

38.70
One important help in breaking out of a cycle of poverty is
a) success in developing export markets.
b) the lack of foreign aid programs.
c) reduced certainty concerning the future of private property rights over capital investments.
d) through increased brain drain.
e) reducing dependence on foreign aid.

38.71
Correct: d)
Difficulty: 3
Page(s): 1027–31
Scramble range: All
Topic: Trade barriers and growth

38.71
Tariffs and quotas imposed by developed countries that restrict imports from developing economies
a) do them harm but it's for their own good.
b) increase the sales of those products in the lucrative developed country market.
c) increases the foreign rate of economic growth if the goods cannot be sold elsewhere in the world.
d) decrease the rate of growth of those developing economies.
e) help these countries develop their own markets.

38.72
Correct: b)
Difficulty: 4
Page(s): 1027–31
Scramble range: All
Topic: Trade and growth

38.72
If Canada engages in free trade with a developing nation,
a) their low-wage labour will eliminate all industry in high-wage Canada.
b) their industries will expand and provide profit to be directed into capital accumulation, thereby increasing future economic growth.
c) Canadian products will ruin the economy of the less developed nation.
d) the development effort will be unaffected.
e) Canada will lose at the expense of this country.

38.73
Correct: e)
Difficulty: 3
Page(s): 1030
Scramble range: All
Topic: Export–led growth

38.73
Which of the following countries has not increased its growth dramatically because of export success?
a) Hong Kong.
b) Japan.
c) Singapore.
d) Taiwan.
e) Nicaragua.

38.74
Correct: b)
Difficulty: 3
Page(s): 1027–31
Scramble range: All
Topic: U.S. policy growth abroad

38.74
The U.S. trade policy called the Generalized System of Preferences lowered tariffs on imports from many developing countries. What was the primary purpose of this act?
a) To wean U.S. consumers from foreign imports.
b) To encourage increased imports from those developing countries.
c) To raise the real income of U.S. producers competing with the imports.
d) To lower the real income of American consumers.
e) To encourage these countries to develop their own independent domestic markets.

38.75
Correct: d)
Difficulty: 2
Page(s): 1017
Scramble range: All
Topic: Measures of development

38.75
The measure of economic development most widely used by economists is the
a) trade deficit.
b) federal budget deficit.
c) unemployment rate.
d) real per capita income.
e) per capita level of debt.

38.76
Correct: c)
Difficulty: 3
Page(s): 1022
Scramble range: All
Topic: Capital flight and growth

38.76
Capital flight from Hong Kong in anticipation of the return of Hong Kong to China in 1997 is likely to
a) stimulate the economy of Hong Kong in the short run.
b) leave unaffected the economy of Hong Kong in the short run, but not the long run.
c) reduce economic growth in both the short run and the long run.
d) stimulate the economy of Hong Kong only in the long run.
e) hurt Hong Kong in the short run, but not in the long run.

38.77
Correct: b)
Difficulty: 3
Page(s): 1021
Scramble range: All
Topic: Human capital

38.77
The Chinese crackdown on the student movement in 1989 may lead to a permanent loss of thousands of some of their best students, who will take refuge abroad. This would be expected to
a) increase per capita wealth of those students who remain in China.
b) decrease the rate of economic growth due to lower human capital stock than would have been available with the full return to China of foreign students.
c) create no change in Chinese economic circumstances.
d) lead to greater capital accumulation in the near future in China.
e) reduce population pressures and hence encourage economic growth.

38.78 (SG 38.1)
Correct: e)
Difficulty: 3
Page(s): 1017
Scramble range: All
Topic: Developing nations

38.78
Which of the following is *not* an attribute of a developing country?
a) Poverty.
b) A low stock of capital.
c) A developing industrial base.
d) A developing commercial base.
e) A stable and high stock of capital.

38.79 (SG 38.2)
Correct: e)
Difficulty: 3
Page(s): 1018
Scramble range: All
Topic: Communist system

38.79
Which of the following relies *least* on the market as a mechanism for allocating resources?
a) Industrial countries.
b) Newly industrialized countries.
c) Developing countries.
d) Oil-rich countries.
e) Communist countries.

38.80 (SG 38.5)
Correct: d)
Difficulty: 3
Page(s): 1018
Scramble range: All
Topic: World Lorenz curve

38.80
The Lorenz curve depicting the distribution of average per capita income across countries lies
a) on the 45° line.
b) to the left of the 45° line.
c) to the right of the 45° line, but not as far out as the Lorenz curve depicting the distribution of income of families within Canada.
d) to the right of the 45° line, and farther out than the Lorenz curve depicting the distribution of income of families within Canada.
e) to the right of the 45° line, roughly as far out as the Lorenz curve depicting the distribution of income of families within Canada.

38.81 (SG 38.7)
Correct: d)
Difficulty: 3
Page(s): 1021
Scramble range: All
Topic: Per capita production function

38.81
Which of the following is *not* a characteristic of a per capita production function?
a) Per capita output increases as the per capita stock of capital increases.
b) The state of technology is held constant for a given per capita production function.
c) The law of diminishing returns applies to the per capita production function.
d) As the stock of capital increases, the per capita production function shifts upward.
e) As technological knowledge advances, the per capita production function shifts upward.

38.82 (SG 38.8)
Correct: a)
Difficulty: 3
Page(s): 1021
Scramble range: All
Topic: Human capital

38.82
Human capital is
a) the skill and knowledge of workers.
b) labour.
c) the machines made by humans.
d) the machines used by humans.
e) the population.

38.83 (SG 38.9)
Correct: e)
Difficulty: 3
Page(s): 1022
Scramble range: All
Topic: Technological change

38.83
Which of the following would be the best way to increase the rate of economic growth?
a) Discover new supplies of natural resources.
b) Educate workers.
c) Increase the population growth rate.
d) Decrease the population growth rate.
e) Develop new technologies.

38.84 (SG 38.13)
Correct: e)
Difficulty: 3
Page(s): 1024–26
Scramble range: All
Topic: Obstacles to economic growth

38.84
Which of the following is *not* a principal obstacle to economic growth for poor countries?
a) Population growth.
b) High number of dependents as a percent of population.
c) Low saving rates.
d) International debt.
e) Multinational corporations.

38.85 (SG 38.15)
Correct: c)
Difficulty: 3
Page(s): 1024
Scramble range: All
Topic: Obstacles to economic growth

38.85
For a given level of saving, investment will be higher the
a) higher the government budget deficit and the higher the current account deficit.
b) higher the government budget deficit and the lower the current account deficit.
c) lower the government budget deficit and the higher the current account deficit.
d) lower the government budget deficit and the lower the current account deficit.
e) higher the income level.

38.86 (SG 38.16)
Correct: a)
Difficulty: 2
Page(s): 1026
Scramble range: All
Topic: Underdevelopment trap

38.86
When a country is locked into a self-reinforcing low-income situation it is said to be in
a) an underdevelopment trap.
b) a liquidity trap.
c) a deindustrialization trap.
d) an undercapitalized trap.
e) a debt trap.

38.87 (SG 38.18)
Correct: d)
Difficulty: 3
Page(s): 1027–30
Scramble range: All
Topic: Trade and development

38.87
Which of the following has been a key ingredient in the most dramatic success stories of economic development?
a) Population control.
b) Foreign aid.
c) Natural resources.
d) Relatively unrestricted international trade.
e) Increased saving levels.

38.88 (SG 38.19)
Correct: a)
Difficulty: 3
Page(s): 1031
Scramble range: All
Topic: *AD* stimulation and growth

38.88
Which of the following will *not* increase the long-run economic growth rate of a poor country?
a) An increase in the rate of growth of aggregate demand.
b) An increase in the growth of technology.
c) An increase in the saving rate.
d) An increase in the rate at which capital is accumulated.
e) A decrease in the rate of population growth.

38.89 (SG 38.20)
Correct: d)
Difficulty: 3
Page(s): 1027
Scramble range: All
Topic: Foreign aid

38.89
Which of the following best characterizes the current general feeling among economists about the role of foreign aid in stimulating economic growth?
a) Foreign aid has almost always had a distinct positive effect on economic growth.
b) Foreign aid has almost always had a distinct negative effect on economic growth.
c) Foreign aid is most helpful if it is used to increase per capita consumption.
d) There is some controversy about the direction of the effect on economic growth but agreement that the level of foreign aid is too small to make a decisive difference.
e) Foreign aid is most helpful when it replaces dependence on international trade.

38.90
Correct: a)
Difficulty: 3
Page(s): 1029
Scramble range: All
Topic: Resource allocation

38.90
Which of the following relies most on command as a mechanism for allocating resources?
a) Communist countries.
b) Newly industrialized countries.
c) Developing countries.
d) Oil-rich countries.
e) Industrial countries.

38.91
Correct: c)
Difficulty: 3
Page(s): 1018–19
Scramble range: All
Topic: Lorenz curve

38.91
A Lorenz curve showing that the distribution of income of families within Canada is nearer to equality than the distribution of average per capita income across countries would lie
a) on the 45° line.
b) to the left of the 45° line.
c) to the right of the 45° line but not as far to the right as the world Lorenz curve.
d) to the the right of the 45° line and farther out than the world Lorenz curve.
e) to the right of the 45° line and equal to the world Lorenz curve.

38.92
Correct: a)
Difficulty: 3
Page(s): 1022
Scramble range: All
Topic: Per capita production function

38.92
Which of the following is characteristic of a per capita production function?
a) Per capita output increases as the per capita stock of capital increases.
b) The state of technology is allowed to vary as output grows.
c) The function shows increasing rather than diminishing returns.
d) As the stock of capital increases, the per capita production function shifts downward.
e) The marginal product of labour is constant.

38.93
Correct: b)
Difficulty: 2
Page(s): 1021
Scramble range: All
Topic: Human capital

38.93
What is the term applied to the skill and knowledge of workers?
a) Marginal revenue product.
b) Human capital.
c) Derived demand.
d) Supply of labour.
e) Labour force.

38.94
Correct: d)
Difficulty: 3
Page(s): 1025
Scramble range: All
Topic: Growth

38.94
Which of the following is considered by economists to be a principal obstacle to economic growth for poor countries?
a) Multinational corporations.
b) Low consumption rates.
c) Lack of population growth.
d) International debt.
e) A lack of sufficient aggregate demand.

38.95
Correct: e)
Difficulty: 3
Page(s): 1026
Scramble range: All
Topic: Underdevelopment trap

38.95
What is known as the "underdevelopment trap"?
a) Lack of liquidity.
b) Decline of population growth that prevents poor countries from having an adequate work force.
c) Too high levels of international debt.
d) Lack of domestic consumption spending caused by overinvestment by foreign corporations.
e) Self-reinforcing low-income equilibrium.

38.96 (SG 38.17)
Correct: e)
Difficulty: 4
Page(s): 1030
Scramble range: All
Topic: Aggregate demand

38.96
Stimulating aggregate demand in the rich countries will
a) raise the growth rate in these countries but not in the developing nations.
b) have no impact on long-run growth rates in the rich countries, but will help the poor countries.
c) lower the inflation rate in the poor countries.
d) stimulate saving in the poor countries.
e) have no impact on the income levels of the poor countries.

38.97
Correct: a)
Difficulty: 3
Page(s): 1026
Scramble range: All
Topic: Growth

38.97
Which of the following has *not* been a key ingredient in the most dramatic success stories of economic development?
a) Restrictions on international trade to protect developing industries.
b) High growth rates of per capita income.
c) High rates of capital accumulation.
d) Fast-paced technological improvement.
e) Lowering population growth.

38.98
Correct: d)
Difficulty: 3
Page(s): 1024
Scramble range: All
Topic: Growth

38.98
Which of the following would increase the long-run economic growth rate of a poor country?
a) A fully anticipated increase in the money supply.
b) An increase in the percentage of income devoted to consumption.
c) An increase in the rate of growth of aggregate demand.
d) An increase in the savings rate.
e) An increase in the inflation rate.

38.99
Correct: b)
Difficulty: 3
Page(s): 1026
Scramble range: All
Topic: Foreign aid

38.99
Which of the following influences on economic growth is generally considered by economists to be too unimportant to make a decisive difference?
a) Total investment in foreign countries.
b) Foreign aid from other countries.
c) Rate of saving in foreign countries.
d) Government budget deficits of foreign countries.
e) Level of trade restrictions.

38.100
Correct: e)
Difficulty: 5
Page(s): 1025
Scramble range: All
Topic: Investment and growth

38.100
Consider Fact 38.1. After the price of silicon rises, the level of investment becomes __________ per capita and the growth rate __________
a) \$100 ; rises.
b) –\$100; falls.
c) \$200; rises.
d) \$300; rises.
e) zero; stays constant.

Fact 38.1
Siliconia is a poor country with no natural resources except sand. Per capita income is \$500 per year, and this entire income is consumed. Per capita income is constant — there is no economic growth. The government sector has a balanced budget and there are no exports or imports. Suddenly the price of silicon increases, and Siliconia is able to export sand at a huge profit. Exports soar from zero to \$400 per capita. Per capita income increases to \$1,000 per year and per capita consumption increases to \$600 per year. There are still no imports, and Siliconia has a current account surplus of \$400 per capita.

38.101
Correct: e)
Difficulty: 5
Page(s): 1025
Scramble range: All
Topic: Investment and growth

38.101
Consider Fact 38.1. Suppose that Siliconia now starts to import capital goods equal to \$400 per capita. Its investment becomes __________ per capita and its net exports become __________ per capita.
a) zero; zero
b) zero; \$400
c) \$100; \$100
d) \$200; -\$200
e) \$400; zero

38.102
Correct: a)
Difficulty: 5
Page(s): 1025
Scramble range: All
Topic: Investment and growth

38.102
Consider Fact 38.1. If the government of Siliconia decides to run a budget deficit of $100 per capita, what will be Siliconia's investment?

a) –$100 per capita.
b) Zero.
c) $100 per capita.
d) $200 per capita.
e) $400 per capita.

Chapter 39 Comparing Economic Systems

39.1
Correct: c)
Difficulty: 2
Page(s): 1036
Scramble range: All
Topic: Economic restructuring in the Soviet Union

39.1
In June 1987, Mikhail Gorbachev presented a new program he called *perestroika*, meaning
a) prosperity.
b) forward looking.
c) restructuring.
d) regulation.
e) democracy.

39.2
Correct: c)
Difficulty: 3
Page(s): 1049
Scramble range: All
Topic: China's Cultural Revolution

39.2
During the Cultural Revolution in the People's Republic of China
a) economic growth experienced a "great leap forward."
b) manufacturing and agricultural productivity increased.
c) productivity decreased in agriculture and industry.
d) more market incentives were used to revolutionize the economy.
e) strong investment was made in human capital.

39.3
Correct: d)
Difficulty: 3
Page(s): 1049
Scramble range: All
Topic: Deng Xiaoping

39.3
Deng Xiaoping stated that China could continue as "one country and two systems." By this he meant China could have an economic
a) system similar to the U.S.S.R. and a political system similar to Canada.
b) and political system similar to the U.S.S.R.
c) and political system similar to Canada.
d) system similar to Canada and a political system similar to the U.S.S.R.
e) system similar to the one already in place and a political system similar to that of Canada.

39.4
Correct: c)
Difficulty: 3
Page(s): 1037
Scramble range: All
Topic: Economic deregulation in the United States

39.4
In the United States, the modern economic deregulation movement began under President
a) John Kennedy in the early 1960s.
b) Richard Nixon in the early 1970s.
c) Jimmy Carter in the late 1970s.
d) Ronald Reagan in the 1980s.
e) Mikhail Gorbachev in 1987.

39.5
Correct: b)
Difficulty: 3
Page(s): 1037
Scramble range: All
Topic: Economic deregulation in the United Kingdom

39.5
Deregulation in the United Kingdom has included the
a) purchasing of more U.S. military hardware.
b) selling of state-owned railroads.
c) selling of the British Broadcasting Corporation.
d) selling of London Bridge.
e) the privatization of Air Canada.

39.6
Correct: e)
Difficulty: 3
Page(s): 1037
Scramble range: All
Topic: Deregulation in Japan

39.6
In Japan, deregulation has included the
a) selling of U.S. government bonds.
b) elimination of rice import quotas.
c) expansion of restrictions in finance and banking.
d) elimination of the Ministry of International Trade and Industry.
e) elimination of restrictions in finance and banking.

39.7
Correct: d)
Difficulty: 2
Page(s): 1037
Scramble range: All
Topic: The economic problem

39.7
Regardless of the economic system, the fundamental economic problem is
a) overproduction.
b) inflation.
c) barter.
d) scarcity.
e) underconsumption.

39.8
Correct: c)
Difficulty: 3
Page(s): 1037
Scramble range: All
Topic: Scarcity

39.8
Scarcity is the relationship between
a) cost and inputs.
b) availability and production possibilities.
c) availability and desirablility.
d) desirability and ability to pay.
e) availability and income.

39.9
Correct: b)
Difficulty: 2
Page(s): 1037
Scramble range: All
Topic: Production possibilities

39.9
The production possibilities frontier represents
a) the best point for the economy.
b) the opportunity costs of production because resources are scarce.
c) all points of technological change which may change either industry.
d) points of less than full employment.
e) various consumption choices of the economy.

39.10
Correct: b)
Difficulty: 3
Page(s): 1037
Scramble range: All
Topic: Production possibilities

39.10
Wasting of resources
a) moves production beyond the production possibilities frontier.
b) moves production inside the production possibilities frontier.
c) moves production along the production possibilities frontier.
d) has nothing to do with production possibilities, only with distribution.
e) has nothing to do with production possibilities, only with consumption.

39.11
Correct: b)
Difficulty: 3
Page(s): 1037
Scramble range: All
Topic: Production possibilities

39.11
If resources are used in a way that is more expensive than some alternative method of producing the identical output, production
a) moves beyond the production possibilities frontier.
b) moves inside the production possibilities frontier.
c) moves along the production possibilities frontier.
d) possibilities remain fixed since the identical output is produced.
e) possibilities remain fixed since the same inputs are used.

39.12
Correct: e)
Difficulty: 3
Page(s): 1037
Scramble range: All
Topic: Production possibilities

39.12
Once an economy is producing at a point on the frontier, more of one good can be produced
a) along with more of all other products.
b) only by expanding the production possibility frontier.
c) only if the economy trades with another economy.
d) at zero opportunity cost only if the economy is a developing economy.
e) only by sacrificing output in another industry.

39.13
Correct: d)
Difficulty: 3
Page(s): 1037
Scramble range: All
Topic: The economic problem

39.13
The economic problem is "solved" when
a) the production possibilities frontier is eliminated.
b) the economy reaches the production possibilities frontier.
c) opportunity costs are reduced.
d) the best point on the production possibilities frontier is reached.
e) there is no more scarcity.

39.14
Correct: a)
Difficulty: 2
Page(s): 1037
Scramble range: All
Topic: The economic problem

39.14
The "best" point on the production possibilities frontier is determined in a market-oriented system by the
a) costs of production and individual preferences.
b) Department of Finance.
c) prime minister.
d) the various committees of parliament.
e) interaction of monopoly and monopsony.

39.15
Correct: c)
Difficulty: 3
Page(s): 1037
Scramble range: All
Topic: The economic problem

39.15
The "best" point on the production possibilities frontier is determined in a communist system by
a) the costs of production and individual preferences.
b) the individual households and sellers.
c) government agencies.
d) the military.
e) the central planner.

39.16
Correct: a)
Difficulty: 3
Page(s): 1037
Scramble range: All
Topic: Solving the economic problem

39.16
The economic system determines whether the production frontier is reached, which production point is reached, and
a) the distribution of that production and income.
b) consumer tastes and preferences.
c) producer talents and capabilities.
d) the population growth rate.
e) the geographical distribution of labour.

39.17
Correct: d)
Difficulty: 3
Page(s): 1038
Scramble range: All
Topic: Economic system/welfare judgement

39.17
All economic systems
a) consider the equality of incomes as a basic human right.
b) consider equality of opportunity as all that is required for social justice.
c) consider equality of results as all that is required for social justice.
d) have their own ideas about what is considered to be right and just.
e) produce on the production possibilities frontier.

39.18
Correct: a)
Difficulty: 2
Page(s): 1038
Scramble range: All
Topic: Different dimensions of economic systems

39.18
Economic systems vary in their laws or rules concerning
a) the ownership of resources and the allocation of those resources.
b) the ownership of resources but not the allocation of those resources.
c) the allocation of resources but not the ownership of those resources.
d) neither the ownership of resources nor the allocation of those resources.
e) the production possibilities frontier.

39.19
Correct: b)
Difficulty: 3
Page(s): 1038
Scramble range: All
Topic: Capitalism

39.19
Capitalism relies primarily on
a) public ownership of resources and command allocation of resources.
b) private ownership of resources and market-determined allocation of resources.
c) public ownership of resources and market-determined allocation of resources.
d) private ownership of resources and command allocation of resources.
e) a mixture of public and private ownership of resources and a mixture of command and market-determined allocation of resources.

39.20
Correct: a)
Difficulty: 3
Page(s): 1038
Scramble range: All
Topic: Socialism

39.20
Socialism relies primarily on
a) public ownership of resources and command allocation of resources.
b) private ownership of resources and market-determined allocation of resources.
c) public ownership of resources and market-determined allocation of resources.
d) private ownership of resources and command allocation of resources.
e) a mixture of public and private ownership of resources and a mixture of command and market-determined allocation of resources.

39.21
Correct: a)
Difficulty: 2
Page(s): 1038
Scramble range: None
Topic: Central planning

39.21
Central planning means
a) command allocation of resources.
b) private ownership of resources.
c) public ownership of resources.
d) private allocation of resources.
e) both a) and c).

39.22
Correct: a)
Difficulty: 2
Page(s): 1038
Scramble range: All
Topic: Capitalist economies

39.22
No economy is purely capitalist, but which is the closest to capitalist of the following?
a) Canada.
b) the U.S.S.R.
c) the People's Republic of China.
d) Hungary.
e) the United Kingdom.

39.23
Correct: e)
Difficulty: 3
Page(s): 1038
Scramble range: All
Topic: Capitalist economies

39.23
No economy is purely capitalist, but which is the closest to capitalist of the following?
a) Poland.
b) Cuba.
c) Saudi Arabia.
d) Sweden.
e) Japan.

39.24
Correct: e)
Difficulty: 2
Page(s): 1038
Scramble range: All
Topic: Socialism

39.24
No economy is purely socialist, but which is the closest to socialist of the following?
a) Yugoslavia.
b) Hong Kong.
c) Japan.
d) the United States.
e) the U.S.S.R.

39.25
Correct: c)
Difficulty: 3
Page(s): 1039
Scramble range: All
Topic: Market socialism

39.25
Market socialism combines
a) public ownership of resources and command allocation of resources.
b) private ownership of resources and market-determined allocation of resources.
c) public ownership of resources and market-determined allocation of resources.
d) private ownership of resources and command allocation of resources.
e) a mixture of public and private ownership of resources and a mixture of command and market-determined allocation of resources.

39.26
Correct: b)
Difficulty: 2
Page(s): 1039
Scramble range: None
Topic: Market socialism

39.26
Market socialist countries include
a) the United States.
b) Yugoslavia.
c) the United Kingdom.
d) the People's Republic of China.
e) both b) and d).

39.27
Correct: c)
Difficulty: 2
Page(s): 1039
Scramble range: None
Topic: Market socialism

39.27
Market socialist countries include
a) Canada.
b) France.
c) Hungary.
d) the German Democratic Republic.
e) both a) and c).

39.28
Correct: d)
Difficulty: 3
Page(s): 1039
Scramble range: All
Topic: Welfare state capitalism

39.28
Welfare state capitalism combines
a) public ownership of resources and command allocation of resources.
b) private ownership of resources and market-determined allocation of resources.
c) public ownership of resources and market-determined allocation of resources.
d) private ownership of resources and command allocation of resources.
e) a mixture of public and private ownership of resources and a mixture of command and market-determined allocation of resources.

39.29
Correct: c)
Difficulty: 2
Page(s): 1039
Scramble range: All
Topic: Welfare state capitalism

39.29
An example of a country that uses welfare state capitalism is
a) the People's Republic of China.
b) the United States.
c) Sweden.
d) Hong Kong.
e) Canada.

39.30
Correct: d)
Difficulty: 3
Page(s): 1039
Scramble range: All
Topic: Pure capitalism

39.30
A country that is purely capitalist puts its greatest concern on preserving
a) the growth of the GDP at all costs.
b) price controls on wages but not interest rates.
c) greed.
d) individual liberty.
e) environmental management.

39.31
Correct: c)
Difficulty: 2
Page(s): 1039
Scramble range: All
Topic: Pure capitalism

39.31
At the foundation of a purely capitalist system is
a) naked human greed and exploitation.
b) the mass of poor people who do most of the work.
c) the establishment and enforcement of private property rights.
d) environmental decay and moral degredation.
e) monopoly producers.

39.32
Correct: d)
Difficulty: 2
Page(s): 1039
Scramble range: All
Topic: Pure capitalism

39.32
In a purely capitalist system, an individual owns all of the following *except* those goods
a) legitimately acquired.
b) legitimately received as gifts.
c) purchased.
d) which are stolen.
e) he or she produces.

39.33
Correct: a)
Difficulty: 3
Page(s): 1039
Scramble range: All
Topic: Pure capitalism

39.33
The proper role of the state in pure capitalism includes
a) preventing fraudulant trades.
b) regulating wages of labour.
c) regulating rents on housing.
d) preventing voluntary trades that occur without fraud.
e) providing a minimum wage.

39.34
Correct: d)
Difficulty: 3
Page(s): 1040
Scramble range: None
Topic: Pure capitalism

39.34
In a capitalist economy, "what" will be produced is determined by
a) local and regional planning boards.
b) national planning boards.
c) the production plans of the capitalist.
d) the tastes and preferences of buyers.
e) both c) and d).

39.35
Correct: c)
Difficulty: 3
Page(s): 1040
Scramble range: None
Topic: Pure capitalism

39.35
In a capitalist economy, "how" goods will be produced is determined by
a) local and regional planning boards.
b) national planning boards.
c) the production decisions of the profit-seeking capitalist.
d) the tastes and preferences of buyers.
e) both c) and d).

39.36
Correct: d)
Difficulty: 3
Page(s): 1040
Scramble range: None
Topic: Pure capitalism

39.36
In a capitalist economy, "for whom" goods will be produced is determined by
a) local and regional planning boards.
b) national planning boards.
c) the prices of the resources.
d) the tastes and preferences of buyers.
e) both c) and d).

39.37
Correct: c)
Difficulty: 3
Page(s): 1040
Scramble range: All
Topic: Socialism

39.37
Socialism assumes that
a) public ownership of capital will enable the rich to exploit the poor.
b) public ownership of capital will enable the capitalists to exploit the labourers.
c) private ownership of capital will enable the rich capitalists to exploit the poor labourers.
d) public ownership of resources will end the economic problem.
e) public ownership of resources will allow labourers to exploit capitalists.

39.38
Correct: b)
Difficulty: 3
Page(s): 1040
Scramble range: All
Topic: Pure socialism

39.38
Under pure socialism, the state owns all resources except
a) capital.
b) human capital and consumer durable capital.
c) raw materials.
d) land.
e) human capital and land.

39.39
Correct: e)
Difficulty: 3
Page(s): 1040
Scramble range: All
Topic: Pure socialism

39.39
Under pure socialism, the state
a) produces and buys all goods.
b) produces, buys, and sells all goods.
c) does not own land, but buys all farm output.
d) does not own the mines, but buys all coal output.
e) produces and sells all goods.

39.40
Correct: e)
Difficulty: 2
Page(s): 1040
Scramble range: All
Topic: Pure socialism

39.40
Under socialism, it is forbidden to
a) be unproductive.
b) vote.
c) use resources efficiently.
d) spend all earned income.
e) earn great wealth or income from large manufacturing activities.

39.41
Correct: b)
Difficulty: 3
Page(s): 1040
Scramble range: All
Topic: Pure socialism

39.41
"From each according to his ability, to each according to his contribution," summarizes the philosophy of income distribution in which type of economic system?
a) Pure capitalism.
b) Pure socialism.
c) Welfare state capitalism.
d) Market socialism.
e) Communism.

39.42
Correct: b)
Difficulty: 3
Page(s): 1040
Scramble range: All
Topic: Socialism

39.42
"From each according to his ability, to each according to his contribution," means that the state will
a) enforce private property rights.
b) determine the prices of the resources in the economy.
c) leave to the marketplace the determination of wages and prices.
d) allow private banks to set their own interest rates.
e) allow private individuals to own land.

39.43
Correct: e)
Difficulty: 3
Page(s): 1040
Scramble range: All
Topic: Communism

39.43
"From each according to his ability, to each according to his need," summarizes the philosophy of income distribution in which type of economic system?
a) Pure capitalism.
b) Pure socialism.
c) Welfare state capitalism.
d) Market socialism.
e) Communism.

39.44
Correct: b)
Difficulty: 3
Page(s): 1040
Scramble range: None
Topic: Communism

39.44
"From each according to his ability, to each according to his need," means that the state will
a) protect private property rights.
b) determine the wages, rents, and interest rates in the economy.
c) leave to the marketplace the determination of wages and prices.
d) allow private banks to set their own interest rates.
e) both c) and d).

39.45
Correct: b)
Difficulty: 3
Page(s): 1040
Scramble range: None
Topic: Socialism and communism

39.45
In a socialist system or a communist system, "what" is produced is determined by
a) local business organizations.
b) the tastes and preferences of the central planners.
c) the production plans of the capitalist.
d) the tastes and preferences of buyers.
e) both c) and d).

39.46
Correct: b)
Difficulty: 3
Page(s): 1040
Scramble range: None
Topic: Socialism and communism

39.46
In a socialist or communist system, "how" goods will be produced is determined by
a) local business organizations.
b) the tastes and preferences of the central planners.
c) the production decisions of the profit-seeking capitalist.
d) the tastes and preferences of buyers.
e) both c) and d).

39.47
Correct: b)
Difficulty: 3
Page(s): 1040
Scramble range: None
Topic: Socialism and communism

39.47
In a socialist or communist system, "for whom" goods will be produced is determined by
a) local business organization and consumer groups.
b) the tastes and preferences of the central planners.
c) the skills of the ordinary labourer.
d) the tastes and preferences of buyers.
e) both c) and d).

39.48
Correct: c)
Difficulty: 3
Page(s): 1040
Scramble range: All
Topic: Advantages of capitalism

39.48
A major advantage of capitalism is the
a) preservation of environmental quality.
b) guarantee of prosperity of all individuals.
c) individual's judgement is used to determine economic actions of the individual.
d) lack of low paying or demeaning jobs.
e) equal distribution of income.

39.49
Correct: a)
Difficulty: 3
Page(s): 1040
Scramble range: All
Topic: Invisible hand of capitalism

39.49
In a system of pure capitalism, every individual labouring to seek his own gain will be led
a) as if by an "invisible hand" to promote the public welfare as well as his own welfare.
b) to an early grave due to the exploitation of labour by the capitalists.
c) by the "visible hand" of regulation to be sure the outcome is fair for all.
d) by the military–industrial complex to increase taxes and spending by the government.
e) as if by an "invisible hand" to promote his own welfare at the cost of the public welfare.

39.50
Correct: e)
Difficulty: 3
Page(s): 1040
Scramble range: All
Topic: Invisible hand of capitalism

39.50
In a system of pure capitalism, every individual labouring to seek his own gain will be led as if by an "invisible hand" to promote the public welfare as well as his own welfare. This statement was made by that defender of capitalism
a) Franklin Roosevelt.
b) John Stuart Mill.
c) Janos Kornai.
d) John Maynard Keynes.
e) Adam Smith.

39.51
Correct: b)
Difficulty: 3
Page(s): 1041
Scramble range: All
Topic: Criticisms of capitalism

39.51
A major disadvantage of capitalism is
a) it leads to materialism.
b) the distribution of income results from an initial distribution of resources that was unjustly determined.
c) the rich get richer as the poor get poorer.
d) that it is inefficient relative to socialism.
e) that it requires knowledge of thousand of prices by each individual in the economy.

39.52
Correct: d)
Difficulty: 3
Page(s): 1040
Scramble range: None
Topic: Advantages of capitalism

39.52
A major advantage of capitalism is that
a) it prevents materialism.
b) the distribution of income results from an initial distribution of resources that was justly determined.
c) the rich get richer as the poor get poorer.
d) it is efficient relative to socialism.
e) both b) and d).

39.53
Correct: a)
Difficulty: 3
Page(s): 1041
Scramble range: All
Topic: Criticisms of capitalism

39.53
A major disadvantage of capitalism is that
a) individuals, such as the mentally ill, may not truly know what is best for themselves.
b) the distribution of income is just.
c) the poor get richer but the rich get poorer.
d) it is inefficient relative to socialism.
e) it requires the knowledge of thousands of prices by each individual in the economy.

39.54
Correct: e)
Difficulty: 3
Page(s): 1040
Scramble range: All
Topic: Socialism

39.54
Advocates of socialism argue that
a) individuals make good decisions and the state makes bad decisions.
b) individuals and the state make equally good choices.
c) the state cannot better process the thousands of prices needed to decide production and consumption as well as each individual in the economy.
d) individuals make bad choices, but the state makes worse choices.
e) the state makes better choices than does the individual.

39.55
Correct: e)
Difficulty: 3
Page(s): 1041
Scramble range: All
Topic: Criticisms of capitalism

39.55
According to critics of capitalism, there is a contradiction in capitalism stemming from the fact that
a) the rich exploit the poor.
b) too much output leads to environmental destruction.
c) it requires knowledge of thousands of prices by each individual in the economy.
d) private individuals enforce public property rights through homespun systems of justice.
e) the state is the monopolist in the enforcement of private property rights.

39.56
Correct: a)
Difficulty: 3
Page(s): 1041
Scramble range: All
Topic: Criticisms of capitalism

39.56
According to critics of capitalism, there is a contradiction in capitalism because
a) individuals and groups can organize and influence government decisions concerning how power is used.
b) too little employment leads to economic decay.
c) the state is the monopsonist in the enforcement of private property rights.
d) private individuals enforce private property rights through murders and other forms of violence.
e) the distribution of income is too equal.

39.57
Correct: d)
Difficulty: 2
Page(s): 1040
Scramble range: All
Topic: Pure capitalism

39.57
Pure capitalism
a) existed in ancient Greece but nowhere else.
b) existed in ancient Greece and Rome, but nowhere else.
c) existed in ancient Greece and in the modern United States, but nowhere else.
d) has never existed.
e) will exist in the new, united Germany.

39.58
Correct: c)
Difficulty: 2
Page(s): 1041
Scramble range: All
Topic: Economic growth in Japan

39.58
The "Japanese economic miracle" refers to Japan's rapid economic growth
a) soon after the Mejii Restoration.
b) between the two world wars.
c) since its defeat in World War II.
d) in the 1960s.
e) in the late 1980s.

39.59
Correct: d)
Difficulty: 3
Page(s): 1041
Scramble range: All
Topic: Japanese economic growth

39.59
In the late 1980s, the Japanese were strong exporters of
a) agricultural products.
b) services.
c) military hardware.
d) high-tech manufactured goods.
e) rice.

39.60
Correct: d)
Difficulty: 3
Page(s): 1042
Scramble range: All
Topic: Japanese economic growth

39.60
Causes of the Japanese rapid economic growth include all of the following *except*
a) small-scale of government.
b) reliance on free market incentives.
c) hard-working, productive people.
d) a bountiful endowment of productive agricultural land.
e) pro-business government intervention.

39.61
Correct: c)
Difficulty: 3
Page(s): 1042
Scramble range: All
Topic: Japanese economic growth

39.61
One cause of the Japanese rapid economic growth is
a) a large, productive government.
b) reliance on Buddhist principles of marketing.
c) low taxes which encourage people to work and save.
d) bountiful endowment of mountainous land.
e) no government intervention in the economy.

39.62
Correct: a)
Difficulty: 3
Page(s): 1042
Scramble range: All
Topic: Japanese economic growth

39.62
One contributor to Japanese industrial growth has been
a) the Ministry of Trade and Industry.
b) reliance on low agricultural prices for consumers.
c) low taxes on consumption inducing people to save a lower portion of earned income and spend more.
d) the defeat of the interests of the land owners.
e) subsidies to industry.

39.63
Correct: e)
Difficulty: 2
Page(s): 1042
Scramble range: All
Topic: Japanese MITI

39.63
The Japanese Ministry of Trade and Industry has encouraged the manufacture of all *except* the following
a) coal.
b) electrical power.
c) steel.
d) shipbuilding.
e) perfume.

39.64
Correct: e)
Difficulty: 3
Page(s): 1042
Scramble range: All
Topic: Japanese MITI

39.64
In the 1960s the Japanese Ministry of Trade and Industry began to
a) subsidize production in the Japanese defence industry.
b) subsidize the importation of rice to increase the real income of consumers.
c) encourage the production of consumer goods.
d) encourage the production of computers.
e) subsidize the production of chemicals and the production of light industrial goods.

39.65
Correct: d)
Difficulty: 3
Page(s): 1042
Scramble range: All
Topic: Japanese MITI

39.65
In the 1980s the Japanese Ministry of Trade and Industry began to
a) subsidize production in the Japanese defence industry.
b) subsidize the importation of rice to increase the real income of consumers.
c) subsidize the production of chemicals and the production of light industrial goods.
d) encourage the production of computers.
e) encourage the production of consumer goods.

39.66
Correct: d)
Difficulty: 3
Page(s): 1042
Scramble range: All
Topic: Japanese MITI

39.66
The Japanese Ministry of Trade and Industry
a) never has or ever will shut down an industry by imposing heavy taxes.
b) has made U.S. industry better off than they would otherwise have been.
c) helped get rice farmers to give up their import protection and their land in order to build more lower-income housing.
d) in the 1970s shut down the aluminum industry when the Japanese process (smelting bauxite to create aluminum) became too expensive when oil prices increased.
e) discouraged the production of computers.

39.67
Correct: c)
Difficulty: 3
Page(s): 1042
Scramble range: All
Topic: Japanese economic growth

39.67
Much of rapid Japanese economic growth has been attributed to
a) low rates of saving by the people.
b) the presence of many major Japanese rivers to transports goods efficiently over long distances.
c) increases in human capital.
d) the introduction of a system of price controls and rationing in markets for consumer goods.
e) the construction of high trade barriers.

39.68
Correct: c)
Difficulty: 3
Page(s): 1042
Scramble range: All
Topic: Japanese economic growth

39.68
Much of rapid Japanese economic growth has been attributed to
a) low rates of education of the people.
b) the presence of much farmland which provides inexpensive foods in much variety.
c) the continued production and sales of technologically advanced consumer goods and, of course, automobiles and trucks.
d) an ample supply of high-quality domestic oil.
e) a high rate of population growth.

39.69
Correct: e)
Difficulty: 2
Page(s): 1042
Scramble range: All
Topic: Welfare state capitalism

39.69
Capitalism that has more socialism mixed in than does the capitalism of the United States or Japan is
a) communism.
b) socialism.
c) European capitalism.
d) fascism.
e) welfare state capitalism.

39.70
Correct: a)
Difficulty: 3
Page(s): 1042
Scramble range: All
Topic: Relative scale of government

39.70
Which of the following is a valid comparison?
a) The scale of government is larger in the European Community than in Japan.
b) The scale of government is larger in the United States than in the European Community.
c) The scale of government in Japan is larger than in the United States.
d) The scale of the government in larger in the European Community than in the U.S.S.R.
e) The scale of government in Canada is larger than in the European Community.

39.71
Correct: b)
Difficulty: 3
Page(s): 1042
Scramble range: All
Topic: Size of government in Europe

39.71
Government expenditures and levels of taxation for most European nations range between
a) 10 percent and 20 percent of GDP.
b) 40 percent and 50 percent of GDP.
c) 50 percent and 60 percent of GDP.
d) 70 percent and 80 percent of GDP.
e) 80 percent and 90 percent of GDP.

39.72
Correct: e)
Difficulty: 3
Page(s): 1042
Scramble range: All
Topic: Nationalized industries

39.72
The nationalized industries in Canada are
a) organized around the market principle.
b) organized by the market socialism principle.
c) increasing in number because of the growing trend toward privatization.
d) usually privately owned and operated.
e) called Crown corporations.

39.73
Correct: d)
Difficulty: 3
Page(s): 1043
Scramble range: All
Topic: Resource endowment in the U.S.S.R.

39.73
The U.S.S.R.
a) is about the same size as Canada, but it is richer and enjoys a greater per capita real income.
b) is about 80 percent Russian and 20 percent ethnic minorities such as Asian and Arab groups.
c) is a nation without many material resources and relies on large amounts of human capital to promote growth.
d) has huge reserves of timber, oil, natural gas, iron ore, and coal.
e) is a market socialist economy.

39.74
Correct: c)
Difficulty: 3
Page(s): 1043
Scramble range: All
Topic: Economic experience in the U.S.S.R.

39.74
After the Bolshevik Revolution, the Soviet economy
a) prospered from 1920 to 1921.
b) remained a market economy until Gorbachev instituted *perestroika.*
c) fell into years of recession and inflation in the early 1920s.
d) became a mixed-capitalist economy under Stalin in the 1920s.
e) immediately went to a socialist economy.

39.75
Correct: c)
Difficulty: 3
Page(s): 1043
Scramble range: All
Topic: Economic experience in the U.S.S.R.

39.75
As a solution to the economic crisis of the early 1920s, Lenin instituted the
a) "New Economic Policy," introducing more market forces and a more open economy.
b) "Keynesian Revolution" by adopting the reforms of the economic advisor to nationalize everything.
c) "New Economic Policy," which led to a crackdown on private initiative and private businesses.
d) policy of "Chevgodnikov" to promote domestic production of consumer goods.
e) policy of "Perestroika" to promote more efficient production.

39.76
Correct: a)
Difficulty: 3
Page(s): 1043
Scramble range: All
Topic: Economic experience in the U.S.S.R.

39.76
The command economy was expanded in the late 1920s as Lenin
a) nationalized the financial, transportation, and manufacturing sectors.
b) nationalized the agricultural sector.
c) introduced market reforms in agriculture, but not in manufacturing.
d) introduced market reforms in manufacturing, but not in agriculture.
e) collectivized the mining sector.

39.77
Correct: e)
Difficulty: 3
Page(s): 1043
Scramble range: All
Topic: Economic experience in the U.S.S.R.

39.77
The command economy was expanded in the 1930s as Stalin
a) nationalized the financial, transportation, and manufacturing sectors.
b) nationalized the mining sector.
c) introduced market reforms in agriculture, but not in manufacturing.
d) introduced market reforms in manufacturing, but not in agriculture.
e) nationalized the agricultural sector.

39.78
Correct: b)
Difficulty: 3
Page(s): 1044–47
Scramble range: All
Topic: Soviet economic planning

39.78
Soviet GOSPLAN is
a) the plan, currently under consideration, calling for free movement of capital and labour across international borders.
b) the state committee responsible for economic planning and execution of the plans.
c) concerned with the production of capital goods only, and not consumer goods.
d) in control of materials but not credit facilities.
e) the new plan for reforms based on increased accountability and decentralization.

39.79
Correct: d)
Difficulty: 3
Page(s): 1047–48
Scramble range: All
Topic: Soviet economic policy

39.79
Key elements of Gorbachev's *perestroika* include all of the following *except*
a) a closer connection between income and performance.
b) reform of planning and pricing.
c) increased independence for state enterprises.
d) decreased reliance on incentives to individuals.
e) reform of accounting methods.

39.80
Correct: a)
Difficulty: 3
Page(s): 1048–49
Scramble range: All
Topic: China's economic reforms

39.80
Which of the following statements is false concerning the economic reforms in agriculture in the People's Republic of China?
a) Led to the downfall of Mao and communism.
b) Led to increased productivity in agriculture.
c) Were begun by Deng Xiaoping in 1978 after the death of Mao.
d) Preceeded only limited deregulation in manufacturing.
e) Included introduction of individual incentives.

39.81 (SG 39.1)
Correct: a)
Difficulty: 3
Page(s): 1037
Scramble range: All
Topic: Production possibilities

39.81
The best any economic system can do is to
a) produce on its production possibility frontier.
b) produce above its production possibility frontier.
c) produce below its production possibility frontier.
d) eliminate scarcity.
e) produce a fair distribution of initial wealth and resources.

39.82 (SG 39.2)
Correct: e)
Difficulty: 2
Page(s): 1039
Scramble range: All
Topic: Welfare state capitalism

39.82
Which economic system is characterized by private ownership of capital and considerable state intervention in the allocation of resources?
a) Capitalism.
b) Socialism.
c) Market socialism.
d) Communism.
e) Welfare state capitalism.

39.83 (SG 39.3)
Correct: a)
Difficulty: 2
Page(s): 1038
Scramble range: All
Topic: Capitalism

39.83
Which economic system is characterized by private ownership of capital and reliance on market allocation of resources?
a) Capitalism.
b) Socialism.
c) Market socialism.
d) Welfare state capitalism.
e) Communism.

39.84 (SG 39.4)
Correct: e)
Difficulty: 2
Page(s): 1039
Scramble range: All
Topic: Market socialism

39.84
Which economic system is characterized by state ownership of capital and reliance on market allocation of resources?
a) Capitalism.
b) Socialism.
c) Communism.
d) Welfare state capitalism.
e) Market socialism.

39.85 (SG 39.5)
Correct: b)
Difficulty: 2
Page(s): 1038
Scramble range: All
Topic: Socialism

39.85
Which economic system is characterized by state ownership of capital and centrally planned allocation of resources?
a) Capitalism.
b) Socialism.
c) Market socialism.
d) Welfare state capitalism.
e) Communism.

39.86 (SG 39.6)
Correct: c)
Difficulty: 4
Page(s): 1040
Scramble range: All
Topic: Communism versus socialism

39.86
What is the principal difference between communism and socialism more generally?
a) There is central planning under communism but not under socialism.
b) Capital is owned by the state under communism but not under socialism.
c) Income is to be distributed according to need under communism and according to contribution under socialism.
d) Income is to be distributed according to contribution under communism and according to need under socialism.
e) Income is to generated according to ability under communism, and according to state need under socialism.

39.87 (SG 39.7)
Correct: a)
Difficulty: 2
Page(s): 1040
Scramble range: All
Topic: Socialism

39.87
Which of the following has a predominantly socialist economic system?
a) China.
b) the United Kingdom.
c) Japan.
d) Sweden.
e) Canada.

39.88 (SG 39.8)
Correct: b)
Difficulty: 3
Page(s): 1041
Scramble range: All
Topic: Japan

39.88
Which of the following is *not* a feature of the Japanese economy that appears to be responsible for its dramatic economic success?
a) Reliance on free-market, capitalist methods.
b) An abundance of natural resources.
c) Small scale of government.
d) Probusiness government intervention by the Ministry of Trade and Industry.
e) Loyal and cooperative people.

39.89 (SG 39.9)
Correct: e)
Difficulty: 3
Page(s): 1043
Scramble range: All
Topic: U.S.S.R.

39.89
Which of the following does *not* exist in the Soviet Union?
a) Money.
b) State enterprises.
c) Markets of any kind.
d) A central planning committee.
e) Resource markets.

39.90 (SG 39.10)
Correct: d)
Difficulty: 3
Page(s): 1045
Scramble range: All
Topic: Turnover tax

39.90
Which of the following methods is most often used by Soviet planners to achieve consumer goods balance if there is an excess of quantity demanded over quantity supplied at the price set by planners?
a) Increasing production.
b) Increasing income taxes.
c) Lowering wages.
d) Imposing a turnover tax.
e) Imposing a quota.

39.91 (SG 39.11)
Correct: b)
Difficulty: 3
Page(s): 1046
Scramble range: All
Topic: Materials balance in the U.S.S.R.

39.91
The Soviet Union allocates raw materials and intermediate goods by using
a) market prices.
b) materials balancing.
c) a survey of the needs of state enterprise managers.
d) feedback from the workers.
e) labour balancing.

39.92 (SG 39.12)
Correct: a)
Difficulty: 3
Page(s): 1047–48
Scramble range: All
Topic: *Perestroika*

39.92
Which of the following is *not* an element of *perestroika*?
a) Elimination of the dominance of the Communist party.
b) Establishment of a direct link of incomes to performance.
c) Increased independence for state enterprises.
d) Reform of accounting methods to calculate enterprises' full cost, revenue, and profit.
e) Requirements that each enterprise achieve the "highest end results."

39.93 (SG 39.13)
Correct: c)
Difficulty: 3
Page(s): 1048
Scramble range: All
Topic: China

39.93
During the Great Leap Forward in China under Mao Zedong,
a) there was a dramatic increase in agricultural production but not industrial production.
b) the application of new technologies resulted in a significant general increase in production.
c) China experienced very slow economic growth.
d) China became a major exporter of grains and cotton.
e) China's educational sector boomed.

39.94 (SG 39.14)
Correct: d)
Difficulty: 2
Page(s): 1048
Scramble range: All
Topic: China

39.94
The People's Republic of China dates from
a) 1917.
b) 1927.
c) 1936.
d) 1949.
e) 1967.

39.95 (SG 39.15)
Correct: b)
Difficulty: 3
Page(s): 1049
Scramble range: All
Topic: Deng Xiaoping

39.95
The economic reforms of 1978 under Deng Xiaoping
a) moved China off the "capitalist road" it had been on under Mao Zedong.
b) abolished collectivized agriculture.
c) have resulted in slower economic growth in China.
d) have made China more dependent on food imports.
e) led to the closing of universities and schools.

39.96 (SG 39.16)
Correct: e)
Difficulty: 3
Page(s): 1050
Scramble range: All
Topic: Socialism and capitalism compared

39.96
Under socialism, when managers of state enterprises are rewarded for reaching the target levels of production, managers have an incentive to produce
a) efficiently but they do not know how.
b) efficiently but there are generally shortages of inputs.
c) efficiently and usually do.
d) inefficiently, as they produce too much output because they are paid per unit of output.
e) inefficiently, as they produce too little output to lower future production quotas.

39.97 (SG 39.17)
Correct: e)
Difficulty: 2
Page(s): 1039
Scramble range: None
Topic: Market socialism

39.97
Which of the following countries has an economic system closest to market socialism?
a) Japan.
b) Soviet Union.
c) Yugoslavia.
d) Hungary.
e) Both c) and d).

39.98 (SG 39.18)
Correct: a)
Difficulty: 3
Page(s): 1045
Scramble range: All
Topic: Five basic balances

39.98
The Soviet Union's basic plan is centred around five basic balances, which include all of the following *except* the
a) foreign exchange balance.
b) consumer goods balance.
c) labour balance.
d) credit balance.
e) materials balance.

39.99 (SG 39.19)
Correct: a)
Difficulty: 3
Page(s): 1052
Scramble range: All
Topic: Economic growth in the U.S.S.R.

39.99
The rate of economic growth in the Soviet Union over the 1950 to 1980 period has been
a) greater than for the United States but less than for Japan.
b) greater than for both the United States and Japan.
c) greater than for Japan but less than for the United States.
d) less than for both the United States and Japan.
e) about the same as for both the United States and Japan.

39.100 (SG 39.20)
Correct: c)
Difficulty: 3
Page(s): 1052–53
Scramble range: All
Topic: Capitalism/socialism compared

39.100
Which of the following is true?
a) Socialist economies have much more equal distributions of income than capitalist or welfare state capitalist countries.
b) Socialist economies tend to grow more slowly when they relax their central planning and command mechanisms and rely on markets and decentralized incentive.
c) Productivity is higher in capitalist economies than in socialist economies.
d) Socialist economies can grow quite rapidly without squeezing consumption to levels below those that would be tolerated in capitalist economies.
e) Socialist economies have much less equal distributions of income than capitalist or welfare state capitalist countries.

39.101
Correct: e)
Difficulty: 4
Page(s): 1051
Scramble range: All
Topic: Comparisons

39.101
In comparing socialism to capitalism, production is
a) more costly under socialism, but higher quantities are produced.
b) less costly under socialism and higher quantities are produced.
c) as costly under socialism but higher quantities are produced.
d) less costly under socialism but lower quantities are produced.
e) more costly under socialism and lower quantities are produced.

39.102
Correct: e)
Difficulty: 4
Page(s): 1051
Scramble range: All
Topic: Comparisons

39.102
Market socialism improves over
a) capitalism by producing higher quantities.
b) socialism by producing lower quantities.
c) capitalism by producing at lower cost.
d) socialism by producing at higher cost.
e) socialism by producing higher quantities.

39.103
Correct: a)
Difficulty: 3
Page(s): 1040
Scramble range: All
Topic: Communism versus socialism

39.103
In which of the following areas is the difference between communism and socialism the greatest?
a) Distribution of income based on contribution or need.
b) Presence or absence of central planning.
c) State or private ownership of capital.
d) Presence or absence of elements of command in the economy.
e) Distribution of working effort.

39.104
Correct: b)
Difficulty: 3
Page(s): 1042
Scramble range: All
Topic: Systems

39.104
Which of the following is among the factors commonly cited to explain the success of the Japanese economy?
a) Abundance of natural resources.
b) Probusiness intervention by the Ministry of Trade and Industry.
c) Great cultural diversity of the workforce.
d) Government ownership of most key industries.
e) An equal distribution of income.

39.105
Correct: d)
Difficulty: 3
Page(s): 1045
Scramble range: All
Topic: Soviet economy

39.105
For what purpose does the Soviet Union use "materials balancing"?
a) Controlling the growth of black markets.
b) Keeping Soviet currency from leaving the country.
c) Pricing consumer goods.
d) Allocating raw materials and intermediate goods.
e) Allocating labour to different industries.

39.106
Correct: a)
Difficulty: 3
Page(s): 1046
Scramble range: All
Topic: Soviet economy

39.106
What is the meaning of "perestroika"?
a) An economic restructuring.
b) Improved Soviet relations with the West.
c) An economic first-strike capability.
d) The paralysis of the Soviet economy by current outmoded methods.
e) Competitive democracy.

39.107
Correct: b)
Difficulty: 2
Page(s): 1049
Scramble range: All
Topic: Chinese economy

39.107
The economic reform of 1978 that abolished collectivized agriculture in China was undertaken by
a) Mao Zedong.
b) Deng Xiaoping.
c) Sun Yat Sen.
d) Chou En Lai.
e) Ho Chi Minh.

39.108
Correct: d)
Difficulty: 2
Page(s): 1039
Scramble range: All
Topic: Yugoslav economy

39.108
Which of the following economic systems best characterizes Yugoslavia?
a) Market capitalism.
b) Welfare state capitalism.
c) Communism.
d) Market socialism.
e) Socialism.

39.109
Correct: b)
Difficulty: 2
Page(s): 1039
Scramble range: All
Topic: British economy

39.109
Which of the following economic systems best characterizes the United Kingdom?
a) Market capitalism.
b) Welfare state capitalism.
c) Communism.
d) Market socialism.
e) Socialism.

39.110
Correct: c)
Difficulty: 3
Page(s): 1052
Scramble range: All
Topic: Growth

39.110
Which of the following nations achieved the highest economic growth rate for 1950 to 1980?
a) United States.
b) Soviet Union.
c) Japan.
d) China.
e) Canada.

39.111
Correct: e)
Difficulty: 4
Page(s): 1046
Scramble range: All
Topic: Shortages

39.111
In the event of a shortage of a good in the Soviet economy, the Soviet planners usually respond by
a) increasing production of the good.
b) decreasing the amount allocated for the intermediate demand for the good.
c) convincing workers to put in more hours.
d) importing some of the good.
e) reducing the quantity allocated for the final demand for the good.

39.112
Correct: d)
Difficulty: 4
Page(s): 1054
Scramble range: All
Topic: Freeing of markets

39.112
Consider Fact 39.1. After the merger of the two economies, in the markets that were previously subsidized prices will
a) rise and as a result quantity traded will rise.
b) fall and as a result quantity traded will fall.
c) rise, but quantity traded will stay the same.
d) rise and as a result quantity traded will fall.
e) fall and as a result quantity traded will rise.

Fact 39.1
East and West Germany recently merged their economies (respectively socialist and capitalist) to produce a united, mostly capitalist economy. Before the merger, the East German economy has some goods that were subsidized (e.g. stoves), some that were taxed (e.g. refrigerators), and some that were illegal and traded in black markets (e.g. microwave ovens). After the merger, all these markets became free, and began trading in a capitalist manner.

39.113
Correct: e)
Difficulty: 4
Page(s): 1054
Scramble range: All
Topic: Freeing of markets

39.113
Consider Fact 39.1. After the merger of the two economies, in the markets that were previously taxed, prices will
a) rise and as a result so will quantity traded.
b) rise and as a result quantity traded will fall.
c) fall but the quantity traded will stay constant.
d) fall and as a result quantity traded will fall.
e) fall and as a result quantity traded will rise.

39.114
Correct: c)
Difficulty: 4
Page(s): 1054
Scramble range: All
Topic: Freeing of markets

39.114
Consider Fact 39.1. After the merger of the two economies, in the black markets prices will
a) fall a little bit and therefore there will be no change in quantity traded.
b) fall a lot and therefore there will be a large fall in quantity traded.
c) fall a lot and therefore there will be a large rise in quantity traded.
d) rise a little and therefore there will a fall in quantity traded.
e) rise a lot and therefore there will be a large fall in quantity traded.